BARCODE ON
NEXT PAGE

W9-BOK-895

YEARBOOK OF AMERICAN & CANADIAN CHURCHES 2005

NON-CIRCULATING

Previous Issues

Year of Publication/Title		*Editor*
1916	Federal Council Year Book	H. K. Carroll
1917	Federal Council Year Book	H. K. Carroll
1918	Yearbook of the Churches	C. F. Armitage
1919	Yearbook of the Churches	C. F. Armitage
1920	Yearbook of the Churches	S. R. Warburton
1922	Yearbook of the Churches	E. O. Watson
1923	Yearbook of the Churches	E. O. Watson
1925	Yearbook of the Churches	E. O. Watson
1927	The Handbook of the Churches	B. S. Winchester
1931	The New Handbook of the Churches	Charles Steizle
1933	Yearbook of American Churches	H. C. Weber
1935	Yearbook of American Churches	H. C. Weber
1937	Yearbook of American Churches	H. C. Weber
1939	Yearbook of American Churches	H. C. Weber
1941	Yearbook of American Churches	B. Y. Landis
1943	Yearbook of American Churches	B. Y. Landis
1945	Yearbook of American Churches	B. Y. Landis
1947	Yearbook of American Churches	B. Y. Landis, G. F. Ketcham
1949	Yearbook of American Churches	G. F. Ketcham
1951	Yearbook of American Churches	G. F. Ketcham
1952	Yearbook of American Churches	B. Y. Landis
1953	Yearbook of American Churches	B. Y. Landis
1954	Yearbook of American Churches	B. Y. Landis
1955	Yearbook of American Churches	B. Y. Landis
1956	Yearbook of American Churches	B. Y. Landis
1957	Yearbook of American Churches	B. Y. Landis
1958	Yearbook of American Churches	B. Y. Landis
1959	Yearbook of American Churches	B. Y. Landis
1960	Yearbook of American Churches	B. Y. Landis
1961	Yearbook of American Churches	B. Y. Landis
1962	Yearbook of American Churches	B. Y. Landis
1963	Yearbook of American Churches	B. Y. Landis
1964	Yearbook of American Churches	B. Y. Landis
1965	Yearbook of American Churches	B. Y. Landis
1966	Yearbook of American Churches	C. H. Jacquet
1967	Yearbook of American Churches	L. B. Whitman
1968	Yearbook of American Churches	L. B. Whitman
1969	Yearbook of American Churches	C. H. Jacquet
1970	Yearbook of American Churches	C. H. Jacquet
1971	Yearbook of American Churches	C. H. Jacquet
1972	Yearbook of American Churches	C. H. Jacquet
1973	Yearbook of American & Canadian Churches	C. H. Jacquet
1974	Yearbook of American & Canadian Churches	C. H. Jacquet
1975	Yearbook of American & Canadian Churches	C. H. Jacquet
1976	Yearbook of American & Canadian Churches	C. H. Jacquet
1977	Yearbook of American & Canadian Churches	C. H. Jacquet
1978	Yearbook of American & Canadian Churches	C. H. Jacquet
1979	Yearbook of American & Canadian Churches	C. H. Jacquet
1980	Yearbook of American & Canadian Churches	C. H. Jacquet
1981	Yearbook of American & Canadian Churches	C. H. Jacquet
1982	Yearbook of American & Canadian Churches	C. H. Jacquet
1983	Yearbook of American & Canadian Churches	C. H. Jacquet
1984	Yearbook of American & Canadian Churches	C. H. Jacquet
1985	Yearbook of American & Canadian Churches	C. H. Jacquet
1986	Yearbook of American & Canadian Churches	C. H. Jacquet
1987	Yearbook of American & Canadian Churches	C. H. Jacquet
1988	Yearbook of American & Canadian Churches	C. H. Jacquet
1989	Yearbook of American & Canadian Churches	C. H. Jacquet
1990	Yearbook of American & Canadian Churches	C. H. Jacquet
1991	Yearbook of American & Canadian Churches	C. H. Jacquet, Alice M. Jones
1992	Yearbook of American & Canadian Churches	Kenneth B. Bedell, Alice M. Jones
1993	Yearbook of American & Canadian Churches	Kenneth B. Bedell
1994	Yearbook of American & Canadian Churches	Kenneth B. Bedell
1995	Yearbook of American & Canadian Churches	Kenneth B. Bedell
1996	Yearbook of American & Canadian Churches	Kenneth B. Bedell
1997	Yearbook of American & Canadian Churches	Kenneth B. Bedell
1998	Yearbook of American & Canadian Churches	Eileen W. Lindner
1999	Yearbook of American & Canadian Churches	Eileen W. Lindner
2000	Yearbook of American & Canadian Churches	Eileen W. Lindner
2001	Yearbook of American & Canadian Churches	Eileen W. Lindner
2002	Yearbook of American & Canadian Churches	Eileen W. Lindner
2003	Yearbook of American & Canadian Churches	Eileen W. Lindner
2004	Yearbook of American & Canadian Churches	Eileen W. Lindner

Seventy-third Issue Annual

KENRICK-GLENNON SEMINARY LIBRARY
3 7050 50001825 6

YEARBOOK OF AMERICAN & CANADIAN CHURCHES 2005

WITHDRAWN
Ref
209
Y39
2005

Edited by Eileen W. Lindner

Prepared and edited for the
National Council of the Churches of Christ in the U.S.A.
475 Riverside Drive, New York, NY 10115-0050

2005-0347

Published and Distributed
by Abingdon Press
Nashville

Kenrick-Glennon
Seminary Library
Charles L. Souvay Memorial

YEARBOOK OF AMERICAN & CANADIAN CHURCHES
2005

Copyright © 2005 by the National Council of the Churches of Christ in the United States of America. All rights reserved. The contents of this book may not be duplicated or transmitted using any mechanical or electronic technology without the permission of the Office of the Yearbook of American & Canadian Churches of the National Council of the Churches of Christ in the U.S.A. For permission to duplicate any of the material found in the *Yearbook* contact the Office of the Yearbook of American & Canadian Churches, 475 Riverside Drive, Room 880, New York, NY 10115-0050.

Telephone: (212) 870-2031
Fax: (212) 870-2817
E-mail: yearbook@ncccusa.org

Printed in the United States of America
ISBN 0-687-325994
ISSN 0195-9034
Library of Congress catalog card number
16-5726

Preparation of this *Yearbook* is an annual project of the National Council of the Churches of Christ in the United States of America.

This is the seventy-third edition of a yearbook that was first published in 1916. Previous editions have been entitled: *Federal Council Yearbook* (1916-1917), *Yearbook of the Churches* (1918-1925), *The Handbook of the Churches* (1927), *The New Handbook of the Churches* (1928), *Yearbook of American Churches* (1933-1972), and *Yearbook of American & Canadian Churches* (1973-2004).

Eileen W. Lindner — *Editor*
Marcel A. Welty — *Associate Editor*
Patrick Bartlett — *Assistant Editor*

Contents

Editor's Preface vii

I

PERSPECTIVES ON AMERICA'S RELIGIOUS LANDSCAPE

Trends & Developments, 2004 9

Whither Global Mission? 16
—Eileen W. Lindner, Ph.D.

II

DIRECTORIES

1. United States Cooperative Organizations, National 23
2. Canadian Cooperative Organizations, National 53
3. Religious Bodies in the United States 61
   Religious Bodies in the United States Arranged by Family 176
4. Religious Bodies in Canada 179
   Religious Bodies in Canada Arranged by Family 209
5. Sources of Religion-Related Research 211
   I. Directory of Selected Research Organizations. 211
   II. Directory of Selected Faith Traditions in America 219
6. United States Regional and Local Ecumenical Bodies 227
   Index of Select Programs for U.S. Regional and Local Ecumenical Bodies 264
7. Canadian Regional and Local Ecumenical Bodies 287
8. Theological Seminaries and Bible Colleges in the United States 290
9. Theological Seminaries and Bible Colleges in Canada 311
10. Religious Periodicals in the United States 317
11. Religious Periodicals in Canada 340
12. Church Archives and Historical Records Collections 347

III

STATISTICAL SECTION

Guide to Statistical Tables 357

1. Membership Statistics in Canada 358
2. Membership Statistics in the United States 365
3. Membership Statistics for the National Council of the Churches of Christ U.S.A. 378
4. Selected Statistics of Church Finances—Canadian Churches 380
5. Selected Statistics of Church Finances—United States Churches 382

Trends in Seminary Enrollment 388

IV

A CALENDAR FOR CHURCH USE

A Calendar for Church Use, 2005–2008 391

V

INDEXES

Organizations 395

Individuals 404

Editor's Preface

This seventy-third edition of the *Yearbook of American & Canadian Churches* once again acknowledges the ever-changing religious context of our times. This 2005 edition is available in both hardcopy and electronic format. The electronic version can be accessed over the Internet using the unique pass code printed on the inside back cover of this volume. Updated information is reflected in the electronic edition twice during the year.

Recognizing the Contributions of Many

The field of church statistics is complex and, of necessity, filled with inconsistencies. In recent years, electronic reporting has enabled greater amounts of time at each data collection level to raise questions and to recalculate and refine reports. We at the *Yearbook* are pleased to take our place in this important task of annually capturing a snapshot of American religious life. Reflection upon such findings tells us much about ourselves as well as the institutional religious life in a country that has been referred to as a "nation with the soul of a church."

Our colleagues—thousands, perhaps tens of thousands, of individuals who keep church records—compile information for each edition of the *Yearbook*. We rely and build upon the efforts of church pastors, deacons, secretaries, and vestrymen and women who carefully review and report church membership statistics and financial giving. We acknowledge the contributions of those at congregational, regional, and especially denominational levels who respond with good cheer (most of the time!) and expeditiously (at least at our second request!) to provide us with the detailed data we require in the format that we request. We hope that being a part of the record and analysis offered by the *Yearbook* contributes to their sense of satisfaction for a job well done.

For various chapters of the *Yearbook* we are indebted to specific individuals for their assistance in gathering, analyzing, and corroborating the information we publish. As she has for the last several years, Nancy Merrill, of the Association of Theological Schools in the United States and Canada, has furnished us with the data and analysis concerning seminary enrollments. Our colleague, Shanta Premawardhana of the National Council of Churches, updated and expanded our Directory of Selected Faith Traditions in America. Our colleague Ernest Rubenstein, Librarian of the Interchurch Center in New York, is a regular and reliable consultant to us. Likewise, Seth Kasten, librarian at the Burke Library of Union Theological Seminary in New York, is ever ready to offer able assistance and counsel. Dale Dickerson of the Evangelical Lutheran Church in America helped us to confirm the dates for the calendar. Cathy Lavendar of the United States Census Bureau confirmed that the Statistical Abstract remains current with *Yearbook* data.

In developing this year's theme chapter on the state of statistical reporting of North America mission personnel abroad, we turned to Jonathan J. Bonk at the Overseas Ministries Study Center in New Haven. His initial suggestions set our research off in the right direction. Later we returned to him with requests to reprint articles from the *International Bulletin of Missionary Research*, and he cheerfully granted permission. Although we did not use excerpts here we found the *Mission Handbook 2004-2006*, edited by Dotsey Welliver and Minette Northcott, to be an indispensable research tool for anyone interested in global mission.

In this 2005 edition we have deleted the chapter entitled "The Electronic Church." That chapter offered a compilation of church related Web sites. We had initiated that chapter several years ago when the Internet was in its infancy and churches were only slowly beginning to establish Web sites. Today, search engines provide excellent coverage in locating church Web sites. Moreover, readers can continue to explore the Yearbook Web site at www.electronicchurch.org.

Annual production of the *Yearbook* requires a variety of skills and commitments within our own editorial offices. Associate Editor, Marcel A. Welty gives leadership and prodigious effort to the logistics of researching, requesting, compiling, confirming, correcting, formatting and preparing data for analysis. Earl Davis is invaluable as the Editor's Assistant, aiding in confirming data and preparing the theme chapter text for publication. Patrick Bartlett joined us late in the year but still in time to give important assistance to the production of this year's edition. Almost as closely associated with us as those we see each day are our colleagues and friends of long standing, John and Sylvia Ronsvalle, of the *empty tomb, inc.* Nationally recognized for their steadfast attention to the patterns of church giving, the Ronsvalles are unfailingly gracious in providing expert assistance and in enabling our own analysis.

On behalf of those readers, we extend our gratitude for the wisdom, skill, patience and generosity of those we acknowledge here. No small group of individuals could hope to have the knowledge needed to compile a text as far-ranging as the *Yearbook*. Our efforts, strengthened by the contributions of all those named above, have led to the 2005 edition of the *Yearbook of American & Canadian Churches*; we wish to express our deepest thanks to each of them.

The 2005 Edition Highlights

- Reports on 217 national church bodies which is reflective of the cultural and constitutional freedom of religion so characteristic of the United States.
- Signals that churches reporting in *Yearbook* statistics reflect continued overall growth of church participation, and account for the religious affiliation of more than 150 million Americans.
- Reports on 217 national church bodies including brief histories, leadership and headquarter information. Is broadly inclusive of the varieties of American Christianity.
- Ranks the 25 largest churches by membership. Only three of the top ten are "mainline" Protestant churches. Reports the fastest-growing churches as: the Catholic Church, the Church of Jesus Christ of Latter-day Saints and the Assemblies of God.
- Offers a special focus on the state of research and statistical information on global missions, 36 years after the *Yearbook* ceased publication of such data.
- Analyzes the financial data from 63 churches representing almost 50 million members and more than $32 billion dollars.
- In this day of increasing awareness of religious pluralism the *Yearbook* offers an updated and expanded Directory of Selected Faith Traditions in America.
- Continues to offer the only accurate and inclusive directory of US local and regional ecumenical bodies with program and contact information.
- Provides listings of theological seminaries and Bible schools, religious periodicals and guides to religious research including church archive listings.
- Provides accurate and timely information through the *Yearbook*'s Internet edition, in its third year. As personnel change, area codes and old E-mail addresses are replaced with new ones, and any new information is submitted to the *Yearbook*, our readers are kept current of those changes through two regular electronic updates throughout the year.

Eileen W. Lindner
Editor
New York, 2004

I

PERSPECTIVES ON AMERICA'S RELIGIOUS LANDSCAPE

Trends & Developments, 2004

Methodological Considerations

The Yearbook of American & Canadian Churches reports annually on data gathered from national religious bodies that reflect the religious affiliations and financial giving patterns of hundreds of millions of Americans. However, these data generally represent information gathered two calendar years prior to the year of publication. For instance, data reported in this 2005 edition of the *Yearbook* reflect information for 2003 that was collected by national church structures in 2004 and reported to the *Yearbook* during 2004 for publication in the 2005 *Yearbook*. This "lag time" often leads our readers to ask if such data is out of date by the time it is printed. In response, we would give a qualified "no." Massive national agencies such as the churches reporting through the *Yearbook* move in their institutional lives at nearly imperceptible rates of speed. Moreover, given the vast size and complexity of such organizations partial data reported more frequently might well have the unintended effect of conveying a sense of "trend" to momentary or regionally isolated patterns of affiliation and/or financial giving. Now in the 73rd year of publication, the *Yearbook* believes that an annual review of data continues to provide an appropriate interval for tracking the changes in institutional patterns.

No single standard for data collection exists to apply across the variety of ecclesiastical structures reported in the *Yearbook*. Moreover, the definitions of membership and related terms differ widely from one church structure to another. This lack of universal definition and collection methodology has frequently led to questions about the validity and reliability of self-reported data. Recognizing the limitations of the data reported herein, we continue to have confidence in the overall value of trends and other findings based on these figures and this methodology. While church data collection and analytical practices differ across various institutional and organizational margins, they tend to be remarkably consistent *within* specific organizations over time. This consistency within organizations brings a greater degree of confidence to the relative data of a given church over time. For the same reason the *relative* size of one church to another as reported here, we believe, provides an accurate picture even while lacking a degree of absolute precision of membership statistics, particularly over time. Thus, we believe that the Southern Baptist Convention is roughly twice the size of the United Methodist Church, for example, and that changes relative to each other over several years are probably an accurate reflection of actual membership trends. Moreover, these data are the most exacting figures presently available, and thus serve as the national standard.

The seven decades of record-keeping represented by the *Yearbook of American & Canadian Churches* is contained in a comprehensive Historic

Table 1
INCLUSIVE MEMBERSHIP 1890–2003

Year	Membership	Source	Year	Membership	Source
1890	41,699,342	CRB	1967	126,445,110	YBAC
1906	35,068,058	CRB	1968	128,469,636	YBAC
1916	41,926,852	CRB	1969	128,505,084	YBAC
1926	54,576,346	CRB	1970	131,045,053	YBAC
1931	59,268,764	CH	1971	131,389,642	YBAC
1932	60,157,392	CH	1972	131,424,564	YBAC
1933	60,812,624	CH	1973	131,245,139	YBAC
1934	62,007,376	CH	1974	131,871,743	YBAC
1935	62,678,177	CH	1975	131,012,953	YBACC
1936	55,807,366	CRB	1976	131,897,539	YBACC
1936	63,221,996	CH	1977	131,812,470	YBACC
1937	63,848,094	CH	1978	133,388,776	YBACC
1938	64,156,895	YBAC	1979	133,469,690	YBACC
1940	64,501,594	YBAC	1980	134,816,943	YBACC
1942	68,501,186	YBAC	1981	138,452,614	YBACC
1944	72,492,699	YBAC	1982	139,603,059	YBACC
1945	71,700,142	CH	1983	140,816,385	YBACC
1946	73,673,182	CH	1984	142,172,138	YBACC
1947	77,386,188	CH	1985	142,926,363	YBACC
1948	79,435,605	CH	1986	142,799,662	YBACC
1949	81,862,328	CH	1987	143,830,806	YBACC
1950	86,830,490	YBAC	1988	145,383,739	YBACC
1951	88,673,005	YBAC	1989	147,607,394	YBACC
1952	92,277,129	YBAC	1990	156,331,704	YBACC
1953	94,842,845	YBAC	1991	156,629,918	YBACC
1954	97,482,611	YBAC	1992	156,557,746	YBACC
1955	100,162,529	YBAC	1993	153,127,045	YBACC
1956	103,224,954	YBAC	1994	158,218,427	YBACC
1957	104,189,678	YBAC	1995	157,984,194	YBACC
1958	109,557,741	YBAC	1996	159,471,758	YBACC
1959	112,226,905	YBAC	1997	157,503,033	YBACC
1960	114,449,217	YBAC	1998*	150,105,525	YBACC
1961	116,109,929	YBAC	1999*	151,161,906	YBACC
1962	117,946,002	YBAC	2000*	152,134,407	YBACC
1963	120,965,238	YBAC	2001	158,952.292	YBACC
1964	123,307,449	YBAC	2002	161,202,780	YBACC
1965	124,682,422	YBAC	2003	163,128,935	YBACC
1966	125,778,656	YBAC			

*Note: The total membership figure for this year excludes the membership of the National Baptist Convention, U.S.A., Inc., which was included in the total membership figure of earlier years.

CRB—Census of Religious Bodies, Bureau of the Census, Washington
CH—*The Christian Herald*, New York
YBAC—*Yearbook of American Churches,* New York
YBACC—*Yearbook of American and Canadian Churches*, New York

Archive on CD-ROM (which contains membership and financial data from 1916–1999). This CD provides a longitudinal backdrop for the analysis that follows. Only through such a longitudinal study of growth and decline in membership are we able to capture and analyze the emerging patterns. Our annual trends analysis should be regarded as a snapshot taken at a discreet moment in history. The meaning of the figures within that snapshot will best be given definition by the larger and longer context of which they are a part.

The reader is invited to utilize both the current edition and the *Yearbook of American & Canadian Churches*' historic CD to test and amplify the analysis that follows. To obtain the Historic Archive on CD-ROM call 1-888-870-3325 or visit www.electronicchurch.org.

Table 2
U.S. MEMBERSHIP CHURCH RANKING: Largest 25 Churches

Denomination Name	Current Ranking (2004 Edition)	Inclusive Membership	Increase (Decrease)
The Catholic Church	1(1)	67,259,768	1.28%
Southern Baptist Convention	2(2)	16,439,603	1.18%
The United Methodist Church	3(3)	8,251,175	0.002%
The Church of Jesus Christ of Latter-day Saints	4(5)	5,503,192	1.71%
The Church of God in Christ	5(4)	5,499,875	***0.00%***
National Baptist Convention, U.S.A., Inc.	6(7)	5,000,000	***0.00%***
Evangelical Lutheran Church in America	7(6)	4,984,925	-1.05%
National Baptist Convention of America, Inc.	8(8)	3,500,000	***0.00%***
Presbyterian Church (U.S.A.)	9(9)	3,241,309	-4.87%
Assemblies of God	10(10)	2,729,562	1.57%
African Methodist Episcopal Church	11(12)	2,500,000	***0.00%***
National Missionary Baptist Convention of America	11(12)	2,500,000	***0.00%***
Progressive National Baptist Convention, Inc.	11(12)	2,500,000	***0.00%***
The Lutheran Church—Missouri Synod (LCMS)	14(11)	2,488,936	-0.95%
Episcopal Church	15(15)	2,320,221	0.57%
Churches of Christ	16(16)	1,500,000	*0.00%*
Greek Orthodox Archdiocese of America	16(16)	1,500,000	*0.00%*
Pentecostal Assemblies of the World, Inc.	16(16)	1,500,000	***0.00%***
American Baptist Churches in the U.S.A.	19(19)	1,433,075	-3.45%
The African Methodist Episcopal Zion Church	20(20)	1,432,795	0.14%
United Church of Christ	21(21)	1,296,652	-2.58%
Baptist Bible Fellowship International	22(22)	1,200,000	0.00%
Christian Churches and Churches of Christ	23(23)	1,071,616	***0.00%***
Jehovah's Witnesses	24(24)	1,041,030	1.82%
The Orthodox Church in America	25(27)	1,000,000	11.11%

Dates and percentages in italics and bold signify that no membership report was submitted for the 2005 edition of the Yearbook.

Last Year's Ranking

Denomination Name	Inclusive Membership Figures Reported in Last Year's Yearbook
The Catholic Church	66,407,105
Southern Baptist Convention	16,247,736
The United Methodist Church	8,251,042
The Church of God in Christ	5,499,875
The Church of Jesus Christ of Latter-day Saints	5,410,544
Evangelical Lutheran Church in America	5,038,006
National Baptist Convention, U.S.A., Inc.	5,000,000
National Baptist Convention of America, Inc.	3,500,000
Presbyterian Church (U.S.A.)	3,407,329
Assemblies of God	2,687,366
The Lutheran Church—Missouri Synod (LCMS)	2,512,714
African Methodist Episcopal Church	2,500,000
National Missionary Baptist Convention of America	2,500,000
Progressive National Baptist Convention, Inc.	2,500,000
Episcopal Church	2,333,628
Churches of Christ	1,500,000
Greek Orthodox Archdiocese of America	1,500,000
Pentecostal Assemblies of the World, Inc.	1,500,000
American Baptist Churches in the U.S.A.	1,484,291
The African Methodist Episcopal Zion Church	1,430,795
United Church of Christ	1,330,985
Baptist Bible Fellowship International	1,200,000
Christian Churches and Churches of Christ	1,071,616
Jehovah's Witnesses	1,022,397
Church of God (Cleveland, Tennessee)	944,857

Table 3
PATTERNS OF U.S. MEMBERSHIP CHANGE OF SELECTED LARGE CHURCHES 2000-2003

Denomination	2000 Membership Change	Percentage Change	2001 Membership Change	Percentage Change	2002 Membership Change	Percentage Change	2003 Membership Change	Percentage Change
The Catholic Church	1,291,546	2.07	1,587,414	2.49	1,136,661	1.74	852,663	1.28
Southern Baptist Convention	108,552	0.68	92,612	0.58	194,816	1.21	191,867	1.18
The United Methodist Church	-36,708	-0.44	-42,494	-0.51	-47,418	-0.57	133	0.002
Evangelical Lutheran Church in America	-23,749	-0.46	-26,042	-0.51	-61,871	-1.21	-53,081	-1.05
The Church of Jesus Christ of Latter-day Saints	95,418	1.87	101,771	1.95	99,946	1.88	92,648	1.71
Presbyterian Church (U.S.A.)	-75,852	-2.13	-29,380	-0.84	-48,623	-1.41	-166,020	-4.87
The Lutheran Church—Missouri Synod	-28,352	-1.10	-14,043	-0.55	-27,331	-1.08	-23,778	-0.95
Assemblies of God	3,029	0.12	49,469	1.92	60,337	2.30	42,196	1.57
American Baptist Churches in the U.S.A.	-17,479	-1.20	5,915	0.41	41,467	2.87	-51,216	-3.45

Table 4
U.S. FINANCIAL SUMMARIES 1996-2003

Year	Number Reporting	Full or Confirmed Members	Inclusive Members	Total Contributions	Per Capita Full or Confirmed Members	Per Capita Inclusive Members	Total Congregational Contributions
1996	55	43,321,039	50,047,599	$24,970,133,464	$576.40	$498.93	$20,422,403,297
1997	58	44,804,383	49,936,836	$25,181,416,276	$562.03	$504.27	$21,212,711,615
1998	62	44,574,101	49,679,497	$26,242,626,313	$588.74	$528.24	$22,202,379,038
1999	62	44,288,906	49,196,965	$26,997,610,588	$609.58	$548.77	$22,801,548,715
2000	65	44,401,451	49,178,675	$29,464,889,024	$663.60	$599.14	$24,475,897,453
2001	62	45,359,589	49,828,003	$31,041,852,581	$684.35	$622.98	$26.587,142,109
2002	59	43,694,611	47,773,814	$31,465,090,286	$720.11	$658.63	$26,908,804,274
2003	**59***	**43,821,419**	**47,659,016**	**$31,804,717,804**	**$725.78**	**$667.34**	**$27,326,662,725**
2003	63	44,211,342	48,266,164	$32,269,713,588	$729.90	$668.58	$27,723,558,838

Year	Per Capita Full or Confirmed Members	Per Capita Inclusive Members	Total Benevolences	Per Capita Full or Confirmed Members	Per Capita Inclusive Members	Benevolences as a Percentage of Total Contributions
1996	$471.42	$408.06	$3,739,584,874	$86.32	$74.72	15%
1997	$473.45	$424.79	$3,968,704,661	$88.58	$79.47	16%
1998	$498.10	$446.91	$4,040,247,275	$90.64	$81.33	15%
1999	$514.84	$463.47	$4,197,087,981	$94.77	$85.31	16%
2000	$551.24	$497.69	$4,988,352,266	$112.35	$101.43	17%
2001	$586.14	$533.58	$4,510,947,817	$99.45	$90.53	15%
2002	$615.84	$563.25	$4,555,191,495	$104.25	$95.35	14%
2003*	**$623.59**	**$573.38**	**$4,680,667,779**	**$106.81**	**$98.21**	**15%**
2003	$627.07	$574.39	$4,748,202,343	$107.40	$98.38	15%

*Same sample of 59 churches listed in 2002, 2003 figures

Table 1 Longitudinal Inclusive Membership

This table represents a longitudinal view of aggregate membership totals for all churches reporting to the *Yearbook*. These data do not reflect the entirety of national church membership since some churches either do not gather such data or do not report them to the *Yearbook*. These figures, moreover, do not include membership of independent congregations, including megachurches. Substantial numbers of church members, therefore, are not accounted for in nationally gathered membership data. With well over 163 million adherents, the churches collectively continue to maintain a substantial organizational and institutional presence within the United States.

Table 2 U.S. Membership Church Ranking

This table allows comparison in size as determined by membership of the largest twenty-five churches in the nation. Dwarfing any single other church is the Catholic Church, reporting more than 67 million adherents. The remainder of the top 25 are Protestant churches with three exceptions; the Greek Orthodox Archdiocese, which is ranked 16th, the Jehovah's Witnesses, which is ranked 24th, and the Orthodox Church in America which is ranked 25th.

The ranking of churches on the basis of membership remains stable, as indicated by the first column of numbers in Table 2. The only notable change is the ranking of the Church of Jesus Christ of Latter-day Saints, which is presently ranked as the fourth-largest church in America in comparison to its ranking as fifth-largest a year ago. Other changes in ranking are due to incidental changes. The Orthodox Church in America was not included in this listing in the 2004 edition of the *Yearbook*. In the 2005 edition it has replaced the Church of God (Cleveland, Tennessee) in the 25th rank.

The patterns of affiliation reflected in this table offer a numerical view and summary of American church history. Protestantism has, since the founding of the Republic, enjoyed cultural hegemony accompanied throughout by a consistent, substantial Catholic presence. Three of the largest twenty-five churches are Pentecostal in belief and practice, reflecting the continuing increase in numbers of adherents to Pentecostal traditions. The Pentecostal churches are: The Church of God in Christ, Assemblies of God, and the Pentecostal Assemblies of the World, Inc.

Likewise, the top fifteen churches, those with membership exceeding two million members, reflect the constancy of the Historic Black Churches. Six of the fifteen largest churches (The Church of God in Christ, National Baptist Convention USA, National Baptist Church of America Inc., National Missionary Baptist Convention of America, Progressive National Baptist Convention, African Methodist Episcopal Church) are predominantly African American churches. This of course is reflective of the historic strength of the church within the African American community.

The Church of Jesus Christ of Latter-day Saints, an American-born church, continues to grow remarkably, now the fourth-largest church in the nation. Among the 15 largest churches the LDS also reports the highest *rate* of growth at 1.712% in the last year, a rate consistent with its previous growth rate. Given the American legacy of religious freedom, new faith traditions and variations on inherited traditions alike have found a receptive climate for growth.

In the last quarter-century much analysis and debate concerning the decline of "mainline" Protestantism has taken place. Whatever the specific rates of growth or decline may be for individual mainline denominations, this ranking illustrates their aggregate prominence in the American religious landscape. Of the top ten largest churches only three are mainline Protestant (United Methodist, Evangelical Lutheran, and Presbyterian Church U.S.A.). These three churches are also the only churches in the top 10 ranking to report an overall decline in membership. In the top twenty-five churches only six are mainline Protestant and all of them report an overall loss of membership for the reporting year. In addition to the three noted above the mainline churches ranked in the top twenty-five include: the Episcopal Church, the American Baptist Churches and the United Church of Christ.

Table 3 Patterns of Membership Gains and Losses

Table 3 offers longitudinal data on *rate* of growth or loss of church membership of a selected group of large churches for four years, 2000-2003.

The three churches with the largest growth measured by percentage of membership are: the Church of Jesus Christ of Latter-day Saints (1.71%), Assemblies of God (1.57%) and the Catholic Church (1.28%).

Finally some small churches, such as the Jehovah's Witnesses report a high rate of membership increase (1.82%) but are not represented in this chart.

Churches experiencing the highest rate of loss of membership are: the Presbyterian Church U.S.A. (4.87%), the American Baptist Churches (3.45%), and the Evangelical Lutheran Church in America (1.05%). For the Presbyterians and Baptists these changes reflect a substantial acceleration of the *rate* of membership loss. For the Lutherans this rate of membership loss is consistent with its own pattern in recent years. A smaller church, the United Church of Christ experienced a rate of loss of membership of 2.58% but that church is not reported in this table. A note of explanation is also warranted concerning the American Baptist Churches. A year ago the Baptists reported a 2.87% *increase* in membership and currently report a 3.45% *decrease* in membership. While this appears to be a very substantial change of both *direction* and *rate* of membership change, it should be interpreted with caution. The American Baptist Churches, unlike many other churches, do not canvas each member congregation each year. Rather, each year a sample is taken and denomination-wide projections are extrapolated from the sample. Hence, some measure of this degree of change must be attributed to the sampling methodology rather than to actual membership loss.

Table 4 Financial Trends

Second only to the interest in membership trends is the interest of the media and the church world alike in the financial trends reported in the *Yearbook*. While not all churches report their financial information to the *Yearbook,* 63 churches have provided full data for the 2005 edition, providing an important glimpse into United States church giving. More than $32 billion dollars are accounted for in the reports of these churches and this, of course, is but a portion of the whole of church giving.

The financial reporting for this 2005 *Yearbook* is based on the financial income reports of the 63 churches reporting figures. The records of those 63 reporting churches are reported in Table 4. However, in order to undertake an accurate analysis of the financial data we have compared the current figures with the figures reported a year ago by the same sample of 59 churches that reported at that time. These figures (controlling for previous year's report) are **boldface** in Table 4.

The over 48 million inclusive members contributed a total of over $32 billion, marking an increase in the total amount of income to the churches of more than $800 million. It is particularly useful to view this increase in its per capita terms. The $669 contributed per person is an increase of $9.95 per person from the previous year. While the increase in per capita giving exceeds the official inflation figure for 2003, it must be remembered that some individuals will be contributing to parishes with a declining number of members. In such settings it is doubtful that this increase will offset the financial loss associated with membership decline.

Benevolence giving for 2003 in our sample of United States churches reporting stands steady at 15%. This ratio of benevolence to total giving is consistent with the figures for the previous year. An interesting comparison can be made with benevolence reported by Canadian churches. While admittedly reporting on a far smaller sample and reflecting a much lower level of giving, the *percentage* of benevolence giving for Canadian churches is consistently in the 19%-20% range compared to the U.S. figure of 15%.

This year's 15% percent U.S. benevolence giving is consistent with previous patterns, but at the low end in the range of benevolent giving over the period of the last decade. This level of giving for benevolence will be the source of sober reflection for some. The overall increase in giving to the churches, at this reporting, is occurring simultaneously with a stagnant posture in benevolence as a percentage. The churches that seek generosity from their supporters have not, at least in this sample, matched that generosity with an increase in their own benevolence giving. The practical consequences of such a decline continues to translate in local settings to less support for church-sponsored day care, fewer soup kitchen meals, less emergency help to persons with medical problems, or reduced transportation to the elderly.

Looking at the full sample reporting financial figures for 2003 (2003 figures without boldface) in Table 4, there is a $2.5 billion dollar increase. However, since the additional six reporting churches include over 2 million additional members, the rate of per capita giving decreases to $650. The percentage of benevolence giving with the larger sample remains constant at 15%.

No one has given greater attention to church giving patterns than John and Sylvia Ronsvalle. For a fulsome discussion of the giving patterns of churches, see their *The State of Church Giving* series of publications, by writing empty tomb, inc. P.O. Box 2404, Champaign, IL 61825, or through www.emptytomb.org.

Whither Global Mission?

Eileen W. Lindner, Ph.D.

In 1968 the Yearbook of American & Canadian Churches, *without comment or explanation, ceased to publish statistical data of American missionary personnel assigned either to home missions or foreign missions. Now, thirty-six years later, we were interested in the ways in which data have been collected, analyzed and reported over the intervening three and a half decades. We also were interested to discover the ways in which missiological literature is related to the practical field of mission. Mission is so central to Christian identity, that it is a prominent topographical feature. This year we asked the question "Whither Global Mission?" and were delighted with what we found as research resources.*

From its earliest days on the North American continent the Christian church in its various manifestations vigorously pursued mission activity as a part of its exercise of religious liberty. Often making the distinction between "home" and "foreign" mission, American Protestantism in particular has been determined to make mission work the hallmark of the church. At its heart mission has been understood to center around the proclamation of the Good News—the telling of the story of Jesus' birth, life, death and resurrection to those who have not heard it.

This evangelical quest is grounded in Jesus' Great Commission to his disciples in which he said, "All authority in heaven and on earth has been given to me. Go, therefore, and make disciples of all nations, baptizing them in the name of the Father and of the Son and of the Holy Spirit, and teaching them to obey everything that I have commanded you." (Matthew 28:18-19, NRSV) Late in the 18th century the modern missionary era was launched with the departure from England of a cobbler turned Baptist pastor, William Carey, who would never return to England but would spend more than forty years in India. He is considered the "father of modern missions" for establishing the Baptist Missionary Society in 1792. He preached mission, saying, "Expect great things from God. Attempt great things for God."

Robust mission enterprises and organizations developed through both the First and Second Great Awakenings in both Europe and North America. Following the Civil War, the mission efforts again stood center stage as missions became central to denominational understanding of what it meant to be "church" and ultimately sought the participation of every member in some aspect of mission at home or abroad. The late 19th century gave unique shape to the American mission movement in both its denominational and parachurch or interdenominational forms.

Perhaps hoping to arouse in America the kind of fervor that had led Hudson Taylor in England to establish the China Inland Mission, evangelist Dwight L. Moody nurtured the mission zeal he found among students. Working first through the Intercollegiate YMCA movement and then through a lecture tour of colleges in New England, Moody established a tradition of missionary service that was to bear fruit long beyond his own ministry. In 1898, the "Mount Herman (Northfield, Massachusetts) 100" college students pledged, at Moody's urging, to become foreign missionaries. Under the direction of John R. Mott, the

Status of Global Mission, 2005, in Context of 20th and 21st Centuries

Year	1900	1970	mid-2000	Trend % p.a.	**mid-2005**	2025
GLOBAL POPULATION						
1. Total population	1,619,625,000	3,692,495,000	6,070,581,000	1.23	**6,453,628,000**	7,851,455,000
2. Urban dwellers	232,695,000	1,362,294,000	2,878,859,000	1.87	**3,158,016,000**	4,572,884,000
3. Rural dwellers	1,386,930,000	2,330,201,000	3,191,722,000	0.64	**3,295,612,000**	3,278,571,000
4. Adult population (over 15s)	1,073,621,000	2,313,053,000	4,241,871,000	1.74	**4,624,300,000**	5,950,587,000
5. Literates	296,146,000	1,476,797,000	3,251,554,000	1.75	**3,546,029,000**	5,015,884,000
6. Nonliterates	777,475,000	836,256,000	990,317,000	1.72	**1,078,271,000**	934,703,000
WORLDWIDE EXPANSION OF CITIES						
7. Metropolises (over 100,000 population)	300	2,400	4,050	2.13	**4,500**	6,500
8. Megacities (over 1 million population)	20	161	402	1.82	**440**	650
9. Urban poor	100 million	650 million	1,400 million	3.09	**1,630 million**	3,000 million
10. Urban slum-dwellers	20 million	260 million	700 million	3.47	**830 million**	1,600 million
GLOBAL POPULATION BY RELIGION						
11. Total of all distinct organized religions	1,000	6,000	9,900	1.76	**10,800**	15,000
12. Christians (total all kinds) (=World C)	558,131,000	1,234,339,000	2,000,836,000	1.31	**2,135,783,000**	2,640,665,000
13. Muslims	199,914,000	549,125,000	1,194,396,000	1.93	**1,313,984,000**	1,825,283,000
14. Hindus	203,003,000	462,379,000	808,104,000	1.49	**870,047,000**	1,065,868,000
15. Nonreligious	3,024,000	532,338,000	762,028,000	0.17	**768,598,000**	806,884,000
16. Chinese universists	380,006,000	231,866,000	390,850,000	0.71	**404,922,000**	431,956,000
17. Buddhists	127,077,000	232,667,000	362,374,000	0.89	**378,809,000**	457,048,000
18. Ethnoreligionists	117,558,000	163,477,000	239,108,000	1.40	**256,341,000**	270,210,000
19. Atheists	226,000	165,391,000	147,212,000	0.58	**151,548,000**	151,742,000
20. New-Religionists (Neoreligionists)	5,951,000	78,324,000	103,846,000	0.81	**108,132,000**	122,188,000
21. Sikhs	2,962,000	10,618,000	23,509,000	1.54	**25,374,000**	31,985,000
22. Jews	12,292,000	15,097,000	14,401,000	1.01	**15,146,000**	16,895,000
23. Non-Christians (=Worlds A and B)	1,061,494,000	2,458,156,000	4,069,745,000	1.19	**4,317,845,000**	5,210,790,000
GLOBAL CHRISTIANITY						
24. Total Christians as % of world (=World C)	34.5	33.4	33.0	0.08	**33.1**	33.6
25. Unaffiliated Christians	36,489,000	105,626,000	105,372,000	0.81	**109,711,000**	112,779,000
26. Affiliated Christians (church members)	521,642,000	1,128,713,000	1,895,464,000	1.34	**2,026,072,000**	2,527,886,000
27. Church attenders	469,303,000	885,777,000	1,359,420,000	1.04	**1,431,573,000**	1,760,568,000
28. Evangelicals	71,726,000	98,358,000	224,790,000	2.21	**250,776,000**	348,648,000
29. Great Commission Christians	77,931,000	227,153,000	650,094,000	1.14	**688,034,000**	853,179,000

Status of Global Mission, 2005, in Context of 20th and 21st Centuries (cont'd)

Year	1900	1970	mid-2000	Trend % p.a.	**mid-2005**	2025
30. Pentecostals/Charismatics/Neocharismatics	981,000	72,223,000	526,916,000	2.24	**588,502,000**	798,320,000
31. Average Christian martyrs per year	34,000	377,000	160,000	1.10	**169,000**	210,000
MEMBERSHIP BY 6 ECCLESIASTICAL MEGABLOCS						
32. Roman Catholics	266,546,000	665,475,000	1,055,651,000	1.17	**1,118,992,000**	1,336,338,000
33. Independents	7,931,000	96,926,000	379,085,000	2.39	**426,672,000**	612,670,000
34. Protestants	103,024,000	211,052,000	347,762,000	1.56	**375,814,000**	491,084,000
35. Orthodox	115,844,000	139,646,000	214,436,000	0.47	**219,501,000**	235,834,000
36. Anglicans	30,571,000	47,409,000	75,164,000	1.18	**79,719,000**	108,257,000
37. Marginal Christians	928,000	11,100,000	29,501,000	2.97	**34,150,000**	49,768,000
MEMBERSHIP BY 6 CONTINENTS, 21 U.N. REGIONS						
38. Africa (5 regions)	8,756,000	117,227,000	346,415,000	2.36	**389,304,000**	595,821,000
39. Asia (4 regions)	20,759,000	94,460,000	302,649,000	2.64	**344,828,000**	498,119,000
40. Europe (including Russia; 4 regions)	368,209,000	467,935,000	532,051,000	-0.04	**531,086,000**	513,706,000
41. Latin America (3 regions)	60,027,000	263,561,000	477,149,000	1.42	**511,908,000**	623,355,000
42. Northern America (1 region)	59,570,000	168,943,000	216,221,000	0.95	**226,685,000**	270,186,000
43. Oceania (4 regions)	4,322,000	14,587,000	20,976,000	1.19	**22,558,000**	26,691,000
CHRISTIAN ORGANIZATIONS						
44. Denominations	1,900	18,800	33,800	1.83	**37,000**	55,000
45. Congregations (worship centers)	400,000	1,450,000	3,448,000	1.50	**3,714,000**	5,000,000
46. Service agencies	1,500	14,100	23,000	1.68	**25,000**	36,000
47. Foreign-mission sending agencies	600	2,200	4,000	1.64	**4,340**	6,000
CONCILIARISM: ONGOING COUNCILS OF CHURCHES						
48. Confessional councils (CWCs, at world level)	40	150	285	1.20	**300**	380
49. International councils of churches	10	36	59	1.10	**62**	80
50. National councils of churches	19	283	598	1.50	**640**	870
51. Local councils of churches	70	2,600	9,000	2.20	**10,000**	15,500
CHRISTIAN WORKERS (clergy, laypersons)						
52. Nationals (citizens; all denominations)	1,050,000	2,350,000	5,104,000	0.97	**5,357,000**	6,500,000
53. Aliens (foreign missionaries)	62,000	240,000	420,000	1.07	**443,000**	550,000
CHRISTIAN FINANCE (in US$, per year)						
54. Personal income of church members, $ p.a.	270 billion	4,100 billion	15,680 billion	2.04	**17,350 billion**	26,000 billion
55. Giving to Christian causes, $ p.a.	8 billion	70 billion	270 billion	4.72	**340 billion**	870 billion

Status of Global Mission, 2005, in Context of 20th and 21st Centuries (cont'd)

Year	1900	1970	mid-2000	Trend % p.a.	**mid-2005**	2025
56. Churches' income, $ p.a.	7 billion	50 billion	108 billion	3.78	**130 billion**	300 billion
57. Parachurch and institutional income, $ p.a.	1 billion	20 billion	162 billion	5.33	**210 billion**	570 billion
58. Cost-effectiveness (cost per baptism, $)	17,500	128,000	330,000	2.80	**349,000**	650,000
59. Ecclesiastical crime, $ p.a.	300,000	5,000,000	16 billion	5.77	**21 billion**	65 billion
60. Income of global foreign missions, $ p.a.	200,000,000	3.0 billion	15 billion	5.70	**20 billion**	60 billion
61. Computers in Christian use (numbers)	0	1,000	328 million	6.05	**440 million**	1,200 million
CHRISTIAN LITERATURE (titles, not copies)						
62. Books about Christianity	300,000	1,800,000	4,800,000	3.08	**5,746,000**	11,800,000
63. Christian periodicals	3,500	23,000	35,000	4.20	**43,000**	100,000
SCRIPTURE DISTRIBUTION (all sources, per year/p.a.)						
64. Bibles, p.a.	5,452,600	25,000,000	53,700,000	4.96	**63,397,000**	180,000,000
65. Scriptures including gospels, selections, p.a.	20 million	281 million	4,600 million	2.24	**5,140 million**	8,000 million
66. Bible density (copies in place)	108 million	443 million	1,400 million	1.97	**1,540 million**	2,280 million
CHRISTIAN BROADCASTING						
67. Total monthly listeners/viewers	0	750,000,000	2,150,000,000	2.30	**2,409,000,000**	3,800,000,000
68. over Christian stations	0	150,000,000	600,000,000	3.13	**700,000,000**	1,300,000,000
69. over secular stations	0	650,000,000	1,810,000,000	1.76	**1,975,000,000**	2,800,000,000
CHRISTIAN URBAN MISSION						
70. Non-Christian megacities	5	65	226	1.14	**239**	300
71. New non-Christian urban dwellers per day	5,200	51,100	129,000	1.79	**141,000**	200,000
72. Urban Christians	159,600,000	660,800,000	1,160,000,000	1.59	**1,255,000,000**	1,720,000,000
CHRISTIAN EVANGELISM						
73. Evangelism-hours per year	5 billion	25 billion	165 billion	3.86	**200 billion**	425 billion
74. Hearer-hours (offers) per year)	10 billion	99 billion	938 billion	6.23	**1,270 billion**	4,250 billion
75. Disciple-opportunities (offers) per capita per year	6	27	155	4.96	**197**	541
WORLD EVANGELIZATION						
76. Unevangelized population (=World A)	879,672,000	1,641,300,000	1,717,522,000	0.95	**1,800,228,000**	2,034,713,000
77. Unevangelized as % of world	54.3	44.4	28.3	-0.28	**27.9**	25.9
78. World evangelization plans since CE 30	250	510	1,500	2.77	**1,720**	3,000

list of those pledging to foreign mission service had grown to 2,010 by 1889 when the Student Volunteer Movement was launched. This student emphasis, in turn, gave rise in 1906 to the Laymen's Missionary Movement. It was John R. Mott who in 1910 provided key staff leadership to the World Missionary Conference in Edinburgh, Scotland. It was this conference that gave shape, strategy, financial underpinnings, and theological grounding to the modern missionary movement that was burgeoning around the world. In 1914, John R. Mott founded the Mission Research Library (MRL) in New York as a center to collect and provide information on myriad mission enterprises abroad. *The Yearbook of American & Canadian Churches,* which began publication in 1916, published data on U.S. and Canadian mission agencies as provided to it by the MRL. For over a half a century the records compiled by the MRL were annually reported, as prepared and analyzed by well-known missiologist R. Pierce Beaver.

Like so much else in the American cultural landscape, the mission enterprise began to change appreciably at mid-century with the rate of change accelerating during the 1960s. In the case of missions the changes were immense. Evangelical and Pentecostal churches in their ascendancy sent ever-increasing numbers of mission personnel abroad. As mainline denominations, long hold over the cultural hegemony within the U.S. began to erode, their foreign mission resources also dwindled. Moreover, the post-colonial era, the Cold War, and a humiliating defeat in Vietnam led these churches to question deeper implications of sending missionaries with their unavoidable western bias throughout the world.

In 1968, the MRL, which had long provided the data on sending/receiving agencies and countries, left its old quarters housed with the National Council of Churches in New York to be gathered into the archives of the American Board of Commissioners for Foreign Mission at Union Seminary in New York. That year, the *Mission Handbook,* published by the MRL, became a joint publication of the MRL and a division of World Vision International, the largest evangelical mission agency. That year too *The Yearbook of American & Canadian Churches* ceased to carry a section on missions and has not reinstated such in the intervening thirty-six years.

While *The Yearbook of American & Canadian Churches* ceased publishing these data, ever-increasing sophistication has taken over the business of monitoring and analyzing mission data. Today the very excellent *Mission Handbook 2004-2006* (19th edition) is available through the Evangelism and Mission Information Service of the Billy Graham Center at Wheaton College (visit www.emisdirect.com). In a format similar to the *Yearbook,* it provides a trove of information describing more than 800 agencies (690 in the U.S. and 120 in Canada) and provides longitudinal comparative data along with substantial analysis.

A second venerable resource for data and analysis of mission sending practices is available from the *International Bulletin of Missionary Research.* As the linear descendent of R. Pierce Beaver's pioneering work in the 1950s, the *Bulletin* is compiled by the Overseas Ministries Study Center in New Haven. In addition to reporting data, this periodical provides reliable analysis and review of the literature in the fields of missiology and evangelism. Two excerpts are used here, with permission, from the January 2005 edition.

"Shifts in the North American Protestant Full-time Missionary Community"

The October 1998 issue of [the *International Bulletin of Missionary Research*] featured a graph entitled "Twentieth-Century Shifts in the North American Protestant Missionary Community." The nineteenth edition of the *Mission Handbook 2004–2006: U.S. and Canadian Protestant Missionaries Overseas* (EMIS, 2004) provides an opportunity to measure the latest changes in the North American Protestant missionary community.

The Mission Handbook reports a grand total of nearly 400,000 North American personnel as of January 1, 2002, including about 350,000 short-termers (serving from two weeks to less than a year). However, the graph accompanying the full article in *IBMR* purposely reflects only full-time overseas missionaries. Short-term data is notoriously misleading. Also not included in the graph are so-called "nonresident" missionaries, persons who minister in, but who do not live in, their place of ministry; their total as of January 1, 2002, was 1,984.

Several points may be observed in the the graph accompanying the full article in *IBMR*:

1. Mainline agencies (Division of Overseas Ministries, National Council of Churches in the U.S.A.; and Canadian Council of Churches, Commission on World Concerns) reflect an increase of 600 missionaries over the number reported in 1996. This change checks a previously unremitting downward slide, dating from 1968.

2. Agencies affiliated with the Interdenominational Foreign Mission Association appear to have gained about 1,400 missionary personnel since 1996. However, the increase reflects the recent addition to IFMA membership of New Tribes Mission (1,496). Without this change in affiliation, IFMA as a whole would have shown a net decline of 100.

3. Agencies affiliated with the Evangelical Fellowship of Mission Agencies appear to have gained about 8,000 missionary personnel since 1996. This increase, however, is due to the addition to the EFMA list of the Southern Baptist Convention International Mission Board (5,437) and Wycliffe Bible Translators (3,907); both agencies were formerly unaffiliated. Without the addition of these two agencies, the EFMA would have shown a net loss of about 1,300 personnel.

4. A newer association of charismatic agencies, Alliance for Missions Advancement (represented by "c" in the 2002 column of the graph, pages 12-13 in the *IBMR* article), reports fewer than 700 missionaries. Only 16 out of 68 AFMA agencies reported data for the current edition of the *Handbook.* It is not known whether this small percentage reflects a paucity of overseas missionaries or simply a failure to report. (Four AFMA agencies maintain membership also in EFMA, creating a double count of about 300 personnel. Three symbols are shaded in the graph on pages 12-13 of the article to indicate this, and the duplication has been eliminated from the grand total of 45,600.)

5. Overall, the graph exhibits a net increase in total personnel of about 2,000 as compared with 1996. Again, this increase is more than accounted

for by just two agencies: the SBC International Mission Board and Wycliffe Bible Translators. In 1996 the two agencies reported a combined total of 7,200 missionaries, while in the latest *Handbook* they report nearly 9,350, recording a gain of 2,150. In other words, as the North American Protestant missionary community enters the twenty-first century, statistical measurement does not indicate much momentum. More often than not, IFMA and EFMA agencies are static or in decline, offsetting the expansion of the few agencies that exhibit significant growth.

Excerpted with permission from the January 2005 International Bulletin of Missionary Research, *p.13, Robert T. Coote.*

In Robert T. Coote's superb summary analysis he ably demonstrates the ways in which the mission patterns of various families of churches within the U.S. continue with the dynamism so characteristic of American religious life. (see box) Studying nearly 400,000 long- and short-term mission personnel he points out the overall growth of the mission enterprise since 1998 but offers a carefully nuanced account of that growth.

Surely the 21st century will bring with it continued changes in the missionary enterprise. Those who wish to follow those changes and interpret their meaning would do well to utilize these two publications noted, as well as the two resources listed below.

The Center for the Study of Global Christianity at Gordon-Conwell Theological Seminary in South Hamilton, Massachusetts, makes available the World Christian Database, an online resource that serves faculty, students, religion scholars, church leaders, missiologists, and journalists seeking information and analysis on the global Christian movement. This site provides the core data set that supports the *World Christian Encyclopedia* and *World Christian Trends*. The WCD provides detailed information on 34,000 Christian denominations and religions in every country of the world. In addition, extensive data is available on 238 countries and 13,000 ethnolinguistic people groups, as well as data on 7,000 cities and 3,000 provinces. Visit the site at www.globalchristianity.org.

The premier issue in October 2003 of *Global Missiology,* an online-only journal that promises "exchanges between researchers, practitioners, and scholars who have an international scope and global concerns," featured an unpublished lecture, "Missions According to Scripture," by Dutch theologian and politician Abraham Kuyper. The editor is Enoch Wan, chair of the Division of Intercultural Studies and director of the doctor of missiology program at Western Seminary in Portland, Oregon. For more information, visit www.globalmissiology.net.

Whither Global Missions? With nearly a half million North Americans engaged in overseas mission work it is clear that the mission impulse remains strong within American Christianity. While there appears to be greater vigor among evangelical and pentecostal churches as sending agencies, Robert Coote's finding that mainline protestants have once again reported an increase in mission activity for the first time in over a quarter-century warrants greater attention to mission patterns. At the start of a new century it appears that American Christians are indeed "attempting great things" in mission.

II

DIRECTORIES

1. United States Cooperative Organizations, National

The organizations listed in this section are cooperative religious organizations that are national in scope. Regional cooperative organizations in the United States are listed in Directory 7, "United States Regional and Local Ecumenical Bodies."

The Alban Institute, Inc.

The Alban Institute is an independent, not-for-profit cradle of learning, grounded in faith and devoted to helping American congregations become greater communities of faithfulness, health, creativity, hospitality and leadership. Alban is the largest congregational resource and advocacy membership organization in the United States, reaching hundreds of thousands of congregants across all faith traditions with our signature of congregation building known as The Alban Way. From Alban's groundbreaking consulting practice, to original research, publications and seminars on leadership, conflict, planning and transitions, The Alban Institute knows what it takes to build vital, enduring communities of faith. Alban draws on a vast reservoir of congregational know-how and wisdom born on the firing line. Clergy and lay leaders seek guidance from the most respected problem solvers, strategists and teachers in the business.

Headquarters

2121 Cooperative Way, Suite 100, Herndon, VA 20171 Tel. (800)486-1318

Media Contact, Dir. of Research, Dr. Ian Evison

Officers

Pres., The Rev. James P. Wind, Ph.D.

American Bible Society

In 1816, pastors and laymen representing a variety of Christian denominations gathered in New York City to establish an organization "to disseminate the Gospel of Christ throughout the habitable world." Since that time the American Bible Society (ABS) has continued to provide God's Word, without doctrinal note or comment, wherever it is needed and in the language and format the reader can most easily use and understand. The ABS is the servant of the denominations and local churches.

The American Bible Society is committed to promoting personal engagement with the Holy Scriptures. A new special emphasis is placed on reaching the souls of America's youth through literacy training and faith-based hip hop music with the goal of changed lives.

Today the ABS serves more than 100 denominations and agencies, and its board of trustees is composed of distinguished laity and clergy drawn from these Christian groups.

Fifty-five years ago the American Bible Society played a leading role in the founding of the United Bible Societies, a federation of 135 national bible societies around the world that enables global cooperation in Scripture translation, publication and distribution in more than 200 countries and territories. The ABS contributes approximately 45 percent of the support provided by the UBS to those national bible societies which request support to meet the total Scripture needs of people in their countries.

The work of the ABS is supported through gifts from individuals, local churches, denominations and cooperating agencies.

Headquarters

National Service Center, 1865 Broadway, New York, NY 10023 Tel. (212)408-1200

Media Contact, Sr. Manager, Media Relations, Roy Lloyd Tel. (212)408-8731 Fax (212)408-1456, rlloyd@americanbible.org

Officers

Chpsn., Rev. R. Lamar Vest
Vice-Chpsn., Dennis Dickerson
Pres., Dr. Eugene B. Habecker
Senior Vice-Pres. for Development, Robert L. Briggs
Senior Vice-Pres. for Bibles.com, John Cruz
Senior Vice-Pres. for Domestic Ministries, Rev. Trevón Gross
Vice-Pres. and General Counsel, Peter Rathbun
Vice-Pres. for Corporate Services, Richard Stewart
Dean, Nida Institute, Dr. Robert Hodgson
Dir. of Internal Audit, Donald Cavanaugh

Dir. for Publishing Services, Bibles.com, Thomas Durakis
Dir. for Finance and Production Services, Bibles.com., Gary Ruth

DEPARTMENT HEADS

Dir. of Strategic Initiatives, Stephen King
Dir. of Operations, Cheryl Berlamino
Dir. of Admin. Services, John Colligan
Dir. of Research, Dr. Joseph Crockett
Chief Technology Officer, Nicholas Garbidakis
Dir. of Operations, Bibles.com, Dr. John Greco
Dir. of The Gallery and Art Initiatives, Dr. Ena Heller
Editorial and Publications Mgr., Charles Houser
Dir. of Direct Response Prog., H. Lee Manis
Dir. of Financial Services, Dennis Morgan
Dir. of Investments, Nicholas Pagano
Dir. of Human Resources, Sharon Roberts
Dir. of Church Relations, John Scott
Dir. of Sales and Marketing, Bibles.com, Brian Sherry
Dir. of Donor Relationship Services, Melinda Trine
Dir. of Relationship Development, Karmen Wynick

American Council of Christian Churches

The American Council of Christian Churches is a Fundamentalist multidenominational organization whose purposes are to provide information, encouragement, and assistance to Bible-believing churches, fellowships, and individuals; to preserve our Christian heritage through exposure of, opposition to, and separation from doctrinal impurity and compromise in current religious trends and movements; to protect churches from religious and political restrictions, subtle or obvious, that would hinder their ministries for Christ; and to promote obedience to the inerrant Word of God.

Founded in 1941, The American Council of Christian Churches (ACCC)is a multi-denominational agency for fellowship and cooperation among Bible-believing churches in various denominations-fellowships, Bible Presbyterian Church, Evangelical Methodist Church, Fellowship of Fundamental Bible Churches (formerly Bible Protestant), Free Presbyterian Church of North America, Fundamental Methodist Church, Independent Baptist Fellowship of North America, Independent Churches Affiliated, along with hundreds of independent churches. The total membership nears 2 million. Each denomination retains its identity and full autonomy, but cannot be associated with the World Council of Churches, National Council of Churches or National Association of Evangelicals.

Headquarters

P.O. Box 5455, Bethlehem, PA 18015 Tel. (610)865-3009 Fax (610)865-3033
Media Contact, Exec. Dir., Dr. Ralph Colas

Officers

Pres., Dr. John McKnight
Vice-Pres., Rev. Mark Franklin
Exec. Sec., Dr. Ralph Colas
Sec., Rev. Craig Griffith
Treas., Rev. Thomas Hamilton.
Commissions, Chaplaincy; Education; Laymen; Literature; Missions; Radio & Audio Visual; Relief; Youth

American Friends Service Committee

Founded, 1917, Regional offices, 9. Founded by and related to the Religious Society of Friends (Quakers)but supported and staffed by individuals sharing basic values regardless of religious affiliation. Attempts to relieve human suffering and find new approaches to world peace and social justice through nonviolence. Work in 22 countries includes development and refugee relief, peace education, and community organizing. Sponsors off-the-record seminars around the world to build better international understanding. Conducts programs with U.S. communities on the problems of minority, groups such as housing, employment, and denial of legal rights. Maintains Washington, D.C. office to present AFSC experience and perspectives to policymakers. Seeks to build informed public resistance to militarism. A co-recipient of the Noble Peace Prize. Programs are multiracial, nondenominational, and international.

Divisions: Community Relations Unit; International Programs; Peacebuilding Unit

Headquarters

1501 Cherry St., Philadelphia, PA 19102
Tel. (215)241-7000 Fax (215)241-727, www.afsc.org
Dir. of Media Relations, Janis Shields

Officers

Presiding Clerk, Paul Lacey
Treas., James Fletcher
Gen. Sec., Mary Ellen McNish

The American Theological Library Association

The American Theological Library Association (ATLA)is a library association that works to improve theological and religious libraries and librarianship by providing continuing education, developing standards, promoting research and experimental projects, encouraging cooperative programs and publishing and disseminating research tools and aids. Founded in 1946, ATLA currently has a membership of more than 245 institutions and 550 individuals.

US COOPERATIVE ORGANIZATIONS

Headquarters

250 S. Wacker Dr., Suite 1600, Chicago, IL, 60606-5889 Tel. (312)454-5100 Fax (312)454-5505

Media Contact, Jonathan West, Web Editor

Officers

Pres., Paul Schrodt, Methodist Theological School in Ohio, 3081 Columbus Pike, P.O. Box 8004, Delaware, OH 43015-8004

Vice-Pres., Paul F. Stuehrenberg, Yale University Divinity School Library, 409 Prospect St., New Haven, CT 06511

Sec., Anne Womack, Vanderbilt University Divinity Library, 419 21st Ave. South, Nashville, TN 37240-0007

Exec. Dir., Dennis A. Norlin, ATLA, 250 S. Wacker Dr., Suite 1600, Chicago, IL 60606-5889

American Tract Society

The American Tract Society is a nonprofit, interdenominational organization, instituted in 1825 through the merger of most of the then-existing tract societies. As one of the earliest religious publishing bodies in the United States, ATS has pioneered in the publishing of Christian books, booklets and leaflets. The volume of distribution has risen to over 35 million pieces of literature annually. For free samples or a free catalog contact 1-800-54-TRACT.

Headquarters

P.O. Box 462008, Garland, TX 75046 Tel. (972)276-9408 Fax (972)272-9642

Media Contact, Dir. of Marketing, Mark A. Brown

Officers

Chpsn., John A. Mawhinney

The American Waldensian Society

The American Waldensian Society (AWS)promotes ministry linkages, broadly ecumenical, between U.S. churches and Waldensian (Reformed)-Methodist constituencies in Italy and Waldensian constituencies in Argentina-Uruguay. Founded in 1906, AWS aims to enlarge mission discovery and partnership among overseas Waldensian-Methodist forces and denominational forces in the U.S.

AWS is governed by a national ecumenical board, although it consults and collaborates closely with the three overseas Waldensian-Methodist boards.

The Waldensian experience is the earliest continuing Protestant experience.

Headquarters

American Waldensian Society, VistaCorn, Suite #1, 1902 Vultee St., Allentown, PA 18103-2958 Tel. (866)825-3373 Fax (610)797-9723, info@waldensian.org, www.waldensian.org

Media Contact, Jack Ferlino

Officers

Pres., The Rev. Francis Rivers '05 PC (USA)

Vice-Pres., The Rev. Gabriella Lettini '05 WC

Sec., Ms. June Rostan '06

Treas., The Rev. Dick Sanner '06 PC (USA)

Exec. Dir., Rev. Frank G. Gibson, Jr.

Appalachian Ministries Educational Resource Center (AMERC)

The mission of AMERC is to promote contextual, cross-cultural education for theological students, faculties, ministers, and other Christian leaders. Working through an ecumenical consortium of theological schools and denominational judicatories, AMERC supports experiential learning about the theological, spiritual, social, economic and environmental aspects of Appalachian culture, especially for rural and small town settings for ministry.

Since 1985 AMERC has provided quality educational programs and learning experiences for seminaries and other religious leaders interested in ministry in Appalachia and other rural areas. The centerpiece of these programs has been and continues to be in-depth, contextually based dialogue with local people engaged in creative ministries, exploring with them social, economic, political, ecological, cultural, and religious issues. Intense theological reflection is used to understand these issues through the eyes of faith, equipping students and other leaders for ministry in the Appalachian context.

In the new millennium AMERC's form of ministry has changed. AMERC is now supporting its consortium of members by providing program grants, technical and library support, and leadership consultation. The consortium seminaries and other groups, in turn, design and offer an even wider variety of experiential programs in rural and small town ministry in the context of Appalachia. Both seminary, for credit, and continuing education courses are offered. In 2000 AMERC launched its grants program for members of the consortium. Since that time AMERC has funded twenty-four winter and summer Travel Seminars, a spring course with an immersion component, a Seminary Faculty Immersion experience and a summer intern program, a consultation and six continuing education events with grants of up to $15,000.

Headquarters

300 Harrison Rd., Berea, KY 40403 Tel. (859)986-8789 Fax (859)986-2576, bpoage@amerc. org, www.amerc.org

Media Contacts, Exec. Dir., Rev. Dr. Bennett D. Poage; Exec. Asst., Marsha Baker

Officers

Chair, Rev. Dr. Leon Carroll, Columbia Theological Seminary

Vice-Chair, Rev. Dr. Bill J. Leonard, Wake Forest University Divinity School
Sec., Ms. Tena Willemsma, Commission on Religion in Appalachia
Treas., Mr. Jim Strand, Berea College

The Associated Church Press

The Associated Church Press was organized in 1916. Its members include periodicals and Web sites of major Protestant, Catholic, Orthodox, and ecumenical groups in the U.S. and Canada and abroad; individual members who supply publishing services on a freelance or student basis; and affiliate members who supply the Christian press with news, information, and vendor services. It is a professional Christian journalistic association seeking to promote excellence among editors and writers, recognize achievements, and represent the interests of the religious press. It sponsors seminars, conventions, awards programs, and workshops for editors, staff people, and business managers. It is active in postal rates and regulations on behalf of the religious press.

Headquarters

Media Contact, Exec. Dir., Mary Lynn Hendrickson, 1410 Vernon St., Stoughton , WI 53589-2248 Tel.(608)877-0011 Fax (608)877-0062, www.theacp.org

Officers

Exec. Dir., Mary Lynn Hendrickson, 1410 Vernon St., Stoughton, WI 53589-2248 Tel. (608)877-0011 Fax (608)877-0062, acpoffice@ earthlink.net
Pres., Victoria A. Rebeck, The Minnesota Connect, 122 W. Franklin, Suite 400, Minneapolis, MN 55404-2472 Tel. (612)870-0058 ext. 232 Fax (612)870-1260, victoria.rebeck@mnumc.org
Vice-Pres., Jerry Van Marter, Presbyterian News Service, 100 Witherspoon St., Louisville, KY 40202-1396 Tel. (502)569-5493 Fax (502)569-8073, jvanmart@ctr.pcusa.org
Past Pres., Bob Terry, The Alabama Baptist, 3310 Independence Dr., Birmingham, AL 35209-5602 Tel. (205)870-4720 Fax (205)870-8957, bterry@alabapnews.org
Treas., Silvia Chavez, The Lutheran, 8765 W. Higgins Rd., Chicago, IL 60631-4189 Tel. (773)380-2543 Fax (773)380-2751, schavez@ elca.org

The Associated Gospel Churches

Organized in 1939, The Associated Gospel Churches (AGC)endorses chaplains primarily for strong evangelical Independent Baptist and Bible Churches to the U.S. Armed Forces. The AGC has been recognized by the U.S. Department of Defense for 65 years as an Endorsing Agency, and it supports a strong national defense. The AGC also endorses Veterans Administration chaplains, police, correctional system and civil air patrol chaplains.

The AGC provides support for its constituent churches, seminaries, Bible colleges and missionaries.

The AGC believes in the sovereignty of the local church, the historic doctrines of the Christian faith and the infallibility of the Bible.

The AGC is a member of the National Conference on Ministry to the Armed Forces (NCMAF)and the Endorsers Conference for Veterans Affairs Chaplaincy (ECVAC).

Headquarters

P.O. Box 733, Taylors, SC 29687 Tel. (864)268-9617 Fax (864)268-0166
Media Contact, Pres., Billy Baugham, D.D.

Officers

Commission on Chaplains, Pres. and Chmn., Billy Baugham, D.D.
Vice-Pres., Rev. Chuck Flesher
Sec.-Treas., Eva Baugham
Exec. Committee, Chaplain (Captain)James Poe, USN Member

Association of Catholic Diocesan Archivists

The Association of Catholic Diocesan Archivists, which began in 1979, has been committed to the active promotion of professionalism in the management of diocesan archives. The Association meets annually; in the even years it has its own summer conference, in the odd years it meets in conjunction with the Society of American Archivists. Publications include Standards for Diocesan Archives, Access Policy for Diocesan Archives and the quarterly Bulletin.

Headquarters

Archives & Records Ctr., 711 West Monroe, IL 60661 Tel. (312)831-0711 Fax (312)736-0488
Media Contact, Ms. Nancy Sandlebac

Officers

Pres., Msgr. Francis J. Weber, 15151 San Fernando Mission Blvd., Mission Hills, CA 91345 Tel. (818)365-1501
Vice-Pres., Dr. Charles Nolan, 1100 Chartres St., New Orleans, LA 70116 Tel. (504)529-2651 Fax (504)529-2001
Sec.-Treas., Sr. Catherine Louise LaCoste, C.S.J., 10291/2 Hayes Ave., San Diego, CA 92103 Tel. (619)298-6608
Newsletter Editor, Nancy Sandleback

Board Members

Kinga Perzynska, P.O. Box 13124, Capital Station, Austin, TX 78711 Tel. (512)476-6296 Fax (512)476-3715
Timothy Cary, P.O. Box 07912, Milwaukee, WI 19807 Tel. (414)769-3407 Fax (414)769-3408
Lisa May, P.O. Box 907, 1700 San Jacinto, Houston, TX 77001 Tel. (713)659-5461 Fax (713)759-9151
John J. Treanor, 711 W. Monroe, Chicago, IL

60661 Tel. (312)736-5150 Fax (312)736-0488

Bernice Mooney, 27 C St., Salt Lake City, UT 84103-2397 Tel. (801)328-8641 Fax (801)328-9680

Association for the Development of Religious Information Services

The Association for the Development of Religious Information Services (ADRIS)was established in 1971 to facilitate coordination and cooperation among information services that pertain to religion. Its goal is a worldwide network that is interdisciplinary, interfaith and interdenominational to serve both administrative and research applications. ADRIS publishes a blog and provides Internet consulting services.

Headquarters

ADRIS Newsletter Office, P.O. Box 210735, Nashville, TN 37221-0735 Tel. (615)429-8744 Fax (508)632-0370, www.adris.org, ICQ 49457096, AIM ed1dodds

Media Contact, Editor., Ed Dodds, P.O. Box 210735, Nashville, TN 37221-0735 Tel. (615)429-8744 Fax (508)632-0370

Association of Gospel Rescue Missions

The Association of Gospel Rescue Missions (AGRM), formerly the International Union of Gospel Missions, is an association of 300 rescue missions and other ministries that serve more than 7 million homeless and needy people in the inner cities of the U.S., Canada and overseas each year. Since 1913, AGRM member ministries have offered emergency food and shelter, evangelical outreach, Christian counsel, youth and family services, prison and jail outreach, rehabilitation and specialized programs for the mentally ill, the elderly, the urban poor and street youth. The AGRM operates RESCUE College, an Internet-based distance education program to prepare and train rescue mission workers. The AGRM sponsors Alcoholics Victorious, a network of Christian support groups.

Headquarters

1045 Swift, Kansas City, MO 64116-4127 Tel. (816)471-8020 Fax (816)471-3718

Media Contact, Exec. Dir., Rev. Stephen E. Burger or Phil Rydman

Officers

Exec. Dir., Rev. Stephen E. Burger

Pres., Mr. Rick Alvis, Box 817, Indianapolis, IN 46206 Tel. (317)635-3575 Fax (317)687-3629

Sec., Rev. James Harriger, 205 Commercial St., Springfield, MO 65803 Tel. (417)831-9980 Fax (417)831-9980

Vice-Pres., Mr. Tom Zobel, Box 461, Salem, OR 97308 Tel. (503)362-3983 Fax (503)399-8673

NATIONAL PROGRAM UNITS AND STAFF

Education, Rev. Michael Liimatta

Exec. Asst., Tammy Sharp

Newsletter & Magazine, Stephen E. Burger; Philip Rydman

Convention, Stephen E. Burger

Business Admin., Len Conner

Historian, Delores Burger

Communications, Phillip Rydman

Expansion, Gary Meek

Development, Ken Fast

Association of Statisticians of American Religious Bodies

This Association was organized in 1934 and grew out of personal consultations held by representatives from the *Yearbook of American Churches, the National (now Official)Catholic Directory,* the Jewish Statistical Bureau, *The Methodist* (now *The United Methodist*), the Lutheran and Presbyterian churches.

ASARB has a variety of purposes: to bring together those officially and professionally responsible for gathering, compiling, and publishing denominational statistics; to provide a forum for the exchange of ideas and sharing of problems in statistical methods and procedure; and to seek such standardization as may be possible in religious statistical data.

Headquarters

c/o John P. Marcum, Presbyterian Church (U.S.A.), 100 Witherspoon St., Room 2623, Louisville, KY 40202-1396 Tel. (502)569-5161 Fax (502)333-7161

Media Contact, Sec.-Treas., John P. Marcum

Officers

Pres., Rich Houseal, Church of the Nazarene, 6401 The Paseo, Kansas City, MO 64131 Tel. (816)333-7000 ext. 2473 Fax (816)361-5202, rhouseal@nazarene.org

1st Vice-Pres., Mary Gautier, Center for Applied Research in the Apostolate, Georgetown University, Washington, DC 20057 Tel. (202)687-8086 Fax(202)687-8083, gautierm@ georgetown.edu

2nd Vice-Pres., Craig This, Office of Research, United Methodist Church, 601 West Riverview Ave., Dayton, OH 45406 Tel. (937)227-9415 Fax (937)227-9407, cthis@gcom-umc.org

Sec.-Treas., John P. Marcum, Presbyterian Church (U.S.A.), 100 Witherspoon St., Louisville, KY 40202-1396 Tel. (502)569-5161 Fax (502)333-7161, jmarcum@ctr.pcusa.org

MEMBERS-AT-LARGE

Larry Steinmetz, yearbook Office, Christian Church (Disciples of Christ), P.O. Box 1986, Indianapolis, IN 46206-1986 Tel. (317)635-3100 Fax (317)635-3700, 1steinmetz@ddi.disciples.org

Major Diana E. Smith, The Salvation Army, 440 West Nyack Road, Box C-635, West Nyack, NY 10994-1739 Tel. (845)620-7382 Fax (845)620-7766, diana_smith@use.salvationarmy.org

The Association of Theological Schools in the United States and Canada

The Association of Theological Schools is the accrediting and program agency for graduate theological education in North America. Its member schools offer graduate professional and academic degrees for church-related professions.

Headquarters

10 Summit Park Drive, Pittsburgh, PA 15275-1103 Tel. (412)788-6505 Fax (412)788-6510

Media Contact, Dir. of Comm., Nancy Merrill Tel. (412)788-6505 ext. 234

Officers

Pres., Cynthia Campbell, McCormick Theological Seminary, Chicago, IL

Vice-Pres., Donald Senior, Catholic Theological Union, Chicago, IL

Sec., Leland V. Eliason, Bethel Theological Seminary, St. Paul, MN

Treas., Thomas R. Johnson, Kirkpatrick and Lockhart, Pittsburgh, PA

Staff

Exec. Dir., Daniel O. Aleshire

Blanton-Peale Institute

Blanton-Peale Institute is dedicated to helping people overcome emotional obstacles by joining mental health expertise with religious faith and values. The Blanton-Peale Graduate Institute provides advanced training in marriage and family therapy, psychotherapy and pastoral care for ministers, rabbis, sisters, priests and other counselors. The Blanton-Peale Counseling Centers provide counseling for individuals, couples, families and groups. Blanton-Peale also offers a nationwide telephone support service for clergy, social service agencies, and other employers and promotes interdisciplinary communication among theology, medicine and the behavioral sciences. Blanton-Peale was founded in 1937 by Dr. Norman Vincent Peale and psychiatrist Smiley Blanton, M.D.

Headquarters

3 W. 29th St., New York, NY 10001 Tel. (212)725-7850 Fax (212)689-3212

Officers

Chpsn., John Allen

Vice-Chpsn., Arthur Caliandro

Sec., Janet E. Hunt

Treas., Mary McNamara

Pres. & CEO, Dr. Holly Johnson

Bread For The World

Bread for the World is a non-profit, nondenominational Christian citizen's movement of 55,000 members, including 2,500 local churches, that advocates specific hunger policy changes and seeks justice for hungry people at home and abroad. Founded in 1974, Bread for the World is supported by more than 45 Protestant, Catholic and Evangelical denominations and church agencies. Rooted in the gospel of God's love in Jesus Christ, its 55,000 members write, call and visit their members of Congress to win specific legislative changes that help hungry people and place the issue of hunger on the nation's policy agenda.

Bread for the World works closely with Bread for the World Institute. The Institute seeks to inform, educate, nurture and motivate concerned citizens for action on policies that affect hungry people.

Headquarters

50 F St. NW, Suite 500, Washington, DC 20001 Tel. (202)639-9400 Fax (202)639-9401

Media Contact, Shawnda Eibl

Officers

Pres., Rev. David Beckmann

Bd. Chpsn., Matthew McHugh.

Bd. Vice-Chpsn., Eleanor Butt Crook

Campus Crusade for Christ International

Campus Crusade for Christ International is an interdenominational, evangelistic and discipleship ministry dedicated to helping fulfill the Great Commission through the multiplication strategy of "win-build-send." Founded in 1951 on the campus of UCLA, the organization now includes 60 plus ministries and special projects reaching out to almost every segment of society. There are more than 27,000 staff members and 226,000 trained volunteers in 190 countries.

Headquarters

100 Lake Hart Dr., Orlando, FL 32832 Tel. (407)826-2000 Fax (407)826-2120

Media Contact, James Woelbern

Officers

Chmn. & Pres., Steve Douglass

Chief Operating Officer, J. Roger Bruehl

Chief Financial Officer, Roger L. Craft

Center for Applied Research in the Apostolate (CARA)

CARA, the Center for Applied Research in the Apostolate is a not-for-profit research organization of the Roman Catholic Church. It operates on the premise that not only theological principles but also findings of the social sciences must be the basis for pastoral care.

CARA's mission since its founding in 1964 has been "to discover, promote, and apply modern techniques and scientific informational resources for practical use in a coordinated and effective approach to the Church's social and religious mission in the modern world, at home and overseas."

CARA performs a wide range of research studies and consulting services. Since its roots are Roman Catholic, many of its studies are done for dioceses, religious orders, parishes, and the United States Conference of Catholic Bishops. Interdenominational studies are also performed. Publishes *The CARA Report,* a research newsletter on Catholic Church-related topics, four times a year and *The Catholic Ministry Formation Directory,* a guide and statistical compilation of enrollments for Catholic seminaries, diaconate formation programs, and lay ministry formation programs.

Headquarters

Georgetown University, Washington, DC 20057-1203 Tel. (202)687-8080 Fax (202)687-8083, cara@georgetown.edu

Media Contact, Exec. Dir., Mary E. Bendyna, RSM, Ph.D.

Officers

Chair, CARA Board of Dir., Bishop John J. Leibrecht

Periodical

The Catholic Ministry Formation Directory

Center on Conscience & War (NISBCO)

CCW (formerly NISBCO), formed in 1940, is a nonprofit service organization supported by individual contributions and related to more than thirty religious organizations. Its purpose is to defend and extend the rights of conscientious objectors to war. CCW provides information on how to register for the draft while documenting one's convictions and as a conscientious objector, how to cope with penalties if one does not cooperate, and how to qualify as a conscientious objector while in the Armed Forces. It also provides information for counselors and the public about conscientious objection, military service and the operation of the draft. It provides information to and support for conscientious objectors in other countries.

As a national resource center it assists research in its area of interest including the peace witness of religious bodies. Its staff provides referral to local counselors and attorneys and professional support for them. Through publications and speaking, CCW encourages people to decide for themselves what they believe about participation in war and to act on the basis of the dictates of their own informed consciences.

Headquarters

1830 Connecticut Ave. NW, Washington, D.C. 20009-5732 Tel. (202)483-2220 Fax (202)483-1246

Media Contact, Exec. Dir., J.E. McNeil

Officers

Exec. Dir., J.E. McNeil

Chpsn., Jonathan Ogle

Sec., James Feldman

Treas., Mary Miller

Center for Parish Development

The Center for Parish Development is an ecumenical, nonprofit research and development agency whose mission is to help church bodies learn to become faithful expressions of God's mission in today's post-modern, post-Christendom world. Founded in 1968, the Center brings to its client-partners a strong theological orientation, a missional ecclesial paradigm with a focus on faithful Christian communities as the locus of mission, research-based theory and practice of major change, a systems approach, and years of experience working with national, regional, and local church bodies.

The Center staff provides research, consulting and training support for church organizations engaging in major change. The Center is governed by a 12-member Board of Directors.

Headquarters

1525 East 55th St., Suite 201, Chicago, IL 60615 Tel. (773)752-1596 Fax (773)752-5093

Media Contact, Office Manager, Beatrice Vansen

Officers

Chpsn., Charles J. Cook, 606 Ratherview Pl., Austin, TX 78768

Vice-Chpsn., Stephen B. Bevens, 5401 S. Cornell Avenue, Chicago, IL 60615

Sec., Delton Krueger, 10616 Penn Ave. S., Bloomington, MN 55431

Exec. Dir., Paul M. Dietterich

Chaplaincy of Full Gospel Churches

The Chaplaincy of Full Gospel Churches (CFGC)is a unique coalition of 150 nondenominational churches and networks of churches united for the purpose of being represented in military and civilian chaplaincies. Since its inception in 1984, CFGC has grown rapidly. Today CFGC represents over 7.5 million American Christians. Additionally, we are connected with another 144 fellowship groups consisting of another 7.5 million members, which gives CFGC the potential of representing a total 15 million.

Churches, fellowships and networks of churches which affirm the CFGC statement of faith that "Jesus is Savior, Lord and Baptizer in the Holy Spirit today, with signs, wonders and gifts following" may join the endorsing agency. CFGC represents its member-networks of churches (consisting of over 60,000 churches nationwide) before the Pentagon's Armed Forces Chaplains Board, the National Conference of Ministry to the Armed Forces, Endorsers Conference for Veterans

Affairs Chaplaincy, Federal Bureau of Prisons, Association of Professional Chaplains, and other groups requiring professional chaplaincy endorsement (state/county/city correctional, healthcare, law enforcement, workplace). The organization also ecclesiastically credentials professional counselors.

Headquarters

2715 Whitewood Dr., Dallas, TX 75233-2713 Tel. (214)331-4373 Fax (214)333-4401

Media Contact, Rev. Dr. E. H. Jim Ammerman

Officers

Pres., Rev. Dr. E. H. Jim Ammerman

Vice-Pres., Col. Walter Ed Drew, U.S. Army Retired

Christian Council on Persons with Disabilities

Created in 1988, the Christian Council on Persons with Disabilities (CCPD)is a coalition of churches, non-profit organizations and individuals advocating an evangelical perspective concerning people with disabilities and their place in God's world. The coalition provides a national voice for Christians involved in disability ministry, framing the Christian community's response to issues relating to disability.

CCPD provides information and responses on issues specifically relating to the church such as accessibility, disability theology and outreach; as well as disability-related issues of concern to the general public such as genetic research, end-of-life care and cloning.

Advocacy, professional development, networking and education are all part of the coalition's activities. Annual conferences (both national and regional), chapter groups and mentoring programs are part of the coalition's strategy in strengthening the network of disability ministry.

Headquarters

1100 West 42nd Street, Suite 223, Indianapolis, IN 46208 Tel. (317)923-CCPD, info@ccpd.org, www.ccpd.org

Officers

Exec. Dir., LisaRose Hall

Vice-Pres., Charlie Chivers, Waupaca, WI

Treas., Stan Higgins, Rohnert Park, CA

Sec., Connie Hutchinson, Placetia, CA

Christian Endeavor International

Christian Endeavor International is a Christ-centered, youth-oriented ministry which assists local churches in reaching young people with the gospel of Jesus Christ, discipling them in the Christian faith, and equipping them for Christian ministry and service in their local church, community and world. It trains youth leaders for effective ministry and provides opportunities for Christian inspiration, spiritual growth, fellowship, and service. Christian Endeavor International reaches across denominational, cultural, racial and geographical boundaries. All materials are on the Internet at www.teamce.com

Headquarters

309 South Main St., Mount Vernon, OH 43050 Tel. (800)260-3234 Fax (740)397-0198, contact@teamce.com

Media Contact, Brett Hutchinson

Officers

Pres., Jonathan Stewart

Exec. Dir., Wesley Whatley

Christian Management Association

Christian Management Association (CMA)provides leadership training, management resources and strategic networking relationship for leaders and managers of Christian organizations and growing churches. Its membership represents senior leaders and departmental managers from more than 1,500 larger Christian organizations and mega-churches in the U.S. CMA publishes *Christian Management Report* magazine, *CMA Management* monthly e-newsletter, *CMA Compensation Handbook* for *Christian Ministries,* www.CMAonline.org Web site, CMA Management Tape Library and other resources. CMA provides the latest leadership and management trends and tools through its annual leadership and management conference for Christian organizations and churches, CEO Dialogues one-day roundtables, CMA Executive Leadership Program, CMA Chapters, CMA Online Job Market, CMA-Sponsored Programs and CMA Money-Savers. It also sponsors the Best Christian Place to Work annual survey and the annual CMA Management Award. Annual membership is open to Christian organizations, ministries and churches. Organizations that provide products or services for Christian organizations and churches may apply for business membership. For complete membership information, go to www.CMAonline.org.

Headquarters

P.O. Box 4090, San Clemente, CA 92674 Tel. (800)727-4CMA Fax (949)487-0927

CEO, John Pearson, john@cmaonline.org

Dir. of Management Resources, DeWayne Herbrandson, dewayne@cmaonline.org

Officers

Chair, Jerry E. White, Pres., The Navigators

Vice-Chair, Mark G. Holbrook, Pres./CEO, ECCU

Treas., Frederick J. Rudy, Consultant

Sec., Mark A. Bankord, Managing Partner, Cap Trust Asset Management

A Christian Ministry in the National Parks

This ministry is recognized by more than 40 Christian denominations and extends the ministry of Christ to the millions of people who live, work and vacation in our National Parks. Ministry Staff Members conduct services of worship in the parks on Sundays. The staff are employed by park concessionaires and have full-time jobs in which their actions, attitudes, and commitment to Christ serve as witness. Room and board are provided at a minimal cost; minimum commitment of 90 days needed.

Officers

Dir., The Rev. Richard P. Camp, Jr.
Deputy Dir., Gordon Compton

Church Growth Center—Home of Church Doctor Ministries

The Church Growth Center is an interfaith, nonprofit, professional organization which exists to bring transformational change of the Christian church toward the effective implementation of the Lord's Great Commission, to make disciples of all people. This effort is done through consultations, resources, and educational events.

Founded in 1978 by Kent R. Hunter, president and chairman of the board, the Church Growth Center offers several services, including church consultations by experienced consultants, cutting-edge resources through The Church Doctor™ Resource Center, and by providing educational events at churches and organizations, providing speakers and resources at seminars, workshops, and conferences. The quarterly newsletter is the *Church Doctor Report.*

Headquarters

P.O.Box 145, 1230 U.S. Highway Six, Corunna, IN 46730 Tel. (800)626-8515 Fax (260)281-2167, www.churchdoctor.org
Media Contact, Asst. to Pres., Cindy Warren

Officers

Pres., Dr. Kent R. Hunter, D.Min, Ph.D.
Vice-Pres., Jim Manthei
Treas., Wayne Register

Church Women United in the U.S.A.

Church Women United in the U.S.A. is a grassroots ecumenical movement of one-half million Protestant, Orthodox, Roman Catholic and other Christian women, organized into more than 1,200 local and state units throughout the United States and Puerto Rico. Founded in 1941, CWU works in coalition with religious and secular groups on issues of peace and justice. CWU hosts three ecumenical worhip services each year, with World Day of Prayer being the most widely celebrated. The priority for 2000-2004 is "Strengthening Families Worldwide in the 21st Century."

NATIONAL OFFICE

475 Riverside Dr., Suite 1626, New York, NY 10115 Tel. (800)CWU-5551 or (212)870-2347 Fax (212)870-2338

LEGISLATIVE OFFICE

CWU Washington Ofc., 100 Maryland Ave. NE, Room 100, Washington, D.C. 20002 Tel. (202)544-8747 Fax (202)544-9133
Legislative Dir., Wash. Ofc., Patricia Burkhardt, pburkhardt@churchwomen.org

UNITED NATIONS OFFICE

475 Riverside Dr., Suite 1626, New York, NY 10115 Tel. (212)661-3856

Officers

Pres., Gail Mengel, Independence, MO
Vice-Pres., Vera Zander, Tucson, AZ
Secretary, Carol Kolsti, Austin, TX
Treasurer, Jane Gray, Columbus, OH
Regional Coordinators, Central, Susan Becker, Madison, WI; East Central, Margaret Tweet, Rock Island, IL; Mid-Atlantic, Blanche Crim, Dover, DE; Northeast, Vivian Love-Jones, Newburg, NY; Northwest, Betty Luginbill, Boise, ID; South Central, Martha Moody Boone, Keithville, LA; Southeast, Mona Hayes, Nashville, TN; Southwest, Martha DeWarf, Tucson, AZ

Churches Uniting in Christ

Churches Uniting in Christ (CUIC)was inaugurated on January 20, 2002, in Memphis, Tennessee as a new relationship among nine communions which agreed to start living more fully into their unity in Christ. CUIC is the successor to the Consultation on Church Union (COCU)which was, in 1962 organized to explore the formation of a uniting church. At the 1999 COCU Plenary the nine-member communions affirmed eight "Marks" of Churches Uniting in Christ and agreed to move into the new relationship of covenanted communion to be called Churches Uniting in Christ. Following confirmation actions by each of the communions, all nine communions officially constituted Churches Uniting in Christ. The nine-member communions are: the African Methodist Episcopal Church, the African Methodist Episcopal Zion Church, the Christian Church (Disciples of Christ), the Christian Methodist Episcopal Church, the Episcopal Church, the International Council of Community Churches, the Presbyterian Church (USA), the United Church of Christ, and the United Methodist Church. Also participating at present is one Partner in Mission and Dialogue, the Evangelical Lutheran Church in America. Other communions are exploring various possibilities for relating to CUIC.

CUIC is a bold venture, expressed through the participating communions' covenant to seek to live a new relationship that bears witness to a church that is truly catholic, truly evangelical, and truly reformed. Among the goals for bearing witness to that unity are two very challenging endeavors: to heed the "emphatic call to 'erase racism' by challenging the system of white privilege that has so distorted life in this society and in the churches themselves;" and to "provide a foundation for the mutual recognition and reconciliation of ordained ministry by the members of Churches Uniting in Christ by the year 2007." Notably, the commitment to address racism is named as a hallmark of the new relationship and, following the inaugural ceremony, on Dr. Martin Luther King, Jr. Day, January 21, 2002, the Heads of Communion signed an Appeal to the Churches to work together for the eradication of racism.

The Ecumenical Officers of each of the communions will carry major responsibility for the engagement of their congregations and members in the CUIC relationship. Neighboring congregations are encouraged to celebrate the Eucharist together; invite the participation of each in services of baptism, ordinations and installation as well as other special events in the congregations' lives; and to discover ways in which they might witness together in combating social justices, especially racism. In addition to the representational Coordinating Council, three task forces will work to enhance the collaborative endeavors of CUIC: Ministry, Racism, and Local and Regional Ecumenism.

Headquarters

700 Prospect Ave., Cleveland, OH 44115-1100 Tel.(216)736-3294 Fax (216)736-3296, cuicwood@ucc.org or cuic@ucc.org

Media Contact: The Rev. Dr. Bertrice Y. Wood

Officers

Dir., The Rev. Dr. Bertrice Y. Wood, 700 Prospect Ave., Cleveland, OH 44115-1100

Pres. of the Coord. Council, Bishop Melvin G. Talbert (United Methodist Church), 108 Rausch Drive, Brentwood, TN 37027

Vice-Pres., Dr. Suzanne Webb (Christian Church/Disciples of Christ), P.O.Box 299, Elyria, OH 44036

Sec., The Rev. C. Dana Krutz (Episcopal Church/USA), Louisiana Interchurch Conference, 660 North Foster Dr., Suite A-225, Baton Rouge, LA 70806

Trea., Elder James N. Tse (Presbyterian Church/USA), 87-17 85th St., Woodhaven, NY 11421

COORDINATING COUNCIL REPRESENTATIVES

African Methodist Episcopal Church, Bishop Vashti McKenzie and Bishop Gregory Ingram

African Methodist Episcopal Zion Church, The Rev. Dr. Harrison Bonner, 12 Eldridge St., Waterbury, CT 06704

Christian Church (Disciples of Christ), The Rev. Dr. Suzanne Webb

Christian Methodist Episcopal Church, Bishop Ronald Cunningham

The Episcopal Church (USA), The Rev. C. Dana Krutz

International Council of Community Churches, Mr. Abraham Wright, 1912-3 Rosemary Hills Drive, Silver Spring, MD 20910

Presbyterian Church (USA), Elder James N. Tse

United Church of Christ, The Rev. Lydia Veliko, 700 Prospect Avenue, Cleveland, OH 44115-1100

The United Methodist Church, Bishop Melvin G. Talbert

Day 1/Episcopal Media Center

Day 1/Episcopal Media Center is an ecumenical organization dedicated to producing media resources from a mainline Protestant point of view. The flagship productions are the weekly radio show, "Day 1," formerly "The Protestant Hour," and the "Day 1" television program (produced in association with Faith & Value Media)airing Sunday mornings on the Hallmark Channel. The Web site www.day1.net provides sermon transcripts and audio resources. Day 1 features preachers from the Cooperative Baptist Fellowship, Episcopal Media Center, Evangelical Lutheran Church in America, Presbyterian Church (U.S.A.), United Church of Christ, and the United Methodist Church.

Headquarters

644 West Peachtree St, Suite 300, Atlanta, GA 30308-1925 Tel. (404)815-9110 Fax (404)815-0258

Media Contact, Nan Ross

Officers

Bd. Chpsn., The Rt. Rev. Charles Duvall

Vice-Chpsns., Ms. Harriet Tumlin Jobson; Ms. Nancy Zintak

Pres., The Rev. Canon Louis C. Schueddig

Vice-Pres., Peter M. Wallace

Treas., William F. Law, Jr.

Sec., Laurin M. McSwain, Esq.

Evangelical Council for Financial Accountability

Founded in 1979, the Evangelical Council for Financial Accountability has the purpose of helping Christ-centered, evangelical, nonprofit organizations earn the public's trust through their ethical practices and financial accountability. ECFA assists its over 1,100 member organizations in making appropriate public disclosure of their financial practices and accomplishments, thus materially enhancing their credibility and support potential among present and prospective donors.

Headquarters

440 W. Jubal Early Drive, Suite 130, Winchester, VA 22601-6319 Tel. (540)535-0103 Fax (540)535-0533

Media Contact, Pres., Paul D. Nelson

Officers

Pres., Paul D. Nelson

Vice-Pres., Dan Busby

Evangelical Press Association

The Evangelical Press Association is an organization of editors and publishers of Christian periodicals which seeks to promote the cause of Evangelical Christianity and enhance the influence of Christian journalism.

Headquarters

P.O. Box 28129, Crystal, MN 55428 Tel. (763)535-4793 Fax (763)535-4794

Media Contact, Exec. Dir., Ronald Wilson

Officers

Pres., David Neff, *Christianity Today,* 465 Gundersen Dr., Carol Stream, IL, 60188

Pres-Elect, Terry White, *Inside Journal,* P.O. Box 17429, Washington, DC 20041-0429

Treas., Lamar Keener, *Christian Times,* P.O. Box 2606, El Cajon, CA 92021

Sec., Jeanette Thomason, *Aspire,* 107 Kenner Ave., Nashville, TN 37205

Advisor, Dean Ridings, *Christian Camp & Conference Journal,* P.O. Box 62189, Colorado Springs, CO 80962-2189

Advisor, Brian Peterson, *New Man,* 600 Rinehart Rd., Lake Mary, FL 32746

Exec. Dir., Ronald Wilson

Faith & Values Media

(See also National Interfaith Cable Coalition, Inc.)

Faith & Values Media is the nation's largest coalition of Jewish and Christian faith groups dedicated to media production, distribution and promotion. It is a service of the National Interfaith Cable Coalition, Inc., established in 1987.

Faith & Values Media member association includes more than 40 faith groups and religious organizations representing 200,000 congregations and 120 million congregants. Its mission is to use television and other media to promote the vitality of religious experience in everyday life.

Award-winning programming from Faith & Values Media is available on the Hallmark Channel and on www.faithstreams.com

Headquarters

74 Trinity Place, Suite 1550, New York, NY 10006 Tel. (212)406-4121 Fax (212)406-4105

Media Contact, Howard Burkat

Officers

Chair, Dr. Daniel Paul Matthews

Vice-Chair, Elder Ralph Hardy, Jr.

Sec., Rabbi Paul J. Menitoff

Treas., Betty Elam

Staff

Pres. and CEO, Edward J. Murray

Exec. Vice-Pres., Beverly Judge

Federation of Christian Ministries

The Federation of Christian Ministries (FCM)is an ecumenical, faith community founded in 1968. FCM stresses inclusiveness, opening its membership to women and men of varying faith backgrounds who share its vision of an ecumenical, nondenominational community. Its ministers work in many ways: pastoring house churches or congregations/parishes; serving as chaplains in nursing homes, correctional facilities, hospitals; offering healing ministries; promoting groups dedicated to peace and justice. FCM is a member of the International Council of Community Churches and a faith group member of the Association for Clinical Pastoral Education. Its educational branch, Global Ministries University, offers online degree completion, both undergraduate and postgraduate, for adult learners in the field of ministry. Contact: GlobalMinistriesUniversity.com.

Headquarters

1905 Bugbee Rd., Ionia, MI 48846-9663 Tel. (800)538-8923 or (616)527-0419 Fax (616)527-0419, info@federationofchristian-ministries.org

Media Contact, Co-Pres., Eileen Mackin Tel.(303)740-7665, cdewall@pcisys.net

Officers

Chairs, Jan & Paul Reithmaier, 7415 K Triwoods Dr., Shrewsbury, MO 63119-4456 Tel. (314)962-6220, p.reithmaier@worldnet.att.net

Pres., Eileen Mackin & Clem DeWall, 11298 E. Maplewood Pl., Englewood, CO 80111-5808 Tel. (303)740-7665, cdewall@pcisys.net.

Treas., Roger J. Fecher, 8330 Catamaran Dr., Indianapolis, IN 46236-9585 Tel. (317)826-8940, rjfecher@aol.com.

Secs., Central Office, Edward & Judy Kalmanek, 1905 Bugbee Rd., Ionia, MI 48846-9663 Tel. (616)527-0419, ejkalmanek@home.ionia.com.

Development Dir.s, Jean & Michael Conley, 45270 Birchcrest Cir., La Quinta, CA 92253-4151 Tel. (760)200-5328, jeannx@aol.com.

Members at Large, Gerald Grudzen, 6331 Mountford Dr., San Jose, CA 95123-5246 Tel. (408)629-6146, grudzen@yahoo.com; William Manseau, 12 Catherwood Rd., Tewksbury, MA 01876-2620 Tel. (978)851-5547.

REGIONAL VICE PRESIDENTS

Pacific Region, Peggy & Phil Ripp, 2869 Donizetti Ct., San Jose, CA 95132-2310 Tel. (408)272-8184, rim656@aol.com.

Mountains & Plains, Rebecca David, 624 E. Dover St., Davenport, IA 52803-2611 Tel. (563)323-5740, irishblue03@earthlink.net

Great Lakes, Carolyn Horvath & Tom Leonhardt, 1709 W. 69th St., Cleveland, OH 44102-2957 Tel. (216)651-4362, cartonhl@earthlink.net.

Southern, Marge & Tom Wilt, 16870 SE 80th Bathhurst Ct., The Villages, FL 32162-8304

Northeast, Michaelita & Thomas Quinn, 93 Post

Rd., Danbury, CT 06810-8367 Tel. (203)792-6968, quinnems@aol.com.

Foundation for a Conference on Faith and Order in North America

A Foundation for a Conference on Faith and Order is a not-for-profit organization dedicated to promoting the unity of the North America churches by keeping before the churches the gospel call to unity in Faith and Order. It engages in educational studies and programs that relate to issues affecting Faith and Order, and promotes, plans, and administers conferences on Faith and Order in North America. The purpose of these conferences is to encourage and promote the unity of the churches in Faith and Order.

Headquarters

99 Park Ave., Suite 298-A, New York, NY 10016 Tel. (212)332-0031

MEMBERS OF THE BOARD

Bishop Vinton Anderson
Dr. Wallace M. Alston, Jr.
Dr. Susan E. Davies
Archbishop Demetrios
Dr. Robert M. Franklin
Dr. Donna Geernaert, SC
The Right Rev. Richard F. Grein
Dr. Robert W. Jenson
Dr. Cheryl Bridges Johns
William Cardinal Keeler
Dr. Kevin W. Mannoia
The Rt. Rev. Victoria Matthews
Bishop Donald J. McCoid
Dr. Richard Mouw
Dr. Willam G. Rusch
Dr. George Vandervelde
Dr. Eldin Villafane
The Rev. Portia Turner Williamson

Friends World Committee for Consultation (Section of the Americas)

The Friends World Committee for Consultation (FWCC)was formed in 1937. There has been an American section as well as a European section from the early days and an African section was organized in 1971. In 1974 the name, Section of the Americas, was adopted by that part of the FWCC with constituency in North, Central, and South America and in the Caribbean area. In 1985 the Asia-West Pacific section was organized. The purposes of FWCC are summarized as follows, To facilitate loving understanding of diversities among Friends while discovering together, with God's help, a common spiritual ground; and to facilitate full expression of Friends' testimonies in the world.

Section of the Americas Headquarters

1506 Race St., Philadelphia, PA 19102 Tel. (215)241-7250 Fax (215)241-7285, americas@fwcc.quaker.org, www.quaker.org/fwcc/americas/americas.html
Media Contact, Exec. Sec., Margaret Fraser

Latin American Office, Guerrero 223 Pte., Zona Centro, Cd. Mante, TAM 89800 Mexico

The Fund for Theological Education, Inc.

Begun in 1954 with the goal of supporting excellence in the profession of ministry, the Fund for Theological Education has enjoyed a long and rich history, providing gifted women and men with nearly 5,000 fellowships and generating innovative new programs for support of persons preparing for ministry and theological teaching. Supported by individuals and grants from a group of U.S. Foundations, FTE envisions new and imaginatve programs to encourage diversity and excellence in the churches and seminaries of North America.

Headquarters

825 Houston Mill Rd., Suite 250, Atlanta, GA 30329 Tel. (404)727-1450 Fax (404)727-1490, fte@thefund.org, www.thefund.org and www.exploreministry.org

Officers

Pres., Ann Svennungsen
Vice-Pres. for Advancement, Jack Gilbert
Dir., Expanding Horizons Partnership, Dr. Sharon Watson Fluker
Dir., Partnership for Excellence, Melissa Wiginton

Glenmary Research Center

The Research Center is a department of the Glenmary Home Missioners, a Catholic society of priests and brothers. The Center was established in 1966 to serve the rural research needs of the Catholic Church in the United States. Its research has led it to serve ecumenically a wide variety of church bodies. Local case studies as well as quantitative research is done to understand better the diversity of contexts in the rural sections of the country. The Center's statistical profiles of the nation's counties cover both urban and rural counties.

Headquarters

1312 Fifth Ave. N., Nashville, TN 37208 Tel. (615)256-1905 Fax (615)251-1472

Officers

Pres., Rev. Daniel Dorsey, P.O. Box 465618, Cincinnati, OH 45246-5618
1st Vice-Pres., Rev. Robert Poandl, P.O. Box 465618, Cincinnati, OH 45246-5618
2nd Vice-Pres., Rev. Dominic Duggins, P.O. Box 465618, Cincinnati, OH 45246-5618
Treas., Ms. Teri Heckenmueller, P.O. Box 465618, Cincinnati, OH 45246-5618
Dir., Kenneth M. Sanchagrin, Ph.D., E-mail ksanchagrin@glenmary.org

Graymoor Ecumenical & Interreligious Institute (GEII)

Graymoor Ecumenical & Interreligious Institute has its roots in the Graymoor Ecumenical Institute which was founded in 1967 by the Franciscan Friars of the Atonement, to respond to the Friars' historical concern for Christian unity in light of the theological and ecumenical developments arising from the Second Vatican Council.

In 1991, in response to developments in both the Institute and the wider ecumenical scene, the Graymoor Ecumenical Institute was expanded into an information and service organization with a mission of Christian unity and inter-religious dialogue. Today, the Graymoor Ecumenical & Interreligious Institute employs several means to accomplish this goal. Among these is the annual Week of Prayer of Christian Unity, "a world-wide observance initiated in 1908 by the Rev. Paul Wattson, cofounder of the Society of the Atonement," the theme and text of which are now chosen and prepared by the Pontificial Council for Promoting Christian Unity and representatives of the World Council of Churches. The Institute publishes the monthly journal *Ecumenical Trends*—to keep clergy and laity abreast of developments in the ecumenical and inter-religious movements; provides membership in, and collaboration with, national and local ecumenical and inter-religious organizations and agencies; and cooperates with individuals engaged in ecumenical and inter-religious work. A new Web site, www.geii.org, has been launched and will continue to be developed as a resource for ecumenical and inter-religious research.

Over the years, the Graymoor Ecumenical & Inter-religious Institute has sponsored and co-sponsored meetings, colloquia, and workshops in areas of ecumenical and inter-religious dialogue.

Headquarters

475 Riverside Dr., Room 1960, New York, NY 10115-1999 Tel. (212)870-2330 Fax (212)870-2001

Staff

Desk for Inter-religious Affairs, Dir., Rev. James Loughran, SA; Tel. (212)870-2330

Desk for Ecumenical Affairs, Assoc. Dir., Lorelei F. Fuchs, SA; Tel. (212)870-2331, lorgeii@aol.com

Ecumenical Research Desk, Assoc. Dir., Rev. Wilfred L. Tyrrell, SA; Tel. (212)870-2332, wltgeii@aol.com

Ecumenical Trends, Editor, Assoc. Dir., Kevin McMorrow, SA; Graymoor, Rt. 9, P.O. Box 300, Garrison, NY 10524-0300 Tel. (845)424-3671 ext. 3323, kmcmorrow@atonementfriars.org

Business Manager/Week of Prayer for Christian Unity Office, Mrs. Veronica Sullivan, Graymoor, Rt. 9, P.O. Box 300, Garrison, NY 10524-0300 Tel. (800)338-2620 ext. 2109 or (854)424-2109 Fax (845)424-2163, rsullivan@atonementfriars.org

Inter-Varsity Christian Fellowship of the U.S.A.

Inter-Varsity Christian Fellowship is a nonprofit, interdenominational student movement that ministers to college and university students and faculty in the United States. Inter-Varsity began in the United States when students at the University of Michigan invited C. Stacey Woods, then General Secretary of the Canadian movement, to help establish an Inter-Varsity chapter on their campus. Inter-Varsity Christian Fellowship-USA was incorporated two years later, in 1941.

Inter-Varsity's uniqueness as a campus ministry lies in the fact that it is student-initiated and student-led. Inter-Varsity strives to build collegiate fellowships that engage their campus with the gospel of Jesus Christ and develop disciples who live out biblical values. Inter-Varsity students and faculty are encouraged in evangelism, spiritual discipleship, serving the church, human relationships, righteousness, vocational stewardship and world evangelization. A triennial missions conference held in Urbana, Illinois, jointly sponsored with Inter-Varsity-Canada, has long been a launching point for missionary service.

Headquarters

6400 Schroeder Rd., P.O. Box 7895, Madison, WI 53707 Tel. (608)274-9001 Fax (608)274-7882

Media Contact, Dir. of Development Services, Carole Sharkey

Officers

Pres. & CEO, Stephen A. Hayner

Vice-Pres., C. Barney Ford; Robert A. Fryling; Samuel Barkat; Ralph Thomas; Jim Malliet

Bd. Chpsn., Virginia Viola

Bd. Vice-Chpsn., E. Kenneth Nielson

Interfaith Impact for Justice and Peace

Interfaith Impact for Justice and Peace is the religious community's united voice in Washington. It helps Protestant, Jewish, Muslim and Catholic national organizations have clout on Capitol Hill and brings grassroots groups and individual and congregational members to Washington and shows them how to turn their values into votes for justice and peace.

Interfaith Impact for Justice and Peace has established the following Advocacy Networks to advance the cause of justice and peace: Justice for Women; Health Care; Hunger and Poverty; International Justice and Peace; Civil and Human Rights. The Interfaith Impact Foundation provides an annual Legislative Briefing for its members.

Members receive the periodic Action alerts on initiatives, voting records, etc., and a free subscription to the Advocacy Networks of their choice.

Headquarters

100 Maryland Ave. N.E., Suite 200, Washington, D.C. 20002 Tel. (202)543-2800 Fax (202)547-8107

Media Contact, Jane Hull Harvey

Officers

Chpsn. of Bd., Jane Hull Harvey, United Methodist Church

MEMBERS

African Methodist Episcopal Church
African Methodist Episcopal Zion Church
Alliance of Baptists
American Baptist Churches, USA, Washington Office; World Relief Office
American Ethical Union
American Muslim Council
Center of Concern
Christian Methodist Episcopal (CME)Church
Christian Church (Disciples of Christ)
Church of the Brethren
Church Women United
Commission on Religion in Appalachia
Episcopal Church
Episcopal Urban Caucus
Evangelical Lutheran Church in America
Federation of Southern Cooperatives-LAF
Federation for Rural Empowerment
Graymoor Ecumenical and Interreligious Institute
Jesuit Social Ministries
Maryknoll Fathers and Brothers
Moravian Church in America
National Council of Churches of Christ, Church World Service; Washington Office
National Council of Jewish Women

NETWORK

Peoria Citizens Committee
Presbyterian Church (USA)
Progressive National Baptist Convention
Presbyterian Hunger Fund
Reformed Church in America
Rural Advancement Fund
Society of African Missions
Southwest Organizing Project
Southwest Voter Registration-Education Project
Toledo Metropolitan Ministries
Union of American Hebrew Congregations
Unitarian Universalist Association
Unitarian Universalist Service Committee
United Church of Christ, Bd. for Homeland Ministries; Bd. for World Ministries; Hunger Action Ofc.; Ofc. of Church in Society
United Methodist Church, Gen. Bd. of Church & Society; Gen. Bd. of Global Ministries Natl. Div.; Gen. Bd. of Global Ministries Women's Div.; Gen. Bd. of Global Ministries World Div.
Virginia Council of Churches
Western Organization of Resource Councils

Interfaith Worker Justice

Interfaith Worker Justice is a network of fifty-six interfaith groups and people of faith who educate and mobilize the U.S. religious community on issues and campaigns to improve wages, benefits and working conditions for workers, especially low-wage workers. The organization rebuilds relationships between the religious community and organized labor.

The organization supports and organizes local interfaith worker justice groups around the country, publishes *Faith Works* six times a year providing, congregations resources and updates on religion-labor work, coordinates the Poultry Justice project to improve conditions for poultry workers, and promotes healthy dialogue between management and unions in religious-owned or sponsored health care facilities.

Headquarters

1020 West Bryn Mawr, 4th floor, Chicago, IL 60660-4627. Tel. (773)728-8400 Fax (773)728-8409
Media Contact, Mike Beckman

Board of Directors

Pres., Rabbi Robert Marx, Congregation Hakafa
Vice-Pres., Rev. Nelson Johnson, Faith Community Church
Sec.-Treas., Rev. Dr. Paul Sherry, National Council of Churches
Action Committee Chair, Ms. Edith Rasell, UCC Minister for Labor Relations
Education Committee Chair, Mr. Tom Chabolla, Catholic Campaign for Human Development
Development Chair, Rev. Clete Kiley, U.S. Conference of Catholic Bishops
Board Development Chair, Ms. Cynthia Nance, University of Arkansas
Dr. Charles Amjad-Ali, Luther Seminary
Mr. Hussam Ayloush, Council on American-Islamic Relations—Southern California
Mr. John Boonstra, Washington Association of Churches
Imam Mahdi Bray, Muslim American Society Freedom Foundation
Ms. Linda Chavez-Thompson, AFL-CIO
Ms. Marilyn Clement, Campaign for a National Health Care Program NOW
Rev. Darren Cushman-Wood, Speedway United Methodist Church
Bishop William DeVeaux, African Methodist Episcopal Church
Bishop Jesse DeWitt**, Retired, United Methodist Church
Dr. Mary Heidkamp, Dynamic Insights International
Ms. Karen Herrling, Catholic Legal Immigration Network, Inc.
Ms. Karen McLean Hessel, Justice for Women, National Council of Churches
Mr. Jeffry Korgen, The Roundtable
Rabbi Mordechai Liebling, Shefa Fund
Ms. Linda Lotz, American Friends Service Committee
Rev. Bennie Mitchell, National Baptist Convention-USA, Inc.
Rev. J. Herbert Nelson, Liberation Community Church/Mid-South Interfaith Committee for Worker Justice
Rev. Sinclair Oubre, Catholic Labor Network

Mr. Mark Pelavin, Religious Action Center for Reform Judaism
Ms. Rosalyn Pelles, Union Community Fund
Sister Mary Priniski, OP, Catholic Committee of the South
Ms. Meg Riley, Unitarian Universalist Association of Congregations
Rev. Michael Rouse*, St. Catherine AME Zion Church
Mr. Chris Sanders, Political Consultant, UFCW
Rev. Jim Sessions*, United Methodist Church
Mr. Thomas Shellabarger, U.S. Conference of Catholic Bishops
Ms. Evely Laser Shlensky*, Commission on Social Action of Reform Judaism (URJ & CCAR)
Rev. Ron Stief, UCC Justice and Witness Ministries Public Life and Social Policy
Mr. Monroe Sullivan, Retired Businessman/ Social Activist
Rev. Phil Tom, Urban Ministry Office, Presbyterian Church USA
Rev. Mark Wendorf, McCormick Theological Seminary
Bishop Gabina Zavala, Archdiocese of Los Angeles
* Former Board Officer
** Former Board President

Special Advisors

Rev. Jim Lawson, Holman United Methodist Church
Rev. Joseph Echols Lowery, Southern Christian Leadership Conference
Rev. Addie Wyatt, Vernon Park Church of God

Administration

Asst. to the Dir., Mike Beckman, mbeckman@nicwj.org
Exec. Dir., Kim Bobo, kbobo@nicwj.org
Deputy Dir., Charese L. Jordan, cjordan@nicwj.org

Issues and Public Policy

Dept. Dir., Tiffany Heath, theath@nicwj.org
Organizer, Nick Tracz, ntracz@nicwj.org

Organizing

Religious Perspectives on Work Prog. Dir., Joy Heine, jheine@nicwj.org
Religious Perspectives on Work Prog. Organizer, Emily Harry, eharry@nicwj.org
National Workers Center Dir., José L. Oliva, joliva@nicwj.org
Organizing Dept. Dir., Kristi Sanford, ksanford@nicwj.org
Worker Center Organizer, Northwest AR, Lucia Hernandez, wrj_lc005@hotmail.com
Worker Center Organizer, Eastern NC, Sallie McLean, smclean@nicwj.org
Worker Center Organizer, Western NC, Francisco Risso, fjrisso@hotmail.com

Fundraising and Finance

Assoc. Development Dir., Aina Gutierrez, agutierrez@nicwj.org
Development Dir., Tina Herpe, therpe@nicwj. org

Interreligious Foundation for Community Organization (IFCO)

IFCO is a national ecumenical agency created in 1966 by several Protestant, Roman Catholic and Jewish organizations, to be an inter-religious, interracial agency for support of community organization and education in pursuit of social justice. Through IFCO, national and regional religious bodies collaborate in development of social justice strategies and provide financial support and technical assistance to local, national and international social-justice projects.

IFCO serves as a bridge between the churches and communities and acts as a resource for ministers and congregations wishing to better understand and do more to advance the struggles of the poor and oppressed. IFCO conducts workshops for community organizers and uses its national and international network of organizers, clergy and other professionals to act in the interest of justice.

Churches, foundations and individual donors use IFCO services as a fiscal agent to make donations to community organizing projects.

IFCO's global outreach includes humanitarian aid shipments through its Pastors for Peace program to Cuba, Haiti, Nicaragua, Honduras, and Chiapas, Mexico.

Headquarters

402 W. 145th St., New York, NY 10031 Tel. (212)926-5757 Fax (212)926-5842
Media Contact, Dir. of Communications, Gail Walker

Officers

Pres., Rev. Schuyler Rhodes
Vice President & Treasurer, Marilyn Clement

The Kairos Institute, Inc.

The Kairos Institute provides quality support, consultation and in-depth educational opportunities to the professional, medical, mental health and religious communities and promotes assistance, consultation, education and care to families of exceptional children. Its clergy consultation service provides care to many denominations and clergy. "Career Path" offers candidate assessment for ordination and consultation for clergy in transition.

Headquarters

107 Green Ave., Madison, NJ 07940 Tel. (973)966-9099 Fax (973)377-8509

Officers

Rev. Robert Clark, Exec. Dir.

The Liturgical Conference

Founded in 1940 by a group of Benedictines, the Liturgical Conference is an independent, ecumenical, international association of persons concerned about liturgical renewal and meaningful worship. The Liturgical Conference is known

KENRICK SEMINARY LIBRARY
5200 GLENNON DRIVE
ST. LOUIS, MO. 63119

chiefly for its periodicals, books, and materials on worship-related concerns in cooperation with various church groups.

Headquarters

P.O.Box 31, Evanston, IL 60201

Officers

Pres., E. Byron Anderson
Vice-Pres., Todd Johnson
Sec., Craig Mueller
Treas., Victor Cinson

Lombard Mennonite Peace Center

The Lombard Mennonite Peace Center (LMPC) is a nonprofit organization with the mission "to proclaim Christ's good news, the gospel of peace and justice—and to be active in the sacred ministry of reconciliation." With an emphasis on equipping clergy and churches to function in healthy ways, LMPC offers training in conflict transformation and in a family systems approach to church leaders' management of themselves and their congregations.

One- and two-day educational workshops and a five-day Mediation Skills Training Institute for Church Leaders are offered throughout the U.S. Ongoing clergy clinics provide church leaders with regular opportunities to reflect on their own functioning. LMPC also provides educational events, consultation and mediation services for congregations and judicatories of all denominations, as well as consultation for individual clergy.

Founded in 1983 as a ministry of a local congregation, LMPC became an independent, 501(c)3 corporation in 1997.

Headquarters

101 W. 22nd St., Suite 206, Lombard, IL 60148
Tel. (630)627-0507 Fax (630)627-0519, admin@lmpeacecenter.org, www.lmpeacecenter.org

Officers

Exec. Dir., Richard G. Blackburn

The Lord's Day Alliance of the United States

The Lord's Day Alliance of the United States, founded in 1888 in Washington, D.C., is the only national organization whose sole purpose is the preservation and cultivation of Sunday, the Lord's Day, as a day of rest and worship. The Alliance also seeks to safeguard a Day of Common Rest for all people regardless of their faith. Its Board of Managers is composed of representatives from 25 denominations. It serves as an information bureau, publishes a magazine, *Sunday*, and furnishes speakers and a variety of materials such as pamphlets, videos, posters, radio spot announcements, cassettes, news releases, articles for magazines and television programs.

Headquarters

2930 Flowers Rd. S., Atlanta, GA 30341-5532
Tel. (770)936-5376 or (800)746-4422 ext. 376 Fax (770)936-5385, tnorton@1dausa.org, www.sundayonline.org
Media Contact, Exec. Dir. & Ed., Rev. Timothy A. Norton

Officers

Pres., Dr. Roger A. Kvam
Pres. Emeritus, Paul J. Craven
Sr. Vice-Pres., Wendell J. Schaal
Vice-Pres., Brian W. Hanse, David C. McNair, Eugene J. Nicodemus, W. David Sapp, William B. Shea
Sec., Donald R. Pepper
Asst. Sec., Betty Jo Craft
Treas., E. Larry Eidson

Lutheran World Relief

Lutheran World Relief (LWR) is an overseas development and relief agency based in Baltimore which responds quickly to natural and man-made disasters and supports more than 160 long-range development projects in countries throughout Africa, Asia, the Middle East and Latin America.

As its mission, Lutheran World Relief works with partners in 50 countries to help people grow food, improve health, strengthen communities, end conflict, build livelihoods, and recover from disasters.

Headquarters

700 Light Street, Baltimore, MD 21230-3850
Tel. (410)230-2700 Fax (410)230-2882

Officers

Pres., Kathryn F. Wolford

The Mennonite Central Committee

The Mennonite Central Committee is the relief and service agency of North American Mennonite and Brethren in Christ Churches. Representatives from Mennonite and Brethren in Christ groups make up the MCC, which meets annually in June to review its program and to approve policies and budget. Founded in 1920, MCC administers and participates in programs of agricultural and economic development, education, health, self-help, relief, peace and disaster service. MCC has about 900 workers serving in 60 countries in Africa, Asia, Europe, Middle East and South, Central and North America.

MCC has service programs in North America that focus both on urban and rural poverty areas. There are also North American programs focusing on such diverse matters as community conciliation, employment creation and criminal justice issues. These programs are administered by two national bodies—MCC U.S. and MCC Canada.

Contributions from North American Mennonite and Brethren in Christ churches provide the largest part of MCC's support. Other sources of financial support include the contributed earnings of volunteers, grants from private and government agencies and contributions from Mennonite churches abroad. The total income in FYE 2001, including material aid contributions, amounted to $63.2 million.

MCC tries to strengthen local communities by working in cooperation with local churches or other community groups. Many personnel are placed with other agencies, including missions. Programs are planned with sensitivity to locally felt needs.

Headquarters

21 S. 12th St., P.O. Box 500, Akron, PA 17501-0500 Tel. (717)859-1151 Fax (717)859-2171

Canadian Office, 134 Plaza Dr., Winnipeg, MB R3T 5K9 Tel. (204)261-6381 Fax (204)269-9875

Media Contact, Exec. Dir., Ronald J.R. Mathies, P.O. Box 500, Akron, PA 17501 Tel. (717)859-1151 Fax (717)859-2171

Officers

Exec. Dirs., Intl., Ronald J.R. Mathies; Canada, Donald Peters; U.S.A., Jose Ortiz

National Association of Ecumenical and Interreligious Staff

NAEIS is an association of professional staff in ecumenical and interreligious work. Founded as the Association of Council Secretaries in 1940, the Association was widened to include program staff in 1971, and renamed the National Association of Ecumenical Staff. It has included staff of any faith engaged in interreligious work since 1994. NAEIS provides means for personal and professional growth, and for mutual support, through national and regional conferences, a newsletter and exchange among its membership.

NAEIS was established to provide creative relationships among them and to encourage mutual support and personal and professional growth. This is accomplished through training programs, through exchange and discussion of common concerns at conferences, and through the publication of the *Corletter,* in collaboration with NCCC Ecumenical Networks.

Headquarters

Janet Leng, Membership Officer, P.O.Box 7093, Tacoma, WA 98406-0093 Tel. (253)759-0142, naeisjan@aol.com

Officers

Pres., 2003-2005, Barbara White, Social Services, Church of God in Christ, 3500 W. Mother Daniel's Way, Milwaukee, WI 53209 Tel. (414)466-1800, uniquebarbara@hotmail.com

Vice-Pres., 2003-2005, The Rev. Samuel Muyskens, Interfaith Ministers—Wichita, 829 North Market Street, Wichita, KS 67214-1157 Tel. (512)451-2062

Immediate Past Pres., Julia Sibley Juras, SC Christian Action Council, P.O. Box 3248, Columbia, SC 29230-3248 Tel. (803)786-7115

Sec., 2003-2005, Rev. Peggy Crawford, Church of Scientology, 1010 Hurley Way, Suite 505, Sacramento, CA 95825 Tel. (916)925-2545

The National Association of Evangelicals

The National Association of Evangelicals (NAE)is a voluntary fellowship of evangelical denominations, churches, organizations and individuals demonstrating unity in the body of Christ by standing for biblical truth, speaking with a representative voice, and serving the evangelical community through united action, cooperative ministry and strategic planning.

The association is comprised of approximately 43,000 congregations nationwide from 50 member denominations and fellowships, as well as several hundred independent churches. The membership of the association includes more than 250 parachurch ministries and educational institutions. Through the cooperative ministry of these members, NAE directly and indirectly benefits more than 27 million people. These ministries represent a broad range of theological traditions, but all subscribe to the distinctly evangelical NAE Statement of Faith. The association is a nationally recognized entity by the public sector with a reputation for integrity and effective service.

The cooperative ministries of the National Association of Evangelicals demonstrate the association's intentional desire to promote cooperation without compromise.

Headquarters

P.O. Box 1325, Azusa, CA 91702 Tel. (626)963-5966

NAE-Washington, 701 G. St., SW, Washington, DC 20024 Tel. (202)789-1011 Fax (202)842-0392

Media Contact, Rev. Rich Cizik, (202)789-1011

Staff

Vice-Pres. of Ministry Development, Rev. John N. Mendez

Vice-Pres. of Governmental Affairs, Rev. Rich Cizik

MEMBER DENOMINATIONS

Advent Christian General Conference
Assemblies of God
Association of Vineyard Churches
Baptist General Conference
The Brethren Church
Brethren in Christ Church
Christian & Missionary Alliance
Christ Community Church
Christian Church of North America
Christian Reformed Church in North America
Christian Union
Church of God, Cleveland, TN
Church of God, Mountain Assembly
Church of the Nazarene

United Brethren in Christ Church
Churches of Christ in Christian Union
Congregational Holiness Church
Conservative Baptist Assoc. of America
Conservative Congregational Christian Conf.
Conservative Lutheran Association
Elim Fellowship
Evangelical Church of North America
Evangelical Congregational Church
Evangelical Free Church of America
Evangelical Friends Intl.-North America
Evangelical Mennonite Church
Evangelical Methodist Church
Evangelical Presbyterian Church
Evangelistic Missionary Fellowship
Fellowship of Evangelical Bible Churches
Fire-Baptized Holiness Church of God of the Americas
Free Methodist Church of North America
General Association of General Baptists
Intl. Church of the Foursquare Gospel
Intl. Pentecostal Church of Christ
Intl. Pentecostal Holiness Church
Mennonite Brethren Churches, USA
Missionary Church, Inc.
Open Bible Standard Churches
Pentecostal Church of God
Pentecostal Free Will Baptist Church
Presbyterian Church in America
Primitive Methodist Church, USA
Reformed Episcopal Church
Reformed Presbyterian Church of N.A.
Salvation Army
Regional Synod of Mid-America (Reformed Church in America)
Wesleyan Church
Worldwide Church of God

National Bible Association

The National Bible Association is an autonomous, interfaith organization of lay people who advocate regular Bible reading and sponsors National Bible Week (Thanksgiving week)each November. Program activities include public service advertising, distribution of nonsectarian literature and thousands of local Bible Week observances by secular and religious organizations. The Association also urges constitutionally acceptable use of the Bible in public school classrooms, i.e.the study of the Bible in literature. All support comes from individuals, corporations and foundations.

Founded in 1940 by a group of business and professional people, the Association offers daily Bible readings in several English and Spanish translations on its Web site and has the IRS nonprofit status of a 501(c)(3)educational association.

Headquarters

1865 Broadway, New York, NY 10023 Tel. (212)408-1390 Fax (212)408-1448
Media Contact, Pres., Thomas R. May

Officers

Chpsn., Philip J. Clements
Vice-Chpsns.; Robert Cavalero; John W. Pugsley; John M. Templeton, Jr., M.D.
Pres., Thomas R. May
Treas., Paul Werner
Sec., J. Marshall Gage

The National Conference for Community and Justice

The National Conference for Community and Justice, founded in 1927 as the National Conference of Christians and Jews, is a human relations organization dedicated to fighting bias, bigotry and racism in America. The NCCJ promotes understanding and respect among all races, religions and cultures through advocacy, conflict resolution and education.

Programmatic strategies include interfaith and interracial dialogue, youth leadership workshops, workplace training, human relations research, and the building of community coalitions. NCCJ has 65 regional offices staffed by approximately 350 people. Nearly 200 members comprise the National Board of Advisors and members from that group form the 27-member National Board of Directors. Each regional office has its own Regional Board of Directors with a total of about 2,800. The National Board of Advisors meets once annually, the National Board of Directors at least three times annually.

Headquarters

475 Park Ave. S., New York, NY 10016 Tel. (212)545-1300 Fax (212)545-8053
Media Contact, Dir. of Communications, Diane Powers

Officers

Pres. & CEO, Sanford Cloud, Jr.

National Conference on Ministry to the Armed Forces

The Conference is an incorporated civilian agency. Representation in the Conference with all privileges of the same is open to all endorsing or certifying agencies or groups authorized to provide chaplains for any branch of the Armed Forces.

The purpose of this organization is to provide a means of dialogue to discuss concerns and objectives and, when agreed upon, to take action with the appropriate authority to support the spiritual ministry to and the moral welfare of Armed Forces personnel.

Headquarters

4141 N. Henderson Rd., Suite 13, Arlington, VA 22203 Tel. (703)276-7905 Fax (703)276-7906
Media Contact, Jack Williamson

Staff

Coord., Jack Williamson
Admn. Asst., Maureen Francis

Officers

Chpsn., David Peterson
Chpsn.-Elect, Robert Jemerson
Sec., Lemuel Boyles
Treas., John Murdoch

National Council of the Churches of Christ in the U.S.A.

The National Council of the Churches of Christ in the U.S.A. ("National Council of Churches")is the nation's leading organization in the movement for Christian unity. Its 36 Protestant, Orthodox, Anglican, Historic African American and Living Peace member churches (denominations)include approximately 45 million congregants in more than 100,000 local congregations nationwide. The NCC was formed in 1950 in Cleveland, Ohio, by the action of representatives of the member churches and by the merger of 12 previously existing ecumenical agencies, each of which had a different program focus. The roots of some of these agencies go back to the 19th century. Council programs include a wide range of activities that further dialogue among churches on issues of doctrine and practice, promote peace, advocate for just public policies, foster interfaith understanding, protect the environment, reduce poverty, and support congregations in worship, education, leadership and social justice ministries. The NCC holds the copyright on the Revised and New Revised Standard Version of the Bible and produces the annual *Yearbook of American and Canadian Churches*.

Headquarters

475 Riverside Drive, Suite 880, New York, NY 10115 Tel. (212)870-2141 Fax (212)870-2817
Media Contact, Communication Department, Tel. (212)870-2227 Fax (212)870-2030

GENERAL OFFICERS

Pres., Bishop Thomas L. Hoyt, Jr.
Gen. Sec., Rev. Dr. Robert W. Edgar
Immediate Past Pres., Ms. Elenie K. Huszagh, Esq.
Pres. Elect, Rev. Michael E. Livingston
Vice-Pres., Admin. & Finance, Ms. Clare J. Chapman
Vice-Pres., Church World Service, Ms. Betty Voskuil
Vice-Pres. at Large, Rev. Dr. Randall R. Lee
Vice-Pres. at Large, Rev. Dr. Thelma Chambers-Young
Sec., Bishop Vicken Aykazian

OFFICE OF THE GENERAL SECRETARY

Gen. Sec., Rev. Dr. Robert W. Edgar, Tel. (212)870-2025 Fax (212)870-2817
Asst. to the Gen. Sec., Ms. Vicki Manning, Tel. (212)870-2025 Fax (212)870-2817

RESEARCH AND PLANNING

Deputy Gen. Sec. for Research and Planning, Rev. Dr. Eileen W. Lindner, Tel. (212)870-2333
Assoc. for Research and Planning, Rev. Marcel A. Welty, Tel. (212)870-2379

DEVELOPMENT

Dir. of Development, Mr. John Briscoe, Tel. (212)870-2923 Fax (212)870-2817
Special Asst. for Planned Giving, Endowment, Rev. Jon Sherry, Tel. (804)928-6222

YEARBOOK OF AMERICAN AND CANADIAN CHURCHES

Editor, Rev. Dr. Eileen W. Lindner, Tel. (212)870-2333
Assoc. Ed. and Technical Coord., Rev. Marcel A. Welty, Tel. (212)870-2379
Asst. to the Ed., Mr. Patrick Bartlett, Tel. (212)870-2031 Fax (212)870-2817
Asst. to the Ed., Mr. Earl Davis, Tel. (212)870-2333

WASHINGTON OFFICE

110 Maryland Ave NE, Washington, DC 20002 Tel. (202)544-2350 Fax(202)543-1297
Assoc. Gen. Sec. for Justice and Advocacy and Dir. Wash. Office, Rev. Brenda Girton-Mitchell, Esq., Tel. (202)544-2350
Dir., Eco-Justice Programs, Ms. Cassandra Carmichael, Tel. (202)544-2350 x 27
Assoc. Gen. Sec. for Faith & Order, Dr. Ann K. Riggs, Tel. (202)544-2350 Wash., D.C.
Communication Officer, Rev. Leslie C. Tune, Tel. (202)544-2350, ext.11
National Religious Partnership for the Environment, Mr. Doug Grace, Tel. (202)544-5530 or (202)544-3110
Dir., FaithfulAmerica.org Electronic Advocacy Program, Mr. Vince Isner, Tel. (202)544-2350 Fax (202)543-1297

OFFICE OF ADMINISTRATION AND FINANCE

Assoc. Gen. Sec. for Admin. and Finance, Ms. Leora Landmesser, Tel. (212)870-3366 Fax (212)870-3112
Asst. Dir. of Admin. and Human Resources, Ms. Joan Gardner, Tel. (212)870-2258 Fax (212)870-3112
Controller, Ms. Karen Wang, Tel. (212)870-3351 Fax (212)870-3454
Dir., Info. Technology, Mr. Julian Devia, Tel. (212)870-2541
Dir., Database Admin., Rev. Marcel A. Welty, Tel. (212)870-2379
Dept. Business Services, Tel. (212)870-2181

FRIENDSHIP PRESS

Business Contact, Leora Landmesser, Assoc. Gen. Sec. for Admin. and Finance, Tel. (212)870-3366 Fax (212)870-3112
Orders: Tel. (800)889-5733 or e-mail Rbray@gbgm-umc.org

BIBLE TRANSLATION AND UTILIZATION

Permissions/licensing inquiries for Revised Standard Version and New Revised Standard Version Bible: See www.ncccusa.org/newbtu/permiss.html and/or contact: nrsv-copyright@aol.com

Other inquiries—Marvin L. Roloff, Tel. (612)330-3300 x301

THE COMMISSIONS:

Justice and Advocacy Commission

Assoc. Gen. Sec. for International Affairs and Peace, Dr. Antonios Kireopoulos, Tel. (212)870-3422 Fax (212)870-2817

Assoc. Gen. Sec. for Justice and Advocacy and Dir. Wash. Office, Rev. Brenda Girton-Mitchell, Esq., Tel. (202)544-2350

Coord., Mobilization to Overcome Poverty, Rev. Dr. Paul Sherry, Tel. (216)736-3710

Prog. Dir., Justice for Women, Rev. Karen Hessel, (212)870-2421 Fax (212)870-2817

Communication Commission

Assoc. Gen. Sec. for Communication, Wesley M. "Pat" Pattillo, Tel. (212)870-2048 Fax (212)870-2030

Dir., Interpretation Resources (Public Requests, EcuLink Newspaper), Ms. Sarah Vilankulu, Tel. (212)870-2228 Fax (212)870-2030 Washington Communication Officer, Rev. Leslie C. Tune, Tel. (202)544-2350 ext. 11 Fax (202)543-1297

Coord. of TV Programming, Ms. Shirley W. Struchen, Tel. (212)870-2227 Fax (212)870-2030

Dir., FaithfulAmerica.org Electronic Advocacy Program, Mr. Vince Isner, Tel. (202)544-2350 Fax (202)543-1297

Education and Leadership Ministries Commission

Assoc. Gen. Sec., Education and Leadership Ministries, Rev. Patrice Rosner, Tel. (212)870-2738

Assoc. Dir., Education and Leadership Ministries, Rev. Garland Pierce, Tel. (212)870-2267

Program Specialist, Ms. Barbara Tilley, Tel. (212)870-2297

Faith and Order Commission

Assoc. Gen. Sec. for Faith and Order, Dr. Ann K. Riggs, Tel. (202)544-2350 Fax (202)543-1297

Interfaith Relations Commission

Assoc. Gen. Sec. for Interfaith Relations, Shanta Premawardhana, Tel. (212)870-2560 Fax (212)870-2817

NCC Related Organizations

Agricultural Missions, Exec. Dir. Dr. Winston Carroo, Tel. (212)870-2554

Interfaith Center for Corporate Responsibility, Exec. Dir., Sr. Patricia Wolf, RSM, Tel. (212)870-2295

Natl. Farm Worker Ministry, Exec. Dir., Ms. Virginia Nesmith, 438 N. Skinner Blvd., St. Louis, MO 63130 Tel. (314)726-6470

Church World Service and Witness

Exec. Dir., Rev. John L. McCullough, Tel. (212)870-2175

Deputy Dir., Operations and CFO, Ms. Joanne Rendall, Tel. (574)264-3102 ext. 332

Chief Development Officer, Rev. Peter D. Crouch, Tel. (574)264-3102 ext. 470

Dir., Human Resources, Mr. Bernard Kirchhoff, Tel. (574)264-3102 ext. 346

Dir., Mission Relationships & Witness Program, Mr. David Weaver, Tel. (212)870-2818

Dir., Education & Advocacy for International Justice & Human Rights, Ms. Rajyashri Waghray, Tel. (212)870-2497

Dir., Social and Economic Development, Mr. Chris Falco, Tel. (212)870-2372

Dir., Emergency Response, Mr. Rick Augsburger, Tel. (212)870-3154

Dir., Immigration & Refugee Program, Rev. Joseph Roberson, Tel. (212)870-2178

Media Contact, Ann Walle, Director of Communications and Marketing, Tel. (212)870-2654

Constituent Bodies (with membership dates)

African Methodist Episcopal Church (1950)
The African Methodist Episcopal Zion Church (1950)
The Alliance of Baptists in the U.S.A. (2000)
American Baptist Churches in the U.S.A. (1950)
The Antiochian Orthodox Christian Archdiocese of North America (1966)
Armenian Apostolic Church, Diocese of the (1957)
Christian Church (Disciples of Christ)(1950)
Christian Methodist Episcopal Church (1950)
Church of the Brethren (1950)
Coptic Orthodox Church (1978)
The Episcopal Church (1950)
Evangelical Lutheran Church in America (1950)
Friends United Meeting (1950)
Greek Orthodox Archdiocese of America (1952)
Hungarian Reformed Church in America (1957)
Intl. Council of Community Churches (1977)
Korean Presbyterian Church in America, Gen. Assembly of the (1986)
Malankara Orthodox Syrian Church, Diocese of America (1998)
Mar Thoma Church (1997)
Moravian Church in America, Northern Province, Southern Province (1950)
National Baptist Convention of America, Inc. (1950)
National Baptist Convention, U.S.A., Inc. (1950)
National Missionary Baptist Convention of America (1995)
Orthodox Church in America (1950)
Philadelphia Yearly Meeting of the Religious Society of Friends (1950)
Polish Natl. Catholic Church of America (1957)
Presbyterian Church (U.S.A.)(1950)
Progressive Natl. Baptist Convention, Inc. (1966)
Reformed Church in America (1950)
Russian Orthodox Church in the U.S.A., Patriarchal Parishes of the (1966)
Serbian Orthodox Church in the U.S.A. & Canada (1957)
The Swedenborgian Church (1966)

US COOPERATIVE ORGANIZATIONS

Syrian (Syriac)Orthodox Church of Antioch (Archdiocese of the U.S. and Canada)(1960)
Ukrainian Orthodox Church of the U.S.A.(1950)
United Church of Christ (1950)
The United Methodist Church (1950)

National Institute of Business and Industrial Chaplains

NIBIC is the professional organization for workplace chaplains, which includes members from a wide variety of faith groups and work settings, including corporations, manufacturing plants, air and sea ports, labor unions and pastoral counseling centers. NIBIC has six membership categories, including Certified, Clinical, Professional, Affiliates and Organizational.

NIBIC works to establish professional standards for education and practice; promotes and conducts training programs; provides mentoring, networking and chaplaincy information; encourages research and public information dissemination; communicates with business leaders and conducts professional meetings. NIBIC publishes a quarterly newsletter and cosponsors *The Journal of Pastoral Care and Counseling*. A public membership meeting and training conference is held annually.

Headquarters

1770 St. James Place, Suite 550, Houston, TX 77056-3471 Tel. (713)266-2456 Fax (713)266-0845
Media Contact, Rev. Diana C. Dale, 1770 St. James Place, Suite 550 Houston, TX 77056-3471 Tel. (713)266-2456 Fax (713)266-0845

Officers

Exec. Dir., Rev. Diana C. Dale, D.Min.
Vice-Pres., Rev. Stephen Holden
Pres., Rev. Timothy Bancroft, D.Min.
Treas., Rev. Gregory Edwards
Board Member, Rev. Robert L. Lewis, Jr., STM

National Interfaith Cable Coalition, Inc. (NICC)

The National Interfaith Cable Coalition, Inc. (NICC)was formed as a not-for-profit 501(c)3 corporation, in December 1987, and is currently doing business as Faith & Values Media. In September 1988, NICC launched a religious cable network called VISN (Vision Interfaith Satellite Network), later known as the Odyssey Channel. In 2001, Odyssey was re-launched as the Hallmark Channel. Faith & Values Media provides 9.5 hours of programming weekly and airs several prime-time holiday/holy day specials on Hallmark each year. The Web presence of Faith & Values Media is www.faithstreams.com, providing video streaming and Video on Demand as well as an extensive library of documents on topics of current interest from member faith groups and others.

Headquarters

74 Trinity Place, Suite 1550, New York, NY 10006 Tel. (212)406-4121 Fax (212)406-4105
Media Contact, Howard Burkat

Officers

Chair, Dr. Daniel Paul Matthews
Vice-Chair, Elder Ralph Hardy, Jr.
Sec., Rabbi Paul J. Menitoff
Treas., Betty Elam

Staff

Pres. and CEO, Edward J. Murray
Exec. Vice-Pres., Beverly Judge

National Interfaith Coalition on Aging

The National Interfaith Coalition on Aging (NICA), a constituent unit of the National Council on Aging, is composed of Protestant, Roman Catholic, Jewish and Orthodox national and regional organizations and individuals concerned about the needs of older people and the religious community's response to problems facing the aging population in the United States. NICA was organized in 1972 to address spiritual concerns of older adults through religious-sector action.

Mission Statement: The National Interfaith Coalition on Aging (NICA), affiliated with the National Council on the Aging (NCOA), is a diverse network of religious and other related organizations and individual members which promotes the spiritual well-being of older adults and the preparation of persons of all ages for the spiritual tasks of aging. NICA serves as a catalyst for new and effective research, networking opportunities, resource development, service provision, and dissemination of information.

Headquarters

c/o NCOA, 300 D St. SW, Suite 801, Washington, D.C. 20024 Tel. (202)479-6655 Fax (202)479-0735
Media Contact, Rita Chow, Ed.D.

Officers

Chpsn., Jane Stenson
Chpsn.-Elect, Rev. Ron Field
Past Chpsn., Rev. Dr. Robert W. Carlson
Sec., Donald R. Koepke
Dir., Dr. Rita K. Chow

National Religious Broadcasters

National Religious Broadcasters is an association of Christian communicators, 1,500 organizations which produce religious programs for radio and television and other forms of electronic mass media or operate stations carrying predominately religious programs. NRB member organizations are responsible for more than 75 percent of all religious radio and television in the United States, reaching an average weekly audience of millions by radio, television, and other broadcast media.

KENRICK SEMINARY LIBRARY
5200 GLENNON DRIVE
ST. LOUIS, MO. 63119

Dedicated to the communication of the Gospel, NRB was founded in 1944 to safeguard free and complete access to the broadcast media. By encouraging the development of Christian programs and stations, NRB helps make it possible for millions to hear the good news of Jesus Christ through the electronic media.

Headquarters

9510 Technology Drive, Manassas, VA 20110 Tel. (703)330-7000 Fax (703)330-7100

Media Contact, Exec. Vice-Pres., Michael Glenn

Officers

Chair, Glenn R. Plummer, Christian Television Network, Detriot, MI

1st Vice-Chair, Michael D. Little, Christian Broadcasting Network, Virginia Beach, VA

2nd Vice-Chair, Bill A. Blount, Blount Communications, Warwick, RI

Sec., William Skelton, Love Worth Finding Ministries, Memphis, TN

Treas., James A. Gwinn, CRISTA Ministries, Seattle, WA

National Woman's Christian Temperance Union

The National WCTU is a not-for-profit, nonpartisan, interdenominational organization dedicated to the education of our nation's citizens, especially children and teens, on the harmful effects of alcoholic beverages, other drugs and tobacco on the human body and the society in which we live. The WCTU believes in a strong family unit and, through legislation, education and prayer, works to strengthen the home and family.

WCTU, which began in 1874 with the motto, "For God and Home and Every Land," is organized in 58 countries.

Headquarters

1730 Chicago Ave., Evanston, IL 60201 Tel. (708)864-1396

Media Contact, Sarah F. Ward, Tel. (765)345-7600

Officers

Pres., Sarah F. Ward, 33 N. Franklin, Knightstown, IN 46148, sarah@wctu.org

Vice-Pres., Rita Wert, 2250 Creek Hill Rd., Lancaster, PA 17601

Promotion Dir., Nancy Zabel, 1730 Chicago Ave., Evanston, IL 60201-4585

Treas., Faye Pohl, P.O. Box 739, Meade, KS 67864

Rec. Sec., Dorothy Russell, 18900 Nestueca Dr., Cloverdale, OR 97112

Member Organizations

Loyal Temperance Legion (LTL), for boys and girls ages 6-12

Youth Temperance Council (YTC), for teens through college age

North American Baptist Fellowship

Organized in 1964, the North American Baptist Fellowship is a voluntary organization of Baptist Conventions in Canada and the United States, functioning as a regional body within the Baptist World Alliance. Its objectives are, (a)to promote fellowship and cooperation among Baptists in North America and (b)to further the aims and objectives of the Baptist World Alliance so far as these affect the life of the Baptist churches in North America. Its membership, however, is not identical with the North American membership of the Baptist World Alliance.

Church membership of the Fellowship bodies is more than 28 million.

The NABF assembles representatives of the member bodies once a year for exchange of information and views in such fields as evangelism and education, missions, stewardship promotion, lay activities and theological education. It conducts occasional consultations for denominational leaders on such subjects as church extension. It encourages cooperation at the city and county level where churches of more than one member group are located.

Headquarters

P.O. Box 6412, Falls Church, VA 22040

Media Contact, Gen. Sec., Dr. Alan Stanford

Officers

Pres., Dr. Harry Gardner, 1655 Manawagonish Rd., Saint John, NB E2M 3Y2 Canada

Vice-Pres., Dr. Derrick Harkins, 4606 16th St. NW, Washington, D.C. 20011

Vice-Pres., Mrs. Bertha Williams, 13520 Corby Rd., Cleveland, OH 44120

Vice-Pres., Dr. Phillip D. Wise, 6109 Chicago Ave., Lubbock, TX 79146

Member Bodies

American Baptist Churches in the USA
Baptist General Conference
Canadian Baptist Federation
General Association of General Baptists
National Baptist Convention of America
National Baptist Convention, USA, Inc.
Progressive National Baptist Convention, Inc.
Seventh Day Baptist General Conference
North American Baptist Conference
Southern Baptist Convention

Oikocredit-Ecumenical Development Cooperative Society

Based in the Netherlands, EDCS is often called "the churches' bank for the poor." EDCS borrows funds from churches, religious communities and concerned individuals and re-lends the funds to enterprises operated by low-income communities. Launched in 1975 through an initiative of the World Council of Churches, EDCS is organized as a cooperative of religious institutions and is governed by annual membership meetings and an elected board of religious leaders and development and financial professionals.

An international network of 15 EDCS Regional Managers is responsible for lending funds to cooperative enterprises and microcredit institutions. At the present time more than $220 million is at work in coffee shops, fishing enterprises, handicraft production, truck farming, and many other commercial ventures owned and operated by poor people.

EDCS is represented in the United States by the Ecumenical Development Corporation-USA (EDC-USA), a 501(c)3 non-profit corporation. American individuals and congregations can invest in EDCS by purchasing one-, three-, and five-year notes paying 0-2% interest that are issued by EDC-USA.

Headquarters

P.O. Box 11000, Washington, D.C. 20008 Tel.(202)265-0607 Fax (202)265-7029, office.us@oikocredit.org, www.oikocredit.org

Media Contact, Regional Manager for North America, Rev. Terry Provance

Officers

Exec. Dir., Rev. Terry Provance
Chpsn., Gary Cook
Vice-Chpsn., Richard Gist
Treas., Mary Pat Brennan

Parish Resource Center, Inc.

Parish Resource Center, Inc. promotes, establishes, nurtures and accredits local Affiliate Parish Resource Centers. Affiliate centers educate, equip and strengthen subscribing congregations of all faiths by providing professional consultants, resource materials and workshops. The Parish Resource Center was founded in 1976. In 2004, there were five free-standing affiliates located in Lancaster, PA; Long Island, NY; Denver, CO.; Dayton, OH and New York City. These centers serve congregations from 49 faith traditions.

Headquarters

633 Community Way, Lancaster, PA 17603 Tel. (717)299-2223 Fax (717)299-7229

Media Contact, Pres., Dr. D. Douglas Whiting

Officers

Chair, Dr. Robert D. Webber
Vice-Chair, Sidney Lovett
Sec.-Treas., Sally Bures
Pres., Dr. D. Douglas Whiting

Pentecostal-Charismatic Churches of North America

The Pentecostal-Charismatic Churches of North America (PCCNA)was organized October 19, 1994, in Memphis, TN. This organizational meeting came the day after the Pentecostal Fellowship of North America (PFNA)voted itself out of existence in order to make way for the new fellowship.

The PFNA had been formed in October 1948 in Des Moines, IA. It was composed of white-led Pentecostal denominations. The move to develop a multiracial fellowship began when the PFNA Board of Administration initiated a series of discussions with African American Pentecostal leaders. The first meeting was held July 10-11, 1992, in Dallas, TX. A second meeting convened in Phoenix, AZ, January 4-5, 1993. On January 10-11, 1994, 20 representatives from each of the two groups met in Memphis to make final plans for a dialogue which was held in Memphis, October 1994.

This racial reconciliation meeting has been called "The Memphis Miracle." During this meeting the PFNA was disbanded, and the PCCNA was organized. The new organization quickly adopted the "Racial Reconciliation Manifesto." Subsequent meetings were held in Memphis, TN (1996), Washington, D.C. (1997), Tulsa, OK (1998), and Hampton, VA (1999)

In an effort to further increase the spirit of reconciliation, the PCCNA meeting of 2000 was held during the North American Renewal Service Committee (NARSC) conference in St. Louis, Missouri. Furthermore, the PCCNA acted as host for the 19th Pentecostal World Conference held in Los Angeles, California, May 2001.

Headquarters

1910 W. Sunset Blvd., Suite 200, Los Angeles, CA 90026-0176 Tel. (213)484-2400 ext. 309 Fax (213)413-3824

Media Contact, Dr. Ronald Williams

PCCNA Executive Board

Co-Chair, Bishop James D. Leggett, International Pentecostal Holiness Church, P.O. Box 12609, Oklahoma City, OK 73157-2609 Tel. (405)787-7110 ext. 3302 Fax (405)787-3650, jdl@iphc.org

Co-Chair, Bishop George D. McKinney, St. Stephen's Church of God in Christ, 5825 Imperial Ave., San Diego, CA 92114 Tel. (619)262-2671 Fax (619)262-8335, ststephens@pcsinter.net

First Vice-Chair, Bishop Oswill Williams, Church of God of Prophecy, Cleveland, TN 37320-3000 Tel. (423)559-5444 Fax (423)559-5219, ossie@wingnet.net

Second Vice-Chair, Rev. Jeff Farmer, Open Bible Standard Churches, 2020 Bell Ave., Des Moines, IA 50315-1096 Tel. (515)288-6761 Fax (515)288-2510

Sec., Dr. Lamar Vest, Church of God, P.O. Box 2430, Cleveland, TN 37320-2430 Tel. (423)478-7137 Fax (423)478-7443

Treas., Dr. Ronald Williams, Int'l Church of the Foursquare Gospel, P.O. Box 26902, Los Angeles, CA 90026 Tel. (213)989-4221 Fax (213)989-4544, ron@foursquare.org

Advisors

Rev. Billy Joe Daugherty, Victory Christian

Center, 7700 South Lewis Ave., Tulsa, OK 74136-7700 Tel. (918)493-1700 Fax (918)491-7795

Rev. Thomas Trask, Assemblies of God, 1445 Boonville Ave., Springfield, MO 65802 Tel. (417)862-2781 ext. 3000 Fax (417)862-8558

Bishop Barbara Amos, Mt. Sinai Holy Church of America, 1010 East 26th St., Norfolk, VA 23504 Tel. (757)624-1950 Fax (757)625-6648

Project Equality, Inc.

Project Equality is a nonprofit national interfaith program for affirmative action and equal employment opportunity.

Project Equality serves as a central agency to receive and validate the equal employment commitment of suppliers of goods and services to sponsoring organizations and participating institutions, congregations and individuals. Employers filing an accepted Annual Participation Report are included in the Project Equality "Buyer's Guide."

Workshops, training events and consultant services in affirmative action, diversity, and equal employment practices in recruitment, selection, placement, transfer, promotion, discipline and discharge are also available to sponsors and participants. Project Equality is a leader in transforming the society to true inclusiveness.

Headquarters

7132 Main St., Kansas City, MO 64114-1406 Tel. (816)361-9222 or toll free (877)PE-IS-EEO Fax (816)361-8997

Media Contact, Pres., Rev. Kirk P. Perucca

Officers

Chpsn., Gloria Folds
Vice-Chpsn., Salvador Mendoza
Sec., Barbara George
Treas., Carla Shaw
Pres., Rev. Kirk P. Perucca

Sponors-Endorsing Organizations

American Baptist Churches in the U.S.A.
American Friends Service Committee
American Jewish Committee
Assoc. Of Junior Leagues, Intl.
Central Conference of American Rabbis
Church of the Brethren
The Episcopal Church
Evangelical Lutheran Church in America
National Council of Churches of Christ in the U.S.A.
National Education Association
Presbyterian Church (USA)
Reorganized Church of Jesus Christ of Latter-Day Saints
The United Methodist Church
Unitarian Universalist Association
United Church of Christ
United Methodist Assoc. of Health & Welfare Ministries
YWCA of the U.S.A.

Religion In American Life, Inc.

Religion In American Life (RIAL)is a unique cooperative program of some 50 major national religious groups (Catholic, Eastern Orthodox, Jewish, Protestant, Muslim, etc.). It provides services for denominationally supported, congregation-based outreach and growth projects such as the current Invite a Friend program. These projects are promoted through national advertising campaigns reaching the American public by the use of all media. The ad campaigns are produced by a volunteer agency with production-distribution and administration costs funded by denominations and business groups, as well as by individuals.

Since 1949, RIAL ad campaign projects have been among the much-coveted major campaigns of The Advertising Council. This results in as much as $35 million worth of time and space in a single year, contributed by media as a public service. Through RIAL, religious groups demonstrate respect for other traditions and the value of religious freedom. The RIAL program also includes seminars and symposia, research and leadership awards and produces a weekly syndicated radio broadcast, *SpiriTalk.*

Headquarters

250 E 87th St., Suite 12F, New York, NY 10128-3116 Tel. (203)355-1220 Fax (203)355-1221

Media Contact, Exec. Admin., Martha Mesiti Tel (203)355-1220

Executive Committee

Natl. Chpsn., Thomas S. Johnson, Chair & CEO, Greenpoint Bank, NY
Chpsn. of Bd., Rev. Dr. Gordon Sommers
Vice-Chpsns., Bishop Khajag Barsamian, Primate (Armenian Church of America); Most Rev. William Cardinal Keeler, (Archbishop of Baltimore); Rabbi Ronald B. Sobel, (Cong. Emanu-El of the City of N.Y.)
Sec., Timothy A. Hultquist (Morgan Stanley Dean Witter)
Treas., Robertson H. Bennett (Smith Barney)

Staff

Pres. & CEO, Robert B. Lennick, Rabbi, D.Min.
Exec. Admin., Martha Mesiti

The Religion Communicators Council, Inc.

RCC is an international, interfaith, interdisciplinary association of professional communicators who work for religious groups and causes. It was founded in 1929 and is the oldest nonprofit professional public relations organization in the world. RCC's more than 600 members include those who work in communications and related fields for church-related institutions, denominational agencies, non and interdenominational organizations and communications firms who primarily serve religious organizations.

Members represent a wide range of faiths,

including Presbyterian, Baptist, Methodist, Lutheran, Episcopalian, Mennonite, Roman Catholic, Seventh-day Adventist, Jewish, Salvation Army, Brethren, Bahá'í, Disciples, Latter-day Saints and others.

On the national level, RCC sponsors an annual three-day convention, and has published seven editions of a *Religious Public Relations Handbook* for churches and church organizations, and a videostrip, *The Church at Jackrabbit Junction*. Members receive a quarterly newsletter (*Counselor*). There are 13 regional chapters.

RCC administers the annual Wilbur Awards competition to recognize high quality coverage of religious values and issues in the public media. Wilbur winners include producers, reporters, editors and broadcasters nationwide. To recognize communications excellence within church communities, RCC also sponsors the annual DeRose-Hinkhouse Awards for its own members.

In 1970, 1980, 1990, and 2000 RCC initiated a global Religious Communications Congress bringing together thousands of persons from western, eastern and third-world nations who are involved in communicating religious faith.

Headquarters

475 Riverside Dr., Room 1355, New York, NY 10115 Tel. (212)870-2171 Fax (212)870-3578

Exec. Dir., Shirley Whipple Struchen, Tel. (212)870-2402, sstruchen@rcn.com, www.religiouncommunicators.org

Officers

Pres., Michael A. Hickcox, Dir. of Comm., New England Conference, UMC, P.O. Box 249, Lawrence, MA 01842-0449 Tel. (978)682-7676 ext. 2 Fax (978)-682-7677, communicate@neumc.org

Vice-Pres., Anuttama Dasa, Dir. of Comm., ISKCON, Hare Krishna, 10310 Oaklyn Drive, Potomac, MD 20854 Tel. (301)299-9707 Fax (301)299-5025, anuttama.acbsp@pamho.net

Religion News Service

Religion News Service (RNS)has provided news and information to the media for almost 70 years. Owned by the Newhouse News Service, it is staffed by veteran jounalists who cover stories on all of the world religions as well as trends in ethics, morality and spirituality.

RNS provides a daily news service, a weekly news service, and photo and graphic services. The daily service is available via the AP Data Features wire, or e-mail. The weekly report is available by wire or e-mail. RNS's Photos Service features stock images, news photography and related graphics. RNS also offers Religion Press Release Services, which distributes press releases and advisories to religion editors. RNS is syndicated in the United States by Universal Press Syndicate and in Canada by Canadian Press.

Headquarters

1101 Connecticut Ave. NW, Suite 350, Washington, D.C. 20036 Tel. (202)463-8777 Fax (202)463-0033, info@religionnews.com, www.religionnews.com

Officers

Editor, David Anderson

Religion Newswriters Association

Founded in 1949, the RNA is a professional association of religion news editors and reporters on secular daily and weekly newspapers, news services, news magazines, radio and television stations. It sponsors seven annual contests for excellence in religion news coverage in the secular press. Annual meetings are held in the fall.

Headquarters

P.O. Box 2037, Westerville, OH 43086 Tel. (614)891-9001 Fax (614)891-9774, mason@religionwriters.com, www.religionwriters.com

Media Contact, Exec. Dir., Debra Mason

Religions for Peace-USA, Inc.

Religions for Peace-USA, formerly the United States Conference of Religions for Peace, began in the 1970s as a program area and chapter of the World Conference of Religions for Peace (now known simply as Religions for Peace), the world's largest representative inter-religious organization. Today, the organization is separately incorporated and registered as an independent 501(c)(3) and focuses its mandate on U.S.-based issues, while retaining a strong link to the international work of Religions for Peace. As the largest and most broadly based representative multi-religious forum in the United States, RFP-USA engages the religious leaders and experts in inter-religious affairs and peace and justice of more than 50 religious traditions. By building on the spiritual, human, and institutional resources of these communities, RFP-USA establishes cooperative efforts among them to address shared challenges. Primary areas of concern for the organization include building inter-religious relationships, creating mutual understanding amidst the country's increasing diversity, and advocating for the responsibility of the U.S. as a citizen of the global community, with particular regard to peace, human rights, and development.

Headquarters

RFP-USA, 777 United Nations Plaza, New York, NY 10017 Tel. (212)338-9140 (212)983-0566

Officers

Sec. Gen./Exec. Dir., Rev. Bud Heckman, bheckman@rfpusa.org

Moderator, The Very Rev. Leonid Kishkovsky

Religious Conference Management Association, Inc.

The Religious Conference Management Association, Inc. (RCMA)is an interfaith, nonprofit, professional organization of men and women who have responsibility for planning and/or managing meetings, seminars, conferences, conventions, assemblies or other gatherings for religious organizations.

Founded in 1972, RCMA is dedicated to promoting the highest professional performance by its members and associate members through the mutual exchange of ideas, techniques and methods.

Today RCMA has more than 3,200 members and associate members.

The association conducts an annual conference and exposition which provides a forum for its membership to gain increased knowledge in the arts and sciences of religious meeting planning and management.

Headquarters

One RCA Dome, Suite 120, Indianapolis, IN 46225 Tel. (317)632-1888 Fax (317)632-7909, www.rcmaweb.org

Media Contact, Exec. Dir., Dr. DeWayne S. Woodring

Officers

Pres., Dr. Jack Stone, Church of the Nazarene, 6401 The Paseo, Kansas City, MO 64131-1213

Vice-Pres., Ms. Linda M. de Leon, General Conference Seventh-Day Adventist Church, 107 Joel Circle, Smithsburg, MD 21783

Sec.-Treas., Dr. Melvin Worthington, Natl. Assoc. of Free Will Baptists, 4878 Ayden Golf Club Rd., Ayden, NC 28513

Exec. Dir., Dr. DeWayne S. Woodring

The Seminary Consortium for Urban Pastoral Education (SCUPE)

Founded in 1976, SCUPE is an interdenominational agency committed to the development of individuals, congregations and organizations for leadership in urban ministry. For individuals, we offer three accredited graduate-level academic programs, the semester and/or summer-term Graduate Theological Urban Studies program for seminary students; an M.A. in Community Development degree developed in partnership with North Park University; and Nurturing the Call, a year-long sequence of graduate courses in theology and ministry for urban pastors who have not previously attended seminary.

SCUPE also consults with other ministries and urban institutions, providing specially designed training programs around issues including diversity, strategic planning, leadership development, and human resource mobilization. We operate an urban ministry resource center and publish the *Resource Review*, as well as other occasional materials, as a service to the urban church. Every two years, SCUPE also organizes the Congress on Urban Ministry as a training and networking event for those in urban ministry.

Headquarters

200 N. Michigan Ave., Suite 502, Chicago, IL 60601 Tel. (312)726-1200 Fax (312)726-0425

Media Contact, Pres., Dr. David Frenchak; Dir. of Development, Mark Walden

Officers

Chair, Rev. Donald Sharp
Vice-Chair, Ms. Cheryl Hammock
Treas., Mr. Case Hoogendoorn
Sec., Dr. Bill VanWyngaarden

Lead Program Staff

Pres., Dr. David Frenchak

Co-Dirs., M.A. in Community Development, Rev. Carol Ann McGibbon & Dr. Arthur Lyons

Dir., Graduate Theological Urban Studies, Rev. Bill Wylie-Kellermann

Coord., Special Events, Ms. Angela Janssen

Dir., Nurturing the Call, Rev. Kazi Joshua

Transnational Association of Christian Colleges and Schools TRACS

TRACS was established in 1979 to promote the welfare, interests, and development of postsecondary institutions, whose mission is characterized by a distinctly Christian purpose, as defined in our Foundational Standards. TRACS is a voluntary, nonprofit, self-governing organization that provides accreditation to Christian postsecondary institutions offering certificates, diplomas, and/or degrees. TRACS is recognized by both the United States Department of Education, and the Council for Higher Education Accredation, as a national accrediting body for Christian institutions, colleges, universities, and seminaries. The geographic territory of TRACS currently consists of the United States and its territories.

Headquarters

P.O. Box 328, Forest, VA 24551 Tel. (434)525-9539 Fax (434)525-9538, info@tracs.org, www.tracs.org

Media Contact: Exec. Dir., Dr. Russell G. Fitzgerald

Officers

Accredition Commission Chairman, Dr. Samuel R. Chand

Exec. Dir., Dr. Russell G. Fitzgerald

Assoc. Exec. Dir., Dr. Jeff McCann

United Ministries in Higher Education

United Ministries in Higher Education is a cooperative effort to provide religious programs and services to those engaged in higher education ministries.

Headquarters

7407 Steele Creek Rd., Charlotte, NC 28217 Tel. (704)588-2182 Fax (704)588-3652

Media Contact, Res. Sec., Linda Danby Freeman

Officers

Treas., Kathy Carson

Personnel Service, Kathy Carson, 11720 Borman Dr., Suite 240, St. Louis, MO 63146 Tel. (314)991-3000 Fax (314)991-2957

Resource Center, Linda Danby Freeman

Participating Denominations

Christian Church (Disciples of Christ)

Presbyterian Church (U.S.A.)

United Church of Christ

United Religions Initiative

The purpose of the United Religions Initiative is to promote enduring, daily interfaith cooperation, to end religiously motivated violence and to create cultures of peace, justice, and healing for the Earth and all living beings.

The United Religions Initiative is a growing, global community of more than 130 Cooperation Circles, involving thousands of people around the world. The URI is inspired by the leadership potential inherent in every individual, leadership that is discovered and deepened through dialogue with others when dreams are shared and cooperative destinies are realized. The individuals who make up the URI network are committed to interfaith peacebuilding, recognizing that for peace to prevail on earth, "peace must begin with me." They believe that by talking with others who come from different faiths, cultures or spiritual traditions all involved can begin to better understand their own beliefs and recognize their common bonds.

The URI seeks to create safe spaces throughout the world where these interfaith partnerships can be seeded, and the ideas and initiatives that they spark can be practically applied. With the mandate in the URI Charter that each Cooperation Circle represent at least three different faith traditions, the very act of coming together builds peace by creating interfaith cooperation among neighbors and within communities where it may never before have been possible. The Charter "Guidelines for Action" affirms the "essentially self-organizing nature" of the Cooperation Circles and empowers CC participants to "choose what they want to do" while providing guidance for community building. The Guidelines assure that all URI activities and actions demonstrate the following heartfelt considerations, (a) sharing the wisdom and cultures of different faith traditions; (b) nurturing cultures of healing and peace; (c) upholding human rights; (d) supporting the health of the entire earth; (e) integrating spirituality in issues of economic justice; and (f) providing grassroot support for all URI activities.

The initial vision for the United Religions Initiative began in 1993 with a dream by its founder, Bishop William Swing. He writes that it came with "a sudden realization that religions, together, have a vocation to be a force for good in the world." In just seven years, tens of thousands of people in more than sixty countries around the world have responded to this vision with a resounding, "Yes!" Their affirmations have taken on myriad forms. For example, during the 72 Hours Project at the turn of the Millennium, more than a million people in 40 countries participated in 200 projects for peace. Highlights included a 12-day interfaith pilgrimage across Pakistan and the celebration of 1 million signatures on a petition to ban handguns in Rio de Janeiro.

Headquarters

P.O. Box 29242, San Francisco, CA 94129-0242 Tel. (415)561-2300 Fax (415)562-2313

Media Contact, Kristin Swenson

Staff

Exec. Dir., Rev. Cn Charles P. Gibbs

Peacebuilding, Barbara H. Hartford & Sarah Talcott

Global Fundraising, Philanthropy, Jennifer Kirk & LaTonya Trotter

Membership and Organizational Development, Sally Mahe & Cory Robertson

Visions for Peace Among Religions Project, Nancy Nielsen

Annual Giving and Knowledge Management, Sarah Talcott

Financial Manager, Ray Signer

Global Council

Pres. and Founding Trustee, Bishop William Swing

AFRICA, Malawi, Joyce N'goma; Uganda, Despina Namwembe; Mozambique, Sabapath Alagiah

ASIA, Pakistan, James Channan; Korea, Jinwol Lee; India, Mohinder Singh

EUROPE, Netherlands, Annie Imbens; United Kingdom, Deepak Naik; Germany, Karimah Stauch

LATIN AMERICA AND THE CARIBBEAN, Argentina, Rosalia Guiterrez; Mexico, Jonathan Rose; Chile, Gerado Gonzalez

MIDDLE EAST, Israel, George Khory; Israel, Yehuda Stolov; Egypt, Mohamed Mosaad

MULTI-REGIONAL/NON-GEOGRAPHIC, Yoland Trevino; Jack Lundin; Munirah Shahidi

NORTH AMERICA, United States of America, Don Frew; United States of America, Kay Lindhal; United States of America, Heng Sure

THE PACIFIC, New Zealand, George Armstrong; Philippines, Bonifacio Quirog; Philippines, Shakuntala Moorjani-Vaswani

TRANSITION ADVISORY COMMITTEE, Iftekhar Hai; Rita Semel; Bob Walter

Vellore Christian Medical College Board (USA), Inc.

The Vellore Christian Medical College Board (USA)has been linked since 1900 to the vision of a young American medical doctor, Dr. Ida S. Scudder, who founded Christian Medical College and Hospital in Vellore, India. Dr. Ida's vision was to train women in all the healing arts so that they could treat women and their families. Today after 100 years of teaching and service the College and Hospital is directed by an Indian woman, Dr. Joyce Ponnaiya. The Vellore Christian Medical College Board (USA)supports the work of Christian Medical College and Hospital in Vellore through exchange personnel programs including volunteers to Vellore and senior CMC staff receiving fellowships to study and work in the United States over 3-month periods. The Vellore Board also assists CMC&H with capital campaigns and high-tech medical equipment.

Headquarters

475 Riverside Dr., Room 243, New York, NY 10115 Tel. (212)870-2640 Fax (212)870-2173, usaboard@vellorecmc.org

Media Contact, Pres., Dr. Louis L. Knowles

Officers

Pres., Dr. Louis L. Knowles

Chair, Mrs. Edwina S. Youth, 211 Blue Ridge Dr., Levittown, PA 19057

Vice-Chair, Mrs. Dorothy R. Williams, 6110 Forest Bend, San Antonio, TX 78240

Sec., Dr. Alexander Kuruvila, 2063 Gainsborough Dr., Riverside, CA 92606

Treas., Mr. Richard L. Vreeland, 182 Ameren Way, Ballwin, MO 63021

World Council of Churches, United States Office

The United States Conference of the World Council of Churches was formed in 1938 when the WCC itself was still in the "Process of Formation." Henry Smith Leiper, an American with many national and international connections, was given the title of "Associate General Secretary" of the WCC and asked to carry out WCC work in the U.S. After the World Council of Churches was officially born in 1948 in Amsterdam, Netherlands, Leiper raised millions of dollars for WCC programs.

Today the U.S. Conference of the WCC is composed of representatives of U.S. member churches of the worldwide body. The U.S. Office of the WCC works to develop relationships among the churches, advance the work of WCC and interpret the council in the United States.

Headquarters

475 Riverside Dr., Room 915, New York, NY 10115 Tel. (212)870-3260 Fax (212)870-2528

Officers

WCC Pres. from North America and Moderator, Rev. Kathryn Bannister, United Methodist Church

Vice-Moderator, Bishop McKinley Young, African Methodist Episcopal Church

Vice-Moderator and Treas., The Very Rev. Leonid Kishkovsky, Orthodox Church in America

Staff

Prog. Exec. for the U.S., Deborah DeWinter, Tel. (212)870-2522

Office Admin., Gloria Feliciano, Tel. (212)870-3260

World Day of Prayer

World Day of Prayer is an ecumenical movement initiated and carried out by Christian women in 170 countries who conduct a common day of prayer on the first Friday of March to which all people are welcome. There is an annual theme for the worship service that has been prepared by women in a different country each year. For 2004 the women of Panama have prepared a worship service on the theme, In Faith, Women Shape the Future. The offering at the WDP is gathered by each WDP national or regional committee and given to help people who are in need.

Headquarters

World Day of Prayer International Comm., 475 Riverside Dr., Room 729, New York, NY 10115 Tel. (212)870-3049 Fax (212)864-8648, wdpic@worlddayofprayer.net

Media Contact, Exec. Dir., Eileen King

Officers

Chairperson, Sylvia Lisk Vanhaverbeke

Treas., Karen Prudente

Africa, Suzie Bayiha II, Assah E. Mgonja

Asia, Junko Matsuura, Woranut Pantupong

Caribbean and North America, Waveney Benjamin; Annette Poitier

Europe, Inge Lise Lollike; Ewa Walter

Latin America, Elisabeth Delmonte, Ormara Nolla

Middle East, Laila Carmi; Nadia Menes

Pacific, Jannice Graham; Joanna S. Matagi-Vilitama

Member at Large for Orthodox Churches, Marija Ciceva-Aleksic

World Methodist Council-North American Section

The World Methodist Council, one of the 30 or so "Christian World Communions," shares a general tradition which is common to all Christians.

The world organization of Methodists and related United Churches is comprised of 74 churches with roots in the Methodist tradition. These churches found in 130 countries have a membership of more than 34 million.

The Council's North American Section, comprised of ten Methodist and United Church denominations, provides a regional focus for the Council in Canada, the United States and Mexico. The North American Section meets at the time of the quinquennial World Conference and Council, and separately as Section between world meetings. The Section met in Rio de Janeiro, Brazil in August 1996 during the 17th World Methodist Conference to elect its officers for the 1997-2001 quinquennium. 2001-2006 officers will be elected in Brighton, England, July 2001.

North American Churches related to the World Methodist Council have a membership of approximately 16 million and a church community of more than 30 million.

Headquarters

P.O. Box 518, Lake Junaluska, NC 28745 Tel. (828)456-9432 Fax (828)456-9433

Media Contact, Gen. Sec., Joe Hale

Officers

Section Pres., Bishop Neil L. Irons, 900 S. Arlington Ave., Room 214, Harrisburg, PA 17109-5097 Tel. (717)652-6705 Fax (717)652-5109

First Vice-Pres., Bishop Thomas L. Hoyt, CME Church

Vice-Pres., Bishop John R. Bryant, AME Church; Bishop Cecil Bishop, AMEZ Church; Bishop Richard D. Snyder, Free Methodist Church; Bishop Gracela Alverez, Methodist Church in Mexico; Bishop Keith Elford, Free Methodist Church of Canada; Rev. Carol Hancock, United Church of Canada; Dr. Jack Stone, Church of the Nazarene; Dr. Earle L. Wilson, The Wesleyan Church; Chairman, Finance Committee, Dr. Donald V. Fites

Treas., Dr. James W. Holsinger, Jr.

Asst. Treas., Edna Alsdurf

General Sec., Dr. Joe Hale

World Officers from North America, Dr. Frances M. Alguire; Dr. Maxie D. Dunnam; Bishop Donald Ming

World Vision

World Vision is a Christian relief and development organization dedicated to helping children and their communities worldwide reach their full potential by tackling the causes of poverty. Motivated by our faith in Jesus, we serve the poor as a demonstration of God's unconditional love for all people. World Vision works with communities in nearly 100 countries to develop long-term solutions that alleviate poverty, provides emergency assistance to children and families affected by natural disasters and civil conflict, and advocates for justice on behalf of the poor. World Vision U.S.—one of 52 national offices in the World Vision Partnership—serves in key United States metropolitan areas, providing intervention for challenged youth, tools that equip strong community leaders, and storehouses that provide essentials for living.

World Vision's Church Relations department facilitates church partnerships, connecting U.S. congregations with critical ministry among people in need locally and internationally. Church opportunities include partnerships with international projects, volunteer options through U.S. programs, and educational programs, including youth-oriented 30 Hour Famine and One Life Revolution, and family-oriented Love Loaf.

Headquarters

P.O. Box 9716, Federal Way, WA 98063-9716 Tel. (253)815-1000

Church Relations Vice-Pres., Steve Haas, Tel. (253)815-2698

Media Contact, Dean Owen, Tel. (253)815-2158

Officers

Pres., Richard Stearns

Sr. Vice-Pres., Scott Jackson; Lawrence Probus; Julie Regnier; Atul Tandon; Bruce Wilkinson

YMCA of the USA

The YMCA is one of the largest private voluntary organizations in the world, serving about 30 million people in more than 100 countries. In the United States, more than 2,000 local branches, units, camps and centers annually serve more than 14 million people of all ages, races and abilities. About half of those served are female. No one is turned away because of an inability to pay.

The Y teaches youngsters to swim, organizes youth basketball games and offers adult aerobics. But the Y represents more than fitness— it works to strengthen families and help people develop values and behavior that are consistent with Christian principles.

The Y offers hundreds of programs, including day camp for children, child care, exercise for people with disabilities, teen clubs, environmental programs, substance abuse prevention, family nights, job training and many more programs, from infant mortality prevention to overnight camping for seniors.

The kind of programs offered at a YMCA will vary; each is controlled by volunteer board members who make their own program, policy, and financial decisions based on the special needs of their community. In its own way, every Y works to build strong kids, strong families, and strong communities.

The YMCA was founded in London, England, in 1844 by George Williams and friends who lived and worked together as clerks. Their goal was to save other live-in clerks from the wicked life of the London streets. The first members were evangelical Protestants who prayed and studied the Bible as an alternative to vice. The Y has always been nonsectarian and today accepts those of all faiths at all levels of the organization.

Headquarters

101 N. Wacker Dr., Chicago, IL 60606 Tel. (312)977-0031 Fax (312)977-9063
Media Contact, Media Relations Manager, Arnie Collins

Officers

Board Chpsn., Daniel E. Emerson
Exec. Dir., David R. Mercer
(Int.)Public Relations Assoc., Mary Pyke Gover

YWCA of the U.S.A.

The YWCA of the U.S.A. is comprised of 313 affiliates in communities and on college campuses across the United States. It serves one million members and program participants. It seeks to empower women and girls to enable them, coming together across lines of age, race, religious belief, economic and occupational status to make a significant contribution to the elimination of racism and the achievement of peace, justice, freedom and dignity for all people.

Headquarters

Empire State Building, 350 Fifth Ave., Suite 301, New York, NY 10118 Tel. (212)273-7800 Fax (212)465-2281
Media Contact, Khristina Lew

Officers

National Pres., Leticia Paez
Sec., Carol O. Markus
Chief Exec. Officer, Margaret Tyndall

Youth for Christ–USA

Founded in 1944, as part of the body of Christ, our vision is to see every young person in every people group in every nation have the opportunity to make an informed decision to be a follower of Jesus Christ and become a part of a local church.

There are 220 locally controlled YFC programs serving in cities and metropolitan areas of the United States.

YFC's Campus Life Club program involves teens who attend approximately 58,236 high schools in the United States. YFC's staff now numbers approximately 1,000. In addition, nearly 10,000 part-time and volunteer staff supplement the full-time staff. Youth Guidance, a ministry for nonschool-oriented youth includes group homes, court referrals, institutional services and neighborhood ministries. The year-round conference and camping program involves approximately 200,000 young people each year. Other ministries include DC Ministries, World Outreach, Project Serve, and Teen Moms. Independent, indigenous YFC organizations also work in 127 countries overseas.

Headquarters

U.S. Headquarters, P.O. Box 228822, Denver, CO 80222 Tel. (303)843-9000 Fax (303)843-9002
Canadian Organization, 2540 5th Ave. NW, Calgary, AB T2N 0T5
Media Contact, Pres., Roger Cross

Officers

United States, Pres., Roger Cross
Intl. Organization, Pres., Jean-Jacques Weiler

2. Canadian Cooperative Organizations, National

In most cases, the organizations listed here work on a national level and cooperate across denominational lines. Regional cooperative organizations in Canada are listed in Directory 8, "Canadian Regional and Local Ecumenical Bodies."

Alcohol and Drug Concerns Inc.

Alcohol and Drug Concerns is a registered, nonprofit, charitable organization that has a long association with the Christian Church. The organization's mission is to empower youth to make positive lifestyle choices relating to alcohol, tobacco, and other drugs.

The organization was granted a national charter in 1987, moving from an Ontario charter dating back to 1934. Among its services are, Choices F.I.T. (Fostering Independent Thinking —a substance abuse prevention resource for grades 4 to 8 teachers; an Institute on Addiction Studies; Making the Leap—a substance abuse prevention resource for grades 7 to 8 teachers created by high school students; Drug and Alcohol Game Show for grades 6 to 9— a classroom activity; education and awareness courses for clients of the Ontario Ministry of Corrections.

Headquarters

4500 Sheppard Ave. E, Ste. 112, Toronto, ON M1S 3R6 Tel. (416)293-3400 Fax (416)293-1142
Media Contact, Robert Walsh, CEO

Officers

Pres., Jean Desgagne, Toronto
Treas., Peter Varley, Toronto
Vice-Pres., Nanci Harris, Toronto
Vice-Pres., Valerie Petroff, Oak Ridges
Vice-Pres., Heidi Stanley, Orillia
Past Pres., Larry Gillians, Napanee
CEO, Robert Walsh

Association of Canadian Bible Colleges

The Association brings into cooperative association Bible colleges in Canada that are evangelical in doctrine and whose objectives are similar. Services are provided to improve the quality of Bible college education in Canada and to further the interests of the Association by means of conferences, seminars, cooperative undertakings, information services, research, publications and other projects.

Headquarters

26 Western St., Sussex, NB E4E 1E6 Tel. (506) 432-4400 Fax (506)432-4425
Media Contact, Sec.-Treas., Dr. Arthur Maxwell, E-mail maxwella@bethany-ca.edu

Officers

Pres., Abe Bergen, Tel. (204)326-6451 Fax (204) 326-6908
Vice-Pres., Dr. Ron Penner, Tel. (604)853-3358 Fax (604)853-3063
Sec.-Treas., Dr. Arthur Maxwell, Tel. (506)432-4400 Fax (506)432-4425
Members-at-Large, Dr. Stephen Roy, Tel. (519)894-8900 Fax (519)894-5331; Waldy Neufeld, Tel. (780)568-3962 Fax (780)568-4431; Dr. Antoinette van Kuik, Tel. (204)433-7488 Fax (204)433-7158

Canadian Bible Society

The Canadian Bible Society is a non-denominational and inter-confessional organization that exists to translate, publish, distribute and encourage the use of the Scriptures, without doctrinal note or comment. Bible Society work was begun in Canada in 1804 by the British and Foreign Bible Society. In 1906, the various auxiliaries of the British and Foreign Bible Society joined together to form the Canadian Bible Society. Today, the Canadian Bible Society has 16 district offices across Canada, a Scripture Translation Office in Kitchener, a French Services Office in Montreal, and a National Support Office in Toronto. Additionally, the Bermuda Bible Society is constituted as an Associate District of the Canadian Bible Society. The Society holds quarterly Board meetings involving one elected representative from each of the districts and from the francophone sector. About 90% of the Society's revenue comes through the generosity of Canadian supporters in the form of donations, bequests and annuity income. Through the Canadian Bible Society's membership in the United States Societies' fellowship, more than 64 million Bibles, Testaments and Portions were distributed globally in 2003. The complete Bible has been published in more than 400 languages, with at least one book of the Bible available in 2,355 languages.

Headquarters

C.B.S. National Support Office, 10 Carnforth Rd., Toronto, ON M4A 2S4 Tel. (416)757-4171 Fax (416)757-3376

Officers

National Dir., Rev. Phyllis M. Nesbitt, 10 Carnforth Rd., Toronto, ON M4A 2S4 Tel. (416)757-4171 Fax (416)757-1292, E-mail pnesbitt@biblesociety.ca
Chief Operating Officer, Mr. Wally Sherwin, 10 Carnforth Rd., Toronto, ON M4A 2S4 Tel. (416)757-4171 Fax (416)757-1292, E-mail wsherwin@biblesociety.ca

Dir. of Scripture Translation, Mr. Hart Wiens, Frederick Mall (2nd Floor), 385 Frederick Street, Kitchener, ON N2H 2P2 Tel. (519)741-8285 Fax (519)741-8357, E-mail hwiens@biblesociety.ca
Dir. du Secteur francophone, M. Serge Rhéaume, 4050 avenue du Parc-Lafontaine, Montreal, QC H2L 3M8 Tel. (514)524-7873 Fax (514)524-6116, E-mail srheaume@societebiblique.ca
Dir. of Ministry Funding, Mr. Erwin van Laar, 10 Carnforth Rd., Toronto, ON M4A 2S4 Tel. (416)757-4171 Fax (416)757-3376, E-mail evanlaar@biblesociety.ca
Production Manager, Ms. Nelly Safari, 10 Carnforth Rd., Toronto, ON M4A 2S4 Tel. (416)757-4171 Fax (416)757-3376, E-mail nsafari@biblesociety.ca
Human Resources Manager/Volunteer Program Coordinator, Mrs. Linda Donohoe, 10 Carnforth Rd., Toronto, ON M4A 2S4 Tel. (416)757-4171 Fax (416)757-3376, E-mail ldonohoe @biblesociety.ca

Canadian Centre for Ecumenism

The Centre has facilitated understanding and cooperation among believers of various Christian traditions and world religions since 1963. An active interdenominational Board of Directors meets annually.

Outreach: *ECUMENISM,* a quarterly publication, develops central themes such as Rites of Passage, Sacred Space, Interfaith Marriages, Care of the Earth, etc. through contributions from writers of various churches and religions in addition to its regular ecumenical news summaries, book reviews and resources.

A specialized library is open to the public for consultation in the areas of religion, dialogue, evangelism, ethics, spirituality, etc.

Conferences and sessions are offered on themes such as Ecumenism and Pastoral Work, Pluralism, World Religions, Prayer and Unity.

Headquarters

2065 Sherbrooke St. W., Montreal, QC H3H 1G6 Tel. (514)937-9176 Fax (514)937-4986
E-mail ccocce@oecumenisme.ca
Web site www.oecomenisme.ca

Officers

Media Contact, Bernice Baranowski
Assoc. Dir., vacant
Dir., vacant
Asst. Dir., Adele Brodeur

The Canadian Council of Churches

The Canadian Council of Churches was organized in 1944. Its basic purpose is to provide the churches with an agency for conference and consultation and for such common planning and common action as they desire to undertake. It encourages ecumenical understanding and action throughout Canada through local councils of churches. It also relates to the World Council of Churches and other agencies serving the worldwide ecumenical movement.

The Council has a Governing Board which meets semiannually and an Executive Committee. Program is administered through two commissions—Faith and Witness, Justice and Peace.

Headquarters

3250 Bloor St. West, 2nd Floor, Toronto, ON M8X 2Y4 Tel. (416)972-9494 ext. 22 Fax (416)236-4532
Media Contact, Rev. Dr. Karen Hamilton
E-mail ccchurch@web.net
http://www.ccc-cce.ca/

Officers

Pres., Bishop Andre Vallee
Vice-Pres., Rev. Michael Winnowski, Fr. Shenork Sovin, Ms. Karen MacKay Llewellyn
Treas., Nancy Bell
Treas. Emeritus, Mr. Jack Hart
Gen. Sec., Rev. Dr. Karen Hamilton

Member Churches

The Anglican Church of Canada
The Armenian Orthodox Church-Diocese of Canada
Baptist Convention of Ontario and Quebec
British Methodist Episcopal Church*
Canadian Conference of Catholic Bishops
Christian Church (Disciples of Christ)
Coptic Orthodox Church of Canada
Christian Reformed Church in North America—Canadian Ministries
Ethiopian Orthodox Church in Canada
Evangelical Lutheran Church in Canada
Greek Orthodox Metropolis of Toronto, Canada
Orthodox Church in America, Diocese of Canada
Polish National Catholic Church
Presbyterian Church in Canada
Reformed Church in Canada
Religious Society of Friends-Canada Yearly Meeting
Salvation Army-Canada and Bermuda
The Ukrainian Orthodox Church
The United Church of Canada
*Associate Member

Canadian Evangelical Theological Association

In May 1990, about 60 scholars, pastors and other interested persons met together in Toronto to form a new theological society. Arising out of the Canadian chapter of the Evangelical Theological Society, the new association established itself as a distinctly Canadian group with a new name. It sponsored its first conference as CETA in Kingston, Ontario, in May 1991.

CETA provides a forum for scholarly contributions to the renewal of theology and church in Canada. CETA seeks to promote theological work which is loyal to Christ and his Gospel, faithful to the primacy and authority of Scripture and responsive to the guiding force of the historic creeds and Protestant confessions of the Christian church. In its newsletters and conferences, CETA seeks presentations that will speak to a general theologically educated audience, rather than to specialists.

CETA has special interest in evangelical points of view upon and contributions to the wider conversations regarding religious studies and church life. Members therefore include pastors, students and other interested persons as well as professional academicians. CETA currently includes about 100 members, many of whom attend its annual conference in the early summer. It publishes the *Canadian Evangelical Review* and supports an active Internet discussion group, which may be accessed by E-mailing ceta-l@egroups.com.

Headquarters

Prof. David Guretzki, Briercrest College, Caronport, Saskatchewan, S0H 0S0
E-mail dguretzki@briercrest.ca
Media Contact, Prof. David Guretzki

Officers

Pres., Prof. David Guretzki
Sec.-Treas., Rev. Dr. Archie Pell
Editor, Canadian Evengelical Review, Dr. Keith Bodner
Exec. Members-at-large, Dr. John Franklin and Dr. Gordon Smith

Canadian Tract Society

The Canadian Tract Society was organized in 1970 as an independent distributor of Gospel leaflets to provide Canadian churches and individual Christians with quality materials proclaiming the Gospel through the printed page. It is affiliated with the American Tract Society, which encouraged its formation and assisted in its founding, and for whom it serves as an exclusive Canadian distributor. The CTS is a nonprofit international service ministry.

Headquarters

P.O. Box 2156, LCD 1, Brampton, ON L6T 3S4 Tel. (905)457-4559 Fax (905)457-0529
Media Contact, Mgr., Donna Croft

Officers

Dir.-Sec., Robert J. Burns
Dir., John Neufeld
Dir., Patricia Burns

Canadian Society of Biblical Studies-Société Canadienne des Études Bibliques

The object of the Society shall be to stimulate the critical investigation of the classical biblical literatures, together with other related literature, by the exchange of scholarly research both in published form and in public forum.

Headquarters

Dept. of Religion and Culture, Wilfrid Laurier University, Waterloo, ON N2L 3C5 Tel. (519)884-0710 ext. 3323 Fax (519)884-9387
Media Contact, Exec. Sec., Michele Murray

Officers

Pres., David J. Hawkin, Dept. of Religious Studies, Memorial University, St. John's, NL A1C 5S7, E-mail dhawkin@mun.ca
Vice-Pres., William Morrow, Queen's Theological College, Kingston, ON K7L 3N6, E-mail morroww@post.queensu.ca
Exec. Sec., Michele Murray, Dept. of Religion, Bishop's University, Lennoxville, PQ J1M 1Z7, E-mail mmurray@ubishops.ca
Treas., Dietmar Neufeld, Department of Classical, Near Eastern and Religious Studies, University of British Columbia, Vancouver, BC V6T 1Z1 Tel. (604)822-4065 Fax (604)822-9431, E-mail dneufeld@interchange. ubc.ca
Prog. Coord., Christine Mitchell, St. Andrews College, 1121 College Dr., Saskatoon, SK S7N 0W3, E-mail ckm365@duke.usask.ca
Comm. Officer, John L. McLaughlin, Faculty of Theology, University of St. Michael's College, 81 St. Mary St., Toronto, ON M5S 1J4, E-mail johnl.mclaughlin@utoronto.ca
Student Liaison Officer, Mona Tokarek LaFosse, Centre for the Study of Religion, University of Toronto, Unit 63, 14 Williamsburg Rd., Kitchener, ON N2E 1W1, E-mail lafosse@ golden.net

The Church Army in Canada

The Church Army in Canada has been involved in evangelism and Christian social service since 1929.

Headquarters

105 Mountain View Dr., Saint John, NB E2J 5B5 Tel. (888)316-8169 Fax (506)642-4005
E-mail bsmith@churcharmy.com
Media Contact, National Dir., Capt. R. Bruce Smith

Officers

National Dir., Capt. R. Bruce Smith
Bd. Chmn., Mr. Peter Bloom

The Churches' Council on Theological Education in Canada, An Ecumenical Foundation

The Churches' Council (CCTE,EF) maintains an overview of theological education in Canada on behalf of its constituent churches and functions as a bridge between the schools of theology and the churches which they serve.

Founded in 1970 with a national and ecumenical mandate, the CCTE,EF provides resources for research into matters pertaining to theological education, opportunities for consultation and cooperation and a limited amount of funding in the form of grants for the furtherance of ecumenical iniatives in theological education.

Headquarters

60 St. Clair Avenue E, Ste. 208, Toronto, ON M4T 1N5 Tel. (416)928-3223 Fax (416)928-3563

Media Contact, Exec. Dir. (interim), Robert Faris

E-mail ccte@look.ca

Officers

Bd. of Dir., Chpsn., Dr. Richard C. Crossman, Waterloo Lutheran Seminary, 75 University Ave. W., Waterloo, ON N2L 3C5

Bd. of Dir., Vice-Chpsn., Dr. Dorcas Gordon, Knox College

Treas., Mr. Brian Cox

Exec. Dir., (interim), Robert Faris

MEMBER ORGANIZATIONS

The General Synod of the Anglican Church of Canada

Canadian Baptist Ministries

The Evangelical Lutheran Church in Canada

The Presbyterian Church in Canada

The Canadian Conference of Catholic Bishops

The United Church of Canada

Evangelical Fellowship of Canada

The Fellowship was formed in 1964. There are 31 denominations, 124 organizations, 1,200 local churches and 11,000 individual members.

Its purposes are, "Fellowship in the gospel" (Phil. Ch.1 vs.5), "the defence and confirmation of the gospel" (Phil. Ch.1 vs.7) and "the furtherance of the gospel" (Phil. Ch.1 vs.12). The Fellowship believes the Holy Scriptures, as originally given, are infallible and that salvation through the Lord Jesus Christ is by faith apart from works.

In national and regional conventions the Fellowship urges Christians to live exemplary lives and to openly challenge the evils and injustices of society. It encourages cooperation with various agencies in Canada and overseas that are sensitive to social and spiritual needs.

Headquarters

Office, 600 Alden Rd. Ste. 300, Markham, ON L3R 0E7 Tel. (905)479-5885 Fax (905)479-4742

Mailing Address, M.I.P. Box 3745, Markham, ON L3R 0Y4

Media Contact, Pres., Dr. Gary Walsh, 600 Alden Rd., Ste. 300, Markham, ON L3R 0E7 Tel. (905)479-5885 Fax (905)479-4742

Officers

Pres., Dr. Gary Walsh

Chair, Dr. Paul Magnus

Vice-Chair, Dr. Rick Penner

Treas., Lt. Col. David Luginbuhl

Past Pres., Dr. Brian Stiller

EXECUTIVE COMMITTEE

Rev. Scott Campbell; Rev. Carson Pue; Ms. Ruth Andrews; Rev. Stewart Hunter; Ms. Jacqueline Dugas; Dr. Rick Penner; Lt. Col. David Luginbuhl; Dr. Ralph Richardson; Rev. Abe Funk; Rev. Gillis Killam; Dr. Paul Magnus; Rev. Winston Thurton

Task Force on Evangelism-(Vision Canada), Interim Chair, Gary Walsh

Social Action Commission, Chpsn., Dr. James Read

Education Commission, Chpsn., Dr. Glenn Smith

Women in Ministry Task Force, Chpsn., Rev. Eileen Stewart-Rhude

Aboriginal Task Force, Co-Chairs, Ray Aldred; Wendy Peterson

Religious Liberties Commission, Chpsn., Dr. Paul Marshall

Task Force on Global Mission, Chpsn., Dr. Geoff Tunnicliffe

Inter-Varsity Christian Fellowship of Canada

Inter-Varsity Christian Fellowship is a non-profit, interdenominational student movement centering on the witness to Jesus Christ in campus communities, universities, colleges and high schools and through a Canada-wide Pioneer Camping program. It also ministers to professionals and teachers through Nurses and Teacher Christian Fellowship.

IVCF was officially formed in 1928-29 by the late Dr. Howard Guinness, whose arrival from Britain challenged students to follow the example of the British Inter-Varsity Fellowship by organizing themselves into prayer and Bible study fellowship groups. Inter-Varsity has always been a student-initiated movement emphasizing and developing leadership in the campus to call Christians to outreach, challenging other students to a personal faith in Jesus Christ and studying the Bible as God's revealed truth within a fellowship of believers. A strong stress has been placed on missionary activity, and the triennial conference held at Urbana, IL (jointly sponsored by U.S. and Canadian IVCF) has been a means of challenging many young people to service in Christian vocations. Inter-Varsity works closely with and is a strong believer in the work of local and national churches.

Headquarters

Unit 17, 40 Vogell Rd., Richmond Hill, ON L4B 3N6 Tel. (905)884-6880 Fax (905)884-6550

Media Contact, Gen. Dir., Rob Regier

Officers

Gen. Dir., Rob Regier

Interchurch Communications

Interchurch Communications is made up of the communication units of the Anglican Church of Canada, the Evangelical Lutheran Church in

Canada, the Presbyterian Church in Canada, the Canadian Conference of Catholic Bishops (English Sector), and the United Church of Canada. ICC members collaborate on occasional video or print coproductions and on addressing public policy issues affecting religious communications.

Headquarters

3250 Bloor St. W., Etobicoke, ON M8X 2Y4

Media Contact, Chpsn., Douglas Tindal, Anglican Church of Canada, 600 Jarvis St., Toronto, ON M4Y 2J6 Tel. (416)924-9199 ext. 286 Fax (416)968-7983

E-mail doug.tindal@national.anglican.ca

MEMBERS

Mr. William Kokesch, Canadian Conference of Catholic Bishops, 90 Parent Ave., Ottawa, ON K1N 7B1 Tel. (613)241-9461 Fax (613)241-8117, E-mail kokesch@cccb.ca

Pres. Keith Knight, Presbyterian Church in Canada, 50 Wynford Dr., Don Mills, ON M3C 1J7 Tel. (416)441-1111 Fax (416)441-2825, E-mail kknight@presbyterian.ca

Religious Television Associates, 3250 Bloor St. W., Etobicoke, ON M8X 2Y4 Tel. (416)231-7680 Fax (416)232-6004

John Howard Society of Ontario

The John Howard Society of Ontario is a registered non-profit charitable organization providing services to individuals, families and groups at all stages in the youth and criminal justice system. The Society also provides community education on critical issues in the justice system and advocacy for reform of the justice system. The mandate of the Society is the prevention of crime through service, community education, advocacy and reform.

Founded in 1929, the Society has grown from a one-office service in Toronto to 17 local branches providing direct services in the major cities of Ontario and a provincial office providing justice policy analysis, advocacy for reform and support to branches.

Headquarters

6 Jackson Pl., Toronto, ON M6P 1T6 Tel. (416) 604-8412 Fax (416)604-8948

Media Contact, Exec. Dir., William Sparks

Officers

Pres., Susan Reid-MacNevin, Dept. of Sociology, Univ. Of Guelph, Guelph, ON N1G 2W1

Vice-Pres., Richard Beaupe, 4165 Fernand St., Hamner, ON B3A 1X4

Treas., Jack Battler, Waterloo, ON

Sec., Peter Angeline, OISE, 252 Bloor St. W., Toronto, ON

Exec. Dir., William Sparks

LOCAL SOCIETIES

Collins Bay; Hamilton; Kingston; Lindsay; London; Niagara; Oshawa; Ottawa; Peel; Peterborough; Sarnia; Sault Ste. Marie; Sudbury; Thunder Bay; Toronto; Waterloo; Windsor

John Milton Society for the Blind in Canada

The John Milton Society for the Blind in Canada is an interdenominational Christian charity founded by Helen Keller whose mandate is producing Christian publications for adults or young people who are blind, deaf-blind or visually impaired. As such, it produces *Insight*, a large-print magazine, *Insound*, a cassette magazine and *In Touch*, a braille magazine. The John Milton Society also features an audio cassette library called the Library in Sound, which contains Christian music, sermons, seasonal materials and workshops. All services are available free upon request to blind persons.

Headquarters

40 St. Clair Ave. E., Ste. 202, Toronto, ON M4T 1M9 Tel. (416)960-3953 Fax (416)960-3570

Media Contact, Ex. Dir., The Rev. Barry R. Brown

Web site www.jmsblind.ca

Officers

Exec. Dir., Rev. Barry R. Brown, E-mail bbrown@jmsblind.ca

Pres., Rev. Gerald Hunt

Lutheran Council in Canada

The Lutheran Council in Canada was organized in 1967 and is a cooperative agency of the Evangelical Lutheran Church in Canada and Lutheran Church-Canada.

The Council's activities include communications, coordinative service and national liaison in social ministry, chaplaincy and scout activity.

Headquarters

302-393 Portage Ave., Winnipeg, MB R3B 3H6 Tel. (204)984-9150 Fax (204)984-9185

Media Contact, Pres., Rev. Ralph Mayan, 3074 Portage Ave., Winnipeg, MB R3K 0Y2 Tel. (204)895-3433 Fax (204)897-4319

Officers

Pres., Bishop Raymond Schultz

Treas., vacant

Sec., Rev. Leon C. Gilbertson

Vice Pres., Rev. Ralph Mayan

Mennonite Central Committee Canada (MCCC)

Mennonite Central Committee Canada was organized in 1964 to continue the work which several regional Canadian inter-Mennonite agencies had been doing in relief, service, immigration and peace. All but a few of the smaller Mennonite groups in Canada belong to MCC Canada.

MCCC is part of the Mennonite Central

Committee (MCC) International which has its headquarters in Akron, Pa. where most of the overseas development and relief projects are administered. In 2000-2001 MCCC's income was $25 million, about 47 percent of the total MCC income. There were 408 Canadians out of a total of 867 MCC workers serving in North America and abroad during the same time period.

The MCC office in Winnipeg administers projects located in Canada. Domestic programs of Voluntary Service, Native Concerns, Peace and Social Concerns, Food Program, Employment Concerns, Ottawa Office, Victim-Offender Ministries, Mental Health and Immigration are all part of MCC's Canadian ministry. Whenever it undertakes a project, MCCC attempts to relate to the church or churches in the area.

Headquarters

134 Plaza Dr., Winnipeg, MB R3T 5K9 Tel. (204)261-6381 Fax (204)269-9875

Communications, Rick Fast, 134 Plaza Dr., Winnipeg, MT R3T 5K9 Tel. (204)261-6381 Fax (204)269-9875

Officers

Exec. Dir., Donald Peters

Project Ploughshares

Founded in 1976, Project Ploughshares is a Canadian ecumenical non-governmental organization that carries out policy research, analysis, dialogue, and public education programs in Canada and internationally to identify, develop, and advance approaches that build peace and prevent war and that promote the peaceful resolution of political conflict. Project Ploughshares is sponsored by the Canadian Council of Churches and is affiliated with the Institute of Peace and Conflict Studies, Conrad Grebel University College, University of Waterloo. Publications include the Ploughshares Monitor (quarterly), the Armed Conflicts Report (annually), Briefings and Working Papers (occasional).

Headquarters

Project Ploughshares, 57 Erb Street West, Waterloo, ON, Canada N2L 6C2 Tel. (519) 888-6541 Fax (519)888-0188

Media Contact: Dir., Ernie Regehr

E-mail plough@ploughshares.ca

Web site www.ploughshares.ca

Officers

Chair, Moira Hutchinson

Treas., Philip Creighton

SPONSORING ORGANIZATIONS

Anglican Church of Canada

Canadian Catholic Organization for Development & Peace

Canadian Unitarian Council

Canadian Voice of Women for Peace

Canadian Yearly Meeting, Religious Society of Friends

Evangelical Lutheran Church in Canada

Mennonite Central Committee Canada

Presbyterian Church in Canada

United Church of Canada

Religious Television Associates

Religious Television Associates was formed in the early 1960s for the production units of the Anglican, Baptist, Presbyterian, Roman Catholic Churches and the United Church of Canada. In the intervening years, the Baptists have withdrawn and the Lutherans have come in. RTA provides an ecumenical umbrella for joint productions in broadcasting and development education. The directors are the heads of the Communications Departments participating in Interchurch Communications.

Headquarters

c/o The United Church of Canada, 3250 Bloor St. W., Etobicoke, ON M8X 2Y4 Tel. (416)231-7680 ext. 4076 Fax (416)231-3103

Media Contact, Shane Chadden

MEMBER ORGANIZATIONS

The Anglican Church of Canada

Canadian Conference of Catholic Bishops

The Canadian Council of Churches

The Evangelical Lutheran Church in Canada

The Presbyterian Church in Canada

The United Church of Canada

Scripture Union

Scripture Union, an international interdenominational missionary movement working in 130 countries, aims to work with churches to make God's Good News known to children, young people and families and to encourage people of all ages to meet God daily through the Bible and prayer.

In Canada, a range of daily Bible guides for people from age four through adult are offered to individuals, churches, and bookstores. Sunday School curriculum and various evangelism and discipling materials are also offered for sale.

A program of youth and family evangelism, including beach missions and community-based evangelistic holiday clubs, is also undertaken.

Headquarters

1885 Clements Rd., Unit 226, Pickering, ON L1W 3V4 Tel. (905)427-4947 Fax (905)427-0334,

Media Contact, Pres., John Irwin, E-mail jirwinc617@rogers.com

Officers

Chair of the Board, Harold Murray, 216 McKinnon Pl. NE, Calgary, AB T2E 7B9, Tel. (403)276-4716, E-mail hjmurray@home.com

Pres., John W. Irwin, 1885 Clements Rd., Unit 226, Pickering, ON L1W 3V4, E-mail jirwinc617@rogers.com

Student Christian Movement of Canada

The Student Christian Movement of Canada was formed in 1921 from the student arm of the YMCA. It has its roots in the Social Gospel movements of the late 19th and early 20th centuries. Throughout its intellectual history, the SCM in Canada has sought to relate the Christian faith to the living realities of the social and political context of each student generation.

The present priorities are built around the need to form more and stronger critical Christian communities on Canadian campuses within which individuals may develop their social and political analyses, experience spiritual growth and fellowship and bring Christian ecumenical witness to the university.

The Student Christian Movement of Canada is affiliated with the World Student Christian Federation.

Headquarters

310 Danforth Ave., Toronto, ON M4K 1N6 Tel. (416)463-4312 Fax (416)466-6854

Media Contact, Natl. Coord., Sheilagh McGlynn

Officers

Natl. Coord., Sheilagh McGlynn, E-mail info@scmcanada.org

Women's Inter-Church Council of Canada

Women's Inter-Church Council of Canada is a national Christian women's council that encourages women to grow in ecumenism, to strengthen ecumenical community, to share their spirituality and prayer, to engage in dialogue about women's concerns and to stand in solidarity with one another. The Council calls women to respond to national and international issues affecting women and to take action together for justice. WICC sponsors the World Day of Prayer and Fellowship of the Least Coin in Canada. Human rights projects for women are supported and a quarterly magazine, *Making Waves*, distributed.

Headquarters

Suite 201, 394 Bloor St. W, Toronto, ON M5S 1X4 Tel. (416)929-5184 Fax (416)929-4064

Media Contact, Comm. Coord., Gillian Barfoot

Officers

Pres., Joyce Christie

Exec. Dir., Rev. Karen Hincke

CHURCH MEMBER BODIES

African Methodist Episcopal
Anglican Church of Canada
Canadian Baptist Ministries
Christian Church (Disciples of Christ)
Evangelical Lutheran Church in Canada
Mennonite Central Committee
Presbyterian Church in Canada
Religious Society of Friends
Roman Catholic Church
The Salvation Army in Canada
United Church of Canada

World Vision Canada

World Vision Canada is a Christian humanitarian relief and development organization. Although its main international commitment is to translate child sponsorship into holistic, sustainable community development, World Vision also allocates resources to help Canada's poor and complement the mission of the church.

World Vision's Reception Centre assists government-sponsored refugees entering Canada. The NeighbourLink program mobilizes church volunteers to respond locally to people's needs. A quarterly publication, *Context*, provides data on the Canadian family to help churches effectively reach their communities. The development education program provides resources on development issues. During the annual 30-Hour Famine, people fast for 30 hours while discussing poverty and raising funds to support aid programs.

Headquarters

1 World Dr., Mississauga, ON L5T 2Y4 Tel. (905)821-3030 Fax (905)821-1356

Media Contact, Philip Maher, Tel. (905)567-2726

Officers

Pres., Dave Toycen

Vice-Pres., Intl. & Govt. Relations, Linda Tripp

Vice-Pres., Natl. Programs, Don Posterski

Vice-Pres., Fin. & Admin., Charlie Fluit

Vice-Pres., Donor Development Group, Brian Tizzard

Young Men's Christian Association in Canada

The YMCA began as a Christian association to help young men find healthy recreation and meditation, as well as opportunities for education in the industrial slums of 19th century England. It came to Canada in 1851 with the same mission in mind for young men working in camps and on the railways.

Today, the YMCA maintains its original mission, helping individuals to grow and develop in spirit, mind and body, but attends to those needs for men and women of all ages and religious beliefs. The YMCA registers 1.5 million participants in 250 communities that are served by 64 autonomous associations across Canada.

The program of each association differs according to the needs of the community, but most offer one or more programs in each of the following categories, health and fitness, child care, employment counseling and training, recreation, camping, community support and outreach, international development and short-term accommodation.

The YMCA encourages people of all ages,

races, abilities, income and beliefs to come together in an environment which promotes balance in life, breaking down barriers and helping to create healthier communities.

Headquarters

42 Charles St. E., 6th Floor., Toronto, ON M4Y 1T4 Tel. (416)967-9622 Fax (416)967-9618
Media Contact, Sol Kasimer

Officers

Chpsn., Ray Mantha
CEO, Sol Kasimer

Young Women's Christian Association of-du Canada

The YWCA of-du Canada is a national voluntary organization serving 44 YWCAs and YM-YWCAs across Canada. Dedicated to the development and improved status of women and their families, the YWCA is committed to service delivery and to being a source of public education on women's issues and an advocate of social change. Services provided by YWCAs and YM-YWCAs include adult education programs, residences and shelters, child care, fitness activities, wellness programs and international development education. As a member of the World YWCA, the YWCA of-du Canada is part of the largest women's organization in the world.

Headquarters

80 Gerrard St. E., Toronto, ON M5B 1G6 Tel. (416)593-9886 Fax (416)971-8084
Media Contact, Int. CEO, Margaret MacKenzie

Officers

Pres., Ann Mowatt

Youth for Christ-Canada

Youth For Christ is an interdenominational organization founded in 1944 by Torrey Johnson. Under the leadership of YFC's 11-member national board of directors, Youth For Christ-Canada cooperates with churches and serves as a mission agency reaching out to young people and their families through a variety of ministries.

YFC seeks to have maximum influence in a world of youth through high-interest activities and personal involvement. Individual attention is given to each teenager through small group involvement and counseling. These activities and relationships become vehicles for communicating the message of the Gospel.

Headquarters

822-167 Lombard Ave., Winnipeg, MB R3B 0V3 Tel. (204)989-0056 Fax (204)989-0067

Officers

Natl. Dir., Randy L. Steinwand

3. Religious Bodies in the United States

The United States, with its staunch constitutional stance on religious freedom and successive waves of immigrants over the last three centuries, has proved to be a fertile soil for the development of varied Christian traditions. In the directory that follows, some 217 distinct church traditions are represented. Many of these groups represent the processes of dividing and re-uniting that are a hallmark of American religious life. Many churches listed here represent those with a long tradition in Europe, Africa, or Asia predating their American tenure. Others are American-born churches. The researcher may be helped by consulting the churches grouped by tradition at the end of this Directory in the section entitled, "Religious Bodies in the United States Arranged by Families." In this section, all the Baptists bodies are listed together, all the Lutheran bodies, Methodists, etc.

The national headquarters of each church supplies the following directory information. Each listing contains a brief description of the church, followed by the national headquarters contact information, which includes a mailing address, telephone and fax numbers, E-mail and Web site addresses (when available), and the name of the media contact. After the headquarters, there are data regarding the church officers or leaders, including names, titles, and contact information (when contact information differs from the headquarters). There is a staggering array of churches, each with its own form of organization; not all of them refer to their leaders as "officers." In some places, the reader will find the term "Bishops," "Board Members," or "Executives" in place of "Officers." Finally, when applicable, each entry contains a list of the names of church publications.

The churches are printed in alphabetical order by the official name of the organization. There are a few instances in which certain churches are more commonly known by another name. In such cases, the reader is referred incidentally within the text to the appropriate official name. Churches that are member communions of the National Council of the Churches of Christ in the U.S.A. are marked with an asterisk (*).

Other useful information about the churches listed here can be found in other chapters or directories within the book: Statistical information for these churches can be found in the tables toward the end of this book in Chapter III. Further, more extensive information about the publications listed in this directory can be found in Directory 11, "Religious Periodicals in the United States."

The organizations listed here represent the denominations to which the vast majority of church members in the United States belong. It does not include all religious bodies functioning in the United States. The Encyclopedia of American Religions (Gale Research Inc., P.O. Box 33477, Detroit MI 48232-5477) contains names and addresses of additional religious bodies.

Advent Christian Church

The Advent Christian Church is a conservative, evangelical denomination which grew out of the Millerite movement of the 1830s and 1840s. The members stress the authority of Scripture, justification by faith in Jesus Christ alone, the importance of evangelism, disciple-making, and world missions and the soon visible return of Jesus Christ.

Organized in 1860, the Advent Christian Church maintains headquarters in Charlotte, N.C., with regional offices in Rochester, N. H., Princeton, N.C., Ellisville, MO., Sumas, WA, and Lenoir, N.C. Missions are maintained in India, Nigeria, Ghana, Japan, Liberia, Croatia, New Zealand, Malaysia, the Philippines, Mexico, South Africa, Namibia, Honduras, China, Kenya, Malawi, Mozambique, Congo, Romania, and Memphis, Tenn.

The Advent Christian Church maintains doctrinal distinctives in three areas—conditional immortality, the sleep of the dead until the return of Christ and belief that the kingdom of God will be established on earth made new by Jesus Christ.

Headquarters

P.O. Box 23152, Charlotte, NC 28227 Tel. (704) 545-6161 ext. 202 Fax (704)573-0712
Media Contact, Exec. Dir., David E. Ross
E-mail: acpub@adventchristian.org
Web site: www.adventchristian.org

Periodicals

Advent Christian News; Maranatha; Leadership Letter

African Methodist Episcopal Church*

This church began in 1787 in Philadelphia when persons in St. George's Methodist Episcopal Church withdrew as a protest against color segregation. In 1816 the denomination was started, led by Rev. Richard Allen, who had been ordained deacon by Bishop Francis Asbury and was subsequently ordained elder and elected and consecrated bishop.

Headquarters

3801 Market St., Suite 300, Philadelphia, PA 29204 Tel. (215)662-0506
E-mail: Administrator@amecnet.org
Web site: www.amecnet.org

Officers

Sr. Bishop, Bishop Philip Robert Cousin, Presiding Bishop, Fourth Episcopal District, 404 East 41st Street, Suite 114, Chicago, IL 60653 Tel. (773)373-6587 Fax (773)373-8356

Chief Ecumenical & Urban Affairs Officer, Bishop E. Earl McCloud, P.O. Box 310043, Atlanta, GA 31131-0043 Tel. (770)475-2966, emccloudjr@aol.com

Pres., Gen. Bd., Bishop Richard Allen Chappelle, Sr., Presiding Bishop, Twelfth Episcopal District, P.O. Box 147, Little Rock, AR 72203-0147 Tel. (501)375-4310 Fax (501)375-0306

Pres., Council of Bishops 2004-2005, Bishop Vashti Murphy McKenzie, Presiding Bishop, Thirteenth Episcopal District, 500 8th Ave. S., Suite 201, Nashville, TN 37203 Tel. (615)242-6814 Fax (615)242-2496

GENERAL OFFICERS

Dr. Clement W. Fugh; Dr. Richard Allen Lewis; Dr. Daryl B. Ingram; Dr. Johnny Barbour; Jr., Dr. George F. Flowers; Dr. Dennis C. Dickerson; Dr. Jerome V. Harris; Dr. James Wade; Dr. Calvin H. Sydnot

Bishop E. Earl McCloud, Ecumenical Officer/Chaplains; Bishop Richard Franklin Norris (First Episcopal Dist.); Bishop Adam Jefferson Richardson, Jr. (Second Episcopal Dist.); Bishop Robert Vaughn Webster (Third Episcopal Dist.); Bishop Philip Robert Cousin, Sr. (Fourth Episcopal Dist.); Bishop John Richard Bryant (Fifth Episcopal Dist.); Bishop William Phillips DeVeaux (Sixth Episcopal Dist.); Bishop Preston Warren Williams, II (Seventh Episcopal Dist.); Bishop Cornal Garnett Henning, Sr. (Eighth Episcopal Dist.); Bishop Theodore Larry Kirkland (Ninth Episcopal Dist.); Bishop Gregory Gerald McKinley Ingram (Tenth Episcopal Dist.); Bishop McKinley Young (Eleventh Episcopal Dist.); Bishop Richard Allen Chappelle, Sr. (Twelfth Episcopal Dist.); Bishop Vashti Murphy McKenzie (Thirteenth Episcopal Dist.); Bishop David Rwhynica Daniels, Jr. (Fourteenth Episcopal Dist.); Bishop Samuel Lawrence Green, Sr. (Fifteenth Episcopal Dist.); Bishop Carolyn Tyler Guidry (Sixteenth Episcopal Dist.); Bishop Paul Jones Mulenga Kawimbe (Seventeenth Episcopal Dist.); Bishop Sarah Frances Davis (Eighteenth Episcopal Dist.); Bishop James Levert Davis (Nineteenth Episcopal Dist.); Bishop Wilfred Jacobus Messiah (Twentieth Episcopal District)

Periodicals

The Christian Recorder; A.M.E. Review; Journal of Christian Education; Women's Missionary Magazine; Voice of Mission; YPD Newsletter

The African Methodist Episcopal Zion Church*

The A.M.E. Zion Church is an independent body, having withdrawn from the John Street Methodist Church of New York City in 1796. The first bishop was James Varick.

Headquarters

Dept. of Records & Research, 3225 West Sugar Creek Rd., Charlotte, NC 28269 Tel.(704)599-4630 Fax (704)688-2549

Media Contact, Gen. Sec-Aud., Dr. W. Robert Johnson, III, E-mail: j1gsa@aol.com

George Washington Carver Walker, Sr., Senior Bishop

BOARD OF BISHOPS
Officers

Pres.*, Warren M. Brown, 12904 Canoe Ct., Fort Washington, MD 20744, E-mail brownamez@aol.com; Office: 8700 Central Ave, Ste. 307, Landover, MD 20785 Tel. (301)499-6890 Fax (301)499-6893, E-mail midatlantic2amez@aol.com

Sec., Clarence Carr, 965 Charlton Tracer, Marietta, GA 30064 Tel. (770)420-9332 Fax (314)867-5255, E-mail southhall@sbcglobal.net, Office: 2645 Hord Ave., St. Louis, MO 63136 Tel. (314)867-8067

Asst. Sec., Kenneth Monroe, P.O. Box 26403, Fayettville, NC 28318 Tel. (910)843-8274 Fax (910)843-8702

Treas., George Washington Carver Walker, Sr., 3225 W. Sugar Creek Rd., Charlotte, NC 28269 Tel. (704)599-5630; Mailing Address: P.O. Box 26770, Charlotte, NC 28221

*Note: Presidency rotates every six (6) months according to seniority.

ACTIVE MEMBERS

George Edward Battle Jr., 18403 Dembridge Lane, Davidson, NC 28036 Tel. (704)895-2236, gebenced@bellsouth.net; Office: Two Wachovia Center, 301 S. Tryon St., Suite 1755, Charlotte, NC 28202 Tel. (704) 332-7600 Fax (704)343-3745

Warren Matthew Brown, 12904 Canoe Ct., Fort Washington, MD 20744, E-mail: namez@aol; Tel. (301)203-1676 Fax. (301)203-6237

Clarence Carr, 965 Charlton Trace, Marietta, GA 30064; Office: 2645 Hord Ave., St. Louis, MO 63136 Tel. (314)867-8067

Samuel Chuka Ekemam, Sr., Office-Mail: A.M.E. Zion Church Area Headquarters, 1 Zion Hill Plaza, (Ugwu Orji),Okigwe Road, P.O. Box 8000, Owerri, Imo State, Nigeria West Africa; Home Phone from US: (1pm-5pm est) 011-234-83-231-303 Alt. Quick Phone: 011-234-803-301-8280; Office Fax from US: 011-234-83-232-271, chukaekemam@hotmail.com

Roy A. Holmes, 22071 Sunset Dr., Richton Park, IL 60471 Tel. (708)748-3725 Fax (708)748-3726

Louis Hunter, Sr., 4255 Laurel Grove Trace, Suwanee, GA 30244 Tel. & Fax (678)714-1566, E-mail louishunter3@aol.com

Nathaniel Jarrett, Jr., 18031 S. Pheasant Lake Dr., Tinley Park, IL 60477 Tel. (708)802-9873 Fax (708)429-3911

James E. McCoy, 2159 Vaughn Lane, Montgomery, AL 36106 Tel. (334)409-9571; 808 S. Lawrence St., Montgomery, AL 36104-5055 Tel. (334)269-6365 Fax (334)269-6369, aflamez@aol.com

Kenneth Monroe, P.O. Box 26403, Fayettville, NC 28318 Tel. (910)843-8274 Fax (910)843-8702

Richard Keith Thompson, P.O. Box 55458, Washington, D.C 20040 Tel. (202)723-8993 Fax (202)722-1840

George Washington Carver Walker, Sr., 3225 W. Sugar Creek Rd., Charlotte, NC 28269 Tel. (704)599-4630 Fax (704)688-2540; Mailing Address: P.O. Box 26770, Charlotte, NC 28221

Milton Alexander Williams, 129 Sagebrush Dr., Belleville, IL 62221, E-mail bishopwilliams82 @aol.com

RETIRED MEMBERS

William Alexander Hilliard, 690 Chicago Blvd., Detroit, MI 48202

John Henry Miller, Sr., Springdale Estates, 8605 Caswell Ct., Raleigh, NC 27612 Tel. (919)848-6915

Cecil Bishop, 2663 Oakmeade Dr., Charlotte, NC 28270 Tel. (704)846-9370 Fax (704)846-9371, PiedBishop@aol.com

Joseph Johnson, 320 Walnut Point Dr., Matthews, NC 28105 Tel. (704)849-0521; Mailing Address: P. O. Box 608, Matthews, NC 28106, djjjj85@alltel.net

Enoch Benjamin Rochester, 32 Trebling Lane, Willingboro, NJ 08046 Tel. (609)871-2759

Marshall H. Strickland, I, 2000 Cedar Circle Dr., Baltimore, MD 21228 Tel. (410)744-7330 Fax (410)788-5510

EPISCOPAL ASSIGNMENTS

Piedmont Episcopal District: Blue Ridge, West Central North Carolina, Western North Carolina, and Jamaica Conferences: Bishop George W. C. Walker, Sr.

Mid-West Episcopal District: Indiana, Kentucky, Michigan, Missouri, Tennessee, Central Africa (Malawi and Mozambique) and South Africa Conferences: Bishop Milton A. Williams

Eastern West Africa Episcopal District: Central Nigeria, Lagos - West Nigeria, Nigeria, Northern Nigeria, Rivers, Mainland, Cross River, South Eastern, and Southern Conferences: Bishop Samuel Chuka Ekemam, Sr.

North Eastern Episcopal District: New England, New York, Western New York, and Bahamas Islands Conferences: Bishop George Edward Battle, Jr.

Eastern North Carolina Episcopal District: Albemarle, Cape Fear, Central North Carolina, North Carolina,Virgin Islands, and South Africa (Zimbabwe) Conferences: Bishop Richard Keith Thompson

South Atlantic Episcopal District: Georgia, Palmetto, Pee Dee, and South Carolina Conferences: Bishop Clarence Carr

Mid-Atlantic I Episcopal District: Allegheny, New Jersey, Ohio, Guyana, Trinidad-Tobago, and Barbados Conferences: Bishop Nathaniel Jarrett, Jr.

Mid-Atlantic II Episcopal District: East Tennessee-Virginia, India, London-Birmingham, Manchester-Midland, Philadelphia-Baltimore, Virginia and Angola Conferences: Bishop Warren M. Brown

Western Episcopal District: Alaska, Arizona, California, Oregon-Washington, Southwest Rocky Mountain, and Colorado Conferences: Bishop Roy A. Holmes

Southwestern Delta: Arkansas, Louisiana, Oklahoma, South Mississippi, West Tennessee-Mississippi and Texas Conferences: Bishop Louis Hunter, Sr.

Alabama/Florida Episcopal District: Alabama, Cahaba, Central Alabama, North Alabama, South Alabama, West Alabama, Florida, and South Florida Conferences: Bishop James E. McCoy

Western West Africa: Cote D'Ivore, East Ghana, Liberia, Mid-Ghana, North Ghana, Togo and West Ghana Conferences: Bishop Kenneth Monroe

GENERAL OFFICERS AND DEPARTMENTS

Address and telephone number for all departments (except where indicated) is 3225 W. Sugar Creek Rd., Charlotte, NC 28269 Tel. (704)599-4630; Mailing address for all departments (except where indicated) is P.O. Box 26770, Charlotte, NC 28221

Department of Records and Research: W. Robert Johnson, III, Gen. Sec.-Aud., Fax (704)688-2549, E-mail j1gsa@aol.com or wajohnson@amezhqtr.org

Department of Finance: Mrs. Shirley Welch, Chief Financial Officer, Fax (704)688-2553, E-mail shwelch@amezhqtr.org

Star of Zion: Michael Lisby, Editor, Fax (704)688-2546, E-mail editor@starofzion.org.

A.M.E. Zion Quarterly Review and Historical Society: James D. Armstrong, Sec.-Editor, P.O. Box 33247, Charlotte, NC 28233, Fax (704)688-2544, E-mail jaarmstrong@amezhqtr. org

Heritage Hall, Livingstone College, Dr. Phyllis Galloway, Dir., 701 W. Monroe St., Salisbury, NC 28144 Tel. (704)216-6094

Department of Overseas Missions and *Missionary Seer*: Kermit DeGraffenreidt, Sec.-Editor, 475 Riverside Drive, Room 1935, New York, NY 10115 Tel. (212)870-2952 Fax (212)870-2808

Department of Brotherhood Pensions and Ministerial Relief: David Miller, Sec.-Treas., Fax (704)599-4580; Mailing Address: P.O. Box 217114, Charlotte, NC 28221, E-mail damiller@amezhqtr.org

Christian Education Department: Raymon Hunt, Sec., Fax (704)688-2550, E-mail rehunt@ amezhqtr.org

Department of Church School Literature: Dr. Mary A. Love, Editor, Fax (704)688-2548, E-mail malove@amezhqtr.org

Department of Church Extension and Home Missions: Terrence J. Jones, Sec.-Treas., Fax (704)688-2552, E-mail tejones@amezhqtr.org

Bureau of Evangelism: Darryl B. Starnes, Dir., P. O. Box 217258, Charlotte, NC 28221-7258, Fax (704)688-2547, E-mail dbstarnesevangel@aol.com

Public Affairs and Convention Manager: George E. McKain, II, Dir., P.O. Box 1417, Summerville, SC 29484 Tel. (843)878-8461 Fax (843)821-1735, E-mail zionpagem2@aol. com; Hqtrs. Tel. (704)599-4630

Department of Health and Social Concerns: Bernard Sullivan, Dir., 292 W. Main Ave., Gastonia, NC 28053 Tel. (704)866-0325 Fax (704)864-7641, E-mail bsullivan@success-inc.org

A.M.E. Zion Publishing House: David Baker, Interim Gen. Manager, Fax (704)688-2541, E-mail: dabaker@amezhqtr.org

JUDICIAL COUNCIL

Honorable Adele M. Riley, 625 Ellsworth Dr., Dayton, OH 45426

Rev. Dr. George L. Blackwell, 220 N. Elm St., Williamston, NC 27892

Rev. Dr. E. Alex Brower, 11510-115th Ave., Jamaica, NY 11434-1204

Rev. Dr. Richard Chappelle, 4026 Huron Ct., Cheswick, PA 15024

Ms. Elmira Jackson, Esq., 194 Wood Hollow Lane, New Rochelle, NY 10804

Neville Tucker, Esq., 865 South Figueroa, Ste. 2640, Los Angeles, CA 90017

Rev. Dr. Jewett L. Walker, 910 Bridle Path Lane, Charlotte, NC 28211

Jerome Willingham, Esq.

Rev. Dr. Reid R. White, Jr., 6608 Cartwright Dr., Columbia, SC 29223

CONNECTIONAL LAY COUNCIL

Pres., David A. Aiken, Sr., 115-21 142nd St., South Ozone Park, NY 11436 Tel. (718)322-1893 Fax (718)529-6045, E-mail laypresident@att.net

First Vice-Pres., Raymond Richmond, Jr., 456 Stillwood Dr., Jackson, MS 39206-5142 Tel. (601)979-2353 or (601)982-7401, E-mail raymondrichmond@ccaixjsums.edu

Second Vice-Pres., Regina W. Rivera, 9701 Magnolia Pointe Place, Glen Allen, VA 23059 Tel. (804)264-2689 Cell (804)307-6104 Fax (804)264-9777, E-mail regrivera@aol.com

Sec., Mary J. Matthews, P.O. Box 3155, Sanford, NC 27331 Tel. (919)499-1187

Treas., Connie B. Williams, 8518 Fansworth, Charlotte, NC 28215 Tel. (704)531-2931 Fax (704)688-2551

Financial Sec., Jerry L. McCombs, P.O. Box 1444, Newton, NC 28658 Tel. (828)464-9609 Fax (828)466-1496 E-mail jlmcableman@charter.net

Chaplain, Annie M. Williams, 2416 Heyward Brockington Rd., Columbia, SC 29203-9081 Tel. (803)754-8561 or (803)647-3570

Editor, "The Laity Speaks", Rhandi M. Stith, Carrington Arms, 33 Lincoln Ave., Apt. 10L, New Rochelle, NY 10801 Tel. (914)235-3596 Fax (914)637-2518, E-mail randhim@aol.com

Pres. Emeritus, Betty V. Stith, Carrington Arms, 33 Lincoln Ave., Apt. 10L, New Rochelle, NY 10801 Tel. (914) 235-3596 Fax (914)637-2518

GENERAL OFFICERS OF THE WOMEN'S HOME & OVERSEAS MISSIONARY SOCIETY

Gen. Pres., Mrs. Barbara L. Shaw, 4002 Maine Ave., Baltimore, MD 21207 Tel. (410)578-8239 Fax (410)578-0261, E-mail bshawmax@comcast.net

First Vice-Pres., Mrs. Margie J. Bonner, 12 Eldridge St., Waterbury, CT 06704 Tel. (203)756-1829

Second Vice-Pres., Dr. Sandra L. Gadson, 1808 Heather Hill Ct., Flossmoor, IL 60422 Tel. (708)957-0114 Fax (708)957- 4629

Exec. Sec., Mrs. Rosetta J. Dunham, P.O. Box 26846, Charlotte, NC 28221-6846 Tel. (704)599-4630 Fax (704)688-2554; In Rock Hill: Tel. (803)324-5877 Fax (803)980-0759, E-mail rodunham@amezhqtr.org

Recording Sec., Mrs. Vivian W. Brown, 3130 Greenvale Way, Decatur, GA 30034 Tel. (770) 593-1566 Fax. (770)593-3454

Gen. Treas., Ms. Pamela Valentine, 692 N. Hawkins Ave., Akron, OH 44313 Tel. (330) 864-4890 Fax (330)796-4050

Gen. Coord. of YAMS, Mrs. Sandra B. Crowder, 301 Geranium Lane, Chesapeake, VA 23325 Tel. (757)424-8884

Sec. of Youth Missionary Society, Mrs. Charlrean B. Mapson, 2214 Oleander Dr., Wilmington, NC 28403 Tel. (910)251-0682 Fax (910)362-9202, E-mail ysec@chuckmapson.net

Superintendent of Buds of Promise, Mrs. Vicki L. Lewis, 110 S. Bayou St., Mobile, AL 36602 Tel. (251)438-4945

Sec., Bureau of Supplies, Mrs. Henrietta Daniels, 7535 Apache Plume Dr., Houston, TX 77071 Tel. (713)729 - 3436

Chair, Life Members Council, Mrs. Julетha N. French, 500 State St., Mobile, AL 36603 Tel. (251)438-4096

Editor, Women's Section, *Missionary Seer*, Mrs. Ruth J. Stevens, 1080 Lincoln Place, Brooklyn, NY 11213 Tel. (718)604-3681 Fax (718)604-2094, E-mail stevens72@msn.com

Periodicals

Star of Zion; Quarterly Review; Church School Herald, Missionary Seer, Vision Focus, Evangel

Albanian Orthodox Archdiocese in America

The Albanian Orthodox Church in America traces its origins to the groups of Albanian immigrants that first arrived in the United States in 1886, seeking religious, cultural and economic freedoms denied them in the homeland.

In 1908 in Boston, the Rev. Fan Stylian Noli (later Archbishop) served the first liturgy in the Albanian language in 500 years, to which Orthodox Albanians rallied, forming their own diocese in 1919. Parishes began to spring up throughout New England and the Mid-Atlantic and Great Lakes states. In 1922, clergy from the United States traveled to Albania to proclaim the self-governance of the Orthodox Church in the homeland at the Congress of Berat.

In 1971 the Albanian Archdiocese sought and gained union with the Orthodox Church in America, expressing the desire to expand the Orthodox witness to America at large, giving it an indigenous character. The Albanian Archdiocese remains vigilant for its brothers and sisters in the homeland and serves as an important resource for human rights issues and Albanian affairs, in addition to its programs for youth, theological education, vocational interest programs and retreats for young adults and women.

Headquarters

523 E. Broadway, S. Boston, MA 02127
Media Contact, Sec., Dorothy Adams, Tel. (617)268-1275 Fax (617)268-3184
Web site: www.oca.org

Officers

Metropolitan Herman, Tel. (617)268-1275
Chancellor, V. Rev. Arthur E. Liolin, 60 Antwerp St., East Milton, MA 02186 Tel. (617)698-3366
Lay Chpsn., William Poist, 40 Forge Village Rd., Westford, MA 01885 Tel. (978)392-0759
Treas., Cynthia Vasil Brown, 471 Capt. Eames Circle, Ashland, MA 01721 Tel. (508)881-0072

Albanian Orthodox Diocese of America

This diocese was organized in 1950 as a canonical body administering to the Albanian faithful. It is under the ecclesiastical jurisdiction of the Ecumenical Patriarchate of Constantinople (Istanbul).

Headquarters

6455 Silver Dawn Lane, Las Vegas, NV 89118 Tel. (702)365-1989 Fax (702)365-1989
Media Contact, His Grace Bishop Ilia

Officers

His Grace Bishop Ilia, 6455 Silver Dawn Lane, Las Vegas, NV 89118 Tel. (702)365-1989 Fax (702)365-1989

The Allegheny Wesleyan Methodist Connection (Original Allegheny Conference)

This body was formed in 1968 by members of the Allegheny Conference (located in eastern Ohio and western Pennsylvania) of the Wesleyan Methodist Church, which merged in 1966 with the Pilgrim Holiness Church to form the Wesleyan Church.

The Allegheny Wesleyan Methodist Connection is composed of persons "having the form and seeking the power of godliness, united in order to pray together, to receive the word of exhortation, and to watch over one another in love, that they may help each other to work out their salvation." There is a strong commitment to congregational government and to holiness of heart and life. There is a strong thrust in church extension within the United States and in missions worldwide.

Headquarters

P.O. Box 357, Salem, OH 44460 Tel. (330)337-9376
Media Contact, Pres., Rev. William Cope
E-mail: awmc@juno.com
Web site: c1web.com/local_info/churches/aw.html

Officers

Pres., Rev. William Cope, P.O. Box 357, Salem, OH 44460
Vice-Pres., Rev. David Blowers, 1231 Conser Dr., Salem, OH 44460
Sec., Rev. Ray Satterfield, 31 S. 12th St., Indiana, PA 15701
Treas., James Kunselman, 1022 Newgarden Ave., Salem, OH 44460

Periodicals

The Allegheny Wesleyan Methodist

The Alliance of Baptists*

The Alliance of Baptists is an association of individuals and churches dedicated to the preservation of historic Baptist principles, freedoms, and traditions, and to the expression of our ministry and mission through cooperative relationships with other Baptist bodies and the larger Christian community.

From its inception in early 1987, the Alliance has stood for those values that have distinguished the Baptist movement from its beginnings nearly four centuries ago—the freedom and accountability of every individual in matters of faith; the freedom of each congregation under the authority of Jesus Christ to determine its own ministry and mission; and religious freedom for all in relationship to the state.

Headquarters

1328 16th St. NW, Washington, DC 20036 Tel. (202)745-7609 Fax (202)745-0023
Media Contact, Exec. Dir., Rev. Dr. Stan Hastey
Web site: www.allianceofbaptists.org

Officers

Exec. Dir., Rev. Dr. Stan Hastey
Assoc. Dir., Jeanette Holt
Pres., Rev. Cherie Smith, Baltimore, MD
Vice-Pres., Rev. Chris Copeland, Atlanta, GA
Sec., Mary Sue Brookshire, San Diego, CA

Periodicals

Connections

The American Association of Lutheran Churches

This church body was constituted on November 7, 1987. The AALC was formed by laity and pastors of the former American Lutheran Church in America who held to a high view of Scripture (inerrancy and infallibility). This church body also emphasizes the primacy of evangelism and world missions and the authority and autonomy of the local congregation.

Congregations of the AALC are distributed throughout the continental United States from Long Island, N.Y., to Los Angeles. The primary decision-making body is the General Convention, to which each congregation has proportionate representation.

Headquarters

801 W. 106th St., Suite 203, Minneapolis, MN 55420-5603 Tel. (952)884-7784 Fax (952) 884-7894,

Media Contact, Admn. Asst., Rev Charles D. Eidum

E-mail: aa2taalc@aol.com

Web site: www.taalc.com

Officers

Presiding Pastor, Rev. Thomas V. Addland

Asst. Presiding Pastor, Rev. John A. Anderson, 310 Seventh St., Ames, IA 50010 Tel. (515)232-3815, jjamiela@aol.com

Sec., Rev. Harold C. Johnson, 7001 San Antonio NE, Suite S, Albuquerque, NM 87109 Tel. (505)828-0172, christrayofhope@juno.com

Treas., Rev. Dale Zastrow, 700 Second Ave. NE, Minot, ND 58703 Tel. (701)839-7474

American Lutheran Theological Seminary (ALTS), Pres., Rev. Dr. Harald Schoubye, 5238 France Ave. S., Minneapolis, MN 55410 Tel. (952)920-8316, altsprof@aol.com

Periodicals

The Evangel

The American Baptist Association

The American Baptist Association (ABA) is an international fellowship of independent Baptist churches voluntarily cooperating in missionary, evangelistic, benevolent and Christian education activities throughout the world. Its beginnings can be traced to the landmark movement of the 1850s. Led by James R. Graves and J.M. Pendleton, a significant number of Baptist churches in the South, claiming a New Testament heritage, rejected as extrascriptural the policies of the newly formed Southern Baptist Convention (SBC). Because they strongly advocated church equality, many of these churches continued doing mission and benevolent work apart from the SBC, electing to work through local associations. Meeting in Texarkana, TX, in 1924, messengers from the various churches effectively merged two of these major associations, the Baptist Missionary Association of Texas and the General Association, forming the American Baptist Association.

Since 1924, mission efforts have been supported in Australia, Africa, Asia, Canada, Central America, Europe, India, Israel, Japan, Korea, Mexico, New Zealand, South America and the South Pacific. An even more successful domestic mission effort has changed the ABA from a predominantly rural southern organization to one with churches in 48 states.

Through its publishing arm in Texarkana, the ABA publishes literature and books numbering into the thousands. Major seminaries include the Missionary Baptist Seminary, founded by Dr. Ben M. Bogard in Little Rock, AR; Texas Baptist Seminary, Henderson, TX; Oxford Baptist Institute, Oxford, MS; and Florida Baptist Schools in Lakeland, FL.

While no person may speak for the churches of the ABA, all accept the Bible as the inerrant Word of God. They believe Christ was the virgin-born Son of God, that God is a triune God, that the only church is the local congregation of scripturally baptized believers and that the work of the church is to spread the gospel.

Headquarters

4605 N. State Line Ave. Texarkana, TX 75503 Tel. (903)792-2783

Media Contact, Public Relations Dir., Steve Reeves

E-mail: bssc@abaptist.org

Web site: www.abaptist.org

Officers

Pres., David Butimore, Sr., 197 W. Railto Ave., Clovis, CA 93612

Vice Pres., Neal Clark, Rt. 1, Box 48A, Daingerfield, TX 75638; John Owen, P.O. Box 142, Bryant, AR 72089; Donald R. Price, 210 W. Mill St., Malvern, 72104

Recording Clerks, Larry Clements, 270 Tracy Dr., Monticello, AR 71655; Lonnie Wiggins, 1114 Occidental St., Redlands, CA 92374

Publications, Editor in Chief, Bill Johnson; Bus. Mgr., Wayne Sewell, 4605 N. State Line Ave., Texarkana, TX 75503

Meeting Arrangements Dir., Edgar N. Sutton, P.O. Box 240, Alexander, AR 72002

Sec.-Treas. of Missions, Randy Cloud, P.O. Box 1050 Texarkana, TX 75504

American Baptist Churches in the U.S.A.*

Originally known as the Northern Baptist Convention, this body of Baptist churches changed its name to American Baptist Convention in 1950 with a commitment to hold the name in trust for all Christians of like faith and mind who desire to bear witness to historical Baptist convictions in a framework of cooperative Protestantism.

In 1972 American Baptist Churches in the U.S.A. was adopted as the new name. Although national missionary organizational developments began in 1814 with the establishment of the American Baptist Foreign Mission Society and continued with the organization of the American Baptist Publication Society in 1824 and the American Baptist Home Mission Society in 1832, the general denominational body was not formed until 1907. American Baptist work at the local level dates back to the organization by Roger Williams of the First Baptist Church in Providence, R. I. in 1638.

Headquarters

American Baptist Churches Mission Center, P.O. Box 851, Valley Forge, PA 19482-0851 Tel. (610)768-2000 Fax (610)768-2320

Media Contact, Dir., Office of Comm., Richard W. Schramm, Tel. (610)768-2077 Fax (610) 768-2320

E-mail: richard.schramm@abc-usa.org

Web site: www.abc-usa.org

Officers

Pres., Margaret Johnson

Vice-Pres., Arlee Griffin, Jr.

Budget Review Officer, Melva Gray

Gen. Sec., A. Roy Medley, Tel. (610)768-2273, roy.medley@abc-usa.org

Assoc. Gen. Sec.-Treas., Cheryl H. Wade, Tel. (610)768-2280, cheryl.wade@abc-usa.org

REGIONAL ORGANIZATIONS

Central Region, ABC of, Fred A. Ansell, 5833 SW 29th St. Suite A, Topeka, KS 66614-5500

Chicago, ABC of Metro, Leonard Thompson, Sr., 8765 W. Higgins Rd., Suite 240, Chicago, IL 60631

Cleveland Baptist Assoc., Dennis E. Norris, 6060 Rockside Woods Blvd., Suite 317, Cleveland, OH 44131

Connecticut, ABC of, Sarah Hallstrand, Interim, 100 Bloomfield Ave., Hartford, CT 06105-1097

Dakotas, ABC of, Riley H. Walker, 1101 W. 22nd St., Sioux Falls, SD 57105-1699

District of Columbia Bapt. Conv., Jeffrey Haggray, 1628 16th St. NW, Washington, DC 20009-3099

Evergreen Baptist Association, Marcia Patton, 409 Third Ave. S., Suite A, Kent, WA 98032

ABC of the Great Rivers Region, J. Dwight Stinnett, P.O. Box 3786, Springfield, IL 62708-3786

Indiana, ABC of, Larry D. Mason, 1350 N. Delaware St., Indianapolis, IN 46202-2493

Indianapolis, ABC of Greater, Larry D. Sayre, 1350 N. Delaware St., Indianapolis, IN 46202-2493

Los Angeles, ABC of, Samuel S. Chetti, 605 W. Olympic Blvd., Suite 700, Los Angeles, CA 90015-1426

Maine, ABC of, Alfred Fletcher, 107 Winthrop St., P.O. Box 617, Augusta, ME 04332-0667

Massachusetts, ABC of, Robert Wallace, Interim, 20 Milton St., Dedham, MA 02026-2967

Metropolitan New York, ABC of, James O. Stallings, 475 Riverside Dr., Room 432, New York, NY 10115-0432

Michigan, ABC of, Michael A. Williams, 4578 S. Hagadorn Rd., East Lansing, MI 48823-5396

Mid-American Baptist Churches, Marshall Peters, 2400 86th St., Suite 15., Des Moines, IA 50322-4380

Nebraska, ABC of, Susan E. Gillies, 6404 Maple St., Omaha, NE 68104-4079

New Jersey, ABC of, Lee Spitzer, 3752 Nottingham Way, Suite 101, Trenton, NJ 08690-3802

New York State, ABC of, William A. Carlsen, 5842 Heritage Landing Dr., East Syracuse, NY 13057-9359

Northwest, ABC of, Charles Revis, 601 S. Ross Point Rd., Post Falls, ID 83854-7726

Ohio, ABC of, Robert H. Roberts, Interim, 136 N. Galway Dr., P.O. Box 376, Granville, OH 43023-0376

Oregon, ABC of, W. Wayne Brown, 0245 SW Bancroft St., Suite G, Portland, OR 97201-4270

Pacific Southwest, ABC of the, Dale V. Salico, 970 Village Oaks Dr., Suite 101, Covina, CA 91724-3679

Pennsylvania & Delaware, ABC of, Clayton R. Woodbury, 106 Revere Lane, Coatesville, PA 19320

Philadelphia Baptist Assoc., James E. McJunkin, Jr., 100 N. 17th St., 5th floor, Philadelphia, PA 19103-2736

Pittsburgh Baptist Assoc., Lawrence O. Swain, 429 Forbes Ave. #1620, Pittsburgh, PA 15219-1604

Puerto Rico, Baptist Churches of, Cristino Diaz-Montanez, Calle Mayaguez #21, San Juan, PR 00917

Rhode Island, ABC of, Donald R. Rasmussen, P.O. Box 330, Exeter, RI 02822

Rochester-Genesee Region, ABC of, Alan Newton, 151 Brooks Ave., Rochester, NY 14619-2454

Rocky Mountains, ABC of, Desmond Hoffmeister, Interim, 3900 Wadsworth Blvd., Suite 365, Lakewood, CO 80235-2220

South, ABC of the, Walter L. Parrish, II, 5124 Greenwich Ave., Baltimore, MD 21229-2393

Vermont-New Hampshire, ABC of, Z. Allen Abbott, Wheeler Professional Park, One Oak Ridge Rd., Bldg. 3, Suite 4A, West Lebanon, NH 03784-3121

West, ABC of the, Paul D. Borden, 2420 Camino Ramon, Suite 140, San Ramon, CA 94583-4207

West Virginia Baptist Convention, James E. Lutz, Interim, P.O. Box 1019, Parkersburg, WV 26102-1019

Wisconsin, ABC of, Arlo R. Reichter, 15330 W. Watertown Plank Rd., Elm Grove, WI 53122-2391

BOARDS

American Baptist Assembly, Green Lake, WI 54941; Pres., Kenneth P. Giacoletto

American Baptist Historical Society, 1106 S. Goodman St., Rochester, NY 14620; or P.O. Box 851, Valley Forge, PA 19482-0851; Admn. Archivist, Deborah B. VanBroekhoven; Pres., Esther Irish

American Baptist Men, Pres., Cody Pollington

American Baptist Women's Ministries, Exec. Dir., Virginia Holmstrom; Pres., Lois Chiles

Bd. of Intl. Ministries, Acting Exec. Dir., Charles H. Jones; Pres., Elizabeth Burger

Bd. of Natl. Ministries, Exec. Dir., Aidsand F. Wright-Riggins; Pres., David Blythe

Ministers & Missionaries Benefit Bd., Exec. Dir., Sumner M. Grant; Pres., George Tooze, 475 Riverside Dr., New York, NY 10115

Minister Council, Dir., Carole (Kate) H. Harvey; Pres., Joseph Kutter

Periodicals

T*omorrow Magazine; The Secret Place; American Baptist Quarterly; American Baptists In Mission*

The American Carpatho-Russian Orthodox Greek Catholic Church

The American Carpatho-Russian Orthodox Greek Catholic Church is a self-governing diocese that is in communion with the Ecumenical Patriarchate of Constantinople. The late Patriarch Benjamin I, in an official Patriarchal Document dated Sept. 19, 1938, canonized the diocese in the name of the Orthodox Church of Christ.

Headquarters

312 Garfield St., Johnstown, PA 15906 Tel. (814)539-4207 Fax (814)536-4699

Media Contact, Chancellor, V. Rev. Protopresbyter Frank P. Miloro, Tel. (814)539-8086 Fax (814)536-4699

E-mail: archdiocese@goarch.org

Web site: www.goarch.org

Officers

Bishop, Metropolitan Nicholas Smisko

Chancellor, V. Rev. Protopresbyter Frank P. Miloro, 249 Butler Ave., Johnstown, PA 15906 Tel. (814)539-9143, acrod@helicon.net

Treas., V. Rev. Protopresbyter Ronald A. Hazuda, 115 East Ave., Erie, PA 16503 Tel. (814)453-4902

Periodicals

The Church Messenger

American Evangelical Christian Churches

Founded in 1944, the AECC is composed of individual ministers and churches who are united in accepting "Seven Articles of Faith." These seven articles are: the Bible as the written word of God; the virgin birth; the deity of Jesus Christ; salvation through the atonement; guidance of our life through prayer; the return of the Saviour; the establishment of the millennial kingdom.

The American Evangelical Christian Churches offers the following credentials: Certified Christian Worker, Commission to Preach, Licensed Minister and Ordained Minister to those who accept the Seven Articles of Faith, who put unity in Christ first and are approved by AECC.

AECC seeks to promote the gospel through its ministers, churches and missionary activities.

Churches operate independently, with all decisions concerning local government left to the individual churches.

The organization also has ministers in Canada, England, Bolivia, Philippines Thailand, Brazil and South America.

Headquarters

P.O. Box 47312, Indianapolis, IN 46227 Tel. (317)788-9280 Fax (317)788-1410

Media Contact, Dr. Charles Wasielewski, Sr., 51 Wells Rd, Barton, NY 13734-1818

E-mail: aeccoffice@infoblvd.net

Web site: www.aeccministries.com

INTERNATIONAL OFFICERS

Mod., Dr. Charles Wasielewski, Box 51, Wells Rd., Barton, NY 13734 Tel. (607)565-4074

Sec., Dr. Gene McClain, 520 Blooming Pike, Morgantown, IN 46160 Tel. (812)597-5021

Treas., Dr. Michael Ward, Sr., 4802 Chervil Ct., Indianapolis, IN 46237 Tel. (317)888-2095

Bd. Member, Dr. Allen Kent, 550 E. Shoeline Dr., Long Beach, CA 90802 Tel. (562)590-7294

Missions Coord., Dr. Douglas Schlemmer, P.O. Box 409, Twin Peaks, CA 92391 Tel. (909)338-6495

REGIONAL MODERATORS

Northwest Region, Rev. Alvin House, P.O. Box 393, Darby MT 59829 Tel. (406)821-3141

Central-West Region, Rev. Charles Clark, Box 314, Rockport, IL 62370 Tel. (217)437-2507

Far West Region, Pastor Richard Cuthbert, 1195 Via Serville, Cathedral City, CA 92234 Tel. (706)321-6682

Lowell Ford, 397 Shamrock Lane, Newark, OH, 43055 Tel. (614)309-3419

Northeast Region, Rev. John Merrill, P.O. Box 183, East Smithfield, PA 18817 Tel. (717)596-4598

East Region, James R. Brown, 17404 W. Washington, Hagerstown, MD 21740 Tel. (301)797-8121

Southeast Region, Rev. James Fullwood, 207 5th Avenue, N.E., Lutz, FL 33549

STATE MODERATORS

Maryland, Rev. James Brown

Delaware, Rev. John W. Coats

New York, Brenda Osborne

Illinois, Dr. Berton G. Heleine

New Jersey, Rev. R. Eugene Hill
Washington, Rev. Kenneth Pope
Michigan, Rev. Art Mirek
Pennsylvania, Rev. Charles Jennings
Indiana, Rev. Jerry Myers

FOREIGN OUTREACH MINISTRIES

American Evangelical Christian Churches-Canada, Regional Moderator, Dr. Stephen K. Massey, 730 Ontario Street, Suite 709, Toronto, Ontario M4X 1N3 Tel. (416)323-9076

Philippine Evangelical Christian Churches, Dir., Rev. Alan A. Olubalang, P.O. Box 540, Cotabato City, Philippines 9600

American Evangelical Christian Churches-Philippines, Regional Moderator, Rev. Oseas Andres, P.O. Box 2695, Central Post Office, 1166 Q.C. Metro Manila, Philippines

Periodicals

The American Evangelical Christian Churches Newsletter- Monthly

American Rescue Workers

Major Thomas E. Moore was National Commander of Booth's Salvation Army when a dispute flared between Booth and Moore. Moore resigned from Booth's Army and due to the fact that Booth's Army was not incorporated at the time, Moore was able to incorporate under said name. The name was changed in 1890 to American Salvation Army. In 1913 the current name American Rescue Workers was adopted.

It is a national religious social service agency which operates on a quasimilitary basis. Membership includes officers (clergy), soldiers-adherents (laity), members of various activity groups and volunteers who serve as advisors, associates and committed participants in ARW service functions.

The motivation of the organization is the love of God. Its message is based on the Bible. This is expressed by its spiritual ministry, the purposes of which are to preach the gospel of Jesus Christ and to meet human needs in his name without discrimination. It is a branch of the Christian Church . . . a Church with a Mission.

Headquarters

Operational Headquarters, 25 Ross Street, Williamsport, PA 17701 Tel. (570)323-8693 Fax (570)323-8694

National Field Office, 11116 Gehr Road, Waynesboro, PA 17268-9101 Tel. (717)762-2965

Media Contact, Natl. Communication Sec./Natl Special Services Dir., Col. Robert N. Coles, Rev., Natl. Field Ofc., Fax (717)762-8109

E-mail: amerscwk@pcspower.net

Web site: www.arwus.com

Officers

Commander-In-Chief & Pres. of Corp., Gen. Claude S. Astin, Jr., Rev

Natl. Bd. Pres., Col. Sam Astin (Claude S. Astin, III)

Ordination Committee, Chpsn., Gen. Paul E. Martin, (Emeritus) Rev.

Natl. Chief Sec., Col. Dawn R. Astin, NQ, 643 Elmira St., Williamsport, PA 17701

Periodicals

The Rescue Herald, Editor in Chief, Col. Beth Ann Martin, 350 Commonwealth NE, Massillon, OH 44646 Tel. (330)834-9967, lbmartine@wcction.com

Amish—please see Old Order Amish Church

Anglican Orthodox Church—please see The Episcopal Orthodox Church

The Antiochian Orthodox Christian Archdiocese of North America*

The spiritual needs of Antiochian faithful in North America were first served through the Syro-Arabian Mission of the Russian Orthodox Church in 1895. In 1895, the Syrian Orthodox Benevolent Society was organized by Antiochian immigrants in New York City. Raphael Hawaweeny, a young Damascene clergyman serving as professor of Arabic language at the Orthodox theological academy in Kazan, Russia, came to New York to organize the first Arabic-language parish in North America in 1895, after being canonically received under the omophorion of the head of the Russian Church in North America. Saint Nicholas Cathedral, now located at 355 State St. in Brooklyn, is considered the "mother parish" of the Archdiocese.

On March 12, 1904, Hawaweeny became the first Orthodox bishop to be consecrated in North America. He traveled throughout the continent and established new parishes. The unity of Orthodoxy in the New World, including the Syrian Greek Orthodox community, was ruptured after the death of Bishop Raphael in 1915 and by the Bolshevik revolution in Russia and the First World War. Unity returned in 1975 when Metropolitan Philip Saliba, of the Antiochian Archdiocese of New York, and Metropolitan Michael Shaheen of the Antiochian Archdiocese of Toledo, Ohio, signed the Articles of Reunification, ratified by the Holy Synod of the Patriarchate. Saliba was recognized as the Metropolitan Primate and Shaheen as Auxiliary Archbishop. A second auxiliary to the Metropolitan, Bishop Antoun Khouri, was consecrated at Brooklyn's Saint Nicholas Cathedral, in 1983. A third auxiliary, Bishop Basil Essey, was consecrated at Wichita's St. George Cathedral in 1992. Two additional bishops were added in 1994, Bishop Joseph Zehlaoui and Bishop Demetri Khoury.

The Archdiocesan Board of Trustees (consisting of 60 elected and appointed clergy and lay members) and the Metropolitan's Advisory

Council (consisting of clergy and lay representatives from each parish and mission) meet regularly to assist the Primate in the administration of the Archdiocese. Currently, there are 240 parishes and missions in the Archdiocese.

Headquarters

358 Mountain Rd., Englewood, NJ 07631 Tel. (201)871-1355 Fax (201)871-7954

Media Contact, Father Thomas Zain, 52 78th St., Brooklyn, NY 11209 Tel. (718)748-7940 Fax (718)855-3608

E-mail: FrJoseph@antiochian.org

Web site: www.antiochian.org

Officers

Primate, Metropolitan Philip Saliba, 358 Mountain Rd., Englewood, NJ 07631

Auxiliary, Bishop Antoun Khouri, 358 Mountain Rd., Englewood, NJ 07631

Auxiliary, Bishop Joseph Zehlaoui, 454 S. Lorraine Blvd., Los Angeles, CA 90020

Auxiliary, Bishop Basil Essey, 1559 N. Woodlawn, Wichita, KS 67208

Periodicals

The Word; Again Magazine

Apostolic Catholic Assyrian Church of the East, North American Dioceses

The Holy Apostolic Catholic Assyrian Church of the East is the ancient Christian church that developed within the Persian Empire from the day of Pentecost. The Apostolic traditions testify that the Church of the East was established by Sts. Peter, Thomas, Thaddaeus and Bartholomew from among the Twelve and by the labors of Mar Mari and Aggai of the Seventy. The Church grew and developed, carrying the Christian gospel into the whole of Asia and islands of the Pacific. Prior to the Great Persecution at the hands of Tamer'leng the Mongol, it is said to have been the largest Christian church in the world.

The doctrinal identity of the church is that of the Apostles. The church stresses two natures and two Qnume in the One person, Perfect God-Perfect man. The church gives witness to the original Nicene Creed, the Ecumenical Councils of Nicea and Constantinople and the church fathers of that era. Since God is revealed as Trinity, the appellation "Mother of God" is rejected for the "Ever Virgin Blessed Mary Mother of Christ." We declare that she is Mother of Emmanuel, God with us!

The church has maintained a line of Catholicos Patriarchs from the time of the Holy Apostles until this present time. Today the present occupant of the Apostolic Throne is His Holiness Mar Dinkha IV, 120th successor to the See of Selucia Ctestiphon.

Headquarters

Catholicos Patriarch, His Holiness Mar Dinkha, IV, Metropolitanate Residence, The Assyrian Church of the East, Baghdad, Iraq

Media Contact, Father Sleiman Shequel, 7201 N. Ashland, Chicago, IL 60626 Tel. (773)465-4777 Fax (773)465-0776

E-mail: ABSoro@aol.com

Web site: www.cired.org/ace.html

BISHOPS—NORTH AMERICAN

Diocese Eastern USA, His Grace Bishop Mar Aprim Khamis, 8908 Birch Ave., Morton Grove, IL 60053 Tel. (847)966-0617 Fax (847) 966-0012; Chancellor to the Bishop, Rev. Chancellor C. H. Klutz, 7201 N. Ashland, Chicago, IL 60626 Tel. (773)465-4777 Fax (773)465-0776

Diocese Western USA, St. Joseph Cathedral, 680 Minnesota Ave., San Jose, CA 95125 Tel. (408)286-7377 Fax (408)286-1236

Diocese of Canada, His Grace Bishop Mar Emmanuel Joseph, St. Mary Cathedral, 57 Apted Ave., Weston, ON M9L 2P2 Tel. (416)744-9311

Comm. on Inter-Church & Religious Ed., His Grace Bishop Mar Bawai, Diocese of Seattle in Washington, 165 NW 65th, Seattle, WA 98117 Tel. (206)789-1843

Apostolic Catholic Orthodox Church

The Apostolic Catholic Orthodox Church (ACOC) is a communion of persons gathered for worship and public ministry outreach within the Christian Apostolic tradition. The ACOC is creedal, renewal-oriented, and is a part of the autocephalous (self-ruling) Old Catholic Movement, which has its origins in the ancient Catholic Church of the Netherlands. The immediate history of the Old Catholic churches comes out of the reform movement that took place after the First Vatican Council (1869-70). The ACOC maintains a friendly relationship with the Old Catholic Church in the Netherlands.

The bishops of the newly forming churches received episcopal consecration in valid apostolic lines from the church of the Netherlands, based in Utrecht, which had been a fully autonomous Catholic church. These churches became known as "Old Catholic" in reference to their insistence upon return to the basic tenets of Apostolic Christianity, and as defined by the seven Ecumenical Councils of the undivided Eastern and Western Christian churches.

The Old Catholic independent church movement came to the United States as early as the 1880s. Bishop DeLandes Berghes, an Austrian nobleman, ordained and consecrated a bishop with valid Old Catholic Apostolic lines, was sent to North America in 1914. Two of the bishops he consecrated in 1916, Carmel Henry Carfora and William Francis Brothers, are from whom the ACOC derives its lines of Apostolic Succession.

The Apostolic Catholic Orthodox Church finds matters of discipline, administration and pastoral care are governed by discernment about ministry in the Spirit of Christ. Clerical celibacy (which is a matter of discipline) is optional among Old Catholics. In the ACOC, Holy Orders are open to both women and men, single or married. Graduate, Seminary and Clinical Pastoral education are required for candidates for ordination. Decisions pertaining to family planning are left to the concience of married couples, through prayer and counseling.

Matters of faith in the Apostolic Catholic Orthodox Church are the same as in other liturgical churches as formulated in the apostles and Nicene Creeds. The offices of bishop, priest, and deacon exist for the service of spiritual leadership in facilitating expressions of life with God—in the celebration of the sacraments, counseling and pastoral care, teaching, and public advocacy of gospel values. The sacraments are never denied to any person on grounds of gender, race, or marital status. The Holy Eucharist is the center of worship for the ACOC and all who are baptized are welcomed at the Lord's Table.

The Apostolic Catholic Orthodox Church emphasizes the importance of the life of the church as community, that all may be one in Christ (John 17), through mutual helpfulness, ministering to one another and all creation in love, through the diversity of personal giftedness and sensitivity to the particular needs of those being served. The church values and promotes spiritually based, courageous, and compassionate ministry to both personal and global needs. Ongoing spiritual growth is to be nourished through sacred study and contemplative prayer. The ACOC values ecumenical dialogue as an expression of the life of the church.

Headquarters

1770 St. James Place, Suite 550, Houston, TX 77056-3471 Tel (713)266-2456 or (713)977-2855 Fax (713)266-0855

Web site: www.apostoliccatholic.org

Officers

Presiding Bishop, Most Rev. Diana C. Dale, 1770 St. James Place, Suite 550, Houston, TX 77056-3471 Tel (713)266-2456, dcdalw@apostoliccatholic.org

Treas., Elizabeth F. Burleigh, J.D., 1770 St. James Place, Suite 550, Houston, TX 77056 Tel (713)334.0499

Ecumenical Officer, Very Rev. Robert L. Lewis Jr., P.O. Box 10483, Rockville, MD 20849 Tel. (240)401-0178

Register Agent, Most Rev. Lance Beizer, J.D., P.O. Box 1121, Campbell, CA 9009-1121

Board Regional Representatives

West, Rev. H. Rogers Thomson, 203 E. Shoreacres Blvd., Shoreacres TX, 77571

Mid-Continent, Rev. Robert M. Palmer, 871 Stone Blvd. Nolensville, TN 37135

Atlantic, Very Rev. Robert L. Lewis Jr.

Other Organizations

Institute of Worklife Ministry, 1770 St. James Place, Suite 550, Houston, TX 77056-3471 Tel (713)266-2456 Fax (713)266-0855, www.apostoliccatholic.org

Periodicals

ACOC Quarterly Bulletin; Worklife Quarterly Newsletter

Apostolic Christian Church (Nazarene)

This body was formed in America by an immigration from various European nations, from a movement begun by Rev. S. H. Froehlich, a Swiss pastor, whose followers are still found in Switzerland and Central Europe.

Headquarters

Apostolic Christian Church Foundation, 1135 Sholey Rd., Richmond, VA 23231 Tel. (804)222-1943 Fax (804)236-0642

Media Contact, Exec. Dir., James Hodges

Officers

Exec. Dir., James Hodges

Apostolic Christian Churches of America

The Apostolic Christian Churches of America was founded in the early 1830s in Switzerland by Samuel Froehlich, a young divinity student who had experienced a religious conversion based on the pattern found in the New Testament. The church, known then as Evangelical Baptist, spread to surrounding countries. A Froehlich associate, Elder Benedict Weyeneth, established the church's first American congregation in 1847 in upstate New York. In America, where the highest concentration today is in the Midwest farm belt, the church became known as Apostolic Christian.

Church doctrine is based on a literal interpretation of the Bible, the infallible Word of God. The church believes that a true faith in Christ's redemptive work at Calvary is manifested by a sincere repentance and conversion. Members strive for sanctification and separation from worldliness as a consequence of salvation, not as a means to obtain it. Security in Christ is believed to be conditional based on faithfulness. Uniform observance of scriptural standards of holiness are stressed. Holy Communion is confined to members of the church. Male members are willing to serve in the military, but do not bear arms. The holy kiss is practiced and women wear head coverings during prayer and worship.

Doctrinal authority rests with a council of elders, each of whom serves as a local elder (bishop). Both elders and ministers are chosen from local congregations, do not attend seminary and serve without compensation. Sermons are delivered extemporaneously as led by the Holy Spirit, using the Bible as a text.

Headquarters

3420 N. Sheridan Rd., Peoria, IL 61604
Media Contact, Sec., William R. Schlatter, 14834 Campbell Rd., Defiance, OH 43512 Tel. (419)393-2621 Fax (419)393-2144, wrschlatter@juno.com
E-mail: Questions@ApostolicChristian.org
Web site: www.apostolicchristian.org

Officers

Sec., Elder (Bishop) William R. Schlatter, 14834 Campbell Rd., Defiance, OH 43512 Tel. (419)393-2621 Fax (419)393-2144

Periodicals

The Silver Lining

Apostolic Episcopal Church

The Apostolic Episcopal Church on Sept. 23-24, 2000 in New York City signed Concordats of Intercommunion with the following Christian Churches—The Anglican Independent Communion, The Ethiopian Orthodox Coptic Archdiocese of North and South America, The Uniate Western Orthodox Catholic Church, and the Byelorussian Orthodox National Church in Exile under the administration of His Beatitude Yury I.

In effect, the Apostolic Episcopal Church thus became a Uniate Western Rite of the Orthodox Church of the East, using the 1928 *Book of Common Prayer*. In 1905, under the guidance of Archbishop Tikhon Bellavin (later Patriarch of Moscow), the Holy Synod in St. Petersburg approved the use of the Anglican Liturgy for Western Rite Orthodox Christians. Today this usage is called the Rite of St. Tikhon and is in use among many Orthodox Western Rite Jurisdictions.

This pilgrimage to Orthodoxy among Anglicans began in 1712 with the Non-Jurors Anglican Hierarchy and faithful. These Non-Jurors were Anglican Clergy who in 1689 refused allegiance to King William III and Queen Mary, the usurpers who had overthrown King James II. In 1712 Metropolitan-Bishop Arsenios of the Alexandrine Patriarchate visited England and received many of these "British Katholicks" into the Orthodox Church.

Headquarters

World Mission HQS and the Editorial Office of the *Tover of St. Cassian*, 80-46 234 St. Jamaica, NY 11427-2116, Attn Editor: the Rt. Rev. Francis C. Spataro DD, Tel. (718)740-4134
The Province of Guyana and the Caribbean, c/o The Rev. Lloyd U. Samuel OCR, P.O. Box 10844, Georgetown, Guyana, South America, 630875.
Ohio OCR Vicariate, the V. Rev. Michael B. Reed, St. Peter the Aleut Mission, 3423 Hunter Dr., N. Olmstead, OH 44070 Tel. (216)779-0272
Queens, NY, OCR Vicariate, the Rev. Pedro Bravo-Guzman, AIELC, P.O. Box 2465, Astoria, NY 11102
Missouri OCR Vicariate, Rt. Rev. Irl A. Gladfelter, M Div., St. Michael's House, 1200 NE 81st Terrace, Kansas City, MO 64118
Pennsylvania OCR Vicariate, Rev. Dr. Sam Guido DD, OCR, St. Paul's Chapel, 620 Main St. Slatington, PA 18080
Shenouda Seminary, Dir., Rev. Dr. Paget Mack, OCR, OSBM, P.O. Box 673, New York, NY 10035
Belgium Mission, St. Michael's, Domein Fort 3, Frans Beirenlaan 2A, 2150 Borsbeek, Belgium
Media Contact, The Rt. Rev. Francis C. Spataro DD, The Vilatte Guild/Society of St. Cassian, 80-46 234 St., Jamaica, NY 11427 Tel. (917) 579-0585
E-mail: vil11427@yahoo.com
Web site: www.cinemaparallel.com/AECSynod.html

Officers

Pres., The Rt. Rev. Francis C. Spataro, DD, OCR, Tel. (718)740-4134 (24-hour number)
Archbishop of the Central & Western Province, USA, Dr. Wayne Ellis, PhD, OCR
AIELC Visitor, The Rt. Rev. Peter P. Brennan, OCR
Vicar for Guyana & the Caribbean: Rev Lloyd U. Samuel, OCR
Vicar for Ohio: The V. Rev. Michael B. Reed, OCR
Vicar for Queens, NY: The Rev. Pedro Bravo-Guzman, OCR
International Primate for the OCR, The M. Rev. Bertil Persson, THD, OCR
Belgium Mission, The Rt. Rev. Walter M. C. Walgraeve, OCR
Missouri OCR Vicariate, Rt. Rev. Irl A. Gladfelter
Pennsylvania OCR Vicariate, Rev. Dr. Sam Guido, DD
Shenouda Seminary, Dir., Rev. Dr. Paget Mack
The Order of Corporate Reunion; The Vilatte Guild/Society of St. Cassian

Periodicals

The Tover of St. Cassian, VIL11427@yahoo.com, www.netministries.org/see/churches/ch04671

Apostolic Faith Mission Church of God

The Apostolic Faith Mission Church of God was founded and organized July 10, 1906, by Bishop F. W. Williams in Mobile, Alabama.

Bishop Williams was saved and filled with the Holy Ghost at a revival in Los Angeles under Elder W. J. Seymour of The Divine Apostolic Faith Movement. After being called into the ministry, Bishop Williams went out to preach the gospel in Mississippi, then moved on to Mobile.

On Oct. 9, 1915, the Apostolic Faith Mission Church of God was incorporated in Mobile under Bishop Williams, who was also the general overseer of this church.

Headquarters

Ward's Temple, 806 Muscogee Rd., Cantonment, FL 32533

Media Contact, Natl. Sunday School Supt., Bishop Thomas Brooks, 3298 Toney Dr., Decatur, GA 30032 Tel. (404)284-7596

Board of Bishops

Presiding Bishop, Donice Brown, 2265 Welcome Cir., Cantonement, FL 32535 Tel. (904)968-5225

Bishop T.C. Tolbert Sr., 226 Elston Ave., Anniston, AL, 36201; Bishop John Crum, 4236 Jackson St., Birmingham, AL, 35217; Bishop Samuel Darden, 25 Taunton Ave., Hyde Park, MA 02136; Bishop James Truss, P.O. Box 495, Lincoln, AL, 35096; Bishop T.C. Tolbert, Jr., 768 Grayton Rd., Ohatchee, AL 36271; Bishop Thomas Brooks, 3298 Toney Drive, Decatur, GA. 30032, Tel. (404)284-7596 Fax: (404)284-7173; Bishop Johnny Cunningham, P.O. Box 472, Century, FL 32535 Tel. (850)256-2443; Bishop Wayne Smiley, 228 Seville Circle, Mary Ester, FL 32569

NATIONAL DEPARTMENTS

Missionary Dept., Pres., Rosa Tolbert, Anniston, AL

Youth Dept., Pres., Johnny Kennedy, Birmingham, AL

Sunday School Dept., Supt., Thomas Brooks, Decatur, GA

Mother Dept., Pres., Mother Bessie Davis, 1003 Northeast St., Pensacola, FL 32501

INTERNATIONAL DEPARTMENTS

Morobia, Liberia, Bishop Beter T. Nelson, Box 3646, Bush Rhode Islane, Morobia, Liberia

Periodicals

The Three-Fold Vision, published quarterly.

The A.F.M. Church of God Apostolic Bible College, Cantonement, FL 32535

Apostolic Faith Mission of Portland, Oregon

The Apostolic Faith Mission of Portland, Oregon, was founded in 1907. It had its beginning in the Latter Rain outpouring on Azusa Street in Los Angeles in 1906.

Some of the main doctrines are justification by faith, which is a spiritual new birth, as Jesus told Nicodemus and as Martin Luther proclaimed in the Great Reformation; sanctification, a second definite work of grace; the Wesleyan teaching of holiness; the baptism of the Holy Ghost as experienced on the Day of Pentecost and again poured out at the beginning of the Latter Rain revival in Los Angeles.

Mrs. Florence L. Crawford, who had received the baptism of the Holy Ghost in Los Angeles, brought this Latter Rain message to Portland on Christmas Day 1906. It has spread to the world by means of literature which is still published and mailed everywhere without a subscription price. Collections are never taken in the meetings and the public is not asked for money.

Camp meetings have been held annually in Portland, Oregon since 1907, with delegations coming from around the world.

Missionaries from the Portland headquarters have established churches in Korea, Japan, the Philippines and many countries in Africa.

Headquarters

6615 SE 52nd Ave., Portland, OR 97206 Tel. (503)777-1741 Fax (503)777-1743

Media Contact, Superintendent, Darrel D. Lee

Web site: www.apostolicfaith.org

Officers

Pres., Rev. Darrel D. Lee

Periodicals

Higher Way

Apostolic Lutheran Church of America

Organized in 1872 as the Solomon Korteniemi Lutheran Society, this Finnish body was incorporated in 1929 as the Finnish Apostolic Lutheran Church in America and changed its name to Apostolic Lutheran Church of America in 1962.

This body stresses preaching the Word of God. There is an absence of liturgy and formalism in worship. A seminary education is not required of pastors. Being called by God to preach the Word is the chief requirement for clergy and laity. The church stresses personal absolution and forgiveness of sins, as practiced by Martin Luther, and the importance of bringing converts into God's kingdom.

Headquarters

P.O. Box 2948, Battle Ground, WA 98604-2948

Media Contact, Sec., Ivan M. Seppala (925)672-3320

Web site: www.apostolic-lutheran.org

Officers

Chair, Richard C. Juuti, RRI, Bentley, AB T0C 0J0 Canada

Treas., Ben Johnson, 98920 Keller Rd., Astoria, OR 97103

Sec., Ivan M. Seppala, 332 Mt. Washington Way, Clayton, CA 94517

Periodicals

Christian Monthly

Apostolic Orthodox Catholic Church of North America

The Christian church was established by the Lord Jesus Christ and His Holy Apostles in Jerusalem in 33 A.D. From Jerusalem, the church spread to other centers of the known world, including Constantinople (founded in 37 A.D.) and Kiev (45 A.D.), founded by St. Andrew the First-Called Holy Apostle. In 864, missionary of the Church of Constantinople further extended the Orthodox christian faith in present-day Russia. In 988, Rus' Prince Vladimir converted and declared Orthodoxy the state religion, while hundreds of thousands were baptized in the Dnieper River at Kiev. The resulting Russian Orthodox Church became the greatest safeguard and body of Orthodox Christians in the world.

The history of American Orthodox Catholic Christianity began in 1794 when Russian Orthodox Church missionaries established the first Orthodox mission on North American soil at present-day Kodiak, Alaska. Their missionary efforts continued down the Pacific coast in 1824, then across the whole continent. Being the canonical founder of Orthodox Christianity in North America, the Russian Orthodox Church maintained and presided over all Orthodox missions, churches, and Christians throughout North America without question or challenge for over 100 years. However, the 1917 Bolshevik Revolution, which resulted in severe persecution and imprisonment of the Russian Orthodox Mother Church, also resulted in the unrestrained rise of old-country nationalism and great ethnic turbulence between Orthodox Catholic Christians and their churches in North America. They separated and divided, often violently, along ethnic and nationalist lines with each creating their own old-world ethnic administrations. The once long-held unity and single Orthodox Church canonical administration in North America was destroyed.

The Apostolic Orthodox Catholic Church (AOCC) is canonically independent and indigenous to North America and comprised of bishops, clergy and faithful possessing unbroken Apostolic Succession since the time of Jesus Christ's appointment of His Twelve Holy Apostles to the present day through American Orthodoxy's Luminary and Defender, Russian Orthodox Prelate-Archbishop Aftimios Ofiesh of Blessed Memory.

The AOCC maintains unquestionable, canonical Apostolic Succession passed on to its bishops through its Russian Orthodox Mother Church by Archbishop Aftimios Ofiesh, his succeeding Bishops Sophronios Beshara and Christopher Contogeorge, their legal successors and through consecrating support of such memorable Orthodox leaders as Russian Patriarchal Exarch of North America Metropolitan Benjamin Fedchenkov and and Albanian Orthodox Church Metropolitan Theophan Noli. In 1945, the Apostolic Succession and Canonicity of these bishops "and their successors" were declared in binding agreement to be unquestionable, valid, authentic and independent by the Orthodox Church Ecumenical Patriarchate of Constantin-ople, and recognition was furthermore attested to in 1951. English-speaking and non-ethnic restrictive, the AOCC's further validity is evidenced by its life, mind, discourse and teaching all being governed and directed in accordance with the Sacred Canons of the Most Ancient Holy Orthodox Catholic Church. The AOCC embraces the ideals and theology of Orthodoxy and freedom which Archbishop Aftimios Ofiesh stood for, taught and passed on by selfless devotion and love for Christ and His Church, and by his personal example.

Headquarters

AOCC Chancery, P.O. Box 1834, Glendora, CA 91740-1834 Tel. (626)335-7369

Media Contact, Vice-Presiding Archbishop, Most Rev. Aftimios L. Sinclair, 4696 SE Horseshoe Ct., Salem, OR 97301 Tel (575)375-6175, baftimii@aol.com

E-mail: aoccna.relations@usa.com

Web site: www.ForMinistry.com/91740AOCCA

Officers

Presiding Bishop, Most Rev. Gorazd

Vice-Presiding Archbishop, Most Rev. Aftimios L. Sinclair

Bishop Sec., Most Rev. Angelo

SYNOD OF BISHOPS & DIOCESES

Most Rev. Gorazd, (C. W. Imgram), Bishop of the Diocese of Los Angeles & Greater Pacific, P.O. Box 1834, Glendora, CA 91740-1834 Tel. (626)335-7369, cwingram@webtv.net

Most Rev. Aftimios II (L. Sinclair), Bishop of the Diocese of the Rocky Mountains & Midwest, 4696 SE Horseshoe Ct., Salem, OR 97301 Tel (503)375-6175, BaftimII@aol.com

Most Rev. John (Kelly), Bishop of the Diocese of New York; Federal Endorser: Military, Federal Prisons & Veteran Admin. Chaplains, NC/MAF-EC/VAC National Board; 4-20 Green Way Ave., Manorville, NY 11949 Tel. (516)878-4172, Bishop-NY@webtv.net

Most Rev. Angelo (Ricci), Bishop of the Diocese of the Eastern States, 37 Shippee School House Rd., Foster, RI 02825 Tel. (401)647-2867

SEMINARY

Holy Trinity Apostolic Orthodox Catholic Seminary, P.O. Box 1834, Glendora, CA 91740-1834

Periodicals

Carpenter's Workshop

Armenian Apostolic Church of America

Widespread movement of the Armenian people over the centuries caused the development of two seats of religious jurisdiction of the Armenian Apostolic Church in the World-the See of Etchmiadzin, in Armenia, and the See of Cilicia, in Lebanon.

In America, the Armenian Church functioned under the jurisdiction of the Etchmiadzin See from 1887 to 1933, when a division occurred within the American diocese over the condition of the church in Soviet Armenia. One group chose to remain independent until 1957, when the Holy See of Cilicia agreed to accept them under its jurisdiction.

Despite the existence of two dioceses in North America, the Armenian Church has always functioned as one church in dogma and liturgy.

Headquarters

Eastern Prelacy, 138 E. 39th St., New York, NY 10016 Tel. (212)689-7810 Fax (212)689-7168

Western Prelacy, 6252 Honolulu Ave., La Crecsenta, CA 91214 Tel. (818)248-7737 Fax (818)248-7745

Media Contact, Vazken Ghougassian

E-mail: prelacy@gis.net

Web site: www.armprelacy.org

Officers

Eastern Prelacy, Prelate, Archbishop Oshagan Choloyan

Eastern Prelacy, Chpsn., Richard Sarajian, Esq.

Western Prelacy, Prelate, Archbishop Moushegh Mardirossian

Western Prelacy, Chpsn., Avo Donoyan

DEPARTMENTS

Eastern Prelacy Offices, Executive Dir., Vazken Ghougassian

AREC, Armenian Religious Educ. Council, Exec. Coord., Deacon Shant Kazanjian

ANEC, Armenian Natl. Educ. Council, Exec. Coord., Gilda Kupelian

Periodicals

Outreach

Armenian Apostolic Church, Diocese of America*

The Armenian Apostolic Church was founded at the foot of the biblical mountain of Ararat in the ancient land of Armenia, where two of Christ's Holy Apostles, Saints Thaddeus and Bartholomew, preached Christianity. In A.D. 303 the historic Mother Church of Etchmiadzin was founded by Saint Gregory the Illuminator, the first Catholicos of all Armenians. This cathedral still stands and serves as the center of the Armenian Church. A branch of this church was established in North America in 1889. The first church building was consecrated in 1891 in Worcester, MA. The first Armenian Diocese was set up in 1898 by the then-Catholicos of All Armenians, Mgrditch Khrimian. Armenian immigrants built the first Armenian church in the new world in Worcester, MA, under the jurisdiction of Holy Etchmiadzin.

In 1927, the churches and the parishes in California were formed into a Western Diocese and the parishes in Canada formed their own diocese in 1984. Other centers of major significance of the Armenian Apostolic Church are the Catholicate of Cilicia, now located in Lebanon, the Armenian Patriarchate of Jerusalem and the Armenian Patriarchate of Constantinople.

Headquarters

Eastern Diocese, 630 Second Ave., New York, NY 10016-4885 Tel. (212)686-0710 Fax (212)779-3558

Western Diocese, 3325 North Glenoaks Blvd., Burbank, CA 91504 Tel. (818)558-7474 Fax (818)558-6333

Canadian Diocese, 615 Stuart Ave., Outremont, QC H2V 3H2 Tel. (514)276-9479 Fax (514)276-9960

Media Contact, Dir., Public Relations, Chris Zakian, Eastern Diocese

Diocesan Council Chpsn., Haig Dadourian, 415 Madison Ave., 7th Floor, New York, NY 10017

Wester Diocese, Pirmate, His Em. Archbishop Vatche Hovsepian, Western Diocese Ofc.

Diocesan Council, Chpsn., Dn. Dr. Varouj Alterbarmakian, 7290 North San Pedro, Fresno, CA 93011

Diocesan Council, Sec., Mr. John Yaldezian, 23221 Aetna St., Woodland Hills, CA 91367 Tel. (B) (818)346-6163

Canadian Diocese, Primate, His Em. Archbishop Hovnan Derderian

Diocesan Council, Chpsn., Mr. Takvor Hopyan, 20 Pineway, Blvd., Willowdale, ON M2H 1A1 Canada, Tel. (B) (416)222-2639

Diocesan Council, Sec., Mr. Vahe Ketli, 750 Montpellier, #909, St. Laurens, QC H4L 5A7 Canada, Tel. (514)747-1347

Web site: www.armenianchurch.org

Officers

Eastern Diocese

Primate, Archbishop Khajag Barsamian, Eastern Diocese Ofc.

Diocesan Council, Chpsn., Haig Dadourian, 415 Madison Ave., 7th Floor, New York, NY 10017

Western Diocese

Primate, His Em. Archbishop Vatche Hovsepian, Western Diocese Ofc.

Diocesan Council, Chpsn., Dn. Dr. Varouj Altebarmakian, 7290 North San Pedro, Fresno, CA 93011

Diocesan Council, Sec., Mr. John Yaldezian, 23221 Aetna St., Woodland Hills, CA 91367 Tel. (B) (818)346-6163

Canadian Diocese

Primate, His Em. Archbishop Hovnan Derderian

Diocesan Council Chpsn, Mr. Takvor Hopyan, 20 Pineway,Blvd., Willowdale, ON M2H 1A1, Canada Tel (B) (416)222-2639

Diocesan Council Sec.., Mr. Vahe Ketli, 750 Montpellier, # 909, St. Laurens, QC H4L 5A7, Canada Tel (R) (514)747-1347

Periodicals

The Armenian Church; The Mother Church

Assemblies of God

From a few hundred delegates at its founding convention in 1914 at Hot Springs, Ark., the

Assemblies of God has become one of the largest church groups in the modern Pentecostal movement with over 50 million adherents worldwide. Throughout its existence it has emphasized the power of the Holy Spirit to change lives and the participation of all members in the work of the church.

The revival that led to the formation of the Assemblies of God and numerous other church groups early in the 20th century began during times of intense prayer and Bible study. Believers in the United States and around the world received spiritual experiences like those described in the Book of Acts. Accompanied by baptism in the Holy Spirit and its initial physical evidence of "speaking in tongues," or a language unknown to the person, their experiences were associated with the coming of the Holy Spirit at Pentecost (Acts 2), so participants were called Pentecostals.

The church also believes that the Bible is God's inspired infallible Word to man, that salvation is available only through Jesus Christ, that divine healing is made possible through Christ's suffering and that Christ will return again for those who love him. In recent years, this Pentecostal revival has spilled over into almost every denomination in a wave of revival sometimes called the charismatic renewal.

Assemblies of God leaders credit their church's rapid and continuing growth to its acceptance of the New Testament as a model for the present-day church. Aggressive evangelism and missionary zeal at home and abroad characterize the denomination.

Assemblies of God believers observe two ordinances—water baptism by immersion and the Lord's Supper, or Holy Communion. The church is trinitarian, holding that God exists in three persons—Father, Son and Holy Spirit.

Headquarters

1445 Boonville Ave., Springfield, MO 65802-1894 Tel. (417)862-2781 Fax (417)862-0133, GenSec@ag.org

Media Contact, Statistician, Sherri L. Doty

E-mail: info@ag.org

Web site: www.ag.org/top

Officers

Gen. Supt., Thomas E. Trask

Asst. Supt., Charles T. Crabtree

Gen. Sec., George O. Wood

Gen. Treas., James E. Bridges

World Missions, Exec. Dir., John Bueno

AG U.S. Missions, Exec. Dir., Charles Hackett

Great Lakes, Charles Crank, 44 N. Girls School Rd., Indianapolis, IN 46214 Tel. (317)554-2114 Fax (317)554-2121

Gulf, L. Alton Garrison, P.O. Box 191670, Little Rock, AR 72219 Tel. (501)568-2194 Fax (501)568-1277

North Central, David Argue, 1111 Old Cheney Rd., Lincoln, NE 68512 Tel. (402)421-1111 Fax (402)421-1179

Northeast, H. Robert Rhoden, P.O. Box 690, Gainesville, VA 20155 Tel. (703)753-0300 Fax (703)753-2879

Northwest, Warren Bullock, P.O. Box 579, Kirkland, WA 98083 Tel. (425)889-5253 Fax (425)889-5750

South Central, J. Don George, 3000 W. Airport Freeway, Irving, TX 75062 Fax (972)399-1919

Southeast, Dan Betzer, 4701 Summerlin Rd., Ft. Myers, FL 33919 Tel. (239)936-6277 Fax (239)936-9365

Southwest, Richard Dresselhaus, c/o General Sec.'s Office, 1445 N. Boonville Ave, Springfield, MO 65802 Tel. (417)862-2781 Fax (417)862-0133

Language Area Spanish, Jesse Miranda, 55 Fair Drive, Costa Mesa, CA 92626 Tel. (714)668-6196 Fax (714)662-5243

Language Area Other, Nam Soo Kim, 130-30 31st Ave., 4th Floor, Flushing, NY 11354 Tel. (718)321-7800 Fax (718)321-9394

Ethnic Fellowship, Zollie Smith, P.O. Box 70, Somerset, NJ 08875 Tel. (732)846-9153 Fax (732)846-5977

INTERNATIONAL HEADQUARTERS

Div. of the Treasury, Gen. Treas., James E. Bridges

Div. of Christian Education, Natl. Dir., Deborah Gill

Div. of Church Ministries, Exec. Liaison, Charles Crabtree

Div. of World Missions, Exec Dir., John Bueno

Div. of Home Missions, Exec. Dir., Charles Hackett

Div. of Publication, Gospel Publishing House, Natl. Dir., Arlyn Pember

Periodicals

Enrichment: A Journal for Pentecostal Ministry; Caring; High Adventure; Club Connection; Pentecostal Evangel; Woman's Touch; Heritage; On Course

Assemblies of God International Fellowship (Independent/ Not affiliated)

April 9, 1906 is the date commonly accepted by Pentecostals as the 20th-century outpouring of God's spirit in America, which began in a humble gospel mission at 312 Azusa Street in Los Angeles. This spirit movement spread across the United States and gave birth to the Independent Assemblies of God (Scandinavian). Early pioneers instrumental in guiding and shaping the fellowship of ministers and churches into a nucleus of independent churches included Pastor B. M. Johnson, founder of Lakeview Gospel Church in 1911; Rev. A. A. Holmgren, a Baptist minister who received his baptism of the Holy Spirit in the early Chicago outpourings, was publisher of Sanningens Vittne, a voice of the Scandinavian Independent Assemblies of God and also served as Sec. of the fellowship for many years; Gunnar Wingren, missionary pioneer in Brazil; and Arthur F. Johnson, who served for many years as chairman of the Scandinavian Assemblies.

In 1935, the Scandinavian group dissolved its incorporation and united with the Independent Assemblies of God of the U.S. and Canada which by majority vote of members formed a new corporation in 1986, Assemblies of God International Fellowship (Independent/Not Affiliated).

Headquarters

6325 Marindustry Dr., San Diego, CA 92121 Tel. (858)677-9701 Fax (858)677-0038

Media Contact, Exec. Dir. & Ed., Rev. T. A. Lanes

E-mail: admin@agifellowship.org

Web site: www.agifellowship.org

Officers

Exec. Dir., Rev. T. A. Lanes

Sec., Rev. George E. Ekeroth

Treas., M. J. Ekeroth

Canada, Sec., Harry Nunn, Sr., 15 White Crest Ct., St. Catherines, ON 62N 6Y1

Associate Reformed Presbyterian Church (General Synod)

The origin of the Associate Reformed Presbyterian Church began in Scotland with the Covenanters of the seventeenth century and Seceder movement of the eighteenth. The Covenanters broke from the established Church of Scotland to eventually form separate "praying societies," which led to the Reformed Presbyterian Church of Scotland. The Seceders, about a hundred years later, became the Associate Church of Scotland.

The Associate Reformed Presbyterian Church stems from the 1782 merger of these two groups in America. in 1822 the "Synod of the South" was granted independent status from the national body. It continued to hold to the 1799 constitution of the church with no changes, and probably consisted of around 2,000 members. The present Associate Reformed Presbyterian Church, (General Synod), is the ongoing denomination resulting from that action, the original "General Synod" of the denomination having become a part of the United Presbyterian Church.

The government is by a three-layered court system, the local "Session," the regional "Presbytery" and the national "General Synod," each of which is composed of both ruling and teaching elders. The standards of the denomination include the Westminster Confession of Faith, the Catechisms and the Forms of Government, Worship and Discipline.

Headquarters

Associate Reformed Presbyterian Center, One Cleveland St., Greenville, SC 29601-3696 Tel. (864)232-8297 Fax (864)271-3729

Media Contact, Principal Clk., Rev. C. Ronald Beard, D.D., 3132 Grace Hill Rd., Columbia, SC 29204 Tel. (803)787-6370.

Moderator, Mr. Frank Hunt, II, One Cleveland St. Greenville, SC 29601

E-mail: dragondraw@aol.com

Web site: www.arpsynod.org

AGENCIES & INSTITUTIONS (in the A.R. Presbyterian Center in Greenville)

Admn. Ser. Dir., Ed Hogan

Christian Education, Dir., Dr. David Vickery

Church Extension, Dir., Rev. Alan Avera

Publications, Editor, Sabrina Cooper

Treas., Guy H. Smith, III

World Witness, Bd. of Foreign Missions, Exec. Sec., John E. Mariner

OTHER INSTITUTIONS

Bonclarken Assembly, Dir., James T. Brice, 500 Pine St., Flat Rock, NC 28731 Tel. (704)692-2223

Erskine College, Pres., Rev. John L. Carson, Ph.D., Due West, SC 29639 Tel. (864)379-8759

Erskine Theological Seminary, Dean, Ralph J. Gore, Jr., Ph.D., Due West, SC 26939 Tel. (864) 379-8885; Vice Pres.: Reverend H. Neely Gaston

Periodicals

The Associate Reformed Presbyterian; The Adult Quarterly

The Association of Free Lutheran Congregations

The Association of Free Lutheran Congregations, rooted in the Northern European revival movements, was organized in 1962 by a Lutheran Free Church remnant which rejected merger with the American Lutheran Church. The original 42 congregations were joined by other like-minded conservative Lutherans, and there has been more than a sixfold increase in the number of congregations. Members subscribe to the Apostles', Nicene and Athanasian creeds; Luther's Small Catechism; and the Unaltered Augsburg Confession. The Fundamental Principles and Rules for Work (1897) declare that the local congregation is the right form of the kingdom of God on earth, subject to no authority but the Word and the Spirit of God.

Distinctive emphases are, (1) the infallibility and inerrancy of Holy Scriptures as the Word of God; (2) congregational polity; (3) the spiritual unity of all believers, resulting in fellowship and cooperation transcending denominational lines; (4) evangelical outreach, calling all to enter a personal relationship with Jesus Christ; (5) a wholesome Lutheran pietism that proclaims the Lordship of Jesus Christ in all areas of life and results in believers becoming the salt and light in their communities; (6) a conservative stance on current social issues.

A two-year Bible school and a theological seminary are in suburban Minneapolis. The AFLC is in fellowship with sister churches in Canada, Brazil, Mexico, and India.

Headquarters

3110 E. Medicine Lake Blvd., Minneapolis, MN 55441 Tel. (763)545-5631 Fax (763)545-0079
Media Contact, Pres., Rev. Robert L. Lee
E-mail: webmaster@aflc.org
Web site: www.aflc.org

Officers

Pres., Rev. Robert L. Lee, 3110 E. Medicine Lake Blvd. Minneapolis, MN 55441 Fax (763) 545-0079 Tel(763)545-5631, Pres.@aflc.org
Vice-Pres., Rev. Elden K. Nelson, 8071 Prairie Trail, Rockford, MN 55373-9342 Tel. (763)545-5631, vpres@aflc.org
Sec., Rev. Brian Davidson, 3110 E. Medicine Lake Blvd., Minneapolis, MN 55441 Tel. (763) 545-5631 Fax (763)545-0079, briand@aflc.org

Periodicals

The Lutheran Ambassador

Association of Vineyard Churches

The Association of Vineyard Churches is a worldwide community of 1300 churches committed to building the church and living under the reign of God. It officially started in Southern California in 1982 under the leadership of John Wimber. The Board of Dirs. in the governing Board for the Association. The form of government is free church and thus the local vineyards are free to govern as they desire as long as they do not violate the faith or practices of the Vineyard community. The association consists of eight regions under the direction of a Regional Overseer. Most regions also have Area Pastoral Care Leaders who give oversight to a small group of pastors in a geographic area. The National Dir. is the CEO of the National Office and works with the National Board to see that the Association achieves its purpose.

Headquarters

5115 Grove West Blvd., Stafford, TX 77477 Tel. (281)313-8463 Fax (281)313-8464
E-mail: info@vineyardusa.org
Web site: vineyardusa.org

Officers

National Dir., Berten A. Waggoner, christian@vineyardusa.org
Sec., Jane Hardesty, janehardesty@vineyardusa.org
Treas., Wendell Richardson
Vineyard Music USA

Periodicals

Cutting Edge

Baptist Bible Fellowship International

Organized on May 24, 1950, in Fort Worth, Texas, the Baptist Bible Fellowship was founded by about 100 pastors and laypeople who had grown disenchanted with the policies and leadership of the World Fundamental Baptist Missionary Fellowship, an outgrowth of the Baptist Bible Union formed in Kansas City in 1923 by fundamentalist leaders from the Southern Baptist, Northern Baptist and Canadian Baptist Conventions. The BBF elected W. E. Dowell as its first Pres. and established offices and a three-year (now four-year with a graduate school) Baptist Bible College.

The BBF statement of faith was essentially that of the Baptist Bible Union, adopted in 1923, a variation of the New Hampshire Confession of Faith. It presents an infallible Bible, belief in the substitutionary death of Christ, his physical resurrection and his premillennial return to earth. It advocates local church autonomy and strong pastoral leadership and maintains that the fundamental basis of fellowship is a missionary outreach. The BBF vigorously stresses evangelism and the international missions office reports 901 adult missionaries working on 110 fields throughout the world.

There are BBF-related churches in every state of the United States, with special strength in the upper South, the Great Lakes region, southern states west of the Mississippi, Kansas and California. There are seven related colleges and one graduate school or seminary.

A Committee of Forty-Five, elected by pastors and churches within the states, sits as a representative body, meeting in three subcommittees, each chaired by one of the principal officers—an administration committee chaired by the Pres., a missions committee chaired by a vice-Pres. and an education committee chaired by a vice-Pres..

Headquarters

World Mission Service Center, Baptist Bible Fellowship Missions Bldg., 720 E. Kearney St., Springfield, MO 65803 Tel. (417)862-5001 Fax (417)865-0794; Mailing Address, P.O. Box 191, Springfield, MO 65801
Media Contact, Mission Dir., Dr. Bob Baird
E-mail: csbc@cherrystreet.org
Web site: www.bbfi.org

Officers

Pres., Rev. Bill Monroe, P.O. Box 12809, Florence, SC 29504 Tel. (843)662-0453 WK (417)-862-5001
First Vice-Pres., Rev. Mike Peper, 4150 Market St., Aston, PA 19014 Tel. (610)497-0700 WK (417)862-5001
Second Vice-Pres., Keith Gillming, 3025 N Lindbergh Blvd., St. Louis, MO 63074 Tel. (314)291-6919

Sec., Rev. Don Elmore, P.O. Box 7150, Springdale, AR 72766 Tel. (479)751-4255
Treas., Rev. Ken Armstrong, 2200 Prairin St., Emporia, KS, Tel. (316)342-4142

Periodicals

The Baptist Bible Tribune; The Preacher

Baptist General Conference

The Baptist General Conference, rooted in the pietistic movement of Sweden during the 19th century, traces its history to Aug. 13, 1852. On that day a small group of believers at Rock Island, Illinois, under the leadership of Gustaf Palmquist, organized the first Swedish Baptist Church in America. Swedish Baptist churches flourished in the upper Midwest and Northeast, and by 1879, when the first annual meeting was held in Village Creek, Iowa, 65 churches had been organized, stretching from Maine to the Dakotas and south to Kansas and Missouri.

By 1871, John Alexis Edgren, an immigrant sea captain and pastor in Chicago, had begun the first publication and a theological seminary. The Conference grew to 324 churches and nearly 26,000 members by 1902. There were 40,000 members in 1945 and 135,000 in 1993.

Many churches began as Sunday schools. The seminary evolved into Bethel, a four-year liberal arts college with 1,800 students, and theological seminaries in Arden Hills, Minnesota. and San Diego, California. Missions and the planting of churches have been main objectives both in America and overseas. Today churches have been established in the United States, Canada and Mexico, as well as twenty countries overseas. In 1985 the churches of Canada founded an autonomous denomination, The Baptist General Conference of Canada.

The Baptist General Conference is a member of the Baptist World Alliance, the Baptist Joint Committee on Public Affairs and the National Association of Evangelicals. It is characterized by the balancing of a conservative doctrine with an irenic and cooperative spirit. Its basic objective is to seek the fulfillment of the Great Commission and the Great Commandment.

Headquarters

2002 S. Arlington Heights Rd., Arlington Heights, IL 60005 Tel. (847)228-0200 Fax (847)228-5376
E-mail: gmarsh@baptistgeneral.org
Web site: www.bgcworld.org

Officers

Pres. & Chief Exec. Officer, Dr. Gerald Sheveland, jsheveland@baptistgeneral.org
Exec., Vice-Pres., Ray Swatkowski, rswatkowski@baptistgeneral.org
Dir. of Mission Advance, Dr. Lou Petrie, lpetrie@baptistgeneral.org
Dir. of Finance, Stephen R. Schultz, sschultz@baptistgeneral.org
Dir. of National Ministries, Rev. Paul Johnson, pauljchp@aol.com
Dir. of International Ministries, Dr. Ronald Larson, rlarson@aol.com

OTHER ORGANIZATIONS

Bd. of Trustees, Bethel College & Seminary, Pres., Dr. George K. Brushaber, 3900 Bethel Dr., St. Paul, MN 55112

Periodicals

BGC World

Baptist Missionary Association of America

A group of regular Baptist churches organized in associational capacity in May, 1950, in Little Rock, Ark., as the North American Baptist Association. The name changed in 1969 to Baptist Missionary Association of America. There are several state and numerous local associations of cooperating churches. In theology, these churches are evangelical, missionary, fundamental and for the most part premillennial.

Headquarters

9219 Sibly Hole Rd., Little Rock, AR, Tel. (501)455-4977 Fax (501)455-3636
Mailing Address, P.O. Box 193920, Little Rock, AR 72219-3920
Media Contact, Dir. of Baptist News Service, Kenneth W. Vanderslice, P.O. Box 97, Jacksonville, TX 75766 Tel. (903)586-2501 Fax (903)586-0378
E-mail: bmaam@bmaam.com
Web site: www.bmaam.com

Officers

Pres., Ronald Morgan, 208 N. Arkansas St., Springhill, LA 71075-2704
Vice-Pres., Leon J. Carmical, 85 Midway Church Rd., Sumrall, MS 39428; David T. Watkins, 1 Pineridge St., Magnolia, AR 71753
Rec. Sec., Rev. Ralph Cottrell, P.O. Box 1203, Van, TX 75790; Don J. Brown, P.O. Box 8181, Laruel, MS 39441; James Ray Raines, 5609 N. Locust, N. Little Rock, AR 72116

DEPARTMENTS

Missions, Gen. Sec., Rev. F. Donald Collins, P.O. Box 193920, Little Rock, AR 72219-3920
Publications, Ed.-in-Chief, Rev. James L. Silvey, 311 Main St., P.O. Box 7270, Texarkana, TX 75505
Christian Education, Bapt. Missionary Assoc. Theological Sem., Pres., Dr. Charley Holmes, Seminary Heights, 1530 E. Pine St., Jacksonville, TX 75766
Baptist News Service, Dir., Rev. Kenneth W. Vanderslice, P.O. Box 97, Jacksonville, TX 75766
Life Word Broadcast Ministries, Dir., Rev. George Reddin, P.O. Box 6, Conway, AR 72032
Armed Forces Chaplaincy, Exec. Dir., Bobby C. Thornton, P.O. Box 240, Flint, TX 75762

BMAA Dept. of Church Ministries, Donny Parish, P.O. Box 10356, Conway, AR 72033
Daniel Springs Encampment, James Speer, P.O. Box 310, Gary, TX 75643
Ministers Resource Services, Craig Branham, 4001 Jefferson St., Texarkana, TX 75501

OTHER ORGANIZATIONS

Baptist Missionary Assoc. Brotherhood, Pres., Bill Looney, 107 Bearskin Dr., Sherwood, AR 72120
National Women's Missionary Auxiliary, Pres., Mrs. Bill Skinner, RR1 Box 213 B, Mineola, TX 75773-9742 Tel. 903-365-2465

Beachy Amish Mennonite Churches

The Beachy Amish Mennonite Church was established in 1927 in Somerset County, Pa. following a division in the Amish Mennonite Church in that area. As congregations in other locations joined the movement, they were identified by the same name. There are currently 97 churches in the United States, nine in Canada and 34 in other countries. Membership in the United States is 7,059, according to the 1996 Mennonite Yearbook.

Beachy Churches believe in one God eternally existent in three persons (Father, Son and Holy Spirit); that Jesus Christ is the one and only way to salvation; that the Bible is God's infallible Word to us, by which all will be judged; that heaven is the eternal abode of the redeemed in Christ; and that the wicked and unbelieving will endure hell eternally.

Evangelical mission boards sponsor missions in Central and South America, Belgium, Ireland, and Kenya, Africa.

The Mission Interests Committee, founded in 1953 for evangelism and other Christian services, sponsors homes for handicapped youth and elderly people, mission outreaches among the North American Indians in Canada and a mission outreach in Europe.

Headquarters

Media Contact, Paul L. Miller, 7809 S. Herren Rd. Partridge, KS 67566 Tel. (620)567-2286

Officers

Amish Mennonite Aid, Sec.-Treas., Vernon Miller, 2675 U.S. 42 NE, London, OH 43140 Tel. (614)879-8616
Mission Interests Committee, Sec.-Treas., Melvin Gingerich, 42555 900W, Topeka, IN 46571 Tel. (219)593-9090
Choice Books of Northern Virginia, Supervisor, Simon Schrock, 4614 Holly Ave., Fairfax, VA 22030 Tel. (703)830-2800
Calvary Bible School, HC 61, Box 202, Calico Rock, AR 72519 Tel. (501)297-8658; Sec.-Treas., Elmer Gingerich, HC 74, Box 282, Mountain View, AR 72560 Tel. (501)296-8764
Penn Valley Christian Retreat, Bd. Chmn., Wayne Schrock, RR 2, Box 165, McVeytown, PA 17015 Tel. (717)529-2935

Periodicals

The Calvary Messenger

Berean Fellowship of Churches

Founded 1932 in North Platte, Nebraska, this body emphasizes conservative Protestant doctrines.

Headquarters

5 Camelot Way, Kearney, NE 68845 Tel (308) 234-5373 Fax (308)234-5373
Media Contact, Pres., Pastor Doug Shada
E-mail: office@bereanfellowship.org
Web site: www.bereanfellowship.org

Officers

Pres., Doug Shada
Vice-Pres., Richard Crocker, 419 Lafayette Blvd., Cheyenne, WY 82009 Tel. (307)635-5914
Sec., Roger Daum, 1510 O Street, Cozad, NE 69130 Tel. (308)784-3675
Treas., Virgil Wiebe, P.O. Box 6103, Lincoln, NE 68506

The Bible Church of Christ, Inc.

The Bible Church of Christ was founded on March 1, 1961 by Bishop Roy Bryant, Sr. Since that time, the church has grown to include congregations in the United States, Africa and India. The church is trinitarian and accepts the Bible as the divinely inspired Word of God. Its doctrine includes miracles of healing, deliverance and the baptism of the Holy Ghost.

Headquarters

1358 Morris Ave., Bronx, NY 10456 Tel. (718)588-2284 Fax (718)992-5597
Media Contact, Pres., Bishop Roy Bryant, Sr.
E-mail: bccbookstore@earthlink.net
Web site: www.thebiblechurchofchrist.org

Officers

Pres., Bishop Roy Bryant, Sr.
Sec., Mother Sissieretta Bryant
Treas., Elder Artie Burney

EXECUTIVE TRUSTEE BOARD

Chpsn., Bishop Christopher Powell, 1069 Morris Ave., Bronx, NY 10456 Tel. (718)992-4653

OTHER ORGANIZATIONS

Christian Bookstore, Mgr., Virginia Allen, Tel. (718)293-1928
Foreign Missions, Pres., Sr. Autholene Smith
Home Missions, Pres., Evangelist Mary Jackson
Minister of Education, Minister Abraham Jones
Ministers of Music, Ray Brown; Tyrone Sumter; Ann Dunston
Prison Ministry Team, Evangelist Marvin Smith
Public Relations, Minister Abraham Jones
Sunday Schools, Gen. Supt., Elder A. M. Jones
Alan Bryant Memorial Institute, Principal, Moses Tolborh, Chocolate City, Monrobia, Liberia

Theological Institute, Pres., Dr. Roy Bryant, Sr.; Dean, Elder A. M. Jones

Vessels Unto Honor Deliverance Ministries, Pres., Elder Antoinette Cannaday

Youth, Pres., Deacon Tommy Robinson

Bishops

Bishop Roy Bryant, Sr., Bishop Eddie Citronnelli, Bishop Christopher Powell

Presiding Elders

Delaware, Elder Edward Cannon, R R Box 70-B5, Daimond Acre, Dagsboro, DE 19939 Tel. (302)732-3351

Mount Vernon, Elder Artie Burney, 100 W. 2nd St., Mount Vernon, NY 10550 Tel. (914)664-4602

Bronx, Elder Anita Robinson, 1358 Morris Ave., Bronx, NY 10456 Tel. (718)588-2284; Annex, Elder Reginald Gullette, 1069 Morris Ave., Bronx, NY 10456 Tel. (718)992-4653

Schenectady, New York, Elder Monica Hope, 1132 Congress St., Schenectady, NY 12303 Tel. (518)382-5625

North Carolina, Elder Darue Bryant, 512 W. Vernon Ave., Kingston, N.C. 28502 Tel. (252) 527-7739

India, Dr. B. Veeraswamy, 46-7-34, Danavaya Peta, Rajahmunry, India, 533103

Periodicals

The Gospel Light; The Challenge

Bible Fellowship Church

The Bible Fellowship Church grew out of divisions in the Mennonite community in Pennsylvania in the 1850s. Traditional church leadership resisted the freedom of expression and prayer meetings initiated by several preachers and church leaders. These evangelical Mennonites formed the Evangelical Mennonite Society. Over the next two decades various like-minded groups in Canada, Ohio and Pennsylvania joined the Society.

In 1959 the Conference became the Bible Fellowship Church and new articles of faith were ratified. They now hold a unique combination of Reformed doctrines with insistence on "Believer Baptism" and Premillennialism.

Headquarters

Bible Fellowship Church, 25 Lemon St., Lititz, PA 17543

Media Contact, David J. Watkins, 2270 Little Rd., Perkiomenville, PA 18074 Tel. (610)754-7463, watkins58@fast.net

E-mail: bfc@bfc.org

Web site: www.bfc.org

Officers

Chmn., Randall A. Grossman, 23 Anglin Dr., Newark, DE 19713

Vice-Chmn., William G. Schlonecker, 1400 Oak Lane, Reading, PA 19604

Sec., David A. Thomann, 745 Village Rd., Lancaster, PA 17602

Asst. Sec., Robert W. Smock, 38 W. Sunset Ave., Ephrata, PA 17522

BOARDS & COMMITTEES

Board of Dir., Bible Fellowship Church

Board of Christian Education

Board of Extension

Bible Fellowship Church Homes, Inc.

Board of Pensions

Board of Pinebrook Bible Conference

Board of Missions Committee on Credentials

Board of Publication and Printing

Board of Victory Valley Camp

Board of Higher Education

Board of Youth & Adults

Committee on Ministerial Candidates

Strategic Planning Committee

Ministerial Relations Committee Conference Judicatory

Periodicals

Fellowship News

Bible Holiness Church

This church came into being about 1890 as the result of definite preaching on the doctrine of holiness in some Methodist churches in southeastern Kansas. It became known as The Southeast Kansas Fire Baptized Holiness Association. The name was changed in 1945 to The Fire Baptized Holiness Church and in 1995 to Bible Holiness Church. It is entirely Wesleyan in doctrine, episcopal in church organization and intensive in evangelistic zeal.

Headquarters

304 Camp Dr., Independence, KS 67301 Tel. (620)331-3049

Media Contact, Gen. Supt., Leroy Newport

Officers

Gen. Supt., Leroy Newport

Gen. Sec., Michael Schaper, 944 Linns Mill Rd., Troy, MO 63379

Gen. Treas., Philip Davolt, 10624 Bluestem, Wichita, KS 67207

Periodicals

The Flaming Sword; John Three Sixteen

Bible Way Church of Our Lord Jesus Christ World Wide, Inc.

This body was organized in 1957 in the Pentecostal tradition for the purpose of accelerating evangelistic and foreign missionary commitment and to effect a greater degree of collective leadership than leaders found in the body in which they had previously participated.

The doctrine is the same as that of the Church of Our Lord Jesus Christ of the Apostolic Faith, Inc., of which some of the churches and clergy were formerly members.

This organization has churches and missions in Africa, England, Guyana, Trinidad and Jamaica, and churches in 25 states in America.

The Bible Way Church is involved in humanitarian as well as evangelical outreach with concerns for urban housing, education and economic development.

Headquarters

4949 Two-Notch Rd., Columbia, SC 29204 Tel. (800)432-5612 Fax (803)691-0583

Media Contact, Chief Apostle, Presiding Bishop Huie Rogers

E-mail: mr.ed5strings@worldnet.att.net

Web site: www.biblewaychurch.org

Officers

Presiding Bishop, Bishop Huie Rogers, 4949 Two Notch Rd., Columbia, SC 29204 Tel. (800) 432-5612 Fax (803)691-0583

Gen. Sec., Bishop Edward Williams, 5118 Clarendon Rd., Brooklyn, NY 11226 Tel. (718) 451-1238

Brethren in Christ Church

The Brethren in Christ Church was founded in Lancaster County, Pa. in about the year 1778 and was an outgrowth of the religious awakening which occurred in that area during the latter part of the 18th century. This group became known as "River Brethren" because of their original location near the Susquehanna River. The name "Brethren in Christ" was officially adopted in 1863. In theology they have accents of the Pietist, Anabaptist, Wesleyan and Evangelical movements.

Headquarters

General Church Office, P.O. Box A, Grantham, PA 17027 Tel. (717)697-2634 Fax (717)697-7714

Media Contact, Dr. Warren L. Hoffman, Mod., Tel. (717)697-2634 Fax (717)697-7714

E-mail: dwinger@messiah.edu

Web site: www.bic-church.org

Officers

Mod., Dr. Warren L. Hoffman

Gen. Sec., Darrell S. Winger

Treas., Elizabeth Brown

OTHER ORGANIZATIONS

General Conference Board, Chpsn., Dr. Mark Garis, 504 Swartley Rd., Hatfield, PA 19440

Bd. for World Missions, Chair, Dr. Grace Holland, 21A Junction Rd., Dillsburg, PA 17019-9469; Exec. Dir., Rev. John Brubaker, P.O. Box 390, Grantham, PA 17027-0390

Bd. for Stewardship Services, Chair, Terry Hoke, Box A, Grantham, PA 17027; Pension Fund Trustees, Chair, Eric Mann

Brethren in Christ Foundation, Elvin H. Peifer, CEO, P.O.Box 290, Grantham, PA 17027-0290

Brethren Church (Ashland, Ohio)

The Brethren Church (Ashland, Ohio) was organized by progressive-minded German Baptist Brethren in 1883. They reaffirmed the teaching of the original founder of the Brethren movement, Alexander Mack, and returned to limited congregational government.

Headquarters

524 College Ave., Ashland, OH 44805 Tel. (419) 289-1708 Fax (419)281-0450

Media Contact, Exec. Dir., Rev. Ken Hunn, Tel; (419)289-1708 Fax (419)281-0450, Ken@brethrenchurch.org

E-mail: brethren@brethrenchurch.org

Web site: www.brethrenchurch.org

Officers

Exec. Dir., Rev. Ken Hunn

Dir. of Pastoral Ministries, Rev. David Cooksey

Dir. of Admin. Services, Mr. Stanley Gentle

Periodicals

The Brethren Evangelist

The Catholic Church

The largest single body of Christians in the United States, The Catholic Church is under the spiritual leadership of His Holiness the Pope. Its establishment in America dates back to the priests who accompanied Columbus on his second voyage to the New World. A settlement, later discontinued, was made in 1565 at St. Augustine, Florida. The continuous history of this Church in the Colonies began at St. Mary's in Maryland, in 1634.

INTERNATIONAL ORGANIZATION

His Holiness the Pope, Bishop of Rome, Vicar of Jesus Christ, Supreme Pontiff of the Catholic Church, Pope John Paul II, Karol Wojtyla (born May 18, 1920; installed Oct. 22, 1978)

APOSTOLIC NUNCIO TO THE UNITED STATES

Archbishop Gabriel Montalvo, 3339 Massachusetts Ave. NW, Washington, DC 20008 Tel. (202)333-7121 Fax (202)337-4036

U.S. ORGANIZATION

United States Conference of Catholic Bishops, 3211 Fourth St. NE, Washington, DC 20017-1194 Tel. (202)541-3000

The United States Conference of Catholic Bishops (USCCB) is an assembly of the hierarchy of the United States and the U.S. Virgin Islands who jointly exercise certain pastoral functions on behalf of the Christian faithful of the United States. The purpose of the Conference is to promote the greater good which the Church offers humankind, especially through forms and programs of the apostolate fittingly adapted to the circumstances of time and place. This purpose is drawn from the universal law of the Church and applies to the episcopal conferences which are established all over the world for the same purpose.

The bishops themselves constitute the membership of the Conference and are served by a staff of over 350 people, priests and religious located at the Conference headquarters in Washington, D.C. There is also a small Office of Film and Broadcasting in New York City and a branch office of Migration and Refugee Services in Miami.

The Conference is organized as a corporation in the District of Columbia. Its purposes under civil law are, "To unify, coordinate, encourage, promote and carry on Catholic activities in the United States; to organize and conduct religious, charitable and social welfare work at home and abroad; to aid in education; to care for immigrants; and generally to enter into and promote by education, publication and direction the objects of its being."

On July 1, 2001 the NCCB and the USCC were combined to form the United states Conference of Catholic Bishops (USCCB). The USCCB continues all of the work formerly done by the NCCB and the USCC with the same staff. The bishops themselves form approximately 50 committees, each with its own particular responsibility.

Web site: www.usccb.org

USCCB GENERAL SECRETARIAT

Gen. Sec., Msgr. William P. Fay

Assoc. Gen. Sec., Mr. Bruce E. Egnew; Msgr. David Malloy; Sr. Lourdes Sheehan, RSM

USCCB OFFICERS

Pres., Bishop Wilton D. Gregory

Vice-Pres., Bishop William S. Skylstad

Treas., Archbishop James P. Keleher

Sec., Archbishop Michael J. Sheehan

USCCB STANDING COMMITTEES

Admin. Committee, Chmn., Bishop Wilton D. Gregory

Exec. Committee, Chmn., Bishop Wilton D. Gregory

Committee on Budget & Finance, Chmn., Archbishop James P. Keleher

Committee on Personnel, Bishop William S. Skylstad

Committee on Priorities & Plans, Chmn., Bishop Wilton D. Gregory

African American Catholics, Chmn., Bishop Gordon D. Bennett, SJ

American Bishops' Overseas Appeal, Chmn., Bishop Wilton D. Gregory

American College Louvain, Chmn., Bishop Edward K. Braxton

Boundaries of Dioceses & Provinces, Chmn., Bishop Wilton D. Gregory

Canonical Affairs, Chmn., Bishop Thomas G. Doran

Church in Latin America, Chmn., Bishop John R. Manz

Consecrated Life, Chmn., Archbishop Jerome G. Hanus, OSB

Diaconate, Chmn., Archbishop William J. Levada

Doctrine, Chmn., Bishop Donald W. Trautman

Ecumenical & Interreligious Affairs, Chmn., Bishop Stephen E. Blaire

Subcommittee on Interreligious Dialogue, Chmn., Bishop Tod D. Brown

Evangelization, Chmn., Bishop Edward J. Slattery

Hispanic Affairs, Chmn., Bishop James A. Tamayo

Home Missions, Chmn., Bishop J. Peter Sartain

Laity, Chmn., Bishop Dale J. Melczek

Subcommittee on Lay Ministry, Chmn., Bishop Gerald F. Kicanas

Subcommittee on Youth & Young Adults, Chmn., Bishop Dennis M. Schnurr

Liturgy, Chmn., Francis Cardinal George, OMI

Marriage & Family Life, Chmn., Bishop J. Kevin Boland

Migration, Chmn., Bishop Thomas G. Wenski

North American College Rome, Chmn., Edwin F. O'Brien

Pastoral Practices, Chmn., Bishop Thomas J. Tobin

Priestly Formation, Chmn., Bishop John C. Nienstedt

Priestly Life & Ministry, Chmn., Archbishop Timothy M. Dolan

Pro-Life Activities, Chmn., William Cardinal Keeler

Relationship Between Eastern & Latin Catholic Churches, Chmn., Archbishop Basil M. Scott, OFM

Science & Human Values, Chmn., Bishop Francis X. DiLorenzo

Selection of Bishops, Chmn., Bishop Wilton D. Gregory

Vocations, Chmn., Bishop Kevin M. Britt

Woman in Society & in the Church, Chmn., Bishop Edward P. Cullen

World Mission, Chmn., Bishop Gregory M. Aymond

USCCB AD HOC COMMITTEES

Agricultural Issues, Chmn., Bishop Ronald M. Gilmore

Aid to the Catholic Church in Central & Eastern Europe, Chmn., Adam Cardinal Maida

Bishops' Life & Ministry, Chmn., Bishop Robert H. Brom

Catholic Charismatic Renewal, Chmn., Bishop Sam G. Jacobs

Catholic Health Care Issues & the Church, Chm., Bishop Robert C. Morlino

Committee for the Special Assembly 2007, Chmn., Bishop Dennis M. Shnurr

Economic Concerns of the Holy See, Chmn., Archbishop John G. Vlazny

National Review Board, Chmn., The Honorable Anne Burke

Native American Catholics, Chmn., Bishop Donald E. Pelotte, SSS

Nomination of Conference Officers, Bishop Bernard J. Harrington

Oversee the Use of the Catechism, Chmn., Archbishop Alfred C. Hughes
Plenary Council Varium, Chmn., Archbishop Daniel M. Buechlein, OSB
Review of Scripture Translations, Chmn., Bishop Arthur J. Serratelli
Sexual Abuse, Chmn., Bishop Harry J. Flynn
Shrines, Chmn., Archbishop James P. Keleher
Spanish Language Bible, Chmn., Bishop Jose H. Gomez
Stewardship, Chmn., Bishop Sylvester D. Ryan

USCCB DEPARTMENTAL COMMITTEES

Catholic Campaign for Human Development, Chmn., Bishop George V. Murry
Communications, Chmn., Bishop Gerald F. Kicanas
Domestic Policy, Chmn., Theodore Cardinal McCarrick
International Policy, Chmn., Bishop John H. Ricard, SSJ
Education, Chmn., Bishop Bernard J. Harrington
Advisory Committee on Public Policy & Catholic Schools, Chmn., Bishop Bernard J. Harrington
Bishops & Catholic College & University Presidents, Chmn., Archbishop John G. Vlazny
Catechesis, Chmn., Archbishop Daniel M. Buechelin, OSB
Sapientia Christiana, Chmn., Bishop Michael F. Burbridge
For information on related organizations and individual dioceses, consult the Official Catholic Directory (published annually by P.J. Kenedy and Sons) and the USCCB Web site (www.usccb.org).

Periodicals

Catholic News Service, L'Osservatore Romano, The Living Light, Origins, Lay Ministry Update, Bishops Committee on the Liturgy Newsletter, Life Insight, SEIA Newsletter on the Eastern Churches and Ecumenism, Law Briefs, Catholic Trends

Christ Catholic Church

The church is a catholic communion established in 1968 to minister to the growing number of people who seek an experiential relationship with God and who desire to make a total commitment of their lives to God. The church is catholic in faith and tradition. Participating cathedrals, churches and missions are located in several states.

Headquarters

405 Kentling Rd., Highlandville, MO 65669 Tel. (417)443-3951
Media Contact, Archbishop, Most Rev. Karl Pruter
E-mail: bishopkarl@juno.com
Web site: christcatholicchurch.freeyellow.com/

Officers

Archbishop, Most Rev. Karl Pruter, P.O. Box 98, Highlandville, MO 65669 Tel. (417)443-3951
Order of St. John of the Cross, Abbot Fr. Frank Bracelin, 1002 16th Place, Kelso, WA 98626

Periodicals

St. Willibrord Journal

Christ Community Church (Evangelical-Protestant)

This church was founded by the Rev. John Alexander Dowie on Feb. 22, 1896 at Chicago, Ill. In 1901 the church founded the city of Zion, IL and moved their headquarters there. Theologically, the church is rooted in evangelical orthodoxy. The Scriptures are accepted as the rule of faith and practice. Other doctrines call for belief in the necessity of repentance for sin and personal trust in Christ for salvation.

The Christ Community Church is a denominational member of The National Association of Evangelicals. It has work in six other nations in addition to the United States. Branch ministries are found in Tonalea, Arizona; Lindenhurst, Illinois; and Toronto, Canada.

Headquarters

2500 Dowie Memorial Dr., Zion, IL 60099 Tel. (847)746-1411 Fax (847)746-1452

Officers

Sr. Pastor, Ken Langley

Christadelphians

The Christadelphians are a body of people who believe the Bible to be the divinely inspired word of God, written by "Holy men who spoke as they were moved by the Holy Spirit" (2 Peter Ch. 1 vs. 21). They believe that the Old Testament presents God's plan to establish his kingdom on earth in accord with the promises He made to Abraham and David; and that the New Testament declares how that plan works out in Jesus Christ, who died a sacrificial death to redeem sinners. They believe in the personal return of Jesus Christ as King, to establish "all that God spoke by the mouth of his holy prophets from of old" (Acts 3:21). They believe that at Christ's return many of the dead will be raised by the power of God to be judged. Those whom God deems worthy will be welcomed into eternal life in the kingdom on earth. Christadelphians believe in the mortality of man; in spiritual rebirth requiring belief and immersion in the name of Jesus; and in a godly walk in this life. They have no ordained clergy, and are organized in a loose confederation of 2,500 autonomous congregations (ecclesias) in approximately 150 countries. They are conscientiously opposed to participation in war. They endeavor to be enthusiastic in work, loyal in marriage, generous in giving, dedicated in preaching, and cheerful in living.

The denomination was organized in 1844 by a medical doctor, John Thomas, who came to the United States from England in 1832, having survived a near shipwreck in a violent storm This experience affected him profoundly, and he vowed to devote his life to a search for the truth of God and a future hope from the Bible.

Headquarters

Media Contact, Trustee, Norman D. Zilmer, Christadelphian Action Society, 1000 Mohawk Dr., Elgin, IL 60120-3148 Tel. (847)741-5253 Fax (847)888-3334

E-mail: Nzilmer@aol.com

Web site: www.christadelphia.org, www.tidings.org, www.wcfoundation.org

Leaders

Co-Ministers, Norman Fadelle, 815 Chippewa Dr., Elgin, IL 60120, nfadelle@juno.com; Norman D. Zilmer, 1000 Mohawk Dr., Elgin, IL 60120, nzilmer@aol.com

Periodicals

Christadelphian Tidings; Christadelphian Advocate

Christian Brethren (also known as Plymouth Brethren)

Christian Brethren churches are bound together by common beliefs and practices but not by central organization. They are committed to the inerrancy of Scripture, to Trinitarian doctrine, and to the evangelical message of salvation by faith apart from works or sacrament. Their most recognizable feature is the weekly observance of the Lord's Supper as the focus of a full-length service of worship, not prearranged and not clergy-led.

Originating in England and Ireland in the late 1820s, the Brethren were influenced by the counsel of Anthony Norris Groves, an English dentist, and the teaching of John Nelson Darby, an Irish clergyman. They recovered aspects of church practice and simplicity that had been obscured in the course of the centuries, such as an unwillingness to establish denominational govering structures and a reluctance to accept sectarian names. The nickname Plymouth Brethren arose spontaneously when a large Plymouth congregation was evangelizing throughout the English countryside. In recent years the term Christian Brethren has replaced Plymouth Brethren for the open branch of the movement in Canada and the British Commonwealth and to some extent in the United States. Neither name has legal status, except where required by national governments. There are no central offices and no corporate property in the U.S.A. or Canada.

In the late 1840s the movement divided. The so-called open assemblies, led initially by George Mueller of orphanage fame, stressed evangelism and foreign missions. It has grown to be the larger of the two branches. The autonomy of local congregations permits variations in practice and generally avoids wide-ranging division.

The other branch focused more on doctrinal and ecclesiastical issues. From it came notable Bible teachers like Darby, William Kelly, C.H. Mackintosh (CHM), and F. W. Grant. Their books have had a wide influence, especially among premillennialists. These assemblies stress the interdependency of congregations. Local church decisions on doctrine and discipline are generally held to be binding on all assemblies. At times, when actions were debatable, division spread throughout the group. By 1900, there were seven or eight main groups. Since 1925, some divisions have been healed, reducing that number to three or four.

Headquarters

Correspondent, James A. Stahr, 327 W. Prairie Ave., Wheaton, Il 60187-3408 Tel. (630)665-3757

RELATED ORGANIZATIONS

Interest Ministries, 2060 Stonington Ave., Suite 101, Hoffman Estates, IL 60195

Christian Missions in Many Lands, P.O. Box 13, Spring Lake, NJ 07762-0013

Stewards Foundation, 14285 Midway Rd., Suite 330, Addison, TX 75001-3622

International Teams, 411 W. River Rd., Elgin, IL 60123

Emmaus Bible College, 2570 Asbury Rd., Dubuque, IA 52001-3044

Stewards Ministries, 18-3 E. Dundee Rd., Suite 100, Barrington, IL 60010

Believers Bookshelf, P.O. Box 261 Sunbury, PA 17801

Christian Church (Disciples of Christ) in the United States and Canada*

Born on the American frontier in the early 1800s as a movement to unify Christians, this body drew its major inspiration from Thomas and Alexander Campbell in western Pennsylvania and Barton W. Stone in Kentucky. Developing separately, the "Disciples," under Alexander Campbell, and the "Christians," led by Stone, united in 1832 in Lexington, Ky.

The Christian Church (Disciples of Christ) is marked by informality, openness, individualism, and diversity. The Disciples claim no official doctrine or dogma. Membership is granted after a simple statement of belief in Jesus Christ and baptism by immersion—although most congregations accept transfers baptized by other forms in other denominations. The Lord's Supper—generally called Communion—is open to Christians of all persuasions. The practice is weekly Communion, although no church law insists upon it.

Thoroughly ecumenical, the Disciples helped organize the National and World Councils of Churches. The church is a member of the Churches

Uniting in Christ. The Disciples and the United Church of Christ have declared themselves to be in "full communion" through the General Assembly and General Synod of the two churches. Official theological conversations have been going on since 1967 directly with the Roman Catholic Church.

Disciples have vigorously supported world and national programs of education, agricultural assistance, urban reconciliation, care of persons with retardation, family planning, and aid to victims of war and calamity. Operating ecumenically, Disciples' personnel or funds work in more than 100 countries outside North America.

Three manifestations or expressions of the church (general, regional and congregational) operate as equals, with strong but voluntary covenantal ties to one another. Entities in each manifestation manage their own finances, own their own property, and conduct their own programs. A General Assembly meets every two years and has voting representation from each congregation.

Headquarters

Disciples Center, 130 E. Washington St., P.O. Box 1986, Indianapolis, IN 46206-1986 Tel. (317)635-3100 Fax (317)635-3700

Media Contact, Communication Ministeries, Exec. Dir., Wanda Bryant Wills

E-mail: cmiller@cm.disciples.org

Officers

Gen. Minister & Pres., William Chris Hobgood, Tel. (317)713-2401 Fax (317)713-2417, chobgood@ogmp.disciples.org

Mod., Charisse Gillette, 3292 Hunter Point, Lexington, KY 40515 Tel. (859)281-3569 Fax (859)281-3547, cgillett@transy.edu

1st Vice-Mod., Douglas Skinner, Northway Christian Church, 7202 Northway Hwy., Dallas, TX 75225 Tel. (214)361-6641 Fax (214)361-9341, doug@northwaychristian.org

2nd Vice-Mod., Manny Collazo, EDS Federal Government, 12000 Research Parkway, Suite 100, Orlando, FL 21826 Tel. (407) 207-8990 Fax (407) 207-8993, Manny.collazo@eds.com

GENERAL OFFICERS

Gen. Minister & Pres., William Chris Hobgood, chobgood@ogmp.disciples.org

Assoc. Gen Min. & Admin. Sec. of the National Convocation, Timothy M. James, tjames@ogmp. disciples.org

ADMINISTRATIVE UNITS

Board of Church Extension (800)366-3383 Fax (314)231-8524, customerservice@cbp21.com

Christian Church Foundation, Inc., Pres., Gary W. Kidwell, Tel. (317)635-3100 or (800)366-8016 Fax (317)635-1991, jcullumb@ccf.disciples.org

Church Finance Council, Inc., Pres., Lois Artis, jedmundson@cfc.disciples.org

Council on Christian Unity, Inc., Pres., Robert K. Welsh, Tel (317)713-2586 Fax (317)713-2588, rozanne@ccu.disciples.org

Disciples of Christ Historical Society, Interim Pres., D. Duane Cummins, 1101 19th Ave. S., Nashville, TN 37212-2196 Tel. (615)327-1444 Fax (615)327-1445, mail@dishistsoc. org

Division of Higher Education, dba Higher Education and Leadership Ministries, Pres., Dennis L. Landon, 11477 Olde Cabin Rd., Suite 310, St. Louis, MO 63141-7130 Tel. (314)991-3000 Fax (314)991-2957, dhe@dhe disciples. org

Division of Homeland Ministries, dba Disciples Home Missions, Pres., Arnold C. Nelson, Jr. Tel. (317)635-3100 or (888)346-2631 Fax (317) 635-4426, homelandministries@hm.disciples. org

Division of Overseas Ministries, Pres., David A. Vargas, Fax (317)635-4323, dom@disciples. org

National Benevolent Association, Pres., Cindy Dougherty, 11780 Borman Dr., St. Louis, MO 63146-4157 Tel. (314)993-9000 Fax (314) 993-9018, nba@nbacares.org

Pension Fund, Pres., James P. Hamlett, 130 E. Washington St., Indianapolis, IN 46204-3645 Tel. (317)634-4504 Fax (317)634-4071, pfcc1@ pension.disciples.org

REGIONAL UNITS OF THE CHURCH

Alabama-Northwest Florida, Regional Minister, John P. Mobley, 861 Highway 52, Helena, AL 35080 Tel. (205)425-5245 Fax (205)425-5246, alnwfl@aol.com

Arizona, Regional Minister, Dennis L. Williams, 4423 N. 24th St., Suite 700, Phoenix, AZ 85016-5544 Tel. (602)468-3815 Fax (602)468-3816, region@arizonadisciples.com

California, Northern-Nevada, Interim Regional Minister & Pres., Paula M. Bishop, 9260 Alcosta Blvd. C-18, San Ramon, CA 94583-4143 Tel. (925)556-9900 Fax (925)556-9904, info@ccncn.org

Canada, Regional Minister, F. Thomas Rutherford, P.O. Box 23030, 417 Wellington St., St. Thomas, ON N5R 6A3 Tel. (519)633-9083 Fax (519)637-6407, ccic@bellnet.ca

Capital Area, Regional Minister, Lari R. Grubbs, 11501 Georgia Ave., Suite 400, Wheaton, MD 20902-1955 Tel (301)942-8266 Fax (301)942-8366, lgrubbs@cccadisciples.org

Central Rocky Mountain Region, Exec. Regional Minister, Ronald L. Parker, 2950 Tennyson #300, Denver, CO 80212-3029 Tel. (303)561-1790 Fax (303)561-1795, info@crmrdoc.org

Florida, Regional Minister, William C. Morrison, Jr., 924 N. Magnolia Ave., Suite 200, Orlando, FL 32803-3845 Tel. (407)843-4652 Fax (407)843-0272, RegionalOffice@floridadisciples.org

Georgia, Interim Regional Minister, Zena S. McAdams, 2370 Vineville Ave., Macon, GA 31204-3163 Tel. (478)743-8649 or (800)755-0485 Fax (478)741-1508, ccinga@bellsouth.net

Great River Region, Exec. Regional Minister, Barbara E. Jones, 9302 Geyer Springs Rd., P.O. Box 192058, Little Rock, AR 72219-2058 Tel. (501)562-6053 or (888)241-5531 Fax (501)562-7089

Idaho, South, Regional Minister, Larry Crist, 6465 Sunrise Ave., Nampa, ID 83686-9461 Tel. (208)468-8976 Fax (208)468-8973, ccsi1@mindspring.com

Illinois and Wisconsin, Regional Minister & Pres., Herbert L. Knudsen, 1011 N. Main St., Bloomington, IL 61701-1753 Tel. (309)828-6293 Fax (309)829-4612, herb@cciwdiciples.org

Indiana, Regional Minister, Richard L. Spleth, 1100 W. 42nd St., Indianapolis, IN 46208-3375 Tel. (317)926-6051 Fax (317)931-2034, cci@ccindiana.org

Kansas, Regional Minister & Pres., Patsie Sweeden, 2914 SW MacVicar Ave., Topeka, KS 66611-1787 Tel. (785)266-2914 Fax (785) 266-0174, ccks@ksmessenger.org

Kansas City, Greater, Regional Minister & Pres., Paul J. Diehl, Jr., 5700 Broadmoor, Suite 702, Mission, KS 66202-2405 Tel. (913)432-1414 Fax (913)432-3598, ksdisciple@aol.com

Kentucky, Gen. Minister, Janet M. Ehrmantraut, 1125 Red Mile Rd., Lexington, KY 40504-2660 Tel. (859)233-1391 Fax (859)233-2079, cck@ccinky.net

Michigan, Regional Minister, Morris Finch, Jr., 2820 Covington Ct., Lansing, MI 48912-4830 Tel. (517)372-3220 Fax (517)372-2705, ccmr@michigandisciples.org

Mid-America Region, Regional Minister, Danny Stewart, 3328 Bennett Lane, P.O. Box 104298, Jefferson City, MO 65110-4298 Tel. (573) 636-8149 Fax (573) 636-2889, ccma@socket.net

Montana, Regional Minister, Ruth A, Fletcher, 1019 Central Ave., Great Falls, MT 59401-3784 Tel. (406)452-7404 Fax (406)452-7404, ccm@imt.net

Nebraska, Regional Minister, Kenneth W. Moore, 1268 S. 20th St., Lincoln, NE 68502-1612 Tel. (402)476-0359 or (800)580-8851 Fax (402)476-0350, ccnebraska@alltel

North Carolina, Regional Minister, John M. Richardson, 509 NE Lee St., P.O. Box 1568, Wilson, NC 27894-1568 Tel. (252)291-4047 Fax (252)291-3338, ccnc@ncdisciples.org

Northeastern Region, Co-Regional Ministers, Lonnie F. Oates & Wesley R. Bourdette, 475 Riverside Dr., Room 1950, New York, NY 10115-1999 Tel (212)870-2734 Fax (870) 2735, n.christian.church@worldnet.att.net

Northwest Region, Regional Minister & Pres., Jack Sullivan, Jr., 6558-35th Ave. SW, Seattle, WA 98126-2899 Tel. (206)938-1008 Fax (206)933-1163, nwrcc@disciplesnw.org

Ohio, Regional Pastor & Pres., William H. Edwards, 38007 Butternut Ridge Rd., Elyria, OH 44035-8457 Tel. (440)458-5112 Fax (440)458-5114, ccio@christianchurchinohio.org

Oklahoma, Regional Pastor, Thomas R. Jewell, 301 NW 36th St., Oklahoma City, OK 73118-8661 Tel. (405)528-3577 Fax (405)528-3584, tjewell@okdisciples.org

Oregon, Co-Regional Ministers, Douglas Wirt & Cathy Myers-Wirt, 0245 SW Bancroft St., Suite F, Portland, OR 97239-4267 Tel. (503)226-7648 Fax (503)226-0598, odmail@oregondisciples.org

Pacific Southwest Region, Regional Minister & Pres., Don W. Shelton, 2401 N. Lake Ave., Altadena, CA 91001-2418 Tel. (626)296-0385 Fax (626)296-1280, pswr@discipleswr

Pennsylvania, Regional Minister, W. Darwin Collins, 105 Water St., Suite 7, New Stanton, PA 15672 Tel. (724)925-1350 Fax (724)925-1358, wdar@padisciples.org

South Carolina, Regional Minister, Sotello V. Long, 1293 Orange Grove Rd., Charleston, SC 29407-3947 Tel. (843)852-4537 Fax (843) 744-5787, rcccsc@aol.com

Southwest Region, Interim Co-Regional Ministers, Robert E. Stewart & Edgar O. Coble, 3209 S. University Dr., Fort Worth, TX 76109-2239 Tel. (817)926-4687 Fax (817) 926-5121, ccsw@ccsw.org

Tennessee, Regional Minister & Pres., Glen J. Stewart, 50 Vantage Way, Suite 251, Nashville, TN 37228-1523 Tel. (615)251-3400 Fax (615)251-3415, ccdctn@yahoo.com

Upper Midwest Region, Regional Minister & Pres., Richard L. Guentert, 3300 University Ave., P.O. Box 41217, Des Moines, IA 50311-0504 Tel. (515)255-3168 Fax (515)255-2625, rg@uppermidwestcc.org

Virginia, Regional Minister, George Lee Parker, 518 Brevard St., Lynchburg, VA 24501-3547 Tel. (434)846-3400 Fax (434)528-4919, ccinva@adelphia.net

West Virginia, Regional Minister, William B. Allen, 1400 Washington Ave., P.O. Box 264, Parkersburg, WV 26102-0264 Tel. (304)428-1681 Fax (304)428-1684, linda@ccwv.org

Periodicals

DiscipleWorld; Call To Unity

Christian Church of North America, General Council

Originally known as the Italian Christian Church, its first General Council was held in 1927 at Niagara Falls, N.Y. This body was incorporated in 1948 at Pittsburgh, Pa., and is described as Pentecostal but does not engage in the "the excesses tolerated or practiced among some churches using the same name."

The movement recognizes two ordinances—baptism and the Lord's Supper. Its moral code is conservative and its teaching is orthodox. Members are exhorted to pursue a life of personal holiness, setting an example to others. A conservative position is held in regard to marriage and divorce. The governmental form is, by and large, congregational. District and National officiaries, however, are referred to as Presbyteries led by Overseers.

The group functions in cooperative fellowship with the Italian Pentecostal Church of Canada and the Evangelical Christian Churches-Assemblies of God in Italy. It is an affiliate member of the Pentecostal Fellowship of North America and of the National Association of Evangelicals.

Headquarters

1294 Rutledge Rd., Transfer, PA 16154-2299
Tel. (724)962-3501 Fax (724)962-1766
Media Contact, Exec. Sec., Christine Marini; Asst., Candace Tarr
E-mail: cnna@nauticom.net
Web site: www.ccna.org

Officers

Executive Bd., Gen. Overseer, Rev. Dennis G. Karaman, 1294 Rutledge Road, Transfer, PA. 16154
Exec. Vice-Pres., Rev. Joseph Shipley, 44-19 Francis Lewis Blvd., Bayside, NY 11361
Asst. Gen. Overseers, Rev. Joseph Shipley 44-19 Francis Lewis Blvd., Bayside, NY 11361; Rev. Trevor Cobarn, 3325 Dry Brook Rd., Falconer, NY 14733 ; Rev. Patrick Bossio, Sr., 667 Capitol, Lincoln Park, MI 48146; Rev. Thomas Geyser, 2 Cynthia Circle, Medway , MA 02062, Rev. Douglas Bedgood, Sr., 442 Trinidad Ln., Teadkwood Village, Largo, FL 33770

DEPARTMENTS

Benevolence, Rev. Eugene De Marco, 136 Dana Dr., New Brighton PA 15066
Home Missions, Rev. Richard George, 3395 Waterside Dr., Akron, OH 44319
Faith, Order & Credentials, Rev. Rev. Joseph Shipley, 44-19 Francis Lewis Blvd, Bayside, NY 11361
Missions, Rev. Mark Charles, 703 Somcenter Rd., Mayfield Hts., OH 44143
Publications Relations, Rev. John Tedesco, 1188 Heron Rd., Cherry Hill, NJ 08003
Lay Ministries, Rev. Carmine Zottoli, 27D Shear Hill Rd., Mahopac, NY 10541
Education, Rev. Lucian Gandolfo, 3141 Highland Dr. Easton, PA. 18045

Periodicals

Vista

Christian Churches and Churches of Christ

The fellowship, whose churches were always strictly congregational in polity, has its origin in the American movement to "restore the New Testament church in doctrine, ordinances and life" initiated by Thomas and Alexander Campbell, Walter Scott and Barton W. Stone in the early 19th century.

Headquarters

Media Contact, No. American Christian Convention Dir., Rod Huron, 4210 Bridgetown Rd., Box 11326, Cincinnati, OH 45211 Tel. (513) 598-6222 Fax (513)598-6471
E-mail: Jowston@cwv.edu
Web site: www.cwv.net/christ'n

CONVENTIONS

North American Christian Convention, Dir., Rod Huron, 4210 Bridgetown Rd., Box 11326, Cincinnati, OH 45211 Tel. (513)598-6222; Mailing Address, Box 39456, Cincinnati, OH 45239
National Missionary Convention, Coord., Walter Birney, Box 11, Copeland, KS 67837 Tel. (316)668-5250
Eastern Christian Convention, Kenneth Meade, 5300 Norbeck Rd., Rockville, MD 20853 Tel. (301)460-3550

Periodicals

Christian Standard; Restoration Herald; Horizons; The Lookout

The Christian Congregation, Inc.

The Christian Congregation is a denominational evangelistic association that originated in 1787 and was active on the frontier in areas adjacent to the Ohio River. The church was an unincorporated organization until 1887. At that time a group of ministers who desired closer cooperation formally constituted the church. The charter was revised in 1898 and again in 1970.

Governmental polity basically is congregational. Local units are semi-autonomous. Doctrinal positions, strongly biblical, are essentially universalist in the sense that ethical principles, which motivate us to creative activism, transcend national boundaries and racial barriers. A central tenet, John 13:34-35, translates to such respect for sanctity of life that abortions on demand, capital punishment and all warfare are vigorously opposed. All wars are considered unjust and obsolete as a means of resolving disputes.

Early leaders were John Chapman, John L. Puckett and Isaac V. Smith. Bishop O. J. Read was chief administrative and ecclesiastic officer for 40 years until 1961. Rev. Dr. Ora Wilbert Eads has been general superintendent since 1961. Ministerial affiliation for independent clergymen is provided.

Headquarters

812 W. Hemlock St., LaFollette, TN 37766
Media Contact, Gen. Supt., Rev. Ora W. Eads, D.D., Tel. (423)562-6330
E-mail: Revalnas@aol.com
Web site: netministries.org/see/churches.exe/ ch10619

Officers

Gen. Supt., Rev. Ora W. Eads, D.D., 812 W. Hemlock St. LaFollette, TN 37766

Christian Methodist Episcopal Church*

The Christian Methodist Episcopal Church (CME) is a historically African American denomination that was established in Jackson, Tennessee in 1870 when a group of former slaves, representing eight annual conferences of the Methodist Episcopal Church South organized the Colored Methodist Episcopal Church in America. In 1954 at its General Conference in Memphis, Tennessee it was overwhelmingly voted to change the term "Colored" to "Christian." On January 3, 1956 the official name became Christian Methodist Episcopal Church. Its boundaries reach from the continental United States, Alaska, Haiti, Jamaica, and the West African countries of Nigeria, Ghana, and Liberia. One of its most significant witnessing arenas has been the education of African Americans. Today the CME Church supports Paine College, August, GA; Lane College, Jackson, TN; Miles College, Birmingham, AL; Texas College, Tyler, TX; and the Phillips School of Theology in Atlanta, GA.

Headquarters

First Memphis Plaza, 4466 Elvis Presley Blvd., Memphis, TN 38116

Media Contact, Exec. Sec., Attorney Juanita Bryant, 3675 Runnymede Blvd., Cleveland Hts., OH 44121 Tel. (216)382-3559 Fax (216)382-3516

E-mail: juanbr4law@aol.com

Officers

Exec. Sec., Attorney Juanita Bryant, 3675 Runnymede Blvd., Cleveland Hts., OH 44121 Tel. (216)382-3559 Fax (216)382-3516, juanbr4law@aol.com

OTHER ORGANIZATIONS

Christian Education, Gen. Sec., Dr. Carmichael Crutchfield, 4466 Elvis Presley Blvd., Suite 214, Box 193, Memphis, TN 38116-7100 Tel. (901)345-0580 Fax (901)345-4118

Lay Ministry, Gen. Sec., Dr. Victor Taylor, 9560 Drake Ave., Evanston, IL 60203, Tel. (800)782-4335 ext. 6029 Fax (312)345-6056, victav@idt.net

Evangelism & Missions, Gen. Sec., Dr. Willie C. Champion, 102 Pearly Top Dr., Glen Heights, TX 75154 Tel. (214)372-9505, champ_dr@ msn.com

Finance, Sec., Dr. Joseph C. Neal, Jr., P.O. Box 75085, Los Angeles, CA 90075 Tel. (323)233-5050

Editor, *The Christian Index*, Dr. Kenneth E. Jones, P.O. Box 431, Fairfield, AL 35064 Tel. (205)929-1640 Fax (205)791-1910, goodoc@ aol.com

Publication Services, Gen. Sec., Rev. William George, 4466 Elvis Presley Blvd., Memphis, TN 38116 Tel. (901)345-0580 Fax (901)767-8514, weg38@aol.com

Personnel Services, Gen. Sec., Rev. Tyrone T. Davis, P.O.Box 74, Memphis, TN 38101-0074 Tel. (901)261-3228, cmegbps@myexcel.com

Women's Missionary Council, Pres., Dr. Elnora P. Hamb, 11321 S. Aberdeen St., Chicago, IL 60643 Tel. (773)264-2273, hamb@sbcglobal.net

BISHOPS

First District, Bishop William H. Graves, Sr., 4466 Elvis Presley Blvd., Suite 222, Memphis, TN 38116 Tel. (901)345-0580

Second District, Bishop E. Lynn Brown, 7030 Reading Rd., Suite 244, Cincinnati, OH 45237 Tel. (513)772-8622

Third District, Bishop Paul A. G. Stewart, Sr., 5925 W. Florissant Ave., St. Louis, MO 63136 Tel. (314)381-3111

Fourth District, Bishop Thomas L. Hoyt, Jr., 109 Holcomb Dr., Shreveport, LA 71103 Tel. (318) 222-6284

Fifth District, Bishop Lawerence L. Reddick, III, 310 18th St., N, Suite 400D, Birmingham, AL 35203 Tel. (205)655-0346

Sixth District, Bishop Othal H. Lakey, 1776 Peachtree Rd. NW, Suite 210, South Tower, Atlanta, GA 30309, Tel. (404)745-9689

Seventh District, Bishop Charles L. Helton, 6524 16th St. NW, Washington, D.C. 20012 and 5937 Ruth Dr., Charlotte, NC 28215 Tel. (704)536-8067

Eighth District, Bishop Marshall Gilmore, Sr., 1616 E. Illinois, Dallas, TX 75216 Tel. (214) 372-9073

Ninth District, Bishop Henry M. Williamson, 3844 W. Slauson Ave., Suite 1, Los Angeles, CA 90043 Tel. (213)294-3830, hwillia531@ aol.com

Tenth District, Bishop Ronald M. Cunningham, P.O. Box 16366, Memphis, TN 38167 Tel. (901)396-2068

Retired, Bishop Caesar D. Coleman, 355 Forest Hill Irene Rd., Cordova, TN 38018; Bishop Oree Broomfield, Sr., 3505 Springrun Dr., Decatur, GA 30032; Bishop Nathaniel L. Linsey, Canterbury Subdivision, 190 Squire Lane, Fayettsville, GA 30214 Tel. (770)460-6897, linseyn@bellsouth.net; Bishop Dotcy I. Isom, 4326 Richwood Place, Memphis, TN 36125

Periodicals

The Christian Index; The Missionary Messenger

The Christian and Missionary Alliance

The Christian and Missionary Alliance was formed in 1897 by the merger of two organizations begun in 1887 by Dr. Albert B. Simpson, The Christian Alliance and the Evangelical Missionary Alliance. The Christian and Missionary Alliance is an evangelical church that stresses the sufficiency of Jesus as Savior, Sanctifier, Healer, and Coming

King and has earned a worldwide reputation for its missionary accomplishments. The Canadian districts became autonomous in 1981 and formed The Christian and Missionary Alliance in Canada.

NATIONAL OFFICE

P.O. Box 35000, Colorado Springs, CO 80935-3500 Tel. (719)599-5999 Fax (719)593-8234
Media Contact, Asst. Vice-Pres. for Advancement, Peter Burgo
E-mail: info@cmalliance.org
Web site: www.cmalliance.org

Officers

Pres., Rev. Peter N. Nanfelt, D.D.
Corp. Vice-Pres., Rev. Abraham H. Poon, D. Min
Corp. Sec., Rev. David L. Goodin
Vice-Pres. for Advancement, Rev. David F. Presher, D. Min.
Vice-Pres. for International Ministries, Rev. Robert L. Fetherlin, D. Min.
Vice-Pres. for National Church Ministries, Rev. Donald A. Wiggins, D. Min.
Vice-Pres. for Operations/Treas., Mr. Duane A. Wheeland, LLD/CPA

BOARD OF DIRECTORS

Chpsn., Rev. Rockwell L. Dillaman, D.D.
Vice-Chpsn., Rev. Robert L. Thune

DISTRICTS

Cambodian, Rev. Nareth May, 1616 S. Palmetto Ave., Ontario, CA 91762 Tel. (909)988-9434
Central, Rev. Gordon F. Meier, D.Min., 1218 High St., Wadsworth, OH 44281 Tel. (330) 336-2911
Central Pacific, Rev. R. Douglas Swinburne, J.R., 715 Lincoln Ave., Woodland, CA 95695 Tel. (530)662-2500
E. Pennsylvania, Rev. J. Wayne Spriggs, 1200 Spring Garden Dr., Middletown, PA 17057 Tel. (717)985-9240
Great Lakes, Rev. Jeffrey P. Brown, 2250 Huron Parkway, Ann Arbor, MI 48104 Tel. (734)677-8555
Haitian, Rev. Emaneuelle Seide, 14 Glen Rd., W. Hempstead, NY 11552 Tel. (516)594-1046
Haitian South, Rev. Joe Kong (Interim Dir.), P.O. Box 35000, Colorado Springs, CO 80935 Tel. (719)265-2052
Hmong, Rev. Timothy T. Vang, 12287 Pennsylvania St., Thornton, CO 80241 Tel. (303)252-1793
Korean, Rev. Hyung J. Moon, 550 Durie Ave. #201, Closter, NJ 07640 Tel. (201)750-6750
Metropolitan, Rev. John F. Soper, P.O. Box 7060, 275 Sussex Ave., Suite B, Newark, NJ 07107 Tel. (973)412-7025
MidAmerica, Rev. Randall S. Burg, 1301 S. 119th St., Omaha, NE 68144 Tel. (402)330-1888
Mid-Atlantic, Rev. Randall B. Corbin, D.Min., Jr., 292 Montevue Lane, Frederick, MD 21702 Tel. (301)620-9934
Midwest, Rev. M. Fred Polding, D. Miss., 260 Glen Ellyn Rd., Bloomingdale, IL 60108 Tel. (630)893-1355
Native American, Rev. Craig S. Smith, 19019 N. 74th Dr., Glendale, AZ 85308 Tel. (623)561-8134
New England, Rev. Richard E. Bush, D.Min., P.O. Box 288, South Easton, MA 02375 Tel. (508)238-3820
Northeastern, Rev. David J. Phillips, 6275 Pillmore Dr., Rome, NY 13440 Tel. (315)336-4720
Northwestern, Rev. Craig L. Strawser, 6425 CTYRD 30 #740, St. Bonifacius, MN 55375 Tel. (952)446-9318
Ohio Valley, Rev . P. David Klinsing, D.Min., 4050 Executive Park Dr., Suite 402, Cincinnati, OH 45241 Tel. (513)733-4833
Pacific NW, Rev. Kelvin J. Gardiner, P.O. Box 1030, Canby, OR 97013 Tel. (503)266-2238
Puerto Rico, Rev. Luis F. Felipa, P.O. Box 191794, San Juan, PR 00919 Tel. (787)281-0101
Rocky Mountain, Rev. Timothy P. Owen, D.Min., 2545 St. Johns Ave., Billings, MT 59102 Tel. (406)656-4233
South Atlantic, Rev. L. Ferrell Towns, 10801 Johnston Rd., Suite 125, Charlotte, NC 28226 Tel. (704)543-0470
South Pacific, Rev. Donald M. Brust, 4130 Adams St., Suite A, Riverside, CA 92504 Tel. (909)351-0111
Southeastern, Rev. Mark T. O' Farrell, D.D., P.O. Box 720430, Orlando, FL 32872-0430 Tel. (407)823-9662
Southern, Rev. Fred G. King, 5998 Deerfoot Parkway, Trussville, AL 35173 Tel. (205)661-9585
Southwestern, Rev. Daniel R. Wetzel, 5600 E. Loop 820 South, Suite 100, Fort Worth, TX 76119 Tel. (817)561-0879
Spanish Central, Rev. C. José Bruno, P.O. Box 5477 McAllen, TX 78504 Tel. (956)565-1600
Spanish Eastern, Rev. Marcelo Realpe, P.O. Box 865, Union City, NJ 07087 Tel. (201)866-7202
Vietnamese, Dr. Tai Anh Nguyen, Th.D., 2275 W. Lincoln Ave., Anaheim, CA 92801 Tel. (714)491-8007
W. Great Lakes, Rev. Gary E. Russell, W6107 Aerotech Dr., Appleton, WI 54914 Tel. (920)734-1123
W. Pennsylvania, Rev. Jeffrey A. Norris, P.O. Box 600, Punxsutawney, PA 15767 Tel. (814)938-6920

NATIONAL ETHNIC ASSOCIATIONS

African American, Pres., Rev. Terrence L. Nichols, 120 Lancaster Way, Vallejo, CA 94591 Tel. (707)310-3926; Exec. Sec., Rev. Gus H. Brown, 688 Diagonal Rd., Akron, OH 44320 Tel. (330)376-4654
Chinese, Pres., Rev. Abraham H. Poon, D.Min., 2360 McLaughlin Ave., San Jose, CA 95122-3560 Tel. (408)280-1021

Dega, Pres., Rev. Ha Giao Cilpam, 3119 Westerwood Dr., Charlotte, NC 28214 Tel. (704) 393-7159
Filipino, Pres., Exec. Dir., Rev. Abednego Ferrer, 20143 Royal Ave., Hayward, CA 94541 Tel. (510)887-6261
Haitian, Pres., Rev. Emmanuel Seide, 14 Glen Rd., West Hempstead, NY. 11552 Tel. (516)594-1046

ETHNIC/CULTURAL MINISTRIES

Arab & South Asian, Rev. Joseph S. Kong, P.O. Box 35000, Colorado Springs, CO 80935 Tel. (719)599-5999 ext. 2052
Alliance Jewish Ministries, Rev. Abraham Sandler, 9820 Woodfern Rd., Philadelphia, PA 19115 Tel. (215)676-5122

Periodicals

Alliance Life

Christian Reformed Church in North America

The Christian Reformed Church represents the historic faith of Protestantism. Founded in the United States in 1857 and active in Canada since 1905, it asserts its belief in the Bible as the inspired Word of God, and is creedally united in the Belgic Confession (1561), the Heidelberg Catechism (1563), and the Canons of Dort (1618-19).

Headquarters

2850 Kalamazoo Ave. SE, Grand Rapids, MI 49560 Tel. (616)224-0744 Fax (616)224-5895
Media Contact, Gen. Sec., Dr. David H. Engelhard
E-mail: btgh@crcna.org
Web site: www.crcna.org

Officers

Gen. Sec., Dr. David H. Engelhard
Exec. Dir. of Ministries, Dr. Peter Borgdorff
Canadian Ministries Dir., Rev. William Veenstra, 3475 Mainway, P.O. Box 5070 STN LCR 1, Burlington, ON L7R 3Y8
Dir. of Finance and Admin., Mr. John Bolt

OTHER ORGANIZATIONS

The Back to God Hour, Dir. of Ministries, Dr. Calvin L. Bremer, International Headquarters, 6555 W. College Dr., Palos Heights, IL 60463
Christian Reformed Home Missions, Dir., Rev. John A. Rozeboom
Christian Reformed World Missions, U.S., Dir., Dr. Gary Bekker
Christian Reformed World Missions, Canada, Dir., Albert Karsten, 3475 Mainway, P.O. Box 5070 STN LCR 1, Burlington, ON L7R 3Y8
Christian Reformed World Relief, U.S., Dir., Andrew Ryskamp
Christian Reformed World Relief, Canada, Dir., H. Wayne deJong, 3475 Mainway, P.O. Box 5070 STN LCR 1, Burlington, ON L7R 3Y8
CRC Publications, Dir., Gary Mulder
Ministers' Pension Fund, Admin., Kenneth Horjus

Periodicals

The Banner

Christian Union

Organized in 1864 in Columbus, Ohio, the Christian Union stresses the oneness of the church with Christ as its only head. The Bible is the only rule of faith and practice and good fruits the only condition of fellowship. Each local church governs itself.

Headquarters

316 Rexford Dr., Fort Wayne, IN 46816-1085 Tel. (260)456-7882 Fax (260)456-7802
Media Contact, Pres., Rev. Phil Harris
Web site: www.christianunion.com

Officers

Pres., Rev. Phil Harris, 316 Rexford Dr., Fort Wayne, IN 46816-1085 Tel. (260)456-7802
Vice-Pres., Rev. Marion Hunerdosse, 1844 West Kansas, Liberty, MD 64068-1919 Tel. (816) 781-5044
Sec., Joseph Cunningham, 1005 N. 5th St., Greenfield, OH 45123 Tel. (937)981-3476
Asst. Sec., Jim Eschenbrenner, 30055 130th Ave., Hedrick, IA 52563-8539 Tel. (641)653-4945
Treas., Rev. Neal Skiles, 80 Licking View Dr., Heath, OH 43056-1530 Tel. (740)522-4845 Fax 740-522-6076, skiles@adelphia.net

Periodicals

The Christian Union Witness, P.O.Box 361, Greenfield, OH 45123 Tel. (937)981-2760, Editor/Manager/Publisher, Joseph Cunningham

Church of the Brethren*

Eight German Pietists/Anabaptists, including their leader, Alexander Mack, founded the Brethren movement in 1708 in Schwarzenau, Germany. Begun in reaction to spiritual stagnation in state churches, the Brethren formed their own movement, modeled on the first-century church. They practice church discipline, believer baptism, anointing, and the love feast. They have no other creed than the New Testament, hold to principles of nonviolence, no force in religion, Christian service, and simplicity. They migrated to the colonies beginning in 1710 and settled at Germantown, Pennsylvania, moving westward and southward over the next 200 years. Emphasis on religion in daily life led to the formation of Brethren Volunteer Service in 1948, which continues today.

Headquarters

Church of the Brethren General Offices, 1451 Dundee Ave., Elgin, IL 60120-1694 Tel. (847) 742-5100 Fax (847)753-6103, generalboard@brethren.org
Brethren Service Center, 500 Main St., P.O. Box 188, New Windsor, MD 21776-0188 Tel.

(410)635-8710 Fax (410)635-8789, bsc_gb@ brethren.org
Washington Office, 337 North Carolina Ave. SE, Washington, DC 20003-2004 Tel. (202)546-3202 Fax (202)544-5852, washington_office_gb @brethren.org
Media Contact, Dir. of News Services, Elgin Office, Cheryl Brumbaugh-Cayford
E-mail: cobweb@brethren.org
Web site: www.brethren.org

Officers

Moderator, Christopher D. Bowman, 210 N. Wall St., Martinsburg, PA 16662-1252 Tel. (814)793-2422 Fax (814)793-3755, mburgcob @nb.net
Moderator, Jim Hardenbrook, 11030 Orchard Ave., Nampa, ID 83651-8258 Tel. (208)466-3321, jobrook@msn.com
Sec., Fred W. Swartz, 10047 Nokesville Rd., Manassas, VA 20110-4131 Tel. (703)369-3947, swartz@emountain.net

GENERAL BOARD STAFF

Gen. Sec., Stanley J. Noffsinger, 1451 Dundee Ave., Elgin, IL 60120-1694 Tel. (847)742-5100 ext. 201 Fax (847)742-8212, snoffsinger_gb@brethren.org
Manager of Office Operations, Jon Kobel, 1451 Dundee Ave., Elgin, IL 60120-1694 Tel. (847)742-5100 ext. 202 Fax (847)742-8212, jkobel_gb@brethren.org
Dir., Human Resources, Mary Lou Garrison, 1451 Dundee Ave., Elgin, IL 60120-1694 Tel. (847)742-5100 ext. 258 Fax (847)742-8212, mgarrison_gb@brethren.org

LEADERSHIP TEAM

Gen. Sec., Stanley J. Noffsinger, 1451 Dundee Ave., Elgin, IL 60120-1694 Tel. (847)742-5100 ext. 201 Fax (847)742-8212, snoffsinger_gb@brethren.org
Exec. Dir., Centralized Resources & CFO/Treas., Judy E. Keyser, 1451 Dundee Ave., Elgin, IL 60120-1694 Tel. (847)742-5100 ext. 270 Fax (847)742-6103, jkeyser_gb@brethren.org
Exec. Dir. & Publisher, Brethren Press, Wendy McFadden, 1451 Dundee Ave., Elgin, IL 60120-1694 Tel. (847)742-5100 ext. 278 Fax (847)742-1407, wmcfadden_gb@brethren.org
Exec. Dir. of Congregational Life Ministries, Delmas L. Keeney, 1451 Dundee Ave., Elgin, IL 60120-1694 Tel. (847)742-5100 ext. 282 Fax 847-742-6103, dkeeney_gb@brethren.org
Exec. Dir. of Global Mission Partnerships, Mervin B. Keeney, 1451 Dundee Ave., Elgin, IL 60120-1694 Tel. (847)742-5100 ext. 226 Fax (847)742-6103, mission_gb@brethren. org
Exec. Dir., Brethren Service Ctr., Roy Winter, P.O. Box 188, New Windsor, MD 21776-0188 Tel. (410)635-8748 Fax (410)635-8739, rwinter_gb@brethren.org

Periodicals

Messenger

Church of Christ

Joseph Smith and five others organized the Church of Christ on April 6, 1830 at Fayette, New York. In 1864 this body was directed by revelation through Granville Hedrick to return in 1867 to Independence, Missouri to the "consecrated land" dedicated by Joseph Smith. They did so and purchased the temple lot dedicated in 1831.

Headquarters

Temple Lot, 200 S. River St., P.O. Box 472, Independence, MO 64051 Tel. (816)833-3995
Media Contact, Gen. Church Rep., William A. Sheldon, P.O. Box 472, Independence, MO 64051 Tel. (816)833-3995
Web site: church-of-christ.com

Officers

Council of Apostles, Sec., Apostle Smith N. Brickhouse, P.O. Box 472, Independence, MO 64051
Gen. Bus. Mgr., Bishop Alvin Harris, P.O. Box 472, Independence, MO 64051

Periodicals

Zion's Advocate

The Church of Christ (Holiness) U.S.A.

The Church of Christ (Holiness) U.S.A. has a divine commission to propagate the gospel throughout the world, to seek the conversion of sinners, to reclaim backsliders, to encourage the sanctification of believers, to support divine healing, and to advance the truth for the return of our Lord and Savior Jesus Christ. This must be done through proper organization.

The fundamental principles of Christ's church have remained the same. The laws founded upon these principles are to remain unchanged. The Church of Christ (Holiness) U.S.A. is representative in form of government; therefore, the final authority in defining the organizational responsibilities rests with the national convention. The bishops of the church are delegated special powers to act in behalf of or speak for the church. The pastors are ordained ministers, who, under the call of God and his people, have divine oversight of local churches. However, the representative form of government gives ministry and laity equal authority in all deliberate bodies. With the leadership of the Holy Spirit, respect, loyalty and love will greatly increase.

Headquarters

329 E. Monument St., P.O. Box 3622, Jackson, MS 39207 Tel. (601)353-0222 Fax (601)353-4002
Media Contact, Sr. Bishop, Maurice D. Bingham, Ed.D.
E-mail: everything@cochusa.com
Web site: www.cochusa.com/main.htm

BOARD OF BISHOPS

Sr. Bishop, Maurice D. Bingham, Ed.D., P.O. Box 6182, Jackson, MS 39308 Tel. (601)353-0222

Eastern Diocese, Bishop Lindsay E. Jones, 1033 Winchester Way, Chesapeake, VA 23320 Tel. (757)547-1653

North Central Diocese, Bishop Bennett Wolfe, 14315 River Oak Court, Florissant, MO 63034 Tel. (314)741-4590

Northern Diocese, Bishop Emery Lindsay, 62 W. 111th Place, Chicago, IL 60628 Tel. (773)821-0088

Pacific Northwest Diocese, Bishop Robert Winn, 3125 W. 54th St., Los Angeles, CA 90043 Tel. (213)295-4166

South Central Diocese, Bishop Joseph Campbell, Jr., P.O. Box 3663, Jackson, MS 39207 Tel. (601)825-6829

Southeastern Diocese, Bishop Victor P. Smith, 3783 Treebark Trail, Decatur, GA 30034 Tel. (404)288-4885

Southwestern Diocese, Bishop Vernon Kennebrew, 13900 Edgemond Drive, Little Rock, AR 72212 Tel. (504)296-7676

Western Diocese, Bishop Robert Winn, 4852 Victoria Ave., Los Angeles, CA 90016

Board Member, Bishop James K. Mitchell, 1580 Waite St., Gary, IN 46404 Tel. (219)944-0051

Church of Christ, Scientist

The Church of Christ, Scientist, was founded in 1879 by Mary Baker Eddy "to commemorate the word and works of our Master [Christ Jesus], which should reinstate primitive Christianity and its lost element of healing" (Church Manual, p. 17). Central to the church's mission is making available worldwide Mrs. Eddy's definitive work on health and Bible-based Christian healing, *Science and Health With Key to the Scriptures*, as well as its publications, Internet sites, and broadcast programs, all of which respond to humanity's search for spiritual answers to today's pressing needs.

The church also maintains an international speakers' bureau to introduce the public to Christian Science and Mrs. Eddy. Christian Science practitioners, living in hundreds of communities worldwide are available full-time to pray with anyone seeking comfort and healing. And Christian Science teachers hold yearly classes for those interested in a more specific understanding of how to practice the Christian Science system of healing.

The worldwide activities and business of the Church are transacted by a five-member Board of Dirs. in Boston. About 2,000 congregations, each democratically organized and governed, are located in approximately 80 countries. The church has no clergy. Worship services are conducted by lay persons elected to serve as Readers. Each church maintains a Reading Room—a bookstore open to the community for spiritual inquiry and research; and a Sunday School where young people discuss the contemporary relevance of ideas from the Bible and *Science and Health*.

Headquarters

The First Church of Christ, Scientist, 175 Huntington Ave., Boston, MA 02115

Media Contact, Mgr., Committees on Publication, Gary A. Jones, Tel. (617)450-3300 Fax (617)450-7397

Web sites: spirituality.com and churchofchristscientist. org

Officers

Bd. of Dir.: Virginia S. Harris; Walter D. Jones; M. Victor Westberg; Mary Metzner Trammell; Nathan Talbot

Pres., Cynthia Neely

Treas., Walter D. Jones

Clk., Nathan Talbot

First Reader, Lyle Young

Second Reader, Suzanne Cowin

Christian Science College Organizations, www.csoconnection.com

Periodicals

The Christian Science Monitor (www.csmonitor.com); *The Christian Science Journal; Christian Science Sentinel; The Herald of Christian Science* (13 languages); *Christian Science Quarterly Bible Lessons* (in 16 languages and English Braille)

Church of God (Anderson, Indiana)

The Church of God (Anderson, Indiana) began in 1881 when Daniel S. Warner and several associates felt constrained to forsake all denominational hierarchies as formal creeds, trusting solely in the Holy Spirit as their overseer and the Bible as their statement of belief.

These people saw themselves at the forefront of a movement to restore unity and holiness to the church, not to establish another denomination, but to promote primary allegiance to Jesus Christ so as to transcend denominational loyalties.

Deeply influenced by Wesleyan theology and Pietism, the Church of God has emphasized conversion, holiness and attention to the Bible. Worship services tend to be informal, accentuating expository preaching and robust singing. There is no formal membership. Persons are assumed to be members on the basis of witness to a conversion experience and evidence that supports such witness. The absence of formal membership is also consistent with the church's understanding of how Christian unity is to be achieved—that is, by preferring the label Christian before all others. The Church of God is congregational in its government. Each local congregation is autonomous and may call any recognized Church of God minister to be its pastor and retain him or her as long as is mutually pleasing.

Ministers are ordained and disciplined by state or provincial assemblies made up predominantly of ministers. National program agencies serve the church through coordinated ministries and resource materials. There are Church of God congregations in 89 foreign countries, most of which are resourced by one or more missionaries. There are slightly more Church of God adherents overseas than in North America.

GENERAL OFFICES

Church of God Ministries, Inc., Gen. Dir. (Pres.), Ronald V. Duncan, P.O. Box 2420, Anderson, IN 46018-2420 Tel. (765) 642-0256 Fax (765) 642-5652; Includes Congregational Ministries, Outreach Ministries, and Resource & Linking Ministries

Media Contact, Communications Coord., Sam Collins, scollins@chog.org

E-mail: JMartin@chog.org

Web site: www.chog.org

OTHER ORGANIZATIONS

Board of Church Extension, Pres., J. Perry Grubbs, Box 2069, Anderson, IN 46018

Board of Pensions, Pres., Jeffery A. Jenness, Box 2299, Anderson IN 46018

Warner Press, Inc., Pres., Eric King, Box 2499, Anderson IN 46018

Anderson University, Pres., James L. Edwards, 1100 E 5th St., Anderson IN 46012

Mid-America Christian University, Pres., John Fozard, 3500 SW 119th St., Oklahoma City OK 73170

Warner Pacific College, Pres., Jay A. Barber, Jr., 2219 SE 68th Ave, Portland OR 97215

Warner Southern College, Pres., Gregory V. Hall, 13895 Hwy 27, Lake Wales, FL 33859

Women of the Church of God, Exec. Dir., Linda J. Mason, Box 2328, Anderson, IN 46018

Periodicals

Missions Magazine; Pathways to God; Communion; People to People; YMI Update

The Church of God in Christ

The Church of God in Christ was founded in 1907 in Memphis, Tennessee, and was organized by Bishop Charles Harrison Mason, a former Baptist minister who pioneered the embryonic stages of the Holiness movement beginning in 1895 in Mississippi.

Its founder organized four major departments between 1910-1916, the Women's Department, the Sunday School, Young Peoples Willing Workers and Home and Foreign Mission.

The church is trinitarian and teaches the infallibility of Scripture, the need for regeneration and subsequent baptism of the Holy Ghost. It emphasizes holiness as God's standard for Christian conduct. It recognizes as ordinances Holy Communion, Water Baptism and Feet Washing. Its governmental structure is basically episcopal, with the General Assembly being the legislative body.

Headquarters

Mason Temple, 938 Mason St., Memphis, TN 38126 Tel. (901)947-9300; Mailing Address, P.O. Box 320, Memphis, TN 38101

Temple Church Of God In Christ, 672 S. Lauderdale St., Memphis, TN 38126 Tel. (901)527-9202

E-mail: ejohncogic@aol.com

Web site: www.cogic.org

GENERAL OFFICES

Office of the Presiding Bishop, Presiding Bishop, Bishop Chandler D. Owens, Tel. (901)947-9338

Office of the Gen. Sec., Gen. Sec., Bishop W. W. Hamilton, Tel. (901)947-9358

Office of the Financial Sec., Sec., Bishop Frank O. White, Tel. (901)947-9310

Office of the Treas., Treas., Bishop Samuel L. Lowe, Tel. (901)947-9381

Office of the Board of Trustees, Chmn., Elder Dwight Green, Tel. (901)947-9326

Office of the Chief Operating Officer at World Headquarters, Elder A.Z. Hall, Jr., 930 Mason Street, Memphis, TN, Tel. (901)947-9358

Office of the Clergy Bureau, Dir., Bishop W.W. Hamilton, Tel. (901)974-9358

Office of Supt. of National Properties, Supt., Elder Marles Flowers, Tel. (901)947-9330

Office of Accounting, Chief Financial Officer, Ms. Sylvia H. Law, Tel. (901)947-9361

Dept. of Evangelism, Pres., Elder Richard White, Atlanta, GA, Tel. (404)361-7020

Dept. of Missions, Pres. Bishop Carlis L. Moody, Tel. (901)947-9316; Vice Pres., Elder Jesse W. Denny

Dept. of Music, Pres., Ms. LuVoinia Whittley, 20205 Augusta Dr., Olympia Fields, IL 60461 Tel. (312)626-1970

Dept. of Sunday Schools, Gen. Supt., Bishop Jerry Macklin, 1027 W. Tennyson Rd., Hayward, CA 94544 Tel. (510)783-9377

Dept. of Women, Pres.-Gen. Supervisor, Mother Willie Mae Rivers, P.O. Box 1052, Memphis, TN 38101 Tel. (901)775-0600

Dept. of Youth (Youth Congress), Pres., Elder J. Drew Sheard, 7045 Curtis Dr., Detroit, MI 48235 Tel. (313)864-7170

Church of God in Christ Book Store, Mgr., Geraldine Miller, 285 S. Main St., Memphis, TN 38103 Tel. (901)947-9304

Church of God in Christ Publishing House, CEO, Dr. David A. Hall, Sr., Tel. (901)947-9342

Board of Publications, Chmn., Bishop R.L.H. Winbush, Tel. (901)947-9342

Church of God in Christ, International

The Church of God in Christ, International was organized in 1969 in Kansas City, Mo., by

14 bishops of the Church of God in Christ of Memphis, Tenn. The doctrine is the same, but the separation came because of disagreement over polity and governmental authority. The church is Wesleyan in theology (two works of grace) but stresses the experience of full baptism of the Holy Ghost with the initial evidence of speaking with other tongues as the Spirit gives utterance.

Headquarters

170 Adelphi St., Brooklyn, NY 11205 Tel. (718) 625-9175
Media Contact, Natl. Sec., Rev. Sis. Sharon R. Dunn
E-mail: laity@cogic.org
Web site: www.cogic.org/main.htm

Officers

Presiding Bishop, Most Rev. Carl E. Williams, Sr.
Vice-Presiding Bishop, Rt. Rev. J. P. Lucas, 90 Holland St., Newark, NJ 07103
Sec.-Gen., Deacon Dennis Duke, 360 Colorado Ave., Bridgeport, CT 06605
Exec. Admin., Horace K. Williams, Word of God Center, Newark, NJ
Women's Dept., Natl. Supervisor, Evangelist Elvonia Williams
Youth Dept., Pres., Dr. Joyce Taylor, 137-17 135th Ave. S., Ozone Park, NY 11420
Music Dept., Pres., Isaiah Heyward
Bd. of Bishops, Chpsn., Bishop J. C. White, 360 Colorado Ave., Bridgeport, CT 06605

Church of God in Christ, Mennonite

The Church of God in Christ, Mennonite was organized the evangelist-reformer John Holdeman in Ohio. The church unites with the faith of the Waldenses, Anabaptists and other such groups throughout history. Emphasis is placed on obedience to the teachings of the Bible, including the doctrine of the new birth and spiritual life, noninvolvement in government or the military, head coverings for the women, beards for the men and separation from the world shown by simplicity in clothing, homes, possessions and lifestyle. The church has a worldwide membership of about 20,150, largely concentrated in the United States and Canada.

Headquarters

P.O. Box 313, 420 N. Wedel Ave., Moundridge, KS 67107 Tel. (620)345-2532 Fax (620)345-2582
Media Contact, Dale Koehn, P.O. Box 230, Moundridge, KS 67107 Tel. (620)345-2532 Fax (620)345-2582
E-mail: dalekoehn.gp@cogicm.org

Periodicals

Messenger of Truth

Church of God (Cleveland, Tennessee)

It is one of America's oldest Pentecostal churches founded in 1886 as an outgrowth of the holiness revival under the name Christian Union. In 1907 the church adopted the organizational name Church of God. It has its foundation upon the principles of Christ as revealed in the Bible. The Church of God is Christian, Protestant, foundational in its doctrine, evangelical in practice and distinctively Pentecostal. It maintains a centralized form of government and a commitment to world evangelization. The first church of Canada was established in 1919 in Scotland Farm, Manitoba. Paul H. Walker became the first overseer of Canada in 1931.

Headquarters

Intl. Offices, 2490 Keith St. NW, Cleveland, TN 37320 Tel. (423)472-3361 Fax (423)478-7066
Media Contact, Dir. of Communications, Michael L. Baker, P.O. Box 2430, Cleveland, TN 37320-2430 Tel. (423)478-7112 Fax (423)478-7066
Web site: www.churchofgod.cc/default_nav40.asp

EXECUTIVES

Gen. Overseer, R. Lamar Vest
Asst. Gen. Overseers, T. L. Lowery; Bill F. Sheeks; Orville Hagan
Sec.-Gen., Gene D. Rice
Canada-Eastern, Rev. Andrew Binda, P.O. Box 2036, Brampton, ON L6T 3TO Tel. (905)793-2213 Fax (905)793-9173
Canada-Western, Rev. Raymond W. Wall, Box 54055, 2640 52nd St. NE, Calgary, AB T1Y 6S6 Tel. (403)293-8817 Fax (403)293-8832
Canada-Quebec-Maritimes, Rev. Jaques Houle, 19 Orly, Granby, QC J2H 1Y4 Tel. (514)378-4442 Fax (514)378-8646
Canada-National, Rev. Ralph R. Glagau, P.O. Box 333, Station B, Etobicoke, ON M9W 5L3 Tel. (416)741-9222 Fax (416)741-3717

DEPARTMENTS

Benefits Board, CEO, Arthur Rhodes
Business & Records, Dir., Julian B. Robinson
Care Ministries, Dir., John D. Nichols
Chaplains Commission, Dir., Robert D. Crick
Communications, Media Ministries, Dir., Michael L. Baker
Education—European Bible Seminary, Dir., John Sims
Education—Hispanic Institute of Ministry, Dir., Jose D. Montanez
Education—International Bible College, Pres., Cheryl Busse
Education—Lee University, Pres., C. Paul Conn
Education—Patten College, Pres., Gary Moncher
Education—Puerto Rico Bible School, Pres., Ildefonso Caraballo
Education—School of Ministry, Chancellor, Paul L. Walker
Education—Theological Seminary, Pres., Steven J. Land
Evangelism & Home Missions, Dir., Larry J. Timmerman

Evangelism—Black Ministries, Dir., Asbury R. Sellers
Evangelism—Cross-Cultural Min., Dir., Wallace J. Sibley
Evangelism—Hispanic Ministry, Dir., Esdras Betancourt
Evangelism—Native American Ministries, Dir., Douglas M. Cline
Lay Ministries, Dir., Leonard Albert
Legal Services, Dir., Dennis W. Watkins
Men/Women of Action, Dir., Hugh Carver
Ministerial Development, Dir., Larry G. Hess
Ministry to Israel, Dir., J. Michael Utterback
Ministry to the Military, Dir.,Robert A. Moore
Music Ministries, Dir., Delton Alford
Pentecostal Resource Center, Dir., Don Smeeton
Pentecostal Research Center, David G. Roebuck
Publications, Dir., Daniel F. Boling
Stewardship, Dir., Al Taylor
Women's Ministries, Coordinator, Oleda Adkinson
World Missions, Dir., Lovell R. Cary
Youth & Christian Education, Dir., John D. Childers

Periodicals

Church of God Evangel; Church of God Evangelica; Save Our World; Ministry Now Profiles

Church of God by Faith, Inc.

Founded 1914, in Jacksonville Heights, Florida, by Elder John Bright, this church believes the word of God as interpreted by Jesus Christ to be the only hope of salvation and Jesus Christ the only mediator for people.

Headquarters

1315 Lane Ave. S., Suite 6, Jacksonville, FL 32205 Tel. (904)783-8500 Fax (904)783-9911
Media Contact, Ofc. Mgr., Sarah E. Lundy
E-mail: natl-hq@cogbf.org
Web site: www.cogbf.org

Officers

Presiding Bishop, James E. McKnight, P.O. Box 121, Gainesville, FL 32601
Treas., Elder John Robinson, 300 Essex Dr., Ft. Pierce, FL 34946
Exec. Sec., David C. Rourk, 207 Chestnut Hill Drive, Rochester, NY. 14617
Ruling Elder, James E. McKnight, Jr., P.O. Box 101, Starke, FL 32091

Church of God General Conference (Oregon, IL and Morrow, GA)

This church is the outgrowth of several independent local groups of similar faith. Some were in existence as early as 1800, and others date their beginnings to the arrival of British immigrants around 1847. Many local churches carried the name Church of God of the Abrahamic Faith. State and district conferences of these groups were formed as an expression of mutual cooperation. A national organization was instituted at Philadelphia in 1888. Because of strong convictions on the questions of congregational rights and authority, however, it ceased to function until 1921, when the present General Conference was formed at Waterloo, Iowa.

The Bible is accepted as the supreme standard of faith. Adventist in viewpoint, the second (premillenial) coming of Christ is strongly emphasized. The church teaches that the kingdom of God will be literal, beginning in Jerusalem at the time of the return of Christ and extending to all nations. Emphasis is placed on the oneness of God and the Sonship of Christ, that Jesus did not pre-exist prior to his birth in Bethlehem and that the Holy Spirit is the power and influence of God. Membership is dependent on faith, repentance and baptism by immersion.

The work of the General Conference is carried on under the direction of the board of directors. With a congregational church government, the General Conference exists primarily as a means of mutual cooperation and for the development of yearly projects and enterprises.

The headquarters and Bible College were moved to Morrow, Ga. in 1991.

Headquarters

P.O. Box 100,000, Morrow, GA 30260 Tel. (404)362-0052 Fax (404)362-9307
Media Contact, Tim Jones
E-mail: info@abc-coggc.org
Web site: www.abc-coggc.org

Officers

Chief Admin. Officer, Mr. Tim Jones, Box 100,000, Morrow, GA 30260 Tel. (404)362-9307, tjones@abc-coggc.org
Chpsn., Pastor Michael Hoffman, 740 W. Oregon Trail, Oregon, IL 61061 Tel. (815)732-6847, hoffon @aol.com
Vice-Chpsn., Pastor Larry Mayberry, 7541 Burlingame SW, Byron Center, MI 49315 Tel. (616)452-3119, larrymayberry@juno.com
Sec., Andrea Anders, 301 N. Ellis St., Salisbury, NC 28144 Tel. (803)461-2150, aanders@suggskelly.com,
Treas., Pastor Dale Bliss, 2696 Wynterpointe Ct., Kokomo IN 46901 Tel. (765)455-9866, dale_ bliss@hotmail.com

OTHER ORGANIZATIONS

Bus. Admn., Operations Manager, Mr. Gary Burnham, Box 100,000, Morrow, GA 30260 Tel. (404)362-0052 Fax (404)362-9307, gburnham@abc-coggc.org
Atlanta Bible College, Pres., Mr. Tim Jones, Box 100,000, Morrow, GA 30260 Tel. (404)362-9307, tjones@abc-coggc.org

Periodicals

T*he Restitution Herald; A Journal From the Radical Reformation; Church of God Progress Journal*

Church of God, Mountain Assembly, Inc.

The church was formed in 1895 and organized in 1906 by J. H. Parks, S. N. Bryant, Tom Moses and William Douglas.

Headquarters

164 N. Florence Ave., P.O. Box 157, Jellico, TN 37762 Tel. (423)784-8260 Fax (423)784-3258

Media Contact, Gen. Sec.-Treas., Rev. James Kilgore

E-mail: cgmahdq@jellico.com

Web site: www.cgmahdq.org

Officers

Gen. Overseer, Rev. Fred R. Cornelius

Asst. Gen. Overseer, World Missions Dir., Rev. Jay Walden

Gen. Sec.-Treas., Rev. James Kilgore

Youth Ministries & Camp Dir., Rev. Nick Hill

Periodicals

The Gospel Herald

Church of God of Prophecy

The Church of God of Prophecy is one of the churches that grew out of the work of A. J. Tomlinson in the first half of the twentieth century. Historically it shares a common heritage with the Church of God (Cleveland, Tennessee) and is in the mainstream of the classical Pentecostal-holiness tradition.

At the death of A.J. Tomlinson in 1943, M.A. Tomlinson was named General Overseer and served until his retirement in 1990. He emphasized unity and fellowship unlimited by racial, social, or political differences. The next General Overseer, Billy D. Murray, Sr., who served from 1990 until his retirement in 2000, emphasized a commitment to the promotion of Christian unity and world evangelization. In July 2000, Fred S. Fisher, Sr. was duly selected to serve as the fourth General Overseer of the Church of God of Prophecy.

From its beginnings, the church has based its beliefs on "the whole Bible, rightly divided," and has accepted the Bible as God's Holy Word, inspired, inerrant and infallible. The church is firm in its commitment to orthodox Christian belief. The Church affirms that there is one God, eternally existing in three persons, Father, Son and Holy Spirit. It believes in the deity of Christ, his virgin birth, his sinless life, the physical miracles he performed, His atoning death on the cross, his bodily resurrection, his ascension to the right hand of the Father and his second coming. The church professes that salvation results from grace alone through faith in Christ, that regeneration by the Holy Spirit is essential for the salvation of sinful men, and that sanctification by the blood of Christ makes possible personal holiness. It affirms the present ministry of the Holy Spirit by whose indwelling believers are able to live godly lives and have power for service. The church believes in, and promotes, the ultimate unity of believers as prayed for by Christ in John 17. The church stresses the sanctity of human life and is committed to the sanctity of the marriage bond and the importance of strong, loving Christian families. Other official teachings include Holy Spirit baptism with tongues as initial evidence; manifestation of the spiritual gifts; divine healing; premillenial second coming of Christ; total abstinence from the use of tobacco, alcohol and narcotics; water baptism by immersion; the Lord's supper and washing of the saints' feet; and a concern for moderation and holiness in all dimensions of lifestyle.

The church is racially integrated on all levels, including top leadership. Women play a prominent role in church affairs, serving in pastoral roles and other leadership positions. The church presbytery has recently adopted plurality of leadership in the selection of a General Oversight Group. This group consists of eight bishops located around the world who, along with the General Overseer, are responsible for inspirational leadership and vision casting for the church body.

The church has local congregations in all 50 states and more than 100 nations worldwide. Organizationally there is a strong emphasis on international missions, evangelism, youth and children's ministries, women's and men's ministries, stewardship, communications, publishing, leadership development and discipleship.

CHURCH OF GOD OF PROPHECY INTERNATIONAL OFFICES

P.O. Box 2910, Cleveland, TN 37320-2910

Media Contact, National Overseer, Levi Clarke, 5145 Tomken Rd, Mississauga, ON L4 W1P1 Tel. (905)625-1278 Fax (905)625-1316.

E-mail: betty@cogop.org

Web site: www.cogop.org

Officers

Gen. Overseer, Bishop Fred S. Fisher, Sr.

General Presbyters, Sherman Allen; Sam Clements; Daniel Corbett; Clayton Endecott; Miguel Mojica; Felix Santiago; Brice Thompson

International Offices Ministries Dirs.

Finance, Communications, and Publishing, Perry Gillum

Global Outreach and Admin. Asst. to the Gen. Presbyters, Randy Howard

Leadership Development and Discipleship Ministries, Larry Duncan.

Periodicals

White Wing Messenger (eng.), *Victory* (Youth Magazine/ Sunday School Curriculum); *The Happy Harvester, White Wing Messenger* (Spanish).

The Church of God (Seventh Day), Denver, Colorado

The Church of God (Seventh Day) began in southwestern Michigan in 1858, when a group of

Sabbath-keepers led by Gilbert Cranmer refused to give endorsement to the visions and writings of Ellen G. White, a principal in the formation of the Seventh-Day Adventist Church. Another branch of Sabbath-keepers, which developed near Cedar Rapids, Iowa, in 1860, joined the Michigan church in 1863 to publish a paper called *The Hope of Israel*, the predecessor to the *Bible Advocate*, the church's present publication. As membership grew and spread into Missouri and Nebraska, it organized the General Conference of the Church of God in 1884. The words "Seventh Day" were added to its name in 1923. The headquarters of the church was in Stanberry, Missouri, from 1888 until 1950, when it moved to Denver.

The church teaches salvation is a gift of God's grace, and is available solely by faith in Jesus Christ, the Savior; that saving faith is more than mental assent, it involves active trust and repentance from sin. Out of gratitude, Christians will give evidence of saving faith by a lifestyle that conforms to God's commandments, including the seventh-day Sabbath, which members observe as a tangible expression of their faith and rest in God as their Creator and Redeemer. The church believes in the imminent, personal, and visible return of Christ; that the dead are in an unconscious state awaiting to be resurrected, the wicked to be destroyed, and the righteous to be rewarded to eternal life in the presence of God on a restored earth. The church observes two ordinances, baptism by immersion and an annual Communion service accompanied by foot washing.

Headquarters

330 W. 152nd Ave., P.O. Box 33677, Denver, CO 80233 Tel. (303)452-7973 Fax (303)452-0657
Media Contact, Pres., Whaid Rose
E-mail: whaidrose@cog7.org
Web site: www.cog7.org

MINISTRIES

Missions Ministries, Dir., William Hicks
Church Planting Dir., Mike Vlad
Home Missions Dir., Mike Vlad
Missions Abroad, Dir., William Hicks
Publications/Bible Advocate Press, Dir., Eddie Villalba
Ministerial Training System, Chair, Harvey Fischer
Young Adult Ministry, Dir., Kristy Lang
Youth Ministry, Dirs., Kurt & Kristi Lang
Women's Ministry, Dir., Mary Ling

Periodicals

The Bible Advocate (English & Spanish); *Pulse* (English & Spanish)

The Church of Illumination

The Church of Illumination was organized in 1908 for the express purpose of establishing congregations at-large, offering a spiritual, esoteric, philosophic interpretation of the vital biblical teachings, thereby satisfying the inner spiritual needs of those seeking spiritual truth, yet permitting them to remain in, or return to, their former church membership.

Headquarters

Beverly Hall, 5966 Clymer Rd., Quakertown, PA 18951 Tel. (800)779-3796
E-mail: bevhall@comcat.com
Web site: www.soul.org

Officers

Media Contact, Dir. Gen., Gerald E. Poesnecker, P.O. Box 220, Quakertown, PA 18951 Tel. (215)536-7048 Fax (215) 536-7058

The Church of Jesus Christ (Bickertonites)

This church was organized in 1862 at Green Oak, Pa., by William Bickerton, who obeyed the Restored Gospel under Sidney Rigdon's following in 1845.

Headquarters

Sixth & Lincoln Sts., Monongahela, PA 15063 Tel. (412)258-3066
Media Contact, Exec. Sec., John Manes, 2007 Cutter Dr., McKees Rocks, PA 15136 Tel. (412)771-4513

Officers

Pres., Dominic Thomas, 6010 Barrie, Dearborn, MI 48126
First Counselor, Paul Palmieri, 319 Pine Dr., Aliquippa, PA 15001 Tel. (412)378-4264
Second Counselor, Robert Watson, Star Rt. 5, Box 36, Gallup, NM 87301
Exec. Sec., John Manes, 2007 Cutter Dr., McKees Rocks, PA 15136 Tel. (412)771-4513

The Church of Jesus Christ of Latter-day Saints

This church was organized April 6, 1830, at Fayette, N.Y., by Joseph Smith. Members believe Joseph Smith was divinely directed to restore the gospel to the earth, and that through him the keys to the Aaronic and Melchizedek priesthoods and temple work also were restored. Members believe that both the Bible and the Book of Mormon (a record of the Lord's dealings with his people on the American continent 600 B.C.– 421 A.D.) are Scripture. Membership is more than eleven million.

In addition to the First Presidency, the governing bodies of the church include the Quorum of the Twelve Apostles, the Presidency of the Seventy, the Quorums of the Seventy and the Presiding Bishopric.

Headquarters

47 East South Temple St., Salt Lake City, UT 84150 Tel. (801)240-1000 Fax (801)240-1167
Media Contact, Dir., Media Relations, Michael Otterson, Tel. (801)240-1111 Fax (801)240-1167
Web site: www.lds.org

Officers

Pres., Gordon B. Hinckley
1st Counselor, Thomas S. Monson
2nd Counselor, James E. Faust
Quorum of the Twelve Apostles, Pres., Boyd K. Packer; L. Tom Perry; David B. Haight; Neal A. Maxwell; Russell M. Nelson; Dallin H. Oaks; M. Russell Ballard; Joseph B. Wirthlin; Richard G. Scott; Robert D. Hales; Jeffrey R. Holland; Henry B. Eyring

AUXILLIARY ORGANIZATIONS

Sunday Schools, Gen. Pres., Cecil O. Samuelson, Jr.
Relief Society, Gen. Pres., Bonnie D. Parkin
Young Women, Gen. Pres., Margaret Nadauld
Young Men, Gen. Pres., F. Melvin Hammond
Primary, Gen. Pres., Coleen K. Menlove

Periodicals

The Ensign; Liahona; Friend Magazine

Church of the Living God (Motto, Christian Workers for Fellowship)

The Church of the Living God was founded by William Christian in April 1889 at Caine Creek, Arkansas. It was the first black church in America without Anglo-Saxon roots and not founded by white missionaries.

Chief Christian, as he is now called, was born a slave in Mississippi on Nov. 10, 1856 and grew up uneducated. In 1875, he united with the Missionary Baptist Church and began to preach. In 1888, he left the Baptist Church and began what was known as Christian Friendship Work. Believing himself to have been inspired by the Spirit of God through divine revelation and close study of the Scriptures, he was led to the truth that the Bible refers to the church as The Church of the Living God (I Timothy. 3:15). In 1889, he established the Church of the Living God organization.

The organization is nondenominational, nonsectarian and Trinitarian and believer in the infallibility of the Scriptures. It emphasizes believer's baptism by immersion, the use of water and unleavened bread element in the Lord's Supper and the washing of feet that is required only when one unites with the church.

The local organizations are known as "Temples" rather than as "Churches" and are subject to the authority of the general assembly. The presiding officer is styled as "chief bishop." The ministry includes bishops, overseers, evangelists, pastors, missionaries and local preachers. The Executive Board is in charge of the operation of the entire organization, in the absence of the Annual Assembly. Synod, Annual, General Assembly meets quadrennialy.

The Church of the Living God, now headquartered in Cincinnati, Ohio, has been in existence for more than 114 years. It is represented by approximately 10,000 members throughout 25 states within the U.S. The presiding officer, Chief Bishop W. E. Crumes, has led the organization for more than 30 years.

Headquarters

430 Forest Ave., Cincinnati, OH 45229 Tel. (513)569-5660 Fax (513)569-5661
Media Contact, Chief Bishop, W. E. Crumes

EXECUTIVE BOARD

Chief Bishop, W. E. Crumes, 430 Forest Ave., Cincinnati, OH 45229
Vice-Chief Bishop, Robert D. Tyler, 3802 Bedford, Omaha, NE 68110
Exec. Sec., Bishop C. A. Lewis, 1360 N. Boston, Tulsa, OK 73111
Gen. Sec., Elder Raymond Powell, Sr., 2159 E. 95th St., Chicago, IL 60617
Gen. Treas., Elder Harry Hendricks, 11935 Cimarron Ave., Hawthorne, CA 90250
Bishop E. L. Bowie, 2037 N.E. 18th St., Oklahoma City, OK 73111
Bishop Leroy Smith, Jr., 1418 Faraday, Peoria, IL 61605
Bishop Jeff Ruffin, 302 E. Monte Way, Phoenix, AZ 85040
Bishop S. E. Shannon, 1034 S. King Hwy., St. Louis, MO 63110
Bishop, Elbert Jones, 4522 Melwood, Memphis, TN 38109
Bishop, Harold Edwards, P.O. Box 411489, Dallas, TX 75249

NATIONAL DEPARTMENTS

Convention Planning Committee
Young People's Progressive Union
Christian Education Dept.
Sunday School Dept.
Natl. Evangelist Bd.
Natl. Nurses Guild
Natl. Women's Work Dept.
Natl. Music Dept.
Natl. Usher Board
Natl. Sec. Office

Periodicals

The Gospel Truth

Church of the Lutheran Brethren of America

The Church of the Lutheran Brethren of America was organized in December 1900. Five independent Lutheran congregations met together in Milwaukee, Wisconsin, and adopted a constitution patterned very closely on that of the Lutheran Free Church of Norway.

The spiritual awakening in the Midwest during the 1890s crystallized into convictions that led to the formation of a new church body. Chief among the concerns were church membership practices, observance of Holy Communion, confirmation practices and local church government.

The Church of the Lutheran Brethren practices a simple order of worship with the sermon as the primary part of the worship service. It believes that personal profession of faith is the primary criterion for membership in the congregation. The Communion service is reserved for those who profess faith in Christ as savior. Each congregation is autonomous and the synod serves the congregations in advisory and cooperative capacities.

The synod supports a world mission program in Cameroon, Chad, Japan and Taiwan. Approximately 40 percent of the synodical budget is earmarked for world missions. A growing home mission ministry is planting new congregations in the United States and Canada. Affiliate organizations operate several retirement, nursing homes, conference and retreat centers.

Headquarters

1020 Alcott Ave. W., Box 655, Fergus Falls, MN 56538 Tel. (218)739-3336 Fax (218)739-5514
Media Contact, Pres., Rev. Joel Egge
E-mail: clba@clba.org
Web site: www.clba.org

Officers

Pres., Rev. Joel Egge
Vice-Pres., Rev. David Rinden
Sec., Rev. Richard Vettrus, 707 Crestview Dr., West Union, IA 52175
Exec. Dir. of Finance, Bradley Martinson
Lutheran Brethren Schools Representative, Dr. Eugene Boe
World Missions, Exec. Dir., Rev. Matthew Rogness
Home Missions, Exec. Dir., Rev. Armin Jahr
Church Services, Exec. Dir., Rev. Brent Juliot
Youth Ministries, Exec. Dir., Nathan Lee

Periodicals

Faith & Fellowship

Church of the Lutheran Confession

The Church of the Lutheran Confession held its constituting convention in Watertown, S.D., in August 1960. The Church of the Lutheran Confession was begun by people and congregations who withdrew from church bodies that made up what was then known as the Synodical Conference over the issue of unionism. Following such passages as I Corinthians 1:10 and Romans 16:17-18, the Church of the Lutheran Confession holds the conviction that mutual agreement with the doctrines of Scripture is essential and necessary before exercise of church fellowship is appropriate.

Members of the Church of the Lutheran Confession uncompromisingly believe the Holy Scriptures to be divinely inspired and therefore inerrant. They subscribe to the historic Lutheran Confessions as found in the Book of Concord of 1580 because they are a correct exposition of Scripture.

The Church of the Lutheran Confession exists to proclaim, preserve and spread the saving truth of the gospel of Jesus Christ, so that the redeemed of God may learn to know Jesus Christ as their Lord and Savior and follow him through this life to the life to come.

Headquarters

501 Grover Rd., Eau Claire, WI 54701 Tel. (715)836-6622
Media Contact, Pres., Daniel Fleischer Tel. (361) 241-5147
E-mail: johnhlau@juno.com
Web site: www.clclutheran.org

Officers

Pres., Rev. John Schierenbeck, 3015 Ave. K NW, Winter Haven, FL 33881
Mod., Prof. Ronald Roehl, 515 Ingram Dr. W., Eau Claire, WI 54701
Vice-Pres., Rev. Mark Bernthal, 3232 West Point Rd., Middleton, WI 53562 Tel. (608)233-2244
Sec., Rev. James Albrecht, 102 Market St., P.O. Box 98 Okebena, MN 55432-2408
Treas., Dr. James Sydow, 500 Grover Rd., Eau Claire, WI 54701
Archivist, Prof. David Lau, 507 Ingram Dr., Eau Claire, WI 54701
Statistician, Dr. James Sydow, 500 Grover Rd., Eau Claire, WI 54701

Periodicals

The Lutheran Spokesman; Journal of Theology

Church of the Nazarene

The Church of the Nazarene resulted from the merger of three independent holiness groups. The Association of Pentecostal Churches in America, located principally in New York and New England, joined at Chicago in 1907 with a largely West Coast body called the Church of the Nazarene and formed the Pentecostal Church of the Nazarene. A southern group, the Holiness Church of Christ, united with the Pentecostal Church of the Nazarene at Pilot Point, Texas, in 1908. In 1919 the word "Pentecostal" was dropped from the name. Principal leaders in the organization were Phineas Bresee, William Howard Hoople, H. F. Reynolds and C. B. Jernigan. The first congregation in Canada was organized in November 1902 by Dr. H. F. Reynolds in Oxford, Nova Scotia.

The Church of the Nazarene emphasizes the doctrine of entire sanctification or Christian Holiness. It stresses the importance of a devout and holy life and a positive witness before the world by the power of the Holy Spirit. Nazarenes express their faith through evangelism, compassionate ministries, and education. Nazarene government is representative, a studied compromise between episcopacy and congregationalism. Quadrennially, the various districts elect delegates to a general assembly at which six general superintendents are elected.

The international denomination has 9 liberal arts colleges, two graduate seminaries, 43 Bible colleges, two schools of nursing, and a junior college.

The church maintains more than 600 missionaries in 119 world areas. World services include medical, educational and religious ministries. Books, periodicals and other Christian literature are published at the Nazarene Publishing House.

The church is a member of the Christian Holiness Partnership, National Association of Evangelicals and the World Methodist Council.

Headquarters

6401 The Paseo, Kansas City, MO 64131 Tel. (816)333-7000 Fax (816)822-9071

Media Contact, Gen. Sec./Headquarters Operations Officer (HOO), Dr. Jack Stone, Tel. (816)333-7000 ext. 2366 Fax (816)362-4983 or (816)822-9071, jstone@nazarene.org

E-mail: ssm@nazarene.org

Web site: www.nazarene.org

Officers

Gen. Supts., Dr. James H. Diehl; Dr. Paul G. Cunningham; Dr. Jerry D. Porter; Dr. Jim L. Bond; Dr. W. Talmadge Johnson; Dr. Jesse C. Middendorf; 6401 The Paseo, Kansas City, MO 64131 Tel. (816)333-7000

Gen. Sec./Headquarters Operation Officer (HOO), Dr. Jack Stone Tel. (816)333-7000 Fax (816) 822-9071, jstone@nazarene.org

Gen. Treas./Headquarters Financial Officer (HFO), Dr. Marilyn McCool, Tel. (816)333-7000 Fax (816)361-6216, mmccool@nazarene. org

Sunday School Ministries Dir., Dr. David Graves, 6401 The Paseo, Kansas City, MO 64131 Tel. (816)333-7000 Fax (816)363-7092, dgraves@nazarene.org

USA/Canada Mission/Evangelism Dir., Dr. Tom Nees, 6401 The Paseo, Kansas City, MO 64131 Tel. (816)333-7000 Fax (816)361-5202, tnees@nazarene.org

Education Commissioner, Dr. Jerry Lambert, 6401 The Paseo, Kansas City, MO 64131 Tel. (816)333-7000 Fax (816)333-2891, jlambert@ nazarene.org

Nazarene Youth International Ministries Dir., Rev. Gary Hartke, 6401 The Paseo, Kansas City, MO 64131 Tel. (816)333-7000 Fax (816)333-4315, ghartke@nazarene.org

World Mission Dir., Dr. Louie Bustle, 6401 The Paseo, Kansas City, MO 64131 Tel. (816)333-7000 Fax (816)363-8216, lbustle@nazarene. org

Periodicals

Holiness Today; Preacher's Magazine; Grow Magazine

Church of Our Lord Jesus Christ of the Apostolic Faith, Inc.

This church body was founded by Bishop R.C. Lawson in Columbus, Ohio, and moved to New York City in 1919. It is founded upon the teachings of the apostles and prophets, Jesus Christ being its chief cornerstone.

Headquarters

2081 Adam Clayton Powell, Jr. Blvd., New York, NY 10027 Tel. (212)866-1700

Media Contact, Exec. Sec., Bishop T. E. Woolfolk, P.O. Box 119, Oxford, NC 27565 Tel. (919)693-9449 Fax (919)693-6115

E-mail: tewmsw@gloryroad.net

Web site: www.apostolic-faith.org

Officers

Board of Apostles, Chief Apostle, Bishop William L. Bonner

Presiding Apostle, Bishop James I. Clark, Jr.; Bishop Frank S. Solomon

Vice-Presiders, Bishop Mathew A. Norwood; Bishop Robert L. Sanders; Bishop Gentle L. Groover; Bishop Wilbur L. Jones

Board of Bishops, Chmn., Bishop Herbert Edwards

Board of Presbyters, Pres., Elder Michael A. Dixon

Exec. Sec., Bishop Thomas E. Woolfolk

Natl. Rec. Sec., Bishop Fred Rubin, Sr.

Natl. Fin. Sec., Bishop Clarence Groover

Natl. Corr. Sec., Bishop Raymond J. Keith, Jr.

Natl Treas., Jonathan K. Jefferson

Periodicals

Contender For The Faith; Minute Book

Church of the United Brethren in Christ

The Church of the United Brethren in Christ had its beginning with Philip William Otterbein and Martin Boehm, who were leaders in the revival movement in Pennsylvania and Maryland from the late 1760s into the early 1800s.

On Sept. 25, 1800, they and others associated with them formed a society under the name of United Brethren in Christ. Subsequent conferences adopted a Confession of Faith in 1815 and a constitution in 1841. The Church of the United Brethren in Christ adheres to the original constitution as amended in 1957, 1961 and 1977.

Headquarters

302 Lake St., Huntington, IN 46750 Tel. (260)356-2312 Fax (260)356-4730 ext. 210

Media Contact, Communications Dir., Steve Dennie

E-mail: sdennie@ub.org

Web site: www.ub.org

Officers

Bishop, Rev. Paul Hirschy

Finance Dir., Janet Bilyew

Dir. of Education, Dir., Dr. G. Blair Dowden

Global Ministries Dir., Rev. Gary Dilley

Communications Dir., Mr. Steve Dennie

Churches of Christ

Churches of Christ are autonomous congregations whose members appeal to the Bible alone to determine matters of faith and practice. There are no central offices or officers. Publications and institutions related to the churches are either under local congregational control or are independent of any congregation. Churches of Christ shared a common fellowship in the 19th century with the Christian Churches/Churches of Christ and the Christian Church (Disciples of Christ). This fellowship ended in the decades following the American Civil War due to erosion of confidence in Scripture among many of those who would go on to form these other groups. This shift in belief embraced theistic evolution, doubted the complete truth of Scripture, and permitted unscriptual practices into the work and worship of the church. Chief among the changes in practice were the use of instrumental music in worship, permitting women to officiate in worship services, and conducting the work of the church through centralized agencies. Churches of Christ, following this division, remained strongly united in their belief in the inerrancy and sufficiency of Scripture. From this standpoint they affirm faith in one God who subsists in three persons: Father, Son, and Holy Spirit; they teach that salvation is through the sacrificial death of Christ and is available to all who come to God through repentance and faith, initially expressed through confession of faith and baptism by immersion. Churches of Christ follow the New Testament pattern to direct every facet of the teaching and work of the church.

Headquarters

Media Contact, Ed., *Gospel Advocate*, Mr. Neil Anderson, 1006 Elm Hill Pike, Nashville, TN 37102 Tel. (800)251-8446 Fax (615)254-7411

Periodicals

Action; Christian Woman; Christian Bible Teacher; The Christian Chronicle; Firm Foundation; Gospel Advocate; Guardian of Truth; Restoration Quarterly; 21st Century Christian; Rocky Mountain Christian; The Spiritual Sword; Word and Work

Churches of Christ in Christian Union

Organized in 1909 at Washington Court House, Ohio, as the Churches of Christ in Christian Union, this body believes in the new birth and the baptism of the Holy Spirit for believers. It is Wesleyan, with an evangelistic and missionary emphasis.

The Reformed Methodist Church merged with the Churches of Christ in Christian Union in 1952.

Headquarters

1426 Lancaster Pike, Box 30, Circleville, OH 43113 Tel. (740)474-8856 Fax (740)477-7766

Media Contact, Dir. of Comm., Rev. Ralph Hux

Officers

Gen. Supt., Dr. Daniel Tipton

Asst. Gen. Supt., Rev. Dan Harrison

Gen. Treas., Mr. Mark Taylor

Gen. Bd. of Trustees, Chpsn., Dr. Daniel Tipton; Vice-Chpsn., Rev. Dan Harrison

District Superintendents, West Central District, Rev. Ron Reese; South Central District, Rev. Don Spurgeon; Northeast District, Rev. Brad Dixon; West Indies District, Rev. Michael Aubrey

Periodicals

The Evangelical Advocate

Churches of God, General Conference

The Churches of God, General Conference (CGGC) had its beginnings in Harrisburg, Pa., in 1825.

John Winebrenner, recognized founder of the Church of God movement, was an ordained minister of the German Reformed Church. His experience-centered form of Christianity, particularly the "new measures" he used to promote it, his close connection with the local Methodists, his "experience and conference meetings" in the church and his "social prayer meetings" in parishioners' homes resulted in differences of opinion and the establishment of new congregations. Extensive revivals, camp meetings and mission endeavors led to the organization of additional congregations across central Pennsylvania and westward through Ohio, Indiana, Illinois and Iowa.

In 1830 the first system of cooperation between local churches was initiated as an "eldership" in eastern Pennsylvania. The organization of other elderships followed. General Eldership was organized in 1845, and in 1974 the official name of the denomination was changed from General Eldership of the Churches of God in North America to its present name.

The Churches of God, General Conference, is composed of 8 conferences in the United States and 1 conference in Haiti. The church has mission ministries in the southwest among Native Americans and is extensively involved in church planting and whole life ministries in Bangladesh, Brazil, Haiti and India.

The General Conference convenes in business session triennially. An Administrative Council composed of 16 regional representatives is responsible for the administration and ministries of the church between sessions of the General Conference.

Headquarters

Legal Headquarters, United Church Center, Room 213, 900 S. Arlington Ave., Harrisburg, PA 17109 Tel. (717)652-0255

Admin. Offices, Gen. Conf. Exec. Dir., Pastor Wayne W. Boyer, 700 E. Melrose Ave., P.O. Box 926, Findlay, OH 45839 Tel. (419)424-1961 Fax (419)424-3343, dir.@cggc.org

Media Contact, Editor, Rachel L. Foreman, P.O. Box 926, Findlay, OH 45839 Tel. (419) 424-1961 Fax (419)424-3343, communications@ cggc.org

E-mail: dir.@cggc.org
Web site: www.cggc.org

Officers

Pres., Pastor Robert L. Eatherton, P.O. Box 366, Columbia City, IN 46725-0366 Tel. (260)244-4042 Fax (260)244-9663, dir.@midwestcggc. org

Sec., Pastor E. David Green, 700 E. Melrose Ave., P.O. Box 1132, Findlay, OH 45839 Tel. (419)423-7694 Fax (419)423-9092, glcdir.@ cggc.org

Treas., Robert E. Stephenson, 700 E. Melrose Ave., P.O. Box 926, Findlay, OH 45839 Tel. (419)424-1961 Fax (419) 424-3433, treas.@ cggc.org

DEPARTMENTS

Cross-Cultural Ministries, Pastor Don Dennison
Pensions, Mr. James P. Thomas
Denominational Communications, Rachel L. Foreman
Church Planting, Pastor Charles A. Hirschy
Youth & Family Ministries, Susan L. Callaway
CGWM—Churches of God Women's Ministries

Periodicals

The Church Advocate; The Gem; The Missionary Signal

Community of Christ

Community of Christ's mission is to proclaim Jesus Christ and promote communities of joy, hope, love, and peace. Founded on April 6, 1830, this Christian denomination is present in nearly 50 nations with approximately 250,000 members worldwide. The church's Temple, located in the international headquarters complex, is dedicated to peace, reconciliation, and healing of the Spirit. Priesthood includes both men and women.

Headquarters

International Headquarters, 1001 W. Walnut, Independence, MO 54050-3562 Tel. (816)833-1000 Fax (816)521-3096

Media Contact; Kendra Friend, kfriend@cofchrist.org; Jennifer Killpack, jkill-pack@cofchrist. org

E-mail: snaylor@cofchrist.org
Web site: www.cofchrist.org

Officers

First Presidency, Pres., W. Grant McMurray, gmc-murray@cofchrist.org; Counselor, Kenneth N. Robinson, krobinson@cofchrist. org; Counselor, Peter A. Judd, pjudd@ cofchrist.org

Council of Twelve Apostles, Pres., Stephen M. Veazey, sveazey@cofchrist.org

Presiding Bishopric, Presiding Bishop, Larry R. Norris, lnorris@cofchrist.org; Counselor, Stassi D. Cramm, scramm@cofchrist.org; Counselor, Stephen M. Jones, sjones@ cofchrist.org

Presiding Evangelist, Danny A. Belrose, dbelrose@cofchrist.org

World Church Sec., A. Bruce Lindgren, blind-gren@cofchrist.org

Public Relations, Kendra Friend, kfriend@ cofchrist.org; Jennifer Killpack, jkillpack@ cofchrist.org, Fax (816)521-3043

Periodicals

Herald; Restoration Witness; Face to Face

Congregational Holiness Church

This body was organized in 1921 and embraces the doctrine of Holiness and Pentecost. It carries on mission work in Mexico, Honduras, Costa Rica, Cuba, Brazil, Guatemala, India, Nicaragua, El Salvador, Venezuela, Panama, Chile, Argentina, Belize, Zimbabwe, Haiti, and Peru.

Headquarters

3888 Fayetteville Hwy., Griffin, GA 30223 Tel. (404)228-4833 Fax (404)228-1177

Media Contact, Gen. Supt., Bishop Ronald Wilson

E-mail: chchurch@bellsouth.net
Web site: www.chchurch.com

EXECUTIVE BOARD

Gen. Supt., Bishop Ronald Smith
1st Asst. Gen. Supt., Rev. William L. Lewis
2nd Asst. Gen. Supt., Rev. Wayne Hicks
Gen. Sec., Rev. Leslee Bailey
Gen. Treas., Rev. Stephen Phillips
World Missions Supt., Rev. Billy Anderson

Periodicals

The Gospel Messenger

Conservative Baptist Association of America (CBAmerica)

The Conservative Baptist Association of America (now known as CBAmerica) was organized May 17, 1947 at Atlantic City, N.J. The Old and New Testaments are regarded as the divinely inspired Word of God and are therefore infallible and of supreme authority. Each local church is independent, autonomous and free from ecclesiastical or political authority.

CBAmerica provides wide-ranging support to its affiliate churches and individuals through nine regional associations. CBA offers personnel to assist churches in areas such as growth and health conflict resolution and financial analysis. The association supports its clergy with retirement planning, referrals for new places of ministry and spiritual counseling. The Conservative Baptist Women's Ministries assists women in the church to be effective in their personal growth and leadership.

Each June or July there is a national conference giving members an opportunity for fellowship, inspiration and motivation.

Headquarters

1501 W. Mineral Ave., Suite B, Littleton, CO 80120-5612 Tel. (888)627-1995 or (720)283-3030 Fax (720)283-3333

Media Contact, Exec. Dir., Dr. Dennis L. Gorton
E-mail: cba@cbamerica.org
Web site: www.cbamerica.org

OTHER ORGANIZATIONS

CBInternational, Exec. Dir., Dr. Hans Finzel, 1501 W. Mineral Ave., Littleton, CO 80120-5612
Mission to the Americas, Exec. Dir., Rev. Rick Miller, Box 828, Wheaton, IL 60189
Conservative Baptist Higher Ed. Council, Dr. Bert Downs, Western Seminary, 5511 SE Hawthorne Blvd., Portland, OR 97215

Periodicals

Front Line Turnings

Conservative Congregational Christian Conference

In the 1930s, evangelicals within the Congregational Christian Churches felt a definite need for fellowship and service. By 1945, this loose association crystallized into the Conservative Congregational Christian Fellow-ship, committed to maintaining a faithful, biblical witness.

In 1948 in Chicago, the Conservative Congregational Christian Conference was established to provide a continuing fellowship for evangelical churches and ministers on the national level. In recent years, many churches have joined the Conference from backgrounds other than Congregational. These churches include Community or Bible Churches and churches from the Evangelical and Reformed background that are truly congregational in polity and thoroughly evangelical in conviction. The CCCC welcomes all evangelical churches that are, in fact, Congregational. The CCCC believes in the necessity of a regenerate membership, the authority of the Holy Scriptures, the Lordship of Jesus Christ, the autonomy of the local church and the universal fellowship of all Christians.

The Conservative Congregational Christian Conference is a member of the World Evangelical Congregational Fellowship (formed in 1986 in London, England) and the National Association of Evangelicals.

Headquarters

7582 Currell Blvd., Suite 108, St. Paul, MN 55125 Tel. (651)739-1474 Fax (651)739-0750

Media Contact, Conf. Min., Mrs. Diane Johnson

E-mail: cccc4@juno.com

Web site: www.ccccusa.org

Officers

Pres., Rev. Larry Scovil, 317 W. 40th St., Scottsbluff, NE 69361
Vice Pres., Rev. Nicholas Granitsas, 68 Enstis St., Revere, MA 02151
Conf. Min., Rev. Clifford R. Christensen, 944 Stratford Law, Burnsville, MN 55337
Controller, Mr. Orrin Bailey, 4260 East Lake Rd., Muskegon, MI 49444
Treas., Rev. Tay Kersey, 8450 Eastwood Rd., Moundsview, MN 55112
Sec., Rev. Peter Murdy, 4 Plympton St., Middleboro, MA 02346
Editor, Mrs. Carol Wells, 2789 Wimbledon Ridge, Woodbury, MN 55125
Historian, Rev. Milton Reimer, 507 Central Ave., New Rockford, ND 58356

Periodicals

Foresee

Conservative Lutheran Association

The Conservative Lutheran Association (CLA) was originally named Lutheran's Alert National (LAN) when it was founded in 1965 by 10 conservative Lutheran pastors and layman meeting in Cedar Rapids, Iowa. Its purpose was to help preserve from erosion the basic doctrines of Christian theology, including the inerrancy of Holy Scripture. The group grew to a worldwide constituency, similarly concerned with maintaining the doctrinal integrity of the Bible and the Lutheran Confessions.

Headquarters

Trinity Lutheran Church, 4101 E. Nohl Ranch Rd., Anaheim, CA 92807 Tel. (714)637-8370
Media Contact, Pres., Rev. P. J. Moore
E-mail: pastorpj@ix.netcom.com
Web site: www.tlcanaheim.com/CLA

Officers

Pres., Rev. P. J. Moore, 4101 E. Nohl Ranch Rd., Anaheim, CA 92807 Tel. (714)637-8370
Vice-Pres., Rev. Dr. R. H. Redal, 409 Tacoma Ave. N., Tacoma, WA 98403 Tel. (206)383-5528
Faith Seminary, Dean, Rev. Dr. Michael J. Adams, 3504 N. Pearl St., P.O. Box 7186, Tacoma, WA 98407 Tel. (888)777-7675 Fax (206)759-1790

Coptic Orthodox Church*

This body is part of the ancient Coptic Orthodox Church of Alexandria, Egypt, which is currently headed by His Holiness Pope Shenouda III, 116th successor to St. Mark the Apostle. Egyptian immigrants have organized many parishes in the United States. Copts exist outside Egypt in Africa, Europe, Asia, Australia, Canada and the United States. The total world Coptic community is estimated at 27 million. The church is in full communion with the other members of the Oriental Orthodox Church family, The Syrian Orthodox Church, Armenian Orthodox Church, Ethiopian Orthodox Church, the Syrian Orthodox Church in India and the Eritrean Orthodox Church.

Headquarters

5 Woodstone Dr., Cedar Grove, NJ 07009
3803 W. Mission Blvd., Pomona, CA 91766 Tel. (909)865-8378 Fax (909)865-8348
Media Contact, Fr. Isaac Boulos Azmy, P.O. Box 4960, Diamond Bar, CA 91765
E-mail: Webmaster@coptic.org
Web site: www.coptic.org

Officers

Bishop of Los Angeles, Bishop Serapion, 3803 W. Mission Blvd., Pomona, CA 91766 Tel. (909)865-8378 Fax (909)865-8348, bishopserapion@lacopts.org

Periodicals

Agape Magazine, El Keraza

Cumberland Presbyterian Church

The Cumberland Presbyterian Church was organized in Dickson County, Tennessee, on Feb. 4, 1810. It was an outgrowth of the Great Revival of 1800 on the Kentucky and Tennessee frontier. The founders were Finis Ewing, Samuel King and Samuel McAdow, ministers in the Presbyterian Church who rejected the doctrine of election and reprobation as taught in the Westminster Confession of Faith.

By 1813, the Cumberland Presbytery had grown to encompass three presbyteries, which constituted a synod. This synod met at the Beech Church in Sumner County, Tenn., and formulated a "Brief Statement" which set forth the points in which Cumberland Presbyterians dissented from the Westminster Confession. These points are—

1. That there are no eternal reprobates;
2. That Christ died not for some, but for all people;
3. That all those dying in infancy are saved through Christ and the sanctification of the Spirit;
4. That the Spirit of God operates on the world, or as coextensively as Christ has made atonement, in such a manner as to leave everyone inexcusable.

From its birth in 1810, the Cumberland Presbyterian Church grew to a membership of 200,000 at the turn of the century. In 1906 the church voted to merge with the then-Presbyterian Church. Those who dissented from the merger became the nucleus of the continuing Cumberland Presbyterian Church.

Headquarters

1978 Union Ave., Memphis, TN 38104 Tel. (901) 276-4572 Fax (901)272-3913
Media Contact, Stated Clk., Rev. Robert D. Rush, Fax (901)276-4578
E-mail: assembly@cumberland.org
Web site: www.cumberland.org

Officers

Mod., Rev. E.G. Sims, 1608 Fountain Heights, Columbia, TN 38401 Tel. (931)490-0167, simseg@aol.com
Stated Clk., Rev. Robert D. Rush, Tel.(901)276-4572 ext. 3325 Fax (901) 276-4578, rdr@ cumberland. org
Gen. Assembly Council, Exec. Dir., Davis Gray, Tel.(901)276-4572 ext. 3316 Fax (901)272-3913, dg@cumberland.org

INSTITUTIONS

Cumberland Presbyterian Children's Home, Exec. Dir., Dr. Judith B. Keith, Drawer G, Denton, TX 76202 Tel. (940)382-5112 Fax (940)387-0821, cpch@cpch.org
Cumberland Presbyterian Center, Tel.(901)276-4572 Fax (901)272-3913 or (901)276-4578
Memphis Theological Seminary, 168 E. Parkway S., Memphis, TN 38104 Tel. (901)458-8232 Fax (901)452-4051
Bethel College, Pres., Dr. Robert Prosser, 325 Cherry St., McKenzie, TN 38201 Tel. (901) 352-4004 Fax (901)352-4069, rprosser@ bethel-college.edu
Historical Foundation, Archivist, Susan K. Gore, 1978 Union Ave., Memphis, TN 38104 Tel. (901)276-8602 Fax (901)272-3913, skg@ cumberland.org

BOARDS

Bd. of Christian Education, Exec. Dir., Claudette Pickle, 1978 Union Ave., Memphis, TN 38104 Tel (901)276-4572 ext. 3323 Fax (901)272-3913, chp@cumberland.org
Bd. of Missions, Exec. Dir., Rev. Michael Sharpe, 1978 Union Ave., Memphis, TN 38104 Tel (901)276-9988 Fax (901)272-3913 mgs@cumberland.org
Bd. of Stewardship, Exec. Sec., Rev. Richard Magrill, 1978 Union Ave., Memphis, TN 38104 Tel (901)276-4572 ext. 3307, jrm@ cumberland.org
Bd. of *The Cumberland Presbyterian*, Editor, Mrs. Patricia White, P.O. Box 935, Antioch, TN 37011 Tel. (615)731-5556, cpmag@comcast.net
Commission on the Ministry, 1978 Union Ave., Memphis, TN 38104 Tel (901)276-4572 ext. 3335 Fax (901) 272-3913

Periodicals

T*he Cumberland Presbyterian; The Missionary Messenger*

Cumberland Presbyterian Church in America

This church, originally known as the Colored Cumberland Presbyterian Church, was formed in May 1874. In May 1869, at the General Assembly meeting in Murfreesboro, Tennessee, Moses Weir of the black delegation sucessfully appealed for help in organizing a separate African church so that blacks could learn self-reliance and independence; they could have more financial assistance; they could minister more effectively among blacks; and they could worship close to the altar, not in the balconies. He requested that the Cumberland Presbyterian Church organize blacks into presbyteries and synods, develop schools to train black clergy, grant loans to assist blacks to secure hymnbooks, Bibles and church buildings and establish a separate General Assembly.

In 1874 the first General Assembly of the Colored Cumberland Presbyterian Church met in Nashville. The moderator was Rev. P. Price and the stated clerk was Elder John Humphrey.

The denomination's General Assembly, the national governing body, is organized around its three program boards and agencies—Finance, Publication and Christian Education, and Missions and Evangelism. Other agencies of the General Assembly are under these three program boards.

The church has four synods (Alabama, Kentucky, Tennessee and Texas), 15 presbyteries and 153 congregations. The CPC extends as far north as Cleveland, Ohio, and Chicago, as far west as Marshalltown, Iowa, and Dallas, Texas, and as far south as Selma, Ala.

Headquarters

Media Contact, Stated Clk., Rev. Dr. Robert. Stanley Wood, 226 Church St., Huntsville, AL 35801 Tel. (205)536-7481 Fax (205)536-7482
E-mail: mleslie598@aol.com
Web site: www.cumberland.org/cpca

Officers

Mod., Rev. Endia Scruggs, 1627 Carroll Rd., Harvest, AL 35749
Stated Clk., Rev. Dr. Robert. Stanley Wood, 226 Church St., Huntsville, AL 35801 Tel. (205)536-7481

SYNODS

Alabama, Stated Clk., Arthur Hinton, 511 10th Ave. NW, Aliceville, AL 35442
Kentucky, Stated Clk., Mary Martha Daniels, 8548 Rhodes Ave., Chicago, IL 60619
Tennessee, Stated Clk., Elder Clarence Norman, 145 Jones St., Huntington, TN 38334
Texas, Stated Clk., Arthur King, 2435 Kristen, Dallas, TX 75216

Disciples of Christ—please see Christian Church (Disciples of Christ) in the United States and Canada

Elim Fellowship

The Elim Fellowship, a pentecostal body established in 1947, is an outgrowth of the Elim Missionary Assemblies formed in 1933.

It is an association of churches, ministers and missionaries seeking to serve the whole Body of Christ. It is of pentecostal conviction and charismatic orientation, providing ministerial credentials and counsel and encouraging fellowship among local churches. Elim Fellowship sponsors leadership seminars at home and abroad and serves as a transdenominational agency sending long-term, short-term and tent-making missionaries to work with national movements.

Headquarters

1703 Dalton Rd., Lima, NY 14485 Tel. (585)582-2790 Fax (585)624-1229
Media Contact, Gen. Sec., Paul Anderson
E-mail: 75551.743@compuserve.com
Web site: www.elimfellowship.org

Officers

Pres., Bernard J. Evans
Vice-Pres., Ron Burgio
Gen. Treas., Stephanie Zeller

Periodicals

Elim Herald

Episcopal Church*

The Episcopal Church entered the colonies with the earliest settlers at Jamestown, Va., in 1607 as the Church of England. After the American Revolution, it became autonomous in 1789 as the Protestant Episcopal Church in the United States of America. (The Episcopal Church became the official alternate name in 1967.) Samuel Seabury of Connecticut was elected the first bishop and consecrated in Aberdeen by bishops of the Scottish Episcopal Church in 1784.

In organizing as an independent body, the Episcopal Church created a bicameral legislature, the General Convention, modeled after the new U.S. Congress. It comprises a House of Bishops and a House of Deputies and meets every three years. A 38-member Executive Council, which meets three times a year, is the interim governing body. An elected presiding bishop serves as Primate and Chief Pastor.

After severe setbacks in the years immediately following the Revolution because of its association with the British Crown and the fact that a number of its clergy and members were Loyalists, the church soon established its own identity and sense of mission. It sent missionaries into the newly settled territories of the United States, establishing dioceses from coast to coast, and also undertook substantial missionary work in Africa, Latin America and the Far East. Today, the overseas dioceses are developing into independent provinces of the Anglican Communion, the worldwide fellowship of 36 churches in communion with the Church of England and the Archbishop of Canterbury.

The beliefs and practices of the Episcopal Church, like those of other Anglican churches, are both Catholic and Reformed, with bishops in the apostolic succession and the historic creeds of Christendom regarded as essential elements of faith and order, along with the primary authority of Holy Scripture and the two chief sacraments of Baptism and Eucharist.

Headquarters

Episcopal Church Center, 815 Second Ave., New

York, NY 10017 Tel. (212)716-6240 or (800) 334-7626 Fax (212)867-0395 or (212)490-3298
Media Contact, Dir. of News Service., Robert Williams, Tel. (212)922-5385
E-mail: cepting@episcopalchurch.org
Web site: www.ecusa.anglican.org

Officers

Presiding Bishop & Primate, Most Rev. Frank Tracy Griswold
Vice-Pres. & Asst. to the Presiding Bishop for Admin., Patricia C. Mordecai
Asst. to the Presiding Bishop for Communication, Barbara L. Braver
Treas., Kurt Barnes
Canon to the Primate and Presiding Bishop, The Rev. Canon Carlson Gerdau
House of Deputies, Pres., The Very Rev. George L. Werner
Exec. Officer of the Gen. Convention, Sec. of the House of Deputies, Sec. of the Domestic and Foreign Missionary Society, and Sec. of the Executive Council, The Rev. Rosemari Sullivan

OFFICE OF THE PRESIDING BISHOP

Presiding Bishop, Most Rev. Frank Tracy Griswold, Tel. (212)922-5322
Vice-Pres. Asst. to the Presiding Bishop for Admin., Patricia Mordecai, Tel. (212)922-5313
Canon to the Presiding Bishop, Rev. Canon Carl Gerdau, Tel. (212)922-5282
Assoc. Dir., Church Deployment Office, Pamela Ramsden, Tel. (212)716-6063
Coord. for Ministry Development, The Rev. Dr. Melford E. Holland, Jr., Tel. (212)922-5246
Exec. Dir., Office of Pastoral Dev., Rt. Rev. F. Clayton Mathews, Tel. (212)716-6163
Exec. Sec., General Board of Examining Chaplains, The Rev. Dr. Richard F. Tombaugh, Tel. (860)233-2271
Chaplaincies, Suffragan Bishop, Rt. Rev., George Packard, Tel. (212)716-6202
Convocation of American Churches in Europe, Bishop-in-Charge, Rt. Rev. Pierre Whalon, Tel. 011-35-1-472-01792
Deputy, Ecumenical and Interfaith Relations, The Rt. Rev. C. Christopher Epting, Tel. (212)716-6220

ADMINISTRATION & FINANCE

Treas. of the Domestic and Foreign Missionary Society and Chief Financial Officer, Kurt Barnes, Tel. (212)922-5296
Controller, Thomas Hershkowitz, Tel. (212)922-5366
Archivist, Mark Duffy, Tel. (512)472-6816
Dir., Human Resources Management, John Colon, Tel. (212)716-6331

SERVICE, EDUCATION & WITNESS

Asst. to the Presiding Bishop for Program, The Rev. James Lemler, Tel. (212)922-5198
Dir., Anglican and Global Relations, The Rev. Canon Patrick Mauney, Tel. (212)716-6223
Editor, *Episcopal Life*, Jerald Hames, Tel. (212)716-6009
Acting Dir., Communications, Robert Williams, Tel. (212)716-6188
Dir., News Service, Robert Williams, Tel. (212)922-5385
Dir., Migration Ministries, Richard Parkins, Tel. (212)716-6252
Dir., Peace & Justice Ministries, The Rev. Canon Brian Grieves, Tel. (212)922-5207
Dir., Ministries with Young People Program, Thomas Chu, Tel. (212)922-5267
Pres., Episcopal Relief and Development, Sandra Swan, Tel. (212)716-6020

BISHOPS IN THE U.S.A.

(C)= Coadjutor; (S)= Suffragan; (A)= Assistant
Presiding Bishop & Primate, Most Rev. Frank Tracy Griswold; Pastoral Dev., The Rt. Rev. F. Clayton Matthews
Alabama, Henry N. Parsley, Jr., 521 N. 20th St., Birmingham, AL 35203 Tel. (205)715-2066
Alaska, Mark MacDonald, 1205 Denali Way, Fairbanks, AK 99701-4137 Tel. (907)452-3040
Albany, Daniel W. Herzog, 68 S. Swan St., Albany, NY 12210-2301 Tel. (518)-465-4737
Arizona, Robert Shahan, 114 W. Roosevelt, Phoenix, AZ 85003-1406 Tel. (602)254-0976
Arkansas, Larry E. Maze, P.O. Box 164668, Little Rock, AR 72216 Tel. (501)372-2168
Atlanta, John Neil Alexander, 2744 Peachtree Rd. NW, Atlanta, GA 30305 Tel. (404)365-1010
Bethlehem, Paul Marshall, 333 Wyandotte St., Bethlehem, PA 18015 Tel. (610)691-5655
California, William E. Swing, 1055 Taylor St., San Francisco, CA 94115 Tel. (415)673-5015
Central Florida, John H. Howe, 1017 E. Robinson St., Orlando, FL 32801 Tel. (407) 423-3567
Central Gulf Coast, Philip M. Duncan II, P.O. Box 13330, Pensacola, FL 32591-3330 Tel. (850)434-7337
Central New York, Gladstone B. Adams, III, 310 Montgomery St., Suite 200, Syracuse, NY 13202 Tel. (315)474-6596
Central Pennsylvania, Michael Creighton, P.O. Box 11937, Harrisburg, PA 17108 Tel. (717) 236-5959
Chicago, William D. Persell, 65 E. Huron St., Chicago, IL 60611 Tel. (312)751-4200
Colorado, Robert J. O'Neill, 1300 Washington St., Denver, CO 80203 Tel. (303)837-1173
Connecticut, Andrew D. Smith, 1335 Asylum Ave., Hartford, CT 06105-2295 Tel. (860)233-4481
Dallas, James M. Stanton, 1630 Garrett Ave., Dallas, TX 75206 Tel. (214)826-8310
Delaware, Wayne P. Wright, 2020 N. Tatnall St., Wilmington, DE 19802 Tel. (302)656-5441

East Carolina, Clifton Daniel, III, P.O. Box 1336, Kinston, NC 28503 Tel. (252)522-0885
East Tennessee, Charles vonRosenberg, 814 Episcopal School Way, Knoxville, TN 37932 Tel. (865)966-2110
Eastern Michigan, Edwin M. Leidel, Jr., 924 N. Niagara St., Saginaw, MI 48602 Tel. (989)752-6020
Eastern Oregon, William O. Gregg, P.O. Box 1548, The Dalles, OR 97058 Tel. (541)298-4477
Easton, James J. Shand, P.O. Box 1027, Easton, MD 21601 Tel. (410)822-1919
Eau Claire, Keith B. Whitmore, 510 S. Farwell St., Eau Claire, WI 54701 Tel. (715)835-3331
El Camino Real, P.O. Box 1903, Monterey, CA 93942 Tel. (831)394-4465
Florida, S. Johnson Howard, 325 Market St., Jacksonville, FL 32202 Tel. (904)356-1328
Fond du Lac, Russell E. Jacobus, P.O. Box 149, Fond du Lac, WI 54936-0149 Tel. (920)921-8866
Fort Worth, Jack L. Iker, 2900 Alemeda Street, Fort Worth, TX 76116 Tel. (817)244-2885
Georgia, Henry Louttit, Jr., 611 East Bay St., Savannah, GA 31401-1296 Tel. (912)236-4279
Hawaii, Richard S. O. Chang, 229 Queen Emma Square, Honolulu, HI 96813 Tel. (808)536-7776
Idaho, Harry B. Bainbridge, III, P.O. Box 936, Boise, ID 83701 Tel. (208)345-4440
Indianapolis, Catherine M. Waynick, 1100 W. 42nd St., Indianapolis, IN 46208 Tel. (317)926-5454
Iowa, Alan Scarfe, 225 37th St., Des Moines, IA 50312-4305 Tel. (515)277-6165
Kansas, Dean E. Wolfe, 835 SW Polk St., Topeka, KS 66612-1688 Tel. (785)235-9255
Kentucky, Edwin F. Gulick, Jr., 425 S. 2nd St., Suite 200, Louisville, KY 40202 Tel. (502)584-7148
Lexington, Stacy F. Sauls, P.O. Box 610, Lexington, KY 40586-0610 Tel. (606)252-6527
Long Island, Orris G. Walker, Jr., 36 Cathedral Ave., Garden City, NY 11530 Tel. (516)248-4800
Los Angeles, J. Jon Bruno; Chester Talton (S), P.O. Box 512164, Los Angeles, CA 90051-0164 Tel. (213)482-2040
Louisiana, Charles E. Jenkins, III, 1623 7th St., New Orleans, LA 70115-4411 Tel. (504)895-6634
Maine, Chilton R. Knudsen, 143 State St., Portland, ME 04101-3799 Tel. (207)772-1953
Maryland, Robert W. Ihloff, 4 University Pkwy., Baltimore, MD 21218 Tel. (410)467-1399
Massachusetts, M. Thomas Shaw, SSJE; Gayle Barbara Harris (S), 138 Tremont St., Boston, MA 02111-1356 Tel. (617)482-5800
Michigan, Wendell N. Gibbs, Jr., 4800 Woodward Ave., Detroit, MI 48201 Tel. (313)832-4400
Milwaukee, Steven A. Miller, 804 E. Juneau Ave., Milwaukee, WI 53202 Tel. (414)272-3028
Minnesota, James L. Jelinek, 1730 Clifton Place #201, Minneapolis, MN 55403 Tel. (612)871-5311
Mississippi, Duncan Montgomery Gray, III, P.O. Box 23107, Jackson, MS 39225-3107 Tel. (601)948-5954
Missouri, G. Wayne Smith, 1210 Locust St., St. Louis, MO 63103 Tel. (314)231-1220
Montana, C. Franklin Brookhart,, 515 North Park Ave., Helena, MT 59601 Tel. (406)442-2230
Navajoland Area Mission, Steven T. Plummer, Box 720, Farmington, NM 87499-0720 Tel. (505)327-7549
Nebraska, Joe G. Burnett, 109 N. 18th St., Omaha, NE 68102 Tel. (402)341-5373
Nevada, Katharine Jefferts Schori, 6135 S. Harrison Dr., Suite 1, Las Vegas, NV 89120 Tel. (702)737-9190
New Hampshire, V. Gene Robinson, 63 Green St., Concord, NH 03301 Tel. (603)224-1914
New Jersey, George E. Councell, 808 W. State St., Trenton, NJ 08618-5326 Tel. (609)394-5281
New York, Mark Sisk, 1047 Amsterdam Ave., New York, NY 10025 Tel. (212)316-7400
Newark, Jack P. Croneberger; 31 Mulberry St., Newark, NJ 07102 Tel. (973)622-4306
North Carolina, Michael B. Curry, 201 St. Albans Dr., Raleigh, NC 27619 Tel. (919)787-6313
North Dakota, Michael Gene Smith, 3600 25 St. SW, Fargo, ND 58104-6861 Tel. (701)235-6688
Northern California, Jerry A. Lamb, P.O. Box 161268, Sacramento, CA 95816 Tel. (916)442-6918
Northern Indiana, Edward S. Little, III, 117 N. Lafayette Blvd., South Bend, IN 46601 Tel. (574)233-6489
Northern Michigan, James A. Kelsey, 131 E. Ridge St., Marquette, MI 49855 Tel. (906)228-7160
Northwest Texas, C. Wallis Ohl, Jr., 1802 Broadway, Lubbock, TX 79401-3016 Tel. (806)763-1370
Northwestern Pennsylvania, Robert D. Rowley, Jr., 145 W. 6th St., Erie, PA 16501 Tel. (814)456-4203
Ohio, Mark Hollingsworth, Jr., 2230 Euclid Ave., Cleveland, OH 44115 Tel. (216)771-4815
Oklahoma, Robert M. Moody, 924 N. Robinson, Oklahoma City, OK 73102-2499 Tel. (405)232-4820
Olympia, Vincent W. Warner, P.O. Box 12126, Seattle, WA 98102 Tel. (206)325-4200
Oregon, Johnny Itty, 11800 SW Military Lane, Portland, OR 97219-8436 Tel. (503)636-5613
Pennsylvania, Charles E. Bennison, Jr., 240 S. 4th St., Philadelphia, PA 19106 Tel. (215)627-6434

Pittsburgh, Robert W. Duncan, Jr., 535 Smithfield St., Pittsburgh, PA 15222 Tel. (412)281-6131
Quincy, Keith L. Ackerman, 3601 N. North St., Peoria, IL 61604-1599 Tel. (309)688-8221
Rhode Island, Geralyn Wolf, 275 N. Main St., Providence, RI 02903-1298 Tel. (401)274-4500
Rio Grande, Terence Kelshaw, 4304 Carlisle Blvd. NE, Albuquerque, NM 87107 Tel. (505)881-0636
Rochester, Jack M. McKelvey, 935 East Ave., Rochester, NY 14607 Tel. (585)473-2977
San Diego, Gethin B. Hughes, 2728 6th Ave., San Diego, CA 92103 Tel. (619)291-5947
San Joaquin, John-David Schofield, 4159 E. Dakota Ave., Fresno, CA 93726 Tel. (559)244-4828
South Carolina, Edward L. Salmon, Jr., P.O. Box 20127, Charleston, SC 29413-0127 Tel. (843)722-4075
South Dakota, Creighton L. Robertson, 500 S. Main Ave., Sioux Falls, SD 57104-6814 Tel. (605)338-9751
Southeast Florida, Leopold Frade, 525 NE 15th St., Miami, FL 33132 Tel. (305)373-0881
Southern Ohio, Herbert Thompson, Jr.; Kenneth Price (S), 412 Sycamore St., Cincinnati, OH 45202 Tel. (513)421-0311
Southern Virginia, David C. Bane, Jr., 600 Talbot Hall Rd., Norfolk, VA 23505 Tel. (757)423-8287
Southwest Florida, John B. Lipscomb, 7313 Merchant Ct., Sarasota, FL 34240 Tel. (941)556-0315
Southwestern Virginia, F. Neff Powell, P.O. Box 2279, Roanoke, VA 24009 Tel. (540)342-6797
Spokane, James E. Waggoner, Jr., 245 E. 13th Ave., Spokane, WA 99202 Tel. (509)624-3191
Springfield, Peter H. Beckwith, 821 S. 2nd St., Springfield, IL 62704 Tel. (217)525-1876
Tennessee, Bertram N. Herlong, 50 Vantage Way, Suite 107, Nashville, TN 37228 Tel. (615)251-3322
Texas, Don A. Wimberly, 3203 W. Alabama St., Houston, TX 77098 Tel. (713)520-6444
Upper South Carolina, Dorsey F. Henderson, Jr., 1115 Marion Street, Columbia, SC 29201 Tel. (803)771-7800
Utah, Carolyn T. Irish, Box 3090, Salt Lake City, UT 84110-3090 Tel. (801)322-4131
Vermont, Thomas C. Ely, 5 Rock Point Rd., Burlington, VT 05401 Tel. (802)863-3431
Virginia, Peter J. Lee, 110 W. Franklin St., Richmond, VA 23220 Tel. (804)643-8451
Washington, John Bryson Chane, Episc. Church House, Mt. St. Alban, Washington, DC 20016-5094 Tel. (202)537-6555
West Missouri, Barry R. Howe, P.O. Box 413227, Kansas City, MO 64141-3227 Tel. (816)471-6161
West Tennessee, Don E. Johnson, 692 Poplar Ave., Memphis, TN 38105 Tel. (901)526-0023
West Texas, James E. Folts, P.O. Box 6885, San Antonio, TX 78209 Tel. (210)824-5387
West Virginia, W. Michie Klusmeyer, P.O. Box 5400, Charleston, WV 25361-0400 Tel. (304) 344-3597
Western Kansas, James Marshall Adams, P.O. Box 2507, Salina, KS 67402-2507 Tel. (785) 825-1626
Western Louisiana, D. Bruce MacPherson, P.O. Box 2031, Alexandria, LA 71309 Tel. (318) 442-1304
Western Massachusetts, Gordon P. Scruton, 37 Chestnut St., Springfield, MA 01103 Tel. (413)737-4786
Western Michigan, Robert Ronald Gepert, 2600 Vincent Ave., Portage, MI 49024 Tel. (269)381-2710
Western New York, J. Michael Garrison, 1114 Delaware Ave., Buffalo, NY 14209 Tel. (716) 881-0660
Western North Carolina, Robert H. Johnson, 900-B Centre Park Dr., Asheville, NC 28805 Tel. (828)225-6656
Wyoming, Bruce Caldwell, 104 S. 4th St., Laramie, WY 82070 Tel. (307)742-6606
Am. Churches in Europe-Jurisdiction, Pierre W. Whalon, The American Cathedral, 23 Avenue Georges V, 75008, Paris, France Tel. 33-1-53-23-84-04

Periodicals

Episcopal Life

The Episcopal Orthodox Church

This body was incorporated in 1964 as a self-governing Orthodox Anglican church. The church is committed to the biblical world view contained in the Holy Scriptures, confessed in the three ancient creeds of the Catholic Church (the Apostles', Nicene, and Athanasian Creeds), experienced in the sacraments, and practiced through the use of orthodox editions of the Book of Common Prayer. The church is the United States member of the Orthodox Anglican Communion, the creation of which it authorized in 1967. The Orthodox Anglican Communion is a fellowship of churches around the world that adhere to orthodox theology. In 1971 the church opened its own theological educational institution. Clergy in the United States are trained at the denomination's school, St. Andrew's Theological College and Seminary.

Headquarters

The Chancery of the Archdiocese, 464 County Home Rd., Lexington, NC 27292 Tel. (336) 236-9565 Fax (336)236-4822
E-mail: eoc@orthodoxanglican.net
Web site: orthodoxanglican.net

Officers

Presiding Bishop, The Most Rev. Dr. Scott E. McLaughlin, abpmclaughlin@orthodoxanglican.net

Periodicals

The Episcopal Orthodox Encounter

The Estonian Evangelical Lutheran Church

For information on the Estonian Evangelical Lutheran Church (EELC), please see the listing in Chapter 4, "Religious Bodies in Canada."

Headquarters

383 Jarvis St., Toronto, ON M5B 2C7
E-mail: konsistoorium@eelk.ee
Web site: www.eelk.ee

The Evangelical Church

The Evangelical Church was born June 4, 1968 in Portland, Oregon, when 46 congregations and about 80 ministers, under the leadership of V. A. Ballantyne and George Millen, met in an organizing session. Within two weeks a group of about 20 churches and 30 ministers from the Evangelical United Brethren and Methodist churches in Montana and North Dakota became part of the new church. Richard Kienitz and Robert Strutz were the superintendents.

Under the leadership of Superintendent Robert Trosen, the former Holiness Methodist Church became a part of the Evangelical Church in 1969, bringing its membership and a flourishing mission field in Bolivia. The Wesleyan Covenant Church joined in 1977, with its missionary work in Mexico, Brownsville, Texas and among the Navajos in New Mexico.

The Evangelical Church in Canada, where T. J. Jesske was superintendent, became an autonomous organization on June 5, 1970. In 1982, after years of discussions with the Evangelical Church of North America, a founding General Convention was held at Billings, Montana, where the two churches united. In 1993 the Canadian conference merged with the Canadian portion of the Missionary Church to form the Evangelical Missionary Church. The new group maintains close ties with their American counterparts. Currently there are nearly 150 U.S. congregations of the Evangelical Church. The headquarters is in Minneapolis, Minnesota.

The following guide the life, program and devotion of this church: faithful, biblical and sensible preaching and teaching of those truths proclaimed by scholars of the Wesleyan-Arminian viewpoint; an itinerant system which reckons with the rights of individuals and the desires of the congregation; local ownership of all church properties and assets.

The church is officially affiliated with the Christian Holiness Partnership, the National Association of Evangelicals, Wycliffe Bible Translators, World Gospel Mission and OMS International. The denomination has nearly 150 missionaries.

Headquarters

Denominational Office, 9421 West River Rd., Minneapolis, MN 55444 Tel. (763)421-2589 Fax (763)424-9230, ecm@usfamily.net
Media Contact, Gen. Supt., Dr. William Vermillion
E-mail: jsditzel@juno.com
Web site: quakertownecna.com/conferences.html

Officers

Gen. Supt., Dr. William Vermillion, 9421 West River Rd., Minneapolis, MN 55444
Denominational Sec., Dr. Bruce Moyer, P.O. Box 29, University Park, IA 52595 Tel. (641)673-8391
Exec. Dir., Evangelical Church Mission, Rev. Duane Erickson, 9421 W. River Rd., Minneapolis, MN 55444

Periodicals

HeatBeat; The Evangelical Challenge

The Evangelical Church Alliance

What is known today as the Evangelical Church Alliance began in 1887 under the name World's Faith Missionary Association. Years later, on March 28, 1928, a nonprofit organization was incorporated in the state of Missouri under the same name. In October, 1931, the name Fundamental Ministerial Association was chosen to reflect the organization's basis of unity.

On July 21, 1958, during the annual convention at Trinity Seminary and Bible College in Chicago, Illinois, a more comprehensive constitution was created and the name was changed to The Evangelical Church Alliance.

The ECA licenses and ordains ministers who are qualified, providing them with credentials from a recognized ecclesiastical body; provides training courses through the Bible Extension Institute for those who have not had the opportunity to attend seminary or Bible school; provides associate membership for churches and Christian organizations, giving opportunity for fellowship and networking with other evangelical ministers and organizations who share the same goals and mission, while remaining autonomous; provides endorsement for military, prison, hospital and other institutional chaplains; provides regional conferences and an annual international Conference where members can find fellowship, encouragement and training; cooperates with churches in finding new pastors when they have openings.

ECA is an international, nonsectarian, evangelical organization.

Headquarters

205 W. Broadway St., P.O. Box 9, Bradley, IL 60915 Tel. (815)937-0720 Fax (815)937-0001
Media Contact, Pres./CEO, Dr. Samuel Goebel
E-mail: info@ecainternational.org
Web site: www.ecainternational.org

Officers

Pres./CEO, Dr. Samuel Goebel

Periodicals

The Evangel

Evangelical Churches—please see Fellowship of Evangelical Churches

The Evangelical Congregational Church

This denomination had its beginning in the movement known as the Evangelical Association, organized by Jacob Albright in 1796. A division that occurred in 1891 in the Evangelical Association resulted in the organization of the United Evangelical Church in 1894. An attempt to heal this division was made in 1922, but a portion of the United Evangelical Church was not satisfied with the plan of merger and remained apart, taking the above name in 1928. This denomination is Wesleyan-Arminian in doctrine, evangelistic in spirit and Methodist in church government, with congregational ownership of local church property.

Congregations are located from New Jersey to Illinois. A denominational center, two retirement villages and a seminary are located in Myerstown, Penn. Three summer youth camps and four camp meetings continue evangelistic outreach. A worldwide missions movement includes conferences in North East India, Liberia, Mexico, Costa Rica, and Japan. The denomination is a member of National Association of Evangelicals.

Headquarters

Evangelical Congregational Church Center, 100 W. Park Ave., Myerstown, PA 17067 Tel. (800)866-7581 Fax (717)866-7383

Media Contact, Bishop, Rev. Michael W. Sigman, Tel. (717)866-7581

E-mail: eccenter@eccenter.com

Web site: www.eccenter.com/church

Officers

Presiding Bishop, Rev. Michael W. Sigman

1st Vice-Chpsn., Rev. Gary Brown

Sec., Rev. Kirk Marks

Conference Attorney, David Roland, Esq.

Treas., Patricia Hartman, Annville, PA

E.C.C. Retirement Village, Exec. Dir., Steven J. Reiter, Fax (717)866-6448

Evangelical School of Theology, Pres., Dr. Dennis Hollinger, Fax (717)866-4667

OTHER ORGANIZATIONS

Evangelism & Discipleship Commission, Chpsn., Bishop Michael Sigman

Leadership Commission, Chpsn., Bishop Michael Sigman

Church Health Commission, Chpsn., Rev. Fred Moury

Church Planting Commission, Chpsn,, Rev. Keith Miller

Church Services Commission, Chpsn., Rev. Keith Miller

Global Ministries Commission, Chpsn., Rev. John Ragsdale

Bd. of Pensions, Pres., William Kautz, New Cumberland, PA; Controller, Douglas White, Myerstown, PA

Periodicals

Window on the World (Global Ministries Commission)

The Evangelical Covenant Church

The Evangelical Covenant Church has its roots in historic Christianity as it emerged during the Protestant Reformation, in the biblical instruction of the Lutheran State Church of Sweden and in the great spiritual awakenings of the 19th century.

The Covenant Church adheres to the affirmations of the Protestant Reformation regarding the Holy Scriptures, believing that the Old and the New Testament are the Word of God and the only perfect rule for faith, doctrine and conduct. It has traditionally valued the historic confessions of the Christian church, particularly the Apostles' Nicene Creed, while at the same time emphasizing the sovereignty of the Word over all creedal interpretations. It has especially cherished the pietistic restatement of the doctrine of justification by faith as basic to its dual task of evangelism and Christian nurture. It recognizes the New Testament emphasis upon personal faith in Jesus Christ as Savior and Lord, the reality of a fellowship of believers that acknowledges but transcends theological differences, and the belief in baptism and the Lord's Supper as divinely ordained sacraments of the church.

While the denomination has traditionally practiced the baptism of infants, in conformity with its principle of freedom it has also recognized the practice of believer baptism. The principle of personal freedom, so highly esteemed by the Covenant, is to be distinguished from the individualism that disregards the centrality of the Word of God and the mutual responsibilities and disciplines of the spiritual community.

Headquarters

5101 N. Francisco Ave., Chicago, IL 60625 Tel. (773)784-3000 Fax (773)784-4366

Media Contact, Sally A. Johnson, sally.johnson@covchurch.org

E-mail: elliott.johnson@covchurch.org

Web site: www.covchurch.org

Officers

Pres., Dr. Glenn R. Palmberg

Vice-Pres., Rev. Donn Engebretson

Admin. V.P., Dr. Mary C. Miller

Financial V.P., Dr. Dean A. Lundgren

ADMINISTRATIVE BOARDS

Exec. Board, Rev. Catherine Gilliard, Chair

Board of Covenant Women Ministries, Exec., Minister, Rev. Ruth Y. Hill

Board of Nominations, Advisory Member, Rev. Dr. Mary C. Miller

Board of the Ordered Ministry, Exec. Minister, Rev. Dr. David Kersten
Board of Pensions & Benefits, Dir. of Pensions, Rev. Dr. Mary C. Miller
Board of Benevolence, Pres. of Covenant Ministries of Benevolence, David A. Dwight, 5145 N. California Ave., Chicago, IL 60625
North Park University, Pres., Dr. David G. Horner, 3225 W. Foster Ave., Chicago, IL 60625; North Park Theological Seminary, Pres. And Dean, Dr. John E. Phelan Jr.

SERVICE ORGANIZATIONS

National Covenant Properties, Pres., David W. Johnson, 5101 N. Francisco, Chicago, IL 60625 Tel. (773)784-3000
Covenant Trust Company, Pres., Charles A. Walles, 5101 N. Francisco, Chicago, IL 60625 Tel. (773)784-9911

REGIONAL CONFERENCES OF THE E.C.C.

Central Conference, Supt., Rev. Herbert M. Freedholm, 3319 W. Foster Ave., Chicago, IL 60625 Tel. (773)267-3060
East Coast Conference, Supt., Rev. Robert C. Dvorak, 52 Missionary Rd., Cromwell, CT 06416 Tel. (860)635-2691
Great Lakes Conference, Supt., Rev. Richard Lucco, 42219 Ann Arbor Rd. E., Plymouth, MI 48170 Tel. (734)451-4670
Midwest Conference, Supt., Rev. Kenneth P. Carlson, 13304 W. Center Rd. #229, Omaha, NE 68144 Tel. (402)334-3060
North Pacific Conference, Supt., Rev. Mark A. Novak, 9311 SE 36th St., Suite 120, Mercer Island, WA 98040 Tel. (206)275-3903
Northwest Conference, Supt., Rev. James A. Fretheim, 3106 47th Ave. S., Minneapolis, MN 55406 Tel. (612) 721-4893
Pacific Southwest Conference, Supt., Rev. Evelyn M. R. Johnson, 1333 Willow Pass Rd., Suite 212, Concord, CA 94502 Tel. (925)677-2140
Southeast Conference, Supt., Rev. Kurt A. Miericke, 1759 W. Broadway St. #7, Oviedo, FL 32765 Tel. (407)977-8009
Canada Conference, Supt., Rev. Jeffrey Anderson, P.O. Box 34025 RPO, Fort Richmond, Winnipeg, MB, Tel. (204)269-3437
Midsouth Conference, Supt., Rev. Garth T Bolinder, 6119 E. 91st St., Suite 2000, Tulsa, OK 74137 Tel. (918)481-9097
E.C.C. of Alaska, Field Dir., P.O. Box 770749, Eagle River, AK 99577 Tel. (907)694-6348

Periodicals

Covenant Companion; Covenant Quarterly; Covenant Home Altar

The Evangelical Free Church of America

In October 1884, 27 representatives from Swedish churches met in Boone, Iowa, to establish the Swedish Evangelical Free Church. In the fall of that same year, two Norwegian-Danish groups began worship and fellowship (in Boston and in Tacoma) and by 1912 had established the Norwegian-Danish Evangelical Free Church Association. These two denominations, representing 275 congregations, came together at a merger conference in 1950.

The Evangelical Free Church of America is an association of local, autonomous churches across the United States and Canada, blended together by common principles, policies and practices. A 12-point statement addresses the major doctrines but also provides for differences of understanding on minor issues of faith and practice.

Overseas outreach includes 500 missionaries serving in 31 countries.

Headquarters

901 E. 78th St., Minneapolis, MN 55420-1300 Tel. (952)854-1300 Fax (952)853-8488
Media Contact, Exec. Dir. of International Mission, Timothy Addington
E-mail: pres.@efca.org
Web site: www.efca.org

Officers

Pres., Dr. William J. Hamel
Exec. Dir. International Mission, Timothy Addington
Exec. Dir. National Ministries, Rev. Steven Hudson
C.F.O., John R. Torvik, CPA
Chair, Brian Cole, 2404 Park Dr., West Des Moines, IA 60265
Sec., Rev. William Culbertson, 958 5th Ave. S., Bloomington, MN 55420
Moderator, Dr. Roland Peterson, 235 Craigbrook Way NE, Fridley, MN 55432
Vice Moderator, Dr. Louis Diaz, 520 E. Roosevelt Rd., Wheaton, IL 60187

Periodicals

EFCA Today

Evangelical Friends International—North American Region

The organization restructured from Evangelical Friends Alliance in 1990 to become internationalized for the benefit of its worldwide contacts. The North America Region continues to function within the United States as EFA formerly did. The organization represents one corporate step of denominational unity, brought about as a result of several movements of spiritual renewal within the Society of Friends. These movements are, (1) the general evangelical renewal within Christianity, (2) the new scholarly recognition of the evangelical nature of 17th-century Quakerism, and (3) EFA, which was formed in 1965.

The EFA is conservative in theology and makes use of local pastors. Sunday morning worship includes singing, Scripture reading, a period of open worship and a sermon by the pastor.

Headquarters

5350 Broadmoor Cir. NW, Canton, OH 44709 Tel. (330)493-1660 Fax (330)493-0852
Media Contact, Gen. Supt., Dr. John P. Williams, Jr.
E-mail: efcer@aol.com
Web site: www.evangelical-friends.org

YEARLY MEETINGS

Evangelical Friends Church, Eastern Region, Wayne Ickes, 5350 Broadmoor Cir. NW, Canton, OH 44709 Tel. (330)493-1660 Fax (330)493-0852
Rocky Mountain YM, John Brawner, 3350 Reed St., Wheat Ridge, CO 80033 Tel. (303)238-5200 Fax (303)238-5200
Mid-America YM, Duane Hansen, 2018 Maple, Wichita, KS 67213 Tel. (316)267-0391 Fax (316)267-0681
Northwest YM, Mark Ankeny, 200 N. Meridian St., Newberg, OR 97132 Tel. (503)538-9419 Fax (503)538-9410
Alaska YM, Sam Williams, P.O. Box 687, Kotzebue, AK 99752 Tel. (907)442-3906
Friends Church Southwest YM, Linda Coop, P.O. Box 1607, Whittier, CA 90609-1607 Tel. (562)947-2883 Fax (562)947-9385

Periodicals

The Friends Voice

Evangelical Lutheran Church in America*

The Evangelical Lutheran Church in America (ELCA) was organized April 30-May 3, 1987, in Columbus, Ohio, bringing together the 2.25 million-member American Lutheran Church, the 2.85 million-member Lutheran Church in America, and the 100,000-member Association of Evangelical Lutheran Churches.

The ELCA is, through its predecessors, the oldest of the major U.S. Lutheran churches. In the mid-17th century, a Dutch Lutheran congregation was formed in New Amsterdam (now New York). Other early congregations were begun by German and Scandinavian immigrants to Delaware, Pennsylvania, New York and the Carolinas.

The first Lutheran association of congregations, the Pennsylvania Ministerium, was organized in 1748 under Henry Melchior Muhlenberg. Numerous Lutheran organizations were formed as immigration continued and the United States grew.

In 1960, The American Lutheran Church (ALC) was created through a merger of an earlier American Lutheran Church, formed in 1930, the Evangelical Lutheran Church, begun in 1917, and the United Evangelical Lutheran Church in America started in 1896. In 1963 the Lutheran Free Church, formed in 1897, merged with the ALC.

In 1962, the Lutheran Church in America (LCA) was formed by a merger of the United Lutheran Church, formed in 1918, with the Augustana Lutheran Church, begun in 1860, the American Evangelical Lutheran Church, founded in 1872, and the Finnish Lutheran Church or Suomi Synod, founded in 1891.

The Association of Evangelical Lutheran Churches arose in 1976 from a doctrinal split with the Lutheran Church-Missouri Synod.

The ELCA, through its predecessor church bodies, was a founding member of the Lutheran World Federation, the World Council of Churches, and the National Council of the Churches of Christ in the USA.

The church is divided into 65 geographical areas or synods. These 65 synods are grouped into nine regions for mission, joint programs and service.

Headquarters

8765 W. Higgins Rd., Chicago, IL 60631 Tel. (773)380-2700 Fax (773)380-1465
Media Contact, Dir. for News, John Brooks, Tel. (773)380-2958 Fax (773)380-2406
E-mail: info@elca.org
Web site: www.elca.org

Officers

Presiding Bishop, Rev. Mark S. Hanson
Sec., Rev. Dr. Lowell G. Almen
Treas., Ms. Christina L. Jackson-Skelton
Vice-Pres., Mr. Carlos F. Pena
Exec. for Admin., Rev. Charles S. Miller
Office of the Presiding Bishop, Interim Exec. Asst. to the Presiding Bishop for Federal Chaplaincies, Rev. Ivan G. Ives; Exec. Asst. to the Presiding Bishop, Ms. Myrna J. Sheie

DIVISIONS

Div. for Congregational Min., Exec. Dir., Rev. M. Wyvetta Bullock; Bd. Chpsn., Rev. Steven T. Kruse; Lutheran Youth Organization, Pres., Leota Thomas-Breitfeld
Div. for Higher Educ. & Schools, Interim Exec. Dir., Ms. Sue E. Rothmeyer; Bd. Chpsn., Dr. Rod Schofield
Div. for Global Mission, Exec. Dir., Rev. Rafael Malpica Padilla; Bd. Chpsn., Ms. S. Christine Mummert
Div. for Ministry, Exec. Dir., Rev. Stanley N. Olson; Bd. Chpsn., Rev. Robert J. Karli
Div. for Outreach, Exec. Dir., Rev. Dr. Richard A. Magnus, Jr.; Bd. Chpsn., Mr. Ronald J. Solimon
Div. for Church in Society, Exec. Dir., Rev. Rebecca S. Larson; Chpsn., Rev. James B. Martin-Schramm

COMMISSIONS

Comm. for Multicultural Ministries, Exec. Dir., Rev. Frederick E.N. Rajan; Chpsn., Ms. Grace G. El-Yateem
Comm. for Women, Exec. Dir., Joanne Chadwick; Chpsn., Ms. Agnes S. McClain

CHURCHWIDE UNITS

Conference of Bishops, Asst. to the Presiding Bishop, Rev. Kathie Bender Schwich; Chpsn., Rev. E. Roy Riley

Development Services, Exec. Dir., The Rev. Donald M. Hallberg; Chpsn., Mr. David D. Swartling, Esq.

ELCA Publishing House, Exec. Dir., Ms. Beth A. Lewis; Bd. Chpsn.,Mr. James Myers

ELCA Bd. of Pensions, Exec. Dir., John G. Kapanke; Bd. Chpsn, Mr. Bradley C. Engel

Women of the ELCA, Exec. Dir., Ms. Linda Post Bushkofsky; Bd. Chpsn., Ms. Mary Ellen Kiesner

DEPARTMENTS

Dept. for Communication, Dir., Rev. Eric C. Shafer

Dept. for Ecumenical Affairs, Dir., Rev. Randall R. Lee; Committee Chpsn., Rev. John K. Stendahl

Dept. for Human Resources, Dir., Ms. Else Thompson

Dept. for Research & Evaluation, Dir., Dr. Kenneth W. Inskeep

Dept. for Synodical Relations, Dir., Rev. Kathie Bender Schwich

SYNODICAL BISHOPS

Region 1

Alaska, Rev. Ronald D. Martinson, 1847 W. Northern Lights Blvd. #2, Anchorage, AK 99517-3343 Tel. (907)272-8899 Fax (907)274-3141

Northwest Washington, Rev. Wm Chris Boerger, 5519 Pinney Ave. N, Seattle, WA 98103-5899 Tel. (206)783-9292 Fax (206)783-9833

Southwestern Washington, Rev. Robert D. Hofstad, 420 121st St. S., Tacoma, WA 98444-5218 Tel. (253)535-8300 Fax (253)535-8315

Eastern Washington-Idaho, Rev. Martin D. Wells, 314 S. Spruce St., Suite A, Spokane, WA 99204-1098 Tel. (509)838-9871 Fax (509)838-0941

Oregon, Rev. Paul R. Swanson, 2800 N. Vancouver Ave., Suite 101, Portland, OR 97227-1643 Tel. (503) 413-4191 Fax (503)413-2407

Montana, Rev. Dr. Richard R. Omland, 2415 13th Ave. S., Great Falls, MT 59405-5199 Tel. (406)453-1461 Fax (406)761-4632

Regional Coord., Mr. Steven H. Lansing, 766-B John St., Seattle, WA 98109-5186 Tel. (206)624-0093 Fax (206)626-0987

Region 2

Sierra Pacific, Rev. David G. Mullen, 401 Roland Way #215, Oakland, CA 94621-2011 Tel. (510)430-0500 Fax (510)430-8730

South West California, Bishop, Rev. Dean W. Nelson, 1300 E. Colorado St., Glendale, CA 91205-1406 Tel. (818)507-9591 Fax (818)507-9627

Pacifica, Rev. Murray D. Finck, 23655 Via Del Rio, Suite B, Yorba Linda, CA 92887-2738 Tel. (714)692-2791 Fax (714)692-9317

Grand Canyon, Rev. Michael J. Neils, Interchurch Center, 4423 N. 24th St., Suite 400, Phoenix, AZ 85016-5544 Tel. (602)957-3223 Fax (602)956-8104

Rocky Mountain, Rev. Allan C. Bjornberg, 455 Sherman St., Suite 160, Denver, CO 80203 Tel. (303)777-6700 Fax (303)733-0750

Regional Coord., Ms. Margaret Schmitt Ajer, 3755 Avocado Blvd., PMB 411, La Mesa, CA 91941 Tel (619)460-9312 Fax (619) 460-9314

Region 3

Western North Dakota, Rev. Duane C. Danielson, 1614 Capitol Way, P.O. Box 370, Bismarck, ND 58502-0370 Tel. (701)223-5312 Fax (701)223-1435

Eastern North Dakota, Rev. Richard J. Foss, 1703 32nd Ave. S., Fargo, ND 58103-5936 Tel. (701)232-3381 Fax (701)232-3180

South Dakota, Rev. Andrea F. DeGroot-Nesdahl, Augustana College, 29th & S. Summit, Sioux Falls, SD 57197-0001 Tel. (605)247-4011 Fax (605)274-4028

Northwestern Minnesota, Rev. Rolf P. Wangberg, Concordia College, 901 8th St. S., Moorhead, MN 56562-0001 Tel. (218)299-3019 Fax (218)299-3363

Northeastern Minnesota, Rev. E. Peter Strommen, 1105 E. Superior St., Upper Suite, Duluth, MN 55802-2085 Tel. (218)724-4424 Fax (218)724-4393

Southwestern Minnesota, Rev. Jon V. Anderson, 175 E. Bridge St., P.O. Box 499, Redwood Falls, MN 56283-0499 Tel. (507)637-3904 Fax (507)637-2809

Minneapolis Area, Rev. Craig E. Johnson, 122 W. Franklin Ave., Suite 600, Minneapolis, MN 55404-2474 Tel. (612)870-3610 Fax (612) 870-0170

Saint Paul Area, Rev. Peter Rogness, 105 W. University Ave., St. Paul, MN 55103-2094 Tel. (651)224-4313 Fax (651)224-5646

Southeastern Minnesota, Rev. Harold L. Usgaard, Assisi Heights, 1001 14th St. NW, Suite 300, Rochester, MN 55901-2511 Tel. (507)280-9457 Fax (507)280-8824

Regional Coord., Rev. Craig A. Boehlke, Luther Seminary, 2481 Como Ave., St. Paul, MN 55108-1445 Tel. (651)649-0454 ext. 232, Fax (651)649-0468

Region 4

Nebraska, Rev. David L. deFreese, 4980 S. 118th St., Suite D, Omaha, NE 68137-2220 Tel. (402)896-5311 Fax (402)896-5354

Central States, Rev. Dr. Gerald L. Mansholt, 3210 Michigan Ave., 4th Floor, Kansas City, MO 64109 Tel. (816)861-6584 Fax (816)861-4753

Arkansas-Oklahoma, Rev. Floyd M. Schoenhals, 693 S. 66th E. Ave., Suite 310, Tulsa, OK 74133-1760 Tel. (918)492-4288 Fax (918) 491-6275

Northern Texas-Northern Louisiana, Rev. Kevin

S. Kanouse, 1230 Riverbend Dr., Suite 105, P.O. Box 560587, Dallas, TX 75356-0587 Tel. (214)637-6865 Fax (214)637-4805

Southwestern Texas, Rev. Ray Tiemann, 1090 Oestreich Dr., Seguin, TX 78155 Tel. (830)379-9900 Fax (830)379-9990

Texas-Louisiana Gulf Coast, Rev. Paul J. Blom, 12707 North Fwy. #580, Houston, TX 77060-1239 Tel. (281)873-5665 Fax (281)875-4716

Acting Regional Coord., Rev. Donald R. Just, 7016 Ameranth Lane, Austin, TX, 78723 Tel. (512)272-9677 Fax (512)272-9699

Region 5

Metropolitan Chicago, Rev. Paul R. Landahl, 1420 West Dickens Ave., Chicago, IL 60614-3004 Tel. (773)248-0021 Fax (773)248-8455

Northern Illinois, Rev. Gary M. Wollersheim, 103 W. State St., Rockford, IL 61101-1105 Tel. (815)964-9934 Fax (815)964-2295

Central-Southern Illinois, Rev. Warren D. Freiheit, 524 S. Fifth St., Springfield, IL 62701-1822 Tel. (217)753-7915 Fax (217) 753-7976

Southeastern Iowa, Rev. Philip L. Hougen, 2635 Northgate Dr., P.O. Box 3167, Iowa City, IA 52244-3167 Tel. (319)338-1273 Fax (319)351-8677

Western Iowa, Rev. Michael A. Last, 318 E. Fifth St., P.O. Box 577, Storm Lake, IA 50588-0577 Tel. (712)732-4968 Fax (712)732-6540

Northeastern Iowa, Rev. Steven L. Ullestad, 201 20th St. SW, P.O. Box 804, Waverly, IA 50677-0804 Tel. (319)352-1414 Fax (319) 352-1416

Northern Great Lakes, Rev. Thomas A. Shrenes, 1029 N. Third St., Marquette, MI 49855-3588 Tel. (906)228-2300 Fax (906)228-2527

Northwest Synod of Wisconsin, Rev. Robert D. Berg, 12 W. Marshall St., P.O. Box 730, Rice Lake, WI 54868-0730 Tel. (715)234-3373 Fax (715)234-4183

East-Central Synod of Wisconsin, Rev. James A. Justman, 16 Tri-Park Way, Appleton, WI 54914-1658 Tel. (920)734-5381 Fax (920) 734-5074

Greater Milwaukee, Rev. Paul W. Stumme-Diers, 1212 S. Layton Blvd., Milwaukee, WI 53215-1653 Tel. (414)671-1212 Fax (414)671-1756

South-Central Synod of Wisconsin, Rev. George G. Carlson, 2909 Landmark Pl., Suite 202, Madison, WI 53713-4237 Tel. (608)270-0201 Fax (608)270-0202

La Crosse Area, Rev. April Ulring Larson, 3462 Losey Blvd. S., La Crosse, WI 54601-7217 Tel. (608)788-5000 Fax (608)788-4916

Regional Coord., Rev. Carl R. Evenson, 675 Deerwood Dr., Suite 4., Neenah, WI 54956-1629 Tel. (920)720-9880 Fax (920)720-9881

Region 6

Southeast Michigan, Rev. Robert A. Rimbo, 218 Fisher Bldg., 3011 W. Grand Ave., Detroit, MI 48202-3011 Tel. (313)875-1881 Fax (313) 875-1889

Northwest Lower Michigan, Rev. Gary L. Hansen, 801 S. Waverly Rd., Suite 201, Lansing, MI 48917-4254 Tel. (517)321-5066 Fax (517)321-2612

Indiana-Kentucky, Rev. James R. Stuck, 911 E. 86th St., Suite 200, Indianapolis, IN 46240-1840 Tel. (317)253-3522 Fax (317)254-5666

Northwestern Ohio, Rev. Marcus C. Lohrmann, 621 Bright Rd., Findlay, OH 45840-6987 Tel. (419) 423-3664 Fax (419)423-8801

Northeastern Ohio, Rev. Marcus J. Miller, 1890 Bailey Rd., Cuyahoga Falls, OH 44221-5259 Tel. (330)929-9022 Fax (330)929-9018

Southern Ohio, Rev. Dr. Callon W. Holloway, Jr., 300 S. 2nd St., Columbus, OH 43215-5001 Tel. (614)464-3532 Fax (614)464-3422

Regional Coord., Marilyn McCann Smith, P.O. Box 91, 119 1/2 N. Main St. Bluffton, OH 45817 Tel. (419)369-4006 Fax (419)369-4007

Region 7

New Jersey, Rev. E. Roy Riley, Jr., 1930 State Highway 33, Hamilton Square, Trenton, NJ 08690-1799 Tel. (609) 586-6800 Fax (609) 586-1597

New England, Rev. Margaret G. Payne, 20 Upland St., Worcester, MA 01607-1624 Tel. (508)791-1530 Fax (508)797-9295

Metropolitan New York, Rev. Stephen P. Bouman, Interchurch Center, 475 Riverside Dr., Suite 1620, New York, NY 10115 Tel. (212)665-0732 Fax (212)665-8640

Upstate New York, Rev. Marie C. Jerge, 890 E. Brighton Ave., Syracuse, NY 13205 Tel. (315) 446-2502 Fax (315)446-4642

Northeastern Pennsylvania, Rev. Dr. David R. Strobel, 4865 Hamilton Blvd., Wescosville, PA 18106-9705 Tel. (610)395-6891 Fax (610)398-7083

Southeastern Pennsylvania, Rev. Roy G. Almquist, 506 Haws Ave., Norristown, PA 19401-4543 Tel. (610)278-7342 Fax (610) 696-2782

Slovak Zion, Rev. Wilma S. Kucharek, 124 Barbero Dr., Torrington, CT 06790, P.O.Box 1003 (06790-1003) Tel. (860)482-6100 Fax (860)482-7463

Regional Coord., Judith A. Spindt, Lutheran Theol. Seminary at Philadelphia, Hagan Hall, 7301 Germantown Ave., Philadelphia, PA 19119-1794 Tel. (215)248-6319 Fax (215) 248-7377

Region 8

Northwestern Pennsylvania, Rev. Ralph E. Jones, 308 Seneca St., 5th Floor, Oil City, PA 16301 Tel. (814)677-5706 Fax (814)676-8591

Southwestern Pennsylvania, Rev. Donald J. McCoid, 9625 Perry Hwy., Pittsburgh, PA 15237-5590 Tel. (412)367-8222 Fax (412) 369-8840

Allegheny, Rev. Gregory R. Pile, 701 Quail Ave., Altoona, PA 16602-3010 Tel. (814)942-1042 Fax (814)941-9259

Lower Susquehanna, Rev. Carol S. Hendrix,

900 S. Arlington Ave., Suite 208, Harrisburg, PA 17109-5031 Tel. (717)652-1852 Fax (717) 652-2504

Upper Susquehanna, Rev. Dr. A. Donald Main, Rt. 192 & Reitz Blvd., P.O. Box 36, Lewisburg, PA 17837-0036 Tel. (570)524-9778 Fax (570)524-9757

Delaware-Maryland, Rev. Dr. H. Gerard Knoche, 700 Light St., Baltimore, MD 21230-3850 Tel. (410)230-2860 Fax (410)230-2871

Metropolitan Washington, D.C., Rev. Theodore F. Schneider, 1030 15th St. NW, Suite 1010, Washington, DC 20005-1503 Tel. (202)408-8110 Fax (202)408-8114

West Virginia-Western Maryland, Rev. Ralph W. Dunkin, The Atrium, 503 Morgantown Avenue, Suite 100, Fairmont, WV 26554-4374 Tel. (304)363-4030 Fax (304)366-9846

Regional Coord., Rev. James E. Miley, Lutheran Theological Sem. at Gettysburg, 61 Seminary Ridge, Gettysburg, PA 17325-1795 Tel. (717)334-6286 ext. 2133 Fax (717)334-0323

Region 9

Virginia, Rev. James F. Mauney, Roanoke College, 221 College Lane, Bittle Hall, P.O. Drawer 70, Salem, VA 24153-0070 Tel. (540)389-1000 Fax (540)389-5962

North Carolina, Rev. Leonard H. Bolick, 1988 Lutheran Synod Dr., Salisbury, NC 28144-4480 Tel. (704)633-4861 Fax (704)638-0508

South Carolina, Rev. David A. Donges, 1003 Richland St., P.O. Box 43, Columbia, SC 29202-0043 Tel. (803)765-0590 Fax (803) 252-5558

Southeastern, Rev. Ronald B. Warren, 100 Edgewood Ave. NE, Suite 1600, Atlanta, GA 30303 Tel. (404)589-1977 Fax (404)521-1980

Florida-Bahamas, Rev. Edward R. Benoway, 3838 W. Cypress St., Tampa, FL 33607-4897 Tel. (813)876-7660 Fax (813)870-0826

Caribbean, Rev. Margarita Martinez, PMB Num 359 Suite 1, 425 CARR 693, Suite 1, Dorado, PR 00646-4802 Tel. (787) 273-8311 Fax (787)796-3365

Regional Coord., Rev. Harvey Huntley, Lutheran Theological Southern Seminary, 4201 N. Main St., Columbia, SC 29203 Tel. (803)461-3263, Fax (803)461-3380

Periodicals

The Lutheran; Lutheran Partners; Lutheran Woman Today; Seeds for the Parish

Evangelical Lutheran Synod

The Evangelical Lutheran Synod had its beginning among the Norwegian settlers who brought with them their Lutheran heritage. The Synod was organized in 1853. It was reorganized in 1918 by those who desired to adhere to the Synod's principles not only in word but also in deed.

The Synod owns and operates Bethany Lutheran College and Bethany Lutheran Theological Seminary. It has congregations in 20 states and maintains foreign missions in Peru, Chile, the Czech Republic, Latvia, and Ukraine. It operates a seminary in Lima, Peru and in Ternopil, Ukraine.

Headquarters

6 Browns Ct., Mankato, MN 56001 Tel. (507) 344-7356 Fax (507)344-7426

Media Contact, Pres., John A. Moldstad

E-mail: gorvick@blc.edu

Web site: www.evluthsyn.org

Officers

Pres., Rev. John A. Moldstad, 6 Browns Ct., Mankato, MN 56001

Sec., Rev. Craig Ferkenstad, State Hwy 22, St. Peter, MN 37777

Vice-Pres., Rev. Glenn Obengerger, 12309 Pacific Ave., Tacoma, WA 98444

OTHER ORGANIZATIONS

Lutheran Synod Book Co., Bethany Lutheran College, 700 Luther Dr., Mankato, MN 56001

Bethany Lutheran Theological Seminary, 6 Browns Court, Mankato, MN 56001

Periodicals

Lutheran Sentinel; Lutheran Synod Quarterly; Young Branches; Oak Leaves; Mission News

Evangelical Mennonite Church—please see Fellowship of Evangelical Churches

Evangelical Methodist Church

The Evangelical Methodist Church was organized in 1946 at Memphis, Tenn., largely as a movement of people who opposed modern liberalism and wished for a return to the historic Wesleyan position. In 1960, it merged with the Evangel Church (formerly Evangelistic Tabernacles) and with the People's Methodist Church in 1962.

Headquarters

P.O. Box 17070, Indianapolis, IN 46217 Tel. (317)780-8017 Fax (317)780-8078

Media Contact, Gen. Conf. Sec.-Treas., Rev. James A. Coulston

E-mail: headquarters@emchurch.org

Web site: www.emchurch.org

Officers

Gen. Supt., Dr. Edward W. Williamson

Gen. Conf. Sec.-Treas., Rev. James A. Coulston

Evangelical Presbyterian Church

The Evangelical Presbyterian Church (EPC), established in March 1981, is a conservative denomination of 9 geographic presbyteries; 8 in the United States and one in Argentina. From its inception with 12 churches, the EPC has grown to 194 churches with a membership of over 72,000.

Planted firmly within the historic Reformed tradition, evangelical in spirit, the EPC places high priority on church planting and development along with world missions. Eighty missionaries serve the church's mission.

Based on the truth of Scripture and adhering to the Westminster Confession of Faith plus its Book of Order, the denomination is committed to the "essentials of the faith." The historic motto "In essentials, unity; in nonessentials, liberty; in all things charity" catches the irenic spirit of the EPC, along with the Ephesians theme, "truth in love."

The Evangelical Presbyterian Church is a member of the World Alliance of Reformed Churches, National Association of Evangelicals, World Evangelical Fellowship and the Evangelical Council for Financial Accountability.

Headquarters

Office of the Gen. Assembly, 17197 N. Laurel Park Dr., Suite 567, Livonia, MI 48152 Tel. (734)742-2020 Fax (734)742-2033

Media Contact, Stated Clerk, Rev. Michael Glodo

E-mail: epchurch@epc.org

Web site: www.epc.org

Officers

Admin. Committee, Chmn., Dr. Ron Dinunzio, Fatih EPC, 200 Mount Fair Ave., Brooksville, FL 34601

Board of Pension & Benefits, Chmn., Mr. John Baird, c/o EPC, 17197 N. Laurel Park Dr., Suite 567, Livonia, MI 48152

Committee on Fraternal Relations, Chmn., Dr. Paul Heidebrecht, 435 Kammes Ct., West Chicago, IL 60185

Committee on National Outreach, Chmn., Rev. Rodger Woodworth, New Hope EPC, 2710 Shadeland Ave., Pittsburgh, PA 15212

Committee on Presbytery Review, Chmn., Dr. Edward Davis, Ward Presbyterian Church, 40000 Six Miles Rd., Northville, MI 48167

Committee on World Outreach, Chmn., Rev. Ed Randal, 17820 NE 101st Court, Redmond, WA 98052

Committee on Ministerial Vocation, Chmn., Rev. Art Hunt, Cornerstone EPC, 9455 Hilton Rd., Brighton, MI 48114

Committee on Christian Educ. & Publ., Chmn., Rev. Waring Porter, All Saints Presbyterian Church, 263 S. McLean, Memphis, TN 38104

Committee on Women's Ministries, Chmn., Dr. Kitsie Hendrix, 813 Ridge Lake Rd. #410, Memphis, TN 38120

Committee on Theology, Chmn., Mr. Tom Werner, 409 Fairway Lane, St. Louis, MO 63122

Committee on Student and Young Adult Ministries, Chmn., Rev. Brian Land, Cornerstone EPC, 1351 S. Mason Rd., Katy, TX 77450

Ad Interim College Committee, Chmn., Rev. Rick Stauffer, Tabernacle EPC, 2432 S. Racoon Rd., Youngstown, OH 44515

PRESBYTERIES

Central South, Stated Clk., Rev. Dennis Flach, New Covenant Evangelical Presbyterian Church, P.O. Box 842, Natchez, MS 39121

East, Stated Clk., Rev. Ron Meyer, Fourth Presbyterian Church, 5500 River Road, Bethesda, MD 20816

Florida, Stated Clk., Rev. Robert Garment, Trinity EPC, 5150 Oleander, Ft. Pierce, FL 34982

Mid-America, Stated Clk., Mr. Dexter Kuhlman, 1926 Prospector Ridge, Ballwin, MO 63011

Mid-Atlantic, Stated Clk., Dr. Howard Shockley, P.O. Box 10, Moore, SC 29369

Midwest, Stated Clk., Mr. John C. Manon, P.O. Box 6047, Auburn, IN 46706-6047

Southeast, Stated Clk., Rev. Bill Sharp, 1222 Village Green Dr., Chattanooga, TN 39343

West, Stated Clk., Mr. Cecil Matthews, 4677 Springmeadow Lane, Castle Rock, CO 80104

St. Andrews, Stated Clk., Rev. Jorge Lumsden, Temperley Church, Gral Paz 191, (1834) Temperley PCIA Buenos Aires, Argentina

Fellowship of Evangelical Bible Churches

Formerly known as Evangelical Mennonite Brethren, this body emanates from the Russian immigration of Mennonites into the United States, 1873–74. Established with the emphasis on true repentance, conversion and a committed life to Jesus as Savior and Lord, the conference was founded in 1889 under the leadership of Isaac Peters and Aaron Wall. The founding churches were located in Mountain Lake, Minnesota, and in Henderson and Jansen, Nebraska. The conference has since grown to a fellowship of 43 churches with approximately 4,500 members in Argentina, Canada, Paraguay and the United States.

Foreign missions have been a vital ingredient of the total ministry. Today one missionary is serving for every 35 members in the home churches. The fellowship does not develop and administer foreign mission fields of its own, but actively participates with existing evangelical "faith" mission agencies. The fellowship has missionaries serving under approximately 40 different agencies around the world.

The church is holding fast to the inerrancy of Scripture, the deity of Christ and the need for spiritual regeneration of man from his sinful natural state by faith in the death, burial and resurrection of Jesus Christ as payment for sin. Members look forward to the imminent return of Jesus Christ and retain a sense of urgency to share the gospel with those who have never heard of God's redeeming love.

Headquarters

3339 N. 109th Plaza, Omaha, NE 68164 Tel. (402)965-3860 Fax (402)965-3871

Media Contact, Admin., Paul Boeker

E-mail: info@febcministries.org

Web site: members.aol.com/febcoma

Officers

Pres., Mr. Gerald Epp, P.O. Box 86, Waldheim, SK S0K 4R0 Tel. (306)945-2023, pres@febcministries.org

Vice-Pres., Rev. Charles Tschetter, 9001 Q St., Omaha, NE 68127-3548

Rec. Sec., Stan Seifert, 1002-3190 Gladwin Road, Abbotsford, BC V2T 5T2 Tel. (604) 852-3253

Admin., Paul Boeker, 3339 N 109th Plaza, Omaha, NE 68164 Tel. (402)965-3860 Fax (402)965-3871, info@febcministries.org

Ministries Coord., Harvey Schultz, 3011 3rd Ave. E., P.O. Box 8, Waldheim, SK S0K 4R0, Tel. (306)945-2220 Fax (306)945-2088, hesals@aol.com

Commission on Churches, Chpsn., Rev. Paul Carpenter, 401 Nebraska St., Box 141, Jansen, NE 68377-0141 Tel. (402)424-2645, jb95208@ alltel.net

Commission on Education, Chpsn., Jeff Friesen, P.O. Box 225, Hebron, NE 68370 Tel. (402)768-4223, hebronbible@yahoo.com

Commission on Missions, Chpsn., Harold Harms, 308 NW Douglas, Dallas, OR 97338-1021, hharms@juno.com

Commission of Trustees, Chpsn., William Ginter, Box 326, Morris, MB ROG 1KO Tel. (204)746-2612, wginter@escape.ca

Commission on Church Planting, Chpsn., Jim Ingle, 806 Leprechaun Lane, Papillion, NE 68046-2111 Tel. (402)339-1221, inglej@cox. net

Commission on Women's Ministries, Chpsn., Ruth Epp, Box 86, Waldheim, SK S0K 4R0 Tel. (306)945-2023, ggepp@sasktel.net

Periodicals

Fellowship Focus

Fellowship of Evangelical Churches

The Evangelical Mennonite Church is an American denomination in the European free church tradition, tracing its heritage to the Reformation period of the 16th century. The Swiss Brethren of that time believed that salvation could come only by repentance for sins and faith in Jesus Christ; that baptism was only for believers; and that the church should be separate from controls of the state. Their enemies called them Anabaptists, since they insisted on rebaptizing believers who had been baptized as infants. As the Anabaptist movement spread to other countries, Menno Simons became its principal leader. In time his followers were called Mennonites.

In 1693 a Mennonite minister, Jacob Amman, insisted that the church should adopt a more conservative position on dress and style of living and should more rigidly enforce the "ban"—the church's method of disciplining disobedient members. Amman's insistence finally resulted in a division within the South German Mennonite groups; his followers became known as the Amish.

Migrations to America, involving both Mennonites and Amish, took place in the 1700s and 1800s, for both religious and economic reasons.

The Evangelical Mennonite Church was formed in 1866 out of a spiritual awakening among the Amish in Indiana. It was first known as the Egly Amish, after its founder Bishop Henry Egly. Bishop Egly emphasized regeneration, separation and nonconformity to the world. His willingness to rebaptize anyone who had been baptized without repentance created a split in his church, prompting him to gather a new congregation in 1866. The conference, which has met annually since 1895, united a number of other congregations of like mind. This group became The Defenseless Mennonite Church in 1898 and has been known as the Evangelical Mennonite Church since 1948. At the 2003 convention the delegates voted to change the name to Fellowship of Evangelical Churches.

Headquarters

1420 Kerrway Ct., Fort Wayne, IN 46805 Tel. (260)423-3649 Fax (260)420-1905

Media Contact, Admin. Asst., Lynette Augsburger

E-mail: fecministries@aol.com

Officers

Pres., Mr. Ronald J. Habegger

Chpsn.., Rev. Roger Andrews, 12509 Chapel Cove, Fort Wayne, IN 46845

Vice-Chpsn., Rev. Steve Shaffer, 3115 W. Forsythe Rd., Peoria, IL 61614

Sec., Mark Wyse, 7183 SR 66, Archbold, OH 43502

Treas., Alan Rupp, 5724 Spring Oat Ct., Fort Wayne, IN 46845

Fellowship of Fundamental Bible Churches

The churches in this body represent the 1939 separation from the Methodist Protestant Church, when some 50 delegates and pastors (approximately one-third of the Eastern Conference) withdrew to protest the union of the Methodist Protestant Church with the Methodist Episcopal Church and the Methodist Episcopal Church South, and what they considered the liberal tendencies of those churches. These churches subsequently changed their name to the Bible Protestant Church. In 1985, this group again changed its name to the Fellowship of Fundamental Bible Churches to more accurately define their position.

As fundamentalists, this group strongly adheres to the historic fundamentals of the faith, including the doctrine of separation. This group accepts a literal view of the Bible and, consequently, accepts premillennial theology and a pre-tribulational rapture.

The churches are currently located in New Jersey, New York, Pennsylvania, Virginia, Michigan, and California. It is a fellowship of independent Bible and Baptist churches. Baptism, by immersion, and the Lord's Supper, as a memorial, are recognized as ordinances. There are currently 21 churches representing 1,500 members. This constituent body is a member of the American Council of Christian Churches.

The Fellowship of Fundamental Bible Churches owns and operates Tri-State Bible Camp and Conference Center in Montague, New Jersey, oversees a mission board called Fundamental Bible Missions, and conducts a Bible Institute called Fundamental Bible Institute.

Headquarters

P.O. Box 206, Penns Grove, NJ 08069

Media Contact, Sec., Rev. Edmund G. Cotton, 80 Hudson St., Port Jervis, NY 12771 Tel. (914)856-7695

E-mail: ffbc-usa@juno.com

Web site: www.churches-ffbc.org

Officers

Pres., Rev. Mark Franklin, 284 Whig Lane, Monroeville, NJ 08343 Tel. (609)881-0057

Vice-Pres., Rev. Gary Myers, P.O. Box 191, Meshoppen, PA 18630 Tel. (717)833-4898

Sec., Rev. Edmund G. Cotton, 80 Hudson St., Port Jervis, NY 12771 Tel. (914)856-7695

Treas., Ken Thompson, 501 N. Main Street, Elmer, NJ 08318 Tel. (865)358-0515

Fellowship of Grace Brethren Churches

A division occurred in the Church of the Brethren in 1882 on the question of the legislative authority of the annual meeting. It resulted in the establishment of the Brethren Church under a legal charter requiring congregational government. This body divided in 1939 with the Grace Brethren establishing headquarters at Winona Lake, Ind., and the Brethren Church at Ashland, Ohio.

Headquarters

Media Contact, Fellowship Coord., Rev. Thomas Avey, P.O. Box 386, Winona Lake, IN 46590 Tel. (219)269-1269 Fax (219)269-4066

E-mail: fgbc@fgbc.org

Web site: www.fgbc.org

Officers

Mod., Dr. Galen Wiley, 22713 Ellsworth Ave., Minerva, OH 44657

1st Mod.-Elect, Dr. James Custer, 2515 Carriage Rd., Powell, OH 43065

2nd Mod.-Elect, Dr. Ron Manahan, 2316 E. Kemo Ave., Warsaw, IN 46580

Fellowship Coord., Rev. Thomas Avey, P.O. Box 386, Winona Lake, IN 46590 Tel. (219)269-1269 Fax (219)269-4066

Sec., Fellowship Coord., Rev. Thomas Avey, P.O. Box 386, Winona Lake, IN 46590

Treas., Thomas Staller, 2311 S. Cost-a-Plenty Drive, Warsaw, IN 46580

OTHER BOARDS

Grace Brethren International Missions, Exec. Dir., Rev. Tom Julien, P.O. Box 588, Winona Lake, IN 46590

Grace Brethren Home Missions, Exec. Dir., Larry Chamberlain, P.O. Box 587, Winona Lake, IN 46590

Grace College & Seminary, Pres., Ronald E. Manahan, 200 Seminary Dr., Winona Lake, IN 46590 Tel. (210)372-5100

Brethren Missionary Herald Co., Pub. & Gen. Mgr., James Bustram, P.O. Box 544, Winona Lake, IN 46590

CE National, Exec. Dir., Rev. Ed Lewis, P.O. Box 365, Winona Lake, IN 46590

Grace Brethren Navajo Ministries, Dir., Steve Galegor, Counselor, NM 87018

Grace Village Retirement Community, Admin., Jeff Carroll, P.O. Box 337, Winona Lake, IN 46590

Natl. Fellowship of Grace Brethren Ministries, Pres., Dr. Steve Taylor, 132 Summerall Ct., Aiken, SC 2980

Women's Missionary Council, Pres., Janet Minnix, 3314 Kenwick Tr. SW, Roanoke, VA 24015

Grace Brethren Men International, Pres., Morgan Burgess, 163 N. Franklin St., Delaware, OH 43015

Free Christian Zion Church of Christ

This church was organized in 1905 at Redemption, Ark., by a company of African American ministers associated with various denominations. Its polity is in general accord with that of Methodist bodies.

Headquarters

1315 S. Hutchinson St., Nashville, AR 71852 Tel. (501)845-4933

Media Contact, Gen. Sec., Shirlie Cheatham

Officers

Chief Pastor, Willie Benson, Jr.

Free Methodist Church of North America

The Free Methodist Church was organized in 1860 in western New York by ministers and laymen who had called the Methodist Episcopal Church to return to what they considered the original doctrines and lifestyle of Methodism. The issues included human freedom (anti-slavery), freedom and simplicity in worship, free seats so that the poor would not be discriminated against and freedom from secret oaths (societies) so the truth might be spoken freely at all times. The founders emphasized the teaching of the entire sanctification of life by means of grace through faith.

The denomination continues to be true to its founding principles. It communicates the gospel and its power to all people without discrimination through strong missionary, evangelistic and educational programs. Six colleges, a Bible college, and numerous overseas schools train the youth of the church to serve in lay and ministerial roles.

Its members covenant to maintain simplicity in life, worship, daily devotion to Christ, responsible stewardship of time, talent and finance.

Headquarters

World Ministries Center, 770 N. High School Rd., Indianapolis, IN 46214 Tel. (317)244-3660 Fax (317)244-1247

Mailing Address, P.O. Box 535002, Indianapolis, IN 46253 Tel. (800)342-5531

Media Contact, Yearbook Ed., P.O. Box 535002, Indianapolis, IN 46253

E-mail: info@fmcna.org

Web site: www.freemethodistchurch.org

Officers

Bishops, Bishop Roger W. Haskins, Jr.; Bishop Joseph F. James; Bishop Leslie L. Krober; Bishop Richard D. Snyder

Gen. Conference Sec., Miss Carol Bartlett

Dir. of Admin. and Finance, Mr. Gary Kilgore

Free Methodist Communications, Gerald Coates

Free Methodist World Missions, Dr. Arthur Brown

Men's Ministries International, Dir., Rev. Jeffrey Johnson

Women's Ministries International, Pres., Gretchen McLaughlin

Periodicals

Light and Life Magazine

Friends General Conference

Friends General Conference (FGC) is an association of fourteen yearly meetings open to all Friends meetings that wish to be actively associated with FGC's programs and services. Friends General Conference includes Baltimore, Canadian, Illinois, Lake Erie, New England, New York, Northern, Ohio Valley, Philadelphia, South Central and Southeastern Yearly Meetings; Alaska Friends Conference, Southern Appalachian Yearly Meeting and Association, and Piedmont Friends Fellowship; plus seven independently affiliated monthly meetings. Friends General Conference is primarily a service organization with the stated purpose of nurturing the spiritual life within its constituency of predominantly unprogrammed Friends. FGC offers services to all Friends, but has no authority over constituent meetings. A Central Committee, to which constituent Yearly Meetings name appointees (in proportion to membership), and its Executive Committee, are responsible for the direction of FGC's programs and services which include a bookstore, conferences, and traveling ministries program. The 1995 Central Committee approved the following Minute of Purpose,

Friends General Conference is a Quaker organization in the unprogrammed tradition of the Religious Society of Friends that primarily serves affiliated yearly and monthly meetings. It is our experience that:

**Faith is based on direct experience of God.

**Our lives witness this experience individually and corporately.

**By answering that of God in everyone, we build and sustain inclusive community.

Friends General Conference provides resources and opportunities that educate and invite members and attenders to experience, individually and corporately, God's living presence, and to discern and follow God's leadings. Friends General Conference reaches out to seekers and to other religious bodies inside and outside the Religious Society of Friends.

Headquarters

1216 Arch St. #2B, Philadelphia, PA 19107 Tel. (215)561-1700 Fax (215)561-0759

Media Contact, Gen. Sec., Bruce Birchard

E-mail: friends@fgcquaker.org

Web site: www.fgcquaker.org

Officers

Gen. Sec., Bruce Birchard, 1216 Arch St. #2B Philadelphia, PA 19107

Presiding Clerk, Marian Beane, 7125 Cardigan Ave, Charlotte, NC 28215

Treas., Mike Hubbart, 907 N. Monroe St. Wilmington, DE 19801

YEARLY MEETINGS

Alaska Friends Conference, Clerk, Bill Schoder-Ehri, 480 Grubstake Ave., Homer, AK, Tel. (907)479-5257, lovenest@ptialaska.net

*Baltimore, Clerk, Lamar Matthew; Staff, Frank Massey, 17100 Quaker Ln., Sandy Spring, MD 20860 Tel. (301)774-7663, bymrsf@ igc.org

*Canadian, Clerk, Rick McCutheon; Staff, Kerry McAdam, 91A Fourth Ave., Ottawa, ON K1S 2L1 Tel. (613)235-8553, cym-office@quaker. ca

Illinois, Clerk, Maurine Pyles; Staff, Sharon Haworth, 608 W. Illinois St. Urbana, IL 61801 Tel. (217)384-9591, shaworth@sbcglobal.net

Lake Erie, Clerk, Sally Weaver Sommer, 118 S. Spring St., Bluffton, OH 45817 Tel. (419)358-0950, sommerjs@bluffton.edu

*New England, Clerk, Deana Chase; Staff, Katharine Clark, 901 Pleasant St., Worcester, MA 01602-1908 Tel. (508)754-6760, neym@neym.org

*New York, Clerk, Linda Chidsey; Staff, Helen Garay Toppins, 15 Rutherford Pl., New York, NY 10003 Tel. (212)673-5750, office@ nyym.org

Northern, Clerk, Pamela Minden, 4322 Upland Dr, Madison, WI 54705 Tel. (608)238-0693
Ohio Valley, Clerk, Cindi Goslee; Staff, Barbarie Hill, 6921 Stonington Rd., Cincinnati, OH 45232 Tel. (513)281-8831, cemg@earthlink. net
Philadelphia, Clerk, Gretchen Castle, 1515 Cherry St., Philadelphia, PA 19102 Tel. (215) 241-7210, joanb@pym.org; Staff, Thomas Jeavons, thomj@pym.org
Piedmont Friends Fellowship, Clerk, Virginia Driscoll, 504 Willowbrookt Dr., Greensboro, NC 27403 Tel. (336)855-5233, virginia.driscoll@ ci.greensboro.nc.us
South Central, Clerk, Warren Wilson-Reiner, 1508 Southport Dr. #146, Austin, TX 78704 Tel. (512)445-0565, w.wilson-reiner@mail. utexas.edu
*Southeastern, Clerk, Dan Vaughn; Staff, Lyn Cope-Robinson, P.O. Box 510975, Melbourne Beach, FL 32951 Tel. (321)724-1162, admin@ seym.org
Southern Appalachian, Clerk, Sharon Annis; Staff, Mary Calhoun, 1950 Nelson Ave, Memphis, TN 38104 Tel. (276)628-5852, moriah@preferred.com
*also affiliated with Friends United Meeting

Periodicals

Newsletter, FGConnections, Friends Journal

Friends International—please see Evangelical Friends International—North American Region

Friends United Meeting*

Friends United Meeting was organized in 1902 (the name was changed in 1963 from the Five Years Meeting of Friends) as a confederation of North American yearly meetings to facilitate a united Quaker witness in missions, peace work Christian education and outreach.

Today Friends United Meeting is comprised of 26 full-member and 3 association member yearly meetings representing about half the Friends in the world. FUM's current work includes programs of mission and service, leadership development and outreach. FUM publishes Christian education curriculum, books of Quaker history and religious thought and a magazine, *Quaker Life*.

Headquarters

101 Quaker Hill Dr., Richmond, IN 47374-1980 Tel. (765)962-7573 Fax (765)966-1293
Media Contact, Gen. Sec., Retha McCutchen
E-mail: info@fum.org
Web site: www.fum.org

Officers

Presiding Clk., Brent McKinney
Treas., Don Garner
Gen. Sec., Retha McCutchen

DEPARTMENTS

World Missions, Dir., Colin Senth
North American Ministries, Dir., Ben Richmond
Quaker Life, Ed., Trish Edwards-Konic
Friends United Press, Ed., Barbara Mays

YEARLY MEETINGS

Baltimore Yearly Meeting, 17100 Quaker Ln., Sandy Spring, MD 20860-1296 Tel. (301)774-7663 or (800)962-4766 Fax (301)774-7087, www.bymrsf@igc.org; Clerk, Lamar Matthew; Gen. Sec., Frank Massey
Bware Yearly Meeting, P.O. Box 179, Suna, Kenya; Gen. Sec., Samuel Kaguni; Gen. Supt., Epainitus Adego; Presiding Clerk, Jonathan M. Sande
Canadian Yearly Meeting, 91-A Fourth Ave., Ottawa ON K1S 2L1 Tel. (613)235-8553 Fax (613)235-1753; Clerk, George McClure; cym @web.net
Central Yearly Meeting, P.O. Box 1510, Kakamega, Kenya, E. Africa; Gen. Supt., Evans Nyenzo
Chavakali Yearly Meeting, P.O. Box 102, Chavakali, Kenya, East Africa; Gen. Sec., Andrew Mukulu; Clerk, Wilson Andenya
Cuba Yearly Meeting, Calle 20 #118 Esquina Paz, Reparto Vista, Alegre 80300, Hoguin, Cuba; Pres., Maria Renya Yi
East Africa Yearly Meeting of Friends, (Kaimosi) P.O. Box 35, Tiriki, Kenya, East Africa; Presiding Clerk, Matthew Tsimbaki; Gen. Sec., Ephraim Konsolo; Gen. Supt., Erastus Kesohole
East Africa Yearly Meeting of Friends (North), P.O. Box 544, Kitale, Kenya, East Africa; Gen. Sec., Geoffrey M. Wukwanja; Gen. Supt., Titus Adira; Presiding Clerk, H.M. Mukwanja
VIHIGA Yearly Meeting of Friends, P.O. Box 160, Vihiga, Kenya, East Africa; Presiding Clerk, Joseph Kisia; Gen. Sec., Lam Kisanya Osodo; Gen. Supt., Gilbert Akenga Oyando
Elgon East Yearly Meeting, P.O. Box 2322, Kitale, Kenya, East Africa; Gen. Supt., Maurice Simiyu; Gen. Sec., Philip Musungu; Presiding Clerk, John Kitui
Elgon Religious Society of Friends, (West) P.O. Box 4, Lugulu Via Webuye, Kenya, East Africa; Gen. Sec., Tom Isiye; Gen. Supt., John Ngoya; Presiding Clerk, Charles Mbachi
Evangelical Friends Church Uganda, P.O. Box 129, Mbale, Uganda, East Africa; Gen. Supt., Simon Tsapwe; Gen. Sec., Peter Kutosi
Great Plains Yearly Meeting, 1262 Richland Rd., Lacon, IL 61540 Tel. (309)246-8397, mesnerret@cconline.net; Clerk, Neil Mesner
Indiana Yearly Meeting, 4715 N. Wheeling Ave., Muncie, IN 47304-1222 Tel. (765)284-6900 Fax (765)284-8925, iyminfo@iym.org; Clerk, Susan Kirkpatrick; Gen. Supt., Alan Weinacht
Iowa Yearly Meeting, Box 657, Oskaloosa, IA 52577-0657 Tel. (641)673-9717 Fax (641)673-9718, wpdc9717@wmpenn.edu; Clerk, Margaret Stoltzfus; Gen. Supt., Ron Bryan

Jamaica Yearly Meeting, 4 Worthington Ave., Kingston 5, Jamaica WI, Tel. (876)926-7371
Kakamega Yearly Meeting, P.O. Box 465, Kakamega, Kenya, East Africa; Gen. Sec., Jonathan Shisanya; Presiding Clerk, Blastus Wawire; Gen. Supt., Meschack Musindi
Lugari Yearly Meeting, P.O. Box 483, Turbo, Kenya, East Africa; Gen. Sec., David A. Mulama; Presiding Clerk, Joshuah Lilande; Gen. Supt., Japheth Vidolo
Malava Yearly Meeting, P.O. Box 26, Malava, Kenya, East Africa; Gen. Sec., Andrew Namasaka Mulongo; Presiding Clerk, Samson Marani; Gen. Supt., Enoch Shinachi
Nairobi Yearly Meeting, P.O. Box 8321, Nairobi, Kenya, East Africa; Gen. Supt., Benson Simiyu; Gen. Sec., Zablon Isaac Malenge; Vice-Presiding Clerk, Nilson Shivachi
New England Yearly Meeting, 901 Pleasant St., Worcester, MA 01602-1908 Tel. (508)754-6760, neym@neym.org; Clerk, Deana Chase; Field Sec., Jonathan Vogel-Borne
New York Yearly Meeting, 15 Rutherford Pl., New York, NY 10003 Tel. (212)673-5750, office@nyym.org; Clerk, Linda Chidsey; Admin. Sec., Helen Garay Toppins
North Carolina Yearly Meeting, 5506 W. Friendly Ave., Greensboro, NC 27410 Tel. (336)292-6957, ncfriends@juno.com; Clerk, Brent McKinney; Gen. Supt., John Porter
Southeastern Yearly Meeting, P.O. Box 510795, Melbourne Beach, FL 32951-0795 Tel. (321)724-1162; Admin. Sec., Lyn Cope-Robinson, seym@bv.net
Tanzania Yearly Meeting, P.O. Box 151, Mugumu, Serengeti, Tanzania; Gen. Supt. & Clerk, Joseph Lavuna Oguma
Tuloi Yearly Meeting, P.O. Box 102, Kapsabet, Kenya, East Africa; Presiding Clerk, Joseph Anyonge Mulama; Gen. Supt., Solomon Mwanzi; Gen. Sec., Frederick Inyangu
Uganda Yearly Meeting, P.O. Box 2384, Mbale, Uganda, East Africa; Gen. Supt., Francis Wamala; Gen. Sec., Andrew H.S. Kurima; Clerk, Sylvester Khasufa
Vokoli Yearly Meetings, P.O. Box 266, Wodanga, Kenya, East Africa; Gen. Sec., Javan Chondo; Presiding Clerk, Hannington Mbato; Gen. Supt., Thomas Kivuya
Western Yearly Meeting, P.O. Box 70, Plainfield, IN 46168 Tel (317)839-2789 and (839)2849 Fax (317)839-2616; Gen. Supt., Curt Shaw; Clerk, Mary Lee Cimer
Wilmington Yearly Meeting, Pyle Center Box 1194, Wilmington, OH 45177 Tel (937)382-2491 Fax (937)382-7077, phackney@wilmington.edu; Clerk, Gary Farlow; Exec. Sec., Marvin Hall

Periodicals

Quaker Life, *Trish Edwards-Konic*

Full Gospel Assemblies International

The Full Gospel Assemblies International was founded in 1962 under the leadership of Dr. Charles Elwood Strauser. The roots of Full Gospel Assemblies may be traced to 1947 with the beginning of the Full Gospel Church of Coatesville, Pennsylvania. As an Assemblies of God Pentecostal church, the Full Gospel Church of Coatesville was active in evangelization and educational ministries to the community. In service to the ministers and students of the Full Gospel Church ministries, the Full Gospel Trinity Ministerial Fellowship was formed in 1962, later changing its name to Full Gospel Assemblies International.

Retaining its original doctrine and faith, Full Gospel Assemblies is Trinitarian, believing that the Bible is God's infallible Word to mankind, baptism in the Holy Spirit according to Acts 2, divine healing is made possible by the sufferings of our Lord Jesus Christ, and in the imminent return of Christ for those who love him.

The body of Full Gospel Assemblies is an evangelical missionary fellowship sponsoring ministry at home and abroad, composed of self-governing ministries and churches. Congregations, affiliate ministries and clerical body are located throughout the United States and more than 15 countries of the world.

Headquarters

International Headquarters: 3018 Lincoln Hwy, Parkesburg, PA
Mailing Address, P.O. Box 1230, Coatesville, PA 19320 Tel. (610)857-2357 Fax (610)857-3109
Media Contact, Simeon Strauser

Officers

Gen. Supt., Dr. AnnaMae Strauser
Exec. Dir. of Ministry, J. Victor Fisk
Exec. Dir of Admin., Simeon Strauser
Exec. Dir. of Communications, Archie Neale
Exec. Sec., Betty Stewart
Exec. Trustee, Edward Popovich

NATIONAL MINISTERS COUNCIL AND TRUSTEES

Chpsn., Simeon Strauser, Sadsburyville, PA
James Capets, Trafford, PA
Donald Schiemant, Marilla, NY
Michael Mathews, Eau Claire, WI
Bette Elgin, Zenia, CA
John Tortoriello, Fort Lauderdale, FL
Raymond Favicha, Spring Hill, FL
Carol Strauser, Parkesburg, PA

Periodicals

Full Gospel Ministries Outreach Report (Q.), Full Gospel Assemblies Int. - Full Gospel Bible Institute, Simeon Strauser, P.O. Box 1230, Coatsville, PA 19320 Tel (610)857-2357, Denominational Code, FGAI

Full Gospel Fellowship of Churches and Ministers International

In the early 1960s a conviction grew in the hearts of many ministers that there should be closer fellowship between the people of God who believed in the apostolic ministry. At the same time, many independent churches were experiencing serious difficulties in receiving authority from the IRS to give governmentally accepted tax-exempt receipts for donations.

In September 1962 a group of ministers met in Dallas, Texas, to form a Fellowship to give expression to the essential unity of the Body of Christ under the leadership of the Holy Spirit—a unity that goes beyond individuals, churches or organizations. This was not a movement to build another denomination, but rather an effort to join ministers, churches and ministry organizations of like mind across denominational lines.

To provide opportunities for fellowship and to support the objectives and goals of local and national ministries, regional conventions and an annual international convention are held.

Headquarters

1000 N. Belt Line Rd., Irving, TX 75061 Tel. (214)492-1254
Media Contact, Sec., Dr. Harry Schmidt
E-mail: fgfcmi@aol.com
Web site: www.fgfcmi.org

Officers

Pres., Dr. Don Arnold, P.O. Box 324, Gadsden, AL 35901
1st Vice-Pres., Dr. Ray Chamberlain
Sec., Dr. Harry Schmidt
Treas., Rev. Gene Evans, P.O. Box 813, Douglasville, GA 30133
CFO, Dr. S.K. Biffle, 1000 N. Belt Line Rd., Irving, TX 75061
Ofc. Sec., Mrs. Anita Sullivan
Receptionist, Mrs. Nita Biffle
Vice-Pres. at Large, Rev. Maurice Hart, P.O. Box 4316, Omaha, NE 68104; Rev. Don Westbrook, 3518 Rose of Sharon Rd., Durham, NC 27705
Chmn. of Evangelism, David Ellis
Chmn. of Mission, Dr. Ray Chamberlain
Chmn. of Youth, Rev. Steven K. Biffle, 3833 Westervill Rd., Columbus, OH 43224
Past Pres., Dr. James Helton

REGIONAL VICE PRESIDENTS

Southeast, Rev. Gene Evans, P.O. Box 813, Douglasville, GA 30133
South Central, Rev. Robert J. Miller, P.O. Box 10621, Killeen, TX 76547
Southwest, Dr. R.G. Dunbar, 121 N. 32nd Street, Colorado Springs, CO 80904
Northeast, Rev. David Ellis, 3636 Winchester Rd., Allertown, PA 18104
North Central, Rev. David Robinson, 1121 Shuler Street, Elgin, IL 60123
Northwest, Rev. Jon R. Engstrom, 19605 12th Ave. W, Lynnwood, WA 98036

Periodicals

Fellowship Tidings

Fundamental Methodist Church, Inc.

This group traces its origin through the Methodist Protestant Church. It withdrew from The Methodist Church and organized on August 27, 1942.

Headquarters

1034 N. Broadway, Springfield, MO 65802
Media Contact, Dist. Supt., Rev. Ronnie Howerton, 1952 Highway H, Monett, MO 65708 Tel. (417)235-3849

Officers

Treas., Wayne Blades, Rt. 1, Crane, MO 65633 Tel. (417)723-8123
Sec., Betty Nicholson, Rt. 2, Box 397, Ash Grove, MO 65604 Tel. (417)672-2268
Dist. Supt., Rev. Ronnie Howerton, 1952 Highway H, Monett, MO 65708 Tel. (417)235-3849

General Association of General Baptists

Similar in doctrine to those General Baptists organized in England in the 17th century, the first General Baptist churches were organized on the Midwest frontier following the Second Great Awakening. The first church was established by the Rev. Benoni Stinson in 1823 at Evansville, Ind.

Stinson's major theological emphasis was general atonement—Christ tasted death for every man. The group also allows for the possibility of apostasy. It practices open Communion and believer's baptism by immersion.

Called "liberal" Baptists because of their emphasis on the freedom of man, General Baptists organized a General Association in 1870 and invited other "liberal" Baptists (e.g., "Free Will" and Separate Baptists) to participate.

The policy-setting body is composed of delegates from local General Baptist churches and associations. Each local church is autonomous but belongs to an association. The group currently consists of more than 60 associations in 16 states, as well as associations in the Philippines, Guam, Saipan, Jamaica, Honduras, and India. Ministers and deacons are ordained by a presbytery.

The denomination operates Oakland City University in Oakland City, Indiana, and nursing homes in Illinois and Missouri. General Baptists belong to the Baptist World Alliance, the North American Baptist Fellowship and the National Association of Evangelicals.

Headquarters

100 Stinson Dr., Poplar Bluff, MO 63901 Tel. (573)785-7746 Fax (573)785-0564
Media Contact, Exec. Dir., Dr. Ron Black

Officers

Mod., Rev. Bill McMillen
Clk., Mr. Tommy Roberts
Exec. Dir., Dr. Ron Black

OTHER ORGANIZATIONS

International Missions, Dir., Rev. Jack Eberhardt
National Missions, Dir., Rev. Ron Byrd
Women's Ministries, Dir., Barbara Wigger
Oakland City University, Dr. James Murray, Chancellor/Pres., 143 N. Lucretia St., Oakland City, IN 47660
Congregational Ministries, Dir., Rev. Mike Warren, 100 Stinson Dr., Poplar Bluff, MO 63901
Pastoral Ministries, Dir., Rev. Fred Brittain, 100 Stinson Dr., Poplar Bluff, MO 63901
Admin., Financial Services, Financial Officer, Linda McDonough, 100 Stinson Dr., Poplar Bluff, MO 63901
Stinson Press, Inc., Pres., Rev. Dale Bates, 400 Stinson Dr., Poplar Bluff, MO 63901
Nursing Home Board, CEO, Rev. Jack Cole, Rt. #3, Box 650, Campbell, MO 63933
Compassionate Care Adoption Agency, Dir., Dr. John Clanton, Rt. 3, Box 12B, Oakland City, IN 47660

General Association of Regular Baptist Churches

This association was founded in May, 1932, in Chicago by a group of churches that had withdrawn from the Northern Baptist Convention (now the American Baptist Churches in the U.S.A.) because of doctrinal differences. Its Confession of Faith, which it requires all churches to subscribe to, is essentially the old, historic New Hampshire Confession of Faith with a premillennial ending applied to the last article.

The churches of the General Association of Regular Baptist Churches voluntarily joined together to accomplish four goals. (1) Champion Biblical truth—committed to communicating the whole counsel of God in its timeless relevance. (2) Impact the world for Christ; obeying the Lord's Great Commission to take the life-changing gospel to the entire world. (3) Perpetuate Its Baptist heritage; faithfully promoting its Scriptural legacy and identity. (4) Advancing GARBC churches; strengthening existing churches and planting new churches for the purposes of evangelism and edification.

Headquarters

1300 N. Meacham Rd., Schaumburg, IL 60173 Tel. (847)843-1600 Fax (847)843-3757
Media Contact, Natl. Rep., Dr. John Greening
E-mail: garbc@garbc.org
Web site: www.garbc.org

Officers

Chpsn., Rev. Bryce Augsburger
Vice-Chpsn., David Warren
Treas., Dr. David Gower
Sec., Rev. David Strope
Natl. Rep., Dr. John Greening

Periodicals

Baptist Bulletin; Energy Newsletter

General Church of the New Jerusalem

The General Church of the New Jerusalem, also called the New Church, was founded in 1897. It is based on the teachings of the 18th Century scientist Emanuel Swedenborg, and stresses the oneness of God, who is the Lord Jesus Christ, a life of faith and love in service to others, in true married love, and in life after death.

Headquarters

P.O. Box 743, Bryn Athyn, PA 19009 Tel. (215)938-2682
Media Contact, Ed., Church Journal, Donald L. Rose, Box 277, Bryn Athyn, PA 19009 Tel. (215)947-6225 Fax (215)947-3078
E-mail: svsimpso@newchurch.edu
Web site: www.newchurch.org

Officers

Presiding Bishop, Rt. Rev. Thomas L. Kline
Sec., Susan V. Simpson
Treas., William W. Buick

Periodicals

New Church Life

General Conference of Mennonite Brethren Churches

A small group, requesting that closer attention be given to prayer, Bible study and a consistent lifestyle, withdrew from the larger Mennonite Church in the Ukraine in 1860. Anabaptist in origin, the group was influenced by Lutheran pietists and Baptist teachings and adopted a quasi-congregational form of church government. In 1874 and years following, small groups of these German-speaking Mennonites left Russia, settled in Kansas and then spread to the Midwest west of the Mississippi and into Canada. Some years later the movement spread to California and the West Coast. In 1960, the Krimmer Mennonite Brethren Conference merged with this body.

Today the General Conference of Mennonite Brethren Churches conducts services in many European languages as well as in Vietnamese, Mandarin and Hindi. It works with other denominations in missionary and development projects in 25 countries outside North America.

Headquarters

4812 E. Butler Ave., Fresno, CA 93727 Tel. (209)452-1713 Fax (209)452-1752
Media Contact, Exec. Sec., Marvin Hein

Officers

Mod., Ed Boschman, 12630 N. 103rd Ave., Suite 215, Sun City, AZ 85351
Asst. Mod., Herb Kopp, 200 McIvor Ave., Winnipeg, NB R20 028

Sec., Valerie Rempel
Exec. Sec., Marvin Hein

Periodicals

Christian Leader

Grace Gospel Fellowship

The Grace Gospel Fellowship was organized in 1944 by a group of pastors who held to a dispensational interpretation of Scripture. Most had ministries in the Midwest. Two prominent leaders were J. C. O'Hair of Chicago and Charles Baker of Milwaukee. Subsequent to 1945, a Bible Institute was founded (now Grace Bible College of Grand Rapids, Mich.), and a previously organized foreign mission (now Grace Ministries International of Grand Rapids) was affiliated with the group. Churches have now been established in most sections of the country.

The body has remained a fellowship, each church being autonomous in polity. All support for its college, mission and headquarters is on a contributory basis.

The binding force of the Fellowship has been the members' doctrinal position. They believe in the Deity and Saviorship of Jesus Christ and subscribe to the inerrant authority of Scripture. Their method of biblical interpretation is dispensational, with emphasis on the distinctive revelation to and the ministry of the Apostle Paul.

Headquarters

Media Contact, Pres., Frosty Hansen, 2125 Martindale SW, P.O. Box 9432, Grand Rapids, MI 49509 Tel. (616)245-0100 Fax (616)241-2542
E-mail: ggfinc@aol.com
Web site: www.ggfusa.org

Officers

Pres., Traynor ("Frosty") Hansen, Jr.

OTHER ORGANIZATIONS

Grace Bible College, Pres., Rev. Ken Kemper, 1011 Aldon St. SW, Grand Rapids, MI 49509
Grace Ministries Intl., Exec. Dir., Dr. Samuel Vinton, 2125 Martindale Ave. SW, Grand Rapids, MI 49509
Prison Mission Association, Gen. Dir., Donald Sommer, P.O. Box 1587, Port Orchard, WA 98366-0140
Grace Publications Inc., Exec. Dir., Wayne Schoonover, 2125 Martindale Ave. SW, Grand Rapids, MI 49509
Bible Doctrines to Live By, Exec. Dir., Lee Homoki, P.O. Box 2351, Grand Rapids, MI 49501

Periodicals

Truth

Greek Orthodox Archdiocese of America*

THE ORTHODOX CHURCH

The Orthodox Church today, numbering over 250 million worldwide, is a communion of self-governing churches, each administratively independent of the other, but united by a common faith and spirituality. Their underlying unity is based on identity of doctrines, sacramental life and worship, which distinguishes Orthodox Christianity. All recognize the spiritual preeminence of the Ecumenical Patriarch of Constantinople who is acknowledged as *primus inter pares*, first among equals. All share full communion with one another. The living tradition of the church and the principles of concord and harmony are expressed through the common mind of the universal episcopate as the need arises. In all other matters, the internal life of each independent church is administered by the bishops of that particular church. Following the ancient priciple of the one people of God in each place and the universal priesthood of all believers, the laity share equally in the responsibility for the preservation and propagation of the Christian faith and Church.

THE GREEK ORTHODOX ARCHIODESE OF AMERICA

Before the establishment of an Archdiocese in the Western Hemisphere there were numerous communities of Greek Orthodox Christians. The first Greek Orthodox community in the Americas was founded in New Orleans, La. by a small colony of Greek merchants. History also records that on June 26,1768 the first Greek colonists landed at St. Augustine, Fla., the oldest city in America. The first permanent community was founded in New York City in 1892, today's Archdiocesan Cathedral of the Holy Trinity and the See of the Archbishop of America. The Greek Orthodox Archdiocese of North and South America was incorporated in 1921 and officially recognized by the State of New York in 1922.

The Greek Orthodox Archdiocese of America is composed of an Archdiocesan District—New York and eight Metropolises: Chicago, San Francisco, Pittsburgh, Boston, Denver, Atlanta, Detroit and New Jersey. It is governed by the Archbishop and the Synod of Bishops. The Synod of Bishops is headed by the Archbishop and comprised of the Metro- politans, who are in charge of a metropolis. It has all the authority and responsibility which the church canons provide for a provincial synod.

Headquarters

8-10 E. 79th St., New York, NY 10021 Tel. (212)570-3500 Fax (212)570-3569
Media Contact, Dir., News and Information/ Public Affairs, Nikki Stephanopoulos, Tel. (212) 570-3530 Fax (212)774-0215, nikki@goarch.org
E-mail: archdiocese@goarch.org
Web site: www.goarch.org

HOLY EPARCHIAL SYNOD OF BISHOPS

His Eminence Archbishop Demetrios, Primate of the Greek Orthodox Archdiocese of America, Exarch of the Atlantic and Pacific Oceans, Chairman of the Holy Synod of Bishops,

Greek Orthodox Church in America, 8-10 East 79th St., New York, NY 10021 Tel. (212)570-3500 Fax (212)570-3592

DIOCESES

His Eminence Metropolitan Iakovos of Chicago, Metropolis of Chicago, 40 E. Burton Place, Chicago, IL 60610 Tel. (312)337-4130 Fax (312)337-9391

His Eminence Metropolitan Anthony of San Francisco, Metropolis of San Francisco, 372 Santa Clara Ave., San Francisco, CA 94127 Tel. (415)753-3075 Fax (415)753-1165

His Eminence Metropolitan Maximos of Pittsburgh, Metropolis of Pittsburgh, 5201 Ellsworth Ave., Pittsburgh, PA 15232 Tel. (412)621-5529 Fax (412)621-1522

His Eminence Metropolitan Methodios of Boston, Metropolis of Boston, 162 Goddard Ave., Brookline, MA 02146 Tel. (617)277-4742 Fax (617)739-9229

His Eminence Metropolitan Isaiah of Denver, Metropolis of Denver, 4610 E. Alameda Ave., Suite D1, Denver, CO 80222 Tel. (303)333-7794 Fax (303)333-7796

His Eminence Metropolitan Alexios of Atlanta, Metropolis of Atlanta, 2480 Clairmont Rd. NE, Atlanta, GA 30329 Tel. (404)634-9345 Fax (404)634-2471

His Eminence Metroplitan Nicholas of Detroit, Metropolis of Detroit, 19405 Renfrew Rd., Detroit, MI 48221 Tel. (313)664-5433 Fax (313)864-5543

Hs Eminence Metropolitan Evangelos of New Jersey, Metropolis of New Jersey, 629 Springfield Rd., Kenilworth, NJ 07033 Tel. (908)686-0003 Fax (908)686-0046

His Grace Bishop Gerasimos of Krateia, Chief Sec.

Auxiliary Bishops, His Grace Bishop Dimitrios of Xanthos; His Grace Bisop Savas of Troas; His Grace Bishop Gerasimos of Krateia; His Grace Bishop Andonios of Phasiane

CLERGY-LAITY CONGRESS

The Clergy-Laity Congress, the highest legislative body of the Archdiocese, is convened biennially and presided over by the Archbishop. It is concerned with all matters, other than doctrinal or canonical, affecting the life, growth and unity of the church, the institutions, finances, administration, educational and philanthropic concerns and its increasing growing role in the life of the nations of the Western Hemisphere. The delegates are the pastors and elected lay representatives.

There are 510 parishes, 810 priests and approximately 1.5 million faithful in the Greek Orthodox Archdiocese of America

THE ARCHDIOCESAN COUNCIL

The Archdiocesan Council is the deliberative body of the Greek Orthodox Archdiocese which meets in the interim period between Clergy-Laity Congresses, held every two years.

Exec. Committee, Chairman, His Eminence Archbishop Demetrios

The Holy Synod of Bishops, Vice-Chairman, Michael Jaharis; Peter Dion; Treas., Nicholas Bouras; George Behrakis; Dr. John Collis; John Pappajohn; John Payiavlas; Georgia Skeadas; Anthony Stefanis; Sec., Catherine Bouffides-Walsh; Legal Counselor to the Archdiocese, Emanuel G. Demos

INSTITUTIONS

Archdiocesan Cathedral of the Holy Trinity, Dean, The Rev. Dr. Robert G. Stephanopoulos, 319-337 E. 74th St., New York, NY 10021 Tel, (212)288-3215 Fax (212)288-5876, www.thecathedral.goarch.org

Hellenic College/Holy Cross School of Theology, Pres., The Rev. Nicholas Triantafilou, 50 Goddard Ave., Brookline, MA 02445 Tel. (617)731-3500 Fax (617)850-1460, admission@hchc.edu

Saint Basil Academy, Dir., The Rev. Constantine L. Sitaras, 79 Saint Basil Rd., Garrison, NY 10524 Tel. (845)424-3500 Fax (845) 424-4172, stbasil@bestweb.net, www.stbasil. goarch.org

St. Michael's Home, Dir., His Grace Bishop Andonios of Phasiane, 3 Lehman Terrace, Yonkers, NY 10705 Tel. (914)476-3374 Fax (914)476-1744, stmichaelshome@msn.com, www.stmichael.goarch.org

ARCHDIOCESE OF NEW YORK

Office of the Archbishop, Dir., Alice Keurian; Office of the Chancellor, Chancellor, His Grace Bishop Savas of Troas; Office of Administration, Exec. Dir., Jerry Dimitriou

ARCHDIOCESAN DEPARTMENTS

Registry, Finance, Stewardship & LOGOS, Religious Education, Greek Education, Communications, Internet Ministries, Information Technologies, Youth and Young Adults, Camping Ministry, Ionian Village Ecumenical, Interfaith/Interchurch Marriages, Archives, Benefits

RELATED ORGANIZATIONS & AUXILIARIES

Ladies Philoptochos Society, Presbyters Council, Sisterhood of Presvyteres, Retired Clergy of America, National Forum of Greek Orthodox Musicians, Hellenic Cultural Center, Archons of the Ecumenical Patriarchate, Archbishop Iakovos Leadership 100 Endowment Fund, St. Photios National Shrine, International Orthodox Christian Charities (IOCC), Orthodox Christian Mission Center, Trinity Children & Family Services.

OTHER JURISDICTIONS OF THE ECUMENICAL PATRIARCHATE IN THE U.S.A.

Albanian Orthodox Diocese in America; Belarusian Council of Orthodox Churches in North America; American Carpatho-Russian Orthodox Greek Catholic Diocese of the USA; Ukrainian Orthodox Church of the USA

Periodicals

The Orthodox Observer, observer@goarch.org
Television Ministry, Greek Orthodox Telecommunications (GOTelecom), www.goarch.org

The Holy Eastern Orthodox Catholic and Apostolic Church in North America, Inc.

Canonically established by the Russian Orthodox Synod of Bishops in North America on Feb. 2, 1927 this church was incorporated on Feb. 1, 1928 by Archbishop Aftimios Ofiesh, the first Archbishop-Pres.. Archbishop Aftimios continued as head of this church until he reposed in July 1966. The name and logo are registered service marks of this church. We are a western rite church but some of our clergy do celebrate the Eastern Liturgy.

The first Synod included Archbishop Aftimios and Bishops Sophronios and Zuk. Over the years many have claimed to be this church, its successor, this church under a different name or having our lines. These are members of the independent movement who claim to have lines of apostolic succession that are traced back to us but not recognized by this or any canonical church since they were not administered in accordance to the Rudder (Canons) of the Orthodox Church.

Headquarters

St. Pachomius Monastery, P.O. Box 8122, Columbus, OH 43201 Tel. (614)297-8055
Primate, Metropolitan Victor
E-mail: tmetropolitan@theocacna.org
Web site: www.theocacna.org

Officers

Archbishop Peter Mar Kepa—Archdiocese of the East
Metropolitan Victor - Archdiocese of the West
Bishop Christopher - Diocese of Houston, Tx.
Bishop Cassian - Diocese of Columbus, Oh.
Bishop Arthur - Diocese of Michigan
Synod Advisors, Archbishop James; Bishop Donald

OTHER ORGANIZATIONS

The Society of Clerks Secular of St. Basil, est. 1931

Holy Ukrainian Autocephalic Orthodox Church in Exile

This church was organized in a parish in New York in 1951 by Ukrainian laymen and clergy who settled in the Western Hemisphere after World War II. In 1954 two bishops, immigrants from Europe, met with clergy and laymen and formally organized the religious body.

Headquarters

103 Evergreen St., West Babylon, NY 11704

Officers

Admin., Rt. Rev. Serhij K. Pastukhiv, Tel. (516) 669-7402

House of God, Which is the Church of the Living God, the Pillar and Ground of the Truth, Inc.

This body, founded by Mary L. Tate in 1919, is episcopally organized.

Headquarters

1301 N. 58th St., Philadelphia, PA 19131
Media Contact, Sec., Rose Canon, 515 S. 57th St., Philadelphia, PA 19143 Tel. (215)474-8913

Officers

Bishop, Raymond W. White, 6107 Cobbs Creek Pkwy., Philadelphia, PA 19143 Tel. (215)748-6338

Hungarian Reformed Church in America*

A Hungarian Reformed Church was organized in New York in 1904 in connection with the Reformed Church of Hungary. In 1922, the Church in Hungary transferred most of its congregations in the United States to the Reformed Church in the U.S. Some, however, preferred to continue as an autonomous, self-supporting American denomination, and these formed the Free Magyar Reformed Church in America. This group changed its name in 1958 to Hungarian Reformed Church in America.

This church is a member of the World Alliance of Reformed Churches, Presbyterian and Congregational, the World Council of Churches and the National Council of Churches of Christ.

Headquarters

Bishop's Office, 13 Grove St., Poughkeepsie, NY 12601 Tel. (914)454-5735

Officers

Bishop, Rt. Rev. Alexander Forro
Chief Lay-Curator, Prof. Stephen Szabo, 464 Forest Ave., Paramus, NJ 07652
Gen. Sec. (Clergy), Rt. Rev. Stefan M. Torok, 331 Kirkland Pl., Perth Amboy, NJ 08861 Tel. (908)442-7799
Gen Sec. (Lay), Zoltan Ambrus, 3358 Maple Dr., Melvindale, MI 48122
Eastern Classes, Dean (Sr. of the Deans, Chair in Bishop's absence), Very Rev. Imre Bertalan, 10401 Grosvenor Pl. #1521, Rockville, MD 20852 Tel. (301)493-5036 Fax (301)571-5111; Lay-Curator, Balint Balogh, 519 N. Muhlenberg St., Allentown, PA 18104
New York Classes, Supervisor, Rt. Rev. Alexander Forro; Lay-Curator, Laszlo B. Vanyi, 229 E. 82nd St., New York, NY 10028
Western Classes, Dean, V. Rev. Andor Demeter, 3921 W. Christy Dr., Phoenix, AZ 85029; Lay-Curator, Zolton Kun, 2604 Saybrook Dr., Pittsburgh, PA 15235

Periodicals

Magyar Egyhaz

Hutterian Brethren

Small groups of Hutterites derive their names from Jacob Hutter, a 16th-century Anabaptist who taught true discipleship after accepting Jesus as Savior, advocated communal ownership of property and was burned as a heretic in Austria in 1536.

Many believers are of German descent and still use their native tongue at home and in church. Much of the denominational literature is produced in German and English. "Colonies" share property, practice non-resistance, dress plainly, do not participate in politics and operate their own schools. There are 428 colonies with 42,000 members in North America. Each congregation conducts its own youth work through Sunday school. Until age 15, children attend German and English school, which is operated by each colony. All youth ages 15 to 20 attend Sunday school. They are baptized as adults upon confession of faith, around age 20.

Headquarters

Media Contact, Philip J. Gross, 3610 N. Wood Rd., Reardon, WA 99029 Tel. (509)299-5400 Fax (509)299-3099

E-mail: philsjg@juno.com

Officers

Smiedleut Chmn., No. 1, Jacob Waldner—Blumengard Colony, Box 13, Plum Coulee, MB R0G 1R0 Tel. (204)829-3527

Smiedleut Chmn., No. 2, Jacob Wipf, Spring Creek Colony, 36562 102 Street, Forbes, ND 58439 Tel. (701)358-8621

Dariusleut, Chmn., No. 1, Martin Walter, Springpoint Colony, Box 249, Pincher Creek, AB T0K 1W0 Tel. (403)553-4368

Lehrerleut, Chmn., Rev. John Wipf, Rosetown Colony, Box 1509, Rosetown, SK S0L 2V0 Tel. (306)882-3344

IFCA International, Inc.

This group of churches was organized in 1930 at Cicero, Illinois, by representatives of the American Council of Undenominational Churches and representatives of various independent churches. The founding churches and members had separated themselves from various denominational affiliations. Founders included J. Oliver Buswell of Wheaton College, Billy McCarrell of Cicero Bible Church and Moody Bible Institute, and M. R. DeHaan of Grand Rapids, MI and Radio Bible Class. Members have included J. Vernon McGee, Charles Ryrie, John Walvoord, and John MacArthur.

The IFCA provides a way for independent churches and ministers to unite in close fellowship and cooperation, in defense of the fundamental teachings of Scripture and in the proclamation of the gospel of God's grace.

Today it consists of 1,000 associated churches and 1200 individual members (pastors, professors, missionaries, chaplains, and other Christian workers.)

Headquarters

3520 Fairlanes, Grandville, MI 49418 Tel. (616)531-1840 Fax (616)531-1814

Mailing Address, P.O. Box 810, Grandville, MI 49468-0810

Media Contact, Exec. Dir., Rev. Les Lofquist

E-mail: office@ifca.org

Web site: www.ifca.org

Officers

Exec. Dir., Rev. Les Lofquist

Pres., Dr. Roy Sprague, Lakewood, WA

Periodicals

The Voice

International Church of the Foursquare Gospel

Founded by Aimee Semple McPherson in 1927, the International Church of the Foursquare Gospel proclaims the message of Jesus Christ the Savior, Healer, Baptizer with the Holy Spirit and Sooncoming King. Headquartered in Los Angeles, this evangelistic missionary body of believers consists of nearly 1,900 churches in the United States and Canada. The International Church of the Foursquare Gospel is incorporated in the state of California and governed by a Board of Directors that directs its corporate affairs. A Foursquare Cabinet, consisting of the Corporate Officers, Board of Directors and District Supervisors of the various districts of the Foursquare Church in the United States and other elected or appointed members, serves in an advisory capacity to the President. and the Board of Directors. Each local Foursquare Church is a subordinate unit of the International Church of the Foursquare Gospel. The pastor of the church is appointed by the Board of Directors and is responsible for the spiritual and physical welfare of the church. To assist and advise the pastor, a church council is elected by the local church members. Foursquare churches seek to build strong believers through Christian education, Christian day schools, youth camping and ministry, Foursquare Women International who support and encourage Foursquare missionaries abroad, local radio and television ministries, the Foursquare World *ADVANCE* Magazine and over 550 Bible colleges worldwide. Worldwide missions remains the focus of the Foursquare Gospel Church, with 38,217 churches and meeting places, 49,287 national pastors, leaders and 4,113,981 members with a combined constituency nearing 5 million in over 140 countries of the world. The church is affiliated with the Pentecostal/Charismatic Churches of North America, the National Association of Evangelicals and the Pentecostal World Conference.

Headquarters

1910 W. Sunset Blvd., Suite 200, P.O. Box 26902, Los Angeles, CA 90026-0176 Tel. (213)989-4234 Fax (213)989-4590

Media Contact, Editor, Dr. Ron Williams

E-mail: comm@foursquare.org

Web site: www.foursquare.org

Officers

Pres., Dr. Paul C. Risser;
Vice-Pres., Dr. Jared D. Roth
Gen. Supervisor, Rev. Glenn C. Burris, Jr.
Dir. of Missions, Rev. Michael Larkin
Corporate Sec., Rev. Arthur J. Gray, II
Treas., Mr. Brent R. Morgan
Board of Dir., Robert Bankhead; Greg Campbell; George Cline; Robert Flores; Jeff Hamilton; Dan Hicks; Ken Johnson; Mike McGovern; Carlos Santiago; Steve Schell; Oscar Shepherd; Mark Simon; Devi Titus; Roger Wheeler;
Foursquare Cabinet, John Honold; Teri Orewiler; Kim Pitner; Sharon Snow; Richard Trees; Ken Authier; Robby Booth; Daniel Brown; Richard Casteel; David Coffey; Dennis Estill; Ken Hart; Jim Hayford; Marty Jenkins; Ron Pinkston; Michael Posey; Scott Reece; Dwight Saunders

SUPPORT MINISTRIES

National Dept. of Youth, Dir., Walter R. Hoefflin
Dept. of Christian Education, Dir., Rod Light
Foursquare Women International, Dir., Kimberly Dirmann

Periodicals

Foursquare World ADVANCE magazine, Editor, Bill Shepson; Dir. of Communications, Brad Abare

International Council of Community Churches*

This body is a fellowship of locally autonomous, ecumenically minded, congregationally governed, non-creedal churches. The Council came into being in 1950 as the union of two former councils of community churches, one formed of black churches known as the Biennial Council of Community Churches in the United States and Elsewhere and the other of white churches known as the National Council of Community Churches.

Headquarters

21116 Washington Pky., Frankfort, IL 60423-3112 Tel. (815)464-5690 Fax (815)464-5692
Media Contact, Exec. Dir., Rev. Michael E. Livingston

Officers

Pres., Grace O'Neal
Vice-Pres., Rev. Herbert Freitag
Vice-Pres., Rev. Leroy McCreary
Sec., Rev. Gary Batey
Treas., Rev. Martin Singley, III

OTHER ORGANIZATIONS

Commission on Laity and Church Relations, Fran Langille
Commission on Ecumenical Relations, Rev. Herman Harmelink, III
Commission on Clergy Relations, Rev. Carol Parrish
Commission on Faith, Justice & Mission, Rev. Dr. Jeffrey Newhall
Women's Christian Fellowship, Pres., Catherine Luckett
Samaritans (Men's Fellowship), Pres., Nicholas Brame
Young Adult Fellowship, Pres., Susan Frazier
Youth Fellowship, Pres., Brittany Gardner

Periodicals

The Christian Community; The Inclusive Pulpit; Key Lay Notes; Clergy Comminique

The International Pentecostal Church of Christ

At a General Conference held at London, Ohio, Aug. 10, 1976, the International Pentecostal Assemblies and the Pentecostal Church of Christ consolidated into one body, taking the name International Pentecostal Church of Christ.

The International Pentecostal Assemblies was the successor of the Association of Pentecostal Assemblies and the International Pentecostal Missionary Union. The Pentecostal Church of Christ was founded by John Stroup of Flatwoods, Kentucky, on May 10, 1917 and was incorporated at Portsmouth, Ohio, in 1927. The International Pentecostal Church of Christ is an active member of the Pentecostal/Charismatic Churches of North America, as well as a member of the National Association of Evangelicals.

The priorities of the International Pentecostal Church of Christ are to be an agency of God for evangelizing the world, to be a corporate body in which people may worship God and to be a channel of God's purpose to build a body of saints being perfected in the image of His Son.

The Annual Conference is held each year during the first full week of August in London, Ohio.

Headquarters

2245 State Rt. 42 SW, P.O. Box 439, London, OH 43140 Tel. (740)852-4722 Fax (740)852-0348
Media Contact, Gen. Overseer, Clyde M. Hughes
E-mail: hqipcc@aol.com
Web site: members.aol.com/hqipcc

EXECUTIVE COMMITTEE

Gen. Overseer, Clyde M. Hughes, P.O. Box 439, London, OH 43140 Tel. (740)852-4722 Fax (740)852-0348
Asst. Gen. Overseer, B.G. Turner, RR5, Box 1286, Harpers Ferry, WV 25425 Tel. (304)535-221 Fax (304)535-1357
Gen. Sec., Asa Lowe, 513 Johnstown Rd., Chesapeake, VA 23322 Tel. (757)547-4329
Gen. Treas., Ervin Hargrave, P.O. Box 439, London, OH 43140 Tel. (740)852-4722 Fax (740)852-0348

Dir. of Global Missions, Dr. James B. Keiller, P.O. Box 18145, Atlanta, GA 30316 Tel. (404)627-2681 Fax (404)627-0702

DISTRICT OVERSEERS

Central District, Lindsey Hayes, 609 Lansing Rd., Akron, OH 44312 Tel. (330)784-3453

Mid-Eastern District, H. Gene Boyce, 705 W. Grubb St., Hertford, NC 27944 Tel. (252)426-5403

Mountain District, Terry Lykins, P.O. Box 131, Staffordsville, KY 41256 Tel. (606)297-3282

New River District, Calvin Weikel, RR. 2, Box 300, Ronceverte, WV 24970 Tel. (304)647-4301

North Central District, Edgar Kent, P.O. Box 275, Hartford, MI 49057 Tel. (616)621-3326

North Eastern District, Wayne Taylor, 806 8th St., Shenandoah, VA 22849 Tel (540)652-8090

South Eastern District, Frank Angie, 2507 Old Peachtree Rd., Duluth, GA 30097 Tel (770)476-5196

Tri-State District, Cline McCallister, 5210 Wilson St., Portsmouth, OH 45662 Tel. and Fax (740)776-6357

Portugese District, Pedro Messias, 34 Woodside Ave., Danbury, CT 06810 Tel. (203)790-9628

OTHER ORGANIZATIONS

Beulah Heights Bible College, Pres., Samuel R. Chand, P.O. Box 18145, Atlanta, GA 30316 Tel. (404)627-2681 Fax (404)627-0702

Women's Ministries, Gen. Pres., Janice Boyce, 121 W. Hunters Tr., Elizabeth City, NC 27909 Tel. and Fax (252)338-3003

Pentecostal Ambassadors, National Youth Dir., Dustin Hughes, P.O. Box 439, London, OH 43140 Tel. (740)852-0448 Fax (740)852-0348

National Christian Education Dept., Dir., Dustin Hughes, P.O. Box 439, London, OH 43140 Tel. (740)852-0448 Fax (740)852-0348

Periodicals

The Bridegroom's Messenger; The Pentecostal Leader

International Pentecostal Holiness Church

This body grew out of the National Holiness Association movement of the last century, with roots in Methodism. Beginning in the South and Midwest, the church represents the merger of the Fire-Baptized Holiness Church founded by B. H. Irwin in Iowa in 1895; the Pentecostal Holiness Church founded by A. B. Crumpler in Goldsboro, North Carolina, in 1898; and the Tabernacle Pentecostal Church founded by N. J. Holmes in 1898.

All three bodies joined the ranks of the pentecostal movement as a result of the Azusa Street revival in Los Angeles in 1906 and a 1907 pentecostal revival in Dunn, N.C., conducted by G. B. Cashwell, who had visited Azusa Street. In 1911 the Fire-Baptized and Pentecostal Holiness bodies merged in Falcon, N.C., to form the present church; the Tabernacle Pentecostal Church was added in 1915 in Canon, Georgia.

The church stresses the new birth, the Wesleyan experience of sanctification, the pentecostal baptism in the Holy Spirit, evidenced by speaking in tongues, divine healing and the premillennial second coming of Christ.

Headquarters

P.O. Box 12609, Oklahoma City, OK 73157-2609 Tel. (405)787-7110 Fax (405)789-3957

E-mail: jdl@iphc.org (for Bishop Leggett)

Web site: www.iphc.org

Officers

Gen. Supt., Bishop James D. Leggett

Vice-Chpsn. & Exec. Dir. of World Missions Ministries, Rev. M. Donald Duncan

Exec. Dir. of Evangelism USA, Dr. Ronald Carpenter, Sr.

Exec. Dir. of Church Education Ministries, Dr. A.D. Beacham, Jr.

Exec. Dir. of Stewardship Ministries & Gen. Sec.-Treas., Rev. Edward W. Wood

OTHER ORGANIZATIONS

The Publishing House (LifeSprings Resources), CEO, Greg Hearn, Franklin Springs, GA 30639

Women's Ministries, Exec. Dir., Mrs. Jewelle Stewart

Men's Ministries, Exec. Dir., Col. Jack Kelley, P.O. Box 53307, Fayetteville, NC 28305-3307

Periodicals

IPHC Experience

Jehovah's Witnesses

Modern-day Jehovah's Witnesses began in the early 1870s when Charles Taze Russell was the leader of a Bible study group in Allegheny City, Pennsylvania. In July 1879, the first issue of *Zion's Watch Tower* and *Herald of Christ's Presence*, now called *The Watchtower* and published in more than 140 languages with a circulation of upwards of 25 million, appeared. In 1884 Zion's Watch Tower Tract Society was incorporated, later changed to Watch Tower Bible and Tract Society. Congregations spread into other states and countries, and followers witnessed from house to house.

By 1913, printed sermons were in four languages in 3,000 newspapers in the United States, Canada and Europe. Hundreds of millions of books, booklets and tracts were distributed. Publication of the magazine now known as *Awake!* Began in 1919. Today, it is published in more than 80 languages and has a circulation of upwards of 22,000,000. In 1931 the name Jehovah's Witnesses, based on Isaiah 43:10-12, was adopted.

During the 1930s and 1940s Jehovah's Witnesses fought many court cases in the interest of preserving freedom of speech, press, assembly and worship. The group has won a total of 43 cases before the United States Supreme Court. A missionary training school was established in 1943, and it has been a major factor in the international expansion of the Witnesses. There are now 6.4 million Witnesses in 235 lands.

Jehovah's Witnesses believe in one almighty God, Jehovah, who is the Creator of all things. They believe in Jesus Christ as God's Son, the first of His creations. While Jesus is now an immortal spirit in heaven, ruling as King of God's Kingdom, he is still subject to his heavenly Father, Jehovah God. Christ's human life was sacrificed as a ransom to open up for obedient mankind the opportunity of eternal life. With Christ in heaven, 144,000 individuals chosen from among mankind will rule in righteousness over an unnumbered great crowd who will survive the destruction of wickedness and receive salvation into an earth cleansed of evil. (Rev. 7:9,10;14:1-5). These, along with the resurrected dead, will transform the earth into a global earthly paradise and will have the prospect of living forever on it.

Headquarters

25 Columbia Heights, Brooklyn, NY 11201-2483 Tel. (718)560-5000
Media Contact, Office of Public Information, J. R. Brown
Editorial Contact, Writing Department, James N. Pellechia
Web site: www.watchtower.org

Officers

Pres. Watch Tower Bible and Tract Society of Pennsylvania, Don Adams

Periodicals

Awake!, The Watchtower

Korean Presbyterian Church in America, General Assembly of the*

This body came into official existence in the United States in 1976 and is currently an ethnic church, using the Korean and English languages.

Headquarters

General Assembly of the Korean Presbyterian Church in America, 17200 Clark Ave., Bellflower, CA 90706 Tel. (714)816-1100 Fax (714)816-1120

Officers

General Sec., Rev. Seung Koo Choi, 3335 W. Lincoln Ave. #327, Anaheim, CA 92801 Tel. (714)928-6131

Periodicals

Moderator, Rev. Dr. Young Chin Huh, 12601 Leda Lane, Garden Grove, CA 92840 Tel. (714)537-2687

Latter-day Saints—please see The Church of Jesus Christ of Latter-day Saints

The Latvian Evangelical Lutheran Church in America

This body was organized into a denomination on Aug. 22, 1975 after having existed as the Federation of Latvian Evangelical Lutheran Churches in America since 1955. This church is a regional constituent part of the Lutheran Church of Latvia Abroad, a member of the Lutheran World Federation and the World Council of Churches.

The Latvian Evangelical Lutheran Church in America works to foster religious life, traditions and customs in its congregations in harmony with the Holy Scriptures, the Apostles', Nicean and Athanasian Creeds, the unaltered Augsburg Confession, Martin Luther's Small and Large Catechisms and other documents of the Book of Concord.

The LELCA is ordered by its Synod (General Assembly), executive board, auditing committee and district conferences.

Headquarters

2140 Orkla Dr., Golden Valley, MN 55427 Tel. (612)722-0174, ucepure@aol.com
Media Contact, Juris Pulins, 9531 Knoll Top Rd., Union, IL 60180 Tel. (815)923-5919
E-mail: pulins@flash.net

Officers

Pres., Rev. Uldis Cepure, Tel. (612)546-3712
Vice-Pres., Rev. Anita Varsbergs, 9908 Shelburne Terr. #312, Gathersburg, MD 20878 Tel. (301) 251-4151
Sec., Girts Kugars, 5209 Douglas Ave., Kalamazoo, MI 49004 Tel. (616)381-3798
Treas., Vilmars Beinikis, 17 John Dr., Old Bethpage, NY 11804 Tel. (516)293-8432

Periodicals

Cela Biedrs; Lelba Zinas

Liberal Catholic Church (International)

Founded as a reorganization of the Dutch Old Catholic Church in 1915-16. In 1941 a controversy broke out in the church regarding whether or not certain teachings of Theosophy (reincarnation, etc.) were to become official teachings of the Church. This was resolved by a court decision holding we (the non-Theosophist party) were the legal Liberal Catholic Church.

Headquarters

741 Cerro Gordo Ave., San Diego, CA 92102 Tel. & Fax (619)239-0637
Web site: www.liberalcatholic.org

Officers

Pres. and Regionary Bishop, The Most Rev. James P. Roberts, Jr., 39 Claire Ave., New Rochelle, NY 10804 Tel. (914)636-7917, bppal32@aol.com
Vice-Pres. and Presiding Bishop, The Most Rev. Charles W. Finn, 741 Cerro Gordo Ave., San

Diego, CA 92102 Tel. & Fax (619)239-0637, abpchas@msn.com
Sec.-Treas., The Most Rev. Dean Bekken, P.O. Box 26044, San Diego, CA 92196-0044 Tel. & Fax (858)689-8610, mrbekken@abac.com
St. Alban Theological Seminary, P.O. Box 2507, Frisco, TX 75034-2507 Tel. (214)636-6719, liberalcatholic@aol.com
St. Alban Press, 741 Cerro Gordo Ave., San Diego, CA 92102 Tel. & Fax (858)689-8610, info@stalbanpress.com

Periodicals

Community, P.O. Box 2507, Frisco, TX 75034-2507 Tel (214)636-6719, liberalcatholic@ aol.com

The Liberal Catholic Church—Province of the United States of America

The Liberal Catholic Church was founded Feb. 13, 1916 as a reorganization of the Old Catholic Church in Great Britain with the Rt. Rev. James I. Wedgwood as the first Presiding Bishop. The first ordination of a priest in the United States was Fr. Charles Hampton, later a Bishop. The first Regionary Bishop for the American Province was the Rt. Rev. Irving S. Cooper (1919-1935).

Headquarters

Pres., The Rt. Rev. William S.H. Downey, 1206 Ayers Ave., Ojai, CA 93023 Tel. (805)646-2573 Fax (805)646-2575
Media Contact, Regionary Bishop, The Rt. Rev. William S.H. Downey
E-mail: w.downey@sbcglobal.net
Web site: www.thelcc.org

Officers

Pres. & Regionary Bishop, The Rt. Rev. William S.H. Downey
Vice-Pres., Rev. L. Marshall Heminway, P.O. Box 19957 Hampden Sta., Baltimore, MD 21211-0957
Sec. (Provincial), Rev. Lloyd Worley, 1232 24th Avenue Ct., Greeley, CO 80631 Tel. (303)356-3002
Provost, Rev. Lloyd Worley
Treas., Rev. Milton Shaw

BISHOPS

Regionary Bishop for the American Province, The Rt. Rev. William S.H. Downey
Aux. Bishops of the American Province, Rt. Rev. Dr. Robert S. McGinnis, Jr., 3612 N. Labarre Rd., Metaire, LA 70002; Rt. Rev. Joseph L. Tisch, P.O. Box 1117, Melbourne, FL 32901; Rt. Rev. Dr. Hein VanBeusekom, 12 Krotona Hill, Ojai, CA 93023; Rt. Rev. Ruben Cabigting, P.O. Box 270, Wheaton, IL 60189; The Rt. Rev. Lawrence Smith 9740 S. Avers Ave., Evergreen Park, IL

Periodicals

Ubique

Lutheran Association, Conservative—please see Conservative Lutheran Association

Lutheran Church—please see American Association of Lutheran Churches

Lutheran Church in America—please see Evangelical Lutheran Church in America

Lutheran Church of America—please see Apostolic Lutheran Church of America

The Lutheran Church—Missouri Synod (LCMS)

The Lutheran Church—Missouri Synod, which was founded in 1847, has more than 6,000 congregations in the United States and works in 78 other countries. It has 2.5 million members and is the second-largest Lutheran denomination in North America.

Christian education is offered for all ages. The North American congregations operate the largest elementary and secondary school systems of any Protestant denomination in the nation, and 17,568 students are enrolled in 12 LCMS institutions of higher learning.

Traditional beliefs concerning the authority and interpretation of Scripture are important. The synod is known for mass-media outreach through *The Lutheran Hour* on radio, *This Is The Life* dramas on television, and the products of Concordia Publishing House, the third-largest Protestant publisher, whose Arch Books children's series has sold more than 60 million copies.

An extensive network of more than 1,000 volunteers in 60 work centers produces Braille, large-type, and audiocassette materials for the blind and visually impaired. There are 25 centers in the U. S. sponsored by LCMS Blind Missions where Blind people are trained for Christian outreach. Lutheran denominations are LCMS; and many denominations use the Bible lessons prepared for developmentally disabled persons.

The involvement of women is high, although they do not occupy clergy positions. Serving as teachers, deaconesses and social workers, women comprise approximately half of total professional workers.

The members' responsibility for congregational leadership is a distinctive characteristic of the synod. Power is vested in voters' assemblies, generally comprised of adults of voting age. Synod decision-making is given to the delegates at triennial national and district conventions, where the franchise is equally divided between lay and pastoral representatives.

Headquarters

The Lutheran Church-Missouri Synod, International Center, 1333 S. Kirkwood Rd., St. Louis, MO 63122-7295

Media Contact, Dir., News & Information, Rev. David Mahsman, Tel. (314)996-1227; Dir., Public Affairs, Mr. David Strand, Tel. (314)996-1229; Manager, News Bureau, Mr. Joe Isenhower, Tel. (314)996-1231 Fax (314) 996-1126
E-mail: infocenter@lcms.org
Web site: www.lcms.org

Officers

Pres., Dr. Gerald B. Kieschnick
1st Vice-Pres., Dr. William R. Diekelman
2nd Vice-Pres., Dr. Paul L. Maier, Kalamazoo, MI
3rd Vice-Pres., Dr. Dean L. Nadasdy, Woodbury, MN
4th Vice-Pres., Dr. Robert L. King, Jefferson City, MO
5th Vice-Pres., Dr. David D. Buegler, Avon, OH
Sec., Dr. Raymond L. Hartwig
Treas., Mr. Thomas Kuchta
Admin. Officer of Bd. of Dir., Dr. Thomas Kuchta (Interim)
Exec. Dir., Human Resources, Barb Ryan, LCMS

BOARD OF DIRECTORS

Rev. Edward Balfour, Cape Elizabeth, ME; Rev. Victor T. Belton, Atlanta, GA; Dr. Betty Duda, Cocoa Beach, FL; Rev. James E. Fandrey, Omaha, NE; Elizabeth Fluegel, Alexandria, VA; Dr. Jean Garton, Benton, AR; Dr. Rev. Raymond L. Hartwig, St. Louis, MO; David Hawk, Ft. Wayne, IN; Dr. Gerald B. Kieschnick, St. Louis, MO; Theodore A. Kober, Billings, MT; Dr. Thomas Kuchta, St. Louis, MO; Dr. Robert T. Kuhn, Oviedo, FL; Julie Martinez, Pagosa Springs, CO; Christan A. Preus, Plymouth, MN; Walter F. Tesch, Milwaukee, WI; Dr. Edwin A. Trapp, Jr., Dallas, TX

BOARDS AND COMMISSIONS

Communication Services, Exec. Dir., Rev. J. Thomas Lapacka
Mission Services, Exec. Dir., Rev. Robert Roegner
Higher Education, Exec. Dir., Dr. William Meyer
Human Care Ministries, Exec. Dir., Rev. Matthew Harrison
District and Congregational Services, Exec. Dir., Dr. LeRoy Wilke
Black Ministry Services, Exec. Dir., Dr. Phillip Campbell
Ministerial Support, Exec. Dir., Dr. Bruce Hartung
Worship, Exec. Dir., Dr. Paul Grime
Theology and Church Relations, Exec. Dir., Dr. Samuel Nafzger

RELATED ORGANIZATIONS

Worker Benefit Plans, Pres. Paul W. Middeke
Lutheran Church—Missouri Synod Foundation, Pres., Rev. Thomas Ries
Lutheran Church Extension Fund, Pres., Dr. Merle Freitag
Concordia Publishing House, Interim Pres., Rev. Paul McCain, 3558 S. Jefferson Ave., St. Louis, MO 63118-3968, Tel. (314)268-1000
Concordia Historical Institute, Dir., Dr. Martin Noland, 801 DeMun Ave., St. Louis, MO 63105, Tel. (314)505-7900
Lutheran Hour Ministries, Exec. Dir., Greg E. Lewis, 660 Mason Ridge Ctr. Dr., St. Louis, MO, 63141, Tel. (314)317-4291
Intl. Lutheran Women's Missionary League, Pres., Linda Reiser, 3558 S. Jefferson Ave., St. Louis, MO 63118-3910, Tel. (314)268-1532
KFUO Radio, Dir., Rev. Dennis Stortz, One Founders Lane, Clayton, MO 63105, Tel, (314)725-3030

Periodicals

The Lutheran Witness (magazine), www.lcms.org/witness
Reporter (newspaper), www.reporter.lcms.org

Lutheran Synod—please see Evangelical Lutheran Synod

Malankara Orthodox Syrian Church, Diocese of America*

It can only be a gift of grace that the faith and tradition of the small community of the early Christians in India has remained alive and vibrant through nearly two thousand years. The church, as old as any other church in the world except Jerusalem, is an apostolic church, established directly by St. Thomas, one of the twelve apostles of Jesus Christ, a privilege not shared by many other churches. The Orthodox Church in India (The Malankara Orthodox Syrian Church) belongs to the family of the five Oriental Orthodox Churches, which include Egypt, Syria, Armenia, and Ethiopia. It has a strength of more than 2 million members in about close to 2,000 parishes mainly in Kerala, a state in India, and increasingly spread all over India and in many parts of the globe, with two dioceses in the western hemisphere, one in the U.S.A. and the other for the parishes in Canada and Europe. Eastern in origin and Asian in its moorings, the Indian Church is, at the same time, a distinctive and respected part of the rich religious mosaic that is India.

A short history

The early Christians of India were known as Thomas Christians and indeed by no other name, until the advent of the Portuguese in the 16th century followed closely by the British. The Malabar Coast, on the southwest tip of India, where Jewish communities had been present many centuries before Christ, was famous for spices that brought many traders to the area. St. Thomas, according to tradition, landed in South India, where there was a preexisting merchant route between the Middle East and India. A strong tradition maintains that the apostle came to Malabar, preached the gospel, baptized local Brahmins (the highest among the four castes in the Hindu society), established seven churches in the area, and made arrangements for the continuation of the ministry by ordaining members from the newly established churches, the same pattern adopted by the other apostles. The local church was self-administered. The Indian Church was autonomous then, and is now like all Orthodox Churches.

The early church in India remained one and at peace, treasuring the same ethnic and cultural characteristics as the rest of the local community. Its members enjoyed the goodwill of the other religious communities as well as the political support of the Hindu rulers. The Thomas Christians welcomed missionaries and migrants from other churches, some of whom sought to escape persecution in their own countries.

On the life of the church in India during the first 15 centuries, the balance of historical evidence and the thrust of local tradition point to its basic autonomy, sustained by the core of its own faith and culture. It received with trust and courtesy missionaries, bishops, and migrants as they came from whichever eastern church—Tigris or Babylon, Antioch or Alexandria. There were times in the long period when the Christians in India had been without a bishop and led by an Archdeacon. And requests were sent, sometimes with success, to one or other of the prelates to help restore the episcopate in India.

The post-Portuguese story of the church in India from the 16th century is relatively well documented. In their combined zeal to colonize and proselytize, the Portuguese might not have readily grasped the way of life of the Thomas Christians who seemed to accommodate differing strands of eastern Christian thought and influence, while preserving the core of their faith. The response of the visitors was to try to bring them under Romo-Syrian prelates, apart from the new converts in the coastal areas under Latin prelates. Pushed beyond a limit, the main body of Thomas Christians rose in revolt and took a collective oath, resolving to preserve the faith and autonomy of their church and to elect its head. Accordingly, Archdeacon Thomas was raised to the title of Mar Thoma. At the request of the Thomas Christians, the Jacobite bishop, Mar Gregorios of Jerusalem, came to India in 1664, and confirmed the Episcopal consecration of Mar Thoma 1 as the head of the Orthodox Church in India.

History repeated itself in another form when British in India encouraged reformation within the Orthodox Church, besides attracting members of the church into Anglican congregations since 1836. Finally the reformist group broke away to form the Mar Thoma Church. The crisis situation was contained with the help of Patriarch Peter III of Antioch who visited India. The outcome was twofold: a reaffirmation of the distinctive identity of the Orthodox Church under its own head and, at some dissonance with the renewal, an enlarged influence of the Patriarch, in the affairs of the Church. Thus a relationship, which started for safeguarding the integrity and independence of the Orthodox Church in India, against the misguided ambitions of the Roman Catholic and Anglican Protestant Churches, opened a long and tortuous chapter. It has become a sore of contention and source for litigation, which still lingers on in the Church. The uncanonical intrusions in the Indian Orthodox Church by the patriarchs of Antioch who cater to the ambitions of disgruntled members and groups by consecrating rival bishops and constituting a parallel administration have been creating problems and divisions in the Church.

Ironically; the Orthodox Church in India has never faced persecution or problems from the prevalent Hindu community or other religious communities in India. In the early stages of the history of the Church, Christians were honored by the members of the Hindu majority community and by the rulers of Kerala belonging to the Hindu community with royal Charters of Privileges. It is a paradox in the history of the Christian Church, that the Indian Orthodox Church faced persecution not from non-Christians, but rather Christians from abroad.

Faith

The Church governs her life by Holy Tradition for which the Holy Bible, the most honored written record of God's revelation, is the first, foremost, and fundamental source. The Liturgy, the Holy Councils and the lives of Saints are part of the Holy Tradition. The Church maintains the same faith as the ancient Church - the faith as was later formulated in the 4th century in the Nicene Creed and in the Councils of Nicea, Constantinople and Ephesus. Jesus Christ, the Son of God, who is consubstantial with the Father, came down from heaven and became man, identifying himself with us in everything except sin. His divinity and humanity were united essentially to become the "one incarnate nature." The Son is begotten by the Father and the Holy Spirit proceeds from the Father. The words 'begotten' and "proceeding" delineate the difference between the Son and the Spirit in their relation to the Father. Indian Orthodox Christians do not believe that there is any special miracle called Immaculate Conception in relation to the origin and birth of the Blessed Virgin Mary. Her bodily assumption is part of the Church's teaching, but not as some central dogma of the church. Believing in the right dogma is not alone the evidence of a true Christian, but the emphasis is also on the way of life, on the way of worship and on the way of disciplining oneself, as on the way of thinking and belief. Every baptized Christian shares in the kingly, priestly and prophetic authority of the Church—though the bishop has a certain fullness of spiritual power which the others in the Church do not have. But the bishop separated from the Church is nothing. It is only in communion with the Church, with the college of priests, deacons and with the people, that he exercises his power of the shepherd. Thus it is conciliar and communitarian in structure. The witness of the Church is a quiet one, based more on worship and holy life of love and service than on preaching and proselytism.

Administration

The Primate of the Church, the Catholicos of the East, is the successor to the apostolic Throne of St. Thomas, the apostle. The Church is divided into dioceses, headed by bishops. The bishops and the Catholicos are monks who are elected by the Church Assembly, consisting of diocesan bishops, laymen and priests representing each parish of the Church, and ratified by the synod, where only bishops are members. The church is administered by the Catholicos *cum* Malankara Metropolitan with the assistance of the Synod and the members of the Managing Committee of priests and laymen elected by the General Assembly of the church. The diocesan metropolitan, appointed by the Catholicos as per the decision of the Managing Committee, presides over the administration of the diocese with the help of a council of priests and laymen elected by the diocesan assembly of parish representatives. The administration of the parish is led by the vicar, appointed by the bishop with the assistance of a council which includes a lay trustee and a secretary elected annually by the general body, consisting the laymen of the parish, and approved by the diocesan metropolitan.

The Formation of the Diocese

The Indian Orthodox Church had its initial footing in the United States over a hundred years ago. Rene Vilathi was consecrated as a bishop under the name Themotheos in 1892 in Colombo, Ceylon (Sri Lanka), who became the first bishop of the Church in the western hemisphere. He moved from one church to another trying both Roman Catholicism and Protestantism and lost connection with the church. He had followers in different parts of the country whose later whereabouts are not certain. None of them were from India, but still the Indian Orthodox Church had its initial footing in the United States through the presence of bishop Themotheos. The Church's participation in the Ecumenical movements of the early 20th century and contacts with the Episcopal Church through the ecumenical movement opened the way for priests and other laymen to visit the United States to attend conferences and to continue higher studies in America. From 1964 onwards in New York, services were held on Sundays and other important feast days. In the sixties, services were occasionally arranged in other major cities, especially in Philadelphia, Chicago and Washington. It was possible mainly because of the presence of priests who were in America for higher studies.

The scarcity of medical professionals in America provided an opportunity for Indians to immigrate to the United States for work, and a good number of them were Orthodox Christians. Hence, in many of the cities parishes were organized. In 1979 the Church formed a new Diocese for the parishes in United States and Canada. The diocese was divided in 1993 to form the diocese of America, which includes all the parishes and congregations in the United States, and another one, the diocese of Canada and Europe, consisting of the parishes in Canada and Europe.

There are about 75 parishes and more than a dozen congregations in the diocese, served by priests and deacons. In major cities like New York, Chicago, Dallas, Houston and Philadelphia the Church has many parishes. Most of the parishes have their own church buildings for worship while others use rented church spaces and halls for worship. Parish life is centered on the Holy Liturgy and the members of the Church give great importance to sacramental life of prayer and fasting. Lent is observed along with major feasts of the Church.

Organizations

The centralized organization for Sunday school, "the Sunday School Association" in the diocese coordinates parish-level Sunday schools where more than 3,000 children are taught about the faith and traditions of the church. A summer program for children called Orthodox Vacation Bible School is very active at present. Mar Gregorios Orthodox Christian Student Movement, a wing for the teenage students and youth in the diocese, with the motto "worship, study and service," helps to bring them together and accomplishes the mission of assisting them in their spiritual, cultural, professional and personal lives. It is a vibrant organization for the growing young generation of the Church in the United States. The Martha Mariam Samajam, a movement of the Church for women, is active in parish and diocesan level coordinates in each parish is centralized in the diocesan level. The diocese has an association for the clergy, which meets occasionally to discuss and resolve the issues and problems that confront the ministry in America. These organizations conduct retreats, workshops, study classes and conferences in the regional and diocesan level at various times of the year. The family Conference of the diocese, usually attended by large number of people from various parishes, held for four to five days during the summer, is an important and colorful annual event of the diocese. The family conference provides a venue for family get-togethers. A quarterly publication called *Diocesan Voice* is published from the diocesan office along with a few other magazines under the auspices of the different organizations and parishes in the diocese.

The Church is active in the Ecumenical movement and is a member of the World Council of

Churches, Christian Conference of Asia, National Council of Churches in India and National Council of Churches of Christ in the United States. The Orthodox Theological Seminary in Kottayam, Kerala, India of the Church which is the oldest theological seminary in India started 175 years ago, is a first rate theological institution and trains students for master and doctoral level studies. The recently started theological seminary of the Church in Nagpur, India, the St. Thomas Orthodox Seminary, is also a graduate level Theological institution. The Church has many institutions, schools and colleges as well as hospitals, all over India. The various monastic orders for men and women add flavor to the spiritual life of the Church.

Headquarters

80-34 Commonwealth Blvd., Bellerose, NY 11426 Tel. (718)470-9844 Fax (718)470-9219

Media Contact, His Grace Mathews Mar Barnabas, Diocesan Metropolitan

E-mail: malankara@malankara.org

Web site: www.malankara.org/american.htm

Officers

Diocesan Metropolitan, His Grace Mathews Mar Barnabas

Diocesan Sec., Rev. Fr. M. Johnson: Sec. to the Metropolitan and Diocesan Office

Periodicals

Diocesan Voice: A quarterly publication of the Diocese*; Family and Youth Conference Souvenir:* An annual publication of the F & Y Conference of the Diocese*; Directory of the Diocese:* Under printing

Mar Thoma Syrian Church of India*

According to tradition, the Mar Thoma Church was established as a result of the apostolic mission of St. Thomas the apostle in 52 AD. Church history attests to the continuity of the community of faithful, throughout the long centuries in India. The liturgy and faith practices of the Church were based on the relationship between the Church in Kerala, India, which St. Thomas founded, with the East-Syrian and Persian Churches. This started in the 3rd century and continued up to the 16th century. In the 17th century, the Malabar Church of St. Thomas (as the Church in Kerala was known) renewed her relationship with the Orthodox Patriarchate of Antioch as part of the resistance to forced Latinization by the Portuguese. This process also led to the development of the Kerala Episcopacy, whereby the first Indian Bishop, Mar Thoma I, was consecrated in Kerala.

The Mar Thoma Church retains her Eastern Orthodoxy. She follows an Orthodox (true) worship form and liturgy, believes in the catholicity of grace, is missionary and evangelistic in approach. She derives Episcopal succession from the Syrian Orthodox Church of Antioch and follows Eastern Reformed Theology. She is independent, autonomous, and indigenous, constitutionally combining democratic values and Episcopal authority. She has been in full communion with the Anglican Church since 1954.

The Diocese of North America was organized in 1988 in order to serve the needs of the immigrant community. It has a membership of around six thousand families in sixty-eight parishes.

Headquarters

Sinai Mar Thoma Center, 2320 S. Merrick Ave., Merrick, New York 11566 Tel. (516)377-3311 Fax (516)377-3322

E-mail: webmaster@marthomachurch.org

Web site: www.marthomachurch.org

Officers

Diocesan Bishop, The Rt. Rev. Dr. Euyakim Mar Coorilos

Diocesan Bishop's Sec., Rev. Dr. John Joseph

Diocesan Treas., Dr. P. John Lincoln

Periodicals

Mar Thoma Messenger

Mennonite Brethren Churches—please see General Conference of Mennonite Brethren Churches

Mennonite Church of God in Christ—please see Church of God in Christ, Mennonite

Mennonite Church U.S.A.

Mennonite Church U.S.A., with 113,000 members, is one of several denominations that trace their beginnings to the Protestant Reformation in the early 1500s. Mennonites hold common core beliefs with other Christian denominations, but they live out God's call in some ways that make them distinct. Mennonites believe in giving ultimate loyalty to God rather than to the nations in which they live. They believe that Jesus revealed a way for people to live peacefully and nonviolently, and they seek to be peacemakers in everyday life.

Mennonite Church U.S.A. is committed to sharing its faith and passion for Jesus with others, and is open to anyone who confesses Jesus Christ as Lord and Savior and wants to live as Jesus taught.

The vision statement of Mennonite Church USA reads, "God calls us to be followers of Jesus Christ and, by the power of the Holy Spirit, to grow as communities of grace, joy, and peace, so that God's healing and hope flow through us to the world."

Mennonite Church U.S.A.—its congregations, area conferences, Executive Board, ministry offices and churchwide agencies—focuses on three priorities:

1. Becoming a missional church, by discerning God's will and joining in God's mission.

2. Developing leaders, young and old, for a missional church.

3. Strengthening relationships with Mennonites and other Christians around the globe to extend the reign of God on earth.

Mennonite Church U.S.A. lists as its strengths a high level of integrity recognized in both society and the religious community; high church attendance (90 percent of members attend church regularly); expanded global awareness through exposure to other world cultures; strong commitment to nonviolence and use of conflict resolution skills; above-average giving to the work of the church; a natural communitarian impulse demonstrated by an emphasis on congregational relationships and mutual accountabilities; strong support of volunteer efforts, relief and service activities; and a holistic theology that holds word and deed together.

Headquarters

Great Plains Office, 722 Main St., P.O. Box 347, Newton, KS 67114 Tel. (316)283-5100 Tollfree (866)866-2872 Fax (316)283-0454

Great Lakes Office, 500 S. Main St., P.O. Box 1245, Elkhart, IN 46515-1245 Tel. (574)294-7523 Tollfree (866)866-2872 Fax (574)293-1892

Media contact, Communications Dir., Barth Hague, Tel. (574)523-3047, barth@mennoniteusa.org

E-mail: info@mennoniteusa.org

Web site: www.mennonitechurchusa.org

Officers

Moderator, Duane Oswald, 1111 E. Herndon Ave., Suite 308, Fresno, CA 93720-3100, Tel. (559)261-9070, doswald@avantehealth.com

Moderator Elect, Roy Williams, 22642 Newfield Ct., Land O'Lakes FL 34639 Tel. (813)966-4244, rrrsjw@aol.com

Exec. Dir., James M. Schrag, 722 Main St., P.O. Box 347, Newton, KS 67114 Tel. (316)283-5100, jims@mennoniteusa.org

Assoc. Exec. Dir., J. Ron Byler, 500 S. Main St., P.O. Box 1245, Elkhart, IN 46515 Tel. (574)294-7523, ronb@mennoniteusa.org

Mennonite Education Agency, Exec. Dir., Carlos Romero, 63846 County Rd. 35, Suite 1, Goshen, IN 46528-9621 Tel (574)642-3164 Fax (574)642-4863, carlosr@mennoniteeducation.org

Mennonite Mission Network, Exec. Dir., Stanley Green, 500 S. Main, Box 370, Elkhart, IN 46515-0370 Tel. (574)294-7523, stanleyg@mennonitemission.net

Mennonite Mutual Aid, Pres., Howard Brenneman, P.O. Box 486, Goshen, IN 46527 Tel. (219)533-9511, howard.brenneman@mma- online.org

Mennonite Publishing Network, Exec. Dir., Ron Rempel, 616 Walnut Ave., Scottdale, PA 15683 Tel. (724)887-8500, rrempel@mph.org

Periodicals

The Mennonite; Leader, Rejoice!; Mennonite Historical Bulletin; Mennonite Quarterly Review; On the Line; Purpose; Story Friends; WITH

Methodist Church—please see The United Methodist Church

Methodist Church, Evangelical—please see Evangelical Methodist Church

Methodist Church, Fundamental—please see Fundamental Methodist Church, Inc.

The Missionary Church

The Missionary Church was formed in 1969 through a merger of the United Missionary Church (organized in 1883) and the Missionary Church Association (founded in 1898). It is evangelical and conservative with a strong emphasis on missionary work and church planting.

There are three levels of church government with local, district and general conferences. There are 11 church districts in the United States. The general conference meets every two years. The denomination operates one college in the United States.

Headquarters

3811 Vanguard Dr., P.O. Box 9127, Ft. Wayne, IN 46899-9127 Tel. (260)747-2027 Fax (260) 747-5331

Media Contact, Pres., Rev. William Hossler

E-mail: mcdenomusa@aol.com

Web site: www.mcusa.org

Officers

Pres., Rev. William Hossler

Vice-Pres., Rev. Joel DeSelm

Sec., Rev. Dave Engbrecht

Treas., Darrel Schlabach

Dir. of U.S. Ministries, Rev. Robert Ransom

Dir. of World Partners USA, Rev. David Mann

Healthy Church Initiatives Coord., Dr. Dan Riemenschneider

Servant Leadership Coord., Rev. Greg Getz

Support Ministries Coord., Rev. Ron Phipps

Pastoral Leadership Institute Dir., Rev. Greg Getz

Dir. of Development/Communications, Dr. Tom Murphy

Dir. of Ad. Services, David Von Gunten

Dir. of Financial Services, Neil Rinehart

Youth Dir., Eric Liechty

Children's Dir., Mrs. Pam Merillat

Sr. Adult Ministry Dir., Dr. Charles Cureton

Missionary Men Liaison, Rev. Ron Phipps

Missionary Women Intl., Pres., Charlotte Beals

Missionary Church Investment Foundation, Mr. Eric Smith

Periodicals

Missionary Church Today

Moravian Church in America (Unitas Fratrum)*

In 1735 German Moravian missionaries of the pre-Reformation faith of Jan Hus came to Georgia, in 1740 to Pennsylvania, and in 1753 to North Carolina. They established the American Moravian Church, which is broadly evangelical, ecumenical, liturgical, "conferential" in form of government and has an episcopacy as a spiritual office. The Northern and Southern Provinces of the church operate on a semi-autonomous basis.

NORTHERN PROVINCE

Headquarters, 1021 Center St., P.O. Box 1245, Bethlehem, PA 18016-1245 Tel. (610)867-7566 Fax (610)866-9223, Media Contact, Ms. Deanna Hollenbach

Provincial Elders' Conference:

Pres., Rev. David L. Wickmann, dave@mcnp.org

Vice-Pres./Sec. & Eastern District Pres., Rev. Gary Straughan, gary@mcnp.org

Vice-Pres. & Western District Pres., Rev. Lawrence Christianson, P.O. Box 386, Sun Prairie, WI 53590, christlr@aol.com

Other Members, Nancy Baldwin; Paul DeTilla; Glenn Hertzog; Stephen Gohdes; Carol Messina

Comptroller, Theresa E. Kunda, 1021 Center St., P.O. Box 1245, Bethlehem, PA 18016-1245, theresa@mcnp.org

Canadian District Pres., Rev. Stephen Gohdes, 600 Arcadia Dr. SE, Calgary, AB T2J 0B8, sgohdes@shaw.ca

SOUTHERN PROVINCE

Headquarters, 459 S. Church St., Winston-Salem, NC 27101 Tel. (336)725-5811 Fax (336) 723-1029, rsawyer@mcsp.org, www.moravian.org (for Moravian Church, Northern and Southern Province)

Provincial Elders' Conference:

Pres., Rev. Dr. Robert E. Sawyer

Vice-Pres., Mrs. Betsy Bombick

Other Members, Ms. Donna Hurt; Rev. Tom Shelton; Rev. Richard Sides

Asst. to Pres., Robert Hunter, rhunter@mcsp.org

ALASKA CONFERENCE

Headquarters, P.O. Box 545, 361 3rd Ave., Bethel, AK 99559, gloria@mcnp.org

Provincial Elders' Conference:

Pres., Rev.Peter Green

Vice-Pres., Carl Ekamrak

Sec., Moses Owen

Treas., Arthur Sharp

Periodicals

The Moravian

Mormons—please see The Church of Jesus Christ of Latter-day Saints

National Association of Congregational Christian Churches

This association was organized in 1955 in Detroit, Michigan, by delegates from Congregational Christian Churches committed to continuing the Congregational way of faith and order in church life. Participation by member churches is voluntary.

Headquarters

P.O. Box 288, Oak Creek, WI 53154 Tel. (414)764-1620 Fax (414)764-0319

Media Contact, Assoc. Exec. Sec., Rev. Dr. Donald P. Olsen, 8473 S. Howell Ave., Oak Creek, WI 53154 Tel. (414)764-1620 Fax (414) 764-0319

E-mail: naccc@naccc.org

Web site: www.naccc.org

Officers

Exec. Sec., Rev. Dr. Thomas M. Richard, 8473 S. Howell Ave., Oak Creek, WI 53154

Assoc. Exec. Sec., Rev. Phil Jackson and Rev. Dr. Donald P. Olsen

Periodicals

The Congregationalist

National Association of Free Will Baptists

This evangelical group of Arminian Baptists was organized by Paul Palmer in 1727 at Chowan, North Carolina. Another movement (teaching the same doctrines of free grace, free salvation and free will) was organized June 30, 1780, in New Durham, N.H., but there was no connection with the southern organization except for a fraternal relationship.

The northern line expanded more rapidly and extended into the West and Southwest. This body merged with the Northern Baptist Convention Oct. 5, 1911, but a remnant of churches reorganized into the Cooperative General Association of Free Will Baptists Dec. 28, 1916, at Pattonsburg, Mo.

Churches in the southern line were organized into various conferences from the beginning and finally united in one General Conference in 1921.

Representatives of the Cooperative General Association and the General Conference joined Nov. 5, 1935 to form the National Association of Free Will Baptists.

Headquarters

5233 Mt. View Rd., Antioch, TN 37013-2306 Tel. (615)731-6812 Fax (615)731-0771

Mailing Address, P.O. Box 5002, Antioch, TN 37011-5002

Media Contact, Exec. Sec., Keith Burden

E-mail: webmaster@nafwb.org

Web site: www.nafwb.org

Officers

Exec. Sec., Keith Burden

Mod., Tim York, P.O. Box 5060, Ashland, KY 41105

DENOMINATIONAL AGENCIES

Free Will Baptist Foundation, Exec. Dir., William Evans

Free Will Baptist Bible College, Pres., Matthew Pinson

Foreign Missions Dept., Dir., Rev. James Forlines
Home Missions Dept., Dir., Rev. Larry Powell
Bd. of Retirement, Dir., Rev. William Evans
Historical Commission, Chpsn., Dr. Darrell Holley, 3606 West End Ave., Nashville, TN 37205
Comm. for Theological Integrity, Chpsn., Rev. Leroy Forlines, 3606 West End Ave., Nashville, TN 37205
Music Commission, Chpsn., Rev. Randy Sawyer, 2316 Union Rd., Gastonia, NC 28054
Media Comm., Chpsn., Rev. Mike Jones, P.O. Box 13266, Florence, SC 29504
Sunday School & Church Training Dept., Dir., Rev. Ron Hunter
Women Nationally Active for Christ, Exec. Sec., Majorie Workman
Master's Men Dept., Dir., Rev. Kenneth Akers

Periodicals

Attack, A Magazine for Christian Men; Free Will Bible College Bulletin; Co-Laborer; Heartbeat; AIM

National Baptist Convention of America, Inc.*

The National Baptist Convention of America, Inc., was organized in 1880. Its mission is articulated through its history, constitution, articles of incorporation and bylaws. The Convention (corporate churches) has a mission statement with fourteen (14) objectives, including fostering unity throughout its membership and the world Christian community by proclaiming the gospel of Jesus Christ; validating and propagating the Baptist doctrine of faith and practice, and its distinctive principles throughout the world; and harnessing and encouraging the scholarly and Christian creative skills of its membership for Christian writing and publications.

Headquarters

Liaison Officer, Dr. Richard A. Rollins, 777 S. R.L. Thornton Fwy., Suite 205, Dallas, TX 75203 Tel. (214)946-8913 Fax (214)946-9619

Officers

Pres., Dr. E. Edward Jones, 1327 Pierre Ave., Shreveport, LA 71103 Tel. (318)221-3701 Fax (318)222-7512
Gen. Rec. Sec., Dr. Clarence C. Pennywell, 2016 Russell Rd., Shreveport, LA 71107
Corres. Sec., Rev. E. E. Stafford, 6614 S. Western Ave., Los Angeles, CA 90047
Liaison Officer, Dr. Richard A. Rollins, 777 S. R.L. Thornton Frwy., Suite 205, Dallas, TX 75203 Tel. (214)946-8913 Fax (214)946-9619

Periodicals

The Lantern

National Baptist Convention, U.S.A., Inc.*

The National Baptist Convention, one of the oldest African American organizations in the nation, traces it history back to 1895. It was formed as a co–solidation of the Baptist Foreign Mission Convention (1880), Consolidated American Baptist Convention (1896), and the National Baptist Educational Convention (1882). Rev. W. H. Alpine of Alabama was the first Pres. of the Baptist Foreign Mission Board, which later became the Baptist Foreign Mission Convention, U.S.A..

The constitution of the convention in 1895 states: "Whereas, It is the sense of the Colored Baptists of the United States of America, convened in the city of Atlanta, Georgia, September 28, 1895 in the several organizations as "The Baptist Foreign Mission Convention of the United States of America," hithero engaged in Mission work on the West Coast of Africa: and the "National Baptist Convention" which has been engaged in mission work in the United States of America; and the "National Baptist Educational Convention," which has sought to look after the educational interest that the interest of the way of the Kingdom of God requires that the several bodies above named should, and do now, unite in one body. Therefore, we do now agree to and adopt the following constitution:

This body shall become known and styled, The National Baptist Convention of the United States of America.

The object of this convention shall be "to do mission work in the United States of America, in Africa, and elsewhere and to foster the cause of education. "Dr. L.M. Luke was elected the first Corresponding Secretary of the Foreign Board. In October, 1896 Rev. L.G. Jordan, pastor of the Union Baptist Church of Philadelphia was selected successor of Luke" (The Epoch of Negro Baptists and The Foreign Mission Board, NBC, USA, Inc. Dr. Edward A. Freeman, The Central Seminary Press 1953.)

In September 1915 at the annual meeting of the convention the constitution was revised with the following changes:

The particular business and object of this Convention shall be to promote a growth and propagation of religion, morality, and intelligence among the races of mankind, by engaging in missionary work in the United States of America, and elsewhere, by fostering the cause of education and publishing and circulating literature, and in providing the necessary ways and means for carrying on such work.

Headquarters

1700 Baptist World Center Dr., Nashville, TN 37207 Tel. (615)228-6292 Fax (615)226-5935

Officers

Pres., Dr. William J. Shaw, 1700 Baptist World Center Dr., Nashville, TN 37207 Tel. (615)228-6292 Fax (615)226-5935
Gen. Sec., Dr. Harry Blake, Mt. Canaan Baptist Church, 1666 Alston St., Shreveport, LA 71101 Tel. (318)227-9993

Periodicals

Mission Herald

National Missionary Baptist Convention of America*

The National Missionary Baptist Convention of America was organized in 1988 as a separate entity from the National Baptist Convention of America, Inc., after a dispute over control of the convention's publishing efforts. The new organization intended to remain committed to the National Baptist Sunday Church School and Baptist Training Union Congress and the National Baptist Publishing Board.

The purpose of the National Missionary Baptist Convention of America is to serve as an agency of Christian education, church extension and missionary efforts. It seeks to maintain and safeguard full religious liberty and engage in social and economic development.

Headquarters

4269 S. Figueroa St., Los Angeles, CA 90037
Tel. (323)846-1950 Fax (323)846-1964
Media Contact, Dr. Melvin Von Wade, Sr.
E-mail: mvwade@nmbca.com
Web site: www.nmbca.com

Officers

Pres., Dr. Melvin Von Wade, Sr., 4269 S. Figueroa St., Los Angeles, CA 90037 Tel. (323) 846-1950 Fax (323)846-1964, mvwade@ nmbca.com
Vice-Pres. at-large, Dr. Harvey E. Leggett, 866 Monroe St., Ypsilanti, MI 48197
Vice-Pres., Ecumenical Affairs, Dr. F. Benjamin Davis, 1535 Dr. A.J. Brown Blvd. N., Indianapolis, IN 46202
Vice-Pres., Auxiliaries, T.J. Prince, 2219 Sea Island Dr., Dallas, TX 75232
Vice-Pres., Boards, Dr. O.E. Piper, 4220 W. 18th St., Chicago, IL 60623
Vice-Pres., Financial Affairs, J.A. Boles, 2001 South J St., Tacoma, WA 98405
Pres., National Baptist Publishing Bd., Dr. T.B. Boyd, III, 6717 Centennial Blvd., Nashville, TN 37209
Gen. Sec., Dr. A. Wayne Johnson, 106 NE Ivy St., Portland, OR 97212 Tel. (503)281-4925 Fax (503)281-6520, gensec@jiacom.net
Corres. Sec., Dr. H.J. Johnson, 2429 South Blvd., Dallas, TX 75215
Treas., Dr. W.N. Daniel, 415 W. Englewood Ave., Chicago, IL 60612
Rec. Sec., Dr. Lonnie Franks, Crocker, TX

National Organization of the New Apostolic Church of North America

The New Apostolic Church of North America claims common origin with the Catholic Apostolic movement in England, which began with the calling of an apostle in 1832. The New Apostolic Church distinguished itself from the parent body in 1863 by recognizing a succession of Apostles.

Headquarters

3753 N. Troy St., Chicago, IL 60618
Media Contact, Sec. & Treas., Ellen E. Eckhardt, Tel. (773)539-3652 Fax (773)478-6691
E-mail: info@nak.org
Web site: www.nak.org

Officers

Pres., Rev. Rev. Richard C. Freund, 1 Mikel Ln., Glen Head, NY 11545-1591
Vice-Pres., Rev. John W. Fendt, Jr., 2 Willets Ln., Plandome, NY 11030-1023
Vice-Pres., Rev. Leonard R. Kolb, 5250 Robinhood Ln., Erle, PA 16509-2563
Vice-Pres. Rev. Karl H. Hoffman, 35 Tradewinds Cir., Tequesta, FL 33469-2041
Treas., Ellen E. Eckhardt, 6380 N. Indian Rd., Chicago, IL 60646
Sec., Ellen E. Eckhardt, 6380 N. Indian Rd., Chicago, IL 60646

National Primitive Baptist Convention, Inc.

Throughout the years of slavery and the Civil War, the Negro population of the South worshipped with the white population in their various churches. At the time of emancipation, their white brethren helped them establish their own churches, granting them letters of fellowship, ordaining their deacons and ministers and helping them in other ways.

The doctrine and polity of this body are quite similar to that of white Primitive Baptists, yet there are local associations and a national convention, organized in 1907.

Each church is independent and receives and controls its own membership. This body was formerly known as Colored Primitive Baptists.

Headquarters

6433 Hidden Forest Dr., Charlotte, NC 28213
Tel. (704)596-1508
Media Contact, Elder T.W. Samuels

Officers

Natl. Convention, Pres., Dr. Thomas W. Samuels, Tel. (704)596-3153
Natl. Convention, Vice-Pres., Elder Ernest Ferrell, Tallahassee, FL
Natl. Convention, Chmn. Bd. of Dirs., Elder Ernest Ferrell, Tallahassee, FL
Natl. Church School Training Union, Pres., Dr. Jonathan Yates, Mobile, AL
Natl. Ushers Congress, Pres., Dea.. Carl Batts, 21213 Garden View Dr., Maple Heights, OH 44137
Publishing Bd., Chpsn., Elder John R. Cox, Birmingham, AL
Women's Congress, Pres., Mother Ann Cartes, Dallas, TX
Natl. Laymen's Council, Pres., Dea. Densimore Robinson, Huntsville, AL

Natl. Youth Congress, Pres., Minister Jacques Mood, Concord, NC

National Spiritualist Association of Churches

This organization is made up of believers that Spiritualism is a science, philosophy and religion based upon the demonstrated facts of communication between this world and the next.

Headquarters

NSAC General Offices, Rev. Sharon L. Snowman, Sec., P.O. Box 217, Lily Dale, NY 14752-0217

Media Contact, Rev. Lelia Cutler, 7310 Midfield St. #1, Norfolk, VA 23505-4126

E-mail: nsac@nsac.org

Web site: www.nsac.org

Officers

Pres., Rev. Lelia Cutler, 7310 Midfield St. #1, Norfolk, VA 23505-4126

Vice-Pres., Rev. Pamla Ashlay, 11811 Watertown Plank Rd., Milwaukee, WI 53226

Sec., Rev. Sharon L. Snowman, P.O. Box 217, Lily Dale, NY 14752 Tel. (716)595-2000 Fax (716)595-2020

Treas., Peter Berg, 12880 Claas Avenue, Holbrook, NY 98499

OTHER ORGANIZATIONS

Dept. of Education, Dir., Rev. Barbara Starr, 4245 Woodmont Rd., Great Cacapon, WV 25422

Dept. of Lyceums, Dir., Rev. Arsenia Williams, 10913 S. Parnell, Chicago, IL 60628

Dept. of Missionaries, Dir., Rev. E. Ann Otzelberger, 4332 Woodlynne Lane, Orlando, FL 32812-7562

Dept. of Phenomenal Evidence, Dir., Revs. Lisa and Thomas Butler, 3415 Socrates Dr., Reno, NV 89512

Dept. of Public Relations, Dir., Mary Montgomery Clifford, 2426 N. Kimball St., Chicago, IL 60647

Dept. of Publications, Dir., John Rothamel, Jr., 7851 Foxfarm Lane, Glen Burnie, MD 21061-6324

NSAC Healing Center, Pres., Rev. Kathleen Rottino, 74 Scenic Dr., Lebanon, CT 06249

NSAC Minsterial Association, Pres., Rev. Barbara Star, NST, 4245 Woodmont Rd., Great Cacapon, WV 25422

National Spiritualist Teachers Club, Pres., Rev. E. Ann Otzelberger, NST, 4332 Woodlynne Lane, Orlando, FL 32812

Spiritualist Healers League, Pres., Rev. E. Annotzelberger, NST

Licentiate Ministers & Certified Mediums Society, Pres., Rev. Janet Tisdale, NST, 1616 N. Alta Mesa Dr. #51, Mesa, AZ 85205

The Stow Memorial Foundation, Sec., Rev. Sharon L. Snowman, P.O. Box 217, Lily Dale, NY 14752 Tel. (716)595-2000 Fax (716)595-2020

Spiritualist Benevolent Society, Inc., P.O. Box 217, Lily Dale, NY 14752

Periodicals

The National Spiritualist (Monthly); *Spotlight*—10 Issues per year (Children's Magazine)

Netherlands Reformed Congregations

The Netherlands Reformed Congregations organized denominationally in 1907. In the Netherlands, the so-called Churches Under the Cross (established in 1839, after breaking away from the 1834 Secession congregations) and the so-called Ledeboerian churches (established in 1841 under the leadership of the Rev. Ledeboer, who seceded from the Reformed State Church), united in 1907 under the leadership of the then 25-year-old Rev. G. H. Kersten, to form the Netherlands Reformed Congregations. Many of the North American congregations left the Christian Reformed Church to join the Netherlands Reformed Congregations after the Kuyperian presupposed regeneration doctrine began making inroads.

All Netherlands Reformed Congregations, office-bearers, and members subscribe to three Reformed Forms of Unity, The Belgic Confession of Faith (by DeBres), the Heidelberg Catechism (by Ursinus and Olevianus), and the Canons of Dort. The Heidelberg Catechism is preached weekly, except on church feast days.

Headquarters

Media Contact, Rev. A.H.Verhoef, 1142 Lakeshore Rd. W, RR#3, St. Catherines, ON L2R 6P9 Tel. (905)935-4934

Other Organizations

Netherlands Reformed Book and Publishing, 1233 Leffingwell NE, Grand Rapids, MI 49505

Periodicals

The Banner of Truth; Paul (mission magazine); *Insight Into* (for young people); *Learning and Living* (for school and home)

New Church—please see General Church of the New Jerusalem

North American Baptist Conference

The North American Baptist Conference was begun by immigrants from Germany. The first church was organized by the Rev. Konrad Fleischmann in Philadelphia in 1843. In 1865 delegates of the churches met in Wilmot, Ontario, and organized the North American Baptist Conference. Today only a few churches still use the German language, mostly in a bilingual setting.

The Conference meets in general session once every three years for fellowship, inspiration and to conduct the business of the Conference through elected delegates from the local churches. The

General Council, composed of representatives of the various Associations and Conference organizations and departments, meets annually to determine the annual budget and programs for the Conference and its departments and agencies. The General Council also makes recommendations to the Triennial Conference on policies, long-range plans and election of certain personnel, boards and committees.

Approximately 60 missionaries serve in Brazil, Cameroon, Japan, Mexico, Nigeria, Philippines, and Russia.

Eight homes for the aged are affiliated with the Conference and 11 camps are operated on the association level.

Headquarters

1 S. 210 Summit Ave., Oakbrook Terrace, IL 60181 Tel. (630)495-2000 Fax (630)495-3301
Media Contact, Marilyn Schaer

Officers

Exec. Dir., Rev. Ron Berg, 1 S. 210 Summit Ave., Oakbrook Terrace, IL 60181, Tel. (630) 495-2000 Fax (630)475-3301, pyntema@nabconf.org

OTHER ORGANIZATIONS

Intl. Missions Dept., Dir., Ron Salzman
Home Missions Dept., Dir., Rev. Bob Walther
Church Extension Investors Fund, Dir., Les D. Collins

Periodicals

NABtoday

North American Old Roman Catholic Church (Archdiocese of New York)

This body is identical with the Roman Catholic Church in faith but differs from it in discipline and worship. The Mass is offered with the appropriate rite either in Latin or in the vernacular. All other sacraments are taken from the Roman Pontifical. This jurisdiction allows for married clergy.

PRIMATIAL HEADQUARTERS

60 St. Felix St., Brooklyn, NY 11217-1206 Tel. (718)855-0600 Fax (718)522-1231
Media Contact, Chancellor, Most Rev. Albert J. Berube

Officers

Primate, The Most Rev. Herve L. Quessy
Chancellor, Most Rev. Albert J. Berube
Diocese of New York, Ordinary, Most Rev. Albert J. Berube
Diocese of Montreal & French Canada, Ordinary, Most Rev. Herve L. Quessy

Old German Baptist Brethren Church

This group separated from the Church of the Brethren (formerly German Baptist Brethren) in 1881 in order to preserve and maintain historic Brethren Doctrine.

Headquarters

Vindicator Ofc. Ed., Steven L. Bayer, 6952 N. Montgomery County Line Rd., Englewood, OH 45322-9748 Tel. (937) 884-7531

Periodicals

The Vindicator

Old Order Amish Church

The congregations of this Old Order Amish group have no annual conference. They worship in private homes. They adhere to the older forms of worship and attire. This body has bishops, ministers and deacons.

Headquarters

Der Neue Amerikanische Calendar, c/o Raber's Book Store, 2467 CR 600, Baltic, OH 43804
LeRoy Beachy, Beachy Amish Mennonite Church, 4324 SR 39, Millerburg, OH 44654, Tel. & Fax (330)893-2883

Old Order (Wisler) Mennonite Church

This body arose from a separation of Mennonites dated 1872, under Jacob Wisler, in opposition to what were thought to be innovations.

The group is in the Eastern United States and Canada. Each state, or district, has its own organization and holds semi-annual conferences.

Headquarters

Media Contact, Amos B. Hoover, 376 N. Muddy Creek Rd., Denver, PA 17517 Tel. (717)484-4849

Open Bible Standard Churches

Open Bible Standard Churches originated from two revival movements, Bible Standard Conference, founded in Eugene, Oregon, under the leadership of Fred L. Hornshuh in 1919, and Open Bible Evangelistic Association, founded in Des Moines, Iowa, under the leadership of John R. Richey in 1932.

Similar in doctrine and government, the two groups amalgamated on July 26, 1935 as "Open Bible Standard Churches, Inc." with headquarters in Des Moines, Iowa.

The original group of 210 ministers has enlarged to incorporate over 2,479 ministers and 1,397 churches in 36 countries. The first missionary left for India in 1926. The church now ministers in Asia, Africa, South America, Europe, Canada, Mexico, Central America, and the Caribbean Islands.

Historical roots of the parent groups reach back to the outpouring of the Holy Spirit in 1906 at Azusa Street Mission in Los Angeles and to the full gospel movement in the Midwest. Both groups were organized under the impetus of pentecostal revival. Simple faith, freedom from fanaticism, emphasis on evangelism and missions and free fellowship with other groups were characteristics of the growing organizations.

The highest governing body of Open Bible Standard Churches meets biennially and is composed of all ministers and one voting delegate per 100 members from each church. A National Board of Directors, elected by the national and regional conferences, conducts the business of the organization. Official Bible College is Eugene Bible College in Oregon.

Open Bible Standard Churches is a charter member of the National Association of Evangelicals and of the Pentecostal/Charismatic Churches of North America. It is a member of the Pentecostal World Conference.

NATIONAL OFFICE

2020 Bell Ave., Des Moines, IA 50315 Tel. (515) 288-6761 Fax (515)288-2510
Media Contact, Exec. Dir., Communications & Resources, Jeff Farmer, Tel. (515)288-6761 Fax (515)288-2510
E-mail: info@openbible.org
Web site: www.openbible.org

Officers

Pres., Jeffrey E. Farmer, jeff@openbible.org
Esq., Sec.-Treas., Teresa A. Beyer, tbeyer@openbible.org
Dir. of Intl. Min., Paul V. Canfield, missions @openbible.org

Periodicals

Message of the Open Bible

The (Original) Church of God, Inc.

This body was organized in 1886 as the first church in the United States to take the name "The Church of God." In 1917 a difference of opinion led this particular group to include the word (Original) in its name. It is a holiness body and believes in the whole Bible, rightly divided, using the New Testament as its rule and government.

Headquarters

P.O. Box 592, Wytheville, VA 24382
Media Contact, Gen. Overseer, Rev. William Dale, Tel. (800)827-9234

Officers

Gen. Overseer, Rev. William Dale
Asst. Gen. Overseer, Rev. Alton Evans

The Orthodox Church in America*

The Orthodox Church of America entered Alaska in 1794 before its purchase by the United States in 1867. Its canonical status of independence (autocephaly) was granted by its Mother Church, the Russian Orthodox Church, on April 10, 1970, and it is now known as The Orthodox Church in America.

Headquarters

P.O. Box 675, Syosset, NY 11791-0675 Tel. (516)922-0550 Fax (516)922-0954
E-mail: info@oca.org
Web site: www.oca.org
Media Contact, Dir. of Communications, V. Rev. John Matusiak, 1 Wheaton Center # 912, IL 60187 Tel. (630)668-5712 Fax (630)668-1706 E-mail: jjm@oca.org

Officers

Primate, Archbishop of Washington, Metropolitan of All America & Canada, Most Blessed Herman
Chancellor, V. Rev. Robert S. Kondratick, P.O. Box 675, Syosset, NY 11791 Tel. (516)922-0550 Fax (516)922-0954 E-mail: rsk@oca.org

SYNOD

Chair, His Beatitude Metropolitan Herman, P.O. Box 675, Syosset, NY 11791
Archbishop of New York, Most Rev. Peter, 33 Hewitt Ave., Bronxville, NY 10708
Archbishop of Pittsburgh & Western PA, Most Rev. Kyrill, P.O. Box 1769, Cranberry Township, PA 16066-1769
Archbishop of Dallas, Archbishop Dmitri, 4112 Throckmorton, Dallas, TX 75219
Bishop of Sitka, Anchorage and Alaska, Rt. Rev. Nikolai, P.O. Box 210569, Anchorage, AK 99521
Archbishop of Detroit, Most Rev. Nathaniel, P.O. Box 309, Grass Lake, MI 49240-0309
Bishop of Chicago, Most Rev. Job, 927 N. LaSalle, Chicago, IL 60610
Bishop of San Francisco, Rt. Rev. Tikhon, 649 N. Robinson St., Los Angeles, CA 90026
Bishop of Ottawa and Canada, Rt. Rev. Seraphim, P.O. Box 179, Spencerville, ON K0E 1X0 Tel. (613)925-5226
Retired Bishop, Rt. Rev. Mark, 9511 Sun Pointe Dr., Boynton Beach, FL 33437
Auxiliary Bishop of Baltimore, Rt. Rev. Nikon, P.O. Box 149, Southbridge, MA 01550 Tel. (508)764-3222
Auxiliary Bishop for the Romanian Episcopate, Rt. Rev. Irineu of Dearborn Heights, 23300, Davison Ave. W, Detriot, MI 48223 Tel. (313)533-3413
Auxiliary Bishop to the Metropolitan, Rt. Rev. Tikhon of South Canaan, St. Tikhon Monastery, P.O. Box 130, South Canann, PA 18459, Tel. (570)937-4067
Auxiliary Bishop for the Diocese of the West, Rt. Rev. Benjamin of Berkeley, 701 Park Place, Bolder City, NV 89005, Tel. (702)293-7208

Retired Bishops

Retired Archbishop, the Most Rev. Lazar, 37323 Hawkins Pickle Rd., Dewdney, BC Canada V0M1H0
Retired Bishop, the Rt. Rev. Varlaam, 37323 Hawkins Pickle Rd., Dewdney, BC Canada V0M1H0
Retired Metropolitan, the Most Blessed Theodosius, P.O. Box 70, Hamlin, PA 18477
Retired Archbishop, the Most Rev. Gregory, P.O. Box 94, Jackson, NJ 08527-0094

Periodicals

The Orthodox Church; Annual Sourcebook and Church Directory, published annually, includes a directory of all parishes, institutions, and communities of the Otrthodox Church of America

The Orthodox Presbyterian Church

On June 11, 1936, certain ministers, elders and lay members of the Presbyterian Church in the U.S.A. withdrew from that body to form a new denomination. Under the leadership of the late Rev. J. Gresham Machen, noted conservative New Testament scholar, the new church determined to continue to uphold the Westminster Confession of Faith as traditionally understood by Presbyterians and to engage in proclamation of the gospel at home and abroad.

The church has grown modestly over the years and suffered early defections, most notably one in 1937 that resulted in the formation of the Bible Presbyterian Church under the leadership of Dr. Carl McIntire. It now has congregations throughout the states of the continental United States.

The denomination is a member of the North American Presbyterian and Reformed Council and the International Council of Reformed Churches.

Headquarters

607 N. Easton Rd., Bldg. E, Box P, Willlow Grove, PA 19090-0920 Tel. (215)830-0900 Fax (215)830-0350

Media Contact, Stated Clerk, Rev. Donald J. Duff

E-mail: duff.1@opc.org

Web site: www.opc.org

Officers

Moderator of Gen. Assembly, The Rev. Larry E. Wilson

Stated Clk., Rev. Donald J. Duff

Periodicals

New Horizons in the Orthodox Presbyterian Church

Patriarchal Parishes of the Russian Orthodox Church in the U.S.A.*

This group of parishes is under the direct jurisdiction of the Patriarch of Moscow and All Russia, His Holiness Aleksy II, in the person of a Vicar Bishop, His Grace Mercurius, Bishop of Zaraisk.

Headquarters

St. Nicholas Cathedral, 15 E. 97th St., New York, NY 10029 Tel. (212)831-6294 Fax (212)427-5003

Media Contact, Sec. to the Bishop, Hierodeacon Joseph, Tel. (212)996-6638

E-mail: bmercurius@ruscon.com

Web site: www.orthodox.net

Officers

Sec. to the Bishop, Hierodeacon Joseph

Pentecostal Assemblies of the World, Inc.

This organization is an interracial Pentecostal holiness of the Apostolic Faith, believing in repentance, baptism in Jesus's name and being filled with the Holy Ghost, with the evidence of speaking in tongues. It originated in the early part of the century in the Middle West and has spread throughout the country.

Headquarters

3939 Meadows Dr., Indianapolis, IN 46205 Tel. (317)547-9541 Fax (317)543-0513

Media Contact, Admin., John E. Hampton, Fax (317)543-0512

Web site: www.pawinc.org

Officers

Presiding Bishop, Norman L. Wagner

Asst. Presiding Bishop, James E. Tyson

Bishops, Arthus Brazier; George Brooks; Ramsey Butler; Morris Golder; Francis L. Smith; Brooker T. Jones; C. R. Lee; Robert McMurray; Philip L. Scott; William L. Smith; Samuel A. Layne; Freeman M. Thomas; James E. Tyson; Charles Davis; Willie Burrell; Harry Herman; Jeremiah Reed; Jeron Johnson; Clifton Jones; Robert Wauls; Ronald L. Young; Henry L. Johnson; Leodis Warren; Thomas J. Weeks; Eugene Redd; Thomas W. Weeks, Sr.; Willard Saunders; Davis L. Ellis; Earl Parchia; Vanuel C. Little; Norman Wagner; George Austin; Benjamin A. Pitt; Markose Thopil; John K. Cole; Peter Warkie; Norman Walters; Alphonso Scott; David Dawkins

Gen. Sec, Suffragan Bishop Edward Roberts

Assist. Gen Sec., Suffragan Bishop A. Glenn Brady

Gen. Treas., Suffragan Bishop Mark C. Tolbert

Asst. Treas., Suffragan Bishop Carl A. Turner

Pentecostal Church of God

Growing out of the pentecostal revival at the turn of the 20th century, the Pentecostal Church of God was organized in Chicago on Dec. 30, 1919, as the Pentecostal Assemblies of the U.S.A. The name was changed to Pentecostal Church of God in 1922; in 1934 it was changed again to The Pentecostal Church of God of America, Inc.; and finally the name became the Pentecostal Church of God (Incorporated) in 1979.

The international headquarters was moved from Chicago, Illinois to Ottumwa, Iowa, in 1927, then to Kansas City, Missouri, in 1933 and finally to Joplin, Missouri, in 1951.

The denomination is evangelical and pentecostal in doctrine and practice. Active membership in the National Association of Evangelicals and the Pentecostal/Charismatic Churches North America is maintained.

The church is Trinitarian in doctrine and teaches the absolute inerrancy of the Scripture from Genesis to Revelation. Among its cardinal beliefs are the doctrines of salvation, which includes regeneration; divine healing, as provided for in the atonement; the baptism in the Holy Ghost, with the initial physical evidence of speaking in tongues; and the premillennial second coming of Christ.

Headquarters

4901 Pennsylvania, P.O. Box 850, Joplin, MO 64802 Tel. (417)624-7050 Fax (417)624-7102

Media Contact, Gen. Sec., Dr. Ronald R. Minor

E-mail: pcg@pcg.org

Web site: www.pcg.org

Officers

Gen. Bishop., Dr. Phil L. Redding
Gen. Sec., Dr. Ronald R. Minor

OTHER GENERAL EXECUTIVES

Dir. of World Missions, Rev. Loyd L. Naten
Dir. of Indian Missions, Dr. C. Don Burke
Dir. of Youth Ministries, Rev. Reggie O. Powers
Dir. of Home Missions/Evangelism, Rev. Stephen E. Oates

ASSISTANT GENERAL SUPERINTENDENTS/BISHOPS

Northwestern Division, Rev. Jamie J. Joiner
Southwestern Division, Rev. Michael W. Jacobsen
North Central Division, Rev. Donald R. Dennis
South Central Division, Rev. Leon A. McDowell
Northeastern Division, Rev. Charles R. Mosier
Southeastern Division, Rev. C.W. Goforth

OTHER DEPARTMENTAL OFFICERS

Bus. Mgr., Rev. R. Alan Greagrey
Dir. of Women's Ministry, Mrs. Sharon K. Redding
Christian Educ., Dir., Mrs. Billie L. Palumbo

Periodicals

The Pentecostal Messenger

Pentecostal Fire-Baptized Holiness Church

Organized in 1918, this group consolidated with the Pentecostal Free Will Baptists in 1919. It maintains rigid discipline over members.

Headquarters

P.O. Box 261, La Grange, GA 30241-0261 Tel. (706)884-7742
Media Contact, Gen. Mod., Wallace B. Pittman, Jr.

Officers

Gen. Treas., Alan Sparkman, 1961 Norjon Circle, Clio, SC 29525 Tel. (843)586-9095
Gen. Sec., Joel Powell, 16841 Springs Mill Rd. Lauringbury, NC 28352 Tel. (901)462-3379
Gen. Mod., Wallace B. Pittman, Jr.
Gen. Supt. Mission Bd., Jerry Powell, Rt. 1, Box 384, Chadourn, NC 28431

The Pentecostal Free Will Baptist Church, Inc.

The Cape Fear Conference of Free Will Baptists, organized in 1855, merged in 1959 with The Wilmington Conference and The New River Conference of Free Will Baptists and was renamed the Pentecostal Free Will Baptist Church, Inc. The doctrines include regeneration, sanctification, the Pentecostal baptism of the Holy Ghost, the second coming of Christ and divine healing.

Headquarters

P.O. Box 1568, Dunn, NC 28335 Tel. (910)892-4161 Fax (910)892-6876
Media Contact, Gen. Supt., Preston Heath
E-mail: pheath@intrstar.net
Web site: www.pfwb.org

Officers

Gen. Supt., Rev. Preston Heath
Asst. Gen. Supt., Jim Wall
Gen. Sec., Mr. Stephen Garriss
Gen. Treas., Mr. Dewayne Weeks
Christian Ed. Dir., Rev. Randy Barker
World Witness Dir., Rev. Hobbs
Gen. Services Dir., Ms. Cathy Muzingo
Ministerial Council Dir., Rev. Ed Taturn
Ladies' Auxiliary Dir., Dollie Davis
Heritage Bible College, Pres., Dr. Dwarka Ramphal
Crusader Youth Camp, Dir., Rev. Randy Barker

OTHER ORGANIZATIONS

Heritage Bible College
Crusader Youth Camp
Blessings Bookstore, 1006 W. Cumberland St., Dunn, NC 28334 Tel. (910)892-2401

Periodicals

The Messenger

Philadelphia Yearly Meeting of the Religious Society of Friends*

PYM traces its roots to the yearly meeting of 1681 in Burlington, New Jersey. For more than three centuries, PYM has served Monthly Meetings and Quarterly Meetings throughout eastern Pennsylvania, southern New Jersey, eastern Maryland and Delaware. In general, the activities of PYM are organized under five Standing Committees—Standing Committee on Worship and Care; Standing Committee on Education; Standing Committee on Peace and Concerns; Standing Committee on Support and Outreach; Standing Committee on General Services.

Headquarters

Philadelphia Yearly Meeting, 1515 Cherry St., Philadelphia, PA 19102-1479 Tel. (215)241-7000 Fax (215)241-7045
Web site: www.pym.org

Officers

Presiding Clerk, Gretchen Castle
Clerk of Interim Meeting, Chris Mahon
Gen. Sec., Thomas Jeavons
Clerk, Standing Committee on Worship and Care, Edward Broadfield & James Morrissey
Clerk, Standing Committee on Education, Deborah Lyons
Clerk, Standing Committee on Peace and Concerns, Howard Cell
Clerk, Standing Committee on Support and Outreach, Frances Dreisbach & Pamela Carter
Clerk, Standing Committee on General Services, Patricia Hunt

Periodicals

PYM News

Pillar of Fire

The Pillar of Fire was founded by Alma Bridwell White in Denver on Dec. 29, 1901 as the Pentecostal Union. In 1917, the name was changed to Pillar of Fire. Alma White was born in Kentucky in 1862 and taught school in Montana where she met her husband, Kent White, a Methodist minister, who was a university student in Denver.

Because of Alma White's evangelistic endeavors, she was frowned upon by her superiors, which eventually necessitated her withdrawing from Methodist Church supervision. She was ordained as Bishop and her work spread to many states, to England, and since her death to Liberia, West Africa, Malawi, East Africa, Yugoslavia, Spain, India and the Philippines.

The Pillar of Fire organization has a college and two seminaries stressing Biblical studies. It operates eight separate schools for young people. The church continues to keep in mind the founder's goals and purposes.

Headquarters

P.O. Box 9159, Zarephath, NJ 08890 Tel. (732)356-0102

Western Headquarters, 1302 Sherman St., Denver, CO 80203 Tel. (303)427-5462

Media Contact, 1st Vice-Pres., Robert B. Dallenbach, 3455 W. 83 Ave., Westminster, CO 80031 Tel. (303)427-5462 Fax (303)429-0910

E-mail: info@zarephath.edu

Web site: www.gospelcom.net/pof

Officers

Pres. & Gen. Supt., Dr. Robert B. Dallenbach

1st Vice-Pres. & Asst. Supt., Rev. Joseph Gross

2nd Vice-Pres./Sec.-Treas., Lois R. Stewart

Trustees, Kenneth Cope; S. Rea Crawford; Lois Stewart; Dr. Donald J. Wolfram; Robert B. Dallenbach; Rob W. Cruver; Joseph Gross

Plymouth Brethren—please see Christian Brethren

Polish National Catholic Church of America*

After a number of attempts to resolve differences regarding the role of the laity in parish administration in the Roman Catholic Church in Scranton, Pennsylvania, this Church was organized in 1897. With the consecration to the episcopacy of the Most Rev. F. Hodur, this Church became a member of the Old Catholic Union of Utrecht in 1907.

Headquarters

Office of the Prime Bishop, 1006 Pittston Ave., Scranton, PA 18505 Tel. (570)346-9131

Media Contact, Prime Bishop, Most Rev. Robert M. Nemkovich, Fax (570)346-2188

E-mail: ads22244@aol.com

Web site: www.pncc.org

Officers

Prime Bishop, Most Rev. Robert M. Nemkovich, 115 Lake Scranton Rd., Scranton, PA 18505

Central Diocese, Bishop, Rt. Rev. Casimir Grotnik, 529 E. Locust St., Scranton, PA 18505

Eastern Diocese, Bishop, Rt. Rev. Thomas J. Gnat, 166 Pearl St., Manchester, NH 03104

Buffalo-Pittsburgh Diocese, Bishop, Rt. Rev. Thaddeus S. Peplowski, 5776 Broadway, Lancaster, NY 14086

Western Diocese, Rt. Rev. Jan Dawidziuk, 920 N. Northwest Hwy., Park Ridge, IL 60068

Canadian Diocese, Bishop, Sede Vacante

Ecumenical Officer, Rev. Anthony Mikovsky

Periodicals

God's Field; Polka

Presbyterian Church—please see Evangelical Presbyterian Church

Presbyterian Church in America

The Presbyterian Church in America is an evangelical, reformed covenant community of churches in the United States and Canada committed to a common doctrinal standard (The Westminster Standards), mutual accountability (representative church government), and cooperative ministry. The PCA traces its historical roots to the First General Assembly of the Church of Scotland of 1560, the establishment of the Presbytery of Philadelphia, 1789, and the General Assembly of the Southern Presbyterian Church, Augusta in 1861. Organized in 1973 by conservative churches formerly associated with the Presbyterian Church in the United States, the Church was first known as the National Presbyterian Church but changed its name in 1974 to the Presbyterian Church in America. The PCA seeks to be "Faithful to the Scriptures, True to the Reformed Faith, and Obedient to the Great Commission." In 1982 the Reformed Presbyterian Church, Evangelical Synod joined the PCA bringing with it a rich tradition that had antecedents in colonial America.

The PCA holds to the ancient creeds of the church such as the Apostles' Creed and the Nicene Creed and has a firm commitment to its doctrinal standards, The Westminster Confession of Faith, Larger and Shorter Catechisms, that have been significant in Presbyterianism since 1645. These doctrinal standards reflect the distinctives of the reformed tradition, Calvinism, and covenant theology. Ministers, ruling elders, and deacons are required to subscribe to the Westminster Standards in good faith. Individuals are received by a Session as communing members of the Church upon their profession of faith in Jesus Christ as Lord and Savior, their promise to live a Christian lifestyle, and their commitment to worship and service in the Church.

The PCA is a connectional Church, led by ruling elders (lay leaders) and teaching elders (ministers). The Session governs a local congregation;

the Diaconate carries out mercy ministries. The Presbytery is responsible for regional matters and the General Assembly is responsible for national matters in the USA and Canada. Cooperative ministry is carried out through over sixty Presbyteries and ten General Assembly Ministries.

The educational institutions of the Church are Covenant College of Lookout Mountain,GA and Covenant Theological Seminary of St. Louis, MO. The PCA and the Orthodox Presbyterian Church participate in a joint publication venture, Great Commission Publications, for the publication of Christian Education materials.

In its ecumenical relations the PCA is a member of the North American Presbyterian and Reformed Council, the National Association of Evangelicals, and the World Reformed Fellowship.

The General Assembly approved a statement of purpose, "It is the purpose of the PCA to bring glory to God as a worshipping and serving community until the nations in which we live are filled with churches that make Jesus Christ and His word their chief joy, and the nations of the world, hearing the Word, are discipled in obedience to the Great Commission."

The Church has grown beyond its origin in the southeastern states to have congregations in forty-nine states in the USA and in several provinces of Canada. Growth is due to the PCA's ministry in evangelism, discipleship, church planting, church renewal, and campus ministry. Indicative of her concern for cross-cultural ministry, the PCA has the largest international missionary force in Presbyterian Church history.

Headquarters

1700 N. Brown Rd., Lawrenceville, GA 30043-8122 Tel. (678)825-1000

E-mail: ac@pcanet.org

Web site: www.pcanet.org

Officers

Moderator, Dr. Skip Ryan, Park Cities PC, 4124 Oak Lawn Ave., Dallas, TX 75219 Tel. (214)224-2500, webmaster@pcpc.org

Stated Clerk/Coord. of Admin., Dr. L. Roy Taylor, 1700 N. Brown Rd., Suite 105, Lawrenceville, GA 30043-8122 Tel. (678)825-1100, ac@pcanet.org

Christian Education & Publications Coord., Dr. Charles Dunahoo, 1700 N. Brown Rd., Suite 102, Lawrenceville, GA 30043-8122 Tel. (678)825-1100, cep@pacnet.org

Mission to the World Coord., Dr. Paul D. Kooistra, 1600 N. Brown Rd., Lawrenceville, GA 30043-8141 Tel. (678)823-0004, mtw@mtw. org

Mission to North America Coord., Dr. James C. Bland, 1700 N. Brown Rd., Suite 101, Lawrenceville, GA 30043-8122 Tel. (678)825-1200, mna@pcanet.org

Reformed University Ministries Coord., Dr. Rod Mays, 1700 N. Brown Rd., Suite 104, Lawrenceville, GA 30043-8122 Tel. (678)825-1070, rum@pcanet.org

PCA Foundation Pres., Mr. Randel Stair, 1700 N. Brown Rd., Suite 103, Lawrenceville, GA 30043-8122 Tel. (678)825-1040, pcaf@pcanet. org

PCA Retirement and Benefits, Inc., Mr. Randel Stair, 1700 North Brown Road, Suite 103, Lawrenceville, GA 30043-8143 Tel. (678)825-1260 Fax (678)825-1261

Ridge Haven Conference Dir., Rev. Morse Up De Graff, P.O. Box 969, Rosman, NC 28772 Tel. (828)862-3916 Fax (828)884-6988, ridgehaven@citcom.net

Covenant College Pres., Dr. Niel Nielson, 14049 Scenic Highway, Lookout Mountain, GA 30750 Tel. (706)820-1560 Fax (706)820-2165, webmaster@covenant.edu

Covenant Theological Seminary Pres., Dr. Bryan Chapell, 12330 Conway Rd., St. Louis, MO 63141 Tel. (314)434-4044 Fax (314)434-4819, president@covenantseminary.edu

Periodicals

Equip, Covenant, Mission Report, The View, Network, byFaith

Presbyterian Church (U.S.A.)*

The Presbyterian Church (U.S.A.) was organized June 10, 1983, when the Presbyterian Church in the United States and the United Presbyterian Church in the United States of America united in Atlanta. The union healed a major division which began with the Civil War when Presbyterians in the South withdrew from the Presbyterian Church in the United States of America to form the Presbyterian Church in the Confederate States.

The United Presbyterian Church in the United States of America had been created by the 1958 union of the Presbyterian Church in the United States of America and the United Presbyterian Church of North America. Of those two uniting bodies, the Presbyterian Church in the U.S.A. dated from the first Presbytery organized in Philadelphia, about 1706. The United Presbyterian Church of North America was formed in 1858, when the Associate Reformed Presbyterian Church and the Associate Presbyterian Church united.

Strongly ecumenical in outlook, the Presbyterian Church (U.S.A.) is the result of at least 10 different denominational mergers over the last 250 years. A restructure, adopted by the General Assembly meeting in June 1993, has been implemented. The Presbyterian Church (U.S.A.) dedicated its new national offices in Louisville, Kentucky in 1988.

Headquarters

100 Witherspoon St., Louisville, KY 40202 Tel. (888)728-7228 Fax (502)569-5018

Media Contact, Assoc. Dir. for Communications,

Ann Giles, Tel. (502)569-5515 Fax (502) 569-8073
E-mail: presytel@pcusa.org
Web site: www.pcusa.org

Officers

Mod., Rich Ufford-Chase
Vice-Mod., Jean Marie Peacock
Stated Clk., Clifton Kirkpatrick

THE OFFICE OF THE GENERAL ASSEMBLY

Tel. (888)728-7228 ext. 5424 Fax (502)569-8005
Stated Clk., Rev. Clifton Kirkpatrick
Strategic Operations, Dir., Rev. Gradye Parsons
Middle Governing Body Relations, Coord., Rev. Gary Torrens
Dept. of the Stated Clerk, Dir., Loyda Aja
Dept. of Constitutional Services, Dir., Rev. Mark Tammen
Ecumenical & Agency Relations, Dir., Rev. Robina Winbush
Dept. of Communication & Technology, Dir., Rev. Kerry Clements
Dept. of Hist., Philadelphia, 425 Lombard St., Philadelphia, PA 19147 Tel. (215)627-1852 Fax (215)627-0509; Dir., Frederick J. Heuser, Jr.; Deputy Dir., Margery Sly

GENERAL ASSEMBLY COUNCIL

Exec. Dir., John J. Detterick
Deputy Exec. Dir., Helen Locklear
Worldwide Ministries Division, Dir., Rev. Marian McClure
Congregational Ministries Division, Dir., Donald G. Campbell
National Ministries Division, Dir., Rev. Curtis A. Kearns, Jr.
Mission Support Services Dir., Joey Bailey

BOARD OF PENSIONS

200 Market St., Philadelphia, PA 19103-3298 Tel. (800)773-7752 Fax (215)587-6215
Chpsn. of the Bd., Earldean V. S. Robbins
Pres., & CEO, Robert W. Maggs, Jr.

PRESBYTERIAN CHURCH (U.S.A.) FOUNDATION

200 E. Twelfth St., Jeffersonville, IN 47130 Tel. (812)288-8841 Fax (502)569-5980
Chpsn. of the Bd., James Henderson
Pres. & CEO, Robert E. Leech

PRESBYTERIAN CHURCH (U.S.A.) INVESTMENT & LOAN PROGRAM, INC.

Tel. (800)903-7457 Fax (502)569-8868
Chpsn. of the Board, Ben McAnally
Pres. & CEO, James L. Hudson

PRESBYTERIAN PUBLISHING CORPORATION

Chpsn. of the Bd., Robert Bohl
Pres. & CEO, Davis Perkins

SYNOD EXECUTIVES

Alaska-Northwest, Rev. Doug Kelly, 217 6th Ave. N., Seattle, WA 98109 Tel. (206)448-6403
Boriquen in Puerto Rico, Rev. Harry Fred Del Valle, Ave. Hostos Edificio 740, Cond. Medical Center Plaza, Suite 216, Mayaguez, PR 00680 Tel. (787)832-8375
Covenant, Rev. Richard D. Brownlee and Rev. Marie T. Cross, 1911 Indian Wood Cir. #B Tel. (419)754-4050
Lakes & Prairies, Rev. Philip Brown, 8012 Cedar Ave. S., Bloomington, MN 55425-1210 Tel. (612)854-0144
Lincoln Trails, Rev. Rev. Paul Gregory Neel, Int., 1100 W. 42nd St., Indianapolis, IN 46208-3381 Tel. (317)923-3681
Living Waters, Rev. P. David Snellgrove, 318 Seaboard Ln., Suite 205, Franklin, TN 37067 Tel. (615)261-4008
Mid-America, Rev. John L. Williams, 6400 Glenwood, Suite 111, Overland Park, KS 66202-4072 Tel. (913)384-3020
Mid-Atlantic, Rev. Roger C. Harp, P.O. Box 27026, Richmond, VA 23261-7026 Tel. (804)342-0016
Northeast, Rev. Frank Poole, Int., 5811 Heritage Landing Dr., East Syracuse, NY 13057-9360 Tel. (315)446-5990
Pacific, Rev. Robert Brinks, 8 Fourth St., Petaluma, CA 94952-3004 Tel. (707)765-1772
Rocky Mountains, Rev. Zane Buxton, 3025 W. 37th Ave., Suite 206, Denver, CO 80211-2799 Tel. (303)477-9070
South Atlantic, Rev. Reginald Parsons, 118 E. Monroe St., Suite 3, Jacksonville, FL 32202 Tel. (904)356-6070
Southern California & Hawaii, Rev. John N. Langfitt, 1501 Wilshire Blvd., Los Angeles, CA 90017-2293 Tel. (213)483-3840
Southwest, Rev. Janet DeVries, 401 E. 4th St. #A, Tucson, AZ 85705 Tel. (520)791-9600
The Sun, Rev. Judy R. Fletcher, 1925 E. Belt Line Rd. #220, Carrollton, TX 75006 Tel. (214)390-1894
The Trinity, Rev. Bruce G. Stevens and Thomas E. Robinson, 3040 Market St., Camp Hill, PA 17011-4599 Tel. (717)737-0421

Periodicals

American Presbyterians, Journal of Presbyterian History; Presbyterian News Service *News Briefs; Church & Society Magazine; Horizons; Presbyterians Today; Interpretation; Presbyterian Outlook*

Primitive Advent Christian Church

This body split from the Advent Christian Church. All its churches are in West Virginia. The Primitive Advent Christian Church believes that the Bible is the only rule of faith and practice and that Christian character is the only test of fellowship and communion. The church agrees with Christian fidelity and meekness; exercises mutual watch and care; counsels, admonishes, or reproves as duty may require and receives the same from each other as becomes the household of faith. Primitive Advent Christians do not believe in taking up arms.

The church believes that three ordinances are set forth by the Bible to be observed by the Christian church, (1) baptism by immersion; (2) the Lord's Supper, by partaking of unleavened bread and wine; (3) feet washing, to be observed by the saints' washing of one another's feet.

Headquarters

Media Contact, Sec.-Treas., Roger Wines, 1971 Grapevine Rd., Sissonville, WV 25320 Tel. (304)988-2668

Officers

Pres., Herbert Newhouse, 7632 Hughart Dr., Sissonville, WV 25320 Tel. (304)984-9277
Vice-Pres., Roger Hammons, 273 Frame Rd., Elkview, WV 25071 Tel. (304)965-6247
Sec. & Treas., Roger Wines, 1971 Grapevine Rd., Sissonville, WV 25320 Tel. (304)988-2668

Primitive Baptists

This large group of Baptists, located throughout the United States, opposes all centralization and modern missionary societies. They preach salvation by grace alone.

Headquarters

P.O. Box 38, Thornton, AR 71766 Tel. (501)352-3694
Media Contact, Elder W. Hartsel Cayce

Officers

Elder W. Hartsel Cayce
Elder Lasserre Bradley, Jr., Box 17037, Cincinnati, OH 45217 Tel. (513)821-7289
Elder S. T. Tolley, P.O. Box 68, Atwood, TN 38220 Tel. (901)662-7417

Periodicals

Baptist Witness; The Christian Baptist

Primitive Methodist Church in the U.S.A.

Hugh Bourne and William Clowes, local preachers in the Wesleyan Church in England, organized a day-long meeting at Mow Cop in Staffordshire on May 31, 1807, after Lorenzo Dow, an evangelist from America, told them of American camp meetings. Thousands attended and many were converted, but the Methodist Church, founded by the open-air preacher John Wesley, refused to accept the converts and reprimanded the preachers.

After waiting for two years for a favorable action by the Wesleyan Society, Bourne and Clowes established The Society of the Primitive Methodists. This was not a schism, Bourne said, for "we did not take one from them ... it now appeared to be the will of God that we ... should form classes and take upon us the care of churches in the fear of God." Primitive Methodist missionaries were sent to New York in 1829. An American conference was established in 1840.

Missionary efforts reach into Guatemala, Spain and other countries. The denomination joins in federation with the Evangelical Congregational Church, the United Brethren in Christ Church and the Southern Methodist Church and is a member of the National Association of Evangelicals.

The church believes the Bible is the only true rule of faith and practice, the inspired Word of God. It believes in one Triune God, the Deity of Jesus Christ, the Deity and personality of the Holy Spirit, the innocence of Adam and Eve, the Fall of the human race, the necessity of repentance, justification by faith of all who believe, regeneration witnessed by the Holy Spirit, sanctification by the Holy Spirit, the second coming of the Lord Jesus Christ, the resurrection of the dead and conscious future existence of all people and future judgments with eternal rewards and punishments.

Headquarters

Media Contact, Pres., Rev. Kerry Ritts, 723 Preston Ln., Hatboro, PA 19040 Tel. (215)675-2639 or (215)672-1576
E-mail: pmconf@juno.com
Web site: www.primitivemethodistchurch.org

Officers

Pres., Rev. Kerry R. Ritts, 723 Preston Ln., Hatboro, PA 19040-2321 Tel. (215)672-1576
Vice-Pres., Rev. Reginald H. Thomas, 110 Pittston Blvd., Wilkes-Barre, PA. 18702-9620 Tel. (570)823-3425
Recording Sec., Rev. Allan Rupert, 207 Whitmore Ave., Mayfield, PA. 18433-1738 Tel. (570)876-2234
Gen. Sec., Rev. David Allen, Jr., 1199 Lawrence St., Lowell, MA 01852-5526 Tel. (978)453-2052, pahson@earthlink.net
Treas., Mr. Raymond C. Baldwin, 18409 Mill Run Ct., Leesburg, VA 20176-4583, rbaldwin32@aol.com

Progressive National Baptist Convention, Inc.*

This body held its organizational meeting in Cincinnati in November, 1961. Subsequent regional sessions were followed by the first annual session in Philadelphia in 1962.

Headquarters

601 50th St. NE, Washington, DC 20019 Tel. (202)396-0558 Fax (202)398-4998
Media Contact, Gen. Sec., Dr. Tyrone S. Pitts

Officers

Pres., Dr. Bennett W. Smith, Sr., St. John Baptist Church, 184 Goodell St., Buffalo, NY 14204
Gen. Sec., Dr. Tyrone S. Pitts

Other Organizations

Dept. of Christian Education, Exec. Dir., Dr. C. B. Lucas, Emmanuel Baptist Church, 3815 W. Broadway, Louisville, KY 40211

Women's Dept., Mildred Wormley, 218 Spring St., Trenton, NJ 08618
Home Mission Bd., Exec. Dir., Rev. Archie LeMone, Jr.
Congress of Christian Education, Pres., Rev. Harold S. Diggs, Mayfield Memorial Baptist Church, 700 Sugar Creek Rd. W., Charlotte, NC 28213
Baptist Global Mission Bureau, Dr. Ronald K. Hill, 161-163 60th St., Philadelphia, PA 19139
Nannie Helen Burroughs School, Tel. (202)398-5266

Protestant Reformed Churches in America

The Protestant Reformed Churches (PRC) have their roots in the sixteenth century Reformation of Martin Luther and John Calvin, as it developed in the Dutch Reformed churches. The denomination originated as a result of a controversy in the Christian Reformed Church in 1924 involving the adoption of the "Three Points of Common Grace." Three ministers in the Christian Reformed Church, the Reverends Herman Hoeksema, George Ophoff, and Henry Danhof, and their consistories (Eastern Avenue, Hope, and Kalamazoo, respectively) rejected the doctrine. Eventually these men were deposed, and their consistories were either deposed or set outside the Christian Reformed Church. The denomination was formed in 1926 with three congregations. Today the denomination is comprised of some twenty-eight churches (more than 7,000 members) in the U.S.A. and Canada. The presbyterian form of church government as determined by the Church Order of Dordt is followed by the PRC. The doctrinal standards of the PRC are the Reformed confessions—the Heidelberg Catechism, Belgic Confession of Faith, and Canons of Dordrecht. The doctrine of the covenant is a cornerstone of their teaching. They maintain an unconditional, particular covenant of grace that God establishes with his elect.

Headquarters

16511 S. Park Ave., South Holland, IL 60473 Tel. (708)333-1314
Media Contact, Stated Clerk, Don Doezema, 4949 Ivanrest Ave., Grandville, MI 49418 Tel. (616)531-1490
E-mail: doezema@prca.org
Web site: www.prca.org

Officers

Stat. Clk., Don Doezema, 4949 Ivanrest Ave., Grandville, MI 49418 Tel. (616)531-1490 Fax (616)531-3033, doezema@prca.org

Periodicals

The Standard Bearer

Quakers—please see Friends General Conference

Quakers, Philadelphia—please see Philadelphia Yearly Meeting of the Religious Society of Friends

Quakers, Conservative—please see Religious Society of Friends (Conservative)

Quakers, International—please see Evangelical Friends International—North American Region

Quakers, Unaffiliated Meetings—please see Religious Society of Friends (Unaffiliated Meetings)

Reformed Catholic Church

The Reformed Catholic Church was founded in 1988, and incorporated in 1989, as an alternative to the structures and strictures of the Roman Catholic Church, yet without denying basic Catholic beliefs of faith and love, spirituality and community, prayer and sacramentality. The Reformed Catholic Church is a federation of independent churches offering a progressive alternative in the Catholic tradition. It is a newly formed rite, as in the tradition of the Orthodox churches of the Catholic tradition and the Old Catholic Church of Utrecht. It remains a Catholic Church, and its priests are considered Catholic priests.

Headquarters

Good Shepherd Rectory, P.O. Box 725, Hampton Bays, NY 11946 Tel. (516)723-2012
Media Contact, Archbishop, Most Rev. Robert J. Allmen, D.D.
E-mail: berzol@apollo3.com
Web site: www.reformedcatholic.org

Officers

Archbishop, Most Rev. Robert J. Allmen, D.D.

Reformed Church in America*

The Reformed Church in America was established in 1628 by the earliest settlers of New York. It is the oldest Protestant denomination with a continuous ministry in North America. Until 1867 it was known as the Reformed Protestant Dutch Church.

The first ordained minister, Domine Jonas Michaelius, arrived in New Amsterdam from The Netherlands in 1628. Throughout the colonial period, the Reformed Church lived under the authority of the Classis of Amsterdam. Its churches were clustered in New York and New Jersey. Under the leadership of Rev. John Livingston, it became a denomination independent of the authority of the Classis of Amsterdam in 1776. Its geographical base was broadened in the 19th century by the immigration of Reformed Dutch and German settlers in the midwestern United States. The Reformed Church now spans the United States and Canada.

The Reformed Church in America accepts as

its standards of faith the Heidelberg Catechism, Belgic Confession and Canons of Dort. It has a rich heritage of world mission activity. It claims to be loyal to reformed tradition which emphasizes obedience to God in all aspects of life.

Although the Reformed Church in America has worked in close cooperation with other churches, it has never entered into merger with any other denomination. It is a member of the World Alliance of Reformed Churches, the World Council of Churches and the National Council of the Churches of Christ in the United States of America. In 1998 it also entered into a relationship of full communion with the Evangelical Lutheran Church in America, Presbyterian Church (U.S.A.), and the United Church of Christ by way of the Formula of Agreement.

Headquarters

475 Riverside Dr., New York, NY 10115 Tel. (212)870-3243 Fax (212)870-2499

Media Contact, Communication Officer, Phil Tanis, 4500 60th St. SE, Grand Rapids, MI 49512 Tel. (616)698-7071 Fax (616)698-6606

E-mail: kbaker@rca.org

Web site: www.rca.org

OFFICERS & STAFF OF GENERAL SYNOD

Pres., The Rev. Steven Vander Molen, 475 Riverside Dr., 18th Floor, New York, NY 10115

Gen. Synod Council, Moderator, The Rev. David Schutt, 475 Riverside Dr., 18th Floor, NY, NY 10115

Gen. Sec., The Rev. Wesley Granberg-Michaelson, 475 Riverside Dr., 18th Floor, New York, NY 10115

Operations and Support, 4500 69th St. SE, Grand Rapids, Michigan 49512

Office for Ministry Services, Dir., The Rev. Dr. Gregg Mast

Congregational Services/Evangelism & Church Development Services, Dir., The Rev. Richard Welscott

Finance Services, Treas., Ms. Susan Converse

Mission Services, Dir., The Rev. Bruce Menning

Strategic Planning, The Rev. Shari Brink

African American Council, Exec. Dir., The Rev. Dr. Glen Missick

Council for Hispanic Ministries, Exec. Sec., The Rev. Brigido Cabrera

Council for Pacific/Asian-American Ministries, Exec. Sec., Ms. Ella Campbell

OTHER ORGANIZATIONS

Board of Benefits Services, Dir., Mr. Jack Dalenberg, 7 Salt Creek Ln., Suite 107, Hinsdale, IL 60521; Pres., The Rev. Robert White; Sec., The Rev. Kenneth Bradsell

RCA Foundation, Dir., Mr. Larryl Humme, 7 Salt Creek Ln., Suite 107, Hinsdale, IL 60521

RCA Building and Extension Fund, Fund Executive, Mr. Paul Karssen, 612 8th St. SE, Orange City, IA 51014

Periodicals

Perspectives; The Church Herald

Reformed Church in the United States

Lacking pastors, early German Reformed immigrants to the American colonies were led in worship by "readers." One reader, schoolmaster John Philip Boehm, organized the first congregations near Philadelphia in 1725. A Swiss pastor, Michael Schlatter, was sent by the Dutch Reformed Church in 1746. Strong ties with the Netherlands existed until the formation of the Synod of the German Reformed Church in 1793.

The Eureka Classis, organized in North and South Dakota in 1910 and strongly influenced by the writings of H. Kohlbruegge, P. Geyser and J. Stark, refused to become part of the 1934 merger of the Reformed Church with the Evangelical Synod of North America, holding that it sacrificed the Reformed heritage. (The merged Evangelical and Reformed Church became part of the United Church of Christ in 1957.) Under the leadership of pastors W. Grossmann and W. J. Krieger, the Eureka Classis in 1942 incorporated as the continuing Reformed Church in the United States.

The growing Eureka Classis dissolved in 1986 to form a synod with four regional classes. An heir to the Reformation theology of Zwingli and Calvin, the Heidelberg Catechism, the Belgic Confession and the Canons of Dort are used as the confessional standards of the church. The Bible is strictly held to be the inerrant, infallible Word of God.

The RCUS supports Dordt College, Mid-America Reformed Seminary, New Geneva Theological Seminary, West Minster Theological Seminary in California, and Hope Haven. The RCUS is the official sponsor to the Reformed Confessing Church of Zaire.

Headquarters

Media Contact, Rev. Frank Walker, Th.M., 6121 Pine Vista Way, Elk Grove City, CA 95758-4205 Tel. (661)827-9885

E-mail: triwheeler@aol.com

Web site: www.rcus.org

Officers

Pres., Rev. Vernon Pollema, 235 James St., Shafter, CA 93263 Tel. (661)746-6907

Vice-Pres., Rev. Robert Grossmann, Th.M., 1905 200th St., Garner, IA 50438 Tel. (515)923-3060

Stated Clk., Rev. Frank Walker, Th.M., 5601 Spring Blossom St., Bakersfield, CA 93313-6025 Tel. (661)827-9885

Treas., Clayton Greiman, 2115 Hwy. 69, Garner, IA 50438 Tel. (515)923-2950

Reformed Episcopal Church

The Reformed Episcopal Church was founded December 2, 1873 in New York City by Bishop George D. Cummins, an Asst. bishop in the

Protestant Episcopal Church from 1866 until 1873. Cummins and other evangelical Episcopalians were concerned about the exclusiveness propagated by what they perceived to be an excessive ritualism then sweeping the church. Throughout the late 1860s evangelicals and ritualists clashed over ceremonies, vestments, open or closed communion, the Articles of Religion, interpretation of the meaning of the sacraments, and the understanding of Apostolic Succession.

In October, 1873, other bishops of the Episcopal Church publicly attacked Cummins in major newspapers for participating in an ecumenical communion service sponsored by the Evangelical Alliance. Cummins resigned from the Episcopal Church and drafted a call to organize a new Episcopal Church for the "purpose of restoring the old paths of their fathers." On December 2, 1873, a Declaration of Principles which expressed the evangelical understanding of the Articles of Religion was adopted. Dr. Charles Edward Cheney of Chicago was elected as bishop to serve with Bishop Cummins. The Second General Council, meeting in May 1874 in New York City, approved a Constitution and Canons and adopted the 1785 Proposed Book of Common Prayer for use in the new Church.

In recent years the Reformed Episcopal Church has revised the Prayer Book to conform to the 1662 and 1928 Books of Common Prayer. The Church still embraces the Thirty Nine Articles of Religion, and has approved the Chicago-Lambeth Quadrilateral of 1886–1888.

Since 1993, the Reformed Episcopal Church has been in official dialogue with the Episcopal Church U.S.A. with occasional meetings at the denominational level.

There are presently five geographic dioceses in the United States and Canada, as well as various missionary jurisdictions including India, Liberia, the West Indies, and others.

The Reformed Episcopal Church is a member of the National Association of Evangelicals.

Headquarters

826 2nd Ave., Blue Bell, PA 19422-1257 Tel. (215)483-1196 Fax (215)483-5235

Media Contact, Rt. Rev. Leonard Riches; Rt. Rev. Royal U. Grote, Jr., Church Growth Office, 211 Byrne Ave., Houston, TX 77009 Tel. (713)862-4929

E-mail: wycliffe@jps.net

Web site: recus.org

Officers

Pres. & Presiding Bishop, Rt. Rev. Leonard W. Riches

Vice-Pres., Rt. Rev. Royal U. Grote, Jr.

Sec., Rev. Walter Banek

Treas., Ven. Jon W. Abboud

OTHER ORGANIZATIONS

Bd. of Foreign Missions, Pres., Dr. Barbara J. West, 316 Hunters Rd., Swedesboro, NJ 08085 Tel. (609) 467-1641

Bd. of Natl. Church Extension, Pres., Rt. Rev. Royal U. Grote, Jr., 211 Byrne Ave., Houston, TX 77009 Tel. (713)862-4929

Publication Society, Pres., Rt. Rev. Royal U. Grote, 211 Byrne Ave., Houston, TX 77009 Tel. (713)862-4929; 7372 Henry Ave., Philadelphia, PA 19128

The Reapers, Pres., Susan Higham, 472 Leedom St., Jenkintown, PA 19046

Committee on Women's Work, Pres., Joan Workowski, 1162 Beverly Rd., Rydal, PA 19046

Committee on Constitutions and Canons, Rev. Canon James T. Payne, P.O. Box 973, Missouri City TX 77495

BISHOPS

Leonard W. Riches, Sr., 85 Smithtown Rd., Pipersville, PA 18947 Tel. (215)483-1196 Fax (215)294-8009

Royal U. Grote, Jr., 211 Byrne Ave., Houston, TX 77009

James C. West, Sr., 408 Red Fox Run, Summerville, SC 29485

Robert H. Booth, 1611 Park Ave., #212, Quakertown, PA 18951

Gregory K. Hotchkiss, 318 E. Main St., Somerville, NJ 08876

George B. Fincke, 155 Woodstock Circle, Vacaville, CA 95687-3381

Daniel R. Morse, 11259 Wexford Dr., Eads, TN 38025

Michael Fedechko, Box 2532, New Liskeard, ON P0J 1P0

Charles W. Dorrington, 626 Blanshard St., Victoria, BC V8W 3G6

Ray R. Sutton, 17405 Muirfield Dr., Dallas TX 75287 Tel. (972)248-6505

Periodicals

Reformed Episcopalians

Reformed Mennonite Church

This is a small group of believers in Pennsylvania, Ohio, Michigan, Illinois, and Ontario, Canada who believe in non-resistance of evil, and non-conformity to the world and who practice separation from unfaithful worship. They believe that Christian unity is the effect of brotherly love and are of one mind and spirit. Their church was established in 1812 by John Herr, who agreed with the teachings of Menno Simon as well as those of Jesus Christ.

Headquarters

Lancaster County only, Reformed Mennonite Church, 602 Strasburg Pike, Lancaster, PA 17602

Media Contact, Bishop, Glenn M. Gross, Tel. (717)795-8695

Officers

Bishop Glenn M. Gross, 906 W. Grantham Rd., Mechanicsburg, PA 17055

Reformed Methodist Union Episcopal Church

The Reformed Methodist Union Episcopal church was formed after a group of ministers withdrew from the African Methodist Episcopal Church following a dispute over the election of ministerial delegates to the General Conference.

These ministers organized the Reformed Methodist Union church during a four-day meeting beginning on January 22, 1885 at Hills Chapel (now known as Mt. Hermon RMUE church), in Charleston, South Carolina. The Rev. William E. Johnson was elected President of the new church. Following the death of Rev. Johnson in 1896, it was decided that the church would conform to regular American Methodism (the Episcopacy). The first Bishop, Edward Russell Middleton, was elected, and "Episcopal" was added to the name of the church. Bishop Middleton was consecrated on Dec. 5, 1896, by Bishop P. F. Stephens of the Reformed Episcopal Church.

Headquarters

1136 Brody Ave., Charleston, SC 29407

Media Contact, Gen. Sec., Brother Willie B. Oliver, P.O. Box 1995, Orangeburg, SC 29116 Tel. (803)536-3293

Officers

Bishop, Rt. Rev. Leroy Gethers, Tel. (803)766-3534

Asst. Bishop, Rt. Rev. Jerry M. DeVoe, Jr.

Gen. Sec., Brother Willie B. Oliver

Treas., Rev. Daniel Green

Sec. of Education, Rev. William Polite

Sec. of Books Concerns, Sister Ann Blanding

Sec. of Pension Fund, Rev. Joseph Powell

Sec. of Church Extension, Brother William Parker

Sec. of Sunday School Union, Sister Wine

Sec. of Mission, Rev. Warren Hatcher

Reformed Presbyterian Church of North America

Also known as the Church of the Covenanters, this church's origin dates back to the Reformation days of Scotland when the Covenanters signed their Covenants in resistance to the king and the Roman Church in the enforcement of state church practices. The Church in America has signed two Covenants in particular, those of 1871 and 1954.

Headquarters

Media Contact, Stated Clk., James K. McFarland, 7408 Penn Ave., Pittsburgh, PA 15208 Tel. (412)731-1177 Fax (412)731-8861

E-mail: rptrustees@aol.com

Web site: www.reformedpresbyterian.org

Officers

Mod., Rev. Ralph E. Joseph, 625 Jeff Davis Ave., Selma, AL 36701-5576 Tel. (334)872-2715

Clk., J. Bruce Martin, 310 Main St., Ridgefield Park, NJ 07660 Tel. (201)440-5993

Asst. Clk., Raymond E. Morton, 411 N. Vine St., Sparta, IL 62286 Tel. (618)443-3419

Stated Clk., James K. McFarland, 7408 Penn Ave., Pittsburgh, PA 15208 Tel. (412)731-1177

Periodicals

The Witness; The Reformed Presbyterian Witness

Reformed Zion Union Apostolic Church

This group was organized in 1869 at Boydton, Va., by Elder James R. Howell of New York, a minister of the A.M.E. Zion Church, with doctrines of the Methodist Episcopal Church.

Headquarters

Rt. 1, Box 64D, Dundas, VA 23938 Tel. (804)676-8509

Media Contact, Bishop G. W. Studivant

Officers

Exec. Brd., Chair, Rev. Hilman Wright, Tel. (804) 447-3988

Sec., Joseph Russell, Tel. (804)634-4520

Religious Society of Friends (Conservative)

These Friends mark their present identity from separations occurring by regions at different times from 1845 to 1904. They hold to a minimum of organizational structure. Their meetings for worship, which are unprogrammed and based on silent, expectant waiting upon the Lord, demonstrate the belief that all individuals may commune directly with God and may share equally in vocal ministry.

They continue to stress the importance of the living Christ and the experience of the Holy Spirit working with power in the lives of individuals who obey it.

YEARLY MEETINGS

North Carolina YM, Robert Gosner, P.O. Box 489, Woodland, NC 27897 Tel. (252)587-2571

Iowa YM, Clerk, Deborah Frisch, 916 41st Street, Des Moines, Iowa 50312-2612

Ohio YM, Clerk, S.S. Smith, 61830 Sandy Ridge Road, Barnesville, OH 43713

Religious Society of Friends (Unaffiliated Meetings)

Though all groups of Friends acknowledge the same historical roots, 19th-century divisions in theology and experience led to some of the current organizational groupings. Many newer yearly meetings, often marked by spontaneity, variety and experimentation, and hoping for renewed Quaker unity, have chosen not to identify with past divisions by affiliating in traditional ways with the larger organizations within the Society. Some of these unaffiliated groups have begun within the past 25 years.

YEARLY MEETINGS

Central Yearly Meeting (I), Supt., Jonathan Edwards, 5597 West County Rd. #700, North Ridgeville, IN 47380 Tel. (765)857-2347 Fax (765)857-2347

Intermountain Yearly Meeting (I), Clerk, Ted Church, 10801 Lagrima de Oro NE, Apt. 86,

Albuquerque, NM 87111 Tel. (505)898-5306 Fax (505)899-0936, tchurch@comcast.net
North Pacific Yearly Meeting (I), Contact,, Helen Dart, 3311 NW Polk, Corvallis, OR 97330 Tel. (541)485-6589 Fax (541)345-7664, npym@ teleport.com
Pacific Yearly Meeting (I), Clerk, Jim Anderson, pacificym@juno.com

Periodicals

Friends Bulletin (for Intermountain, Pacific & North Pacific Yearly Meetings)

Reorganized Church of Jesus Christ of Latter-day Saints—please see Community of Christ

The Romanian Orthodox Church in America

The Romanian Orthodox Church in America is an autonomous Archdiocese chartered under the name of "Romanian Orthodox Archdiocese in America." The diocese was founded in 1929 and approved by the Holy Synod of the Romanian Orthodox Church in Romania in 1934. The Holy Synod of the Romanian Orthodox Church granted ecclesiastical autonomy in American Diocese on July 12, 1950. The Diocese continues to hold dogmatic and canonical ties with the Holy Synod and the Romanian Orthodox Patriarchate of Romania.

In 1951, approximately 40 parishes with their clergy from the United States and Canada separated from this church. In 1960, they joined the Russian Orthodox Greek Catholic Metropolia, now called the Orthodox Church in America, which reordained for these parishes a bishop with the title "Bishop of Detroit and Michigan."

On June 11, 1973 the Holy Synod of the Romanian Orthodox church elevated the Bishop of Romanian Orthodox Missionary Episcopate in America to the rank of Archbishop.

Headquarters

P.O. Box 27, Skokie, IL 60076-0027 Tel. (847)674-3900 Fax (847)674-4110
Media Contact, Archdiocesan Sec., V. Rev. Fr. Nicholas Apostola, 44 Midland St., Worcester, MA 01602-4217 Tel. (508)845-0088 Fax (508)845-8850, nicholas.apostola@verizon.net
E-mail: archnicolae@aol.com
Web site: www.romarch.org

Officers

Archbishop, His Eminence Dr. Nicolae Condrea, P.O. Box 27, Skokie, IL 60076-0027 Tel. (847)674-3900 Fax (847)674-4110, archnicolae@aol.com
Vicar, V. Rev. Fr. Ioan Ionita, 17601 Wentworth Ave., Lansing, IL 60438-2074 Tel. & Fax (708)474-0340, tintari@aol.com
Inter-Church Relations, Dir., V. Rev. Fr. Nicholas Apostola, 44 Midland St., Worcester, MA 01602-4217 Tel. (508)845-0088 Fax (508) 845-8850, nicholas.apostola@verizon.net

Periodicals

Credinta-The Faith

The Romanian Orthodox Episcopate of America

This body of Eastern Orthodox Christians of Romanian descent is part of the Autocephalous Orthodox Church in America. For complete description and listing of officers, please see chapter 3, "Religious Bodies in the United States."

Headquarters

2535 Grey Tower Rd., Jackson, MI 49201 Tel. (517)522-4800
Mailing Address, P.O. Box 309, Grass Lake, MI 49240-0309
Media Contact, Ed.-Sec., Rev. Archdeacon David Oancea, P.O. Box 185, Grass Lake, MI 49240-0185 Tel (517)522-3656
E-mail: roeasolia@aol.com
Web site: www.roea.org

Officers

Ruling Hierarch, Most Rev. Archbishop Nathaniel Popp

Periodicals

Solia-The Herald; Good News- Buna Vestire (in Canada only)

Russian Orthodox Church—please see Patriarchal Parishes of the Russian Orthodox Church in the USA

The Russian Orthodox Church Outside of Russia

This group was organized in 1920 to unite in one body of dioceses the missions and parishes of the Russian Orthodox Church outside of Russia. The governing body, set up in Constantinople, was sponsored by the Ecumenical Patriarchate. In November 1950, it came to the United States. The Russian Orthodox Church Outside of Russia emphasizes being true to the old traditions of the Russian Church. It is not in communion with the Moscow Patriarchate.

Headquarters

75 E. 93rd St., New York, NY 10128 Tel. (212)534-1601 Fax (212)426-1086
Media Contact, Dep. Sec., Bishop Gabriel

SYNOD OF BISHOPS

Pres., His Eminence Metropolitan Laurus
Sec., Bishop of Manhattan, Gabriel, Tel. (212) 722-6577

Periodicals

Living Orthodoxy; Orthodox Family; Orthodox Russia; Pravoslavnaya Rus; Pravoslavnaya Zhisn; Orthodox America

The Salvation Army

The Salvation Army, founded in 1865 by William Booth (1829–1912) in London,

England, and introduced into America in 1880, is an international religious and charitable movement organized and operated on a paramilitary pattern and is a branch of the Christian church. To carry out its purposes, The Salvation Army has established a widely diversified program of religious and social welfare services which are designed to meet the needs of children, youth and adults in all age groups.

Headquarters

615 Slaters Ln., Alexandria, VA 22313 Tel. (703)684-5500 Fax (703)684-5538

Media Contact: National Community Rel. & Dev. Sec., Major George Hood, Tel. (703)684-5526 Fax (703)684-5538, george_hood@usn. salvationarmy.org

Officers

Natl. Commander, Commissioner W. Todd Bassett

Natl. Chief Sec., Lt. Colonel Larry Bosh

Natl. Community Relations and Develepment Sec., Dir., Major George Hood

TERRITORIAL ORGANIZATIONS

Central Territory, 10 W. Algonquin Rd., Des Plaines, IL 60016 Tel. (847)294-2000 Fax (847)294-2299; Territorial Commander, Commissioner Kenneth Baillie

Eastern Territory, 440 W. Nyack Rd., P.O. Box C-635, West Nyack, NY 10994 Tel. (914)620-7200 Fax (914)620-7766; Territorial Commander, Commissioner Lawrence Moretz

Southern Territory, 1424 Northeast Expressway, Atlanta, GA 30329 Tel. (404)728-1300 Fax (404)728-1331; Territorial Commander, Commissioner Philip Needham

Western Territory, 180 E. Ocean Blvd., Long Beach, CA Tel. (562)436-7000 Fax (562)491-8792; Territorial Commander, Commissioner Linda Bond

Periodicals

The War Cry

The Schwenkfelder Church

The Schwenkfelders are the spiritual descendants of the Silesian nobleman Caspar Schwenkfeld von Ossig (1489-1561), a scholar, reformer, preacher and prolific writer who endeavored to aid in the cause of the Protestant Reformation. A contemporary of Martin Luther, John Calvin, Ulrich Zwingli and Phillip Melanchthon, Schwenkfeld sought no following, formulated no creed and did not attempt to organize a church based on his beliefs. He labored for liberty of religious belief, for a fellowship of all believers and for one united Christian church.

He and his cobelievers supported a movement known as the Reformation by the Middle Way. Persecuted by state churches, ultimately 217 Schwenkfelders exiled from Silesia emigrated to Pennsylvania in six migrations, 1731–1734. The largest migration, about 180, landed at Philadelphia Sept. 22, 1734. In 1782, the Society of Schwenkfelders, the forerunner of the present Schwenkfelder Church, was formed. The church was incorporated in 1909.

The Schwenkfelder Church is a voluntary association of six Schwenkfelder Churches at Palm, Worcester, Lansdale, Norristown and two in Philadelphia, Penn.

They practice adult baptism, dedication and baptism of children, and observe the Lord's Supper regularly with open Communion. In theology, they are Christo-centric; in polity, congregational; in missions, world-minded; in ecclesiastical organization, ecumenical.

The ministry is recruited from graduates of accredited theological seminaries. The churches take leadership in ecumenical concerns through ministerial associations, community service and action groups, councils of Christian education and other agencies.

Headquarters

105 Seminary St., Pennsburg, PA 18073 Tel. (215)679-3103

Media Contact, David W. Luz

Officers

Mod., David W. Luz, Pennsburg, PA

Sec., Pat Gramm, Central Schwenkfelder Church, Worcester, PA 19490

Treas., Linda Anders, Souderton, PA

Periodicals

The Schwenkfeldian

Separate Baptists in Christ

The Separate Baptists in Christ are a group of Baptists found in Indiana, Ohio, Kentucky, Tennessee, Virginia, West Virginia, Florida and North Carolina dating back to an association formed in 1758 in North Carolina and Virginia.

Today this group consists of approximately 100 churches. They believe in the infallibility of the Bible, the divine ordinances of the Lord's Supper, feetwashing, baptism and that those who endureth to the end shall be saved.

The Separate Baptists are Arminian in doctrine, rejecting both the doctrines of predestination and eternal security of the believer.

At the 1991 General Association, an additional article of doctrine was adopted. "We believe that at Christ's return in the clouds of heaven all Christians will meet the Lord in the air, and time shall be no more," thus leaving no time for a literal one-thousand-year reign. Seven associations comprise the General Association of Separate Baptists.

Headquarters

Media Contact, Clk., Greg Erdman, 10102 N. Hickory Ln., Columbus, IN 47203 Tel. (812)526-2540

E-mail: mail@separatebaptist.org

Web site: www.separatebaptist.org

Officers

Mod., Rev. Jim Goff, 1020 Gagel Ave., Louisville, KY 40216

Asst. Mod., Rev. Jimmy Polston, 785 Kitchen Rd., Mooresville, IN 46158 Tel. (317)831-6745

Clk., Greg Erdman, 10102 N. Hickory Ln., Columbus, IN 47203 Tel. (812)526-2540

Asst. Clk., Rev. Mattew Cowan, 174 Oak Hill School Rd., Lot 30, Smiths Grove, KY 42171 Tel. (270)678-5599

Serbian Orthodox Church in the U.S.A. and Canada*

The Serbian Orthodox Church is an organic part of the Eastern Orthodox Church. As a local church it received its autocephaly from Constantinople in 1219 A.D.

In 1921, a Serbian Orthodox Diocese in the United States of America and Canada was organized. In 1963, it was reorganized into three dioceses, and in 1983 a fourth diocese was created for the Canadian part of the church. The Serbian Orthodox Church in the U.S.A. and Canada received its administrative autonomy in 1928. However, it remains canonically an integral part of the Serbian Orthodox Patriarchate with its see in Belgrade. The Serbian Orthodox Church is in absolute doctrinal unity with all other local Orthodox Churches.

Headquarters

St. Sava Monastery, P.O. Box 519, Libertyville, IL 60048 Tel. (847)367-0698

E-mail: oea@oea.serbian-church.net

Web site: oea.serbian-church.net

BISHOPS

Metropolitan of Midwestern America, Most Rev. Metropolitan Christopher

Bishop of Canada, Georgije, 5A Stockbridge Ave., Toronto, ON M8Z 4M6 Tel. (416)231-4009

Bishop of Eastern America, Rt. Rev. Bishop Mitrophan, P.O. Box 368, Sewickley, PA 15143 Tel. (412)741-5686

Diocese of Western America, Bishop Jovan, 2541 Crestline Terr., Alhambra, CA 91803 Tel. (818)264-6825

OTHER ORGANIZATIONS

Brotherhood of Serbian Orth. Clergy in U.S.A. & Canada, Pres., V. Rev. Nedeljko Lunich, Joliet, IL, Merrilville, IN

Federation of Circles of Serbian Sisters

Serbian Singing Federation

Periodicals

The Path of Orthodoxy

Seventh-day Adventist Church

The Seventh-day Adventist Church grew out of a worldwide religious revival in the mid-19th century. People of many religious persuasions believed Bible prophecies indicated that the second coming or advent of Christ was imminent.

When Christ did not come in the 1840s, a group of these disappointed Adventists in the United States continued their Bible studies and concluded they had misinterpreted prophetic events and that the second coming of Christ was still in the future. This same group of Adventists later accepted the teaching of the seventh-day Sabbath and became known as Seventh-day Adventists. The denomination organized formally in 1863.

The church was largely confined to North America until 1874, when its first missionary was sent to Europe. Today, over 55,822 congregations meet in 204 countries. Membership exceeds 13 million and increases between four and five percent each year.

In addition to a mission program, the church has the largest worldwide Protestant parochial school system, with approximately 6,471 schools with more than 1,254,000 students on elementary through college and university levels.

The Adventist Development and Relief Agency (ADRA) helps victims of war and natural disasters, and many local congregations have community service facilities to help those in need close to home.

The church also has a worldwide publishing ministry with 55 printing facilities producing magazines and other publications in more than 347 languages and dialects. In the United States and Canada, the church sponsors a variety of radio and television programs, including *Christian Lifestyle Magazine, It Is Written, Breath of Life, Ayer, Hoy, y Mañana, Voice of Prophecy, and La Voz de la Esperanza.*

The North American Division of Seventh-day Adventists includes 58 Conferences which are grouped together into nine organized Union Conferences. The various Conferences work under the general direction of these Union Conferences.

Headquarters

12501 Old Columbia Pike, Silver Spring, MD 20904-6600 Tel. (301)680-6000

Media Contact, Dir., Archives & Statistics, Bert Haloviak

E-mail: kjones@gc.adventist.org

Web site: www.adventist.org

WORLD-WIDE OFFICERS

Pres., Jan Paulsen

Sec., Matthew A. Bediako

Treas., Robert E. Lemon

WORLDWIDE DEPARTMENTS

Adventist Chaplaincy Ministries, Dir., Martin W. Feldbush

Children's Ministries, Dir., Linda Koh

Education, Dir., C. Garland Dulan

Communication, Dir., Rajmund Dabrowski

Family Ministries, Dir., Ronald M. Flowers

Health Ministries, Dir., Allan R. Handysides
Ministerial Assoc., Dir., James A. Cress
Public Affairs & Religious Liberty, Dir., John Graz
Publishing, Dir., Jose Luis Campos
Sabbath School & Personal Ministries, James W. Zackrison
Stewardship, Dir., Benjamin C. Maxson
Trust Services, Jeffrey K. Wilson
Women's Ministries, Ardis D. Stenbakken
Youth, Baraka G. Muganda

NORTH AMERICAN OFFICERS

Pres., Don C. Schneider
Vice-Pres., Debra Brill; James W. Gilley; Gerald Kovalski; Alvin M. Kibble; Manuel Vasquez
Sec., Roscoe J. Howard, III
Assoc. Sec., Rosa T. Banks
Treas., Juan R. Prestol
Assoc. Treas., Michael Park; Del L. Johnson; Kenneth W. Osborn

NORTH AMERICAN ORGANIZATIONS

Atlantic Union Conf., P.O. Box 1189, South Lancaster, MA 01561-1189; Pres., Donald G. King
Canada, Seventh-day Adventist Church in Canada (see Ch. 4)
Columbia Union Conf., 5427 Twin Knolls Rd., Columbia, MD 21045; Pres., Harold L. Lee
Lake Union Conf., P.O. Box C, Berrien Springs, MI 49103; Pres., Walter L. Wright
Mid-America Union Conf., P.O. Box 6128, Lincoln, NE 68506; Pres., Dennis N. Carlson
North Pacific Union Conf., P.O. Box 871150, Vancouver, WA 98687; Pres., Jere D. Patzer,
Pacific Union Conf., P.O. Box 5005, Westlake Village, CA 91359; Pres., Thomas J. Mostert, Jr
Southern Union Conf., P.O. Box 849, Decatur, GA 30031; Pres., Gordon L. Retzr
Southwestern Union Conf., P.O. Box 4000, Burleson, TX 76097; Pres., Max A. Trevino

Periodicals

ADRA Works; The Adventist Chaplain; Adventist Review; ASI Magazine; AWR Trans Missions; Children's Friend; Christian Record; College and University Dialogue; Collegiate Quarterly; Cornerstone Youth Resource Magazine; Cornerstone Connections; Elder's Digest; Encounter; For God and Country; Geoscience Reports; Guide; It is Written Channels; The Journal of Adventist Education; Kid's Ministry Ideas; Liberty; Lifeglow; Listen; Literature Evangelist; Message; Ministry; Mission—children, youth, adult; Origins; Our Little Friend; Primary Treasure; Publishing Mirror; Sabbath School Teaching Aids; Sabbath School Program Helps; Sabbath School Leadership; Shabbat Shalom; Shepherdess International Journal; Signs of the Times; Vibrant Life; Voice of Prophecy News; Winner; Women of Spirit; Young and Alive; Youth Ministry ACCENT

Seventh Day Baptist General Conference, USA and Canada

Seventh Day Baptists emerged during the English Reformation, organizing their first churches in the mid-1600s. The first Seventh Day Baptists of record in America were Stephen and Ann Mumford, who emigrated from England in 1664. Beginning in 1665 several members of the First Baptist Church at Newport, R.I. began observing the seventh day Sabbath, or Saturday. In 1671, five members, together with the Mumfords, formed the first Seventh Day Baptist Church in America at Newport.

Beginning about 1700, other Seventh Day Baptist churches were established in New Jersey and Pennsylvania. From these three centers, the denomination grew and expanded westward. They founded the Seventh Day Baptist General Conference in 1802.

The organization of the denomination reflects an interest in home and foreign missions, publications and education. Women have been encouraged to participate. From the earliest years religious freedom has been championed for all and the separation of church and state advocated.

Seventh Day Baptists are members of the Baptist World Alliance and Baptist Joint Committee. The Seventh Day Baptist World Federation has 17 member conferences on six continents.

Headquarters

Seventh Day Baptist Center, 3120 Kennedy Rd., P.O. Box 1678, Janesville, WI 53547-1678
Tel. (608)752-5055 Fax (608)752-7711
Media Contact, Ex. Dir., Robert Appel; Financial Dir., Calvin Babcock
E-mail: sdbgen@inwave.com
Web site: www.seventhdaybaptist.org

OTHER ORGANIZATIONS

Seventh Day Baptist Missionary Society, Exec. Dir., Kirk Looper, 119 Main St., Westerly, RI 02891
Seventh Day Bapt. Bd. of Christian Ed., Exec. Dir., Rev. Andrew Camenga., Box 115, Alfred Station, NY 14803
Women's Soc. of the Gen. Conference, Pres., Mrs. Marjorie Jacob, P.O. Box 122, Pomona Park, FL 32181-0122
American Sabbath Tract & Comm. Council, Dir. of Communications, Rev. Kevin J. Butler, 3120 Kennedy Rd., P.O. Box 1678, Janesville, WI 53547
Seventh Day Baptist Historical Society, Historian, Don A. Sanford, 3120 Kennedy Rd., P.O. Box 1678, Janesville, WI 53547
Seventh Day Baptist Center on Ministry, Dir. of Pastoral Services, Rev. Gordon Lawton, 3120 Kennedy Rd., P.O. Box 1678, Janesville, WI 53547

Periodicals

Sabbath Recorder

Southern Baptist Convention

The Southern Baptist Convention was organized on May 10, 1845, in Augusta, Georgia. Cooperating Baptist churches are located in all 50 states, the District of Columbia, Puerto Rico, American Samoa and the Virgin Islands. The members of the churches work together through 1,194 district associations and 41 state conventions or fellowships. The Southern Baptist Convention has an Executive Committee and 12 national agencies—four boards, six seminaries, one commission, and one auxiliary organization.

The purpose of the Southern Baptist Convention is "to provide a general organization for Baptists in the United States and its territories for the promotion of Christian missions at home and abroad and any other objects such as Christian education, benevolent enterprises, and social services which it may deem proper and advisable for the furtherance of the Kingdom of God." (Constitution, Article II)

The Convention exists in order to help the churches lead people to God through Jesus Christ.

From the beginning, there has been a mission desire to share the Gospel with the peoples of the world. The Cooperative Program is the basic channel of mission support. In addition, the Lottie Moon Christmas Offering for Foreign Missions and the Annie Armstrong Easter Offering for Home Missions support Southern Baptists' world mission programs.

In 2003, there were more than 5,300 foreign missionaries serving in foreign countries and approximately 5,200 home missionaries serving in North America.

Headquarters

901 Commerce St., Nashville, TN 37203 Tel. (615)244-2355

Media Contact, Vice-Pres. for Convention Relations, A. William Merrell, Tel. (615)244-2355 Fax (615)782-8684

E-mail: bmerrell@sbc.net

Web site: www.sbc.net

Officers

Pres., Bobby Welsh, 118 North Palmetto Ave., Daytona Beach, FL 32114

Recording Sec., John Yeats, P.O. Box 12130, Oklahoma City, OK 73112

Exec. Committee, Pres., Morris H. Chapman; Vice-Pres., Business & Finance, Jack Wilkerson; Vice-Pres., Convention News, Will Hall; Vice-Pres., Convention Relations, A. William Merrell; Vice-Pres., Convention Policy, Augie Boto; Vice-Pres., Cooperative Program, David E. Hankins

GENERAL BOARDS AND COMMISSIONS

International Mission Board, Pres., Jerry A. Rankin, 3806 Monument Ave., Richmond, VA 23230 Tel. (804)353-0151 ext. 1207

North American Mission Board, Pres., Robert E. Reccord, 4200 N. Point Pkwy., Alpharetta, GA 30022-4176 Tel. (770)410-6000

Annuity Board, Pres., O.S. Hawkins, 2401 Cedar Springs Rd, Dallas, TX 75201 Tel. (214)720-0511

LifeWay Christian Resources, Pres., James T. Draper, Jr., One Lifeway Plaza, Nashville, TN 37234 Tel. (615)251-2000

Ethics and Religious Liberty Commission, Pres., Richard D. Land, 901 Commerce St., Suite 550, Nashville, TN 37203 Tel. (615)244-2495

STATE CONVENTIONS

Alabama, Rick Lance, 2001 E. South Blvd., Montgomery, AL 36116 Tel. (334)288-2460

Alaska, David N. Baldwin, 1750 O'Malley Rd., Anchorage, AK 99516 Tel. (907)344-9627

Arizona, Steve Bass, 2240 N. Hayden Rd., Suite 100 Scottsdale, AZ 85257 Tel. (480)945-0880

Arkansas, Emil Turner, 525 West Capitol, Little Rock, AR 72201 Tel. (501)376-4791 ext. 5102

California, Fermin A. Whittaker, 678 E. Shaw Ave., Fresno, CA 93710 Tel. (559)229-9533 ext. 230

Colorado, Mark Edlund, 7393 S. Alton Way, Centennial, CO 80112 Tel. (303)771-2480 ext. 222

District of Columbia, Rev. Jeffrey Haggray, 1628 16th St. NW, Washington, DC 20009 Tel. (202)265-1526

Florida, John Sullivan, 1230 Hendricks Ave., Jacksonville, FL 32207 Tel. (904)396-2351 ext 8101

Georgia, Dr. J. Robert White, 2930 Flowers Rd. S., Atlanta, GA 30341 Tel. (770)936-5200

Hawaii, Veryl F. Henderson, 2042 Vancouver Dr., Honolulu, HI 96822 Tel. (808)946-9581 ext. 229

Illinois, Wendell Lang, Exec. Dir, 3085 Stevenson Dr, Springfield, IL 62794 Tel. (217)786-2600

Indiana, Stephen P. Davis, 900 N. High School Rd., Indianapolis, IN 46224 Tel. (317)241-9317

Baptist Convention of Iowa, Jimmy L. Barrentine, Suite 27, 2400 86th St., Des Moines, IA 50322 Tel. (515)278-4369

Kansas-Nebraska, R. Rex Lindsay, 5410 SW Seventh St., Topeka, KS 66606 Tel. (785)273-4880

Kentucky, Bill F. Mackey, 10701 Shelbyville Rd., Middletown, KY 40253-0433 Tel. (502) 245-4101

Louisiana, Dean Doster, 1250 MacArthur Dr., Alexandria, LA 71303 Tel. (318)448-3402

Maryland-Delaware, David H. Lee, 10255 Old Columbia Rd., Columbia, MD 21046 Tel. (410)290-5290

Michigan, Michael R. Collins, 8420 Bunyan Lake Rd., Fenton, MI 48430, Tel. (810)714-1955

Minnesota-Wisconsin, Leo Endel, Exec. Dir., 519 16th St. SE, Rochester, MN 55904 Tel. (507)282-3636

Mississippi, James R. Futral, 515 Mississippi St., Jackson, MS 39201 Tel. (601)968-3800
Missouri, Exec. Dir., David Clippard, 400 E. High Street, Jefferson City, MO 65101 Tel. (573)635-7931 ext. 200
Montana, Jeffert A. Clark, 1130 Cerise Rd., Billings, MT 59101-7396 Tel. (406)252-7537
Nevada, Thane Barnes, Exec. Dir., 406 California Ave., Reno, NV 89509 Tel. (775) 786-0406
New England, James Wideman, 87 Lincoln St., Northborough, MA 01532 Tel. (508)393-6013 ext. 224
New Mexico, Claude W. Cone, 5325 Wyoming NE, Albuquerque, NM 87109 Tel. (505)924-2300 ext. 11
New York, J.B. Graham, 6538 Collamer Rd., East Syracuse, NY 13057 Tel. (315)433-1001
North Carolina, James H. Royston, 205 Convention Dr., Cary, NC 27511 Tel. (919) 467-5100 ext. 102
Northwest, Jeff Iorg, 3200 NE 109th Ave., Vancouver, WA 98682 Tel. (360)882-2100 ext. 121
Ohio, Exec. Dir., Jack P. Kwok, 1680 E. Broad, Columbus, OH 43203 Tel. (614)258-8491 ext. 777
Oklahoma, Anthony L. Jordan, 3800 N. May Ave., Oklahoma City, OK 73112 Tel. (405) 942-3800
Pennsylvania-South Jersey, David C. Waltz, 4620 Fritchey St., Harrisburg, PA 17109 Tel. (717)652-5856
South Carolina, B. Carlisle Driggers, 190 Stoneridge Dr., Columbia, SC 29210 Tel. (803)765-0030 ext. 1500
Tennessee, James M. Porch, 5001 Maryland Way, Brentwood, TN 37027 Tel. (615)371-2090
Texas, (BGCT) Baptist General Convention of Texas, Charles R. Wade, 333 N. Washington, Dallas, TX 75246 Tel. (214)828-5300
Texas, (SBTC) Southern Baptists of Texas, James W. Richards, 4500 State Hwy. 360, Grapevine, TX 76051 Tel. (817)552-2500
Utah-Idaho, Tim Clark, 12401 South 450 East #G-1, Draper, UT 84020 Tel. (801)572-5350
Virginia, (BGAV) Baptist General Association of Virginia, John V. Upton, Jr., 2828 Emerywood Pkwy, Richmond, VA 23226 Tel. (804)915-2430 ext. 223
Virginia, (SBCV) Southern Baptist Conservatives of Virginia, H. Doyle Chauncey, 4101 Cox Rd., Suite 100, Glen Allen, VA 23060 Tel. (804)270-1848
West Virginia, Terry L. Harper, Number One Missions Way, Scott Depot, WV 25560 Tel. (304)757-0944
Wyoming, Randy Sprinkle, 3925 Casper Mountain Rd., Casper, WY 82601 Tel. (307) 472-4087

FELLOWSHIPS

Dakota Southern Baptist Fellowship, W.D. "Doc" Lindsey, P.O. Box 6028, Bismarck, ND 58506 Tel. (701)255-3765
Montana Southern Baptist Fellowship, Jeffery A. Clark, 1130 Cerise Rd., Billings, MT 59101 Tel. (406)252-7537
Canadian Convention of Southern Baptists, Gerry Taillon, 100 Convention Way, Cochrane, AB T4C 2G2 Tel. (403)932-5688

Periodicals

The Commission; SBC Life; On Mission

Southern Methodist Church

Organized in 1939, this body is composed of congregations desirous of continuing in true Biblical Methodism and preserving the fundamental doctrines and beliefs of the Methodist Episcopal Church, South. These congregations declined to be a party to the merger of the Methodist Episcopal Church, The Methodist Episcopal Church, South and the Methodist Protestant Church into The Methodist Church.

Headquarters

P.O. Box 39, Orangeburg, SC 29116-0039 Tel. (803)536-1378 Fax (803)535-3881
Media Contact, Pres., Rev. Bedford F. Landers
E-mail: smchq@juno.com

Officers

Pres., Rev. Bedford F. Landers
Dir. of Admin. & Finance, Rev. Cicel Clark
Dir. of Foreign Missions, Rev. Paul Zellmek, P.O. Box 39, Orangeburg, SC 29116-0039
Southern Methodist College, P.O. Box 1027, Orangeburg, SC 29116-1027
The Eastern Conf., Vice-Pres., Rev. John T. Hucks, Jr., 221 Pinewood Dr., Rowesville, SC 29133
Alabama-Florida-Georgia Conf., Vice-Pres., Rev. Bob Waites, 220 South Trace Lane, Hoover, AL 35244
Mid-South Conf., Vice-Pres., Rev. Dr. H. J. Hutchins, Route 1, Box 275C, Bailey, MS 39320
South-Western Conf., Vice-Pres., Rev. Ira Schilling, 106 Albert Dr., Haughton, LA 71037
Gen. Conf., Treas., Rev. Cicel Clark, P.O. Drawer A, Orangeburg, SC 29116-0039

Periodicals

The Southern Methodist

Sovereign Grace Believers

The Sovereign Grace Believers are a contemporary movement that began its stirrings in the mid-1950s when some pastors in traditional Baptist churches returned to a Calvinist-theological perspective.

The first "Sovereign Grace" conference was held in Ashland, Kentucky, in 1954 and since then conferences of this sort have been sponsored by various local churches on the West Coast, Southern and Northern states and Canada. This movement is a spontaneous phenomenon concerning reformation at the local church level.

Consequently, there is no interest in establishing a Sovereign Grace Baptist "Convention" or "Denomination." Each local church is to administer the keys to the kingdom.

Most Sovereign Grace Believers formally or informally relate to the "First London" (1646), "Second London" (1689) or "Philadelphia" (1742) Confessions.

There is a wide variety of local church government in this movement. Many Calvinist Baptists have a plurality of elders in each assembly. Other Sovereign Grace Believers, however, prefer to function with one pastor and several deacons.

Membership procedures vary from church to church but all require a credible profession of faith in Christ, and proper baptism as a basis for membership.

Calvinistic Baptists financially support gospel efforts (missionaries, pastors of small churches at home and abroad, literature publication and distribution, radio programs, etc.) in various parts of the world.

Headquarters

Media Contact, Corres., Jon Zens, P.O. Box 548, St. Croix Falls, WI 54024 Tel. (651)465-6516 Fax (651)465-5101
E-mail: jon@searchingtogether.org
Web site: www.searchingtogether.org

Periodicals

Searching Together, Sound of Grace

The Swedenborgian Church*

Founded in North America in 1792 as the Church of the New Jerusalem, the Swedenborgian Church was organized as a national body in 1817 and incorporated in Illinois in 1861. Its biblically based theology is derived from the spiritual, or mystical, experiences and exhaustive biblical studies of the Swedish scientist and philosopher Emanuel Swedenborg (1688–1772).

The church centers its worship and teachings on the historical life and the risen and glorified present reality of the Lord Jesus Christ. It looks with an ecumenical vision toward the establishment of the kingdom of God in the form of a universal church, active in the lives of all people of goodwill who desire and strive for freedom, peace and justice for all. It is a member of the NCCC and active in many local councils of churches.

With churches and groups throughout the United States and Canada, the denomination's central administrative offices and its seminary, "Swedenborg House of Studies," are located in Newton, Massachusetts and Berkeley, California. Affiliated churches are found in Africa, Asia, Australia, Canada, Europe, the United Kingdom, Japan, South Korea and South America. Many philosophers and writers have acknowledged their appreciation of Swedenborg's teachings.

Headquarters

11 Highland Ave., Newtonville, MA 02460 Tel. (617)969-4240 Fax (617)964-3258
Media Contact, Central Ofc. Mgr., Martha Bauer
E-mail: manager@swedenborg.org
Web site: www.swedenborg.org

Officers

Pres., Rev. Christine Laitner, 10 Hannah Court, Midland, MI 48642
Vice-Pres., James Erickson, 1340 Snelling Ave, N., St. Paul, MN 55108
Rec. Sec., Gloria Toot, 10280 Gentlewind Dr., Montgomery, OH 45242
Treas., Lawrence Conant, 290 Berlin St., Apt. 89, Clinton, MA 01510 Tel. (978)368-6269
Ofc. Mgr., Martha Bauer

Periodicals

The Messenger; Our Daily Bread

Syrian (Syriac) Orthodox Church of Antioch*

The Syrian Orthodox Church of Antioch traces its origin to the Patriarchate established in Antioch by St. Peter the Apostle. It is under the supreme ecclesiastical jurisdiction of His Holiness the Syrian Orthodox Patriarch of Antioch and All the East, now residing in Damascus, Syria. The Syrian Orthodox Church—composed of several archdioceses, numerous parishes, schools and seminaries—professes the faith of the first three Ecumenical Councils of Nicaea, Constantinople and Ephesus, and numbers faithful in the Middle East, India, the Americas, Europe and Australia.

The first Syrian Orthodox faithful came to North America during the late 1800s, and by 1907 the first Syrian Orthodox priest was ordained to tend to the community's spiritual needs. In 1949, His Eminence Archbishop Mor Athanasius Y. Samuel came to America and was appointed Patriarchal Vicar in 1952. The Archdiocese was officially established in 1957. In 1995, the Archdiocese of North America was divided into three separate Patriarchal Vicariates (Eastern United States, Western United States and Canada), each under a hierarch of the Church.

There are 24 official archdiocesan parishes and one mission congregation in the United States, located in Arizona, California, District of Columbia, Florida, Indiana, Illinois, Massachusetts, Michigan, New Jersey, New York, Oregon, Rhode Island and Texas. In Canada, there are six official parishes—three in the Province of Ontario and two in the Province of Quebec and one in the Province of Alberta.

Headquarters

Archdiocese of the Eastern U.S., 260 Elm Ave., Teaneck, NJ 07666 Tel. (201)801-0660 Fax (201)801-0603
Archdiocese of the Western U.S., 417 E.

Fairmount Rd., Burbank, CA 91501 Tel. (818)845-5089 Fax (818)845-5436
Media Contact, Archdiocesan Gen. Sec., Very Rev. Chorepiscopus John Meno, 260 Elm Ave., Teaneck, NJ 07666 Tel. (201)907-0122 Fax (201)907-0551
E-mail: hasio@syrianorthodoxchurch.org
Web site: www.syrianorthodoxchurch.org

Officers

Archdiocese for Eastern U.S., Archbishop, Mor Cyril Aphrem Karim
Archdiocese of Los Angeles and Environs, Archbishop, Mor Clemis Eugene Kaplan

Syro-Russian Orthodox Catholic Church

The Syro-Russian Orthodox Catholic Church was originally established in May of 1892 as the American Orthodox Catholic Archdiocese of America, and this was canonized by His Holiness Ignatius Peter III, Patriarch of Antioch. It was this same Patriarch that issued the Bull for the consecration of its first Archbishop Metropolitan, Timotheos Vilathi, as named by Patriarch Ignatius. The Syro-Russian Archdiocese also has a few Western Rite parishes under its jurisdiction. The Synod of Bishops is referred to as the "Romano Byzantine Synod of Bishops" but the currently favored term is the Syro-Russian Synod of Bishops. This jurisdiction is the Byzantine Rite continuation of what Archbishop Timotheos established in the United States. First parishes of this jurisdiction were established in Wisconsin among Belgians, Italians, Slavs, and other ethnic groups. After Archbishop Timotheos' consecration, parishes were later formed in Ohio, Illinois, and New York, and some missionary work begun in Canada.

After much disagreement with the Patriarchate concerning administration and the Council of Chalcedon, which the Patriarchate did not accept concerning the two natures of Christ, a Consistory was convened on January 1, 1910 concerning the future of the Archdiocese of America. The Bishops agreed upon and decided that, "Our reality as a branch, a part of the true Catholic and Orthodox Church of God, is not dependent upon the recognition of any ecclesiastical authority outside the Councils of our own American Ecclesiastical Consistory and National Synod of Bishops and Clergy." Archbishop Timotheos believed strongly in the truths of the Council of Chalcedon, and the right of the American Church to name its own bishops, and from then on the Church was known as Autocephalous and severed from the Patriarchate of Antioch. However, after this time several schisms occurred that gave way to some heretical newly established "churches" that caused the Church to eventually be renamed "Syro-Russian Orthodox Catholic." In the 1970s, after the retirement for health reasons of Archbishop John, Archbishop Joseph of Blessed Memory became the newly enthroned Metropolitan Hierarch of the Church. He possessed Apostolic Succession from both the Syrian and Russian Orthodox Churches later giving the Synod the name of Syro-Russian Orthodox Catholic Church. In 1987, before his death, a meeting was held at St. Paul's Monastery in LaPorte, Indiana and Very Right Reverend Archimandrite Stephen (Thomas) was duly elected Metropolitan Hierarch. He was consecrated Bishop on October 18, 1987, by Archbishop Joseph assisted by Archbishop George and Bishop Norman at St. Mary's Chapel, LaPorte, Indiana, and the following year enthroned as metropolitan Archbishop Hierarch. Archbishop Stephen has caused the Church to grow throughout the world. In 1994-96, he endured many sufferings as the result of some clergy who went astray and since deposed of their faculties and offices. Since that time, the Church has experienced peace, growth, and new viability. The Divine Liturgy of St John Chrysostom is the official liturgy of the Church. In addition, as with all other Orthodox Churches, the Liturgy of Saint Basil is used ten times a year, and the Presanctified Liturgy as prescribed. The Traditions of Holy Orthodoxy are observed in the administration of the Holy Mysteries (Sacraments) and, as is practice in the Russian Orthodox Church, Holy Myron (Chrism) is consecrated by the Metropolitan Hierarch on Holy Thursday and distributed to the clergy of the Church.

Some western customs exist within the Church. Hyperveneration is given to icons that memorialize the saints and events in the life of Jesus Christ and the Holy Theotokos Mary. It follows the Gregorian Calendar and the Orthodox date of Pascha (Easter), and the Julian Calendar is allowed. The Syro-Russian Orthodox Catholic Church, strongly believes in the separation of Church and State, and healing by licensed practitioners is allowed but only by the clergy is the Mystery of Holy Unction administered. The Synodal Metropolinate has received official recognition from the Hellenic (Greek) Orthodox Church of Athens, and has been involved in ecumenical dialogue with the Orthodox Patriarchate of Jerusalem, the True Orthodox Church of Greece, The Macedonian Orthodox Church, and several Old Calendar jurisdictions. There is one monastic order, The Monastic Community of Saint Basil, which is open to men and women and is headquartered in England. The Synod of Bishops is composed of the following: Archbishop Stephen (United States), Bishop Benjamin (Bangladesh), Bishop George (United Kingdom), Bishop John (India), Chorbishop Joseph (Belgium), Bishop-elect Ricardo (Cuba), Bishop Samuel (Nigeria), Bishop Seraphim (California), and retired Chorbishop John (United States). The Vicariate of Pakistan is currently served by a Vicar General, Very Reverend

Father John Asir, as the result of an episcopal vacancy there. Vicars serve the mission territories of Belgium, Kenya, and Tanzania. The Church of Bangladesh recently united with the Syro-Russian Orthodox Catholic Church. Two Russian Orthodox parishes in England have united with the Synod, and a Romanian parish and monastery in the United States has also followed. Clergy are trained for the Church through St Mark's (RBC) Seminary of Fairfax Virginia; St. Basil's Seminary of Havana, Cuba; Holy Trinity Seminary (Lahore Pakistan) or Holy Apostles School and College (Dar es Salaam Tanzania). A distance education program for mature candidates is offered through St. Mark / Romano Byzantine College (Virginia). The national headquarters at this time is located at St. Mary the Theotokos Pro-Cathedral in Duluth, Minnesota.

Headquarters

St. Mary the Theotokos Pro-Cathedral, 5907 Grand Ave., Duluth, MN 55087 Tel. (218)624-0202 Fax (218)590-8435

E-mail: rbsocc@juno.com

Officers

Vicar General, Rev. Fr. Timothy Kjera, 5907 Grand Ave., Duluth MN 55807 Tel. (218)590-8435, fr_timothy_kjera@hotmail.com .

Archdiocesan Chaplain, Very Rev Patrick Lemming, 304 Grace Ave., Sevierville TN 37862 Tel. (865)429-3641.

Periodicals

Orthodox Christian Herald

Triumph the Church and Kingdom of God in Christ Inc. (International)

This church was given through the wisdom and knowledge of God to the late apostle Elias Dempsey Smith on Oct. 20, 1897, in Issaquena County, Mississippi, while he was pastor of a Methodist church.

The Triumph Church, as this body is more commonly known, was founded in 1902. Its doors opened in 1904 and it was confirmed in Birmingham, Alabama, with 225 members in 1915. It was incorporated in Washington, D.C. in 1918 and currently operates in 31 states and overseas. The general church is divided into 13 districts, including the Africa District.

Triumphant doctrine and philosophy are based on the principles of life, truth and knowledge; the understanding that God is in man and expressed through man; the belief in manifested wisdom and the hope for constant new revelations. Its concepts and methods of teaching the second coming of Christ are based on these and all other attributes of goodness.

Triumphians emphasize that God is the God of the living, not the God of the dead.

Headquarters

213 Farrington Ave. SE, Atlanta, GA 30315

Media Contact, Bishop C. W. Drummond, 7114 Idlewild, Pittsburg, PA 15208 Tel. (412)731-2286

Officers

Chief Bishop, Bishop C. W. Drummond, 7114 Idlewild, Pittsburgh, PA 15208 Tel. (412)731-2286

Gen. Bd of Trustees, Chmn., Bishop Leon Simon, 1028 59th St., Oakland, CA 94608 Tel. (415)652-9576

Gen. Treas., Bishop Hosea Lewis, 1713 Needlewood Ln., Orlando, FL 32818 Tel. (407)295-5488

Gen. Rec. Sec., Bishop Zephaniah Swindle, Box 1927, Shelbyville, TX 75973 Tel. (409)598-3082

True Orthodox Church of Greece (Synod of Metropolitan Cyprian), American Exarchate

The American Exarchate of the True (Old Calendar) Orthodox Church of Greece adheres to the tenets of the Eastern Orthodox Church, which considers itself the legitimate heir of the historical Apostolic Church.

When the Orthodox Church of Greece adopted the New, or Gregorian, Calendar in 1924, many felt that this breach with tradition compromised the Church's festal calendar, based on the Old, or Julian, Calendar, and its unity with world Orthodoxy. In 1935, three State Church Bishops returned to the Old Calendar and established a Synod in Resistance, the True Orthodox Church of Greece. When the last of these Bishops died, the Russian Orthodox Church Abroad consecrated a new Hierarchy for the Greek Old Calendarists and, in 1969, declared them a Sister Church.

In the face of persecution by the State Church, some Old Calendarists denied the validity of the Mother Church of Greece and formed two synods, now under the direction of Archbishop Chrysostomos of Athens and Archbishop Andreas of Athens. A moderate faction under Metropolitan Cyprian of Oropos and Fili does not maintain communion with the Mother Church of Greece, but recognizes its validity and seeks a restoration of unity by a return to the Julian Calendar and traditional ecclesiastical polity by the State Church. About 1.5 million Orthodox Greeks belong to the Old Calendar Church.

The first Old Calendarist communities in the United States were formed in the 1930s. The Exarchate under Metropolitan Cyprian was established in 1986. Placing emphasis on clergy education, youth programs, and recognition of the Old Calendarist minority in American Orthodoxy, the Exarchate has encouraged the establishment of monastic communities and missions. Cordial contacts with the New Calendarist and other Orthodox communities are encouraged. A center for theological training and Patristic studies has been established at the Exarchate headquarters in Etna, California.

In July 1994, the True Orthodox Church of Greece (Synod of Metropolitan Cyprian), the True Orthodox Church of Romania, the True Orthodox Church of Bulgaria, and the Russian Orthodox Church Abroad entered into liturgical union, forming a coalition of traditionalist Orthodox bodies several million strong.

Headquarters

St. Gregory Palamas Monastery, P.O. Box 398, Etna, CA 96027-0398 Tel. (530)467-3228 Fax (530) 467-5828

Media Contact, Exarch in America, His Eminence, Archbishop Chrysostomos

Officers

Acting Synodal Exarch in America, His Grace Bishop Auxentios

Chancellor of the Exarchate, The Very Rev. Raphael Abraham, 3635 Cottage Grove Ave. SE, Cedar Rapids, IA 52403-1612

Periodicals

Orthodox Tradition (quarterly theological journal)

Ukrainian Orthodox Church of the U.S.A.*

The Ukrainian Orthodox Church of the U.S.A. has its origin in the ancient lands of Rus-Ukraine (present day Ukraine). It was to the inhabitants of these lands that the Apostle Andrew first preached the gospel. Christianization began early in the history of Rus-Ukraine by missionaries from the Orthodox Christian See of Constantinople. In 988 AD, the Saintly Prince Volodymyr, crowned a process of Christian Evangelization begun in the 4th century, by personally accepting Orthodox Christianity and inspiring his subjects to do the same. The baptism of Volodymyr, his household and the inhabitants of Kyiv altered the face of Kyivan Rus-Ukraine and Slavic history for all time. Kyiv became the spiritual heart of Orthodox Christians in Rus-Ukraine. It was from this See that missionaries were sent into every corner of St. Volodymyr's realm. Through their efforts the gospel was preached and new communities were established. The Mother Church of Kyiv and its See of Saint Sophia, modeled after Constantinople's See of the same name, gave birth to many Orthodox Christian centers and communities in the west, east and north of the Dnipro river, among them the Orthodox Christian See of Moscow, Russia (Rosia).

The Ukrainian Orthodox Church of U.S.A. ministers to the needs of the faithful whose ancestral roots are in Ukraine. The Church found haven in America in the early 1920s. Its first bishop, Metropolitan Ioan (John) Teodorovych, arrived from Ukraine in 1924 and shepherded the church as Metropolitan until his death in 1971. His successor, Archbishop Mstyslav, arrived in the U.S.A. in 1950, and shepherded the Church as Metropolitan from 1971 until his death in 1993. It was Metropolitan Mstyslav who, as a consequence of Ukraine's independence, was named Patriarch of Kyiv and All Ukraine, in 1990. Previous to 1996 there were two Ukrainian Orthodox jurisdictions in the U.S.A.. Formal unification of the Ukrainian Orthodox Church of the U.S.A., shepherded by His Beatitude Metropolitan Constantine, and the Ukrainian Orthodox Church of America, shepherded by His Grace Bishop Vsevolod, was concluded in November 1996.

Headquarters

Saint Andrew the Firstcalled Apostle Ukrainian Orthodox Church Center, P.O. Box 495, South Bound Brook, NJ 08880 Tel. (732)356-0090 Fax (732)356-5556

Media Contact, Consistory Pres., His Eminence Antony, Archbishop of New York

E-mail: uocofusa@aol.com

Web site: www.uocofusa.org

Officers

Metropolitan, His Beatitude Constantine, 1803 Sidney St., Pittsburgh, PA 15203

Central Eparchy, Eparchial Bishop, Metropolitan Constantine; Eparchial Seat, St. Volodymyr Cathedral, 5913 State Rd., Parma, OH 44134 Tel. (440)885-1509; Eparchial Territory: Florida, Georgia, Ohio, Western Pennsylvania

Eastern Eparchy, Eparchial Bishop, Archbishop Antony; Eparchial Seat, St. Volodymyr Cathedral, 160 West 82nd St., New York, NY 10024 Tel. (212)873-8550; Eparchial Territory: Connecticut, Deleware, Massachusetts, Maryland, New Jersey, New York, Pennsylvania and Rhode Island

Western Eparchy, Eparchial Bishop, Archbishop Vsevolod; Eparchial Seat, St. Volodymyr Cathedral, 2230-50 W. Cortez St., Chicago, IL 60622 Tel. (312)278-2827; Eparchial Territory: Arizona, California, Colorado, Illinois, Indiana, Michigan, Minnesota, North Dakota, Nebraska, Oregon, Washington, Wisconsin, Ontario Province

Council of Bishops of the Ukranian Orthodox Church of the U.S.A., Chair, Metropolitan Constantine; Sec., Archbishop Antony; Member, Archbishop Vsevolod

METROPOLITAN COUNCIL MEMBERS

Vice-Chair, Archimandrite Andriy

Protopresbyter William Diakiw

Protopresbyter Frank Estocin, JCB

Protopriest John Nakonachny

Protopriest Michael Kochis

Protopriest Eugene Meschisen

Protopriest Bazyl Zawierucha

English Language Sec., Dr. Gayle Woloschak

Mr. Emil Skocypec

Dr. Paul Micevych

Ukranian Language Sec., Dr. George Krywolap
Dr. Anatol Lysyj
Mrs. Helen Greenleaf
Mr. Michael Kapeluck
Ukrainian Orthodox League, Pres., Daria Pishko
United Ukrainian Orthodox Sisterhoods, Pres., Mrs. Nadia Mirchuk
Saint Andrew Society, Pres., Mr. Michael Heretz

CONSISTORY

Consistory Pres., His Eminence Antony, Archbishop of New York, P.O. Box 495, S. Bound Brook, NJ 08880 Tel. (732)356-0090 Fax (732)356-5556, uocofusa@aol.com
Vice-Pres., Protopresbyter Willam Diakiw
Sec., Protopriest Frank Estocin
Treas., Mr. Emil Skocypec
Member, Protopriest John Nakonachny
Member, Protopriest Bazyl Zawierucha
Member, Dr. George Krywolap

Periodicals

Ukrainian Orthodox Word; Vira

Unitarian Universalist Association of Congregations

History: The Unitarian Universalist Association (UUA), created in 1961 through a consolidation of the Universalist Church of America with the American Unitarian Association, combines two liberal religious traditions. The religion traces its roots back to Europe, where in 1569 the Transylvanian king, John Sigismund (1540-1571), issued an edict of religious freedom. The religious philosophy led to the organization of the Universalists in this country in 1793, and the Unitarians (organized here in 1825).

Beliefs: Founders of Universalism believed in universal salvation of all humans by God, while founders of Unitarianism believed in the unity of God (as opposed to the Trinity). Unitarian Universalism is a liberal, creedless religion with Judeo-Christian roots. It draws also from Eastern, humanist, and other religious traditions, and encourages its members to seek religious truth out of their own reflection and experience. The denomination teaches tolerance and respect for other religious viewpoints, and affirms the worth and dignity of every person.

Organization and Government: The Unitarian Universalist Association consists of more than 1,010 congregations in the United States and Canada, with more than 220,000 members, and is served by more than 1,100 ministers. The Association is the fastest-growing liberal religion in North America, and this year completed its twenty-first consecutive year of growth, at an average annual rate of nearly two percent. Each member congregation within the UUA is governed independently. In North America, the Association is made up of 20 districts (served by a District Executive who is a member of the UUA staff), with each congregation having district affiliation. The Association is governed by an elected Board of Trustees, chaired by an elected Moderator. An elected President, three vice Presidents, and Directors of five departments form the executive staff that administers the daily activities of the Association.

The General Assembly, held each June in a different UUA district, serves as the Association's annual business meeting. The UUA includes Departments of Ministry and Professional Leadership; Lifespan Faith Development; Congregational Services; Identity Based Ministries; District Services; Advocacy and Witness; Financial Development; and Communications. *The World*, published bimonthly, is the denominational journal. Beacon Press, an internationally honored publishing house, is wholly owned by the Unitarian Universalist Association.

Headquarters

25 Beacon Street, Boston, MA 02108 Tel. (617)742-2100 Fax (617)367-3237
Media Contact, John Hurley, Dir. of Information, Tel. (617)742-2100 ext. 131
E-mail: jhurley@uua.org
Web site: www.uua.org

Officers

Pres., The Rev. William Sinkford
Moderator, Gini Courter
Executive Vice Pres., Kathleen C. Montgomery

Periodicals

UU World; InterConnections

The United Catholic Church, Inc.

In 1996, a group of Independent Catholic Bishops, meeting in Synod, asked then Bishop, Robert M. Bowman to draw up guidelines for "inclusivity." Under these guidelines a fellowship of independent Catholic churches and clergy was born under the leadership of current Archbishop Robert M. Bowman. This fellowship was incorporated in the State of Florida as a not-for-profit corporation in August 1996 for the purposes of educating and ordaining clergy, organizing dioceses, parishes and ministries, conducting religious services, entering into various affiliations with other Christian churches, and educating the public on religious, moral and social issues.

Headquarters

Media Contact: Archbishop Robert M. Bowman, 5017 Bellflower Ct., Melbourne, FL 32940 Tel. (321)752-5955, catholic@rmbowman. com
E-mail: catholic@rmbowman.com
Web site: www.united-catholic-church.org

Officers

Dir. of Parish Development, Bishop Senia Fix, 23 Atrium St., Englishtown, NJ 07726, generic 3000@cs.com

Vicar General, Bishop Lawrence Michael Miller, 2007 Christiana Meadows, Bear, DE 19701-2839 Tel. (302)325-4004, metroform@msn. om
Dir. of Vocations & Religious Life, Bishop Lawrence M. Cameron, 1375 Sylvania Ave., Toledo, OH 43612 Tel. (734)243-3186, pilgromUCC@toledolink.com

Periodicals

The United Catholic Quarterly

United Christian Church

The United Christian Church originated about 1864. There were some ministers and laymen in the United Brethren in Christ Church who disagreed with the position and practice of the church on infant baptism, voluntary bearing of arms and belonging to oath-bound secret combinations. This group developed into the United Christian Church, organized at a conference held in Campbelltown, Pennsylvania, on May 9, 1877. The principal founders of the denomination were George Hoffman, John Stamn and Thomas Lesher. Before they were organized, they were called Hoffmanites.

The United Christian Church has district conferences, a yearly general conference, a general board of trustees, a mission board, a board of Directors of the United Christian Church Home, a camp meeting board, a young peoples' board and local organized congregations.

It believes in the Holy Trinity and the inspired Holy Scriptures with the doctrines they teach. The church practices the ordinances of Baptism, Holy Communion and Foot Washing.

It welcomes all into its fold who are born again, believe in Jesus Christ as Savior and Lord and have received the Holy Spirit.

Headquarters

c/o John P. Ludwig, Jr., 523 W. Walnut St., Cleona, PA 17042 Tel. (717)273-9629
Media Contact, Presiding Elder, John P. Ludwig, Jr.

Officers

Presiding Elder, Elder John P. Ludwig, Jr.
Conf. Sec., Mr. Lee Wenger, 1625 Thompson Ave., Annville, PA 17003
Conf. Moderator, Elder Gerald Brinser, 2360 Horseshoe Pike, Annville, PA 17003

OTHER ORGANIZATIONS

Mission Board, Pres., Elder John P. Ludwig, Jr.; Sec., Elder David Heagy, 4129 Oak St., Lebanon, PA 17042; Treas., LeRoy Bomgardner, 1252 Royal Rd., Annville, PA 17003

United Church of Christ*

The United Church of Christ was constituted on June 25, 1957 by representatives of the Congregational Christian Churches and the Evangelical and Reformed Church, in Cleveland, Ohio.

The Preamble to the Constitution states, "The United Church of Christ acknowledges as its sole head, Jesus Christ... It acknowledges as kindred in Christ all who share in this confession. It looks to the Word of God in the Scriptures, and to the presence and power of the Holy Spirit...It claims...the faith of the historic Church expressed in the ancient creeds and reclaimed in the basic insights of the Protestant Reformers. It affirms the responsibility of the Church in each generation to make this faith its own in... worship, in honesty of thought and expression, and in purity of heart before God.... it recognizes two sacraments, Baptism and the Lord's Supper."

The creation of the United Church of Christ brought together four unique traditions:

(1) Groundwork for the Congregational Way was laid by Calvinist Puritans and Separatists during the late 16th-early 17th centuries, then achieved prominence among English Protestants during the civil war of the 1640s. Opposition to state control prompted followers to emigrate to the United States, where they helped colonize New England in the 17th century. Congregationalists have been self-consciously a denomination from the mid-19th century.

(2) The Christian Churches, an 18th-century American restorationist movement emphasized Christ as the only head of the church, the New Testament as their only rule of faith, and "Christian" as their sole name. This loosely organized denomination found in the Congregational Churches a like disposition. In 1931, the two bodies formally united as the Congregational Christian Churches.

(3) The German Reformed Church comprised an irenic aspect of the Protestant Reformation, as a second generation of Reformers drew on the insights of Zwingli, Luther and Calvin to formulate the Heidelberg Catechism of 1563. People of the German Reformed Church began immigrating to the New World early in the 18th century, the heaviest concentration in Pennsylvania. Formal organization of the American denomination was completed in 1793. The church spread across the country. In the Mercersburg Movement, a strong emphasis on evangelical catholicity and Christian unity was developed.

(4) In 19th-century Germany, Enlightenment criticism and Pietist inwardness decreased longstanding conflicts between religious groups. In Prussia, a royal proclamation merged Lutheran and Reformed people into one United Evangelical Church (1817). Members of this new church migrated to America. The Evangelicals settled in large numbers in Missouri and Illinois, emphasizing pietistic devotion and unionism; in 1840 they formed the German Evangelical Church Society in the west. After union with other Evangelical church associations, in 1877 it took the name of the German Evangelical Synod of North America.

On June 25, 1934, this Synod and the

Reformed Church in the U.S. (formerly the German Reformed Church) united to form the Evangelical and Reformed Church. They blended the Reformed tradition's passion for the unity of the church and the Evangelical tradition's commitment to the liberty of conscience inherent in the gospel.

Headquarters

700 Prospect Ave., Cleveland, OH 44115 Tel. (216)736-2100 Toll-free (866)822-8224 (866-UCC-UCC4) Fax (216)736-2103

Media Contact, Ms. Barbara A. Powell, Tel. (216)736-2175 Fax (216)736-2223

E-mail: kellys@ucc.org

Web site: www.ucc.org

Officers

Gen. Minister and Pres., Rev. John H. Thomas
Assoc. Gen. Minister, Ms. Edith A. Guffey
Exec. Minister, Wider Church Ministries, Vacant
Exec. Minister, Justice and Witness Ministries, Ms. Bernice Powell Jackson
Exec. Minister, Local Church Ministries, Rev. José A. Malayang
Chair, Exec. Council, Rev. M. Winston Baldwin, Jr.
Vice-Chair, Exec. Council, Ms. Reba Walker
Mod., Gen. Synod , Rev. Norman W. Jackson
Asst. Mod., Gen. Synod, Ms. Annie Wynn Neal
Asst. Mod., Gen. Synod, Mr. Eric C. Smith

ORGANIZATIONS

Office of General Ministries, National Office, 700 Prospect Ave., Cleveland, OH 44115 Tel. (216)736-2100 Fax (216)736-2103, Gen. Minister and Pres., Rev. John H. Thomas; Assoc. Gen. Minister, Ms. Edith A. Guffey

Justice and Witness Ministries, National Offices (as above), Tel. (216)736-3700 Fax (216)736-3703; Franklinton Center at Bricks, P.O. Box 220, Whitakers, NC, Tel. (252)437-1723 Fax (252)437-1278; Washington Office, 110 Maryland Ave. NE, Room 207, Washington, DC, Tel. (202)543-1517 Fax (202)543-5994, Exec. Minister, Ms. Bernice Powell Jackson; Exec. Assoc., Rev. Carl P. Wallace

Local Church Ministries, Tel. (216)736-3800 Fax (216)736-3803, Exec. Minister, Rev. José A. Malayang

Wider Church Ministries, National Offices (as above), Tel. (216)736-3200 Fax (216)736-3203; Disciples of Christ Division of Overseas Ministries, P.O. Box 1986, Indianapolis, IN 46206 Tel. (317)635-3100 Fax (317)635-4323, Exec. Minister, Ms. Olivia Masih White; Exec. Assoc. to the Exec. Minister, Rev. William R. Johnson

Pension Boards, Main Office, 475 Riverside Drive, New York, NY 10115 Tel. (212)729-2700 Fax (212)729-2701; National Office, 700 Prospect Ave., Cleveland, OH 44115 Tel. (216)736-2271 Fax (216)736-2274, Exec. Vice-Pres., Mr. Michael A. Downs

United Church Foundation, Inc., 475 Riverside Drive, New York, NY 10115 Tel. (212)729-2600 Fax (212)729-2601, Exec. Vice-Pres., Mr. Donald G. Hart

Council for American Indian Ministry, 471 3rd St., Box 412, Excelsior, MN 55331 Tel. (952)474-3532, Exec. Dir., Rev. Kim Mammedaty

Council for Health and Human Services Ministries, National Office (as above), Tel. (216)736-2250 Fax (216)736-2251, Exec. Dir., Rev. Bryan W. Sickbert

CONFERENCES

Western Region

California, Northern & Nevada, Rev. Mary Susan Gast, 21425 Birch St., Hayward, CA 94541-2131

California, Southern, Rev. Daniel F. Romero and Rev. Jane E. Heckles, 2401 N. Lake Ave., Altadena, CA 91001

Hawaii, Rev. Charles Buck, 15 Craigside Pl., Honolulu, HI 96817

Montana & Northern Wyoming, Rev. Lynne Simcox, 2016 Alderson Ave., Billings, MT 59102

Central Pacific, Rev. Hector Lopez and Rev. Eugene Ross, 0245 SW Bancroft St., Suite E, Portland, OR 97201

Rocky Mountain, Rev. Tom Rehling, 1140 W. 5th Ave., Denver, CO 80204

Southwest, Rev. Ann C. Rogers-Witte, 4423 N. 24th St., Suite 600, Phoenix, AZ 85016

Pacific Northwest, 6218 Beacon Ave. S., Seattle, WA 98108; Rev. Randall Hyvonen, 411 S. Washington St., Spokane, WA 99204

West Central Region

Iowa, Rev. Lark Hapke, 600 42nd St., Des Moines, IA 50312

Kansas & Oklahoma, Rev. David Hansen, 1245 Fabrique, Wichita, KS 67218

Minnesota, Rev. David McMahill, 122 W. Franklin Ave., Room 323, Minneapolis, MN 55404

Missouri, Mid-South, Rev. A. Gayle Engel, 461 E. Lockwood Ave., St. Louis, MO 63119

Nebraska, Rev. Ruddy Dunkerson, 825 M St. #201, Lincoln, NE 68508

Northern Plains, Rev. Wade Schemmel, 1200 E. Highland Acres Rd., Bismarck, ND 58501

South Dakota, Rev. Gene E. Miller, 3500 S. Phillips Ave., #121, Sioux Falls, SD 57105-6864

Great Lakes Region

Illinois, Rev. Jane Fisler Hoffman, 1840 Westchester Blvd. #200, Westchester, IL 60154

Illinois South, Rev. Gene Kraus, Box 325, 1312 Broadway, Highland, IL 62249

Indiana & Kentucky, Rev. Stephen C. Gray, 1100 W. 42nd St. #350, Indianapolis, IN 46208

Michigan, Rev. Kent J. Ulery, P.O. Box 1006, 5945 Park Lake Rd., East Lansing, MI 48826

Ohio, Rev. William Hulteen, 6161 Busch Blvd. #95, Columbus, OH 43229

Wisconsin, Rev. David Moyer, 4459 Gray Rd., Box 435, De Forest, WI 53532-0495

Southern Region

Florida, Rev. James E. Boler, 924 Magnolia Ave. #250, Orlando, FL 32803

South Central, Rev. Mark H. Miller, 6633 E. Hwy. 290 #200, Austin, TX 78723-1157

Southeast, Rev. Timothy C. Downs, 756 W. Peachtree St. NW, Atlanta, GA 30308

Southern, Rev. Steve Camp, 216 S. Antioch Ave., Box 215, Elon, NC 27244

Middle Atlantic Region

Central Atlantic, Rev. John R. Deckenback, 916 S. Rolling Rd., Baltimore, MD 21228

New York, Rev. Geoffrey A. Black, 5800 Heritage Landing Drive, Suite 2D, East Syracuse, NY 13057

Penn Central, Rev. Marja Coons-Torn, 900 S. Arlington Ave. #112, Harrisburg, PA 17109

Penn Northeast, Rev. Alan C. Miller, 431 Delaware Ave., Palmerton, PA 18071

Pennsylvania Southeast, Rev. F. Russell Mittman, 505 S. Second Ave., P.O. Box 26400, Collegeville, PA 19426

Penn West, Rev. Alan McLarty, 320 S. Maple Ave., Greensburg, PA 15601

Puerto Rico, Rev. Luis Rosario, Box 8609, Caguas, PR 00762

New England Region

Connecticut, Rev. Davida Foy Crabtree, 125 Sherman St., Hartford, CT 06105

Maine, Rev. Jean M. Alexander, Rev. David R. Gaewski, 28 Yarmouth Crossing Dr., P.O. Box 966, Yarmouth, ME 04096

Massachusetts, Rev. Nancy Taylor, 1 Badger Rd., Framingham, MA 01702

New Hampshire, Rev. Bill McConnell, Rev. Susan Henderson, 140 Sheep Davis Rd, Pembroke, NH 03275

Rhode Island, Rev. Carl Beyer, 56 Walcott St., Pawtucket, RI 02860

Vermont, Rev. Arnold I. Thomas, 32 N. Main St., Randolph, VT 05060

Nongeographic

Calvin Synod, Rev. Koloman K. Ludwig, 7319 Tapper Ave., Hammond, IN 46324

Periodicals

United Church News; Common Lot

United Holy Church of America, Inc.

The United Holy Church of America, Inc. is an outgrowth of the great revival that began with the outpouring of the Holy Ghost on the day of Pentecost. The church is built upon the foundation of the apostles and prophets, Jesus Christ being the cornerstone.

During a revival of repentence, regeneration and holiness of heart and life that swept through the South and West, the United Holy Church was born. The founding fathers had no desire to establish a denomination but were pushed out of organized churches because of this experience of holiness and testimony of the Spirit-filled life.

On the first Sunday in May 1886, in Method, North Carolina, what is today known as the United Holy Church of America, Inc. was born. The church was incorporated on Sept. 25, 1918.

Baptism by immersion, the Lord's Supper and feet washing are observed. The premillennial teaching of the second coming of Christ, divine healing, justification by faith, sanctification as a second work of grace and Spirit baptism are accepted.

Headquarters

5104 Dunstan Rd., Greensboro, NC 27405 Tel. (336)621-0669

Media Contact, Gen. Statistician, Ms. Jacquelyn B. McCain, 1210 N. Euclid Ave., Apt. A, St. Louis, MO 63113-2012 Tel. (314)367-8351 Fax (314)367-1835

E-mail: books@mohistory.org

GENERAL ADMINISTRATION

Gen. Pres., The Rt. Rev. Odell McCollum, 707 Woodmark Run, Gahanna, OH 43230, Tel. (614)475-4713 Fax (614)475-4713

Gen. Vice-Pres., Bishop Elijah Williams, 901 Briarwood St., Reidsville, NC 27320 Tel. (919)349-7275

Gen. 2nd Vice-Pres., The Rt. Rev. Kenneth O. Robinson, Sr., 33 Springbrook Rd., Nanuet, NY 10954-4423 Tel. (914)425-8311 Fax (914)352-2686

Gen. Rec. Sec., Rev. Mrs. Elsie Harris, 2304 Eighth St., Portsmouth, VA 23704 Tel. (757)399-0926

Asst. Rec. Sec., Mrs. Cassandra Jones, 3869 JoAnn Dr., Cleveland, OH 44122 Tel. (216)921-0097

Gen. Fin. Sec., Vera Perkins-Hughes, P.O. Box 6194, Cleveland, OH, Tel. (216)851-7448

Asst. Fin. Sec., Bertha Williams, 4749 Shaw Dr., Wilmington, NC 28405 Tel. (919)395-4462

Gen. Corres. Sec., Ms. Gwendolyn Lane, 3069 Hudson St., Columbus, OH 43219

Gen. Treas., Louis Bagley, 8779 Wales Dr., Cincinnati, OH 45249 Tel. (513)247-0588

General Officers

Gen. Pres. Missionary Dept., Rev. Ardelia M. Corbett, 519 Madera Dr., Youngstown, OH 44504 Tel. (216)744-3284

Gen. Evangelism & Extension Dept., Pres., Elder Clifford R. Pitts, 3563 N. 14th St., Milwaukee, WI 53206 Tel. (414)244-1319

Gen. Bible Church School Dept., Superintendent, Robert L. Rollins, 1628 Avondale Ave., Toledo, OH 43607 Tel. (419) 246-4046

Gen. Y.P.H.A., Pres., Elder James W. Brooks, Rt. 3 Box 105, Pittsboro, NC 27312 Tel. (919) 542-5357

Gen. Ushers Department, Pres., Ms. Sherly M. Hughes, 1491 E. 191st St. #H-604, Euclid, OH 44117 Tel. (216)383-0038

Gen. Educ. Dept., Elder Roosevelt Alston, 168 Willow Creek Run, Henderson, NC 27636 Tel. (919)438-5854

Gen. Music Dept., Chair, Rosie Johnson, 2009 Forest Dale Dr., Silver Spring, MD 20932

Gen. Historian, Dr. Chester Gregory, Sr., 1302 Lincoln Woods Dr., Baltimore, MD 21228 Tel. (410)788-5144

Gen. Counsel, Mr. Joe L. Webster, Esq., Attorney-at-Law, P.O. Box 2301, Chapel Hill, NC 27515-2301 Tel. (919)542-5150

UHCA Academy, Dir., Ms. Stephanie Davis, The United Holy Church of America, Inc., 5104 Dunstan Road, Greensboro, NC 27405 Tel. (336)621-0069

Gen. Statistician, Ms. Jacquelyn B. McCain, 1210 N. Euclid Ave., Apt. A, St. Louis, MO 63113-2012 Tel. (314)367-8351 Fax (314) 367-1835

PRESIDENTS OF CONVOCATIONAL DISTRICTS

Barbados Dist., The Rt. Rev. Jestina Gentles, 5 West Ridge St., Britton's Hill, St. Michael, BH2 Barbados, West Indies, Tel. (246)427-7185

Bermuda Dist., The Rt. Rev. Calvin Armstrong, P.O. Box 234, Paget, Bermuda, Tel. (441)296-0828 or (441)292-8383

Central Western Dist., Bishop Bose Bradford, 6279 Natural Bridge, Pine Lawn, MO 63121 Tel. (314)355-1598

Ghana, West Africa Dist., The Rt. Rev. Robert Blount, 231 Arlington Ave., Jersey City, NJ 07035 Tel. (201)433-5672

New England Dist., The Rt. Rev. Lowell Edney, 85 Woodhaven St., Mattapan, MA 02126 Tel. (617)296-5366

Northern Dist., The Rt. Rev. Kenneth O. Robinson, Sr., 33 Springbrook Rd., Nanuet, NY 10954 Tel. (914)425-8311

Northwestern Dist., The Rt. Rev. M. Daniel Borden, 8655 North Melody Lane, Macedonia, OH 44056 Tel. (330)468-0270

Pacific Coast Dist., The Rt. Rev. Irvin Evans, 235 Harvard Rd., Linden, NJ 07036 Tel. (908)925-6138

Southeastern Dist., The Rt. Rev. James C. Bellamy, 1825 Rockland Dr. SE, Atlanta, GA 30316 Tel. (404)241-1821

Southern Dist.—Goldsboro, The Rt. Rev. Ralph E. Love, Sr., 200 Barrington Rd., Greenville, NC 27834 Tel. (252)353-0495

Southern Dist.—Henderson, The Rt. Rev. Jesse Jones, 608 Cecil Street, Durham, NC 27707 Tel. (919)682-8249

St. Lucia Dist., The Rt. Rev. Carlisle Collymore, P.O. Box 51, Castries, St. Lucia, West Indies, Tel. (758)452-5835

Virginia Dist., The Rt. Rev. Albert Augson, 1406 Melton Ave., Richmond, VA 23223 Tel. (804) 222-0463

West Virginia Dist., The Rt. Rev. Alvester McConnell, Route 3, Box 263, Bluefield, WV 24701 Tel. (304)248-8046

Western North Carolina Dist., The Rt. Rev. Elijah Williams, 901 Briarwood St., Reidsville, NC 27320-7020 Tel. (336)349-7275

United House of Prayer for All People

The United House of Prayer for All People was founded and organized as a hierarchical church in the 1920s by the late Bishop C. M. Grace, who had built the first House of Prayer in 1919 in West Wareham, Mass., with his own hands. The purpose of the organization is to establish, maintain and perpetuate the doctrine of Christianity and the apostolic faith throughout the world among all people; to erect and maintain houses of prayer and worship where all people may gather for prayer and to worship the almighty God in spirit and in truth, irrespective of denomination or creed, and to maintain the apostolic faith of the Lord and Savior, Jesus Christ.

Headquarters

1117 7th St. NW, Washington, D.C. 20001 Tel. (202)289-0238 Fax (202)289-8058

Media Contact, Apostle S. Green

Officers

CEO, Bishop S.C. Madison, 1665 N. Portal Dr. NW, Washington, D.C. 20012 Tel. (202)882-3956 Fax (202)829-4717

NATIONAL PROGRAM STAFF

The Gen. Assembly, Presiding Officer, Bishop S. C. Madison, 1665 N. Portal Dr. NW, Washington, D.C. 20012 Tel. (202)882-3956 Fax (202)829-4717

Gen. Council Ecclesiastical Court, Clerk, Apostle R. Price, 1665 N. Portal Dr. NW, Washington, D.C. 20012 Tel. (202)882-3956 Fax (202)829-4717

Nationwide Building Program, Gen. Builder, Bishop S. C. Madison, 1665 N. Portal Dr. NW, Washington, D.C. 20012 Tel. (202)882-3956 Fax (202)829-4717

Special Projects, Dir., Apostle S. Green

Annual Truth & Facts Publication, Exec. Editor, Bishop S.C. Madison, 1665 N. Portal Dr. NW, Washington, D.C. 20012 Tel. (202)882-3956 Fax (202)829-4717

The United Methodist Church*

The United Methodist Church was formed April 23, 1968, in Dallas by the union of the Methodist Church and the Evangelical United Brethren Church. The two churches shared a common historical and spiritual heritage. The Methodist Church resulted in 1939 from the unification of three branches of Methodism: the Methodist Episcopal Church, the Methodist Episcopal Church, South, and the Methodist Protestant Church.

The Methodist movement began in 18th-century England under the preaching of John Wesley, but the Christmas Conference of 1784 in Baltimore is regarded as the date on which the organized Methodist Church was founded as an ecclesiastical organization. It was there that Francis Asbury was elected the first bishop in this country.

The Evangelical United Brethren Church was formed in 1946 with the merger of the Evangelical Church and the Church of the United Brethren in Christ, both of which had their beginnings in Pennsylvania in the evangelistic movement of the 18th and early 19th centuries. Philip William Otterbein and Jacob Albright were early leaders of this movement among the German-speaking settlers of the Middle Colonies.

Headquarters

Information, InfoServ, United Methodist Information Service, Dir., Mary Lynn Holly, Tel. (800)251-8140 Fax (615)742-5423

Media Contact, Dir., United Methodist News Service, Tel. (615)742-5470 Fax (615)742-5469, newsdesk@umcom.umc.org

E-mail: infoserv@umcom.umc.org

Web site: www.umc.org

Officers

General Conference, Sec., Carolyn M. Marshall, 204 N. Newlin St., Veedersburg, IN 47987

Council of Bishops, Pres., Bishop Sharon Brown Christopher, 400 Chatham Rd., Suite 100, Springfield, IL 62704-1495 Tel. (217)726-8071 Fax (217)726-8074, ilareaumc@aol.com; Sec., Bishop Sharon Zimmerman Rader, 750 Windsor St., Suite 303, Sun Prairie, WI 53590-2149 Tel. (608)837-8526 Fax (608) 837-0281, episcopaloffice@wisconsinumc.org

NORTH CENTRAL JURISDICTIONAL BISHOPS

Chicago Episcopal Area, Bishop C. Joseph Sprague, 77 W. Washington St., Suite 1820, Chicago, IL 60602-2904 Tel. (312)346-9766 ext. 101 Fax (312)214-9031, jsprague@umcnic.org

Dakotas Episcopal Area, Bishop Michael J. Coyner, 3910 25th St. S., Fargo, ND 58104-6880 Tel. (701)232-2241 Fax (701)232-2615, bishopconyer@juno.com

Illinois Episcopal Area, Bishop Sharon Brown Christopher, 400 Chatham Rd., Suite 100, Springfield, IL 62704-1495 Tel. (217)726-8071 Fax (217)726-8074, ilareaumc@aol.com

Indiana Episcopal Area, Bishop Woodie W. White, 1100 W. 42nd St., Suite 210, Indianapolis, IN 46208-3382 Tel. (317)924-1321 Fax (317)924-1380, bishopwhite@inareaumc.org

Iowa Episcopal Area, Bishop Gregory V. Palmer, 500 E. Court Ave., Suite C, Des Moines, IA 50309-2019 Tel. (515)283-1996 ext. 102 Fax (515)283-8672, bishop.palmer@iaumc.org

Michigan Episcopal Area, Bishop Linda Lee (2164 University Park Dr., Suite 250, Okemos, MI 48864), P.O. Box 25068, Lansing MI 48909-5068 Tel. (517)347-4030 Fax (517) 347-4003, mareaumc@tir.com

Minnesota Episcopal Area, Bishop John L. Hopkins, 122 W. Franklin Ave., Room 200, Minneapolis, MN 55404-2472 Tel. (612)870-4007 Fax (612)870-3587, jhopkins@msn.com

Ohio East Episcopal Area, Bishop Jonathan D. Keaton (8800 Cleveland Ave. NW), P.O. Box 2800, North Canton, OH 44720-0800 Tel. (330)499-3972 ext. 112 Fax (330)497-4911, jonathan@eocumc.com

Ohio West Episcopal Area, Bishop Bruce R. Ough, 32 Wesley Blvd., Worthington, OH 43085-3585 Tel. (614)844-6200 ext. 215 Fax (614)781-2625, bishop@wocumc.org

Wisconsin Episcopal Area, Bishop Sharon Zimmerman Rader, 750 Windsor St., Suite 303, Sun Prairie, WI 53590-2149 Tel. (608)837-8526 Fax (608)837-0281, episcopaloffice@wisconsinumc.org

NORTHEASTERN JURISDICTIONAL BISHOPS

Albany Episcopal Area, Bishop Susan M. Morrison, 215 Lancaster St., Albany, NY 12210-1131 Tel. (518)426-0386 Fax (518) 426-0347, albepisarea@worldnet.att.net

Boston Episcopal Area, Bishop Susan W. Hassinger (276 Essex St., 5th Fl. -01840), P.O. Box 249, Lawrence, MA 01842-0449 Tel. (978)682-7555 ext. 30 Fax (978)682-9555, bishopsoffice@neumc.org

Harrisburg Episcopal Area, Bishop Neil L. Irons, 303 Mulberry Dr., Suite 100, Mechanicsburg, PA 17050-3141 Tel. (717)766-7871 ext. 3100 Fax (717)766-3210, bishop@cpcumc.org

New Jersey Episcopal Area, Bishop Alfred Johnson, 1001 Wickapecko Dr., Ocean, NJ 07712-4733 Tel. (732)359-1010 Fax (732) 359-1019, bishop@gnjumc.org

New York Episcopal Area, Bishop Ernest Shaw Lyght, 20 Soundview Ave., White Plains, NY 10606-3302 Tel. (914)615-2221 Fax (914) 615-2246, bishop@nyac.com

New York West Episcopal Area, Bishop Violet L. Fisher, 1010 East Ave., Rochester, NY 14607-2220 Tel. (585)271-3400 Fax (585)271-3404, nywaumc@frontiernet.net

Philadelphia Episcopal Area, Bishop Peter D. Weaver (Madison & Monroe Blvd.), P.O. Box 820, Valley Forge, PA 19482-0820 Tel. (610)666-9090 ext. 233 Fax (610) 666-9181, bishop@epaumc.org

Pittsburgh Episcopal Area, Bishop Hae-Jong Kim (1204 Freedom Rd.), P.O. Box 5002, Cranberry Township, PA 16066-1902 Tel.

(724)776-1499/1599 Fax (724)776-1683, haejongkim@aol.com

Washington Episcopal Area (D.C.), Bishop Felton Edwin May, 100 Maryland Ave. NE, Suite 510, Washington, DC 20002-5611 Tel. (202) 546-3110 Fax (202)546-3186, bishopmay@ bwcumc.org

West Virginia Episcopal Area, Bishop S. Clifton Ives, United Methodist Center, 900 Washington St. E., Suite 300, Charleston, WV 25301-1710 Tel. (304)344-8330 Fax (304) 344-8330, wvareaumc@aol.com

SOUTH CENTRAL JURISDICTIONAL BISHOPS

Arkansas Episcopal Area, Bishop Janice Riggle Huie, 723 Center St., Little Rock, AR 72201-4399 Tel. (501)324-8019 Fax (501)324-8018, bishophuie@arumc.org

Dallas Episcopal Area, Bishop William B. Oden (3300 Mockingbird Ln., Room 358,-75205), P.O. Box 600127, Dallas, TX 75360-0127 Tel. (214)522-6741 Fax (214)528-4435, dallasbishop@hpumc.org

Fort Worth Episcopal Area, Bishop Ben R. Chamness, 464 Bailey Ave., Fort Worth, TX 76107-2153 Tel. (817)877-5222 Fax (817)332-4609, bishop@ctcumc.org

Houston Episcopal Area, Bishop Alfred L. Norris, 5215 Main St., Houston, TX 77002-9792 Tel. (713)528-6881 Fax (713)529-7736, ijarratt@methodists.net

Kansas Episcopal Area, Bishop Albert Frederick Mutti (4201 SW 15th St.), P.O. Box 4187, Topeka, KS 66604-0187 Tel. (785)272-0587 Fax (785)272-9135, kansasbishop@kansas east.org

Louisiana Episcopal Area, Bishop William W. Hutchinson, 527 North Blvd., Baton Rouge, LA 70802-5700 Tel. (225)346-1646 ext. 212 Fax (225)387-3662, laumc@premier.net

Missouri Episcopal Area, Bishop Ann Brookshire Sherer, 4800 Santana Cir., Suite 100, Columbia, MO 65203-7138 Tel. (573)441-1770 Fax (573)441-0765, sherer@ecunet.org

Nebraska Episcopal Area, Bishop Rhymes H. Moncure, Jr. (2641 N. 49th St.), P.O. Box 4553, Lincoln, NE 68504-0553 Tel. (402)466-4955 Fax (402)466-7931, bishop@umcneb. org

Northwest Texas-New Mexico Episcopal Area, Bishop D. Max Whitfield, 7920 Mountain Rd. NE, Albuquerque, NM 87110-7805, Tel (505)255-8786 Fax (505)255-8738, whitmax@nmconfum.com

Oklahoma Episcopal Area, Bishop Bruce P. Blake (2420 N. Blackwelder Ave.), P.O. Box 60467, Oklahoma City, OK 73106-0467 Tel. (405)530-2025 Fax (405)530-2040, cnoble@okumc.org

San Antonio Episcopal Area, Bishop Joel N. Martinez (16400 Huebner Rd., 78248), P.O. Box 781688, San Antonio, TX 78278-1688 Tel. (210)408-4500 Fax (210)408-4501, bishop@umcswtx.org

SOUTHEASTERN JURISDICTIONAL BISHOPS

Alabama-West Florida Episcopal Area, Bishop Larry M. Goodpaster, 312 Interstate Park Dr., Montgomery, AL 36109-5408 Tel. (334)277-1787 Fax (334)277-0109, bishop.awf@knology.net

Birmingham Episcopal Area, Bishop Robert E. Fannin, 898 Arkadelphia Rd., Birmingham, AL 35204-5011 Tel. (205)322-8665 Fax (205)322-8938, rfannin@umcna.bsc.edu

Charlotte Episcopal Area, Bishop Charlene P. Kammerer (3400 Shamrock Dr., 28215), P.O. Box 18750, Charlotte, NC 28218-0750 Tel. (704)535-2260 Fax (704)535-9160, jclark@ wnccumc.org

Columbia Episcopal Area, Bishop J. Lawrence McCleskey, 4908 Colonial Dr., Suite 108, Columbia, SC 29203-6000 Tel. (803)786-9486 Fax (803)754-9327, bishop@umcsc.org

Florida Episcopal Area, Bishop Timothy Wayne Whitaker (1122 E. McDonald St., 33801), P.O. Box 1747, Lakeland, FL 33802-1747 Tel. (863)688-4427 Fax (863)687-0568, bishop@ flumc.org

Holston Episcopal Area, Bishop Ray W. Chamberlain, Jr. (9915 Kingston Pike, Suite C, 37922), P.O. Box 32939, Knoxville, TN 37930-2939 Tel. (865)690-4080 Fax (865) 690-7112, bishop@holston.org

Louisville Episcopal Area, Bishop James R. King, Jr., 7400 Floydsburg Rd., Crestwood, KY 40014-8202 Tel. (502)425-4240 Fax (502) 425-9232, jking@kyumc.org

Mississippi Episcopal Area, Bishop Kenneth L. Carder (321 Mississippi St., 39201), P.O. Box 931, Jackson, MS 39205-0931 Tel. (601)948-4561 Fax (601)948-5981, bishop@mississippi-umc.org

Nashville Episcopal Area, Bishop William W. Morris, 520 Commerce St., Suite 201, Nashville, TN 37203-3714 Tel. (615)742-8834 Fax (615)742-3726, umcoffice@aol.com

North Georgia Episcopal Area, Bishop G. Lindsey Davis (4511 Jones Bridge Cir. NW 30092), P.O. Box 922997 Norcross, GA 30010-2997 Tel. (678)533-1360 Fax (678) 533-1361, bishop@ngumc.org

Raleigh Episcopal Area, Bishop Marion M. Edwards (1307 Glenwood Ave., Room 203), P.O. Box 10955, Raleigh, NC 27605-0955 Tel. (919)832-9560 ext. 243 Fax (919)832-4721, bishopmme@nccumc.org

Richmond Episcopal Area, Bishop Joe E. Pennel, Jr. (10330 Staples Mill Rd.), P.O. Box 1719, Glen Allen, VA 23060-0659 Tel. (804)521-1100 Fax (804)521-1171, bod@vaumc.org

South Georgia Episcopal Area, Bishop B. Michael Watson (3370 Vineville Ave., Suite

101,-31204), P.O. Box 13616, Macon, GA 31208-3616 Tel. (478)475-9286 Fax (478) 475-9248, bishopsga@aol.com

WESTERN JURISDICTIONAL BISHOPS

Denver Episcopal Area, Bishop Warner H. Brown, Jr., 2200 S. University Blvd., Denver, CO 80210-4797 Tel. (303)733-3736 ext. 601 Fax (303)733-5047, bishop@bishopbrown.org

Los Angeles Episcopal Area, Bishop Mary Ann Swenson (110 S. Euclid Ave. 91101), P.O. Box 6006, Pasadena, CA 91102-6006 Tel. (626)568-7312 Fax (626)568-7377, calpacbishop@earthlink.net

Phoenix Episcopal Area, Bishop William W. Dew, Jr., 1550 E. Meadowbrook Ave., Phoenix, AZ 85014-4040 Tel. (602)266-6956 ext. 209 Fax (602)279-1355, bishop@ desertsw.org

Portland Episcopal Area, Bishop Edward W. Paup, 1505 SW 18th Ave., Portland, OR 97201-2599 Tel. (503)226-1530 Fax (503)228-3189, bishop@umoi.net

San Francisco Episcopal Area, Bishop Beverly J. Shamana (1276 Halyard Dr., 95691), P.O. Box 980250, West Sacramento, CA 95798-0250 Tel. (916)374-1510 Fax (916)372-9062, bishop@calnevumc.org

Seattle Episcopal Area, Bishop Elias G. Galvan, 2112 3rd Ave., Suite 301, Seattle, WA 98121-2333 Tel. (206)728-7674 Fax (206)728-8442, bishop@pnwumc.org

Periodicals

Mature Years; El Intérprete; New World Outlook; Newscope; Interpreter; Methodist History; Christian Social Action; Pockets; Response; Social Questions Bulletin; United Methodist Reporter; Quarterly Review; Alive Now; Circuit Rider; El Aposento Alto; Weavings—A Journal of the Christian Spiritual Life; The Upper Room

United Pentecostal Church International

The United Pentecostal Church International came into being through the merger of two oneness Pentecostal organizations: the Pentecostal Church, Inc., and the Pentecostal Assemblies of Jesus Christ. The first of these was known as the Pentecostal Ministerial Alliance from its inception in 1925 until 1932. The second was formed in 1931 by a merger of the Apostolic Church of Jesus Christ with the Pentecostal Assemblies of the World.

The church contends that the Bible teaches that there is one God who manifested himself as the Father in creation, in the Son in redemption, and as the Holy Spirit in regeneration; that Jesus is the name of this absolute deity and that water baptism should be administered in his name, not in the titles Father, Son and Holy Ghost (Acts Ch.2 vs.38, Ch.8 vs.16, and Ch.19 vs.6).

The fundamental doctrine of the United Pentecostal Church International, as stated in its Articles of Faith, is "the Bible standard of full salvation, which is repentance, baptism in water by immersion in the name of the Lord Jesus Christ for the remission of sins, and the baptism of the Holy Ghost with the initial sign of speaking with other tongues as the Spirit gives utterance."

Further doctrinal teachings concern a life of holiness and separation, the operation of the gifts of the Spirit within the church, the second coming of the Lord, and the church's obligation to take the gospel to the whole world.

Headquarters

8855 Dunn Rd., Hazelwood, MO 63042 Tel. (314)837-7300 Fax (314)837-4503

Media Contact, Gen. Sec.-Treas., Rev. Jerry Jones

Officers

Gen. Supt., Rev. Kenneth F. Haney

Asst. Gen. Supts., Rev. Jesse F. Williams and Rev. Randy Keyes

Gen. Sec.-Treas., Rev. Jerry Jones

Dir. of Foreign Missions, Rev. Bruce Howell

Gen. Dir. of Home Missions, Rev. Jack Cunningham

Editor-in-Chief, Rev. J. L. Hall

Gen. Sunday School Dir., Rev. Gary Erickson

Youth Pres., Rev. Todd Gaddy

Other Organizations

Pentecostal Publishing House, Mgr., Rev. Marvin Curry

Ladies Ministries, Pres., Gwyn Oakes

Harvestime Radio Broadcast, Dir., Rev. N. A. Ursham and Coord., Rev. J. Hugh Rose

Stewardship Dept., Dir., Rev., Stephen Drur

Division of Education, Supt., Rev. Arless Glass

Word Aflame Publications, Editor, Rev. Richard Davis

Public Relations, Contact Church Admin.

Historical Society & Archives

Urshan Graduate School of Theology

Periodicals

The Pentecostal Herald; World Harvest Today; The North American Challenge; Conqueror; Reflections; Forward; Apostolic Man

The United Pentecostal Churches of Christ

In a time when the Church of Jesus Christ is challenged to send the "Evening Light Message" to the uppermost part of the earth, a group of men and women came together on May 29, 1992 at the Pentecostal Church of Christ in Cleveland, Ohio to form what is now called The United Pentecostal Churches of Christ.

Organized and established by Bishop Jesse Delano Ellis, II, the United Pentecostal Churches of Christ is about the business of preparing people to see the Lord of Glory. The traditional barriers of yesteryear must not keep saints or like faith apart ever again and this fellowship of Pentecostal, Apostolic Independent Churches have discovered the truth of Our Lord's Prayer in the seventeenth chapter of Saint John, "that they may all be One."

The United Pentecostal Churches of Christ is a fellowship of holiness assemblies which has membership in the universal Body of Christ. As such, we preserve the message of Christ's redeeming love through his atonement and declare holiness of life to be his requirement for all men who would enter into the Kingdom of God. We preach repentence from sin, baptism in the Name of Jesus Christ, a personal indwelling of the Holy Spirit, a daily walk with the Lord and life after death. Coupled with the cardinal truths of the church are the age-old customs of ceremony and celebration.

Headquarters

10515 Chester Ave. (at University Circle), Cleveland, OH 44106 Tel. (216)721-5935 Fax (216)721-6938; Contact Person, Public Relations., Rev. W. Michelle James Williams

Regional Office, 493-5 Monroe St., Brooklyn, NY 11221 Tel. (718)574-4100 Fax (718)574-8504; Contact Person, Sec. General., Rev. Rodney McNeil Johnson

Officers

Presiding Bishop and Gen. Overseer, Bishop J. Delano Ellis, II, Cleveland, OH

Asst. Presiding Bishop, Bishop Carl Halloway Montgomery, II, Baltimore, MD

Sec. General, Bishop James R. Chambers, Brooklyn, NY

Pres. of Pentacostal Youth Congress, Overseer Darryl D. Woodson, Memphis, TN

Periodicals

The Pentecostal Flame

United Zion Church

A branch of the Brethren in Christ, which settled in Lancaster County, Pennsylvania, the United Zion Church was organized under the leadership of Matthias Brinser in 1855.

Headquarters

United Zion Retirement Community, 722 Furnace Hills Pk., Lititz, PA 17543

Media Contact, Bishop Charles Brown, 4041 Shanamantown Rd., Annville, PA 17003 Tel. (717)867-1133

Officers

Gen. Conf. Mod., Bishop Charles Brown, 4041 Shanamantown Rd., Annville, PA 17003 Tel. (717)867-1133

Asst. Mod., Rev. Leon Eberly

Gen. Conf. Sec., Rev. Clyde Martin

Gen. Conf. Treas., Kenneth Kleinfelter, 919 Sycamore Lane, Lebanon, PA 17042

Unity of the Brethren

Czech and Moravian immigrants in Texas (beginning about 1855) established congregations which grew into an Evangelical Union in 1903, and with the accession of other Brethren in Texas, into the Evangelical Unity of the Czech-Moravian Brethren in North America. In 1959, it shortened the name to the original name used in 1457, the Unity of the Brethren (*Unitas Fratrum, or Jednota Bratrska*).

Headquarters

4009 Hunter Creek, College Station, TX 77845

Media Contact, Sec. of Exec. Committee, Ginger McKay, 148 N. Burnett, Baytown, TX 77520

Officers

Pres., Kent Laza, 4009 Hunter Creek, College Station, TX 77845

1st Vice-Pres., Rev. Michael Groseclose, 902 Church St., Belleville, TX 77418 Tel. (512)365-6890

Sec. of Exec. Committee, Ginger McKay, 148 N. Burnett, Baytown, TX 77520

Fin. Sec., Rev. Joseph Polasek, 4241 Blue Heron, Bryan, TX 77807

Treas., Arranna Jakubik, P.O. Box 408, Snook, TX 77878

OTHER ORGANIZATIONS

Bd. of Christian Educ., Dr., Donald Ketcham, 900 N. Harrison, West, TX 76691

Brethren Youth Fellowship, Pres., Jamie Brooke Bryan, 1231 Four Corners, West, TX 76691

Friends of the Hus Encampment, Jim Baletka, 727 San Benito, College Station, TX 77845

Christian Sisters Union, Pres., Janet Pomykal, P.O. Box 560, Brenham, TX 77834

Sunday School Union, Pres., Dorothy Kocian, 107 S. Barbara Dr., Waco, TX 76705

Youth Dir., Kimberly Stewart, 1500 Lawnmont Dr., Apt. 208, Round Rock, TX 78664

Periodicals

Brethren Journal, Editor, Rev. Milton Maly, 6703 FM 2502, Brenham, TX 77833; Bus Mngr., Jean Maly, 6703 FM 2502, Brenham, TX 77833

Universal Fellowship of Metropolitan Community Churches

The Universal Fellowship of Metropolitan Community Churches was founded Oct. 6, 1968 by the Rev. Troy D. Perry in Los Angeles, with a particular but not exclusive outreach to the gay community. Since that time, the Fellowship has grown to include congregations throughout the world.

The group is Trinitarian and accepts the Bible as the divinely inspired Word of God. The Fellowship has two sacraments, baptism and holy communion, as well as a number of traditionally recognized rites such as ordination.

This Fellowship acknowledges "the Holy Scriptures interpreted by the Holy Spirit in conscience and faith, as its guide in faith, discipline, and government." The government of this Fellowship is vested in its General Council (consisting of Elders and District Coordinators), clergy and church delegates, who exert the right of control in all of its affairs, subject to the provisions of its Articles of Incorporation and By-Laws.

Headquarters

8704 Santa Monica Blvd., 2nd Floor, West Hollywood, CA 90069-4548 Tel. (310)360-8640 ext. 226 Fax (310)360-8680

Media Contact, Dir. of Communications, Jim Birkett

E-mail: communications@ufmcchq.com

Web site: www.ufmcchq.com

Officers

Mod., Rev. Elder Troy D. Perry

Vice-Mod., Rev. Elder Nancy L. Wilson

Treas., Rev. Elder Donald Eastman

Clk., Rev. Elder Darlene Garner

Elder Mel Johnson, PMB #63, 2261 Market St., San Francisco, CA 94114-1600

Rev. Elder Nori Rost, 214 S. Prospect St., Colorado Springs, CO 80903

Rev. Elder Hong Kia Tan, 72 Fleet Rd., Hampstead, London, NW3 2QT England

Deputy Chief Exec. Officer, Jane Wagner, 8704 Santa Monica Blvd., 2nd Floor, West Holywood, CA 90069-4548

Dir., Communications, Jim Birkett, 8704 Santa Monica Blvd., 2nd Floor, West Hollywood, CA 90069-4548

OTHER COMMISSIONS & COMMITTEES

Min. of Global Outreach, Field Dir., Rev. Judy Dahl

Commission on the Laity, Chpsn., Stan Kimer

Clergy Credentials & Concerns, Admin., Rev. Justin Tanis

UFMCC AIDS Ministry, AIDS Liaison., Rev. Robert Griffin

Chief Financial Officer, Margaret Mahlman, 8704 Santa Monica Blvd., 2nd Floor, West Hollywood, CA 90069-4548

Periodicals

Keeping in Touch; UFMCC E-Mail News Service (free)

Volunteers of America

Volunteers of America is a national, nonprofit, spiritually based organization that provides local human service programs and opportunities for individual and community involvement through 39 local affiliate offices and the National Services Housing and Health Care Division. Founded in 1896 by Christian social reformers Ballington and Maud Booth, Volunteers of America provides more than 100 different types of programs and services in more than 400 communities nationwide. Programs include services for abused and neglected children, youth at risk, the elderly, people with disabilities, homeless individuals and families, and many others. Volunteers of America is one of the nation's largest providers of affordable housing for seniors, and low income families and individuals. It also provides a national Prison After-Care program that engages local congregations of all denominations as mentors to newly released prisoners. It employs 14,000 individuals whose work is assisted by more than 40,000 committed volunteers.

Headquarters

1660 Duke St., Alexandria, VA 22314-3427 Tel. (800)899-0089

E-mail: voa@voa.org

Web site: www.voa.org

Officers

Chpsn., Frances Hesselbein

Pres., Charles W. Gould, 1660 Duke St., Alexandria, VA. 22314 Tel. (703)341-5000

Dir., of Ecclesiastical Services, Harry V. Quiett, 1660 Duke St., Alexandria, VA. 22314 Tel. (703)341-5054 Fax (703)341-7000, hquiett@voa.org

39 local affiliate offices and one National Services Division. Information accessible through the national Web site: www.voa.org

Periodicals

Spirit Magazine; No Limits To Caring; Era of the Founders and *Ministry of Service*

The Wesleyan Church

The Wesleyan Church was formed on June 26, 1968, through the union of the Wesleyan Methodist Church of America (1843) and the Pilgrim Holiness Church (1897). The headquarters was established at Marion, Ind., and relocated to Indianapolis in 1987.

The Wesleyan movement centers around the beliefs, based on Scripture, that the atonement in Christ provides for the regeneration of sinners and the entire sanctification of believers. John Wesley led a revival of these beliefs in the 18th century.

When a group of New England Methodist ministers led by Orange Scott began to crusade for the abolition of slavery, the bishops and others sought to silence them. This led to a series of withdrawals from the Methodist Episcopal Church. In 1843, the Wesleyan Methodist Connection of America was organized and led by Scott, Jotham Horton, LaRoy Sunderland, Luther Lee and Lucius C. Matlack.

During the holiness revival in the last half of the 19th century, holiness replaced social reform as the major tenet of the Connection. In 1947 the name was changed from Connection to Church and a central supervisory authority was set up.

The Pilgrim Holiness Church was one of many independent holiness churches which came into existence as a result of the holiness revival. Led by Martin Wells Knapp and Seth C. Rees, the International Holiness Union and Prayer League was inaugurated in 1897 in Cincinnati. Its purpose was to promote worldwide holiness evangelism and the Union had a strong missionary emphasis from the beginning. It developed into a church by 1913.

The Wesleyan Church is now spread across most of the United States and Canada and in more than 70 other countries. The Wesleyan World Fellowship was organized in 1972 to unite Wesleyan mission bodies developing into mature churches. The Wesleyan Church is a member of the Christian Holiness Partnership, the National Association of Evangelicals and the World Methodist Council.

Headquarters

P.O. Box 50434, Indianapolis, IN 46250 Tel. (317)774-7900

Media Contact, Gen. Sec., Dr. Ronald D. Kelly, Tel. (317)744-3922 Fax (317)744-3924, kellyr@wesleyan.org

E-mail: generalsecretary.org

Web site: www.wesleyan.org

General Superintendents

Dr. Earle L. Wilson, Tel. (317)570-5146 Fax (317)774-3932, wilsone@wesleyan.org

Dr. Thomas E. Armiger, Tel. (317)570-5147 Fax (317)744-3933, armigert@wesleyan.org

Dr. David W. Holdren, Tel. (317)570-5148 Fax (317)774-3934, holdrend@wesleyan.org

General Officers

Gen. Sec., Dr. Ronald D. Kelly, Tel. (317)774-3933 Fax (317)570-5280, kellyr@wesleyan. org

Gen. Treas., Donald M. Frase, Tel. (317)774-3841 Fax (317)570-5285, frased@wesleyan. org

Gen. Publisher, Mr. Donald D. Cady, Tel. (317)744-3853 Fax (317)570-5370, cadyd@ wesleyan.org

Gen. Dir. of Communications, Dr. Norman G. Wilson, Tel. (317)774-7907 Fax (317)774-7913, wilsonn@wesleyan.org

Gen. Dir. of Sunday School & Discipleship, Dr. Ray E. Barnwell, Sr., Tel. (317)774-3888 Fax (317)744-3880, barnwelr@wesleyan.org

Gen. Dir. of Evangelism & Church Growth, Dr. Jerry Pence, Tel. (317)744-3900 Fax (317) 774-3899, pencej@wesleyan.org

Gen. Dir. of Education & the Ministry, Rev. Kerry D. Kind, Tel. (317)774-3911 Fax (317)774-3915, kindk@wesleyan.org

Gen. Dir. of World Missions, Dr. Donald L. Bray, Tel. (317)774-7950 Fax (317)774-7948, brayd@wesleyan.org

Auxiliaries/Subsidiary Agencies

Stewardship Ministries, Gen. Dir., Rev. Larry J. Moore, Tel. (317)774-7338 Fax (317)774-7341, moorej@wesleyan.org

Wesleyan Investment Foundation, Gen. Dir., Dr. Craig A. Dunn, Tel. (317)774-7300 Fax (317)774-7321, wif@wesleyan.org

Wesleyan Pension Fund, Gen. Dir., Dr. Craig A. Dunn, Tel. (317)774-7300 Fax (317)774-7321, dunnc@wesleyan.org

Wesleyan Women, Mrs. Martha Blackburn, Tel. (317)774-7974 Fax (317)774-7975, blackburnm@wesleyan.org

Wesleyan Kids for Mission, Mrs. Peggy Camp, Tel. (317)774-7974, blackburnm@wesleyan.org

Wesleyan Men, Dr. Jerry Pence, Tel. (317)774-3900 Fax (317)774-3899, pencej@wesleyan.org

Address Service, Tel. (317)744-7900

Archives & Historical Library, Tel. (317)774-7996

Computer Information Services, Tel. (317)774-7922

Wesleyan Publishing House, Tel. (317)744-3954

Periodicals

Wesleyan Life; Wesleyan World

Wesleyan Holiness Association of Churches

This body was founded Aug. 4, 1959 near Muncie, Indiana by a group of ministers and laymen who were drawn together for the purpose of spreading and conserving sweet, radical, scriptural holiness. These men came from various church bodies. This group is Wesleyan in doctrine and standards.

Headquarters

1141 North US Hwy 27, Fountain City, IN 47341-9757 Tel. (765)584-3199

Media Contact, Gen. Sec.-Treas., Rev. Robert W. Wilson, RR3 Box 218, Selinsgrove, PA 17870

Officers

Gen. Supt., Rev. John Brewer

Asst. Gen. Supt., Rev. Armen O. Rhoads, 7812 Portland Ave., Tacoma, WA 98404

Gen. Sec.-Treas., Rev. Robert W. Wilson, RR3 Box 218, Selinsgrove, PA 17870 Tel. (570)539-9821

Gen. Youth Pres., Rev. Nathan Shockley, 504 W. Tyrell St., St. Louis, MI 48880 Tel. (517)681-2591

Periodicals

Eleventh Hour Messenger

Wisconsin Evangelical Lutheran Synod

Organized in 1850 at Milwaukee, Wisconsin, by three pastors sent to America by a German mission society, the Wisconsin Evangelical Lutheran Synod still reflects its origins, although it now has congregations in 50 states and three Canadian provinces. It supports missions in 26 countries.

The Wisconsin Synod federated with the Michigan and Minnesota Synods in 1892 in order to more effectively carry on education and mission enterprises. A merger of these three Synods followed in 1917 to give the Wisconsin Evangelical Lutheran Synod its present form.

Although at its organization in 1850 WELS turned away from conservative Lutheran theology, today it is ranked as one of the most conservative Lutheran bodies in the United States. WELS confesses that the Bible is the verbally inspired, infallible Word of God and subscribes without reservation to the confessional writings of the Lutheran Church. Its interchurch relations are determined by a firm commitment to the principle that unity of doctrine and practice are the prerequisites of pulpit and altar fellowship and ecclesiastical cooperation. It does not hold membership in ecumenical organizations.

Headquarters

2929 N. Mayfair Rd., Milwaukee, WI 53222
Tel. (414)256-3888 Fax (414)256-3899
CCFS Administrator, Rev. Ronald Roth
E-mail: webbin@sab.wels.net
Web site: www.wels.net

Officers

Pres., Rev. Karl R. Gurgel, 2929 N. Mayfair Rd., Milwaukee, WI 53222,
1st Vice-Pres., Rev. Wayne D. Mueller, 2929 N. Mayfair Rd., Milwaukee, WI 53222 Tel. (414)256-3888 Fax (414)256-3899
2nd Vice-Pres., Rev. Jon Mahnke, 6001 Blossom Ave., San Jose, CA 95123-4005
Sec., Teacher Steven Lemke, 1108 Ontario Ave., Sheboygan, WI, 53081

OTHER ORGANIZATIONS

Bd. for Ministerial Education, Admin., Rev. Peter Kruschel
Bd. for Parish Services, Admin., Rev. Bruce Becker
Bd. for Home Missions, Admin., Rev. Harold J. Hagedorn
Bd. for World Missions, Admin., Rev. Daniel Koelpin

Periodicals

Wisconsin Lutheran Quarterly; Forward in Christ; Lutheran Leader; The Lutheran Educator; Mission Connection

Religious Bodies in the United States Arranged by Family

The following list of religious bodies appearing in the Directory Section of the *Yearbook* shows the "families," or related clusters into which American religious bodies can be grouped. For example, there are many communions that can be grouped under the heading "Baptist" for historical and theological reasons. It should not be assumed, however, that all denominations under one family heading are necessarily consistent in belief or practice. The family clusters tend to represent historical factors more often than theological or practical ones. These family categories provide one of the major pitfalls when compiling church statistics because there is often a tendency to combine the statistics by "families" for analytical and comparative purposes. Such combined totals are deeply flawed, even though they are often used as variables for sociological analysis. The arrangement by families offered here is intended only as a general guide for conceptual organization when viewing the broad sweep of American religious culture.

Religious bodies that can not be categorized under family headings appear alphabetically and are not indented in the following list.

Adventist Bodies

Advent Christian Church
Church of God General Conference (Oregon, IL and Morrow, GA)
Primitive Advent Christian Church
Seventh-day Adventist Church

American Evangelical Christian Churches
American Rescue Workers

Anglican Bodies

Episcopal Church
The Episcopal Orthodox Church
Reformed Episcopal Church

Apostolic Christian Church (Nazarene)
Apostolic Christian Churches of America
Apostolic Episcopal Church
Association of Vineyard Churches

Baptist Bodies

The Alliance of Baptists
The American Baptist Association
American Baptist Churches in the U.S.A.
Baptist Bible Fellowship International
Baptist General Conference
Baptist Missionary Association of America
Conservative Baptist Association of America
General Association of General Baptists
General Association of Regular Baptist Churches
National Association of Free Will Baptists
National Baptist Convention, U.S.A., Inc.
National Missionary Baptist Convention of America
National Primitive Baptist Convention, Inc.
North American Baptist Conference
Primitive Baptists
Progressive National Baptist Convention, Inc.
Separate Baptists in Christ
Seventh Day Baptist General Conference, USA and Canada
Southern Baptist Convention
Sovereign Grace Believers

Berean Fellowship of Churches

Brethren (German Baptists)

Brethren Church (Ashland, Ohio)
Church of the Brethren
Fellowship of Grace Brethren Churches
Old German Baptist Brethren

Brethren, River

Brethren in Christ Church
United Zion Church

The Catholic Church
Christ Community Church (Evangelical-Protestant)
Christadelphians
Christian Brethren (also known as Plymouth Brethren)
The Christian Congregation, Inc.
The Christian and Missionary Alliance
Christian Union
The Church of Christ (Holiness) U.S.A.
Church of Christ, Scientist
The Church of Illumination
Church of the Living God
Church of the Nazarene

Churches of Christ—Christian Churches

Christian Church (Disciples of Christ) in the United States and Canada
Christian Churches and Churches of Christ
Churches of Christ

Churches of Christ in Christian Union

Churches of God

Church of God (Anderson, Indiana)

The Church of God (Seventh Day), Denver, Colorado

Churches of the New Jerusalem

General Church of the New Jerusalem
The Swedenborgian Church

Conservative Congregational Christian Conference

Eastern Orthodox Churches

Albanian Orthodox Archdiocese in America
Albanian Orthodox Diocese of America
The American Carpatho-Russian Orthodox Greek Catholic Church
The Antiochian Orthodox Christian Archdiocese of North America
Apostolic Catholic Assyrian Church of the East, North American Dioceses
Apostolic Orthodox Catholic Church of North America
Greek Orthodox Archdiocese of America
The Holy Eastern Orthodox Catholic and Apostolic Church in North America, Inc.
Holy Ukrainian Autocephalic Orthodox Church in Exile
The Orthodox Church in America
Patriarchal Parishes of the Russian Orthodox Church in the U.S.A.
The Romanian Orthodox Church in America
The Romanian Orthodox Episcopate of America
The Russian Orthodox Church Outside of Russia
Serbian Orthodox Church in the U.S.A. and Canada
The Syro-Russian Orthodox Catholic Church
True Orthodox Church of Greece (Synod of Metropolitan Cyprian), American Exarchate
Ukrainian Orthodox Church of the U.S.A.

The Evangelical Church
The Evangelical Church Alliance
The Evangelical Congregational Church
The Evangelical Covenant Church
The Evangelical Free Church of America
Fellowship of Fundamental Bible Churches
Free Christian Zion Church of Christ

Friends

Evangelical Friends International–North American Region
Friends General Conference
Friends United Meeting
Philadelphia Yearly Meeting of the Religious Society of Friends
Religious Society of Friends (Conservative)
Religious Society of Friends (Unaffiliated Meetings)

Grace Gospel Fellowship
House of God, Which is the Church of the Living God, the Pillar and Ground of the Truth, Inc.
IFCA International, Inc.
International Council of Community Churches
Jehovah's Witnesses

Latter Day Saints (Mormons)

Church of Christ
The Church of Jesus Christ (Bickertonites)
The Church of Jesus Christ of Latter-day Saints
Community of Christ

The Liberal Catholic Church—Province of the United States of America

Lutheran Bodies

The American Association of Lutheran Churches
Apostolic Lutheran Church of America
The Association of Free Lutheran Congregations
Church of the Lutheran Brethren of America
Church of the Lutheran Confession
Conservative Lutheran Association
The Estonian Evangelical Lutheran Church
Evangelical Lutheran Church in America
Evangelical Lutheran Synod
The Latvian Evangelical Lutheran Church in America
The Lutheran Church—Missouri Synod
Wisconsin Evangelical Lutheran Synod

Mennonite Bodies

Beachy Amish Mennonite Churches
Bible Fellowship Church
Church of God in Christ, Mennonite
Fellowship of Evangelical Bible Churches
Fellowship of Evangelical Churches
General Conference of Mennonite Brethren Churches
Hutterian Brethren
Mennonite Church, USA
Old Order Amish Church
Old Order (Wisler) Mennonite Church
Reformed Mennonite Church

Methodist Bodies

African Methodist Episcopal Church
The African Methodist Episcopal Zion Church
Allegheny Wesleyan Methodist Connection (Original Allegheny Conference)
Bible Holiness Church
Christian Methodist Episcopal Church
Evangelical Methodist Church
Free Methodist Church of North America
Fundamental Methodist Church, Inc.
Primitive Methodist Church in the U.S.A.
Reformed Methodist Union Episcopal Church
Reformed Zion Union Apostolic Church
Southern Methodist Church
The United Methodist Church
The Wesleyan Church

The Missionary Church

Moravian Bodies

Moravian Church in America (Unitas Fratrum)
Unity of the Brethren

National Association of Congregational Christian Churches
National Organization of the New Apostolic Church of North America
National Spiritualist Association of Churches
North American Old Roman Catholic Church (Archdiocese of New York)

Old Catholic Churches

Apostolic Catholic Orthodox Church
Christ Catholic Church
Liberal Catholic Church (International)
The United Catholic Church, Inc.

Oriental Orthodox Churches

Armenian Apostolic Church of America
Armenian Apostolic Church, Diocese of America
Coptic Orthodox Church
Syrian (Syriac) Orthodox Church of Antioch

Pentecostal Bodies

Apostolic Faith Mission Church of God
Apostolic Faith Mission of Portland, Oregon
Assemblies of God
Assemblies of God International Fellowship (Independent/Not affiliated)
The Bible Church of Christ, Inc.
Bible Way Church of Our Lord Jesus Christ World Wide, Inc.
Christian Church of North America, General Council
The Church of God In Christ
Church of God in Christ, International
Church of God (Cleveland, Tennessee)
Church of God, Mountain Assembly, Inc.
Church of God of Prophecy
Church of Our Lord Jesus Christ of the Apostolic Faith, Inc.
Congregational Holiness Church
Elim Fellowship
Full Gospel Assemblies International
Full Gospel Fellowship of Churches and Ministers International
International Church of the Foursquare Gospel
The International Pentecostal Church of Christ
International Pentecostal Holiness Church
Open Bible Standard Churches
The (Original) Church of God, Inc.
Pentecostal Assemblies of the World, Inc.
Pentecostal Church of God
Pentecostal Fire-Baptized Holiness Church
The Pentecostal Free Will Baptist Church, Inc.
Pillar of Fire
United Holy Church of America, Inc.
United Pentecostal Church International
The United Pentecostal Churches of Christ

Polish National Catholic Church of America

Reformed Bodies

Associate Reformed Presbyterian Church (General Synod)
Christian Reformed Church in North America
Cumberland Presbyterian Church
Cumberland Presbyterian Church in America
Evangelical Presbyterian Church
Hungarian Reformed Church in America
Korean Presbyterian Church in America, General Assembly of the
Netherlands Reformed Congregations
The Orthodox Presbyterian Church
Presbyterian Church in America
Presbyterian Church (U.S.A.)
Protestant Reformed Churches in America
Reformed Church in America
Reformed Church in the United States
Reformed Presbyterian Church of North America
United Church of Christ

Reformed Catholic Church
The Salvation Army
The Schwenkfelder Church

Thomist Churches

Malankara Orthodox Syrian Church, Diocese of America
Mar Thoma Syrian Church of India

Triumph the Church and Kingdom of God in Christ Inc. (International)
Unitarian Universalist Association of Congregations

United Brethren Bodies

Church of the United Brethren in Christ
United Christian Church

United House of Prayer
Universal Fellowship of Metropolitan Community Churches
Volunteers of America
Wesleyan Holiness Association of Churches

4. Religious Bodies in Canada

A large number of Canadian religious bodies were organized by immigrants from Europe and elsewhere, and a smaller number sprang up originally on Canadian soil. In the case of Canada, moreover, many denominations that transcend the U.S.-Canada border have headquarters in the United States.

A final section in this directory lists churches according to denominational families. This can be a helpful tool in finding a particular church if you don't know the official name. Complete statistics for Canadian churches are found in the statistical section in Chapter 3: Table 1 contains membership figures, and Table 4 contains giving figures. Addresses for periodicals are found in the directory entitled, "Religious Periodicals in Canada."

The Anglican Church of Canada

Anglicanism came to Canada with the early explorers such as Martin Frobisher and Henry Hudson. Continuous services began in Newfoundland about 1700 and in Nova Scotia in 1710. The first Bishop, Charles Inglis, was appointed to Nova Scotia in 1787. The numerical strength of Anglicanism was increased by the coming of American Loyalists and by massive immigration both after the Napoleonic wars and in the later 19th and early 20th centuries.

The Anglican Church of Canada has enjoyed self-government for over a century since 1893 and is an autonomous member of the worldwide Anglican Communion. The General Synod, which normally meets triennially, consists of the Archbishops, Bishops and elected clerical and lay representatives of the 30 dioceses. Each of the Ecclesiastical Provinces—Canada, Ontario, Rupert's Land and British Columbia—is organized under a Metropolitan and has its own Provincial Synod and Executive Council. Each diocese has its own Diocesan Synod.

Headquarters

Church House, 80 Hayden St., Toronto, ON M4Y 3G2 Tel. (416)924-9192 (Switchboard) (416)924-9199 (Voice mail) Fax (416)968-7983, Web www.anglican.ca

Media Contact, Mr. Sam Galati Vianney (Sam) Carriere

General E-mail info@national.anglican.ca

GENERAL SYNOD OFFICERS

Primate of the Anglican Church of Canada, vacant (election May 2004)

Prolocutor, Ms. Dorothy Davies-Flindall

Gen. Sec., Ven. James B. Boyles

Treas., Gen. Synod, Mr. James Cullen

DEPARTMENTS & DIVISIONS

Faith, Worship & Ministry, Dir., Rev. Canon Alyson Barnett-Cowan

Financial Management and Dev., Dir., Mr. James Cullen

Inform. Resources Dir., Mr. Vianney (Sam) Carriere

Partnerships, Dir., Dr. Eleanor Johnson

Pensions, Dir., Ms. Judith Robinson

Primate's World Relief and Dev. Fund, Dir., Mr. Andrew Ignatieff

METROPOLITANS (ARCHBISHOPS)

British Columbia, The Most Rev. David P. Crawley, 1876 Richter St., Kelowna, BC V1Y 2M9 Tel. (250)762-3306 Fax (250)762-4150

Ecclesiastical Province of, Canada, The Most Rev. Andrew S. Hutchison, 1444 Union Ave., Montreal, QC H3A 2B8 Tel. (514) 843-6577 Fax (514) 843-32221, E-mail bishops.office@ montreal. anglican.ca

Ontario, The Most Rev. Terence E. Finlay, 135 Adelaide St. East, Toronto, ON M5C 1L8 Tel. (416)363-6021 Fax (416)363-3683, E-mail tfinlay@toronto.anglican.ca

Rupert's Land, The Most Rev. John R. Clarke, Box 6868, Peace River, AB T8S 1S6 Tel. (780) 624-2767 Fax (780) 624-2365, E-mail bpath@telusplanet.net

DIOCESAN BISHOPS

Algoma, The Rt. Rev. Ronald Ferris, Box 1168, Sault Ste. Marie, ON P6A 5N7 Tel. (705)256-5061 Fax (705)946-1860, E-mail dioceseofalgoma@on.aibn.com

Arctic, The Rt. Rev. Andrew P. Atagotaalnuk, 4910 51st St., Box 190, Yellowknife, NT X1A 2N2 Tel. (867)873-5432 Fax (867) 873-8478, E-mail diocese@theedge.ca

Athabasca, The Most Rev. John R. Clarke, Box 6868, Peace River, AB T8S 1S6 Tel. (780)624-2767 Fax (780)624-2365, E-mail bpath@telusplanet.net

Brandon, Rt. Rev. James D. Njegovan, Box 21009 WEPO, Brandon, MB R7B 3W8 Tel. (204)727-7550 Fax (204)727-4135, E-mail bishopbdn@mts.net

British Columbia, vacant, 900 Vancouver St., Victoria, BC V8V 3V7 Tel. (250)386-7781 Fax (250)386-4013, E-mail bishop@acts.bc.ca

Caledonia, The Rt. Rev. William J. Anderson, Box 278, Prince Rupert, BC V8J 3P6 Tel. (250)624-6013 Fax (250)624-4299, E-mail synodofc@citytel.net

Calgary, Bishop, The Rt. Rev. Barry C.B. Hollowell, #560, 1207 11th Ave., SW, Salgary, AB T3C 0M5, Tel. (403)243-3673 Fax (403)243-2182, Diocesan E-mail synod@calgary.anglican.ca

Cariboo, for matters pertaining to clergy and Anglican parishes of the Central Interior: The Rev. Canon Gordon Light, 608 Sutherland Ave.,

CANADIAN RELIGIOUS BODIES

Kelowna, BC V1Y 5X1, Tel (250)763-0099 Fax (250)762-9173, E-mail apci@ silk. net

Central Newfoundland, The Rt. Rev. Donald A. Young, 34 Fraser Rd., Gander, NF A1V 2E8 Tel. (709)256-2372 Fax (709)256-2396, E-mail bishopcentral@nfld.net

Eastern Newfoundland and Labrador, The Rt. Rev. Donald F. Harvey, 19 King's Bridge Rd., St. John's, NF A1C 3K4 Tel. (709)576-6697 Fax (709)576-7122, E-mail dharvey@anglicanenl.nf.net

Edmonton, The Rt. Rev. Victoria Matthews, 10035–103 St., Edmonton, AB T5J 0X5 Tel. (780)439-7344 Fax (780)439-6549, E-mail bishopv@telusplanet.net

Fredericton, The Rt. Rev. Claude E.W. Miller, 115 Church St., Fredericton, NB E3B 4C8 Tel. (506)459-1801 Fax (506)459-8475, E-mail bishfton@nbnet.nb.ca

Huron, The Rt. Rev. Bruce H. W. Howe, 190 Queens Ave., London, ON N6A 6H7 Tel. (519)434-6893 Fax (519)673-4151, E-mail bishops@huron.anglican.ca

Keewatin, Rt. David N. Ashdown, 915 Ottawa St., Keewatin, ON P0X 1C0 Tel. (807)547-3353 Fax (807)547-3356, E-mail diocese ofkeewatin@gokenora.com

Kootenay, Archbishop, The Most Rev. David P. Crawley, 1876 Richter St., Kelowna, BC V1Y 2M9 Tel. (250)762-3306 Fax (250)762-4150, E-mail diocese_of_kootenay@telus.net

Montreal, The Most Rev. Andrew S. Hutchison, 1444 Union Ave., Montreal, QC H3A 2B8 Tel. (514)843-6577 Fax (514)843-3221, E-mail bishops.office@montreal.anglican.ca

Moosonee, The Rt. Rev. Caleb J. Lawrence, Box 841, Schumacher, ON P0N 1G0 Tel. (705) 360-1129 Fax (705)360-1120, E-mail dmoose@ domaa.ca

New Westminster, The Rt. Rev. Michael C. Ingham, 580-401 W. Georgia St., Vancouver, BC V6B 5A1 Tel. (604)684-6306 Fax (604) 684-7017, E-mail bishop@vancouver.anglican. ca

Niagara, The Rt. Rev. Ralph Spence, 252 James St. N., Hamilton, ON L8R 2L3 Tel. (905)527-1278 Fax (905)527-1281, E-mail bishop@niagara.anglican.ca

Nova Scotia and Prince Edward Is., The Rt. Rev. Frederick J. Hiltz, 5732 College St., Halifax, NS B3H 1X3 Tel. (902)420-0717 Fax (902) 425-0717, E-mail office@nspeidiocese.ca

Ontario, The Rt. Rev. George L. R. Bruce, 90 Johnson St., Kingston, ON K7L 1X7 Tel. (613)544-4774 Fax (613)547-3745, E-mail synod@ontario.anglican.ca

Ottawa, The Rt. Rev. Peter R. Coffin, 71 Bronson Ave., Ottawa, ON K1R 6G6 Tel. (613)232-7124 Fax (613)232-7088, E-mail dayadmin@ ottawa.anglican.ca

Qu'Appelle, The Rt. Rev. Duncan D. Wallace, 1501 College Ave., Regina, SK S4P 1B8 Tel. (306)522-1608 Fax (306)352-6808, E-mail quappelle@ca sasktel.net

Quebec, The Rt. Rev. Bruce Stavert, 31 rue des Jardins, Quebec, QC G1R 4L6 Tel. (418)692-3858 Fax (418)692-3876, E-mail synodoffice@ quebec.anglican.ca

Rupert's Land, The Rt. Rev. Donald D. Phillips, 935 Nesbitt Bay, Winnipeg, MB R3T 1W6 Tel. (204)922-4200 Fax (204)922-4219, E-mail general@rupertsland.ca

Saskatchewan, The Rt. Rev. Anthony Burton, 1308 5th Ave. East, Prince Albert, SK S6V 2H7 Tel. (306)763-2455 Fax (306)764-5172, E-mail synod@sasktel.net

Saskatoon, The Archbishop, vacant, Box 1965, Saskatoon, SK S7K 3S5 Tel. (306)244-5651 Fax (306)933-4606,
E-mail anglicanbishop@sasktel.net

Toronto, The Most Rev. Terence E. Finlay, 135 Adelaide St. East, Toronto, ON M5C 1L8 Tel. (416)363-6021 Fax (416)363-3683, E-mail tfinlay@toronto.anglican.ca

Western Newfoundland, The Rt. Rev. Percy D. Coffin, 25 Main St., Corner Brook, NF A2H 1C2 Tel. (709)639-8712 Fax (709)639-1636, E-mail dsownc@nf.aibn.com

Yukon, The Rt. Rev. Terry Buckle, Box 4247, Whitehorse, YT Y1A 3T3 Tel. (867)667-7746 Fax (867)667-6125, E-mail synof@dioyukon. org

Periodicals

Anglican Journal (national newspaper); *Ministry Matters*

The Antiochian Orthodox Christian Archdiocese of North America

The approximately 100,000 members of the Antiochian Orthodox community in Canada are under the jurisdiction of the Antiochian Orthodox Christian Archdiocese of North America, with headquarters in Englewood, N.J. There are churches in Edmonton, Winnipeg, Halifax, London, Ottawa, Toronto, Windsor, Montreal, Saskatoon, Hamilton, Vancouver, Charlottestown, PEI, Calgary, Mississauga.

Headquarters

Metropolitan Philip Saliba, 358 Mountain Rd., Englewood, NJ 07631 Tel. (201)871-1355 Fax (201)871-7954

Web site www.antiochian.org

Media Contact, Rev. Fr. Thomas Zain, 355 State Street, Brooklyn, NY 11217 Tel. (718)855-6225 Fax (718)855-3608, E-mail abouna@aol.com

Periodicals

The Word; Again; Handmaiden

Apostolic Christian Church (Nazarene)

This church was formed in Canada as a result of immigration from various European countries.

The body began as a movement originated by the Rev. S. H. Froehlich, a Swiss pastor, whose followers are still found in Switzerland and Central Europe.

Headquarters

Apostolic Christian Church Foundation, 1135 Sholey Rd., Richmond, VA 23231 Tel. (804) 222-1943

Media Contact, James Hodges

Officers

Exec. Dir., James Hodges

The Apostolic Church in Canada

The Apostolic Church in Canada is affiliated with the worldwide organization of the Apostolic Church with headquarters in Great Britain (www.apostolicworld.net). A product of the Welsh Revival (1904 to 1908), its Canadian beginnings originated in Nova Scotia in 1927. Today its main centers are in Nova Scotia, Ontario and Quebec. This church is evangelical, fundamental and Pentecostal, with special emphasis on the ministry gifts listed in Ephesians 4:11-12.

Headquarters

27 Castlefield Ave., Toronto, ON M4R 1G3

Media Contact, Pres., Rev. D. Karl Thomas, 220 Adelaide St. London, ON N6B-3H4 Tel. (519) 438-7036 Fax (705)742-2948, E-mail nlcrevival @goldon.net

Web site www.apostolic.ca

Officers

Pres., Rev. D. Karl Thomas, 220 Adelaide St., London, ON N6B 344 Tel. (519)438-7036 Fax (519)438-5800, E-mail nlcrevival@goldon.net

Natl. Sec., Rev. James Hackner, R.R. #1 Uxbridge, ON L9P-1R1 Tel. (905)852-3563

Periodicals

Canadian News Up-Date; The News Magazine of the Apostolic Church in Canada

Apostolic Church of Pentecost of Canada Inc.

This body was founded in 1921 at Winnipeg, Manitoba, by Pastor Frank Small. Doctrines include belief in eternal salvation by the grace of God, baptism of the Holy Spirit with the evidence of speaking in tongues, water baptism by immersion in the name of the Lord Jesus Christ.

Headquarters

#119-2340 Pegasus Way NE, Calgary, AB T2E 8M5

Media Contact, Dir. Of Admin. and Finance, Rev. Wes Mills Tel. (403)273-5777 Fax (403) 273-8102

E-mail acop@acop.ca

Web site www.acop.ca

Officers

Mod., Rev. Wes Mills

Mission Dir., Rev. Brian Cooper

Periodicals

Fellowship Focus; Apostolic Women's Ministry (AWM) Newsletter; Apostolic Children's Ministry Newsletter

Armenian Evangelical Church

Founded in 1960 by immigrant Armenian evangelical families from the Middle East, this body is conservative doctrinally, with an evangelical, biblical emphasis. The polity of churches within the group differ with congregationalism being dominant, but there are presbyterian Armenian Evangelical churches as well. Most of the local churches have joined mainline denominations. All of the remaining Armenian Evangelical (congregational or presbyterian) local churches in the United States and Canada have joined with the Armenian Evangelical Union of North America.

Headquarters

Armenian Evangelical Church of Toronto, 2851 John St., P.O. Box 42015, Markham, ON L3R 5R0 Tel. (905)305-8144

Media Contact, Chief Editor, Rev. Yessayi Sarmazian

A.E.U.N.A. Officers

Min. to the Union, Rev. Karl Avakian, 1789 E. Frederick Ave., Fresno, CA 93720

Mod., Rev. Bernard Geulsgeugian

Officers

Min., Rev. Yessayi Sarmazian

Periodicals

Armenian Evangelical Church

Armenian Holy Apostolic Church—Canadian Diocese

The Canadian branch of the ancient Church of Armenia founded in A.D. 301 by St. Gregory the Illuminator was established in Canada at St. Catharines, Ontario, in 1930. The diocesan organization is under the jurisdiction of the Holy See of Etchmiadzin, Armenia. The Diocese has churches in St. Catharines, Hamilton, Toronto, Ottawa, Vancouver, Mississauga, Montreal, Laval, Windsor, Halifax, Winnipeg, Edmonton and Calgary.

Headquarters

Diocesan Offices, Primate, Canadian Diocese, Archbishop Hovnan Derderian, 615 Stuart Ave., Outremont, QC H2V 3H2 Tel. (514)276-9479 Fax (514)276-9960

Media Contact, Exec. Dir., Deacon Hagop Arslanian; Sec., Silva Mangassarian

E-mail adiocese@aol.com

Web site www.canarmdiocese.org

Officers

Sec., Silva Mangassarian

Webmaster, Albert Yeglikian

Associated Gospel Churches

The Associated Gospel Churches (AGC) traces its historical roots to the 1890s. To counteract the growth of liberal theology evident in many established denominations at this time, individuals and whole congregations seeking to uphold the final authority of the Scriptures in all matters of faith and conduct withdrew from those denominations and established churches with an evangelical ministry. These churches defended the belief that "all Scripture is given by inspiration of God" and also declared that the Holy Spirit gave the identical word of sacred writings of holy men of old, chosen by him to be the channel of his revelation to man.

At first this growing group of independent churches was known as the Christian Workers' Churches of Canada, and by 1922 there was desire for forming an association for fellowship, counsel and cooperation. Several churches in southern Ontario banded together under the leadership of Dr. P. W. Philpott of Hamilton and Rev. H. E. Irwin, K. C. of Toronto.

When a new Dominion Charter was obtained on March 18, 1925, the name was changed to Associated Gospel Churches. Since that time the AGC has steadily grown, spreading across Canada by invitation to other independent churches of like faith and by actively beginning new churches.

Headquarters

1500 Kerns Rd., Burlington, ON L7P 3A7 Tel. (905)634-8184 Fax (905)634-6283
E-mail admin@agcofcanada.com
Web site www.agcofcanada.com
Media Contact, Admin. Asst., Donna Leung, 1500 Kerns Rd., Burlington, ON L7P 3A7 Tel. (905)634-8184 Fax (905)634-6283, E-mail donna@agcofcanada.com

Officers

Pres., Rev. A.F. (Bud) Penner, 1500 Kerns Rd., Burlington, ON L7P 3A7 Tel. (905)634-8184 Fax (905)634-6283
Mod., Rev. David Collins, 599 Bayly St. E., Ajax, ON L1Z 1L4 Tel. (905)686-4450
Sec.-Treas., Mr. Charles Lyle, 1245 Stephenson Dr., Burlington, ON L7S 2L9 Tel. (905)633-8960

Periodicals

Insidedge

Association of Regular Baptist Churches (Canada)

The Association of Regular Baptist Churches was organized in 1957 by a group of churches for the purpose of mutual cooperation in missionary activities. The Association believes the Bible to be God's word, stands for historic Baptist principles, and opposes modern ecumenism.

Headquarters

17 Laverock St., Tottenham, ON L0G 1W0 Tel. (905)936-3786

Officers

Chmn., Rev. S. Kring, 67 Sovereen St., Delhi, ON N4B 1L7

Baptist Convention of Ontario and Quebec

The Baptist Convention of Ontario and Quebec is a family of 386 churches in Ontario and Quebec, united for mutual support and encouragement and united in missions in Canada and the world.

The Convention was formally organized in 1888. Its one educational institution—McMaster Divinity College was founded in 1887. The Convention works through the all-Canada missionary agency, Canadian Baptist Ministries. The churches also support the Sharing Way, the relief and development arm of Canadian Baptist Ministries.

Headquarters

195 The West Mall, Ste. 414, Etobicoke, ON M9C 5K1 Tel. (416)622-8600 Fax (416) 622-2308
Media Contact, Exec. Min., Dr. Ken Bellous

Officers

Past Pres., Mr. Roger Harris
Pres., Rev. John Torrance
1st Vice-Pres., Mr. Evan Whitehead
2nd Vice Pres., Mrs. Marie Toompuu
Treas.-Bus. Admn., Nancy Bell
Exec. Min., Dr. Ken Bellous

Periodicals

The Canadian Baptist

Baptist General Conference of Canada

The Baptist General Conference was founded in Canada by missionaries from the United States. Originally a Swedish body, BGC Canada now includes people of many nationalities and is conservative and evangelical in doctrine and practice.

Headquarters

4306-97 St. NW, Edmonton, AB T6E 5R9 Tel. (780)438-9127 Fax (780)435-2478
Media Contact, Exec. Dir., Rev. Abe Funk

Officers

Exec. Dir., Rev. Abe Funk, 4306-97 St. NW, Edmonton, AB T6E 5R9 Tel. (780)438-9127 Fax (780)435-2478
Exec. Dir., Gordon Sorensen, BGC Stewardship Foundation

DISTRICTS

Baptist Gen. Conf.- Central Canada,
Baptist General Conference in Alberta, Exec. Min., Dr. Cal Netterfield, 5011 122nd A St., Edmonton, AB T6H 3S8 Tel. (780)438-9126 Fax (780)438-5258

British Columbia Baptist Conference, Exec. Min., Rev. Walter W. Wieser, 7600 Glover Rd., Langley, BC V2Y 1Y1 Tel. (604)888-2246 Fax (604)888-0046

Baptist General Conf. in Saskatchewan,

Baptist Union of Western Canada

Headquarters

302,902-11 Ave., SW, Calgary, AB T2R 0E7

Media Contact, Exec. Min., Dr. Gerald Fisher

Officers

Pres., Mr. Bill Mains, 4576 Rainer Crescent, Prince George, BC V2K 1X4

Exec. Minister, Dr. Gerald Fisher, 302, 902-11 Ave SW, Calgary, AB T2R 0E7

Alberta Area Minister, Rev. Ed Dyck, 302, 902-11 Ave SW, Calgary, AB T2R 0E7

BC Area Minister, Dr. Paul Pearce, 201, 20349-88th Ave., Langely, BC V1M 2K5

SK-MB Area Minister, Dr. Robert Krahn, 414 Cowley Place, Saskatoon, SK S7N 3X2

Carey Theological College, Principal, Dr. Brian Stelck, 5920 Iona Dr., Vancouver, BC V6T 1J6

Baptist Resources Centre, 302, 902-11 Ave SW, Calgary, AB T2R 0E7

The Bible Holiness Movement

The Bible Holiness Movement, organized in 1949 as an outgrowth of the city mission work of the late Pastor William James Elijah Wakefield, an early-day Salvation Army officer, has been headed since its inception by his son, evangelist Wesley H. Wakefield, its Bishop-General.

It derives its emphasis on the original Methodist faith of salvation and scriptural holiness from the late Bishop R. C. Horner. It adheres to the common evangelical faith in the Bible, the deity and the atonement of Christ. It stresses a personal experience of salvation for the repentant sinner, of being wholly sanctified for the believer and of the fullness of the Holy Spirit for effective witness.

Membership involves a life of Christian love and evangelistic and social activism. Members are required to totally abstain from liquor and tobacco. They may not attend popular amusements or join secret societies. Divorce and remarriage are forbidden. Similar to Wesley's Methodism, members are, under some circumstances, allowed to retain membership in other evangelical church fellowships. Interchurch affiliations are maintained with a number of Wesleyan-Armenian Holiness denominations.

Year-round evangelistic outreach is maintained through open-air meetings, visitation, literature and other media. Noninstitutional welfare work, including addiction counseling, is conducted among minorities. There is direct overseas famine relief, civil rights action, environment protection and antinuclearism. The movement sponsors a permanent committee on religious freedom and an active promotion of Christian racial equality.

The movement has a world outreach with branches in the United States, India, Nigeria, Philippines, Ghana, Liberia, Cameroon, Kenya, Zambia, South Korea, Mulawi, and Tanzania. It also ministers to 89 countries in 42 languages through literature, radio and audiocassettes.

Headquarters

Box 223, Postal Stn. A, Vancouver, BC V6C 2M3 Tel. (250)492-3376

Media Contact, Bishop-General, Evangelist Wesley H. Wakefield, P.O. Box 223, Postal Station A, Vancouver, BC V6C 2M3 Tel. (250)492-3376

DIRECTORS

Bishop-General, Evangelist Wesley H. Wakefield, (Intl. Leader)

Evangelist M. J. Wakefield, Penticton, BC

Pastor Vincente & Mirasal Hernando, Phillipines

Pastor & Mrs. Daniel Stinnett, 1425 Mountain View W., Phoenix, AZ 85021

Pastor Monday S. Attai, Abak, Akwalbom, Nigeria, West Africa

Pastor Choe Chong Dee, Cha Pa Puk, S. Korea

Pastor S. A. Samuel, Andra, India

Pastor and Mrs. Daniel Vandee, Ghana, W. Africa

Pastor L.W. Hutchings, Protean, Vancouver, B.C.

Periodicals

Hallelujah!

Brethren in Christ Church, Canadian Conference

The Brethren in Christ, formerly known as Tunkers in Canada, arose out of a religious awakening in Lancaster County, Pennsylvania late in the 18th century. Representatives of the new denomination reached Ontario in 1788 and established the church in the southern part of the present province. Presently the conference has congregations in Ontario, Alberta, Quebec and Saskatchewan. In theology they have accents of the Pietist, Anabaptist, Wesleyan and Evangelical movements.

Headquarters

Brethren in Christ Church, Gen. Ofc., P.O. Box A, Grantham, PA 17027-0901 Tel. (717)697-2634 Fax (717)697-7714

Canadian Headquarters, Bishop's Ofc., 416 North Service Rd. E., Suite 1, Oakville, ON L6H 5R2 Tel. (905)339-2335

Media Contact, Mod., Dr. Warren L. Hoffman, Brethren in Christ Church Gen. Ofc.

Officers

Mod., Bishop Brian Bell, 416 North Service Road, Suite 1, Oakville, ON L6H 5R2 Tel. (905)339-2335 Fax (905)337-2120

Sec., Betty Albrecht, RR 2, Petersburg, ON N0B 2H0
Sec., Carole Phillips, 416 North Service Rd. E., Suite 1, Oakville, ON L6H 5R2

Periodicals

Evangelical Visitor; "Yes," Shalom

British Methodist Episcopal Church of Canada

The British Methodist Episcopal Church was organized in 1856 in Chatham, Ontario and incorporated in 1913. It has congregations across the province of Ontario.

Headquarters

430 Grey Street, London, ON N6B 1H3
Media Contact, Gen. Sec., Rev. Jacqueline Collins, 47 Connolly St., Toronto, ON M6N 4Y5 Tel. (416)653-6339

Officers

Gen. Supt., Rt. Rev. Dr. Douglas Birse, R.R. #5, Thamesville, ON N0P 2K0 Tel. (519)692-3628
Asst. Gen. Supt., Maurice M. Hicks, 3 Boxdene Ave., Scarborough, ON M1V 3C9 Tel. (416) 298-5715
Gen. Sec., Rev. Jacqueline Collins, 47 Connolly St., Toronto, ON M6N 4Y5 Tel. (416)653-6339
Gen. Treas., Ms. Hazel Small, 7 Wood Fernway, North York, ON M2J 4P6 Tel. (416)491-0313

Periodicals

B.M.E. Church Newsletter

Canadian and American Reformed Churches

The Canadian and American Reformed Churches accept the Bible as the infallible Word of God, as summarized in The Belgic Confession of Faith (1561), The Heidelberg Cathechism (1563) and The Canons of Dort (1618-1619). The federation was founded in Canada in 1950 and in the United States in 1955.

Headquarters

Synod, 607 Dynes Rd., Burlington, ON L7N 2V4
Canadian Reformed Churches, Ebenezer Canadian Reformed Church, 607 Dynes Rd., Burlington, ON L7N 2V4
Theological College, Dr. N. H. Gootjes, 110 W. 27th St., Hamilton, ON L9C 5A1 Tel. (905)575-3688 Fax (905)575-0799
Media Contact, Rev. G. Nederveen, 3089 Woodward Ave., Burlington, ON L7N 2M3 Tel. (905)681-7055 Fax (905)681-7055

Periodicals

Reformed Perspective, A Magazine for the Christian Family; Evangel, The Good News of Jesus Christ; Clarion, The Canadian Reformed Magazine; Diakonia-A Magazine of Office-Bearers; Book of Praise; Koinonia, A periodical of the Ministers of the CanRC; Horizon, A quarterly magazine published by the League of CanRC Women Societies; A Gift from Heaven, A Reformed Bible course.

Canadian Baptist Ministries

The Canadian Baptist Ministries has four federated member bodies, (1) Baptist Convention of Ontario and Quebec, (2) Baptist Union of Western Canada, (3) the United Baptist Convention of the Atlantic Provinces, (4) Union d'Églises Baptistes Françaises au Canada (French Baptist Union). Its main purpose is to act as a coordinating agency for the four groups for mission in all five continents.

Headquarters

7185 Millcreek Dr., Mississauga, ON L5N 5R4 Tel. (905)821-3533 Fax (905)826-3441
Media Contact, Communications, David Rogelstad
E-mail daver@cbmin.org
Web site www.cbmin.org

Officers

Pres., Doug Coomas
Gen. Sec., Rev. Gart Nelson, E-mail NelsonG@ cbmin.org

Canadian Conference of Mennonite Brethren Churches

The conference was incorporated November 22, 1945.

Headquarters

3-169 Riverton Ave., Winnipeg, MB R2L 2E5 Tel. (204)669-6575 Fax (204)654-1865
Media Contact, Exec. Dir., Dave Wiebe

Officers

Mod., Willie Reimer, 101-239 Midpark, Calgary, AB T2X 1M2 Tel. (403)254-2823
Asst. Mod., Paul Loewen, 2940 Clearbrook Rd., Abborsford, BC V2T 228 Tel. (604)853-3358
Sec., Marilyn Hiebert, 101-32310 Frasenway, Abborsford, BC V2T 1X1 Tel. (604)853-6990

Periodicals

Mennonite Brethren Herald; Mennonitische Rundschau; IdeaBank; Le Lien; Expression; Chinese Herald; Mennonite Historian

Canadian Convention of Southern Baptists

The Canadian Convention of Southern Baptists was formed at the Annual Meeting, May 7–9, 1985, in Kelowna, British Columbia. It was formerly known as the Canadian Baptist Conference, founded in Kamloops, British Columbia, in 1959 by pastors of existing churches.

Headquarters

100 Convention Way, Cochrane, AB T4C 2G2 Tel. (403)932-5688 Fax (403)932-4937

Media Contact, Exec. Dir.-Treas., Rev.Gerald Taillon

E-mail office@ccsb.ca

Officers

Exec. Dir.-Treas., Gerald Taillon, 17 Riverview Close, Cochrane, AB T4C 1K7

Pres., Alan Braun, 334 Norton St., Penticton, BC V2A 4H7

Periodicals

The Baptist Horizon

Canadian District of the Moravian Church in America, Northern Province

The work in Canada is under the general oversight and rules of the Moravian Church, Northern Province, general offices for which are located in Bethlehem, Pennsylvania. For complete information, see "Religious Bodies in the United States" section of the Yearbook.

Headquarters

1021 Center St., P.O. Box 1245, Bethlehem, PA 18016-1245

Media Contact, Ms. Deanna Hollenbach

Officers

Pres., Rev. Stephen Gohoes, 600 Acadia Dr. SE Calgary, AB T2J OB8 E-mail sgohdes@shaw.ca

Periodicals

The Moravian

Canadian Evangelical Christian Churches

The Canadian Evangelical Christian Church is an international, full-gospel new apostolic denomination, emphasizing the New Testament apostolic paradigm pattern which recognizes the ministry gifts beyond the apostle, prophet, evangelist, pastor and teacher to spread the gospel, according to Ephesians 4:11,12. The congregations are associated through full-gospel doctrine that is in combination with Calvinistic and Arminian beliefs. Each and every congregation is connected with CECC as congregational and ordination is supervised by National Office.

Headquarters

General Superintendent, Rev. David P. Lavigne, 410-125 Lincoln Rd., Waterloo, ON N2J 2N9 Tel. (519)880-9110 Toll free (888)981-8881 Fax (519)725-5578

E-mail cecc@rogers.com

Web sites www.cecconline.org, cetsonline.com

Officers

Gen. Supt., Rev. David P. Lavigne, 410-125 Lincoln Rd., Waterloo, ON N2J 2N9 Tel. (519)725-5578 Toll free (888)981-8881 Fax (519)725-5578, E-mail cecc@rogers.com

Exec. Dir., Rev. Otto Ferber, 139 Ste. Ann Ave., Box 237, St. Agatha, ON N0B 2L0 Tel. (519) 886-8809

Gen. Sec., Rev. Bill St. Pierre, Box 7, Oro, ON N3P 1B9 Tel. (888)297-5551

Canadian Yearly Meeting of the Religious Society of Friends

Canadian Yearly Meeting of the Religious Society of Friends was founded in Canada as an offshoot of the Quaker movement in Great Britain and colonial America. Genesee Yearly Meeting, founded 1834, Canada Yearly Meeting (Orthodox), founded in 1867, and Canada Yearly Meeting, founded in 1881, united in 1955 to form the Canadian Yearly Meeting. Canadian Yearly Meeting is affiliated with Friends United Meeting and Friends General Conference. It is also a member of Friends World Committee for Consultation.

Headquarters

91A Fourth Ave., Ottawa, ON K1S 2L1 Tel. (613)235-8553 Toll Free (888)296-3222 Fax (613)235-1753

Media Contact, Gen. Sec.-Treas.

E-mail cym-office@quaker.ca

Officers

Gen. Sec.-Treas., vacant

Clerk, Rick McCutcheon

Archivist, Jane Zavitz Bond

Archives, Arthur G. Dorland, Pickering College, 389 Bayview St., Newmarket, ON L3Y 4X2 Tel. (416)895-1700

Periodicals

The Canadian Friend; Quaker Concern

Christ Catholic Church International

Christ Catholic Church International now has churches and/or missions in 14 countries spread over four continents. They are located in the United States, Canada, Poland, Bahamas, Ukraine, Trinidad-Tobago, Germany, Vietnam, Colombia, Paraguay, Australia, Croatia, Kenya and the Philippines. Some countries have active churches and missions; some just missions and/or prayer groups.

CCCI is an Orthodox-Catholic Communion tracing Apostolic Succession through the Old Catholic and Orthodox Catholic Churches.

The church ministers to a growing number of people seeking an experiential relationship with their Lord and Savior Jesus Christ in a sacramental- and Scripture-based church.

Headquarters

5567 East 97th Place, Thornton, CO 80229

Media Contact, The Rt. Rev. John W. Brown, 1504-75 Queen St., Hamilton, ON L8R 3J3 Tel. (905)527-9089 Fax (905)354-9934, E-mail bishopjohn@primus.ca

E-mail cbrad99@aol.com
Web site www3.sympatico.ca/dwmullan

PRESIDING ARCHBISHOP

The Most Rev. Curtis Bradley, 5567 E 97th Pl., Thornton, CO 80229 Tel. (303)451-0683, E-mail cbrad99@aol.com

ARCHBISHOPS

The Most Rev. Donald Wm. Mullan, 6190 Barker St., Niagara Falls, ON L2G 1Y4 Tel. (905)354-2329 Fax (905)357-9934, E-mail dmullan1@cugeco.ca

The Most Rev. Jose Ruben Garcia Matiz, Calle 52 Sur #24A-35-Bq. #1, Ap. 301, Santa Fe de Bogota, D.C., Colombia, South America Tel. 57-71447 87, E-mail jorugama@col1.telecom.com.co

BISHOPS

The Rt. Rev. John Wm. Brown, 1504-75 Queen St., N. Hamilton, ON L8R 3J3 Tel. (905)522-6240, E-mail bishopjohn@primus.ca

The Rt. Rev. Gerard La Plante, 715 E 51st Ave., Vancouver, BC V5X 1E2 Tel. (604)327-1066 Fax (604)327-1066, E-mail oldcatholic@ elus.ca

The Rt. Rev. Luis Fernando Hoyos Maldonado, A.A. 24378 Santa Fe de Bogota, D.C., Colombia, South America Tel. 57-276-68-16, E-mail jourgama@col1.telecom.com.co

The Rt. Rev. L.M. (Mac) McFerran, #206-6020 East Boulevard, Vancouver, BC Tel. (604)261-2494

The Rt. Rev. Jose Moises Moncada Quevedo, A.A. 24378 Santa Fe de Bogota, D.C., Colombia, South America Tel. 57-276-68-16, E-mail jourgama@col1.telecom.com.co

The Rt. Rev. Jerome Robben, PO Box 566, Chesterfield, MO 63006-0566 Tel. (314)205-8422, E-mail abbajn17@aol.com

The Rt. Rev. Andrzej J. Sarwa, ul. Krucza 16 27-600 Sandomierz, Poland Tel.-Fax 084-(0-15) 833-21-41, E-mail andrzej-san@poczta.wp.pl

The Rt. Rev. Robert Smith, 824 Royal Oak Dr., Orlando, FL 32809 Tel (407)240-7833, E-mail yshwa@webtv.net

The Most Rev. Mar Melchizedek, P.O. Box 346, Seward, NE 68434, Tel. (402)643-9365

The Rt. Rev. John Gilbert-Cougar, Box 7305, D.L. Atkinson Station, Pasadena, TX 77508-7308

The Rt. Rev. Bill Quinlan, 3359 Swans Rd. NE, Newark, OH 43055

The Rt. Rev. Ker Smith, 76-770 Hialalai Rd., Kailua-Kona, HI 96740

Periodicals

St. Luke Magazine

Christian Brethren (also known as Plymouth Brethren)

The Christian Brethren are a loose grouping of autonomous local churches, often called "assemblies." They are firmly committed to the inerrancy of Scripture and to the evangelical doctrine of salvation by faith alone apart from works or sacrament. Characteristics are a weekly Breaking of Bread and freedom of ministry without a requirement of ordination. For their history, see "Religious Bodies in the United States" in the Directories section of this Yearbook.

CORRESPONDENT

James A. Stahr, 327 W. Praire Ave., Wheaton, IL 60187 Tel. (630)665-3757

RELATED ORGANIZATIONS

Christian Brethren Church in the Province of Quebec, P.O. Box 1054, Sherbrooke, QC J1H 5L3 Tel. (819)820-1693 Fax (819)821-9287

Kawartha Lakes Bible College, Box 1101, Peterborough, ON K9J 7H4 Tel. (705)742-2437

Mount Carmel Bible School, 4725 106th Ave., Edmonton, AB T6A 1E7 Tel. (780)465-3015

MSC Canada, Administrator, William Yuille, 509-3950 14th Ave., Markham, ON L3R 0A9 Tel. (905)947-0468 Fax (905)947-0352

Vision Ministries Canada, Dir., Gord Martin, P.O. Box 28032, Waterloo, ON N2L 6J8 Tel. (519)725-1212 Fax (519)725-9421

Periodicals

News of Quebec

Christian Church (Disciples of Christ) in Canada

Disciples have been in Canada since 1810, and were organized nationally in 1922. This church served the Canadian context as a region of the whole Christian Church (Disciples of Christ) in the United States and Canada.

Headquarters

Christian Church in Canada, PO Box 23030, 417 Wellington St., St. Thomas, ON N5R 6A3 Tel. (519)633-9083 Fax (519)637-6407

E-mail ccic@netrover.com

Media Contact, Reg. Min., F. Thomas Rutherford

Officers

Mod., Peter Fountain, PO Box 344, Milton, NS B0T 1P0 Tel. (902)354-5988, E-mail pjfountain@auracom.com

Reg. Min., F. Thomas Rutherford, PO Box 23030, 417 Wellington St., St. Thomas, ON N5R 6A3 Tel. (519)633-9083 Fax (519)637-6407, E-mail ccic@netrover.com

Christian Churches/Churches of Christ

First congregation organized: Cross Roads Christian Church, Cross Roads, Prince Edward Island, Canada, 1810, by "Scotch Baptists" influenced by James and Robert Haldane of Edinburgh. Since the 1820s when the writings of Thomas and Alexander Campbell were widely circulated and reprinted in periodicals, these congregations have identified with the 19th-century "Restoration Movement" (also known as "Stone-Campbell Movement"), which came to be known as

"Disciples of Christ." In late 19th-century. Ontario, some congregations separated over the use of musical instruments into a group known as the a capella Churches of Christ. From the 1880s to the 1930s, Disciples of Christ migrating from Ontario and emigrating from the United States organized congregations in Manitoba, Saskatchewan, Alberta, and British Columbia. From about 1948, when the Disciples of Christ in Canada first moved toward and, then, declared a formal denominational structure in 1968, 65-70 congregations across Canada did not identify with this structure, preferring to remain free, congregationally governed fellowships. While especially in western Canada these congregations cooperate and fellowship with congregations identified with the Disciples of Christ in Canada, a capella Churches of Christ, and people and congregations of several other traditions, they generally tend to identify with the interpretation of the Restoration or Stone-Campbell Movement as exemplified by U.S. Christian Churches and Churches of Christ in affinity with the North American Christian Convention, an annual, non-delegated, preaching and teaching convention. (See "The Movement in Canada," *Encyclopedia of the Stone-Campbell Movement.* Grand Rapids, Mich.: Eerdmans, 2004).

Headquarters

Media Contact: Russell E. Kuykendall, 25 Grenville Street, 1507, Toronto, ON M4Y 2X5 Tel (416)895-1098

E-mail kuykendall@canada.com

PARA-CHURCH INSTITUTIONS

Mortgage financing for congregations and para-church institutions: Church of Christ Development Company, Edmonton, Alberta

Church-planting associations: Partners in Atlantic Canada Evangelism, Impact Ontario, and Alberta Church Planting Association

Degree-granting colleges: Maritime Christian College, Charlottetown, PEI, and Alberta Bible College, Calgary, AB

Cross-cultural missions: Church of Christ Mission Jamaica; Church of Christ Mission India; Global Missionary Ministries (Central Europe); Frontier Labourers for Christ Canada (Thailand, Laos, and Myanmar); Graceland Ministries (Poland); Terri Scruggs, Partners with Nationals, Wycliffe Bible Translators; Benevolent Social Services of India; and others

Christian camps: Canoe Cove (PEI), Ontario Christian Assembly, Camp Christian (Pine Lake, AB), Pine Ridge Christian (Grande Prairie, AB), and Double VM (Lumby, BC)

Annual fellowship meetings: Maritime Christian Fellowship, Ontario Christian Missionary Conference, Western Canada Christian Convention (with Disciples of Christ and a capella Churches of Christ), and the North American Christian Convention.

Christian and Missionary Alliance in Canada

A Canadian movement, dedicated to the teaching of Jesus Christ the Saviour, Sanctifier, Healer and Coming King, commenced in Toronto in 1887 under the leadership of the Rev. John Salmon. Two years later, the movement united with the Christian Alliance of New York, founded by Rev. A. B. Simpson, becoming the Dominion Auxiliary of the Christian Alliance, Toronto, under the presidency of the Hon. William H. Howland. Its four founding branches were Toronto, Hamilton, Montreal, and Quebec. The movement focused on the deeper life and missions. In 1980, the Christian and Missionary Alliance in Canada became autonomous. Its General Assembly is held every two years.

NATIONAL OFFICE

30 Carrier Dr, Suite 100, Toronto, ON M9W 5T7 Tel. (416)674-7878 Fax (416)674-0808

Media Contact, Dir. of Comm., Barrie Doyle

E-mail info@cmacan.org

Officers

Pres., Dr. Franklin Pyles, pylesf@cmacan.org

Vice-Pres.-Global Ministries, Dr. Ray Downey, downeyr@cmacan.org

Vice-Pres.-Fin., Paul D. Lorimer, lorimerp@cmacan.org

Vice-Pres.-Canadian Ministries, Rev. C. Stuart Lightbody, lightbodys@cmacan.org

Vice-Pres.-Advancement, Rev. David Freeman, freemand@cmacan.org

Chairman of the Board, Dr. T. V. Thomas

Secretary of the Board, Connie Driedger

Periodicals

Alliance Life

Christian Reformed Church in North America

Canadian congregations of the Christian Reformed Church in North America have been formed since 1908. For detailed information about this denomination, please refer to the listing for the Christian Reformed Church in North America in Chapter 3, "Religious Bodies in the United States."

Headquarters

Canadian Office, 3475 Mainway, P.O. Box 5070 STN LCR 1, Burlington, ON L7R 3Y8 Tel. (905)336-2920 Fax (905)336-8344

Media Contact, Dir. of Comm., Mr. Henry Hess, Canadian Office

Web site www.crcna.org

Officers

Gen. Sec., Dr. David H. Engelhard, U.S. Office

Exec. Dir.-Ministries, Dr. Peter Borgdorff, U.S.Office

Dir. of Fin. & Admin., Mr. John Bolt, U.S. Office

Periodicals

The Banner

Church of God (Anderson, Ind.)

This body is one of the largest of the groups that have taken the name "Church of God." Its headquarters are at Anderson, Indiana. It originated about 1880 and emphasizes Christian unity.

Headquarters

Western Canada Assembly, Chpsn., Horst Depner, 4717- 56th St., Camrose, AB T4V 2C4 Tel. (780)672-0772 Fax (780)672-6888

Eastern Canada Assembly, Chpsn., Jim Wiebe, 38 James St., Dundas, ON L9H 2J6

Media Contact for Western Canada, Exec. Dir. Of Ministry Services, John D. Campbell, 4717 56th St., Camrose, AB T4V 2C4 Tel. (780) 672-0772 Fax (780)672-6888

E-mail admincoo@cable-lynx.net, baughman@cable-lynx.net

Web site, www.chog.ca

Periodicals

The Gospel Contact; The Messenger

Church of God in Christ (Mennonite)

The Church of God in Christ, Mennonite was organized by the evangelist-reformer John Holdeman in Ohio. The church unites with the faith of the Waldenses, Anabaptists and other such groups throughout history. Emphasis is placed on obedience to the teachings of the Bible, including the doctrine of the new birth and spiritual life, noninvolvement in government or the military, a head covering for women, beards for men and separation from the world shown by simplicity in clothing, homes, possessions and lifestyle. The church has a worldwide membership of about 20,150, largely concentrated in the United States and Canada.

Headquarters

P.O. Box 313, 420 N. Wedel Ave., Moundridge, KS 67107 Tel. (620)345-2532 Fax (620)345-2582

Media Contact, Dale Koehn, P.O.Box 230, Moundridge, KS 67107 Tel. (620)345-2532 Fax (620)345-2582

Periodicals

Messenger of Truth

Church of God (Cleveland, Tenn.)

It is one of America's oldest Pentecostal churches founded in 1886 as an outgrowth of the holiness revival under the name Christian Union. In 1907 the church adopted the organizational name Church of God. It has its foundation upon the principles of Christ as revealed in the Bible. The Church of God is Christian, Protestant, foundational in its doctrine, evangelical in practice and distinctively Pentecostal. It maintains a centralized form of government and a commitment to world evangelization.

The first church in Canada was established in 1919 in Scotland Farm, Manitoba. Paul H. Walker became the first overseer of Canada in 1931.

Headquarters

Intl. Offices, 2490 Keith St., NW, Cleveland, TN 37320 Tel. (423)472-3361 Fax (423)478-7066

Media Contact, Dir. of Comm., Michael L. Baker, P.O. Box 2430, Cleveland, TN 37320-2430 Tel. (423)478-7112 Fax (423)478-7066

Executives

Gen. Overseer, R. Lamar Vest

Asst. Gen. Overseers, T.L. Lowery, Bill F. Sheeks, Orville Hagan

Gen. Sec.-Treasurer, Gene D. Rice

DEPARTMENTS

Benefits Board, CEO, Arthur Rhodes

Business & Records, Dir., Julian B. Robinson

Care Ministries, Dir., John D. Nichols

Chaplains Commission, Dir. Robert D. Crick

Communications, Media Ministries, Director, Michael L. Baker

Education—European Bible Seminary, Dir., John Sims

Education—Hispanic Institute of Ministry, Dir., Jose D. Montanez

Education—International Bible College, Pres., Cheryl Busse

Education—Lee University, Pres. C. Paul Conn

Education—Patten College, Chancellor, Bebe Patten

Education—Puerto Rico Bible School, Pres., Iledfonso Caraballo

Education—School of Ministry, Chancellor, Paul L. Walker

Education—Theology Seminary, President, Stephen J. Land

Evangelism & Home Missions, Dir.,

Canada-Eastern, Rev. Canute Blake, P.O. Box 2036, Brampton, ON L6T 3TO Tel. (905)793-2213 Fax (905)793-9173

Canada-Western, Rev. Raymond W. Wall, Box 54055, 2640 52 St. NE, Calgary, AB T1Y 6S6 Tel. (403)293-8817 Fax (403)293-8832

Canada-Quebec-Maritimes, Rev. Jacques Houle, 19 Orly, Granby, QC J2H 1Y4 Tel. (514)378-4442 Fax (514)378-8646

Periodicals

Church of God Evangel, Editorial Evangelica

The Church of God of Prophecy Canada East

The Church of God of Prophecy is one of the churches that grew out of the work of A. J. Tomlinson in the first half of the twentieth century. Historically it shares a common heritage with the Church of God (Cleveland, Tennessee) and is in the mainstream of the classical Pentecostal-holiness tradition.

At the death of A.J. Tomlinson in 1943, M.A. Tomlinson was named General Overseer and served until his retirement in 1990. He emphasized unity and fellowship unlimited by racial, social, or political differences. The next General Overseer, Billy D. Murray, Sr., who served from 1990 until his retirement in 2000, emphasized a commitment to the promotion of Christian unity and world evangelization. In July 2000, Fred S. Fisher, Sr. Was duly selected to serve as the fourth General Overseer of the Church of God of Prophecy.

From its beginnings, the Church has based its beliefs on "the whole Bible, rightly divided," and has accepted the Bible as God's Holy Word, inspired, inerrant and infallible. The church is firm in its commitment to orthodox Christian belief. The Church affirms that there is one God, eternally existing in three persons, Father, Son and Holy Spirit. It believes in the deity of Christ, His virgin birth, His sinless life, the physical miracles He performed, His atoning death on the cross, His bodily resurrection, His ascension to the right hand of the Father and his Second coming. The church professes that salvation results from grace alone through faith in Christ, that regeneration by the Holy Spirit is essential for the salvation of sinful men, and that sanctification by the blood of Christ makes possible personal holiness. It affirms the present ministry of the Holy Spirit by whose indwelling believers are able to live godly lives and have power for service. The church believes in, and promotes, the ultimate unity of believers as prayed for by Christ in John 17. The church stresses the sanctity of human life and is committed to the sanctity of the marriage bond and the importance of strong, loving Christian families. Other official teachings include Holy Spirit baptism with tongues as initial evidence; manifestation of the spiritual gifts; divine healing; premillenial second coming of Christ; total abstinence from the use of tobacco, alcohol and narcotics; water baptism by immersion; the Lord's supper and washing of the saints' feet; and a concern for moderation and holiness in all dimensions of lifestyle.

The Church is racially integrated on all levels, including top leadership. Women play a prominent role in church affairs, serving in pastoral roles and other leadership positions. The church presbytery has recently adopted plurality of leadership in the selection of a General Oversight Group. This group consists of eight bishops located around the world who, along with the General Overseer, are responsible for inspirational leadership and vision casting for the church body.

The Church has local congregations in all 50 states and more than 100 nations worldwide. Organizationally there is a strong emphasis on international missions, evangelism, youth and children's ministries, women's and men's ministries, stewardship, communications, publishing, leadership development and discipleship.

INTERNATIONAL OFFICES

P.O. Box 2910, Cleveland, TN 37320-2910
Media Contact, National Overseer, Levi Clarke, 5145 Tomken Rd, Mississauga, ON L4 W1P1 Tel. (905) 625-1278 Fax (905)-625-1316.
Web site www.cogop.ca

Officers

Gen. Overseer, Bishop Fred S. Fisher, Sr.
General Presbyters, Sherman Allen, Sam Clements, Daniel Corbett, Clayton Endecott, Miguel Mojica, José Reyes, Sr., Felix Santiago, Brice Thompson

INTERNATIONAL OFFICES MINISTRIES DIRECTORS

Finance, Communications, and Publishing, Perry Gillum
Global Outreach and Administrative Asst. to the General Presbyters, Randy Howard
Leadership Development and Discipleship Ministries, Larry Duncan.

Periodicals

White Wing Messenger (ENG); *Victory* (Youth Magazine/Sunday School Curriculum); *The Happy Harvester; White Wing Messenger* (Spanish).

The Church of Jesus Christ of Latter-Day Saints in Canada

The Church has had a presence in Canada since the early 1830s. Joseph Smith and Brigham Young both came to Eastern Canada as missionaries. There are now 157,000 members in Canada in more than 400 congregations.

Leading the Church in Canada are the presidents of more than 40 stakes (equivalent to a diocese). World headquarters is in Salt Lake City, UT (See U.S. Religious Bodies chapter of the Directories section of this Yearbook).

Headquarters

50 East North Temple St., Salt Lake City, UT 84150
Media Contact, Public Affairs Dir., Bruce Smith, 1185 Eglinton Ave., Box 116, North York, ON M3C 3C6 Tel. (416)431-7891 Fax (416)438-2723

Church of the Lutheran Brethren

The Church of the Lutheran Brethren of America was organized in December 1900. Five independent Lutheran congregations met together in Milwaukee, Wisconsin, and adopted a constitution patterned very closely to that of the Lutheran Free Church of Norway.

The spiritual awakening in the Midwest during the 1890s crystallized into convictions that led to the formation of a new church body. Chief among the concerns were church membership practices, observance of Holy Communion, confirmation practices and local church government.

The Church of the Lutheran Brethren practices

a simple order of worship with the sermon as the primary part of the worship service. It believes that personal profession of faith is the primary criterion for membership in the congregation. The Communion service is reserved for those who profess faith in Christ as savior. Each congregation is autonomous and the synod serves the congregations in advisory and cooperative capacities.

The synod supports a world mission program in Cameroon, Chad, Japan and Taiwan. Approximately 40 percent of the synodical budget is earmarked for world missions. A growing home mission ministry is planting new congregations in the United States and Canada. Affiliate organizations operate several retirement-nursing homes, conference and retreat centers.

Headquarters

1020 Alcott Ave., W., P.O. Box 655, Fergus Falls, MN 56538 Tel. (218)739-3336 Fax (218)739-5514

Media Contact, Rev. Brent Juliot

E-mail rmo@clba.org

Web site www.clba.org

Officers

Pres., Rev. Arthur Berge, 72 Midridge Close SE, Calgary, AB T2X 1G1

Vice-Pres., Rev. Luther Stenberg, PO Box 75, Hagen, SK S0J 1B0

Sec., Mr. Alvin Herman, 3105 Taylor Street E., Saskatoon, SK S7H 1H5

Treas., Edwin Rundbraaten, Box 739, Birch Hills, SK S0J 0G0

Youth Coord., Rev. Harold Rust, 2617 Preston Ave. S., Saskatoon, SK S7J 2G3

Periodicals

Faith and Fellowship

Church of the Nazarene in Canada

The first Church of the Nazarene in Canada was organized in November, 1902, by Dr. H. F. Reynolds. It was in Oxford, Nova Scotia. The Church of the Nazarene is Wesleyan Arminian in theology, representative in church government and warmly evangelistic.

Headquarters

20 Regan Rd., Unit 9, Brampton, ON L7A 1C3 Tel. (905)846-4220 Fax (905)846-1775

Media Contact, Gen. Sec., Dr. Jack Stone, 6401 The Paseo, Kansas City, MO 64131 Tel. (816)333-7000 Fax (816)822-9071

E-mail national@nazarene.ca

Web site www.nazarene.ca

Officers

Natl. Dir., Dr. William E. Stewart, 20 Regan Rd. Unit 9, Brampton, ON L7A 1C3 Tel. (905)846-4220 Fax (905)846-1775

Exec. Asst., John T. Martin, 20 Regan Rd. Unit 9, Brampton, ON L7A 1C3 Tel. (905)846-4220 Fax (905)846-1775

Churches of Christ in Canada

Churches of Christ are autonomous congregations, whose members appeal to the Bible alone to determine matters of faith and practice. There are no central offices or officers. Publications and institutions related to the churches are either under local congregational control or independent of any one congregation.

Churches of Christ shared a common fellowship in the 19th century with the Christian Churches-Churches of Christ and the Christian Church (Disciples of Christ). Fellowship was broken after the introduction of instrumental music in worship and centralization of churchwide activities through a missionary society. Churches of Christ began in Canada soon after 1800, largely in the middle provinces. The few pioneer congregations were greatly strengthened in the mid-1800s, growing in size and number.

Members of Churches of Christ believe in the inspiration of the Scriptures, the divinity of Jesus Christ, and immersion into Christ for the remission of sins. The New Testament pattern is followed in worship and church organization.

Headquarters

Media Contact, Man. Ed., *Gospel Herald*, Max Craddock, 5 Lankin Blvd., ON M4J 4W7 Tel. (416)461-7406 Fax (416)424-1850

E-mail maxc@strathmorecofc.ca

Periodicals

Gospel Herald

Community of Christ

Founded April 6, 1830, by Joseph Smith, Jr., the church was reorganized under the leadership of the founder's son, Joseph Smith III, in 1860. The Church is established in 38 countries including the United States and Canada, with nearly a quarter of a million members. A biennial world conference is held in Independence, Missouri. The current president is W. Grant McMurray.

Headquarters

World Headquarters Complex, 1001 W. Walnut, Independence, MO 64050 Tel. (816)833-1000 Fax (816)521-3095

Ontario Regional Ofc., 390 Speedvale Ave. E., Guelph, ON N1E 1N5

Media Contact, Public Relations Coordinator, Susan Naylor

CANADA EAST MISSION CENTRE OFFICERS

Pres., Ken Barrows, 390 Speedvale Ave E., Guelph, ON N1E 1N5 Tel. (519)822-4150, E-mail ken@communityofchrist.ca

Financial Officer, Jim Poirier, 390 Speedvale Ave. E., Guelph, ON N1E 1N5 Tel. (519)822-4150, E-mail jim@communityofchrist.ca

CANADA WEST MISSION CENTRE OFFICERS

Pres., Darrell Belrose, 194 Tuscarora Circle

NW, Calgary AB T3L 2B8 Tel. (403)241-9616 E-mail darrellcswm@shaw.ca
Financial Officer, Bob Hodgson, 181 Hamptons Square NW, Calgary AB T3A 5C3 Tel. (403)241-8221, E-mail bobwcmc@shaw.ca

Periodicals

Saints Herald

Congregational Christian Churches in Canada

This body originated in the early 18th century when devout Christians within several denominations in the northern and eastern United States, dissatisfied with sectarian controversy, broke away from their own denominations and took the simple title "Christians." First organized in 1821 at Keswick, Ontario, the Congregational Christian Churches in Canada was incorporated on Dec. 4, 1989, as a national organization. In doctrine the body is evangelical, being governed by the Bible as the final authority in faith and practice. It believes that Christian character must be expressed in daily living; it aims at the unity of all true believers in Christ that others may believe in him and be saved. In church polity, the body is democratic and autonomous. It is also a member of The World Evangelical Congregational Fellowship.

Headquarters

241 Dunsdon St. Ste. 405, Brantford, ON N3R 7C3 Tel. (519)751-0606 Fax (519)751-0852
Media Contact, Past Pres., Jim Potter, 8 Church St., Waldemar, ON L0N 1G0 Tel. (519)928-5561

Officers

Pres., Rev. Michael Shute
Exec. Dir., Rev.David Schrader
Sec., Rev. Ron Holden

Convention of Atlantic Baptist Churches

The Convention of Atlantic Baptist Churches is the largest Baptist Convention in Canada. Through the Canadian Baptist Ministries, it is a member of the Baptist World Alliance.

In 1763 two Baptist churches were organized in Atlantic Canada, one in Sackville, New Brunswick and the other in Wolfville, Nova Scotia. Although both these churches experienced crises and lost continuity, they recovered and stand today as the beginning of organized Baptist work in Canada.

Nine Baptist churches met in Lower Granville, Nova Scotia in 1800 and formed the first Baptist Association in Canada. By 1846 the Maritime Baptist Convention was organized, consisting of 169 churches. Two streams of Baptist life merged in 1905 to form the United Baptist Convention. This is how the term "United Baptist" was derived. Today there are 554 churches within 21 associations across the Convention.

The Convention has two educational institutions, Atlantic Baptist University in Moncton, New Brunswick, a Christian Liberal Arts University, and Acadia Divinity College in Wolfville, Nova Scotia, a Graduate School of Theology. The Convention engages in world mission through Canadian Baptist Ministries, the all-Canada mission agency. In addition to an active program of home mission, evangelism, training, social action and stewardship, the Convention operates ten senior citizen complexes and a Christian bookstore.

Headquarters

1655 Manawagonish Rd., Saint John, NB E2M 3Y2 Tel. (506)635-1922 Fax (506)635-0366
Media Contact, Exec. Minister, Dr. Harry G. Gardner
E-mail cabc@baptist.atlantic.ca
Web site www.baptist.atlantic.ca

Officers

Pres. (2004-2005), Mr. George H. Powell, 3 Elton Place, St. John's, WL A1A 5B8 Tel. (709)722-5007
Vice-Pres. (2004-2005), Dr. Ralph Richardson, 129 Athabaska Ave., Riverview, NB E1B 2T2 Tel. (506)863-8456
Exec. Min., Dr. Harry G. Gardner, 1655 Manawagonish Rd., Saint John, NB E2M 3Y2 Tel. (506)635-1922 Fax (506)635-0366, E-mail harry.gardner@baptist-atlantic.ca
Dir. of Operations., Daryl MacKenzie, 1655 Manawagonish Rd., Saint John, NB E2M 3Y2 Tel. (506)635-1922 Fax (506)635-0366, E-mail daryl.mackenzie@baptist-atlantic.ca
Dir. of Atlantic Baptist Mission, Dr. Malcolm Beckett, 1655 Manawagonish Rd., Saint John, NB E2M 3Y2 Tel. (506)635-1922 Fax (506) 635-0366, E-mail malcolm.beckett@baptist-atlantic.ca
Dir. of Youth and Family, Rev. Bruce Fawcett, 1655 Manawagonish Rd., Saint John, NB E2M 3Y2 Tel. (506)635-1922 Fax (506)635-0366, E-mail bruce.fawcett@baptist-atlantic.ca
Dir. Of Development, Rev. Greg Jones, 1655 Manawagonish Rd., Saint John, NB E2M 3Y2 Tel. (506)635-1922 Fax (506)635-0366, E-mail greg.jones@baptist-atlantic.ca
Part-time Dir. Of Public Witness and Social Concern, Dr. Lois P. Mitchell c/o 1655 Manawagonish Rd., Saint John, NB E2M 3Y2 Tel. (506)635-1922 Fax (506)635-0366, E-mail lois.mitchell@baptist-atlantic.ca

The Coptic Orthodox Church in Canada

The Coptic Orthodox Church in North America was begun in Canada in 1964 and was registered in the province of Ontario in 1965. The Coptic Orthodox Church has spread rapidly since then. The total number of local churches in both Canada and the USA exceeded one hundred. Two dioceses, a monastery with a bishop, monks and novices, and two theological seminaries were established in the U.S.A.

The Coptic Orthodox Church is the church of Alexandria founded in Egypt by St. Mark the Apostle in the first century A.D. She is a hierarchical church and the administrative governing body of each local church is an elected Board of Deacons approved by the Bishop. The current patriarch of the church is H. H. Pope Shenouda III, Pope of Alexandria and Patriach of the see of St. Mark. The Coptic Orthodox Church is a member of the Canadian Council of Churches.

Headquarters

St. Mark's Coptic Orthodox Church, 41 Glendinning Ave., Scarborough, ON M1W 3E2 Tel. (416)494-4449 Fax (416)494-2631

Media Contact, Fr. Ammonius Guirguis, Tel. (416)494-4449 Fax (416)494-2631, E-mail frammonius@coptorthodox.ca

E-mail mail@coptorthodox.ca

Web site www.stmark.toronto.on.coptorthodox.ca

Elim Fellowship of Evangelical Churches and Ministers

The Elim Fellowship of Evangelical Churches and Ministers, a Pentecostal body, was established in 1984 as a sister organization of Elim Fellowship in the United States.

This is an association of churches, ministers and missionaries seeking to serve the whole body of Christ. It is Pentecostal and has a charismatic orientation.

Headquarters

379 Golf Road, RR#6, Brantford, ON N3T 5L8 Tel. (519)753-7266 Fax (519)753-5887

Ofc. Mgr., Larry Jones

E-mail elim@bfree.on.ca

Web site Bfree.ON.ca/comdir/churchs/elim

Officers

Pres., Howard Ellis, 102 Ripley Crescent., Kitchener, ON N2N 1V4

Vice-Pres., Rev. Errol Alchin, 1694 Autumn Crescent, Pickering, ON L1V 6X5

Sec.-Treas., Larry Jones, 107 Hillside Ave., Paris ON K2G 4N1

Council of Elders

Rev. Bud Crawford, Brampton, ON

Rev. Howard Ellis, Kitchener, ON

Rev. Bernard Evans, Lima, New York

Rev. Claude Favreau, Drummondville, Quebec

Rev. Aubrey Phillips, Blairsville, Georgia

The Estonian Evangelical Lutheran Church Abroad

The Estonian Evangelical Lutheran Church (EELC) was founded in 1917 in Estonia and reorganized in Sweden in 1944. The teachings of the EELC are based on the Old and New Testaments, explained through the Apostolic, Nicean and Athanasian confessions, the unaltered Confession of Augsburg and other teachings found in the Book of Concord.

Headquarters

383 Jarvis St., Toronto, ON M5B 2C7 Tel. (416)925-5465 Fax (416)925-5688

Media Contact, Archbishop, Rev. Udo Petersoo

E-mail udo.petersoo@eelk.ee

Web site www.eelk.ee/~e.e.l.k.

Officers

Archbishop, The Rev. Udo Petersoo

Gen. Sec., Mr. Ivar Nippak

Sec./Clerk, Mrs. Evi Jaaguste

Periodicals

Eesti Kirik

The Evangelical Covenant Church of Canada

A Canadian denomination organized in Canada at Winnipeg in 1904 which is affiliated with the Evangelical Covenant Church of America and with the International Federation of Free Evangelical Churches, which includes 31 federations in 26 countries.

This body believes in the one triune God as confessed in the Apostles' Creed, that salvation is received through faith in Christ as Savior, that the Bible is the authoritative guide in all matters of faith and practice. Christian Baptism and the Lord's Supper are accepted as divinely ordained sacraments of the church. As descendants of the 19th century northern European pietistic awakening, the group believes in the need of a personal experience of commitment to Christ, the development of a virtuous life and the urgency of spreading the gospel to the "ends of the world."

Four Core Values: To be a Missional Church; To be a Biblical Church; To be a Devotional Church; and to be a Connnectional Church.

Four Ministry Priorities: Leadership Development; Church Planting & Mission; Church Renewal/ Transition; and Christian Services.

Headquarters

PO Box 34025, RPO Fort Richmond, Winnipeg, MB R3T 5T5

Media Contact, Supt., Jeff Anderson

Officers

Pres./Supt., Rev. Jeff Anderson, PO 34025, RPO Fort Richmond, Winnipeg, MB R3T 5T5

Chpsn., Rod Johnson, Box 217, Norquay, SK S0A 2V0

Sec., Judy Nelson, Box 194, Norquay, SK S0A 2V0

Treas., Ingrid Wildman, Box 93, Norquay, SK S0A 2V0

Periodicals

The Covenant Messenger

Evangelical Free Church of Canada

The Evangelical Free Church of Canada traces its beginning back to 1917 when the church in Enchant, Alberta opened its doors. Today the denomination has 139 churches from the West Coast to Quebec. Approximately 80 missionaries are sponsored by the EFCC in 17 countries. The Evangelical Free Church is the founding denomination of Trinity Western University in Langley, British Columbia. Church membership is 7,920, average attendance is 18,496

Headquarters

Mailing Address, P.O. Box 850 LCD1, Langley, BC V3A 8S6 Tel. (604)888-8668 Fax (604) 888-3108

Location, 7600 Glover Rd., Langley, BC

Media Contact, Exec. Sec., Carol Jones, P.O. Box 850 LCD1, Langley, BC V3A 8S6 Tel. (604)888-8668 Fax (604)888-3108

E-mail efcc@twu.ca

Web site www.efcc.ca

Officers

Pres., Dr. Ron Unruh, P.O.Box 850 LCD 1, Langley, BC, Canada V3A 8S6 Tel (604)888-8668, Fax (604) 888-3108, E-mail efcc@ twu.ca

Periodicals

The Pulse

Evangelical Lutheran Church in Canada

The Evangelical Lutheran Church in Canada was organized in 1985 through a merger of The Evangelical Lutheran Church of Canada (ELCC) and the Lutheran Church in America—Canada Section.

The merger is a result of an invitation issued in 1972 by the ELCC to the Lutheran Church in America—Canada Section and the Lutheran Church—Canada. Three-way merger discussions took place until 1978 when it was decided that only a two-way merger was possible. The ELCC was the Canada District of the ALC until autonomy in 1967.

The Lutheran Church in Canada traces its history back more than 200 years. Congregations were organized by German Lutherans in Halifax and Lunenburg County in Nova Scotia in 1749. German Lutherans, including many United Empire Loyalists, also settled in large numbers along the St. Lawrence and in Upper Canada. In the late 19th century, immigrants arrived from Scandinavia, Germany and central European countries, many via the United States. The Lutheran synods in the United States have provided the pastoral support and help for the Canadian church.

Headquarters

302-393 Portage Avenue, Winnipeg, MB R3B 3H6 Tel. (204)984-9150 Fax (204)984-9185

Media Contact, Bishop, Rev. Raymond L. Schultz

Periodicals

Canada Lutheran; Esprit

The Evangelical Mennonite Conference

The Evangelical Mennonite Conference is a modern church of historic Christian convictions, tracing its indebtedness to the Radical Reformation, which, in turn, is rooted in the Protestant Reformation of the 16th century. The center of faith, and of Scripture, is found in Jesus Christ as Saviour and Lord.

The church's name was chosen in 1959. Its original name, Kleine Gemeinde, which means "small church," reflected its origins as a renewal movement among Mennonites in southern Russia. Klaas Reimer, a minister, was concerned about a decline of spiritual life and discipline in the church, and inappropriate involvement in the Napoleonic War. About 1812, Reimer and others began separate worship services, and two years later were organized as a small group.

Facing increasing government pressure, particularly about military service, the group migrated to North America in 1874 to 1875. Fifty families settled in Manitoba and 36 in Nebraska. Ties between the groups weakened and eventually the U.S. group gave up its KG identity. The KG survived several schisms and migrations, dating from its years in Russia through the 1940s.

As an evangelical church, The Evangelical Mennonite Conference holds that Scripture has final authority in faith and practice, a belief in Christ's finished work, and that assurance of salvation is possible. As Mennonite, the denomination has a commitment to discipleship, baptism upon confession of faith, community, social concern, nonviolence and the Great Commission. As a conference, it seeks to encourage local churches, to work together on evangelism and matters of social concern, and relates increasingly well to other denominations.

In the year 2000 its membership surpassed 7,000, with many more people as treasured adherents and a wider circle of ministry influence. Membership is for people baptized on confession of faith (usually in adolescence or older). Children are considered safe in Christ until they reach an age where they are accountable for their own spiritual decision and opt out; they are considered part of the church, while full inclusion occurs upon personal choice.

The Conference has 50 churches from British Columbia to Ontario (33 in Manitoba) and roughly 147 mission workers in 25 countries. The cultural make-up of the Conference is increasingly diverse, though its Dutch-German background remains dominant nationally. Ten churches have pastors or leaders who are of non-Dutch-German background.

Some churches have a multiple leadership pattern (ministers and deacons can be selected from within the congregation); others have new patterns. Most churches support their leading minister full time. Its church governance moved from a bishop system to greater local congregational autonomy. It currently functions as a conference of churches with national boards, a conference council, and a moderator.

Women can serve on most national boards, as conference council delegates, as missionaries, and within a wide range of local church activities; while they can be selected locally, they cannot currently serve as nationally recognized or commissioned ministers.

It is a supporting member of Mennonite Central Committee and the Evangelical Fellowship of Canada. About 80 percent of its national budget goes toward mission work in Canada and other countries.

Headquarters

Box 1268, 440 Main St., Steinbach, MB R0A 2A0 Tel. (204)326-6401 Fax (204)326-1613
Media Contact, Conf. Pastor, David Thiessen
E-mail emconf@mts.net

Officers

Conf. Mod., Harvey Plett
General Sec., Len Barkman
Conf. Pastor, David Thiessen
Bd. of Missions, Exec. Sec., Len Barkman
Bd. of Missions, Foreign Sec., Lester Olfert
Bd. of Church Ministries, Exec. Sec.-Editor, Terry M. Smith
Canadian Sec., Conf. Pastor, David Thiessen
Conf. Youth Minister, Gerald Reimer

Periodicals

The Messenger

Evangelical Mennonite Mission Conference

This group was founded in 1936 as the Rudnerweider Mennonite Church in Southern Manitoba and organized as the Evangelical Mennonite Mission Conference in 1959. It was incorporated in 1962. The Annual Conference meeting is held in July.

Headquarters

Box 52059, Niakwa P.O., Winnipeg, MB R2M 5P9 Tel. (204)253-7929 Fax (204)256-7384
Media Contact, Lil Goertzen,
E-mail lil@emmc. ca
E-mail emmc@mb.sympatico.ca

Officers

Mod., David Penner, 906-300 Sherk St., Leamington, ON N8H 4N7
Vice-Mod., Carl Zacharias, R.R. 1, Box 205, Winkler, MB R6W 4A1
Sec., Darrell Dyck, R.R. 1, Box 186, Winkler, MB R6W 4A1
Dir. of Conference Ministries, Jack Heppner
Dir. of Missions, Rev. Leonard Sawatzky
Business Admin., Henry Thiessen

OTHER ORGANIZATIONS

The Gospel Message, Box 1622, Saskatoon, SK S7K 3R8 Tel. (306)242-5001 Fax (306)242-6115; 210-401 33rd St. W., Saskatoon, SK S7L 0V5 Tel. (306)242-5001
Radio Pastor, Rev. Ed Martens

Periodicals

EMMC Recorder

The Evangelical Missionary Church of Canada

This denomination was formed in 1993 with the merger of The Evangelical Church of Canada and The Missionary Church of Canada. The Evangelical Missionary Church of Canada maintains fraternal relations with the worldwide body of the Missionary Church, Inc. and with the Evangelical Church of North America.The Evangelical Church of Canada was among those North American Evangelical United Brethern Conferences which did not join the EUB in merging with the Methodist Church in 1968. The Missionary Church of Canada is Anabaptist in heritage. Its practices and theology were shaped by the Holiness Revivals of the late 1800s. The Evangelical Missionary Church consists of 135 churches in two conferences in Canada.

Headquarters

4031 Brentwood Rd., NW, Calgary, AB T2L 1L1 Tel. (403)250-2759 Fax (403)291-4720
Media Contact, Exec. Dir., Missions and Admin., G. Keith Elliott
E-mail info@emcc.ca

Officers

Pres. and Canada East District, Dist. Supt., Rev. Phil Delsaut, 130 Fergus Ave., Kitchener, ON N2A 2H2 Tel. (519)894-9800, E-mail pdelsaut@emcced.ca
Canada West District, Acting Dist. Supt., Rev. Don Adolf, 4031 Brentwood Rd., NW, Calgary, AB T2L 1L1 Tel. (403)291-5525 Fax (403)291-4720, E-mail don@emcwest.ca

The Fellowship of Evangelical Baptist Churches in Canada

This organization was founded in 1953 by the merging of the Union of Regular Baptist Churches of Ontario and Quebec with the Fellowship of Independent Baptist Churches of Canada.

Headquarters

679 Southgate Dr., Guelph, ON N1G 4S2 Tel. (519)821-4830 Fax (519)821-9829
Media Contact, Pres., Rev. Terry D. Cuthbert
E-mail president@fellowship.ca

Officers

Pres., Rev. Terry D. Cuthbert
Chmn., Rev. Dan Shurr

Periodicals

B.C. Fellowship Baptist; The Evangelical Baptist; Intercom

Foursquare Gospel Church of Canada

The Western Canada District was formed in 1964 with the Rev. Roy Hicks as supervisor.

Prior to 1964 it had been a part of the Northwest District of the International Church of the Foursquare Gospel with headquarters in Los Angeles, California.

A Provincial Society, the Church of the Foursquare Gospel of Western Canada, was formed in 1976; a federal corporation, the Foursquare Gospel Church of Canada, was incorporated in 1981 and a national church formed. The provincial society was closed in 1994.

Headquarters

#100 8459 160th St., Surrey, BC V3S 3T9

Media Contact, Pres. & Gen. Supervisor, Timothy J. Peterson, #100-8459 160th St., Surrey, BC V3S 3T9 Tel. (604)543-8414 Fax (604)543-8417

E-mail fgcc@canada.com

Officers

Pres. & Gen. Supervisor, Timothy J. Peterson

Periodicals

VIP Communique

Free Methodist Church in Canada

The Free Methodist Church was founded in New York in 1860 and expanded in 1880. It is Methodist in doctrine, evangelical in ministry and emphasizes the teaching of holiness of life through faith in Jesus Christ.

The Free Methodist Church in Canada was incorporated in 1927 after the establishment of a Canadian Executive Board. In 1959 the Holiness Movement Church merged with the Free Methodist Church. Full autonomy for the Canadian church was realized in 1990 with the formation of a Canadian General Conference. Mississauga, Ontario, continues to be the location of the Canadian Headquarters.

The Free Methodist Church ministers in 70 countries through its World Ministries Center in Indianapolis, Indiana.

Headquarters

4315 Village Centre Ct., Mississauga, ON L4Z 1S2 Tel. (905)848-2600 Fax (905)848-2603

Media Contact, Dan Sheffield

E-mail ministrycentre@fmc-canada.org

Web site www.fmc-canada.org

Officers

Bishop, Rev. Keith Elford

Dir. of Admn. Ser., Norman Bull

Dir. Of Global and Intercultural Ministries, Rev. Dan Sheffield

Supt., Personnel, Rev. Alan Retzman

Supt., Growth Ministries, in transition

Periodicals

Mosaic

Free Will Baptists

As revival fires burned throughout New England in the mid- and late 1700s, Benjamin Randall proclaimed his doctrine of Free Will to large crowds of seekers. In due time, a number of Randall's converts moved to Nova Scotia. One such believer was Asa McGray, who was to become instrumental in the establishment of several Free Baptist churches. Local congregations were organized in New Brunswick. After several years of numerical and geographic gains, disagreements surfaced over the question of music, Sunday school, church offerings, salaried clergy and other issues. Adherents of the more progressive element decided to form their own fellowship. Led by George Orser, they became known as Free Christian Baptists.

The new group faithfully adhered to the truths and doctrines which embodied the theological basis of Free Will Baptists. Largely through Archibald Hatfield, contact was made with Free Will Baptists in the United States in the 1960s. The association was officially welcomed into the Free Will Baptist family in July 1981, by the National Association.

Headquarters

5233 Mt. View Rd., Antioch, TN 37013-2306 Tel. (615)731-6812 Fax (615)731-0771

Media Contact, Mod., Dwayne Broad, RR 3, Bath, NB E0J 1E0 Tel. (506)278-3771

Officers

Mod., Dwayne Broad

Promotional Officer, Dwayne Broad

General Church of the New Jerusalem

The Church of the New Jerusalem, also called the New Church, is a Christian church founded on the Bible and the writings of Emanuel Swedenborg (1688-1772). These writings were first brought to Ontario in 1835 by Christian Enslin.

Headquarters

c/o Olivet Church, 279 Burnhamthorpe Rd., Etobicoke, ON M9B 1Z6 Tel. (416)239-3054 Fax (416)239-4935

Media Contact, Exec. Vice-Pres., Rev. Michael D. Gladish

E-mail Mgladish@interlog.com

Web site www.newchurch.org

Officers

Pres., Rt. Rev. P. M. Buss, Bryn Athyn, PA 19009

Exec. Vice-Pres., Rev. Michael D. Gladish

Sec., Carolyn Bellinger, 110 Chapel Hill Dr., Kitchener, ON N2G 3W5

Treas., James Bellinger, 2 Shaver Court, Etobicoke, ON M9B 4P5

Greek Orthodox Metropolis of Toronto (Canada)

Greek Orthodox Christians in Canada are under the jurisdiction of the Ecumenical Patriarchate of Constantinople (Istanbul).

Headquarters

86 Overlea Blvd., Toronto, ON M4H 1C6 Tel. (416)429-5757 Fax (416)429-4588
Media Contact, Orthodox Way Committee
E-mail greekomt@on.aibn.com

Officers

Metropolitan Archbishop of the Metropolis of Toronto (Canada), His Eminence Metropolitan Archbishop Sotirios

Periodicals

Orthodox Way

Independent Assemblies of God International (Canada)

This fellowship of churches has been operating in Canada for over 58 years. It is a branch of the Pentecostal Church in Sweden. Each church within the fellowship is completely independent.

Headquarters

1211 Lancaster St., London, ON N5V 2L4 Tel. (519)451-1751 Fax (519)453-3258
Media Contact, Gen. Sec., Rev. Harry Wuerch
E-mail h.wuerch@rogers.com

Officers

Gen. Sec., Rev. Harry Wuerch, 1211 Lancaster St., London, ON N5V 2L4
Treas., Rev. David Ellyatt, 1795 Parkhurst Ave., London, ON N5V 2C4, E-mail david.ellyatt@odyssey.on.ca

Periodicals

The Mantle (published in March, July & October)

Independent Holiness Church

The former Holiness Movement of Canada merged with the Free Methodist Church in 1958. Some churches remained independent of this merger and they formed the Independent Holiness Church in 1960, in Kingston, Ontario. The doctrines are Methodist and Wesleyan. The General Conference is every three years.

Headquarters

Rev. R. E. Votary, 1564 John Quinn Rd., R.R.1, Greely, ON K4P 1J9 Tel. (613)821-2237
Media Contact, Gen. Sec., Dwayne Reaney, 5025 River Rd. RR #1, Manotick, ON K4M 1B2 Tel. (613)692-3237

Officers

Gen. Supt., Rev. R. E. Votary, 1564 John Quinn Rd., Greeley, ON K4P 1J9
Gen. Sec., Dwayne Reaney
Additional Officers, E. Brown, 104-610 Pesehudoff Cresc., Saskatoon, SK S7N 4H5; D. Wallace, 1456 John Quinn Rd., R#1, Greely, ON K4P 1J9

Periodicals

Gospel Tidings

The Italian Pentecostal Church of Canada

This body had its beginnings in Hamilton, Ontario, in 1912 when a few people of an Italian Presbyterian Church banded themselves together for prayer and received a Pentecostal experience of the baptism in the Holy Spirit. Since 1912, there has been a close association with the teachings and practices of the Pentecostal Assemblies of Canada.

The work spread to Toronto, then to Montreal, where it also flourished. In 1959, the church was incorporated in the province of Quebec. The early leaders of this body were the Rev. Luigi Ippolito and the Rev. Ferdinand Zaffuto. The churches carry on their ministry in both the English and Italian languages.

Headquarters

6724 Fabre St., Montreal, QC H2G 2Z6 Tel. (514)279-1100 Fax (514)279-1131
Media Contact, Gen. Sec., Rev. John DellaForesta, 12216 Pierre Baillargeon, Montreal, QC H1E 6R7 Tel. (514)494-6969 Fax (514)279-1131

Officers

Gen. Supt., Rev. Davidl Mortelliti, 6724 Fabre St., Montreal, QC H2G 2Z6 Tel. (514)279-1100 Fax (514)279-1131
Gen. Sec., Rev. John DellaForesta, 12216 Pierre Baillargeon, Montreal, QC H1E 6R7 Tel. (514)494-6969
Gen. Treas., Rev. David Quackenbush, 686 Ossington, Toronto ON M6G 3Y7, Tel. (416)532-3951 Fax (416)532-0267
Overseer, Rev. David DiStaulo, 5811 Maurice Duplessis, Montreal QC H1G 1Y2, Tel. (514)328-3131

Periodicals

Voce Evangelica-Evangel Voice

Jehovah's Witnesses

For a description of Jehovah's Witnesses see "Religious Bodies in United States" in this edition of the Yearbook.

Headquarters

25 Columbia Heights, Brooklyn, NY 11201-2483 Tel. (718)560-5600 Fax (718)560-8850
Canadian Branch Office, Box 4100, Halton Hills, ON L7G 4Y4 Tel. (888)301-4259
Media Contact, Office of Public Information, J. Richard Brown
Media Contact, Office of Public Information in Canada, Mark Ruge
Editorial Contact, Writing Department, James N. Pellechia

Lutheran Church-Canada

Lutheran Church-Canada was established in 1959 at Edmonton, Alberta, as a federation of Canadian districts of the Lutheran Church-

Missouri Synod; it was constituted in 1988 at Winnipeg, Manitoba, as an autonomous church.

The church confesses the Bible as both inspired and infallible, the only source and norm of doctrine and life and subscribes without reservation to the Lutheran Confessions as contained in the Book of Concord of 1580.

Headquarters

3074 Portage Ave., Winnipeg, MB R3K 0Y2 Tel. (204)895-3433 Fax (204)897-4319, E-mail info@lutheranchurch.ca

Media Contact, Dir. of Comm., Ian Adnams, communications@lutheranchurch.ca

Officers

Pres., Rev. Ralph Mayan, 3074 Portage Ave., Winnipeg, MB R3K 0Y2 Tel. (204)-895-3433, Fax (204)832-3018, E-mail president@ lutheran church.ca

Pres. Emeritus, Rev. Dr. Edwin Lehman, 686 Lee Ridge Road, Edmonton AB T6K 0P2 Tel. (780)462-9608, Fax (780)468-2172, E-mail edwinlehman@shaw.ca

Honorary Pres., Rev. Dr. Elroy Treit, 74-3180 East 58 Avenue, Vancouver BC V5S 3S8 Tel. (604)434-9700

Vice-Pres., Rev. James Fritsche, 1541 St. Mary's Road., Winnipeg, MB R2M 3V8 Tel. (204)256-5548, Fax (204)257-8542, E-mail jefritsche@shaw.ca

Vice-Pres., Rev. Robert C. Krestrick, 78 John St., W. Waterloo, ON N2L 1B8 Tel. (519) 745-5027 Fax (519)745-7165, E-mail rekrestick@ sympatico.ca

Vice-Pres., Rev. Nolan D. Astley, 2925-57A Lloydminster, AB T9V 1W5 Tel. (780)875-9797 Fax (780)875-9799, E-mail luthfrst@ telusplanet.net

Sec., Rev. Michael P. Dorn, 243209 Garden Rd., NE Calgary, AB T1X 1E1 Tel.(403)285-2288 Fax(403)285-2855, E-mail mdorn@princeofpeace.ca

Treas., Mr. Dwayne Cleave, 3074 Portage Avenue, Winnipeg, MB R3K 0Y2 Tel. (204)895-3433 Fax (204)897-4319, E-mail treasurer@lutheranchurch.ca

DISTRICT OFFICES

Alberta-British Columbia, Pres., Rev. D. Schiemann, 7100 Ada Blvd., Edmonton, AB T5B 4E4 Tel. (403)474-0063 Fax (403)477-9829, E-mail info@lccabc.ca

Central, Pres., Rev. T. Prachar, 1927 Grant Dr., Regina, SK S4S 4V6 Tel. (306)586-4434 Fax (306)586-0656, E-mail tprachar@accesscomm.ca

East, Pres., Rev. A. Maleske, 275 Lawrence Ave., Kitchener, ON N2M 1Y3 Tel. (519)578-6500 Fax (519)578-3369, E-mail lcced@aol.com

Periodicals

The Canadian Lutheran

Mennonite Church Canada

Mennonite Church Canada (formerly Conference of Mennonites in Canada) was founded in 1903 by 15 praire congregations. In the late 1990s it merged with the Mennonite Church to become Mennonite Church Canada.

The first Mennonites came to Canada in 1786, moving from Pennsylvania in Conestoga wagons. Over the next 150 years, more arrived by ship from Europe, in at least four successive waves.

Its members hold to traditional Christian beliefs, believer's baptism and congregational polity. They emphasize practical Christianity, opposition to war, service to others and personal ethics.

Some people who have joined the Canadian Mennonite body in recent years have arrived from Asia, from Africa, or from Latin and South America. Native brothers and sisters, whose people were here long before the first Conestoga wagons arrived, have added their voices to the mix.

Meanwhile, French-speaking and English-speaking Canadians from the wider community have enriched the Mennonite people. Together we are Christian believers moving into the future under the umbrella of the Mennonite Church Canada.

Mennonite Church Canada is affiliated with Mennonite Church U.S.A., whose offices are at Newton, Kansas and Elkhart, Indiana. (See, Mennonite Church USA description in the section "Religious Bodies in the United States").

The first annual sessions were held in July, 1903. Further immigration from Russia in the 1920s and 1940s increased the group which is now located in all provinces from New Brunswick to British Columbia. In recent years a variety of other ethnic groups, including native Canadians, have joined the conference. This conference is affiliated with Mennonite Church USA whose offices are at Newton, Kansas. (See, Mennonite Church USA description in the section "Religious Bodies in the United States").

Headquarters

600 Shaftesbury Blvd., Winnipeg, MB R3P 0M4 Tel. (204)888-6781 Fax (204)831-5675

Media Contact, Dan Dyck

E-mail ddyck@mennonitechurch.ca

Web site www.mennonitechurch.ca

Officers

Chpsn., Henry Krause

Gen. Sec., Dan Nighswander

Periodicals

Canadian Mennonite

North American Baptist Conference

Churches belonging to this conference emanated from German Baptist immigrants of more than a century ago. Although scattered across Canada and the U.S., they are bound together by a common heritage, a strong spiritual unity, a Bible-centered faith and a deep interest in missions.

Note, The details of general organization, officers, and periodicals of this body will be found in the North American Baptist Conference directory in the "Religious Bodies in the United States" section of this Yearbook.

Headquarters

1 S. 210 Summit Ave., Oakbrook Terrace, IL 60181 Tel. (630)495-2000 Fax (630)495-3301

Media Contact, Marilyn Schaer

Officers

Exec. Dir., Dr. Philip Yntema

Periodicals

N.A.B. Today

The Old Catholic Church of Canada

The church was founded in 1948 in Hamilton, Ontario. The first bishop was the Rt. Rev. George Davis. The Old Catholic Church of Canada accepts all the doctrines of the Eastern Orthodox Churches and, therefore, not papal infallibility or the Immaculate Conception. The ritual is Western (Latin Rite) and is in the vernacular language. Celibacy is optional.

Headquarters

2185 Sheridan Park Drive, Apt. 105, Mississauga, ON L5K 1C7 Tel. (905)855-3643

Media Contact, Bishop, The Right Rev. Pat Davies, Vicar General

Officers

Vicar General and Auxiliary Bishop, The Rt. Rev. A.C. Keating, PhD., 5066 Forest Grove Crest, Burlington, ON L7L GG6 Tel. (905)681-9983

Old Order Amish Church

This is the most conservative branch of the Mennonite Church and direct descendants of Swiss Brethren (Anabaptists) who emerged from the Reformation in Switzerland in 1525. The Amish, followers of Bishop Jacob Ammann, became a distinct group in 1693. They began migrating to North America about 1736; all of them still reside in the United States or Canada. They first migrated to Ontario in 1823 directly from Bavaria, Germany and later from Pennsylvania and Alsace-Lorraine. Since 1953 more Amish have migrated to Ontario from Ohio, Indiana and Iowa.

In 2003 there were 27 congregations in Ontario, each being autonomous. No membership figures are kept by this group, and there is no central headquarters. Each congregation is served by a bishop, two ministers and a deacon, all of whom are chosen from among the male members by lot for life.

CORRESPONDENT

Pathway Publishers, David Luthy, Rt. 4, Aylmer, ON N5H 2R3

Periodicals

Blackboard Bulletin; Herold der Wahreit; The Budget; The Diary; Die Botschaft; Family Life; Young Companion

Open Bible Faith Fellowship of Canada

This is an evangelical, full gospel fellowship of churches and ministries emphasizing evangelism, missions and the local church for success in the present harvest of souls. OBFF was chartered January 7, 1982.

Headquarters

Niagara Celebration Church, P.O. Box 31020, St. Catharines, ON L2N 7S5 Tel. (905)646-0970

Officers

Sec.-Treas., George Woodward

Dir., Jim Buslon

Dir., Lindsey Burt

Dir., Mike Welch

Dir., Christer Ihreborg

Orthodox Church in America (Archdiocese of Canada)

The Archdiocese of Canada of the Orthodox Church in America was established in 1916. First organized by St. Tikhon, martyr Patriarch of Moscow, previously Archbishop of North America, it is part of the Russian Metropolia and its successor, the autocephalous Orthodox Church in America.

The Archdiocesan Council meets twice yearly, the General Assembly of the Archdiocese takes place every three years. The Archdiocese is also known as "Orthodox Church in Canada."

Headquarters

P.O. Box 179, Spencerville, ON K1S 2R6 Tel. (613)925-5226, E-mail rhutcheon@hotmail.com

Officers

Bishop of Ottawa & Canada, The Rt. Rev. Seraphim

Chancellor, V. Rev. Dennis Pinach, 9930-167 Street, Edmonton, AB T5P 4W7

Treas., Nikita Lopoukhine, 55 Clarey Ave., Ottawa, ON K1S 2R6

Sec., Protodeacon Cyprian Hutcheon, P.O. Box 179, Spencerville, ON K1S 2R6

ARCHDIOCESAN COUNCIL

Clergy Members, Rev. Lawrence Farley; Rev. R.S. Kennaugh; Rev. Larry Reinheimer; Igumen Irenee Rochon; Rev. John Jillions; Rev. Ovest Olekshy

Lay Members, David Grier; John Hadjinicolaou;

Mother Sophia (Zion); David Rystephanuk; Rod Tkachuk; Sandra Ellis; Alexei Vassiouchkine
Ex Officio, Chancellor; Treas.; Sec.

Periodicals

Canadian Orthodox Messenger

Patriarchal Parishes of the Russian Orthodox Church in Canada

This is the diocese of Canada of the former Exarchate of North and South America of the Russian Orthodox Church. It was originally founded in 1897 by the Russian Orthodox Archdiocese in North America.

Headquarters

St. Barbara's Russian Orthodox Cathedral, 10105 96th St., Edmonton, AB T5H 2G3
Media Contact, Roman Lopushinsky, 11620 134 Ave., Edmonton, AB T5E 1K9 Tel./Fax (780)455-6314

Officers

Admn., Archbishop of Kashira, Most Rev. Mark, 10812-108 St., Edmonton, AB T5H 3A6 Tel. (780)420-9945

The Pentecostal Assemblies of Canada

This body is incorporated under the Dominion Charter of 1919 and is also recognized in the Province of Quebec as an ecclesiastical corporation. Its beginnings are to be found in the revivals at the turn of the century, and most of the first Canadian Pentecostal leaders came from a religious background rooted in the Holiness movements.

The original incorporation of 1919 was implemented among churches of eastern Canada only. In the same year, a conference was called in Moose Jaw, Saskatchewan, to which the late Rev. J. M. Welch, general superintendent of the then-organized Assemblies of God in the U.S., was invited. The churches of Manitoba and Saskatchewan were organized as the Western District Council of the Assemblies of God. They were joined later by Alberta and British Columbia. In 1921, a conference was held in Montreal, to which the general chairman of the Assemblies of God was invited. Eastern Canada also became a district of the Assemblies of God, joining Eastern and Western Canada as two districts in a single organizational union.

In 1920, at Kitchener, Ontario, eastern and western churches agreed to dissolve the Canadian District of the Assemblies of God and unite under the name the Pentecostal Assemblies of Canada.

Today the Pentecostal Assemblies of Canada operates throughout the nation and in about 30 countries around the world. Religious services are conducted in more than 25 different languages in the 1,100 local churches in Canada. Members and adherents number about 230,000. The number of local churches includes approximately 100 Native congregations.

Headquarters

2450 Milltower Court, Mississauga, ON L5N 5Z6, Tel. (905)542-7400 Fax (905)542-7313

Officers

Gen. Supt., Rev. William D. Morrow
Asst. Supt., for Ministerial Services, Rev. David E. Hazzard
Asst. Supt. for Financial Resources, Rev. David Ball

DISTRICT SUPERINTENDENTS

British Columbia, Rev. D.R. Wells, 20411 Douglas Crescent, Langley, BC V3S 4B6 Tel. (604)533-2232 Fax (604)533-5405
Alberta, Rev. Lorne D. McAlister, 10585-111 St., #101, Edmonton, AB T5H 3E8 Tel. (403)426-0084 Fax (403)420-1318
Saskatchewan, Rev. J. I. Guskjolen, 3488 Fairlight Dr., Saskatoon, SK S7M 3Z4 Tel. (306)683-4646 Fax (306)683-3699
Manitoba, Rev. R.W. Pierce, 187 Henlow Bay, Winnipeg, MB R3Y 1G4 Tel. (204)940-1000 Fax (204)940-1009
Western Ontario, Rev. D.A Shepherd, 3214 S. Service Rd., Burlington, ON L7N 3J2 Tel. (905)637-5566 Fax (905)637-7558
Eastern Ontario and Quebec, Rev. R. T. Hilsden, Box 337, Cobury, ON K9A 4K8 Tel. (905)373-7374 Fax (905)373-1911
Quebec, Rev. G.C. Connors, 911, Boul Roland-Therrien, Longueuil, QC JAJ 4L3, Tel (4005) 442-2732 Fax (405) 442-3818
Maritime Provinces, Rev. Douglas Moore, Box 1184, Truro, NS B2N 5H1 Tel. (902)895-4212 Fax (902)897-0705

BRANCH CONFERENCES

Slavic Conferences, Eastern District, Rev. A. Muravski, 445 Stevenson Rd., Oshawa, ON L1J 5N8 Tel (905) 576-3584; Western District, Rev. Michael Brandebura, 4108-134 Ave., Edmonton, AB T5A 3M2 Tel (780) 743-2410 Fax (780) 473-2410
Finnish Conference, Rev. E. Ahonen, 1920 Argyle Dr., Vancouver, BC V5P 2A8 Tel (604)321-0555 Fax (604)321-0555

Periodicals

Testimony (the official magazine of the Pentecostal Assemblies of Canada); *Enrich* (national leadership magazine); *Contact* (magazine for those 50 years +); *HonorBound* (magazine for men)

The Pentecostal Assemblies of Newfoundland

This body began in 1911 and held its first meetings at Bethesda Mission at St. John's. It was incorporated in 1925 as The Bethesda Pentecostal Assemblies of Newfoundland and changed its name in 1930 to The Pentecostal Assemblies of Newfoundland.

Headquarters

57 Thorburn Rd., Box 8895, Stn. "A," St. John's, NF A1B 3T2 Tel. (709)753-6314 Fax (709)753-4945

Media Contact, Gen. Sup't., A. Earl Batstone, 57 Thorburn Rd., Box 8895, Stn. "A," St. John's, NF A1B 3T2

E-mail paon@paon.nf.ca

GENERAL EXECUTIVE OFFICERS

Gen. Sup't. A. Earl Batstone, 57 Thorburn Rd., Box 8895, Stn. "A," St. John's, NF A1B 3T2

Gen. Sec.-Treas., Clarence Buckle, 57 Thorburn Rd., Box 8895, Stn. "A," St. John's, NF A1B 3T2

Ex. Dir. of Home Missions, Barry Q. Grimes, 57 Thorburn Rd., Box 8895, Stn. "A," St. John's, NF A1B 3T2

Ex. Dir. of Ch. Ministries, Robert H. Dewling, 57 Thorburn Rd., Box 8895, Stn. "A," St. John's, NF A1B 3T2

PROVINCIAL DIRECTORS

Sunday School Ministries, Alvin F. Peddle, Box 40, Baytona, NF A0G 2J0

Children's Ministries, Lorinda R. Moulton, Box 56, New Harbour, NF A0B 2P0

Women's Ministries, Nancy L. Hunter, 12 Harp Place, Paradise, NF A1L 1G9

Men's Ministries, Norman C. Joy, 2 Firgreen Ave., Mount Pearl, NF A1N 1T7

Youth Ministries, B. Dean Brenton, Box 21100, St. John's, NF A1B 3L5

Mature Adult Ministries, Clayton Rice, 29 Diana Rd., St. John's, NF A1B 1H7

Family Ministries, Eva M. Winsor, 26 Ireland Dr., Grand Falls-Windsor, NF A2A 2S6

AUXILLIARY SERVICES

Chaplain for Institutions, Roy A. Burden, 293 Frecker Dr., St. John's, NF A1E 5T8

Pentecostal Senior Citizens Home Administrator, Beverley Bellefleur, Box 130, Clarke's Beach, NF A0A 1W0

Evergreen Manor, Summerford, NF A0G 4E0

Pastoral Enrichment Ministries, Gary D. & Eva M. Winsor, 26 Ireland Dr., Grand Falls-Windsor, NF A2A 2S6

Chaplain, Memorial University of Newfoundland, Gregory R. Dewling, Memorial University of Newfoundland, Box 102, St. John's, NF A1C 5S7

Emmanuel Convention Centre Administrator, Ronald M. Dicks, Box 1558, Lewisporte, NF A0G 3A0

World Missions Promotions, A. Scott Hunter, 12 Harp Place, Paradise, NF A1L 1G9

Managing Editor, *Good Tidings*, Burton K. Janes, 57 Thornburn Rd., Box 8895, Stn. "A", St. John's, NF A1B 3T2

Periodicals

Good Tidings

Presbyterian Church in America (Canadian Section)

Canadian congregations of the Reformed Presbyterian Church, Evangelical Synod, became a part of the Presbyterian Church in America when the RPCES joined PCA in June 1982. Some of the churches were in predecessor bodies of the RPCES, which was the product of a 1965 merger of the Reformed Presbyterian Church in North America, General Synod and the Evangelical Presbyterian Church. Others came into existence later as a part of the home missions work of RPCES. Congregations are located in seven provinces, and the PCA is continuing church extension work in Canada. The denomination is committed to world evangelization and to a continuation of historic Presbyterianism. Its officers are required to subscribe to the Reformed faith as set forth in the Westminster Confession of Faith and Catechisms.

Headquarters

Media Contact, Dr. Dominic Aquila, Editor PCANet.org, New Geneva Seminary, 3622 East Galley Rd., Colorado Springs, CO, 80909 Tel. (719)573-5395 Fax (719)573-5398, E-mail daquila6@aol.com

Periodicals

Equip for Ministry; Multiply; Network

Presbyterian Church in Canada

This is the nonconcurring portion of the Presbyterian Church in Canada that did not become a part of the United Church of Canada in 1925.

Headquarters

50 Wynford Dr., Toronto, ON M3C 1J7 Tel. (416)441-1111 Fax (416)441-2825

Media Contact, Principal Clk., Rev. Stephen Kendall or Assoc. Sec. for Resource Production & Comm., Mr. Keith Knight

Web site www.presbyterian.ca

Officers

Principal Clk., Rev. Stephen Kendall

Periodicals

Channels; The Presbyterian Message; Presbyterian Record; Glad Tidings; La Vie Chrétienne

Reformed Church in Canada

The Canadian region of the Reformed Church in America was organized under the General Synod of the Reformed Church in America. The RCA in Canada has 41 churches which include three classes (lower assemblies). The Reformed churches in Canada are member congregations of the Reformed Church in America and the Regional Synod of Canada (one of eight RCA regional synods established by its General

Synod) and three classes, Ontario, Canadian Prairies and British Columbia.

The first ordained minister, Domine Jonas Micahelius, arrive in New Amsterdam from The Netherlands in 1628. Throughout the colonial period, the Reformed Church lived under the authority of the Classis of Amsterdam. Its churches were clustered in New York and New Jersey. Under the leadership of Rev. John Livingston, it became a denomination independent of the authority of the Classis of Amsterdam in 1776. Its geographical base was broadened in the 19th century by the immigration of Reformed Dutch and German settlers in the midwestern United States. The Reformed Church now spans the United States and Canada. The Reformed Church in America accepts as its standards of faith the Heidelberg Catechism, Belgic Confession and Canons of Dort. It has a rich heritage of world mission activity. It claims to be loyal to Reformed tradition which emphasizes obedience to God in all aspects of life.

Although the Reformed Church in America has worked in close cooperation with other churches, it has never entered into merger with any other denomination. It is a member of the World Alliance of Reformed Churches, the World Council of Churches and the National Council of the Churches of Christ in the United States of America. In 1998 it also entered into a relationship of full communion with the Evangelical Lutheran Church in America, Presbyterian Church (U.S.A.), and the United Church of Christ by way of the Formula of Agreement.

Headquarters

475 Riverside Dr., 18th Floor, New York, NY 10115 Tel. (212)870-3243 Fax (212)870-2499

Media Contact, Comm. Officer, Phil Tanis, 4500 60th St., SE, Grand Rapids, MI 49512 Tel. (616)698-7071 Fax (616)698-6606

Web site www.rca.org

OFFICERS AND STAFF OF GENERAL SYNOD

Regional Synod of Canada, Synod Executive, Mr. Fred Algera, 1985 Beke Rd. RR#4, Cambridge, ON N1R 5S5

Pres., The Rev. Steven Vander Molen, 475 Riverside Dr., 18th Floor, New York, NY 10115

Gen. Synod Council Moderator, The Rev. David Schutt, 475 Riverside Dr., 18th Floor, New York, NY 10115

Gen. Sec., The Rev. Wesley Granberg-Michaelson, 475 Riverside Dr., 18th Floor, New York, NY 10115; 4500 60th St. S.E., Grand Rapids, MI 49512

Operations and Support, Dir. & Asst. Sec., The Rev. Kenneth Bradsell

Office for Ministry Services, Dir., The Rev. Dr. Gregg Mast

Congregational Servcies-Evangelism & Church Development Services, Dir., The Rev. Richard Welscott

Finance Services, Treas., Ms. Susan Converse

The Reformed Episcopal Church of Canada

The Reformed Episcopal Church is a separate entity. It was established in Canada by an act of incorporation given royal assent on June 2, 1886. It maintains the founding principles of episcopacy (in historic succession from the apostles), Anglican liturgy and Reformed doctrine and evangelical zeal. In practice it continues to recognize the validity of certain nonepiscopal orders of evangelical ministry. The Church has reunited with the Reformed Episcopal Church and is now composed of two Dioceses in this body—the Diocese of Central and Eastern Canada and the Diocese of Western Canada and Alaska.

Headquarters

Box 2532, New Liskeard, ON P0J 1P0 Tel. (705)647-4565 Fax (705)647-4565

Media Contact, Pres., Rt. Rev. Michael Fedechko, M. Div., D.D.

E-mail fed@nt.net

Web site www.reformedepiscopal.com

Officers

Pres., Rt. Rev. Michael Fedechko, 320 Armstrong St., New Liskeard, ON P0J 1P0

Sec., Janet Dividson, 224 Haliburton, New Liskeard, ON P0J 1P0

BISHOPS

Diocese of Central & Eastern Canada, Rt. Rev. Michael Fedechko, 320 Armstrong St., New Liskeard, ON P0J 1P0 Tel. (705)647-4565 Fax (705)647-4565

Diocese of Western Canada & Alaska, Rt. Rev. Charles W. Dorrington, 54 Blanchard St., Victoria, BC V8X 4R1 Tel. (604)744-5014 Fax (604)388-5891

Periodicals

The Messenger

Reinland Mennonite Church

This group was founded in 1958 when 10 ministers and approximately 600 members separated from the Sommerfelder Mennonite Church. In 1968, four ministers and about 200 members migrated to Bolivia.The church has work in five communities in Manitoba and one in Ontario

Headquarters

Bishop William H. Friesen, P.O. Box 96, Rosenfeld, MB R0G 1X0 Tel. (204)324-6339

Media Contact, Deacon, Henry Wiebe, Box 2587, Winkler, MB R6W 4C3 Tel. (204)325-8487

The Roman Catholic Church in Canada

The largest single body of Christians in Canada, the Roman Catholic Church is under the spiritual leadership of His Holiness the Pope. Catholicism in Canada dates back to 1534, when the first Mass was celebrated on the Gaspé Peninsula on July 7, by a priest accompanying Jacques Cartier. Catholicism had been implanted earlier by fishermen and sailors from Europe. Priests came to Acadia as early as 1604. Traces of a regular colony go back to 1608 when Champlain settled in Quebec City. The Récollets (1615), followed by the Jesuits (1625) and the Sulpicians (1657), began the missions among the native population. The first official Roman document relative to the Canadian missions dates from March 20, 1618. Bishop François de Montmorency-Laval, the first bishop, arrived in Quebec in 1659. The church developed in the East, but not until 1818 did systematic missionary work begin in western Canada.

In the latter 1700s, English-speaking Roman Catholics, mainly from Ireland and Scotland, began to arrive in Canada's Atlantic provinces. After 1815 Irish Catholics settled in large numbers in what is now Ontario. The Irish potato famine of 1847 greatly increased that population in all parts of eastern Canada.

By the 1850s the Catholic Church in both English and French-speaking Canada had begun to erect new dioceses and found many religious communities. These communities did educational, medical and charitable work among their own people as well as among Canada's native peoples. By the 1890s large numbers of non-English and non-French-speaking Catholics had settled in Canada, especially in the Western provinces. In the 20th century the pastoral horizons have continued to expand to meet the needs of what has now become a very multicultural church.

The Canadian Conference of Catholic Bishops is the national association of the Latin and Eastern Catholic Bishops of Canada. Its main offices are in Ottawa, Ontario.

CANADIAN ORGANIZATION

Conférence des évêques catholiques du Canada - Canadian Conference of Catholic Bishops, 2500 Don Reid Drive, Ottawa, ON K1H 2J2 Tel. (613)241-9461 Fax (613)241-9048, E-mail cecc@cccb.ca, Web site www.cccb.ca

Media Contact, M. Sylvain Salvas, salvas@ cecc.ca (French Sector); Deacon William Kokesch, Kokesch@cccb.ca (English Sector) Tel. (613)241-7538 or (800)769-1147, E-mail publi@cccb.ca

GENERAL SECRETARIAT OF THE CANADIAN CONFERENCE OF CATHOLIC BISHOPS

Gen. Sec., Msgr. Mario Paquette, P.H.

Assoc. Gen. Sec., M. Benoît Bariteau (French Sector); Mr. Bede Hubbard (English Sector)

EXECUTIVE COMMITTEE

Pres., Most Rev. Brendan M. O'Brien

Vice-Pres., Most Rev. André Gaumond

Co-Treas., Most Rev. Pierre Morissette and Most Rev. V. James Weisgerber

EPISCOPAL COMMISSIONS – NATIONAL LEVEL

Social Affairs, Most Rev. Blaise Morand

Canon Law, Most Rev. James Wingle

Relations with Assoc. of Clergy, Consecrated Life & Laity, Most Rev. André Richard, C.S.C.

Evangelization of Peoples, Most Rev. Vincent Cadieux, O.M.I.

Christian Unity, Religious Relations with the Jews, and Interfaith Dialogue, Most Rev. François Lapierre, P.M.E.

Theology, Most Rev. Eugène Cooney

EPISCOPAL COMMISSIONS—SECTOR LEVEL

Communications sociales, Most Rev. Martin Veillette

Social Communication, Most Rev. Frederick Henry

Éducation chrétienne, Most Rev. André Vallée, P.M.E

Christian Education, Most Rev. Richard Grecco

Liturgie, Most Rev. Dorylas Moreau

Liturgy, Most Rev. Gerald Wiesner, O.M.I.

OFFICES

Affaires sociales-Social Affairs, Dir., Mr. Joe Gunn

Communications, Dir., M. Sylvain Salvas, Dir. (French Sector); Deacon William Kokesch (English Sector)

Droit canonique—inter-rites-Canon Law—Inter-rite, Msgr. Mario Paquette, P.H. Secr.

Éditions-Publications, Dir., Dr. Vicki Bennett

Éducation chrétienne,

Évangelisation des peuples-Evangelization of Peoples,

Liturgie-Liturgy, Dir., M. Gaëtan Baillargeon (French Sector); Rev. Camille Jacques, O.S.M. (English Sector)

National Office of Religious Education, Dir., Ms. Joanne Chafe

Christian Unity, Religious Relations with the Jews, and Interfaith Dialogue: Dir., Sr. Mary Jean Goulet, C.S.C.

Relations avec les associations du clergé, de la vie conseacrée et du laïcat-Relations with Association of Clergy, Consecrated Life and Laity, Sec.: Ms. Jennifer Leddy

Théologie-Theology, Dir., P. Richard Côté, O.M.I.

Tribunal d'appel du Canada—The Canadian Appeal Tribunal, Msgr. Alan McCormack, P.H., Vicaire judiciaire-Judicial Vicar

REGIONAL EPISCOPAL ASSEMBLIES

Atlantic Episcopal Assembly—Assemblée des évêques de l'Atlantique, Pres., Most Rev. Raymond Lahey; Vice Pres., Most Rev. Terrence Prendergast, S.J. and Most Francois Thibodeau, C.J.M.; Sec.-Treas., Léo Grégoire,

I.V. Dei; Tel. (506)735-5578 Fax (506)735-4271

Assemblée des évêques du Québec, Pres., Most Rev. Raymond St-Gelais C.S.C.; Vice Prés., Most Rev. Gilles Cazabon, O.M.I.; Sec. Gen., M. Pierre Gaudette; Tel. (514)274-4323 Fax (514)274-4383

Ontario Conference of Catholic Bishops—Conférence des évêques catholiques de l'Ontario, Pres., Most Rev. Richard Smith; Vice Pres., Most Rev. Richard Grecco; Sec.-Treas., Mr. Thomas J. Reilly; Tel. (416)923-1423 Fax (416)923-1509

Western Catholic Conference-Conférence Catholique de L'Ouest, Pres., Most Rev. V. James Weisgerber; Vice Pres., Most Rev. Frederick B. Henry; Sec.-Treas., Rt. Rev. Peter Novecosky, O.S.B.; Tel. (306)682-1788 Fax (306)682-1766

Militaryy Ordinariate-Ordinariat Militaire, Bishop, Most Rev. Donald J. Theriault, Military Ordinariate of Canada, Canadian Forces Support Unit (Ottawa), Uplands Site Building 469, Ottawa, ON K1A 0K2 Tel. (613)990-7824 Fax (613)991-1056

Canadian Religious Conference, Sec. Gen., Sr. Margaret Toner, SCIC. 4135, rue de Rouen, Montréal, Québec H1V 1G5 Tel. (514)259-0856 Fax (514)259-0857

Organisme catholizque pour la vie et la famille/Catholic Organization for Life and Family, Co-Dir., Ms. Michèle Boulva (French Sector); Ms. Jennifer Leddy (English Sector); Tel. (613)241-9461 Fax (613)241-9048, E-mail ocvfcolf@cccb.ca

Periodicals

National Bulletin on Liturgy; Foi et Culture (Bulletin natl. de liturgie); *Caravan*

Romanian Orthodox Church in America (Canadian Parishes)

The first Romanian Orthodox immigrants in Canada called for Orthodox priests from their native country of Romania. Between 1902 and 1914, they organized the first Romanian parish communities and built Orthodox churches in different cities and farming regions of western Canada (Alberta, Saskatchewan, Manitoba) as well as in the eastern part (Ontario and Quebec).

In 1929, the Romanian Orthodox parishes from Canada joined with those of the United States in a Congress held in Detroit, Michigan, and asked the Holy Synod of the Romanian Orthodox Church of Romania to establish a Romanian Orthodox Missionary Episcopate in America. The first Bishop, Policarp (Morushca), was elected and consecrated by the Holy Synod of the Romanian Orthodox Church and came to the United States in 1935. He established his headquarters in Detroit, with jurisdiction over all the Romanian Orthodox parishes in the United States and Canada.

In 1950, the Romanian Orthodox Church in America (i.e. the Romanian Orthodox Missionary Episcopate in America) was granted administrative autonomy by the Holy Synod of the Romanian Orthodox Church of Romania, and only doctrinal and canonical ties remain with this latter body.

In 1974 the Holy Synod of the Romanian Orthodox Church of Romania recognized and approved the elevation of the Episcopate to the rank of the Romanian Orthodox Archdiocese in America and Canada and completed the administrative autonomy.

Headquarters

Romanian Orthodox Archdiocese in America and Canada, 5410 N. Newland Ave., Chicago, IL 60656 USA

Officers

Archbishop, Most Rev. Nicolae Condrea,5410 N. Newland Ave., Chicago, IL 60656 Tel. (773)774-1677 Fax (773)774-1805, E-mail archnicolee@aol.com

Vicar, V. Rev. Fr. Ioan Ionita, 17527 Wenthworth Ave., Lansing, IL 60438 Tel. (708)889-9768

Secretary, V. Rev. Fr. Nicholas Apostola, 44 Midland St. Worchester, MA 01602-4217 Tel. (508)845-0088 Fax (508)752-8180

Periodicals

Credinte —The Faith

The Romanian Orthodox Episcopate of America (Jackson, MI)

This body of Eastern Orthodox Christians of Romanian descent is part of the Autocephalous Orthodox Church in America. For complete description and listing of officers, please see chapter 3, "Religious Bodies in the United States."

Headquarters

2535 Grey Tower Rd., Jackson, MI 49201 Tel. (517)522-4800

Mailing Address, P.O. Box 309, Grass Lake, MI 49240-0309

Media Contact, Ed.-Sec., Rev. Archdeacon David Oancea, P.O. Box 185, Grass Lake, MI 49240-0185 Tel. (517)522-3656

E-mail chancery@roea.org

Web site www.roea.org

Officers

Ruling Hierarch, Most. Rev. Archbishop Nathaniel Popp

Dean of All Canada, Very Rev. Daniel Nenson, 2855 Helmsing St., Regina, SK S4V 0W7 Tel. (306)761-2379

Periodicals

Solia - The Herald; Good News- Buna Vestire (in Canada only)

The Salvation Army in Canada

The Salvation Army, an evangelical branch of the Christian Church, is an international movement founded in 1865 in London, England. The ministry of Salvationists, consisting of clergy (officers) and laity, comes from a commitment to Jesus Christ and is revealed in practical service, regardless of race, color, creed, sex or age.

The goals of The Salvation Army are to preach the gospel, disseminate Christian truths, instill Christian values, enrich family life and improve the quality of all life.

To attain these goals, The Salvation Army operates local congregations, provides counseling, supplies basic human needs and undertakes spiritual and moral rehabilitation of any needy people who come within its influence.

A quasi-military system of government was set up in 1878, by General William Booth, founder (1829–1912). Converts from England started Salvation Army work in London, Ontario, in 1882. Two years later, Canada was recognized as a Territorial Command, and since 1933 it has included Bermuda. An act to incorporate the Governing Council of The Salvation Army in Canada received royal assent on May 19, 1909.

Headquarters

2 Overlea Blvd., Toronto, ON M4H 1P4 Tel. (416) 425-2111
Media Contact, Major Len Miller, Tel. (416)425-6153 Fax (416)425-6157
E-mail len-miller@can.salvationarmy.org
Web site www.salvationarmy.ca

Officers

Territorial Commander, Commissioner Bill Luttrell
Territorial Pres., Women's Organizations, Commissioner Gwen Lutterell
Chief Sec., Col. Bob Redhead
Sec. for Personnel, Lt. Col. Wayne Pritchett
Bus. Adm. Sec., Lt. Col. Susan McMillan
Fin. Sec., Major Paul Goodyear
Program Sec., Lt. Col. David Luginbuhl
Public Rel., Major Len Millar
Property Sec., Major Neil Watt

Periodicals

The War Cry; Faith & Friends; En Avant!; The Edge; Horizons

Serbian Orthodox Church in the U.S.A. and Canada, Diocese of Canada

The Serbian Orthodox Church is an organic part of the Eastern Orthodox Church. As a local church it received its autocephaly from Constantinople in A.D. 1219. The Patriarchal seat of the church today is in Belgrade, Yugoslavia. In 1921, a Serbian Orthodox Diocese in the United States of America and Canada was organized. In 1963, it was reorganized into three dioceses, and in 1983 a fourth diocese was created for the Canadian part of the church. The Serbian Orthodox Church is in absolute doctrinal unity with all other local Orthodox Churches.

Headquarters

7470 McNiven Rd., RR 3, Campbellville, ON L0P 1B0 Tel. (905)878-0043 Fax (905)878-1909
Media Contact, Rt. Rev. Georgije
E-mail vladika@istocnik.com
Web site www. istocnik.com

Officers

Serbian Orthodox Bishop of Canada, Rt. Rev. Georgije
Dean of Western Deanery, V. Rev. Mirko Malinovic, 924 12th Ave., Regina, SK S4N 0K7 Tel. (306)352-2917
Dean of Eastern Deanery, V. Rev. Zivorad Subotic, 351 Mellville Ave., Westmount, QC H3Z 2Y7 Tel.-Fax (514)931-6664

Periodicals

Istocnik, Herald of the Serbian Orthodox Church— Canadian Diocese

Seventh-day Adventist Church in Canada

The Seventh-day Adventist Church in Canada is part of the worldwide Seventh-day Adventist Church with headquarters in Silver Spring, Maryland (See "Religious Bodies in the United States" section of this Yearbook for a fuller description.) The Seventh-day Adventist Church in Canada was organized in 1901 and reorganized in 1932.

Headquarters

1148 King Street East, Oshawa, ON L1H 1H8 Tel. (905)433-0011 Fax (905)433-0982
Media Contact, Nilton D. Amorim

Officers

Pres., Daniel R. Jackson
Sec., Nilton D. Amorim
Treas., Gerald M. Northam

DEPARTMENTS

Under Treas., Brent Burdick
Asst. Treas., Joyce Jones
Computer Services, Brian Ford
Education, Mike Lekic
Family Ministries, Celest Corkum, Ken Corkum
Sabbath School and Personal Ministries, Gary Hodder
Trust Services, Brent Burdick
ADRA Canada, Oliver Lofton-Brook

Periodicals

Canadian Adventist Messenger

Syriac Orthodox Church of Antioch

The Syriac Orthodox Church professes the faith of the first three ecumenical councils of

Nicaea, Constantinople and Ephesus and numbers faithful in the Middle East, India, the Americas, Europe and Australia. It traces its origin to the Patriarchate established in Antioch by St. Peter the Apostle and is under the supreme ecclesiastical jurisdiction of His Holiness the Syrian Orthodox Patriarch of Antioch and All the East, now residing in Damascus, Syria.

The Archdiocese of the Syrian Orthodox Church in the U.S. and Canada was formally established in 1957. In 1995, the Archdiocese of North America was divided into three separate Patriarchal Vicariates, including one for Canada. The first Syrian Orthodox faithful came to Canada in the 1890s and formed the first Canadian parish in Sherbrooke, Quebec. Today five official parishes of the Archdiocese exist in Canada—two in Quebec and three in Ontario. There is also an official mission congregation in Calgary, Alberta and Ottawa, Ontario.

Headquarters

Archdiocese of Canada, The New Archdiocesan Centre, 4375 Henri-Bourassa Ouest, St.-Laurent, Quebec H4L 1A5, Canada Tel. (514) 334-6993 Fax (514)334-8233

Officers

Archbishop Mor Timotheos Aphrem Aboodi

Ukrainian Orthodox Church of Canada

Toward the end of the 19th century many Ukrainian immigrants settled in Canada. In 1918, a group of these pioneers established the Ukrainian Orthodox Church of Canada (UOCC), today the largest Ukrainian Orthodox Church beyond the borders of Ukraine. In 1990, the UOCC entered into a eucharistic union with the Ecumenical Patriarchate at Constantinople (Istanbul).

Headquarters

Ukrainian Orthodox Church of Canada, Office of the Consistory, 9 St. Johns Ave., Winnipeg, MB R2W 1G8 Tel. (204)586-3093 Fax (204)582-5241

Media Contacts, Rev. Fr. Andrew Jarmus, 9 St. John's Ave., Winnipeg, MB R2W 1G8 Tel. (204)586-3093 Fax (204)582-5241; Ms. M. Zurek, 9 St. Johns Ave., Winnipeg, MB R2W 1G8 Tel. (204)586-3093 Fax (204)582-5241

E-mail consistory@uocc.ca

Web site www. uocc.ca

Officers

Primate, Most Rev. Metropolitan Wasyly Fedak, 9 St. Johns Ave., Winnipeg, MB R2W 1G8 Tel. (204)586-3093 Fax (204)582-5241

Chancellor, Rt. Rev. Fr. William Makarenko

Periodicals

Visnyk-The Herald-Le Messager (newspaper); *Ridna Nyva* (almanac-annual)

Union d'Eglises Baptistes Françaises au Canada

Baptist churches in French Canada first came into being through the labors of two missionaries from Switzerland, Rev. Louis Roussy and Mme. Henriette Feller, who arrived in Canada in 1835. The earliest church was organized in Grande Ligne (now St.-Blaise), Quebec in 1838.

By 1900 there were 7 churches in the province of Quebec and 13 French-language Baptist churches in the New England states. The leadership was totally French Canadian.

By 1960, the process of Americanization had caused the disappearance of the French Baptist churches. During the 1960s, Quebec as a society, began rapidly changing in all its facets, education, politics, social values and structures. Mission, evangelism and church growth once again flourished. In 1969, in response to the new conditions, the Grande Ligne Mission passed control of its work to the newly formed Union of French Baptist Churches in Canada, which then included 8 churches. By 2003 the French Canadian Baptist movement had grown to include 32 congregations present in three provinces: Quebec, New Brunswick, and Ontario.

The Union d'Églises Baptistes Françaises au Canada is a member body of the Canadian Baptist Ministries and thus is affiliated with the Baptist World Alliance.

Headquarters

2285 Avenue Papineau, Montreal, QC H2K 4J5 Tel. (514)526-6643 Fax (514)526-9269

Media Contact, Gen. Sec., Rev. Roland Grimard

Officers

Sec. Gen., Rev. Roland Grimard

Periodicals

www.UnionBaptiste.com (Internet)

Union of Spiritual Communities of Christ (Orthodox Doukhobors in Canada)

The Doukhobors are Canadians of Russian origin living primarily in the western provinces of Canada, but their beginnings in Russia are unknown. The name "Doukhobors," or "Spirit Wrestlers," was given them in derision by the Russian Orthodox clergy in Russia as far back as 1785. The Doukhobors were persecuted by the church for rejecting Orthodoxy, and following the counsel of their leader, Peter V. Verigin, earned the wrath of the Tsarist government by destroying all of their weapons and adopting pacifism in 1895. In 1899 the Tsarist government allowed 8,000 Doukhobors to leave Russia in response to an international uproar over their persecution by the church and state. They made their way to Canada with the assistance of Count Leo Tolstoy, who saw in these people the living embodiment of his philosophy, the Religious

Society of Friends, commonly known as Quakers and other people of good will. Originally settled in Saskatchewan, by 1911 the majority followed Verigin to Bristish Columbia because of government efforts to assismilate them.

The teaching of the Doukhobors is penetrated with the gospel spirit of love. Worshiping God in the spirit, they affirm that the outward church and all that is performed in it and concerns it has no importance for them; the church is where two or three are gathered together, united in the name of Christ. They do not believe in icon worship or in intermediaries between themselves and God. Their spiritual teachings are founded on ancient tradition, which they call the "Book of Life," because it lives in their memory and hearts. In this book are psalms composed by their elders and leaders, partly formed out of the contents of the Bible, partly out of their historical experience. These are committed to memory by each succeeding generation. Doukhobors observe complete pacifism and non-violence, are lacto-vegetarians, and attempt to maintain a communal lifestyle.

The majority of Canadian Doukhobors were reorganized in 1938 by Peter P. Verigin, son of P.V. Verigin, shortly before his death, into the Union of Spiritual Communities of Chris to distinguish themselves from a radical offshoot who call themselves Sons of Freedom, and whose embrace of nudity and depradations has been sensationalized by the media and has stigmatized all Doukhobors. Today the USCC is governed by Trustees elected from member communities and administered by an elected Executive Committee headed by Honourary Chairman, John J. Verigin, CM OBC. The USCC executes the will and protects the interests of its member communities and its members living beyond south central British Columbia where the USCC is headquartered. The USCC is the largest organization of Doukhobors and maintains relations with other Doukhobor groups across Canada, in the USA, the Russian Federation, the Ukraine, and Georgia. The USCC also cooperates with other non-governmental organizations working non-violently to promote peace and justice, and respect for human dignity and ecological integrity.

Headquarters

USCC Central Office, Box 760, Grand Forks, BC V0H 1H0 Tel. (250)442-8252 Fax (250) 442-3433

Media Contact, John J. Verigin, Sr.

Officers

Hon. Chmn. of the Exec. Comm., John J. Verigin, Sr.

Chpsn., Fred Bojey

Periodicals

ISKRA

United Brethren Church in Canada

Founded in 1767 in Lancaster County, Pennsylvania, missionaries came to Canada about 1850. The first class was held in Kitchener in 1855, and the first building was erected in Port Elgin in 1867.

The Church of the United Brethren in Christ had its beginning with Philip William Otterbein and Martin Boehm, who were leaders in the revivalistic movement in Pennsylvania and Maryland during the late 1760s.

Headquarters

302 Lake St., Huntington, IN 46750 Tel. (219)356-2312 Fax (219)356-4730

GENERAL OFFICERS

Pres., Rev. Brian Magnus, 120 Fife Rd., Guelph, ON N1H 6Y2 Tel. (519)836-0180

Treas., Brian Winger, 2233 Hurontario St., Apt. 916, Mississauga, ON L5A 2E9 Tel. (905)275-8140

The United Church of Canada

The United Church of Canada was formed on June 10, 1925, through the union of the Methodist Church, Canada, the Congregational Union of Canada, the Council of Local Union Churches and 70 percent of the Presbyterian Church in Canada. The union culminated years of negotiation between the churches, all of which had integral associations with the development and history of the nation.

In fulfillment of its mandate to be a uniting as well as a United Church, the denomination has been enriched by other unions during its history. The Wesleyan Methodist Church of Bermuda joined in 1930. On January 1, 1968, the Canada Conference of the Evangelical United Brethren became part of The United Church of Canada. At various times, congregations of other Christian communions have also become congregations of the United Church.

The United Church of Canada is a full member of the World Methodist Council, the World Alliance of Reformed Churches (Presbyterian and Congregational), and the Canadian and World Councils of Churches. The United Church is the largest Protestant denomination in Canada.

NATIONAL OFFICES

General Council Office, 3250 Bloor St. W., Ste. 300, Etobicoke, ON M8X 2Y4 Tel. (416)231-5931 Fax (416)231-3103

Media Contact, Communications Officer, Mary Frances Denis

GENERAL COUNCIL

Mod., Rt. Rev. Peter B. Short

Gen. Sec., Rev. James H. Sinclair

GENERAL COUNCIL MINISTERS

Planning Processes, vacant
Programs for Mission & Ministry, Rev. Bruce Gregersen
Racial Justice, Omega C. Bula
Regional Relations, Rev. Carol L. Hancock
Resources for Mission & Ministry, Ian S. Fraser
Archivist, Sharon Larade, 73 Queen's Park Cr., E., Toronto, ON M5C 1K7 Tel. (416)585-4563 Fax (416)585-4584, E-mail uccvu.archives@ utoronto.ca, Web site www.united-church. ca/archives

ADMINISTRATIVE UNITS (EXECUTIVE MINISTERS)

Ethnic Ministries, Exec. Min., Rev. Richard C. Choe
Faith Formation and Education, Exec. Min., Rev. Steven Chambers
Financial Services, Exec. Officer, Ron Olsen
Financial Stewardship, Exec. Min., Rev. Gary Magarrell
Information Technology Services, Exec. Officer, Peter Tebbutt
Justice, Global & Ecumenical Relations, Exec. Min., vacant
Ministries in French, Exec. Min., Rev. Pierre Goldberger
Ministry & Employment Policies & Services, Exec. Min., Michael Burke
Resource Production and Distribution, Exec. Min., Juliet Huntly
Support to Local Ministries, Exec. Min., vacant

CONFERENCE EXECUTIVE SECRETARIES

Alberta and Northwest, Rev. Lynn I. Maki, 9911-48 Ave., NW, Edmonton, AB T6E 5V6 Tel. (780)435-3995 Fax (780)438-3317, E-mail coffice@anwconf.com
All Native Circle, Speaker, Cheryl Jourdain, 367 Selkirk Ave., Winnipeg, MB R2W 2M3 Tel. (204)582-5518 Fax (204)582-6649, E-mail allnative@mts.net
Bay of Quinte, Rev. Wendy Bulloch, P.O. Box 700, 67 Mill St., Frankford, ON K0K 2C0 Tel. (613)398-1051 Fax (613)398-8894, E-mail bayq.conference@sympatico.ca
British Columbia, Rev. Douglas Goodwin, 4383 Rumble St., Burnaby, BC V5J 2A2 Tel. (604)431-0434 Fax (604)431-0439, E-mail bcconf@bc.united-church.ca
Hamilton, Rev. Fred Monteith, Box 100, Carlisle, ON L0R 1H0 Tel. (905)659-3343 Fax (905)659-7766, E-mail office@hamconf.org
London, W. Peter Scott, 759 Hyde Park Rd., Ste 252, London, ON N6H 3K2 Tel. (519)672-1930 Fax (519)439-2800, E-mail lonconf@ execulink.com
Manitoba and Northwestern Ontario, K. Virginia Coleman, 170 Saint Mary's Rd., Winnipeg, MB R2H 1H9 Tel. (204)233-8911 Fax (204)233-3289, E-mail office@confmnwo. mb.ca
Manitou, Rev. Rev. William Kunder, 319 McKenzie Ave., North Bay, ON P1B 7E3 Tel. (705)474-3350 Fax (705)497-3597, E-mail office@manitouconference.ca
Maritime, Rev. Catherine H. Gaw, 32 York St., Sackville, NB E4L 4R4 Tel. (506)536-1334 Fax (506)536-2900, E-mail info@marconf.ca
Montreal and Ottawa, Rev. Brian Cornelius (acting), 225-50 Ave., Lachine, QC H8T 2T7 Tel. (514)634-7015 Fax (514)634-2489, E-mail lachine@istar.ca
Newfoundland and Labrador, Rev. William G. Bartlett, 320 Elizabeth Ave., St. John's, NF A1B 1T9 Tel. (709)754-0386 Fax (709)754-8336, E-mail unitedchurch@nfld.net
Saskatchewan, Rev. G. Robert Campbell, 418 A. McDonald St., Regina, SK S4N 6E1 Tel. (306)721-3311 Fax (306)721-3171, E-mail ucskco@sasktel.net
Toronto, Rev. David W. Allen, 65 Mayall Ave., Downsview, ON M3L 1E7 Tel. (416)241-2677 Fax (416)241-2689, E-mail torontoconference@bellnet.ca

Periodicals

United Church Observer; Mandate; Aujourd'hui Credo

United Pentecostal Church in Canada

This body, which is affiliated with the United Pentecostal Church, International, with headquarters in Hazelwood, Missouri, accepts the Bible standard of full salvation, which is repentance, baptism by immersion in the name of the Lord Jesus Christ for the remission of sins and the baptism of the Holy Ghost, with the initial signs of speaking in tongues as the Spirit gives utterance. Other tenets of faith include the Oneness of God in Christ, holiness, divine healing and the second coming of Jesus Christ.

Headquarters

United Pentecostal Church Intl., 8855 Dunn Rd., Hazelwood, MO 63042 Tel. (314)837-7300 Fax (314)837-4503
Media Contact, Gen. Sec.-Treas., Rev. C. M. Becton

DISTRICT SUPERINTENDENTS

Atlantic, Rev. Harry Lewis, P.O. Box 1046, Perth Andover, NB E0J 1V0
British Columbia, Rev. Paul V. Reynolds, 13447-112th Ave., Surrey, BC V3R 2E7
Canadian Plains, Rev. Johnny King, 615 Northmount Dr., NW, Calgary, AB T2K 3J6
Central Canadian, Rev. Clifford Heaslip, 4215 Roblin Blvd., Winnipeg, MB R3R 0E8
Newfoundland, Jack Cunningham
Nova Scotia, Superintendent, Rev. John D. Mean, P.O. Box 2183, D.E.P.S., Dartmouth, NS B2W 3Y2
Ontario, Rev. Carl H. Stephenson, 63 Castlegrove Blvd., Don Mills, ON M3A 1L3

Universal Fellowship of Metropolitan Community Churches

The Universal Fellowship of Metropolitan Community Churches is a Christian church which directs a special ministry within, and on behalf of, the gay and lesbian community. Involvement, however, is not exclusively limited to gays and lesbians; U.F.M.C.C. tries to stress its openness to all people and does not call itself a "gay church."

Founded in 1968 in Los Angeles by the Rev. Troy Perry, the U.F.M.C.C. has more than 300 member congregations worldwide. Congregations are in Vancouver, Edmonton, Windsor, London, Toronto, Ottawa (2), Guelph, Fredericton, Winnipeg, Halifax, Barrie and Belleville.

Theologically, the Metropolitan Community Churches stand within the mainstream of Christian doctrine, being "ecumenical" or "interdenominational" in stance (albeit a "denomination" in their own right).

The Metropolitan Community Churches are characterized by their belief that the love of God is a gift, freely offered to all people, regardless of sexual orientation and that no incompatibility exists between human sexuality and the Christian faith.

The Metropolitan Community Churches in Canada were founded in Toronto in 1973 by the Rev. Robert Wolfe.

Headquarters

Media Contact, Marcie Wexler, 33 Holly St., #1117, Toronto, ON M4S 2G8 Tel. (416)487-8429 Fax (416)932-1836

Officers

Eastern Canadian District, Rev. Marcie Wexler, 33 Holly St., #1117, Toronto, ON M4S 2G8 Tel. (416)487-8429

The Wesleyan Church of Canada

This group is the Canadian portion of The Wesleyan Church which consists of the Atlantic and Central Canada districts. The Central Canada District of the former Wesleyan Methodist Church of America was organized at Winchester, Ontario, in 1889 and the Atlantic District was founded in 1888 as the Alliance of the Reformed Baptist Church, which merged with the Wesleyan Methodist Church in July, 1966.

The Wesleyan Methodist Church and the Pilgrim Holiness Church merged in June, 1968, to become The Wesleyan Church. The doctrine is evangelical and Wesleyan Arminian and stresses holiness beliefs. For more details, consult the U.S. listing under The Wesleyan Church.

Headquarters

The Wesleyan Church Intl. Center, P.O. Box 50434, Indianapolis, IN 46250-0434

Media Contact, Dist. Supt., Central Canada, Rev. Donald E. Hodgins, 17 Saint Paul St., Belleview, ON K8N 1A4 Tel. (613)966-7527 Fax (613)968-6190

DISTRICT SUPERINTENDENTS

Central Canada, Rev. Donald E. Hodgins, 17 Saint Paul St., Belleview, ON K8N 1A4, E-mail ccd@on.aibn.com

Atlantic, Rev. Dr. H. C. Wilson, 1600 Main St., Ste. 216, Moncton, NB E1E 1G5, E-mail ncwilson@nbnet.nb.ca

Periodicals

Central Canada;The Clarion

Religious Bodies in Canada Arranged by Families

The following list of religious bodies appearing in the Directory Section of the *Yearbook* shows the "families," or related clusters into which Canadian religious bodies can be grouped. For example, there are many communions that can be grouped under the heading "Baptist" for historical and theological reasons. It should not be assumed, however, that all denominations under one family heading are necessarily consistent in belief or practice. The family clusters tend to represent historical factors more often than theological or practical ones. These family categories provide one of the major pitfalls when compiling church statistics because there is often a tendency to combine the statistics by "families" for analytical and comparative purposes. Such combined totals are deeply flawed, even though they are often used as variables for sociological analysis. The arrangement by families offered here is intended only as a general guide for conceptual organization when viewing the broad sweep of Canadian religious culture.

Religious bodies that cannot be categorized under family headings appear alphabetically and are not indented in the following list.

The Anglican Church of Canada
Apostolic Christian Church (Nazarene)
Armenian Evangelical Church
Associated Gospel Churches

Baptist Bodies

Association of Regular Baptist Churches (Canada)
Baptist Convention of Ontario and Quebec
Baptist General Conference of Canada
Baptist Union of Western Canada
Canadian Baptist Ministries
Canadian Convention of Southern Baptists
Convention of Atlantic Baptist Churches
The Fellowship of Evangelical Baptist Churches in Canada
Free Will Baptists
North American Baptist Conference
Union d'Eglises Baptistes Françaises au Canada

Brethren in Christ Church, Canadian Conference
Canadian District of the Moravian Church in America, Northern Province
Canadian Evangelical Christian Churches
Canadian Yearly Meeting of the Religious Society of Friends
Christ Catholic Church International
Christian Brethren (also known as Plymouth Brethren)
Christian and Missionary Alliance in Canada
Church of God (Anderson, Ind.)
Church of the Nazarene in Canada

Churches of Christ-Christian Churches

Christian Church (Disciples of Christ) in Canada
Christian Churches / Churches of Christ
Churches of Christ in Canada

Congregational Christian Churches in Canada

Eastern Orthodox Churches

The Antiochian Orthodox Christian Archdiocese of North America
Greek Orthodox Metropolis of Toronto (Canada)
Orthodox Church in America (Canada Section)
Patriarchal Parishes of the Russian Orthodox Church in Canada
Romanian Orthodox Church in America (Canadian Parishes)
The Romanian Orthodox Episcopate of America (Jackson, MI)
Serbian Orthodox Church in the U.S.A. and Canada, Diocese of Canada
Ukrainian Orthodox Church of Canada

The Evangelical Covenant Church of Canada
Evangelical Free Church of Canada
The Evangelical Missionary Church of Canada
General Church of the New Jerusalem
Jehovah's Witnesses

Latter-day Saints (Mormons)

The Church of Jesus Christ of Latter-day Saints in Canada
Community of Christ

Lutheran Bodies

Church of the Lutheran Brethren
The Estonian Evangelical Lutheran Church
Evangelical Lutheran Church in Canada
Lutheran Church—Canada

Mennonite Bodies

Canadian Conference of Mennonite Brethren Churches
Church of God in Christ (Mennonite)
The Evangelical Mennonite Conference

Evangelical Mennonite Mission Conference
Mennonite Church (Canada)
Old Order Amish Church
Reinland Mennonite Church

Methodist Bodies

British Methodist Episcopal Church of Canada
Free Methodist Church in Canada
Independent Holiness Church
The Wesleyan Church of Canada

The Old Catholic Church of Canada
Open Bible Faith Fellowship of Canada

Oriental Orthodox Churches

Armenian Holy Apostolic Church - Canadian Diocese
The Coptic Orthodox Church in Canada
Syriac Orthodox Church of Antioch

Pentecostal Bodies

The Apostolic Church in Canada
Apostolic Church of Pentecost of Canada Inc.
The Bible Holiness Movement
Church of God (Cleveland, Tenn.)
The Church of God of Prophecy in Canada
Elim Fellowship of Evangelical Churches and Ministers
Foursquare Gospel Church of Canada
Independent Assemblies of God International (Canada)
The Italian Pentecostal Church of Canada
The Pentecostal Assemblies of Canada
Pentecostal Assemblies of Newfoundland
United Pentecostal Church in Canada

Reformed Bodies

Canadian and American Reformed Churches
Christian Reformed Church in North America
Presbyterian Church in America (Canadian Section)
Presbyterian Church in Canada

Reformed Church in Canada
The Reformed Episcopal Church of Canada
The Roman Catholic Church in Canada
The Salvation Army in Canada
Seventh-day Adventist Church in Canada
Union of Spiritual Communities of Christ (Orthodox Doukhobors in Canada)
United Brethren Church in Canada
The United Church of Canada
Universal Fellowship of Metropolitan Community Churches

5. Sources of Religion-Related Research
I. Directory of Selected Research Organizations

The editorial office of the *Yearbook of American & Canadian Churches* receives innumerable requests for data about churches, religious organizations, attendance patterns, and comparative religion concerns. Sometimes we are able to furnish the requested data, but more often we refer the inquirer to other research colleagues in the field. We are always interested in and aided by such requests, and we find ourselves informed by each question.

In response to such inquiries, the "Sources in Religion-Related Research" directory was initiated in the 1999 edition of the *Yearbook*. In addition to asking each organization to provide a brief overall description, each was also asked to indicate any special research foci (i.e. denominational, congregational, interfaith, gender, etc.). Further, each organization is asked to identify the sociological, methodological, or theological approaches that serve to guide their research, and to describe any current or recent research projects. Lastly, we asked for a list of recurrent publications. Below, the organizations' responses to these questions are reported as clearly and completely as is possible. Contact information appears just beneath the title of each organization. In most cases, the organization's Web site provides very detailed information about current research projects.

Numerous other research centers in the area of American religious life, each with specific areas of concern, conduct timely and significant research. We hope that readers will find utility in this directory and we invite them to identify additional sources by e-mail: yearbook@ncccusa.org or by Fax: (212)870-2817.

American Academy of Religion (AAR)

AAR Executive Office
825 Houston Mill Rd., Ste. 300
Atlanta, GA 30329
Tel. (404)727-7920
Fax (404)727-7959
Email: aar@aarweb.org
Web site: www.aarweb.org
Pres., Dr. Jane Dammen McAuliffe
Exec. Dir., Dr. Barbara DeConcini

The AAR is the major learned society and professional association for scholars whose object of study is religion. Its mission— in a world where religion plays so central a role in social, political and economic events, as well as in the lives of communities and individuals— is to meet a critical need for ongoing reflection upon and understanding of religious traditions, issues, questions and values. As a learned society and professional association of teachers and research scholars, the American Academy of Religion has more than 8,500 members who teach in some 1,500 colleges, universities, seminaries, and schools in North America and abroad. The Academy is dedicated to furthering knowledge of religion and religious institutions in all their forms and manifestations. This is accomplished through Academy-wide and regional conferences and meetings, publications, programs, and membership services. Within a context of free inquiry and critical examination, the Academy welcomes all disciplined reflection on religion— both from within and outside of communities of belief and practice— and seeks to enhance its broad public understanding.

At the AAR's annual meeting, more than 8,000 scholars gather to share research and collaborate on scholarly projects. The annual meeting sessions are grouped into more than 70 program units, each representing an ongoing community of scholars who are collectively engaged in pursuing knowledge about a specific religious tradition or a specific aspect of religion. In addition, the AAR's ten regional organizations sponsor smaller annual meetings that are similar in structure to the Academy-wide meeting. All of the world's major religious traditions, as well as indigenous and historical religions, are explored in the work of AAR members.

Current or Recent Research

Currently, for example, the AAR offers teaching workshops for both junior and senior scholars. It is organizing efforts to gather data on the field to facilitate departmental planning and funding. A full explanation of the many current research projects is available on the AAR Web site, which is listed above.

Periodicals

The Journal of the American Academy of Religion is the scholarly periodical of the AAR. In addition, the AAR publishes a quarterly newsletter, *Religious Studies News*, AAR Edition.

American Religion Data Archive (ARDA)

Department of Sociology
The Pennsylvania State University
211 Oswald Tower
University Park, PA 16802-6207
Tel. (814)865-6258
Fax (814)863-7216
Email: arda@pop.psu.edu
Web site: www.TheARDA.com
Dir., Dr. Roger Finke

The American Religion Data Archive (ARDA) is an Internet-based archive that stores and distributes information from more than 250 major data collections on American religion. Online features include interactive maps of state and county church membership rates, denominational profiles for counties, states, metropolitan areas, and the nation, basic statistics for all survey questions, and many other features. With the exception of the 2000 Religious Congregations and Membership Study, all data files can be downloaded. The ARDA (www.TheARDA.com) is supported by the Lilly Endowment and is housed in the Social Science Research Institute at the Penn State University.

Association of Theological Schools (ATS)

10 Summit Park Dr.
Pittsburgh, PA 15275-1103
Tel. (412)788-6505
Fax (412)788-6510
Email: ats@ats.edu
Web site: www.ats.edu
Exec. Dir., Daniel O. Aleshire
Dir. of Comm. and Membership Services, Nancy Merrill

The mission of The Association of Theological Schools in the United States and Canada (ATS) is to promote the improvement and enhancement of theological schools to the benefit of communities of faith and the broader public. The Association seeks to fulfill this mission by engaging in four core areas of work, (1) accreditation, (2) leadership education for administrative officers and faculty, (3) development of theological education, which involves the study of critical issues in theological education, and (4) communications and data.

The Association is a membership organization of approximately 250 graduate schools of theology, including Protestant, Roman Catholic, and Orthodox schools, both freestanding seminaries and university-related divinity schools. A full list of members is available on the above Web site.

Current or Recent Research

Current research is addressing the effective formation of seminary students for religious vocation and ministerial leadership. The project encompasses several goals: (1) increased understanding of the character of theological learning that includes intellectual content, professional skill, personal formation, and spiritual maturity; (2) effective assessment of theological learning in the context of the Master of Divinity degree program, in particular, and in the context of ministerial practice, (3) information about the relationship between the goals of theological learning and selected characteristics of current theological students, and (4) development of models of assessment of student learning for use by ATS member schools. Over the course of this four-year project, the Association will commission five research studies that will focus on: (1) current practices of educational assessment being employed in ATS schools, (2) best practices of educational assessment in graduate, professional education for human services professions, (3) a review of the literature on higher education outcomes assessment, (4) characteristics of students currently enrolled in theological education programs of study, and (5) church-denominational perspectives of the strengths and weaknesses of recent graduates of ATS schools.

Periodicals

Fact Book on Theological Education is published annually and provides statistical data on the member institutions. The Association publishes a journal, *Theological Education*, bi-annually, a bi-monthly newsletter entitled *Colloquy*, and the formal institutional documents of the Association entitled *Bulletin*, part 2 of which is the ATS membership list.

Auburn Theological Seminary

3041 Broadway
New York, NY 10027
Tel. (212)662-4315
Fax (212)663-5214
Email: krh@auburnsem.org
Web site: www.auburnsem.org
Dir., Dr. Barbara G. Wheeler
Exec. Vice-Pres., Rev. Katharine R. Henderson

Auburn Theological Seminary's mission is to strengthen religious leadership. It carries out its mission through programs of non-degree theological education for clergy and laity; through programs for Presbyterian students enrolled at its partner institution, Union Seminary in New York City; and by conducting research on theological education at its Center for the Study of Theological Education. Auburn, located on Union Seminary's campus, was founded in 1818 in Auburn, New York.

Auburn Seminary is related by covenant agreement with Presbyterian Church (U.S.A.), but most of its programs are ecumenical, and many have a multi-faith focus. The Center for the Study of Theological Education includes rabbinical schools and Protestant and Roman Catholic seminaries and divinity schools in its studies.

Research is conducted using a variety of methods, including survey and ethnographic research, structured interview and documentary research, research reports on surveys and case studies. Reports of findings are frequently published with accompanying information on the history of the issue being studied and with theological commentaries written from a variety of perspectives.

Current or Recent Research

The Center is undertaking a systematic study of U.S. and Canadian M.Div. graduates from across the religious spectrum in order to find out how graduates have used their theological training, how many are in ministry five and ten years after graduation, and how they look back and assess their seminary experience. A second study underway is on seminary institutional advancement. Through analysis of available data, site visits and interviews, the researchers will examine the techniques, costs, best practices and barriers to effective fundraising in theological schools.

Periodicals

Auburn Studies is an occasional bulletin in which the Center publishes its research results. Research reports are also available on Auburn's Web site (listed above).

The Barna Group, Ltd.

1957 Eastman Ave.
Ventura, CA 93003
Tel. (805)658-8885
Fax (805)658-7298
Email: barna@barna.org
Web site: www.barna.org
Pres., George Barna
Vice-Pres., David Kinnaman

The Barna Group conducts primary research related to cultural change, people's lifestyles, values, attitudes, beliefs and religious practices.

Its vision is to provide current accurate and reliable information, in bite-sized pieces and at reasonable costs, to its clients to facilitate strategic decisions. Barna also produces many research-based books, reports, and ministry tools to help churches understand the national context of ministry. The organization works with churches from all Christian denominations.

It conducts projects based upon existing needs in the Church at-large, or for its clients specifically. Methodologically, The Barna Group uses both qualitative approaches (focus groups, depth interviews) and quantitative approaches (cross-sectional surveys, longitudinal studies, panel research). Data collection methods include telephone surveys, mail surveys, in-person interviews, on-line surveys, self-administered surveys, and focus groups.

Current or Recent Research

The Barna Group conducts more than 50 studies each year, covering a broad range of topics. Some of the recent non-proprietary studies completed are focused on understanding the state of the Church; the habits of highly effective churches; worship efficacy; the unchurched; strategies and techniques for developing lay leaders; understanding effective discipleship processes; pastoral profiles; beliefs, behaviors and core attitudes of ministry donors; Biblical knowledge, and many others.

Periodicals

The Barna Group offers a free bi-weekly report, *The Barna Update*, on current information related to faith matters from its national non-proprietary research. This information is free to those who register for it at the Web site (listed above).

Center for the Study of Religion and American Culture

Indiana University
Purdue University at Indianapolis
425 University Blvd, Room 341
Indianapolis, IN 46202-5140
Tel. (317)274-8409
Fax (317)278-3354
Email: pgoff@iupui.edu
Web site: www.iupui.edu/~raac
Dir., Dr. Phillip Goff
Prog. Coord., Rebecca Vasko

The Center for the Study of Religion and American Culture is a research and public outreach institute devoted to the promotion of the understanding of the relation between religion and other features of American culture. Research methods are both interdisciplinary and multidisciplinary. Established in 1989, the Center is based in the School of Liberal Arts and Indiana University-Purdue University at Indianapolis. Center activities include national conferences and symposia, commissioned books, essays, bibliographies, and research projects, fellowships for younger scholars, data-based communication about developments in the field of American religion, a newsletter devoted to the promotion of Center activities, and the semi-annual scholarly periodical, *Religion and American Culture, A Journal of Interpretation.*

Current or Recent Research

The Center is presently overseeing two intiatives. The "Young Scholars in American Religion Program" is a multi-year project to assist early-career scholars in developing their teaching skills and research agendas. The "Centers and Institutes Project," meanwhile, brings together those organizations dedicated to the academic study of religion in the U.S. in order to discuss common problems and solutions, as well as to identify areas for cooperative efforts. The work of these various centers and institutes will be highlighted in future issues of the *Newsletter from the Center for the Study of Religion and American Culture* and the Center's reception at the annual meeting of the American Academy of Religion.

We continue to explore other areas of potential research in the relation between religion and other aspects of American culture. As these projects materialize, they will be announced on this Web site and in the *Newsletter*.

Periodicals

Religion and American Culture, A Journal of Interpretation. Center books include the series, "The Public Expressions of Religion in America."

empty tomb, inc.

301 North Fourth Street
P.O. Box 2404
Champaign, IL 61825-2404
Tel. (217)356-9519
Fax (217)356-2344
Email: research@emptytomb.org
Web site: www.emptytomb.org
CEO, John L. Ronsvalle
Exec. Vice-Pres., Sylvia Ronsvalle

empty tomb, inc. is a Christian research and service organization. On a local level, it coordinates direct services to people in need in cooperation with area congregations. On a national level, it studies church member giving patterns of historically Christian churches, including Roman Catholic, mainline and evangelical Protestant, Anabaptist, Pentecostal, Orthodox, and fundamentalist communions. empty tomb publishes the annual *State of Church Giving* series. Also, empty tomb offers a mission funding incentive program, Mission Match, in an effort to help reverse the negative giving trends indicated by national data.

Current or Recent Research

Current research monitors and analyzes church member giving patterns, and is published in *The State of Church Giving* series produced by empty tomb, inc.

Periodicals

The State of Church Giving series is an annual publication. It considers denominational giving data, analysis of giving and membership trends, and other estimates of charitable giving. Each edition features a chapter on giving issues relevant to church giving patterns. Past *State of Church Giving* special focus chapters are posted on empty tomb's Web site, www.emptytomb.org.

The Hartford Institute for Religion Research of Hartford Seminary

Hartford Seminary
77 Sherman Street
Hartford, CT 06105
Tel. (860)509-9543
Fax (860)509-9551
Email: hirr@hartsem.edu
Web site: www.hirr.hartsem.edu
Dir. of Research, Dr. David A. Roozen
Admin. Asst., Mary Jane Ross

The Hartford Institute for Religion Research of Hartford Seminary was established in 1981, formalizing a research program initiated by the seminary in 1974. Until recently it was known as the Center for Social and Religious Research. The Institute's work is guided by a disciplined understanding of the interrelationship between (a) the inner life and resources of American religious institutions and (b) the possibilities and limits placed on those institutions by the social and cultural context into which God has called them.

Its twenty-one year record of rigorous, policy-relevant research, anticipation of emerging issues, commitment to the creative dissemination of learning, and strong connections to both theological education and the church has earned the Institute an international reputation as an important bridge between the scholarly community and the practice of ministry.

Current or Recent Research

Some of the titles of current projects at the Institute are, "Organizing Religious Work for the 21st Century, Exploring 'Denominationalism,'" "Cooperative Congregational Studies Project," "Congregational Consulting Services," "New England Religion Discussion Society (NERDS)," and "Congregational Studies Team." Descriptions of these programs are available on the Institute's Web site, listed above.

Periodicals

Praxis is Hartford Seminary's magazine, which focuses on the activities and faculty of the Seminary.

Institute for Ecumenical and Cultural Research

P.O. Box 6188
Collegeville, MN 56321-6188
Tel. (320)363-3366
Fax (320)363-3313
Email: iecr@iecr.org
Web site: www.iecr.org
Exec. Dir., Dr. Patrick Henry, (Dr. Don B. Ottenhoff, June 1)
Admin. Asst., Stephanie Hart

The Institute for Ecumenical and Cultural Research brings together well-trained, creative, articulate men and women for careful thought and dialogue in a place of inquiry and prayer. The Resident Scholars Program welcomes researchers and their families for either individual semesters or for an entire academic year. Resident scholars work on their own projects but meet once a week for seminars, and have other occasions for conversation. Each scholar presents a public lecture. Ecumenism happens at the Institute as people come to know one another in community. The Institute is an independent corporation, but shares in the Benedictine and academic life of Saint John's Abbey and University, and of nearby Saint Benedict's Monastery and the College of Saint Benedict. In the summer the Institute uses its facilities for invitational consultations on subjects considered by the Board of Directors to be of special ecumenical interest.

In the Resident Scholars Program, the subjects of research are determined by the interests of the applicants who are invited to come by the Admissions Committee. While most of the work tends to be in traditional theological areas, we encourage people in all fields to consider applying, both because ecumenism is of concern across the spectrum of disciplines, and because the term "cultural" in our title extends our reach beyond theology and religious studies. In particular cases, work done here may have a denominational, congregational, or interfaith focus, but the Institute does not prescribe or delimit, in any narrow way, what is appropriate.

Current or Recent Research

Recent summer consultations have had the following titles, "Ecumenical Formation: The Heart of the Matter," and "Igniting Biblical Imagination." Among subjects dealt with in earlier years are "Prayer in the Ecumenical Movement," "Virtues for an Ecumenical Heart," "The Price of Disunity," "Living Faithfully in North America Today," "Orthodoxy at Home in North America," "Transmitting Tradition to Children and Young People," "The Nature of Christian Hope," "Women and the Church," "Jewish and Christian Relatedness to Scripture," "Confessing Christian Faith in a Pluralistic Society."

Periodicals

Ecumenical People, Programs, Papers is an bi-annual newsletter containing brief sketches of resident scholars, reports on Institute programs, and, in nearly every issue, there is an "An Occasional Paper" on a subject of ecumenical interest. The newsletter is free.

Institute for the Study of American Evangelicals (ISAE)

Wheaton College
Wheaton, IL 60187
Tel. (630)752-5437
Fax (630)752-5516
Email: isae@wheaton.edu
Web site: www.wheaton.edu/isae
Dir., Dr. Edith Blumhofer
Research and Resource Asst., Katria Delac

Founded in 1982, the Institute for the Study of American Evangelicals is a center for research and functions as a program of Wheaton College. The purpose of the ISAE is to encourage and support research on evangelical Christianity in the United States and Canada. The institute seeks to help evangelicals develop a mature understanding of their own heritage and to inform others about evangelicals' historical significance and contemporary role. For the most part, the ISAE focuses on historical research, with occasional sociological or economic researchers participating in the projects.

Current or Recent Research

One recently completed project entitled "Hymnody in American Protestantism" was a research project focusing on the history of hymnology in American religious life. We have published two books from this project: *Singing the Lord's Song in a Strange Land* by the University of Alabama Press and *Wonderful Words of Life: Hymns in American Protestant History and Theology* published by William B. Eerdmans.

Two new projects include "Confessional Traditions and American Christianity," a grant from the Lilly Endowment, Inc., and "The Changing Face of American Evangelicalism," a grant from the Henry Luce Foundation.

Periodicals

Evangelical Studies Bulletin (ESB) is designed to aid both the scholar and the layman in his or her education and research of evangelicalism. Issued quarterly, the bulletin contains articles, book reviews, notices, a calendar of events, and bibliographic information on the latest dissertations, articles and books related to the study of evangelicals.

Institute for the Study of American Religion

P.O. Box 90709
Santa Barbara, CA 93190-0709
Tel. (805)967-7721
Fax (805)683-4876
Email: jgordon@linkline.com
Web site: www.americanreligion.org
Dir., Dr. J. Gordon Melton
Assoc. Dir., Dr. James Beverley

The Institute for the Study of American Religion was founded in 1968 in Evanston, Illinois as a religious studies research facility with a particular focus upon the smaller religions of the United

States. Those groups that it serves have been known under a variety of labels including sect, cult, minority religion, alternative religion, non-conventional religion, spiritual movement, and new religious movement.

In the 1970s the Institute extended its attention to Canada and in the 1990s developed an even more global focus. In 1985, the institute moved to its present location in Santa Barbara, California. Over the years the institute built a large collection of both primary and secondary materials on the religious groups and movements it studied. In 1985 this collection of more than 40,000 volumes and thousands of periodicals and archival materials was deposited with the Davidson Library at the University of California in Santa Barbara. The reference material exists today as the American Religions Collection and is open to scholars and the interested public. The institute continues to support the collection with donations of additional materials.

Current or Recent Research

Today the institute has two main foci. It monitors all of the religious denominations, organizations, and movements functioning in North America and regularly publishes reports drawing from that activity in a series of reference books. The most important of these reference books is the *Encyclopedia of American Religions* (Detroit, Gale Group, 7th edition, 2002). Among the most called-for information is factual data on the many new and more controversial religious movements, which are popularly labeled as "cults." The institute's second focus developed out of its more recent refocusing on the international scene, provoked by the international life of most of the religious groups which it has studied in previous decades.

J.M. Dawson Institute of Church-State Studies at Baylor University

P.O. Box 97308
Waco, TX 76798-7308
Tel. (254)710-1510
Fax (254)710-1571
Email: derek_davis@baylor.edu
Web site: www.baylor.edu/~Church_State
Dir., Dr. Derek Davis
Admin. Asst., Wanda Gilbert

Baylor University established the J.M. Dawson Institute of Church-State Studies in 1957, so named in honor of an outstanding alumnus, an ardent advocate of religious liberty, and a distinguished author of publications on church and state. The Institute is the oldest and most well-established facility of its kind located in a university setting. It is exclusively devoted to research in the broad field of church and state and the advancement of religious liberty around the world.

From its inception in 1957, the stated purpose of the Institute has been to stimulate academic interest and encourage research and publication in the broad area of church-state relations. In carrying out its statement of purpose, the Institute has sought to honor a threefold commitment, to be interfaith, interdisciplinary, and international.

Current or Recent Research

Some current research includes government persecution of minority religions in Europe; original intent of Founding Fathers regarding religion and public life; Christian Right views on political activism; conservative versus moderate Baptist views on church-state relations; role of civil religion in America; international treaties and religious liberty.

Periodicals

Journal of Church and State is the only scholarly journal expressly devoted to church-state relations.

The Louisville Institute

1044 Alta Vista Road
Louisville, KY 40205-1798
Tel. (502) 992-5432
Fax (502) 894-2286
Email: info@louisville-institute.org
Web site: www.louisville-institute.org
Exec. Dir., Dr. James W. Lewis

The Louisville Institute is a Lilly Endowment program for the study of American religion based at the Louisville Presbyterian Seminary. As a program of Lilly Endowment, the Louisville Institute builds upon the endowment's long-standing support of both leadership education and scholarly research on American religion. The distinctive mission of the Louisville Institute is to enrich the religious life of

American Christians and to encourage the revitalization of their institutions by bringing together those who lead religious institutions with those who study them, so that the work of each might stimulate and inform the other. The Louisville Institute seeks to fulfill its mission through a coordinated strategy of grantmaking and convening within a programmatic focus on three issues. The first, Christian faith and life, concerns the character and role of the theology and spirituality that are effectively at work in the lives of American Christians. The second, religious institutions, asks how America's religious institutions might respond most constructively in the midst of the bewildering institutional reconfiguration occurring in American society.

The third, pastoral leadership, explores various strategies for improving the quality of religious leadership in North America. The several grant programs of the Louisville Institute offer financial support to a broad range of projects that seek to address both the mission of the Louisville Institute to bring pastors and academics together and the Institute's focus on Christian faith and life, religious institutions, and pastoral leadership. Although many of these grants support research projects, an increasing number of them support other types of projects that contribute to the work of the Louisville Institute.

Current or Recent Research

Please see the Louisville Institute Web site (listed above) for lists of recent grants made by the Louisville Institute.

Periodicals

Intersections newsletter

The Pluralism Project

Harvard University
201 Vanserg Hall
25 Francis Avenue
Cambridge, MA 02138
Tel. (617)496-2481
Fax (617)496-2428
Email: staff@pluralism.org
Web site: www.pluralsm.org
Dir., Dr. Diana L. Eck
Managing Dir., Grove Harris

The Pluralism Project was developed by Dr. Diana L. Eck at Harvard University to study and document the growing religious diversity of the United States, with a special view to its new immigrant religious communities. The religious landscape of the U.S. has radically changed in the past 30 years. In light of these changes, how Americans of all faiths begin to engage with one another in shaping a positive pluralism is one of the most important questions American society faces in the years ahead. In addressing these phenomena, the Project has three goals: 1) To document some further changes taking place in America's cities and towns by beginning to map their new religious demography with old and new mosques and Islamic centers, Sikh gurdwaras, Hindu and Jain temples, Buddhist temples and meditation centers, Zoroastrian and Taoist religious centers. 2) To begin to study how these religious traditions are changing as they take root in American soil and develop in a new context. How are they beginning to recreate their community life, religious institutions, rites and rituals, and forms of transmission in the cultural environment of the United States? 3) To explore how the United States is changing as we begin to appropriate this new religious diversity in our public life and institutions, and in emerging forms of interfaith relationships.

The Pluralism Project has the most comprehensive archive anywhere of the print materials of America's new immigrant religious communities, newsletters, serial publications, anniversary programs, handbooks, prayer books, calendars, and educational materials. The Project files also include research papers as well as a variety of materials donated directly by centers.

The Pluralism Project On-Line Directory maintains an extensive directory of religious centers in the United States. At present, this directory exists in a sortable database, with listings of nearly 3,000 centers across the U.S.

Current or Recent Research

The Pluralism Project produced a CD-ROM called *On Common Ground: World Religions in America*, to present some of the wide range of work that had emerged from three years of research. A further grant from the Ford Foundation has enabled the Project to extend its research on the American religious landscape.

II. Directory of Selected Faith Traditions in America

Compiling a directory of faith groups is an arduous but rewarding task in religiously plural America, In part, because the very self-understanding and definition of community varies so greatly from faith group to faith group. In order to present a reasonably parallel and well-balanced listing of organizations for each faith, care must be taken not to impose categories or terms from one's own universe of understanding upon other contexts. The very terms, "church," "membership," "denomination," "hierarchy" which are essential constructs of certain Christian universes of understanding, are rendered meaningless when applied to other faith groups.

Further, it is important to remember that many religious traditions lack a centralized organization that speaks for the whole of the community. Often, this lack of centralization reflects the existence of several distinct forms or branches of the religion. In some instances, different ethnic groups immigrating to the U.S. bring with them a distinctive form of their religion, which is particular to their culture of origin. In other cases, plural forms of a faith exist resulting from theological, political, or economic differences. Still other faith groups may be more tightly organized, but the religious center that provides guidance in matters of faith and, perhaps, even organizational discipline may not be in the United States. Hence, the organizations before us are not necessarily religious hierarchical organizations, but are often groups assembled for other purposes that are associated with a particular faith group, or subdivision of that faith group. Caution is advised in regarding these entries as one might regard a "church headquarters."

The compilation of any directory relies upon the existence of some common organizational structure within all the entities listed. Yet, when compiling a directory of faith groups, it cannot be assumed such organizational parallels exist. Oblique ways must be found to adequately represent individual faith groups. The many religious communities in the United States are associated with myriad organizations of all different types. Some of these are primarily places of worship; others are organizations seeking to represent either the religious community as a whole or some particular constituency within it. Others are community centers; some are educational groups; some are organizations particularly for women or youths; and some are political action groups. Still others are peace organizations or relief organizations. That said, a directory of this sort cannot include an exhaustive list of organizations for each faith group nationwide. The omission of any particular organization or branch of any of the major faith groups listed does not reflect a deliberate attempt to homogenize the rich pluralities that exist within faith groups. Instead, the listings that follow are intended to provide the interested reader with a few initial contacts within each religious community.

Despite the above cautions, this directory provides a rich resource for readers and researchers who wish to learn more about other faith groups. The agencies listed here consist of organizations of importance within the communities they represent, and serve as excellent introductory points of contact with those communities.

In some cases, these religious communities are in a state of flux; the Internet is an excellent way to keep contact with changing religious organizations. There is a plethora of information available about nearly all religious traditions online, but sites vary widely in their accuracy and reliability. Nearly any Internet search engine will provide extensive links to information about specific religious traditions.

For directory information about national interfaith organizations in the United States, please see Directory 1, "U.S. Cooperative Organizations." For directory information on local interfaith organizations, please see Directory 7, "U.S. Regional and Local Ecumenical Bodies."

BAHA'ISM

Baha'ism was founded in Persia during the late 19th century by Mirza Hussein Ali Nuri, also known as Baha'ullah, which means "Glory of God" in Arabic. Baha'i is an outgrowth of an earlier Persian religious movement called Babism, which was initiated by Mirza Ali Muhammad, who was referred to as the "Bab." In 1844, the Bab prophesied that in nineteen years, a divine manifestation of God would appear. Shortly afterward, the Babis endured a massive period of persecution in which the Bab was martyred. In 1863, Baha'ullah, a close follower of the Bab, claimed that he, himself, was this divine manifestation of God. Further, he claimed that he was the last in a line of such divine figures, which included Zoroaster, the Buddha, Christ, and Muhammad. Along these lines, Baha'ullah's teachings called for a religious universalism in which moral truths could be gleaned from all faiths. His son, Abd al-Baha, spread his father's teachings to the Western world, insisting on certain social principles such as universal equality of the sexes, or races, and of religious adherence.

The Baha'i National Center of the U.S.A.
and, **The National Spiritual Assembly of the Bahà'ìs of the United States**
1233 Central Street

Evanston, IL 60201
(847)869-9039
Web site: www.us.bahai.org

This center can provide information about the Baha'i faith and provide contacts with Baha'i organizations throughout the country and the world. There are over 1,400/1,700 Baha'i local spiritual assemblies in the United States. The community is very concerned about issues involving peace, justice, racial unity, economic development, and education (among others) and has available resources on a number of these issues as well as on Baha'i scriptures and theology. The Web site listed above is the official Baha'i Web site in the U.S.A.

The National Spiritual Assembly of the Bahá'ís of the United States is the administrative body for the Bahá'ís of the U.S. The Assembly consists of 9 members chosen by 171 delegates representing all the adult Bahá'ís of the continental U.S.A. The Assembly directs, coordinates and stimulates the activities of individuals and local Spiritual Assemblies. It participates with other National Spiritual Assemblies in the election of the international governing body of the Faith, the Universal House of Justice, which is held in Haifa, Israel, every five years.

BUDDHISM

Buddhism began in northern India between the 6th–5th centuries B.C.E. with the teachings of Siddhartha Gautama, who is called the Buddha, which means "The One Who is Enlightened."

Buddhism grew out of the Hindu tradition of the time, but it rejected certain fundamental philosophical, cosmological, social, hierarchical, and scriptural aspects of that tradition, which set the two deeply apart from each other. Most Buddhists believe that suffering is the central predicament of life, and that desires are the source of this suffering. One need only remove desires and it follows that suffering disappears as well. Buddhism has grown in different directions over the centuries among many different cultures, and its traditions have varied widely. All are usually characterized by an emphasis on meditation and compassion. Buddhism is divided into three major branches: *Theravada*, "the way of the Elders," *Mahayana,* "the Great Vehicle," and *Vajrayana*, "the indestructible vehicle" or path of devotion. Buddhism spread through parts of South Asia, the Himalayan region, all over China, Japan, and Korea, and deeply into Southeast Asia. Although its origins are Indian, Buddhism is almost entirely absent from that country. In the past hundred and fifty years, Buddhism has spread to the Western world. In this religious tradition, with few national bodies and great variation among particular branches and cultural expressions, organization is more localized than in some other faith groups.

American Buddhist Congress
3835 E. Thousand Oaks Blvd., Ste. 450
Westlake Village, CA 91362
Tel. (877)7BUDDHA, (877)728-3342

An association of leaders from a variety of Buddhist traditions in the U.S.

Buddhist Churches of America
1710 Octavia St.
San Francisco, CA 94109
Tel. (415)776-5600
Fax (415)771-6293
Rev. Koshin Ogui

The national body of Japanese Shin tradition was founded in 1899. It provides programmatic resources for local temples around the U.S.

Buddhist Council of the Midwest
2400 Prairie
Evanston, IL 60201
Tel. (847)869-4975
Web site: members.ymc.net/jfred

A regional organization active in coordinating activities among the Buddhist communities in the Midwest.

Buddhist Sangha Council of Southern California
933 S. New Hampshire Ave.
Los Angeles, CA 90006
Tel. (213)739-1270
Fax (213)386-6643

The umbrella organization of Buddhist communities in Southern California.

Texas Buddhist Council
8727 Radio Rd.
Houston, TX 77075
The regional coordinating body for Buddhists in Texas.

The Buddhist Peace Fellowship
P. O. Box 3470
Berkeley, CA 94703
Tel. (510)655-6169
Fax (510)655-1369
E-mail: bpf@bpf.org
Web site: www.bpf.org
A national organization through which Buddhists of many traditions work for peace and justice.

HINDUISM

Hinduism has been evolving since roughly 1500 B.C.E. and has its origins in India. Most of the inhabitants of India are still Hindus, but many have emigrated to Europe, North America, East Africa, South and Southeast Asia. The beliefs and practices of Hinduism vary so deeply and widely throughout India, and are so diffused throughout every aspect of life, that one may describe Hinduism not so much as a tradition, but more accurately as the collection of many traditions, encompassed by the great history and geography of India. Throughout its history, Hinduism has had an enormous propensity for the absorption of new elements into its practices and its understanding of deity. There is no central authority or priestly hierarchy that regulates the evolution of Hinduism, very few traditions are shared by all Hindus; adaptations and evolutions can and do occur, but usually at the regional level. Simultaneously, ancient practices and beliefs persist in some places, where elsewhere, they have been long since replaced or never occurred. Nevertheless, all Hindus believe in the authority of the *Vedas*, the ancient scriptural tradition of India. All accept the *dharma*, or "way," of the four *varnas,* or social classes, which constitute the complex caste system, which is interwoven in the practice of the religion. Further, most Hindus worship Shiva or Vishnu or Devi, in addition to individual devotions to other deities or divine manifestations. Most Hindus are vegetarians.

The International Society for Krishna Consciousness
North American Communications
10310 Oaklyn Dr.
Potomac, MD 20854
Tel. (301)299-9707
Fax (301)299-5025
E-mail: anuttama.acbsp@com.bbt.se
Communications Dir., Anuttama Dasa

Council of Hindu Temples of North America
45-57 Bowne St.
Flushing, NY 11355
Tel. (800)99HINDU, (800)994-4638
Sec.-Treas., Dr. Uma Mysorekar
One of a number of Hindu organizations, which connect Hindus in certain regions of the U.S.

American Hindus Against Defamation
8914 Rotherdam Ave.
San Diego, CA 92129
Tel. (619)484-4564
E-mail: ajay@hindunet.org
Director, Mr. Ajay Shah
A new organization devoted to defending Hindus from stereotyping and discriminatory or defamatory acts/speech.

ISLAM

Islam began in 7th century Arabia under the leadership of the Prophet Muhammad, to whom God (*Allah* in Arabic) revealed a collection of verses known as the *Holy Qur'an*. The word *islam* means "making peace through submission" and in the context of religion, it means "submission to the will of God." A person who practices Islam is a Muslim, meaning, "one who is submitting to the will of God." A Muslim follows the teachings of the *Holy Qur'an*, which was presented to humankind by

Muhammad, but which is the very word of the one and only God, and is therefore perfect and complete. Integral to the Muslim tradition are the "Five Pillars of Islam," which are the five obligations each Muslim must uphold. The first of these is the *shahadah*, or profession of faith, which states, "There is no God but God, and Muhammad is his prophet." The second obligation is that a Muslim prays five times each day at prescribed times. Thirdly, a Muslim must pay the *zakat*, which is a form of mandatory almsgiving. Fourth, a Muslim is required to fast from dawn until sunset during the month of *Ramadan*, the ninth month of the Muslim year. And finally, if able, once in his/her lifetime, every Muslim is required to make a pilgrimage called the *Hajj* to the holy city of Mekkah, where the *ka'bah* is housed, a stone structure, built by Abraham and Ishmael. Early in the history of the Islam, the religion split into two distinct branches, known as the Sunni and the Shiah, both of which contain sub-branches. Muslims worldwide constitute an enormous community that is rapidly spreading throughout North America as a result of recent immigration as well as conversion.

The Islamic Society of North America (ISNA)
P.O. Box 38
Plainfield, IN 46168
Tel. (317)839-8157
Web site: www.isna.net
Gen. Sec., Dr. Sayyid M. Syeed

The Islamic Society of North America grew out of the Muslim Students Association and is one of the oldest national Muslim organizations in the United States. It has a varied program primarily serving the Muslim community, but also seeks to promote friendly relations between Muslims and non-Muslims. It has a speakers' bureau, film loans, library assistance program, and several other services. It has also has a number of publications. Since ISNA is well represented throughout much of the United States, it is a good initial contact. It has been very active in the area of interfaith relations.

The Islamic Circle of North America (ICNA)
166-26 89th Ave.
Jamaica, NY 11432
Tel. (718)658-1199
Web site: www.icna.org

The Islamic Circle of North America is a smaller national organization than ISNA, but is involved in many of the same activities. They also have a presence in many different parts of the country and provide a number of resources both to Muslims and non-Muslims. ICNA also has been very active in the world of interfaith relations.

The Muslim American Society
The Ministry of W. Deen Mohammed
P.O. Box 1944
Calumet City, IL 60409

This is the community of Imam W. Deen Mohammed and represents the largest single grouping of orthodox African-American Muslims in the United States. It is important to distinguish this group from the Nation of Islam (Black Muslims). African Americans constitute probably the largest single group of Muslims in the United States. Given the loose structure of the organization, it is often both possible and helpful to make contact with a local mosque in your area.

Muslim Public Affairs Council (MPAC)
3010 Wilshire Blvd., Ste. 217
Los Angeles, CA 90010
Tel. (213)383-3443
Fax (213)383-9674
Exec. Dir., Salam Al-Marayati

MPAC seeks to establish a vibrant American Muslim community that will enrich American society through promoting the Islamic values of mercy, justice, peace, human dignity, freedom and equality for all.

Council for American-Islamic Relations (CAIR)
453 New Jersey Ave. SE
Washington, DC 20003-4034
Tel. (202)488-8787
Fax (202)488-0833
E-mail: cair@cair-net.org

CAIR's mission is to enhance understanding of Islam, encourage dialogue, protect civil liberties, empower American Muslims and build coalitions that promote justice and mutual understanding.

JAINISM

Jainism was founded in the 6th century B.C.E. in India by Vardhamana Jnatiputra —also known as Nataputta Mahavira, whom the Jains call Jina, which means "Spiritual Conqueror." Mahavira was a contemporary of the Buddha, and to some extent, Buddhism was an important rival to Jainism at the time. Both grew out of the Hindu tradition but rejected certain of its aspects. Jains honor a number of saints, or prophets from remote history called *tirthankaras,* who had liberated themselves from the bondage of *karma,* and hence from the cycle of reincarnation Mahavira is the 24th of these *tirthankaras*. Emulating these saints, one may free the soul from the shackles of *karma* and rebirth, by observing the "three jewels" of "right faith," "right knowledge," "and right conduct." There is a strong emphasis in Jainism on peacefulness, moderation, and the refusal to injure animals in any way. There are religious orders, called *yatis,* which observe strict vows. The laity hold a pious respect for the *yatis*. There are two main branches of Jainism, the *Digambara* ("sky-clad" or "naked") and the *Svetambara* ("white-clad"). Despite the fact that the Jains constitute a relatively small proportion of the Indian population, they have a great influence on the Hindu community. The essential philosophy of nonviolence had a great effect on the teachings of Gandhi in this century.

Federation of Jain Associations in North America
P.O. Box 700
Getzville, NY 14068
Tel./Fax (716)636-5342
E-mail: jainahq@jaina.org

Siddhachalam/International Mahavira Jain Mission
65 Mud Pond Rd.
Blairstown, NJ 07285
Tel. (908)362-9793
A residential center for the teaching of the Jain way of life in the United States.

JUDAISM

Judaism is one of the world's oldest religions, encompassing a rich and complex tradition that has evolved over centuries and has given rise to, or influenced, other major world traditions. Numerous expressions of Judaism have always coexisted with one another, as they do today. The central concern shared by all is to live in relation to God and to follow God's will. Jews understand themselves to be in covenant with God, who is the one transcendent God, Creator of the Universe. God revealed the Torah to the people of Israel as his way of life. History brought the Jewish people into contact with many cultures and civilizations, contacts that continuously transformed the nature of their worship, the understanding of God's law, and even their conceptualization of peoplehood. At the time of the second Diaspora, or great migration of Jews throughout the Middle East, North Africa, and Europe at the beginning of the common era, was the rise of the rabbinical tradition, with its emphasis on the study of Scripture. Today's Judaism has grown out of these roots. In the 19th century, Reform Judaism arose in Europe and the United States as one Jewish response to modernity. Conservative Judaism and Reconstructionism are branches of Jewish practice that first developed in America. Orthodox Judaism also has a number of modern forms.

American Jewish Committee
165 East 56th St.
New York, NY 10022
Tel. (212)751-4000
Fax (212)750-0326
Web site: www.ajc.org
Exec. Dir., David A. Harris
Founded in 1906, the AJC protects the rights and freedoms of Jews worldwide; combats bigotry and anti-Semitism and promotes democracy and human rights for all. It is an independent community-relations organization, with strong interest in inter-religious relations and public policy advocacy. The AJC publishes the *American Jewish Yearbook*, and *Commentary* magazine.

The Anti-Defamation League of B'nai B'rith
823 United Nations Plaza
New York, NY 10017

Tel. (212)885-7707
Fax (212)867-0779
Web site: www.adl.org
National Dir., Abraham H. Foxman

Since 1913, the Anti-Defamation League has been involved in combating and documenting anti-Semitism. It also works to secure fair treatment for all citizens through law, education and community relations.

Jewish Council for Public Affairs
443 Park Ave. S., 11th Floor
New York, NY 10016
Tel. (212)684-6950
Fax (212)686-1353
Web site: www.jewishpublicaffairs.org
Exec. Dir., Hannah Rosenthal

This national coordinating body for the field of Jewish community relations comprises 13 national and 122 local Jewish communal agencies. Through the Council's work, and in its collaboration with other religious groups, its constituent agencies work on public policy issues, both international and domestic.

Jewish Reconstructionist Federation
7804 Montgomery Ave., Ste. 9
Elkins Park, PA 19027
Tel. (212)782-8500
E-mail: jfrnatl@aol.com
Exec. Dir., Rabbi Mordechai Liebling

Fosters the establishment and ongoing life of Reconstructionist congregations and fellowship groups. Publishes *The Reconstructionist* and other materials. Rabbis who relate to this branch of Judaism are often members of the Reconstructionist Rabbinical Association.

Union of Reform Judaism
633 Third Ave.
New York, NY 10017
Tel. (212)650-4000
Fax (212)650-4169
Web site: www.urj.org
Pres., Rabbi Eric H. Yoffie

The central congregational body of Reform Judaism, founded in 1873. It serves approx. 875 affiliated temples and its members through religious, educational, cultural and administrative programs, women's men's and youth organizations. *Reform Judaism* is one of its publications. The Central Conference of American Rabbis is the affiliated rabbinical body.

Religious Action Center of Reform Judaism
2027 Massachusetts Ave. NW
Washington, DC 20036
Tel. (202)387-2800
Fax (202)667-9070
E-mail: rac@urj.org
Exec. Dir., Rabbi David Saperstein

The Religious Action Center pursues social justice and religious liberty by mobilizing the American Jewish community and serving as its advocate in the capitol of the United States.

The Union of Orthodox Jewish Congregations of America
11 Broadway
New York, NY 10004-1003
Tel. (212)563-4000
Fax (212)564-9058
Web site: www.ou.org
Exec. Vice-Pres., Rabbi Tzvi Hersh Weinreb

The national central body of Orthodox synagogues since 1898, providing *kashrut* supervision, women's and youth organizations, and a variety of educational, religious and public policy programs and activities. Publishers of *Jewish Action* magazine and other materials. The Rabbinical Council of America is the related organization for Orthodox rabbis.

The United Synagogue of Conservative Judaism
155 Fifth Ave.
New York, NY 10010-6802
Tel. (212)533-7800
Fax (212)353-9439
Web site: www.uscj.org
Exec. Vice-Pres., Rabbi Jerome M. Epstein

The international organization of 800 congregations, founded in 1913. Provides religious, educational, youth, community and administrative programming. Publishes *United Synagogue Review* and other materials. The Rabbinical Assembly is the association of Conservative rabbis.

NATIVE AMERICAN TRADITIONAL SPIRITUALITY

Native American spirituality is difficult to define or categorize because it varies so greatly across the continent. Further, it is deeply entwined with elements of nature that are associated with different geographical regions. For example, while Plains Indians possess a spiritual relationship with the buffalo, indigenous peoples from the Northwest share a similar relationship with salmon. Hence, the character of Native American spirituality is dependent, to some extent, on the surrounding geography and its incumbent ecosystems. Despite this great variety, there are some similarities which allow us to consider the many Native American forms of spirituality together: Contrary to popular belief, Native American peoples are monotheistic; they do not worship the sun or buffalo or salmon, but rather understand that these elements of nature are gifts from the "Great Mystery," and are parts of it. Today, while still working toward religious freedom in the United States, Native Americans are also struggling to protect sacred sites, which they consider to be comparable to "churches." But since these sites are actually part of the land, not man-made structures, many are constantly under attack for the natural resources they contain. Such exploitation of these resources is an offense to the Native American sense of spirituality, which views resources like timber, oil, and gold, as gifts from the Great Mystery. The struggle to protect and respect these sacred sites is a universal and essential part of Native American spirituality.

National Congress of American Indians (NCAI)
1301 Connecticut Ave. NW, Ste. 200
Washington, DC 20036
Tel. (202) 466-7767
Fax (202) 466-7797
E-mail: jdossett@ncia.org
Web site: www.ncai.org
Exec. Dir., Jacqueline Johnson

The National Congress of American Indians (NCAI), founded in 1944, is the oldest, largest and most representative national Indian organization serving the needs of a broad membership of American Indian and Alaska native governments. NCAI stresses the need for unity and cooperation among tribal governments and people for the security and protection of treaty and sovereign rights. As the preeminent national Indian organization, NCAI is organized as a representative congress aiming for consensus on national priority issues.

The NCAI Web site contains links for a directory of Indian nations in the continental U.S. and Alaska as well as a directory of tribal governments. There are also links to other Native American Web sites.

Native American Rights Fund (NARF)

1506 Broadway
Boulder, CO 80302
Tel. (303) 447-8760
Fax (303) 433-7776
E-mail: pereira@narf.org
Web site: www.narf.org
Exec. Dir., John Echohawk

The Native American Rights Fund is the non-profit legal organization devoted to defending and promoting the legal rights of the Indian people. NARF attorneys, most of whom are Native Americans, defend tribes who otherwise cannot bear the financial burden of obtaining justice in the courts of the United States. The NARF mission statement outlines five areas of concentration: 1) Preservation of tribal existence; 2) Protection of tribal natural resources; 3) Promotion of human rights; 4) Accountability of government; 5) Development of Indian law.

SIKHISM

Sikhism was founded by Guru Nanak during the 15th and 16th centuries C.E. in the state of Punjab in northwestern India. Nanak was greatly influenced by the teachings of Kabir, a Muslim who became deeply inspired by Hindu philosophies. Kabir's poems called for a synthesis between Islam and Hinduism. In the footsteps of Kabir's wisdom, Nanak drew upon elements of Bhakti Hinduism and Sufi Islam: He stressed the existence of a universal, single God, who transcends religious distinctions. Union with God is accomplished through meditation and surrender to the divine will. Nanak also called for the belief in reincarnation, *karma*, and also the cyclical destruction and recreation of the universe. However, he rejected the caste system, the devotion to divine incarnations, priesthood, idol worship, all of which were elements of the Hindu tradition. Nanak was the first of ten *gurus*, or teachers. The fourth guru built the Golden Temple in Amritsar, the Sikh religious center. The fifth guru compiled the *Adi Granth*, a sort of hymnbook of spiritual authority. All male Sikhs are initiated into the religious brotherhood called the *Khalsa*. Members of this order vow never to cut their beard or hair, to wear special pants, to wear an iron bangle as an amulet against evil, to carry a steel dagger, and a comb.

The Sikh Center of Orange County
2514 West Warner Ave.
Santa Ana, CA 92704
Tel. (714) 979-9328
Web site: www.sikhcenter.org

The Sikh Center of Orange County describes itself as follows: "Our mission, in following the tradition and teaching of our honorable Guru Nanak, is to provide accurate, reliable and complete religious, social and cultural teachings and understanding of Sikhism and the people who practice it."

6. United States Regional and Local Ecumenical Bodies

One of the many ways Christians and Christian churches relate to one another locally and regionally is through ecumenical bodies. The membership in these ecumenical organizations is diverse. Historically, councils of churches were formed primarily by Protestants, but many local and regional organizations now include Orthodox and Roman Catholics. Many are made up of congregations or judicatory units of churches. Some have a membership base of individuals. Others foster cooperation between ministerial groups, community ministries, coalitions, or church agencies. While "council of churches" is a term still commonly used to describe this form of cooperation, other terms such as "conference of churches," "ecumenical councils," "churches united," "metropolitan ministries," are coming into use. Ecumenical organizations that are national in scope are listed in Director 1, "United States Cooperative Organizations."

An increasing number of ecumenical bodies have been exploring ways to strengthen the inter-religious aspect of life in the context of religious pluralism in the U.S. today. Some organizations in this listing are fully interfaith agencies primarily through the inclusion of Jewish congregations in their membership. Other organizations nurture partnerships with a broader base of religious groups in their communities, especially in the areas of public policy and inter-religious dialogue.

This list does not include all local and regional ecumenical and interfaith organizations in existence today. The terms regional and local are relative, making identification somewhat ambiguous. Regional councils may cover sections of large states or crossstate borders. Local councils may be made up of several counties, towns, or clusters of congregations. State councils or state-level ecumenical contacts exist in 45 of the 50 states. These state-level or multi-state organizations are marked with a "*." The organizations are listed alphabetically by state.

ALABAMA

Greater Birmingham Ministries

2304 12th Ave. N, Birmingham, AL 35234-3111 Tel. (205)326-6821 Fax (205)252-8458
E-mail: robert@gbm.org
Web site: www.gbm.org
Media Contact, Robert Montgomery
Exec. Dir., Scott Douglas
Economic Justice, Co-Chairs, Helen Holdefer, Betty Likis
Direct Services, Chair, Patty Warren
Faith in Community, Chair, Patricia Ross
Finance & Fund-Raising, Chair, Richard Ambrose
Pres., Tom Forsee
Treas., Helen Tibbs Wilson
Major Activities: Direct Service Ministries (Food, Utilities, Rent and Nutrition Education, Shelter); Alabama Arise (Statewide legislative network focusing on low income issues); Economic Justice Issues (Low Income Housing and Advocacy, Health Care, Community Development, Jobs Creation, Public Transportation); Faith in Community Ministries (Interchurch Forum, Interpreting and Organizing, Bible Study)

Interfaith Mission Service

701 Andrew Jackson Way NE, Huntsville, AL 35801 Tel. (256)536-2401 Fax (256)536-2284
E-mail: ims@hiwaay.net
Exec. Dir., Susan J. Smith
Pres., Richard C. Titus
Major Activities: Foodline & Food Pantry; Local FEMA Committee; Ministry Development; Clergy Luncheon; Workshops; Response to Community Needs; Information and Referral; Interfaith Understanding; Christian Unity; Homeless Needs; School Readiness Screenings

ALASKA

Alaska Christian Conference

Episcopal Diocese of Alaska, 1205 Denali Way, Fairbanks, AK 99701-4178 Tel. (907)452-3040
E-mail: mmcdonald@gci.net
Media Contact, Pres., Rt. Rev. Mark MacDonald
Pres., Rt. Rev. Mark MacDonald
Vice-Pres., Rev. David I. Blanchett, 1100 Pullman Drive, Wasilla, AK 99654 Tel. (907) 352-2517
Treas., Carolyn M. Winters, 2133 Bridgewater Drive, Fairbanks, AK 99709-4101 Tel. (907) 456-8555
Major Activities: Legislative & Social Concerns; Resources and Continuing Education; New Ecumenical Ministries; Communication; Alcoholism (Education & Prevention); Family Violence (Education & Prevention); Native Issues; Ecumenical-Theological Dialogue; HIV-AIDS Education and Ministry; Criminal Justice

ARIZONA

Arizona Ecumenical Council*

4423 N. 24th St., Ste. 750, Phoenix, AZ 85016 Tel. (602)468-3818 Fax (602)468-3311

E-mail: aec@aecunity.org
Web site: www.aecunity.org
Media Contact, Exec. Dir., Rev. Jan Olav Flaaten, Tel. (602)468-3818 Fax (602)468-3311, Cell (602)670-1594
Exec. Dir., Rev. Jan Olav Flaaten
Pres., Bishop Michael Neils
Major Activities: Facilitating collaboration among the 20 judicatories for Theological Dialogue, Services of Prayer, Public Policy and Social Justice, Church Leadership School (called Survival School), Local Ecumenism (encouraging and being a resource for local ecumenical groupings), Earth Care Commission (presents annual "Caring for Creation" conference), Arizonans for the Protection of Exploited Children and Adults (APECA), Disaster Relief, Nonviolence Education for Youth, Souper-Bowl

Arkansas Interfaith Conference*

P.O. Box 151, Scott, AR 72142 Tel. (501)961-2626
E-mail: aicark@aol.com
Media Contact, Conf. Exec., Mimi Dortch
Conf. Exec., Mimi Dortch
Pres., Rev. Steve Copley. 6701 JFK Blvd., Gielett, AR 72116 (Methodist)
Sec., Imam John Hasan. P.O.Box 1607, Little Rock, AR 72203. (Muslim)
Treas., Jim Davis, Box 7239, Little Rock, AR 72217 (Catholic)
Major Activities: Institutional Ministry; Interfaith Executives' Advisory Council; Interfaith Relations; Church Women United; Our House-Shelter; Legislative Liaison; Ecumenical Choir Camp; Tornado Disaster Relief; Camp for Jonesboro School Children Massacre; Welfare Reform Work; Med Center Chaplaincy; Peace Service

CALIFORNIA

California Council of Churches-California Church Impact*

2715 K Street, Suite D, Sacramento, CA 95816 Tel. (916)442-5447 Fax (916)442-3036
E-mail: cccinfo@calchurches.org
Web site: www.calchurches.org
Media Contact, Exec. Dir., The Rev. Rick Schlosser
Exec. Dir., The Rev. Rick Schlosser
Major Activities: Monitoring State Legislation; California IMPACT Network; Legislative Principles; Food Policy Advocacy; Family Welfare Issues; Health; Church-State Issues; Violence Prevention; Child Care Program-Capacity Coordinator to Increase Quality Child Care within California for the Working Poor; Building Bridges of Understanding: An Interfaith Response to Septerber 11.

The Council of Churches of Santa Clara County

1710 Moorpark Avenue, San Jose, CA 95128 Tel. (408)297-2660 Fax (408)297-2661
E-mail: councilchurches@aol.com
Media Contact, Interim Exec. Dir., Rev. R. Richard Roe
Interim Exec. Dir., Rev. R. Richard Roe
Pres., Rev. James Friedrich
Major Activities: Social Education-Action; Ecumenical and Interfaith Witness; Affordable Housing; Environmental Ministry; Family-Children; Convalescent Hospital Ministries; Gay Ministry; Strengthening Congregations for Ministry

The Ecumenical Council of Pasadena Area Churches

P.O. Box 41125, 444 E. Washington Blvd., Pasadena, CA 91114-8125 Tel. (626)797-2402 Fax (626)797-735
E-mail: ecpac@prodigy.net
Exec. Dir., Rev. Frank B. Clark
Major Activities: Christian Education; Community Worship; Community Concerns; Christian Unity; Ethnic Ministries; Hunger; Peace; Food, Clothing Assistance for the Poor; Emergency Shelter

Ecumenical Council of San Diego County

1880 Third Ave., #13, San Diego, CA 92101
E-mail: nrankin@ecsd.org
Web site: www.ecsd.org
Exec. Dir. (interim), Nancy Rankin
Pres. Jane Barry
Treas., Rev. Robert Ard
Major Activities: Interfaith Shelter Network-Rational Shelter and El Nido Transitional Living Program; Emerging Issues; Faith Order & Witness; Worship & Celebration; Ecumenical Tribute Dinner; Advent Prayer Breakfast; Seminars and Workshops; Called to Dance Assn.; Children's Sabbath Workshops and Events; Edgemoor Chaplaincy; Stand for Children events; Continuing Education for Clergy and Laypersons; Inter-Religious Council; Sacred Spaces Church Tour

Fresno Metro Ministry

1055 N. Van Ness, Ste. H, Fresno, CA 93728 Tel. (559)485-1416 Fax (559)485-9109
E-mail: metromin@fresnometmin.org
Web site: www.fresnometmin.org
Media Contact, Exec. Dir., Rev. Walter P. Parry
Exec. Dir., Rev. Walter P. Parry
Pres., Tony Gonzalez
Major Activities: Hunger Relief & Nutrition Advocacy; Cultural Diversity and Anti-Racism; Health Care Advocacy; Environmental Health and Quality; Access and Public Health; Public Education Concerns; Children's Needs; Ecumenical & Interfaith Celebrations & Cooperation; Youth Needs; Community Network Building; Human Services Facilitation; Anti-Poverty

Efforts; Low-Income and Immigrant Leadership Development related to public policies

Interfaith Council of Contra Costa County

1543 Sunnyvale Ave., Walnut Creek, CA 94596 Tel. (925)933-6030 Fax (925)952-4554

Chaplains, Rev. Charles Tinsley; Rev. Duane Woida; Rev. Harold Wright; Laurie Maxwell

Pres., Rev. Steve Harms

Treas., Robert Bender

Major Activities: Institutional Chaplaincies, Community Education, Interfaith Cooperation; Social Justice

Interfaith Service Bureau

2212 K. St., Sacramento, CA 95816-4923 Tel. (916)456-3815 Fax (916)456-3816

E-mail: isbdexter@aol.com

Media Contact, Exec. Dir., Dexter McNamara

Exec. Dir., Dexter McNamara

Pres., Richard Montgomery

Vice-Pres., Lloyd Hanson

Major Activities: Religious and Racial Cooperation and Understanding; Welfare Reform Concerns; Refugee Resettlement & Support; Religious Cable Television; Violence Prevention; Graffiti Abatement

Marin Interfaith Council

1510 5th Avenue, San Rafael, CA 94901-1807 Tel. (415)456-9657 Fax (415)456-6959

E-mail: admin@marinifc.org

Web site: marininterfaithcouncil.org

Media Contact, Exec. Dir., Rev. Carol Hovis

Exec. Dir., Rev. Carol Hovis

Major Activities: Interfaith Dialogue; Education; Advocacy; Convening; Interfaith Worship Services & Commemorations

Northern California Inter-religious Conference

534 22nd St., Oakland, CA 94612 Tel. (510)433-0822 Fax (510)433-0813

E-mail: ncic@igc.org

Web site: ncic.home.igc.org

Media Contact, Pres., Rev. Phil Lawson

Exec. Dir., Catherine Coleman

Pres., Rev. Phil Lawson

Vice-Pres., Esther Ho

Sec., Robert Forsberg

Major Activities: Peace with Justice Commission; Inter-religious Relationships Commission; Public Policy Advocacy; Welfare Reform, Founding member of California Council of Churches and of California Interfaith Power and Light; Soul of Justice, a spiritual and leadership concepts interactive performance troupe of teens and young adults; death penalty moratorium; video produced for sale for congregations-organizations to study legal, theological and social implications of marriage and same-gender marriage, widening our circle of religious groups participating; a cooperating circle of URL.

Pacific and Asian American Center for Theology and Strategies (PACTS)

Graduate Theological Union, 2400 Ridge Rd., Berkeley, CA 94709 Tel. (510)849-0653

E-mail: pacts@igc.org

Media Contact, Dir., Kyle Minura

Dir., Kyle Minura

Pres., Ronald Nakasone

Major Activities: Collect and Disseminate Resource Materials; Training Conferences; Public Seminars; Women in Ministry; Racial and Ethnic Minority Concerns; Journal and Newsletter; Hawaii & Greater Pacific Programme; Sale of Sadao Watanabe Calendars; Informational Forums on Peace & Social Justice in Asian Pacific American Community and Asia-Pacific Internationally; Forums & Conferences for Seminarians Asian Pacific Heritage; holistic health and healing ministries; affirming support groups for gay, lesbian, transgender, and questioning Asian and Pacific Islanders.

Pomona Inland Valley Council of Churches

1753 N. Park Ave., Pomona, CA 91768 Tel. (909)622-3806 Fax (909)622-0484

Media Contact, Dir. of Dev., Mary Kashmar

Pres., The Rev. Henry Rush

Acting Exec. Dir., The Rev. La Quetta Bush-Simmons

Sec., Ken Coates

Treas., Anne Ashford

Major Activities: Advocacy and Education for Social Justice; Ecumenical Celebrations; Hunger Advocacy; Emergency Food and Shelter Assistance; Farmer's Market; Affordable Housing; Transitional Housing

San Fernando Valley Interfaith Council

10824 Topanga Canyon Blvd., No. 7, Chatsworth, CA 91311 Tel. (818)718-6460 Fax (818)718-0734

E-mail: info@sfvic.org

Web site: www.sfvic.org

Media Contact, Comm. Coord., Eileen Killoren, ext. 3002

Pres., Barry Smedberg, ext. 3011

Chair, Board of Dir., Rev. Bernard (Bob) Bonnot, PhD

Major Activities: Seniors Multi-Purpose Centers; Nutrition & Services; Meals to Homebound; Meals on Wheels; Interfaith Reporter; Interfaith Relations; Social Adult Day Care; Hunger-Homelessness; Volunteer Care-Givers;

Clergy Gatherings; Food Pantries and Outreach; Social Concerns; Aging; Hunger; Human Relations; Immigration Services; Self-Sufficiency Program for Section 8 Families

South Coast Interfaith Council

759 Linden Ave., Long Beach, CA 90813 Tel. (562)983-1665 Fax (562)983-8812
E-mail: scic@earthlink.net
Web site: www.southcoastecumenical.org
Media Contact, Exec. Dir., Rev. Ginny Wagener
Exec. Dir., Rev. Ginny Wagener
Farmers' Markets, Rev. Dale Whitney
Pres., Rev. Dr. Reinhard Krauss
Centro Shalom, Amelia Nieto
Good Samaritan Counseling Ctr., Dr. William Scar
Major Activities: Homeless Support Services; Farmers' Markets; CROP Hunger Walks; Church Athletic Leagues; Community Action; Easter Sunrise Worships; Inter-religious Dialogue; Justice Advocacy; Martin Luther King, Jr. Celebration; Violence Prevention; Long Beach Interfaith Clergy; Publishing Area Religious Directories

Southern California Ecumenical Council

195 So. Hill Ave., Pasadena, CA 91106 Tel. (626)578-6371 Fax (626)578-6358
E-mail: scec1@scec1.net
Web site: www.scec1.net
Media Contact, Exec. Dir., Rev. Albert G. Cohen
Exec. Dir., Rev. Albert G. Cohen
Pres., Fr. Ashag Khatchadourian
Treas., Rev. Paul Lance
Sec., Ms. Lucy Guernsey
Vice-Pres. Special Events, Dr. Gwynne Guibord
Second Vice-Pres., Carol Kostura
Members at Large, Rev. Dr. Efstathios Mylonas; Ms. Laura Ramirez; Fr. Alexei Smith
Faith and Order Chair, Rev. Dr. Rod Parrott
Past Pres., Rev. Donald Smith
Major Activities: Consultation with the regional religious sector concerning the well-being and spiritual vitality of this most diverse and challenging area

Westside Interfaith Council

P.O. Box 1402, Santa Monica, CA 90406 Tel. (310)394-1518 Fax (310)576-1895
Media Contact, Rev. Janet A. Bregar
Exec. Dir., Rev. Janet A. Bregar
Major Activities: Meals on Wheels; Community Religious Services; Convalescent Hospital Chaplaincy; Homeless Partnership; Hunger & Shelter Coalition

COLORADO

Colorado Council of Churches*

3690 Cherry Creek S. Dr., Denver, CO 80209 Tel. (303)825-4910 Fax (303)744-8605
E-mail: jrryan7@qwest.net
Web site: www.coloradocouncilofchurches.org
Media Contact, Council Exec., Rev. Dr. James R. Ryan
Pres., Rev. Janet Schlenker
Staff Assoc., Dori Wilson
Major Activities: Addressing issues of Christian Unity, Justice, and Environment

Interfaith Council of Boulder

3700 Baseline Rd., Boulder, CO 80303 Tel. (303)494-8094
Media Contact, Pres., Stan Grotegut, 810 Kalma Ave., Boulder, CO 80304 Tel. (303)443-2291
Pres., Stan Grotegut
Major Activities: Interfaith Dialogue and Programs; Thanksgiving Worship Services; Food for the Hungry; Share-A-Gift; Monthly Newsletter

CONNECTICUT

Association of Religious Communities

325 Main St., Danbury, CT 06810 Tel. (203)792-9450 Fax (203)792-9452
E-mail: arc325@aol.com
Media Contact, Exec. Dir., Rev. Phyllis J. Leopold
Exec. Dir., Rev. Phyllis J. Leopold
Pres., The Rev. Mark Lingle
Major Activities: Refugee Resettlement; Family Counseling; Family Violence Prevention; Affordable Housing, Inter-Faith Dialogue, Racial Justice

The Capitol Region Conference of Churches

60 Lorrain St., Hartford, CT 06105 Tel. (860)236-1295 Fax (860)236-8071
E-mail: crcc@conferenceofchurches.org
Web site: www.conferenceofchurches.org
Media Contact, Exec. Dir., Rev. Shelley Copeland
Exec. Dir., Rev. Shelley Copeland
Pastoral Care & Training, Dir., Rev. Kathleen Davis
Aging Project, Dir., Barbara Malcolm
Community Organizer, Joseph Wasserman
Broadcast Ministry Consultant, Ivor T. Hugh
Pres., Mr. David O. White
Major Activities: Organizing for Peace and Justice; Aging; Legislative Action; Cooperative Broadcast Ministry; Ecumenical Cooperation; Interfaith Reconciliation; Chaplaincies; Low-Income Senior Empowerment; Anti-Racism Education

Center City Churches

40 Pratt Street,, Ste. 210, Hartford, CT 06103-1601 Tel. (860)728-3201 Fax (860)549-8550
E-mail: info@centercitychurches.org
Web site: www.centercitychurches.org

Media Contact, Exec. Dir., Paul C. Christie
Exec. Dir., Paul C. Christie
Pres., Marie LaMarre Ford
Treas., Frank Lord
Major Activities: Senior Services; Family Resource Center; Energy Bank; Food Pantry; Assistance & Advocacy; After-School Tutoring and Arts Enrichment; Summer Day Camp; Housing for persons with AIDS; Community Soup Kitchen

Christian Community Action

168 Davenport Ave., New Haven, CT 06519 Tel. (203)777-7848 Fax (203)777-7848
E-mail: cca@ccahelping.org
Web site: www.ccahelping.org
Media Contact, Exec. Dir., The Rev. Bonita Grubbs
Exec. Dir., The Rev. Bonita Grubbs
Major Activities: Emergency Food Program; Used Furniture & Clothing; Security and Fuel; Emergency Housing for Families; Advocacy; Transitional Housing for Families

Christian Conference of Connecticut*

60 Lorraine St., Hartford, CT 06105 Tel. (860)236-4281 Fax (860)236-9977
E-mail: ssidorak@aol.com
Web site: www.christconn.org
Media Contact, Exec. Dir., Rev. Dr. Stephen J. Sidorak, Jr.
Exec. Dir., The Rev. Dr. Stephen J. Sidorak, Jr.
Pres., The Rt. Rev. Andrew D. Smith
Vice-Pres., The Rev. Dr. Robert C. Dvorak
Sec., The Rev. Samuel N. Slie
Treas., Mr. Minot B. Nettleton
Major Activities: Communications; Institutional Ministries; Connecticut Ecumenical Small Church Project; Ecumenical Forum; Faith & Order; Social Concerns; Public Policy; Peace and Justice Convocation; Restorative Justice & Death Penalty; Inter-religious Dialogue ; Anti-Nuclear Activities; Problem Gambling; Jewish-Christian Dialogue

Council of Churches of Greater Bridgeport, Inc.

180 Fairfield Ave., Bridgeport, CT 06604 Tel. (203)334-1121 Fax (203)367-8113
E-mail: ccgb@ccgb.org
Web site: www.ccgb.org
Media Contact, Exec. Dir., Rev. John S. Kidd
Exec. Dir., Rev. John S. Kidd
Pres. Rev. Dr. Brian Schofield-Bodt
Vice-Pres., Bonnie McWain
Sec., Valerie Peterkin
Treas., Roger Perry
Major Activities: Youth in Crisis; Youth In Crisis Hotline, Responses & Safe Places; Host Home Shelter Care; Criminal Justice Services for Ex-offenders; Jail Ministry; Hunger Outreach and Networking; Ecumenical & Inter-Religious Relations, Prayer and Celebration; Covenantal Ministries; Homework Help; Summer Programs; Race Relations-Bridge Building

Council of Churches and Synagogues of Southwestern Connecticut

461 Glenbrook Rd, Stamford, CT 06901 Tel. (203)348-2800 Fax (203)358-0627
E-mail: council@flvax.ferg.lib.ct.us
Web site: www.interfaithcouncil.org
Media Contact, Comm. Ofc., Lois Alcosser
Exec. Dir., Jack Penfield, Interim Director
Major Activities: Partnership Against Hunger; The Food Bank of Lower Fairfield County; Friendly Visitors and Friendly Shoppers; Senior Neighborhood Support Services; Christmas in April; Interfaith Programming; Prison Visitation; Friendship House; Help a Neighbor; Operation Fuel; Teaching Place

Greater Waterbury Interfaith Ministries, Inc.

84 Crown St., Waterbury, CT 06704 Tel. (203)756-7831 Fax (203)419-0024
Media Contact, Exec. Dir., Carroll E. Brown
Exec. Dir., Carroll E. Brown
Pres., The Rev. Dr. James G. Bradley
Major Activities: Emergency Food Program; Emergency Fuel Program; Soup Kitchen; Ecumenical Worship; Christmas Toy Sale; Annual Hunger Walk

Manchester Area Conference of Churches

P.O. Box 3804, Manchester, CT 06045-3804 Tel. (860)647-8003
Media Contact, Exec. Dir., Denise Cabana
Exec. Dir., Denise Cabana
Dir. of Community Ministries, Joseph Piescik
Dept. of Ministry Development, Dir., Karen Bergin
Pres., Rev. Charles Ericson
Vice-Pres., Theresa Ghabrial
Sec., Jean Richert
Treas., Clive Perrin
Major Activities: Provision of Basic Needs (Food, Fuel, Clothing, Furniture); Emergency Aid Assistance; Emergency Shelter; Soup Kitchen; Reentry Assistance to Sex Offenders; Pastoral Care in Local Institutions; Interfaith Day Camp; Advocacy for the Poor; Ecumenical Education and Worship

New Britain Area Conference of Churches (NEWBRACC)

830 Corbin Ave., New Britain, CT 06052 Tel. (860)229-3751 Fax (860)223-3445
Media Contact, Exec. Dir., Michael Gorzoch
Exec. Dir., Michael Gorzoch
Pastoral Care-Chaplaincy, Rev. Ron Smith; Rev.

Will Baumgartner; Rev. Rod Rinnel
Pres., Rev. Anne Marie Meyerhoffer
Treas., Joyce Chmura
Major Activities: Worship; Social Concerns; Emergency Food Bank Support; Communications—Mass Media; Hospital; Elderly Programming; Homelessness and Hunger Programs; Telephone Ministry

DELAWARE

The Christian Council of Delaware and Maryland's Eastern Shore*

2020 N. Tatnall Street, Wilmington, DE 19802 Tel. (302)-656-5441
Web site: www.demdsynod.org
Media Contact, Pres., Bishop Wayne P. Wright, Diocese of Delaware, 2020 N. Tatnall Street, Wilmington, DE 19802
Pres., Bishop Wayne P. Wright, Diocese of Delaware, 2020 N. Tatnall Street, Wilmington, DE 19802
Major Activities: Exploring Common Theological, Ecclesiastical and Community Concerns; Racism; Prisons

DISTRICT OF COLUMBIA

The Council of Churches of Greater Washington

5 Thomas Circle N.W., Washington, DC 20005 Tel. (202)722-9240 Fax (202)722-9240
Media Contact, Exec. Dir., The Rev. Rodger Hall Reed, Sr.
Pres., The Rev. Lewis Anthony
Exec. Dir., The Rev. Rodger Hall Reed, Sr.
Prog. Officer, Daniel M. Thompson
Major Activities: Promotion of Christian Unity-Ecumenical Prayer & Worship; Coordination of Community Ministries; Summer Youth Employment; Summer Camping—Inner City Youth; Supports wide variety of social justice concerns

InterFaith Conference of Metropolitan Washington

1426 Ninth St., NW, Washington, DC 20001-3344 Tel. (202)234-6300 Fax (202)234-6303
E-mail: ifc@ifcmw.org
Web site: www.ifcmw.org
Media Contact, Exec. Dir., Rev. Dr. Clark Lobenstine
Exec. Dir., Rev. Dr. Clark Lobenstine
Admin. Sec., Judy Bond
Pres., Mrs. Carole Miller
First Vice-Pres., Siva Subramanian, M.D.
Chair, Rev. Dr. Robert Maddo
Sec., Mrs. Iris Lav
Treas., Sheikh Bassam Estwani
Major Activities: Helps end hunger, homelessness, and racism. Strengthens families and youth and deepens understanding by bringing together 10 world religions to build a just, compassionate community in metropolitan Washington, D.C.

FLORIDA

Christian Service Center for Central Florida, Inc.

808 W. Central Blvd., Orlando, FL 32805-1809 Tel. (407)425-2523 Fax (407)425-9513
Web site: www.christianservicecenter.org
Media Contact, Exec. Dir., Robert F. Stuart
Exec. Dir., Robert F. Stuart
Family Emergency Services, Dir., Rev. Haggeo Gautier
Fresh Start, Dir., Rev. Haggeo Gautier
Pres., Dr. Bryan Fulwider
Treas., Peter Reinert
Sec., Terry Bitner
Major Activities: Provision of Basic Needs (food, clothing, shelter); Emergency Assistance; Noontime Meals; Collection and Distribution of Used Clothing; Shelter & Training for Homeless; Children's After-School and Summer Programs

Florida Council of Churches*

523 Spring Oaks Blvd., Altamonte Springs, FL 32714 Tel. (407)265-7376 Fax (630)839-0114
E-mail: fced@aol.com
Web site: www.floridachurches.org
Media Contact, Exec. Dir., Rev. Fred Morris
Exec. Dir., Rev. Fred Morris
Major Activities: Justice and Peace; Disaster Response; Legislation & Public Policy; Local Ecumenism; Farmworker Ministry; Cherishing the Creation (Environmental Stewardship)

GEORGIA

Georgia Christian Council*

P.O. Box 7193, Macon, GA 31209-7193 Tel. (478)743-2085 Fax (478)743-2085
E-mail: lccollins@juno.com
Media Contact, Exec. Dir., Rev. Leland C. Collins
Exec. Dir., Rev. Leland C. Collins
Pres., Bishop B. Michael Watson, 3370 Vincville, Ave., Suite 101, Macon, GA 31204
Sec., Dr. Willis Moore, 5312 W. Mountain St., Suite 200, Stone Mountain, GA 30083-2073
Major Activities: Local Ecumenical Support and Resourcing; Legislation; Rural Development; Racial Justice; Networking for Migrant Coalition; Aging Coalition; GA To GA With Love; Medical Care; Prison Chaplaincy; Training for Church Development; Souper Bowl; Disaster Relief; Clustering; Development of Local Ecumenism; Prison Ministry; Hunger Advocacy; Family Advocacy; Developing Discipleship

The Regional Council of Churches of Atlanta

2195 Defoor Hills Rd., Suite L, Atlanta, GA 30318 Tel. (404)389-0590 Fax (404)389-0594

E-mail: info@rccatl.org
Web site: www.rccatl.org
Pres., Rev. Anthony M. Alford, Sr.
Vice-Pres., Rev. Kimberleigh Buchanan
Vice-Pres., Dr. R. Alan Culpepper
Vice-Pres., Dr. Mark A. Lomax
Vice-Pres., Rev. Adrian C. H. Pleus
Sec., Dr. C.P. Huang
Treas., Ms. Dorothy James
Exec. Dir., Roy Craft
Office Coord., Ethel Ware Carter
Major Activities: Refugee Services; Commission on Children and Youth; Supervised Ministry; Homeless; Ecumenical and Inter-religious Events; Persons With Handicapping Conditions; Women's Concerns; Task Force on Prison Ministry; Quarterly Forums on Ecumenical Issues; Faith and Order Concerns; Interracial and Intercultural Emphasis

IDAHO

The Regional Council for Christian Ministry, Inc.

237 N. Water, Idaho Falls, ID 83403 Tel. (208) 524-9935
Exec. Sec., Wendy Schoonmaker
Major Activities: Island Park Ministry; Community Food Bank; Community Observances; Community Information and Referral Service; F.I.S.H.

ILLINOIS

Churches United of the Quad City Area

630 9th St., Rock Island, IL 61201 Tel. (309)786-6494 Fax (309)786-5916
E-mail: mjones@churchesunited.net
Web site: www.churchesunited.net
Media Contact, Exec. Dir., Rev. Ronald Quay
Exec. Dir., Ronald Quay
Prog. Manager, Anne E. Wachal
Pres., Mr. Joseph Lindsay
Pres. Elect, Mrs. Sandra Frericks
Treas., Mr. Bill Schmidt
Major Activities: Jail Ministry; Hunger Projects; Minority Enablement; Criminal Justice; Radio-TV; Peace; Local Church Development; Living Wage

Community Renewal Society

332 South Michigan Ave. Suite 500, Chicago, IL 60604 Tel. (312)427-4830 Fax (312)427-6130
E-mail: csmorris@crs-ucc.org
Web site: www.crs-ucc.org
Media Contact, Exec. Dir., Dr. Calvin S. Morris

Contact Ministries of Springfield

1100 E. Adams, Springfield, IL 62703 Tel. (217) 753-3939 Fax (217)753-8643
E-mail: rtarrcm@springnetl.com
Media Contact, Exec. Dir., Rita Tarr
Exec. Dir., Rita Tarr
Major Activities: Information; Referral and Advocacy; Ecumenical Coordination; Low Income Housing Referral; Food Pantry Coordination; Prescription & Travel Emergency; Low Income Budget Counseling; 24 hours on call; Emergency Shelter On-site Women with Children

Evanston Ecumenical Action Council

P.O. Box 1414, Evanston, IL 60204 Tel. (847) 475-1150 Fax (847)475-2526
Web site: members.aol.com/eeachome/eeac.html
Media Contact, Comm. Chpsn., Ken Wylie
Hospitality Ctr. for the Homeless, Dir., Sue Murphy
Co-Pres., Rev. Ted Miller; Rev. Hardist Lane
Treas., Caroline Frowe
Major Activities: Interchurch Communication and Education; Peace and Justice Ministries; Coordinated Social Action; Soup Kitchens; Multi-Purpose Hospitality Center for the Homeless; Worship and Renewal, Racial Reconciliation, Youth Work

Greater Chicago Broadcast Ministries

112 E. Chestnut St., Chicago, IL 60611-2014 Tel. (312)988-9001 Fax (312)988-9004
E-mail: gcbm@ameritech.net
Media Contact, Exec. Dir., Lydia Talbot
Pres., Bd. of Dir., Rev. Phil Blackwell
Exec. Dir., Lydia Talbot
Admin. Asst., Margaret Early
Major Activities: Television, Interfaith-Ecumenical Development; Social Justice Concerns

The Hyde Park & Kenwood Interfaith Council

5745 S. Blackstone Ave., Chicago, IL 60637 Tel. (773)752-1911 Fax (773)752-2676
Media Contact, Exec. Dir., Lesley M. Radius
Exec. Dir., Lesley M. Radius
Pres., Rev. David Grainger
Sec., Barbara Krell
Major Activities: Interfaith Work; Hunger Projects; Community Development

Illinois Conference of Churches*

522 East Monroe, Ste. 208, Springfield, IL 62701 Tel. (217)522-7099 Fax (217)522-7100
E-mail: adminstaff@ilconfchurches.org
Web site: ilconfchurches.org
Media Contact, Exec. Dir., Rev. David A. Anderson, E-mail davidanderson@ilconfchurhces.org
Exec. Dir., Rev. David A. Anderson
Pres., Rev. Donald E. Mason
Major Activities: Unity and Relationships Commission, Council of Judicatory Executives;

Ecumenical Forums & Retreats; Triennial Ecumenical Assembly; Church and Society Commission, Public Policy Ecumenical Network; Global Ecumenism on Cuba; Racism; Economic Justice; Universal Health Care

Oak Park-River Forest Community of Congregations

P.O. Box 3365, Oak Park, IL 60303-3365 Tel. (708)386-8802 Fax (708)386-1399
Web site: www.mcs.net/~grossman/comcong.htm
Media Contact, Patricia C. Koko
Admin. Sec., Patricia C. Koko
Pres., Ms. Marguerite Rourke
Treas., Mr. Gerald Parker
Major Activities: Community Affairs; Ecumenical-Interfaith Affairs; Youth Education; Food Pantry; Senior Citizens Worship Services; Interfaith Thanksgiving Services; Good Friday Services; UNICEF Children's Fund Drive; Blood Drive; Literacy Training; CROP-CWS Hunger Walkathon; Work with Homeless Through PADS (Public Action to Deliver Shelter); Diversity Education

Peoria Friendship House of Christian Service

800 N.E. Madison Ave., Peoria, IL 61603 Tel. (309)671-5200 Fax (309)671-5206
Media Contact, Exec. Dir., Beverly Isom
Pres. of Bd., David Dadds
Major Activities: Children's After-School; Teen Programs; Recreational Leagues; Senior Citizens Activities; Emergency Food/Clothing Distribution; Emergency Payments for Prescriptions, Rent, Utilities; Community Outreach; Economic Development; Neighborhood Empowerment; GED Classes; Family Literacy; Mother's Group; Welfare to Work Programs

INDIANA

The Associated Churches of Fort Wayne & Allen County, Inc.

602 E. Wayne St., Fort Wayne, IN 46802 Tel. (219)422-3528 Fax (219)422-6721
E-mail: vernchurch@aol.com
Web site: www.associatedchurches.org
Media Contact, Exec. Dir., Rev. Vernon R. Graham
Exec. Dir., Rev. Vernon R. Graham
Admin. Asst., Elaine Williamson
Foodbank, Dir., Ellen Graham; John Kaiser; Loren Rossi; Lora Ganote
Dir. of Prog. Development & Mission Outreach, Ellen Graham
Dir. of Weekday Religious Education, Kathy Rolf
Pres., Thomas Szymczak, 1711 Black Bear Dr., Ft. Wayne, IN 46808
Treas., Rev. Alycia Smith, 3223 Hobson Rd., Ft. Wayne, IN 46805
Major Activities: Weekday Religious Ed.; Church Clusters; Church and Society Commission; Overcoming Racism; A Baby's Closet; Hunger Walk; Campus Ministry; Feeding the Babies; Food Bank System; Peace & Justice Commission; Welfare Reform; Endowment Development; Child Care Advocacy; Advocates Inc.; Ecumenical Dialogue; Children Feeding Children; Vincent House (Homeless); A Learning Journey (Literacy); Reaching Out in Love; The Jail Ministry; The Samaritan Counseling Center; Habitat for Humanity.

Christian Ministries of Delaware County

401 E. Main St., Muncie, IN 47305 Tel. (317)288-0601 Fax (317)282-4522
E-mail: christianministries@netzero.net
Web site: www.christianministries.ws
Media Contact, Exec. Dir., Marie Evans
Exec. Dir., Marie Evans
Pres., Dr. J. B. Black, Jr.
Treas., Joan McKee
Major Activities: Baby Care Program; Youth Ministry at Detention Center; Community Church Festivals; Food Pantry; Emergency Assistance; CROP Walk; Social Justice; Family Life Education; Homeless Shelter (sleeping room only); Clothing and household items available free; workshops for low income clients; homeless apartments available-short stays only at no cost; provide programs and workshops for pastors and churches in community; work with schools sponsoring programs.

Church Community Services

629 S. 3rd Street, Elkhart, IN 46516-3241 Tel. (574)295-5593 Fax (574)295-5593
E-mail: ccs6293rd@aol.com
Web site: www.soupofsuccess.com
Media Contact, Rev. Jeni Hiett Umble
Exec. Dir., Rev. Jeni Hiett Umble
Major Activities: Financial Assistance for Emergencies; Food Pantry; Information and Referral; Clothing Referral; Rent Assistance; Medication Vouchers; Transportation Vouchers; Job and Life Skills Training Program for Women

The Church Federation of Greater Indianapolis, Inc.

1100 W. 42nd St., Ste. 345, Indianapolis, IN 46208 Tel. (317)926-5371 Fax (317)926-5373
E-mail: churches@churchfederationindy.org
Web site: www.churchfederationindy.org
Media Contact, Comm. Consultant, Julie Foster
Exec. Dir., Rev. Dr. Angelique Walker-Smith
Pres., Rev. Dr. Joh Wantz
Treas., Hugh Moore
Major Activities: "Preserving Christian Diversity

& Impacting Our Society-Through Unity in Christ": Organizing, Energizing, Mobilizing Since 1912 (John 17:20-23), Benevolence Ministry-C.R.O.P. (Church World Service; Celebration of Hope Partnership (Racial Reconciliation); Clergy ID Badge Program; Faith and Fathers; FaithFest!; Family Congregation and Mentoring Program(FCMP); Greater Indianapolis Urban Forum; Hispanic-Latino Forum; Loving Our Children/Children's Sabbath; Greater Indianapolis Prayer Network to Stop the Violence-Ecumenical Project for Reconciliation and Healing; TV Broadcasts; Loaves and Fishes Advocacy Network

Evansville Area Community of Churches, Inc.

713 N. 2nd Ave., Evansville, IN 47710 Tel. (812) 425-3524 Fax (812)425-3525
E-mail: eacc@evansville.net
Media Contact, EACC Administrator and Weekday Director, Janet Battram
Weekday Dir., Janet Battram
Pres., Rev. G. Philip Hoy
Vice-Pres., Evelyn Cave
Sec., Rev. C. E. Erickson
Treas., Paul Farmer
Major Activities: Food Pantry System; Jail Ministry; Weekday Christian Ed.; Ecumenical and Community Service & Activities

Indiana Partners for Christian Unity and Mission

P.O. Box 88790, Indianapolis, IN 46208-0790 Tel. (800)746-2310 Fax (315)292-5990
E-mail: indunity@aol.com
Web site: www.ipcum.org
Media Contact, James V. Dougans
Pres., Rev. Timothy D. Bonney
Treas., Mrs. Marilyn Moffett
Major Activities: Initiating dialogue on issues of social concern by organizing conferences on the death penalty, racism, welfare reform and violence; facilitating communication through an electronic newsletter and Web site; promoting the National Day of Prayer and the Week of Prayer for Christian Unity; and advancing Churches Uniting in Christ.

Interfaith Community Council, Inc.

702 E. Market St., New Albany, IN 47150 Tel. (812)948-9248 Fax (812)948-9249
E-mail: icc@digicove.com
Web site: www.interfaithinc.org
Media Contact, Exec. Dir., Houston Thompson
Exec. Dir., Houston Thompson
RSVP, Dir., Ceil Sperzel
Major Activities: Emergency Assistance; Retired Senior Volunteer Program; New Clothing and Toy Drives; Emergency Food Distribution; Homeless Prevention; Kids' Café; Youth Development Services

Kentuckiana Interfaith Community **(see listing under Kentucky)**

Lafayette Urban Ministry

525 N. 4th St., Lafayette, IN 47901 Tel. (317) 423-2691 Fax (317)423-2693
Media Contact, Exec. Dir., Joseph Micon
Exec. Dir., Joseph Micon
Advocate Coord., Rebecca Smith
Public Policy Coord., Harry Brown
Pres., John Wilson
Major Activities: Social Justice Ministries with and among the Poor

United Religious Community of St. Joseph County

2015 Western Ave., Suite 336, South Bend, IN 46629 Tel. (574)282-2397 Fax (574)282-8014
E-mail: cmayernick@urcsjc.org
Web site: www.urcsjc.org
Media Contact, Exec. Dir., Rev. Carol L. Mayernick
Exec. Dir., Rev. Carol L. Mayernick
Pres., Rev. Lorin Clemenz
Refugee Prog. Dir., Carol McDonnell
Victim Impact Panel Dir., Martha Sallows
Advocacy Centers Dir., Carol Thon
Major Activities: Religious Understanding; Interfaith-Ecumenical Education; Interfaith Newsletter "Torch"; CROP Walk; UDare2Care Interfaith Youth Event; On-site Prayer Ministry; Peacemaker Awards; Hunger Education; Housing and Homelessness Issues; Clergy Education and Support; Refugee Resettlement; Victim Assistance; Advocacy for the Needy

West Central Neighborhood Ministry, Inc.

1316 Broadway, Fort Wayne, IN 46802-3304 Tel. (219)422-6618 Fax (219)422-9319
Media Contact, Exec. Dir., Andrea S. Thomas
Exec. Dir., Andrea S. Thomas
Office Mgr., J. R. Stopperich
Neighborhood Services Dir., Carol Salge
Senior Citizens Dir., Gayle Mann
Youth Dir., Laura Watt
Major Activities: After-School Programs; Teen Drop-In Center; Summer Day Camp; Summer Overnight Camp; Information and Referral Services; Food Pantry; Nutrition Program for Senior Citizens; Senior Citizens Activities; Tutoring; Developmental Services for Families & Senior Citizens; Parent Club

IOWA

Churches United, Inc.

1035 3rd Ave., Suite 202, Cedar Rapids, IA 52403-2463 Tel. (319)366-7163 Fax (319) 366-7163
E-mail: churchesunited@yahoo.com
Web site: www.churchesunitedcr.org

Media Contact, Exec. Dir., Karla Twedt-Ball
Exec. Dir., Karla Twedt-Ball
Pres., Rev. David Loy
Treas., Rachel Bartol, 450 19th St. NW, Cedar Rapids, IA 52405
Major Activities: Communication-resource center for member churches; Community Information and Referral; Ecumenical City-wide Celebrations

Des Moines Area Religious Council

3816 36th St., Ste. 204, Des Moines, IA 50310 Tel. (515)277-6969 Fax (515)274-8389
E-mail: info@dmreligious.org
Web site: dmreligious.org
Media Contact, Exec. Dir., Forrest Harms
Exec. Dir., Forrest Harms
Pres., Fr. Jim Kiernan
Pres. Elect, Cindy Morton
Treas., Jim Houser
Major Activities: Outreach and Nurture; Education; Social Initiatives Advocacy; Mission; Emergency Food Pantry; Ministry to Widowed; Child Care Assistance, Compassion in Action

Ecumenical Ministries of Iowa (EMI)*

3300 University Ave., P.O. Box 41487, Des Moines, IA 50311 Tel. (515)274-2278 Fax (515) 274-2278
E-mail: emofiowa@aol.com
Web site: www.iowachurches.org
Media Contact, Comm. Coord., Mary Swalla Holmes
Exec. Dir., Rev. Sarai Schnucker Beck
Major Activities: Facilitating the denominations' cooperative agenda of resourcing local expression of the church; Assess needs & develop responses through Justice and Unity Commissions

Iowa Religious Media Services*

3816 36th St., Des Moines, IA 50310 Tel. (515)277-2920 Fax (515)277-0842
E-mail: questions@irms.org
Web site: www.irms.org
Media Contact, Director
Exec. Dir., Sharon E. Strohmaier
Educ. Consultant, Kevin Mayer
Major Activities: Media Library for Churches in seven Denominations in the Midwest; Provide Video Production Services for Churches, Nonprofit & Educational organizations; will rent media to churches in the continental U.S. (details on the Web site)

KANSAS

Cross-Lines Cooperative Council

736 Shawnee Ave., Kansas City, KS 66105 Tel. (913)281-3388 Fax (913)281-2344
E-mail: rhea@cross-lines.org
Web site: www.cross-lines.org
Media Contact, Dir. of Dev., Theresa Swartwood
Exec. Dir., Lou Rose
Dir. of Prog., Rev. Noel Chase
Major Activities: Emergency Assistance; Family Support Advocacy; Crisis Heating-Plumbing Repair; Thrift Store; Work Camp Experiences; School Supplies; Christmas Store

Interfaith Ministries-Wichita

829 N. Market, Wichita, KS 67214-3519 Tel. (316)264-9303 Fax (316)264-2233
E-mail: smuyskens@ifmnet.org
Web site: www.ifmnet.org
Media Contact, Exec. Dir., Sam Muyskens
Exec. Dir., Rev. Sam Muyskens
Adm. Asst., Kathy Freed
ASAP Haiti, Dir. Bonnie Chadick
Homeless and Housing Services, Dir., Sandy Swank
Special Projects, Dir., Ashley Davis
Development, Dir., Karen Dobbin
Campaign to End Childhood Hunger, Karole Bradford
Community Ministry/Restorative Justice/Family Group Conferencing/Racial Justice Coord., Jeannine Little
Faith in Action, Coord., Richard Hanley
GoZones! Dir., Johanna Wilson
Major Activities: Communications; Urban Education; Inter-religious Understanding; Community Needs and Issues; Theology and Worship; Hunger; Family Life; Multi-Cultural Concerns

Kansas Ecumenical Ministries*

5833 SW 29th St., Topeka, KS 66614-2499 Tel. (785)272-9531
E-mail: kemstaff@ecunet.org
Media Contact, Exec. Dir., Dr. Joe M. Hendrixson
Pres., Rev. Marvin Zehr
Vice-Pres., Rev. Nancy Gammill
Sec., Tom McGraw
Exec. Dir., Dr. Joe M. Hendrixson
Pres., Winnie Crapson
Vice-Pres., Marvin Zehr
Sec., Rev. Art Jaggard
Major Activities: State Council of Churches; Legislative Activities; Program Facilitation and Coordination; Education; Mother-to-Mother Program; Rural Concerns; Hate group monitoring; Children & Families; Faith and Order

KENTUCKY

Eastern Area Community Ministries

P.O. Box 43049, Louisville, KY 40253-0049 Tel. (502)244-6141 Fax (502)254-5141
E-mail: easternacm@cs.com
Media Contact, Acting Exec. Dir., Sharon Eckler

Acting Exec. Dir., Sharon Eckler
Board Pres., Rev. Elwood Sturtevant
Board Sec., Mary Stephens
Board Treas., Homer Lacy, Jr.
Youth and Family Services, Rachael Elrod
Older Adult Services, Assoc. Prog. Dir., Joni Snyder
Neighborhood Visitor Prog., Acting Prog. Dir., Jane Parker
Major Activities: Emergency Assistance; Clothes Closet; Meals on Wheels; Community Worship Services; Good Start for Kids; Juvenile Court Diversion; Community Development; Transient Fund; Ministerial Association; Juvenile Court Diversion

Fern Creek-Highview United Ministries

7502 Tangelo Dr., Louisvlle, KY 40228 Tel. (502)239-7407 Fax (502)239-7454
E-mail: ferncreek.ministries@crnky.org
Media Contact, Exec. Dir., Kay Sanders, 7502 Tangelo Dr., Louisville, KY 40228 Tel. (502) 239-7407
Exec. Dir., Kay Sanders
Pres., David Pooler
Major Activities: Ecumenically supported social service agency providing services to the community, including Emergency Financial Assistance, Food-Clothing, Health Aid Equipment Loans, Information-Referral, Advocacy, Checks; Holiday Programs, Life Skills Training; Mentoring; Case Management; Adult Day Care Program

Hazard-Perry County Community Ministries, Inc.

P.O. Box 1506, Hazard, KY 41702-1506 Tel. (606)436-0051 Fax (606)436-0071
Media Contact, Gerry Feamster-Roll
Exec. Dir., Gerry Feamster-Roll
Chair, Sarah Hughes
Vice-Chair, Susan Duff
Sec., Virginia Campbell
Treas., Margaret Adams
Major Activities: Food Pantry-Crisis Aid Program; Day Care; Summer Day Camp; After-school Program; Christmas Tree; Family Support Center; Adult Day Care; Transitional Housing

Highlands Community Ministries

1140 Cherokee Rd., Louisville, KY 40204 Tel. (502)451-3695 Fax (502) 451-3609
E-mail: hcmexecu@hotmail.com
Web site: www.hcmlou.org
Media Contact, Exec. Dir., Stan Esterle
Exec. Dir., Stan Esterle
Major Activities: Welfare Assistance; Children Day Care; Adult Day Health Care; Social Services for Elderly; Housing for Elderly and Handicapped; Ecumenical Programs; Interfaith Programs; Community Classes; Activities for Children; Neighborhood and Business Organization

Kentuckiana Interfaith Community

P.O. Box 7128, Louisville, KY 40257 Tel. (502) 587-6265 Fax (502)540-5017
E-mail: interfaith@bellsouth.net
Web site: www.neighborhoodlink.com/org/kic
Media Contact, Exec. Dir., Dr. Roy Fuller
Pres., Steven Johns-Boehme
Vice-Pres., Ron Gaddie
Treas., Fr. Bill Hammer
Major Activities: Christian-Jewish, Islamic, Bahai Ministries in KY, Southern IN; Consensus Advocacy; Interfaith Dialogue; Community Hunger Walk; Racial Justice Forums; Network for Neighborhood-based Ministries; Hunger & Racial Justice Commission; Faith Channel—Cable TV Station, Horizon News Paper; Police-Comm. Relations Task Force; Ecumenical Strategic Planning; Networking with Seminaries & Religious-Affiliated Institutions

Kentucky Council of Churches*

1500 Leestown Rd., Suite 108, Lexington, KY 40511 Tel. (859)269-7715 Fax (859)269-1240
E-mail: kcc@kycouncilofchurches.org
Web site: www.kycouncilofchurches.org
Media Contact, Exec. Dir., Nancy Jo Kemper
Exec. Dir., Rev. Dr. Nancy Jo Kemper
Pres., The Rev. Ron Gaddie
Kentucky Interchurch Disaster Recovery Prog. Coord., Mr. Harper Davis
Dir. Assoc. for Local Ecumenism, Rev. W. Chris Benham Skidmore
Major Activities: Christian Unity; Public Policy; Justice; Disaster Response; Peace Issues; Anti-Racism; Health Care Issues; Local Ecumenism; Rural Land-Farm Issues; Gambling; Capital Punishment

Ministries United South Central Louisville (M.U.S.C.L., Inc.)

1207 Hart Avenue, Louisville, KY 42013 Tel. (502)363-9087 Fax (502)363-9087
Media Contact, Exec. Dir., Rev. Antonio (Tony) Aja, M.Div., Tel. (502)363-2383, E-mail Tony_Aja@pcusa.org
Ex. Dir., Rev. Antonio (Tony) Aja, M.Div.
Airport Relocation Ombudsman, Rev. Phillip Garrett, M.Div. Tel. (502)361-2706, philombud@aol.com
Senior Adults Prog., Dir., Mrs. Jeannine Blakeman, BSSW
Emergency Assistance, Dir., Mr. Michael Hundley
Low-Income Coord., Ms. Wanda Irvio
Youth Services, Dir., Rev. Bill Sanders, M.Div.
Volunteers Coord., Mrs. Carol Stemmle

Northern Kentucky Interfaith Commission, Inc.

901 York St., P.O. Box 72296, Newport, KY 41072 Tel. (859)581-2237 Fax (859)261-6041
E-mail: nkyinterfaith@isoc.net
Web site: www.nkyinterfaith.com
Media Contact, Exec. Dir., Rev. Tim Hungler
Pres., Rev. Tom Parker
Sec., Ms. Judy Norris
Treas., Ms. Peggy McEntee
Admin. Asst., Pat McDermott
Major Activities: Understanding Faiths; Meeting Spiritual and Human Needs; Enabling Churches to Greater Ministry

Paducah Cooperative Ministry

1359 S. 6th St., Paducah, KY 42003 Tel. (270) 442-6795 Fax (270)442-6812
E-mail: pcministry@hotmail.com
Media Contact, Dir., Heidi Suhrheinrich
Dir., Heidi Suhrheinrich
Chair, Rev. Larry McBride
Vice-Chair, Tommy Tucker
Major Activities: Programs for Hungry, Elderly, Poor, Homeless, Handicapped, Undereducated

St. Matthews Area Ministries

201 Biltmore Rd., Louisville, KY 40207 Tel. (502) 893-0205 Fax (502)893-0206
Media Contact, Exec. Dir., Dan G. Lane
Exec. Dir., Dan G. Lane
Child Care, Dir., Janet Hennessey
Dir. Assoc., Eileen Bartlett
Major Activities: Child Care; Emergency Assistance; Youth Services; Interchurch Worship and Education; Housing Development; Counseling; Information & Referral; Mentor Program; Developmentally Disabled

South East Associated Ministries (SEAM)

6500 Six Mile Ln., Ste. A, Louisville, KY 40218 Tel. (502)499-9350
Media Contact, Mary Beth Helton
Exec. Dir., Mary Beth Helton
Life Skills Center, Dir., Robert Davis
Youth Services, Dir., Bill Jewel
Pres., David Ehresman
Treas., Bill Trusty
Major Activities: Emergency Food, Clothing and Financial Assistance; Life Skills Center (Programs of Prevention and Case Management and Self-Sufficiency Through Education, Empowerment, Support Groups, etc.); Bloodmobile; Ecumenical Education and Worship; Juvenile Court Diversion; TEEN Court; Teen Crime & the Community

South Louisville Community Ministries

Peterson Social Services Center, 4803 Southside Dr., Louisville, KY 40214 Tel. (502)367-6445 Fax (502)361-4668
E-mail: slcm@slcm.org
Web site: www.slcm.org
Media Contact, Exec. Dir., J. Michael Jupin
Bd. Chair, Greg Greenwood
Bd. Vice-Chair, Jim Woodward
Bd. Treas., Greg Greenwood
Exec. Dir., Rev. J. Michael Jupin
Major Activities: Food, Clothing & Financial Assistance; Home Delivered Meals; Transportation; Ecumenical Worship; Juvenile Ct. Diversion Program; Affordable Housing; Adult Day Care; Truancy Prevention; Dare to Care Kids Café

LOUISIANA

Greater Baton Rouge Federation of Churches and Synagogues

3112 Convention St., Baton Rouge, LA 70806 Tel. (225)267-5600 Fax (225)267-5100
Web site: gbrfed.org
Media Contact, Exec. Dir., Rev. Jeff Day
Exec. Dir., Rev. Jeff Day
Admin. Asst., Ashley Griffin
Pres., Rev. Amy Mercer
Pres.-Elect, Joyce Robinson
Treas., Melvin Davis
Major Activities: Combating Hunger; Interfaith Relations; Interfaith Concert; Race Relations; Interfaith Caregivers (Faith in Action)

Greater New Orleans Federation of Churches

4640 S. Carrollton Ave, Suite 2B, New Orleans, LA 70119-6077 Tel. (504)488-8788 Fax (504) 488-8823
Exec. Dir., Rev. J. Richard Randels
Major Activities: Information and Referral; Food Distribution (FEMA); *Forward Together* TV Program; Sponsors seminars for pastors (e.g. church growth, clergy taxes, etc.); Police Chaplaincy; Fire Chaplaincy

Louisiana Interchurch Conference*

527 North Boulevard, Fourth Floor, Baton Rouge, LA 70802 Tel. (225)924-0213 Fax (225) 927-7860
E-mail: lainterchurch@aol.com
Media Contact, Exec. Dir., Rev. C. Dana Krutz
Exec. Dir., Rev. C. Dana Krutz
Pres., The Most Rev. Michael Jarrell
Major Activities: Ministries to Aging; Prison Reform; Liaison with State Agencies; Ecumenical Dialogue; Institutional Chaplains; Racism; Environmental

MAINE

Maine Council of Churches*

19 Pleasant Ave., Portland, ME 04103 Tel. (207) 772-1918 Fax (207)772-2947
E-mail: info@mainecouncilofchurches.org
Web site: www.mainecouncilofchurches.org
Media Contact, Comm. Dir., Karen Caouette

Exec. Dir., Thomas C. Ewell
Assoc. Dir., Douglas Cruger
Admin. Asst., Sandra Buzzell
Pres., Br. Francis Blouin
Treas., Rev. Richard Swan
Major Activities: Criminal Justice Reform/ Restorative Justice; Economic Justice; Environmental Justice; Peace Issues; Civil Rights

MARYLAND

Central Maryland Ecumenical Council*

Cathedral House, 4 E. University Pkwy., Baltimore, MD 21218 Tel. (410)467-6194 Fax (410)554-6387
E-mail: cmec@bcpl.net
Media Contact, Exec. Dir., Martha Young
Pres., Rev. Iris Farabee-Lewis
Major Activities: Interchurch Communications and Collaboration; Information Systems; Ecumenical Relations; Urban Mission and Advocacy; Staff for Judicatory Leadership Council; Commission on Dialogue; Commission on Church & Society; Commission on Admin. & Dev.; Ecumenical Choral Concerts; Ecumenical Worship Services

Community Ministries of Rockville

114 West Montgomery Ave., Rockville, MD 20850 Tel. (301)762-8682 Fax (301)762-2939
E-mail: cmr114cmr@aol.com
Media Contact, Managing Dir., Agnes Saenz
Exec. Dir. & Comm. Min., Mansfield M. Kaseman
Managing Dir., Agnes Aaenz
Major Activities: Shelter Care; Emergency Assistance; Elderly Home Care; Affordable Housing; Political Advocacy; Community Education; Education to Recent Immigrants

Community Ministry of Montgomery County

114 West Montgomery Ave., Rockville, MD 20850 Tel. (301)762-8682 Fax (301)762-2939
Media Contact, Exec. Dir., Rebecca Wagner
Exec. Dir., Rebecca Wagner
Major Activities: Interfaith Clothing Center; Emergency Assistance Coalition; The Advocacy Function; Information and Referral Services; Friends in Action; Thanksgiving Hunger Drive; Thanksgiving in February; Community Based Shelter

MASSACHUSETTS

Attleboro Area Council of Churches, Inc.

7 North Main St., Ste. 200, Attleboro, MA 02703 Tel. (508)222-2933 Fax (508)222-2008
E-mail: aacc@naisp.net
Media Contact, Pres., Bd. of Dir., Rev. Ruth Shaver
Exec. Adm., Kathleen Trowbridge
Staff Asst., Food 'n Friends Program Dir., Dorothy Embree
Hosp. Chplns., Rev. Dr. William B. Udall; Rev. Lynn MacLagan
Pres., Rev. Ruth Shaver, Minister of Christian Ed. And Family Life, Second Congregational Ch., 50 Pk. St., Attleboro, MA 02703
Treas., Mr. Richard Shaw, 70 Stanson Dr., N. Attleboro, MA 02760
Major Activities: Hospital Chaplaincy; personal Growth-Skill Workshops; Ecumenical Worship; Interfaith Worship; Media Resource Center; Referral Center; Communications-Publications; Community Social Action; Food 'n Friends Kitchens; Nursing Home Volunteer Visitation Program; Clergy Fellowship-Learning Events

The Cape Cod Council of Churches, Inc.

P.O. Box 758, Hyannis, MA 02601 Tel. (508) 775-5073
E-mail: cccounchur@capecod.net
Media Contact, Exec. Dir., Diane Casey-Lee
Exec. Dir., Diane Casey-Lee
Chaplain, Cape Cod Hospital, Rev. William Wilcox
Chaplain, Falmouth Hospital, Rev. Allen Page
Chaplain, House of Correction & Jail, Rev. Thomas Shepherd
Chaplain, Rehabilitation Hospital of the Cape and Islands, Mrs. Elizabeth Stommel
Service Center & Thrift Shop, P.O. Box 125, Dennisport, MA 02639 Tel. (508)394-6361
Major Activities: Pastoral Care; Social Concerns; Religious Education; Emergency Distribution of Food, Clothing, Furniture; Referral and Information; Church World Service; Interfaith Relations; Media Presence; Hospital & Jail Chaplaincy; Arts & Religion

Cooperative Metropolitan Ministries

474 Centre St., Newton, MA 02158 Tel. (617) 244-3650 Fax (617)630-9172
E-mail: coopmet@aol.com
Web site: www.coopment.org
Media Contact, Exec. Dir., Claire Kashuck
Exec. Dir., Claire Kashuck
Board Pres., Robert Stephens
Treas., Ricardo Neal
Clerk, Rev. John Odams
Major Activities: Low Income; Suburban-Urban Bridges; Racial and Economic Justice

Council of Churches of Greater Springfield

39 Oakland St., Springfield, MA 01108 Tel. (413)733-2149 Fax (413)733-9817
Media Contact, Asst. to Dir., Andrea Skeene
Exec. Dir., Rev. Karen L. Rucks
Community Min., Dir. Don A. Washington
Pres., The Rev. Dr. David Hunter

Treas., John Pearson, Esq

Major Activities: Advocacy; Emergency Fuel Fund; Peace and Justice Division; Community Ministry; Hospital and Jail Chaplaincies; Pastoral Service; Crisis Counseling; Christian Social Relations; Relief Collections; Ecumenical and Interfaith Relations; Church-Community Projects and Community Dialogues; Publication, *Knowing My Neighbor—Religious Beliefs and Traditions at Times of Death*

Greater Lawrence Council of Churches

117A S. Broadway, Lawrence, MA 01843 Tel. (978)686-4012

E-mail: pointer53a@aol.com

Media Contact, Exec. Dir., David Edwards

Exec. Dir., David Edwards

Pres., Carol Rabs

Vice-Pres., Rev. Michael Graham

Admin. Asst., Linda Sullivan

Major Activities: Ecumenical Worship; Radio Ministry; Hospital and Nursing Home Chaplaincy; Church Women United; After-school Children's Program; Vacation Bible School

Inter-Church Council of Greater New Bedford

412 County St., New Bedford, MA 02740-5096 Tel. (508)993-6242 Fax (508)991-3158

E-mail: administration@inter-churchcouncil.org

Web site: www.inter-churchcouncil.org

Media Contact, Min., Rev. Edward R. Dufresne, Ph.D.

Exec. Min., Rev. Edward R. Dufresne, Ph.D.

Pres., The Rev. David Lima

Treas., George Mock

Major Activities: Counseling; Spiritual Direction; Chaplaincy; Housing for Elderly and Disabled; Urban Affairs; Community Spiritual Leadership; Parish Nurse Ministry; Accounting and Spiritual Care for the Developmentally Challenged; Ecumenical and Interfaith Ministries; Advocacy for the Homeless; Support for Urban Schhol District; Opposition to Expanded Gambling

Massachusetts Commission on Christian Unity

82 Luce St, Lowell, MA 01852 Tel. (978)453-5423 Fax (978)453-5423

E-mail: kgordonwhite@msn.com

Media Contact, Exec. Dir., Rev. K. Gordon White

Exec. Sec., Rev. K. Gordon White

Pres., Rev. Fr. Edward O'Flaherty, Ecumenical Officer, Roman Catholic Archdiocese of Boston

Major Activities: Faith and Order Dialogue with Church Judicatories; Guidelines & Pastoral Directives for Inter-Church Marriages; Guidelines for Celebrating Baptism in an Ecumenical Context

Massachusetts Council of Churches*

14 Beacon St., Suite 416, Boston, MA 02108 Tel. (617)523-2771 Fax (617)523-1483

E-mail: www.council@masscouncilofchurches.org

Web site: www.masscouncilofchurches.org

Media Contact, Dir., Rev. Dr. Diane C. Kessler

Exec. Dir., Rev. Dr. Diane C. Kessler

Adjunct Assoc. Dir., Rev. Betsy Sowers

Pres., Rev. John Stendahl

Vice-Pres., Fr. John Maheras

Sec., Ms. Anne Nickerson

Treas., Mr. Robert Sarly

Major Activities: Christian Unity; Education and Evangelism; Social Justice & Individual Rights; Ecumenical Worship; Services and Resources for Individuals and Churches

Worcester County Ecumenical Council

4 Caroline St., Worcester, MA 01604 Tel. (508)757-8385 Fax (508)795-7704

E-mail: worcecumen@aol.com

Media Contact, Exec. Dir., Rev. Allyson D. Platt

The Rev. Allyson D. Platt, worcecumen@aol.com

Pres., Mrs. Fran Langille

Major Activities: Ecumenical worship and dialogue networking congregations together in partnerships of mission, education and spiritual renewal. Clusters of Churches; Ecumenical Worship and Dialogue; Interfaith Activities; Resource Connection for Churches; Group Purchasing Consortium

MICHIGAN

Bay Area Ecumenical Forum

103 E. Midland St., Bay City, MI 48706 Tel. (517)686-1360

Media Contact, Rev. Karen Banaszak

Major Activities: Ecumenical Worship; Community Issues; Christian Unity; Education; CROP Walk

Berrien County Association of Churches

275 Pipestone, Benton Harbor, MI 49022 Tel. (616)926-0030

Media Contact, Sec., Mary Ann Hinz

Pres., Carol Stockman

Dir., Street Ministry, Rev. Yvonne Hester

Major Activities: Street Ministry; CROP Walk; Community Issues; Fellowship; Christian Unity; Hospital Chaplaincy Program; Annual County Church Directory and Monthly Newsletter; Resource Guide for Helping Needy; Distribution of Worship Opportunity—Brochure for Tourists

Grand Rapids Area Center for Ecumenism (GRACE)

207 East Fulton, Grand Rapids, MI 49503-3210 Tel. (616)774-2042 Fax (616)774-2042
E-mail: dbaak@graceoffice.org
Web site: www.graceoffice.org
Media Contact, Rev. David P. Baak
Leadership Team: Rev. David P. Baak; Lisa H. Mitchell; Rev. David G. May
Major Activities: AIDS Care Network (Client Services Education-Volunteer Services); Hunger Walk ; Education-Relationships; (Ecumenical Lecture, Christian Unity Worship-Events, Interfaith Dialogue Conference); (Affiliates, ACCESS-All County Churches Emergency Support System, FISH for My People-transportation); Racial Justice Institute; West Michigan Call to Renewal (Response to Poverty Advocacy) AIDS Care Network (Client Services Education-Volunteer Services); Hunger Walk ; Education-Relationships; (Ecumenical Lecture, Christian Unity Worship-Events, Interfaith Dialogue Conference); (Affiliates, ACCESS-All County Churches Emergency Support System, FISH for My People-transportation); Publications (*Grace In-Site*); Racial Justice Institute; West Michigan Call to Renewal (Response to Poverty Advocacy); Faith In Motion (Mass Transit and Land Use); Restorative Justice Coalition

Greater Flint Council of Churches

310 E. Third St., Suite 600, Flint, MI 48502 Tel. (810)238-3691 Fax (810)238-4463
E-mail: gfcc1929@aol.com
Media Contact, Coord., Mrs. Constance D. Neely
Publicity Chair, Barbara Spaulding Westcott
Pres., Rev. Zoltan S. Sutto
Major Activities: Christian Education; Christian Unity; Christian Missions; Nursing Home Visitor; Church in Society; American Bible Society Materials; Interfaith Dialogue; Church Teacher Exchange Sunday; Directory of Area Faiths and Clergy; Thanksgiving & Easter Sunrise Services; CROP Walks

In One Accord

157 Capital Ave., NE, Battle Creek, MI 49017-3928 Tel. (269)966-2500 Fax (269)660-6665
E-mail: inoneaccordmi@aol.com
Web site: www.skyWeb site.com/in-one-accord
Media Contact, Exec. Dir., Rev. Ron L. Keller
Pres., Rev. Craig Tatum
Vice-Pres., Joy Rogers
Exec. Dir., Rev. Ron L. Keller
Treas., Paula McDaniel
Sec., Mrs. Carla Dearing
Major Activities: CROP Walk; Week of Prayer for Christian Unity; Ecumenical Worship; Faith Health Network; Martin Luther King Jr. Community Service, Church Softball & Volleyball Leagues; Clergy Support Groups; Burmese Refugee Resettlement; Neighborhood Improvement Program; Racism Action Group; Building Spirituality In the Schools; Coordinated lisiting of area churches and partners; Clergy Forums.

The Jackson County Interfaith Council

425 Oakwood, P.O. Box 156, Clarklake, MI 49234-0156 Tel. (517)529-9721
Major Activities: Chaplaincy at Institutions and Senior Citizens Residences; Martin L. King, Jr. Day Celebrations; Ecumenical Council Representation; Radio and TV Programs; Food Pantry; Inter-religious Events; Clergy Directory

The Metropolitan Christian Council: Detroit-Windsor

1300 Sutie, 28 W. Adams, Detroit, MI 48226 Tel. (313)962-0340 Fax (313)962-9044
E-mail: councilweb@aol.com
Web site: users.aol.com/councilweb
Media Contact, Rev. Richard Singleton
Exec. Dir., Rev. Richard Singleton
Meals for Shut-ins, Prog. Dir., John Simpson
Admin. Asst., Mrs. Elaine Kisner
Web Calendar Supervisor, Mr. Gerald Morgan
Major Activities: Theological and Social Concerns; Ecumenical Worship; Educational Services; Electronic Media; Print Media; Meals for Shut-Ins; Summer Feeding Program

Michigan Ecumenical Forum*

809 Center St., Ste. 5, Lansing, MI 48906 Tel. (517)485-4395 Fax (517)482-8751
E-mail: ecumenicalforum@aol.com
Major Activities: Communication and Coordination; Support and Development of Regional Ecumenical Fora; Ecumenical Studies; Fellowship and Celebration; Church and Society Issues; Continuing Education

Muskegon County Cooperating Churches

1095 Third St., Suite 10, Muskegon, MI 49441-1976 Tel. (231)727-6000 Fax (231)722-1230
Media Contact, Prog. Coord., Delphine Hogston
President, Dr. Bill D. Page
Major Activities: Local Faith Community Information Source, Racial Reconciliation, Dialogue, & Healing; Multiracial Family Support; Responsible Fathers Empowerment; Ecumenical Worship; Faith News TV Ministry; CROP Walk Against Hunger; Jewish-Christian Dialogue; Environmental Issues, Social Justice Issues, Pastoral Support, Homeless Sheltering

Subsidiary Organizations:
Muskegon Responsible Fathers' Initiative
Tel. (231)725-7268 Fax (231)728-4558

Media Contact, Prog. Coord., Christopher Sandford
Major Activities: Responsible Fathers Empowerment; Providing education, job skills & support for fathers to connect and support their children financially, emotionally, & spiritually; Fatherhood skills for incarcerated fathers; Teen Pregnancy Prevention

Community Uniting for Peace
Media Contact, Sec., Delphine Hogston
Major Activities: Advocacy to remove the effects of Racism; Community Civil Rights Health Assessment Survey; Responsible Consumer Spending Initiative; Monthly Community Dialogue on Racial Issues

Interfaith Hospitality Network in Muskegon
Media Contact, Delphine Hogston
Major Activities: Helping congregations shelter homeless families

Community Connects Choir
Media Contact, Sherri Slater
Major Activities: Winter Holiday Concert. Intentionally interracial, intergenerational, ecumenical singing blending gospel and traditional music. Supports other diverse music opportunities for the community.

In the City for Good—Muskegon
Media Contact, Kryssis Bjork
Major Activities: Bringing together residents, churches, schools, and businesses for hands-on activities to promote cultural diversity and community good. Back-to-school fairs including health screenings, summer work projects, and quarterly gatherings. Focus is on urban areas of Muskegon County.

MINNESOTA

Arrowhead Interfaith Council*

102 W. 2nd St., Duluth, MN 55802 Tel. (218) 722-7166
E-mail: president@arrowheadinterfaith.org
Web site: www.arrowheadinterfaith.org
Media Contact, Pres., Doug Bowen-Bailey
Pres., Doug Bowen-Bailey
Sec., Sister Lois Eckes
Treas., David Carlson
Major Activities: Inter/Faith Dialogue; Joint Religious Legislative Coalition; Corrections Chaplaincy; Human Justice and Community Concerns; Community Seminars; Children's Concerns

Community Emergency Assistance Program (CEAP)

6840 78th Ave N, Brooklyn Park, MN 55445 Tel. (763)566-9600 Fax (763)566-9604
E-mail: smklein@isd.net
Web site: www.ceap.homestead.com
Media Contact, Exec. Dir., Stephen Klein
Exec. Dir., Stephen Klein
Major Activities: Provision of Basic Needs (Food, Clothing); Emergency Financial Assistance for Shelter; Home Delivered Meals; Chore Services and Homemaking Assistance; Family Loan Program; Volunteer Services

Greater Minneapolis Council of Churches

1001 E. Lake St., P.O. Box 7509, Minneapolis, MN 55407-0509 Tel. (612)721-0772 Fax (612) 722-8669
E-mail: info@gmcc.org
Web site: www.gmcc.org
Media Contact, Dir. of Comm., Darcy Hanzlik
Pres. and CEO, Rev. Dr. Gary B. Reierson, reierson@gmcc.org
Chair, Dorothy Bridges
Treas., Lester Swenson
Division Indian Work, Vice-Pres. & Exec. Dir., Noya Woodrich
Dir. of Prog., Denise Estey
Russ Ewald Ctr. for Urban Service, Dir., Bruce Bjork
Minnesota FoodShare, Dir., Barbara Thell
Handyworks, Dir., Katherine Panasuk
Correctional Chaplains, Rev. Susan Allers Hatlie; Rev. Thomas Van Leer; Rev. Paula Nordhem; Rev. James Njoroge
Discover Learning Centers, Coord., Kathleen Richardson
Div. of Indian Work, Dir., Youth Program, Louise Matson
Adult Services, Denise Estey
Teen Indian Parents, Leslie Walking Elk
Finance & Admin., Vice-Pres. and CFO, Dennis Anderson
Advancement, Sr. Vice-Pres., Don R. Riggs
Urban Immersion Service Retreats, Dir., Mike Manhard
Metro Paint-A-Thon, Coord., Julie Kinkaid
Discover Support Groups, Coord., Briana Franzmeier
Projct Re-Entry, Dir., Brian Herron
Project Keeping The Faith, Dir., Hillary Freeman
Minnesota Churches Anti-Racism Initiative, Co-Dirs., James Addington and Carmen Valenzuela
Church and Community Initiatives, Coord., Bridget Ryan
Major Activities: Indian Work (Emergency Assistance, Youth Leadership, self-sufficiency, Jobs Program, Teen Indian Parents Program, and Family Violence Program); Minnesota FoodShare; Metro Paint-A-Thon; Correctional Chaplaincy Program; HandyWorks; Anti-racism Initiative; Child Advocacy; Social Justice Advocacy; Home Renovation; Affordable Housing; Urban Immersion Service Retreats; Welfare Reform; Economic Self-Sufficiency; Discover Support Groups; Job Readiness; Discover Learning Centers; Church and Community Initiatives; Immigrant and Refugee Services; Community Health Promotion; Correctional Aftercare; Restorative Justice

The Joint Religious Legislative Coalition

122 W. Franklin Ave., Rm. 315, Minneapolis, MN 55404 Tel. (612)870-3670 Fax (612)870-3671
E-mail: info@jrlc.org
Web site: www.jrlc.org
Media Contact, Exec. Dir., Brian A. Rusche
Exec. Dir., Brian A. Rusche
Research Dir., Dr. James Casebolt
Network Organizer, Jody McCardle
Major Activities: Lobbying at State Legislature; Researching Social Justice Issues and Preparing Position Statements; Organizing Grassroots Citizen's Lobby

Metropolitan Interfaith Council on Affordable Housing (MICAH)

122 W. Franklin Ave., #310, Minneapolis, MN 55404 Tel. (612)871-8980 Fax (612)813-4501
E-mail: info@micah.org
Web site: www.micah.org
Media Contact, Exec. Dir., Joy Sorensen Navarre
Exec. Dir., Joy Sorensen Navarre
Assoc. Dir., José Trejo
Congregational Organizers, Jodi Nelson; Jean Pearson; Rev. John Buzza; Rev. John Buzza
Sec., Sue Watlov Phillips
Pres., Rev. Paul Robinson
Vice-Pres., Nancy L. Anderson
Treas., Joseph Holmberg
Past Pres., Kristine Reynolds
Major Activities: The Metropolitan Interfaith Council on Affordable Housing, MICAH, seeks to live out the prophetic vision that calls us "to do justice, to love mercy and to walk humbly with God." (Micah 6:8). We envision a metropolitan area where everyone without exception has a safe, decent and affordable home. MICAH will realize this vision through organizing congregations of faith and community partners to change the political climate and public policies so that all communities preserve and build affordable housing. MICAH's faith-based organizing creates power that produces results. During the past five years MICAH: Mobilized congregations to build community support for 1,348 affordable homes for families with very low incomes. Prevented the demolition and gentrification of 1,919 structurally sound apartments. Half of the tenants were people of color or people with disabilities. Earned HUD's 1999 National Best Practices Award and the Headwaters Fund Social Justice Award in 2001.

Minnesota Council of Churches*

122 W. Franklin Ave., Rm. 100, Minneapolis, MN 55404 Tel. (612)870-3600 Fax (612)870-3622
E-mail: mcc@mnchurches.org
Web site: www.mnchurches.org
Media Contact, Exec. Dir., Rev. Peg Chemberlin, E-mail chemberlinp@mnchurches.org
Exec. Dir., Rev. Peg Chemberlin, chemberlinop @mn.churches.org
Dir. of Prog., Rev. Deborah Manning, manningd@mnchurches.org
Unity & Relationships, Organizer, Cindy Kennedy, kennedyc@mnchurches.org
Refugee Services, Dir., Joel Luedtke, luedtkej@mnchurches.org
Indian Ministry, Field Organizer,
Comm., Dir., Christopher Dart, dartcel@mnchurches. org
Finance & Facilities, Dir., Douglas Swanson, swansond@mnchurches.org
Tri-Council Coord. Commission, Co-Dirs., James Addington; Carmen Valenzuela
Joint Religious Legislative Coalition, Research Dir. & Admin. Asst., James Casebolt
Joint Religious Legislative Coalition, Exec., Brian A. Rusche
Pres. Bishop James Jelinek
Major Activities: Minnesota Church Center, Rural Life-Ag Crisis; Racial Reconciliation; Indian Ministry; Legislative Advocacy; Refugee Services; Service to Newly Legalized-Undocumented persons; Unity & Relationships, Sexual Exploitation within the Religious Community; Jewish-Christian Relations; Muslim-Christian Relations; Tri-Council Coordinating Commission (Minnesota Churches Anti-Racism Initiative); Hindu-Christian Relations; Peace Works; Minnesota Foodshare

St. Paul Area Council of Churches

1671 Summit Ave, St. Paul, MN 55105 Tel. (651)646-8805 Fax (651)646-6866
E-mail: info@spacc.org
Web site: www.spacc.org
Media Contact, Mary Kane
Exec. Dir., Rev. Grant Abbott
Dir. of Development, Kristi Anderson
Congregations in Community, Bob Walz
Congregations Concerned for Children, Peg Wangensteen
Project Spirit, Darcel Hill
Project Home, Sara Liegl
Dept. of Indian Work, Sheila WhiteEagle
Pres. of the Board, John Anderson
Treas., James Verlautz
Sec., Art Sidner
Major Activities: Education and Advocacy Regarding Children and Poverty; Assistance to Churches Developing Children's Parenting Care Services; Ecumenical Encounters and Activities; Indian Ministries; Leadership in Forming Cooperative Ministries for Children and Youth; After-School Tutoring; Assistance to Congregations; Training Programs in Anti-racism; Shelters for homeless

Tri-Council Coordinating Commission

122 W. Franklin, Rm. 100, Minneapolis, MN 55404 Tel. (612)871-0229 Fax (612)870-3622

E-mail: naja@gmcc.org

Web site: www.gmcc.org/tcc.html

Media Contact, Co.-Dir., R. James Addington; Assoc. Rev. Carmen Valenzuela

Exec. Committee, Rev. Peg Chemberlin; Rev. Gary Reierson; Rev. Thomas Duke

Major Activities: Anti-Racism training and organizational consultation; Institutional anti-racism team development and coaching; training and coaching of anti-racism trainers and organizers (in cooperation with Cross Roads Ministry)

MISSISSIPPI

Mississippi Religious Leadership Conference*

P.O. Box 68123, Jackson, MS 39286-8123 Tel. (601)924-7430 Fax (601)924-7430

E-mail: mrlc@netdoor.com

Media Contact, Exec. Dir., Rev. Paul Griffin Jones, II, Th.D., PhD.

Exec. Dir., Rev. Paul Griffin Jones, II, Th.D., PhD.

Chair, Bishop Duncan Gray, III

Treas., Rev. Jim White

Major Activities: Cooperation among Religious Leaders; Lay-Clergy Retreats; Social Concerns Seminars; Disaster Task Force; Advocacy for Disadvantaged

MISSOURI

Council of Churches of the Ozarks

P.O. Box 3947, Springfield, MO 65808-3947 Tel. (417)862-3586 Fax (417)862-2129

E-mail: ccozarks@ccozarks.org

Web site: www.ccozarks.org

Media Contact, Comm. Dir., Susan Jackson

Exec. Dir., Dr. David W. Hockensmith, Jr.

Chief Operating Officer, Julie Guillebeau

Major Activities: Ministerial Alliance; Child Care Food Program-FDA Food Program; Child Care Resource & Referral; Connections Handyman Service; Crosslines-Food and Clothing Pantry; Daybreak Adult Day Care Center; Long-Term Care Ombudsman Programs; Ozarks Food Harvest; Retired and Senior Volunteer Program; Sigma House-Treatment Center for Alcohol and Drug Abuse; Therapeutic Riding of the Ozarks

Ecumenical Ministries

829 Jefferson St., Fulton, MO 65251 Tel. (573) 642-6065 Fax (573)592-0247

E-mail: emfulton@coin.org

Web site: www.callaway.county.missouri.org/em

Media Contact, Admin. Asst., Karen Luebbert

Chair, Bd. of Dir.; Rev. Seamus Doyle

Major Activities: Kingdom Respite Care and Hospice; CROP Hunger Walk; Little Brother and Sister; Unity Service; Senior Center Bible Study; County Jail Ministry; Fulton High School Baccalaureate Service, HAVEN House; Missouri Youth Treatment Center Ministry, Parish Nurses of Callaway

Interfaith Community Services

200 Cherokee St., P.O. Box 4038, St. Joseph, MO 64504-0038 Tel. (816)238-4511 Fax (816) 238-3274

E-mail: daveb@ponyexpress.net

Web site: www.inter-serv.org

Media Contact, Exec. Dir., David G. Berger

Exec. Dir., David G. Berger

Major Activities: Child Development; Neighborhood Family Services; Group Home for Girls; Retired Senior Volunteer Program; Nutrition Program; Mobile Meals; Southside Youth Program; Church and Community; Housing Development; Homemaker Services to Elderly; Emergency Food, Rent, Utilities; AIDS Assistance; Family Respite; Family and Individual Casework.

Interfaith Partnership of Metropolitan St. Louis

418 E. Adams Ave., Kirkwood, MO 63122 Tel. (314)821-3808 Fax (314)821-6361

E-mail: ipstlouis@mindspring.com

Web site: home.mindspring.com/~ipstlouis

Media Contact, Barbara Russell

Dir., Barbara Russell

Pres., The Rev. Dr. Warren Crews

Cabinet Chair: Riley Leag

Major Activities: Speaking out with a concerted faith voice on public issues; Celebrating our diversity encouraging respect for our faith traditions through interfaith dialogue, music events, dinner programs, and public forums.; Projects that promote bridge-building across racial, religious, and cultural divides, and health promotion through congregational health initiatives; Projects responding to hunger, natural disasters, environmental restoration, improving impoverished neighborhoods

MONTANA

Montana Association of Churches*

180 24th St. W., Ste. G, Billings, MT 59102 Tel. (406)656-9779 Fax (406)656-2156

E-mail: montanachurches@earthlink.net

Web site: www.montana-churches.org

Media Contact, Exec. Dir., Margaret MacDonald

Exec. Dir., Margaret E. MacDonald

Admn. Asst., Hung Vu

Pres., Fr. Jay Peterson, Box 1399, Great Falls, MT 59403

Past Pres., Rev. Jessica Crist, 401 4th Ave. N., Great Falls, MT 59401-2310

Treas., Rev. Barbara Archer, 2210 Pryor Lane, Billings, MT 59102
Sec., Rev. Donald Guthrie, 1833 Daniel Dr., Missoula, MT 59802
Major Activities: Montana Christian Advocates Network; Christian Unity; Junior Citizen Camp; Public Information; Ministries Development; Social Ministry; Renewing the Public Church, Montana Faith-Health Cooperative, Partnership For Rural Life

NEBRASKA

Interchurch Ministries of Nebraska*

215 Centennial Mall S., Suite 411, Lincoln, NE 68508-1888 Tel. (402)476-3391 Fax (402) 202-2005
E-mail: mecham5@hotmail.com
Web site: www.interchurchministries.org
Media Contact, Exec., Mrs. Marilyn P. Mecham
Pres., Rev. Dr. Kenneth W. Moore
Treas., Ms. Susan Gillies
Exec., Mrs. Marilyn Mecham
Adm. Asst., Sharon K. Kalcik
Health Ministry Coord., Ronnette L. Sailors
Domestic Violence Program Coord., Patricia L. Brown
Community Resource Specialist: Caroline Walles
Major Activities: Interchurch Planning and Development; Indian Ministry; Rural Church Strategy; United Ministries in Higher Education; Disaster Response; Rural Response Hotline; Health Ministry; Community Organizing Initiative Planning; Peace with Justice; Angel Connection; Domestic Violence Program; Faith-Based Initiative

Lincoln Interfaith Council

140 S. 27th St., Ste. B, Lincoln, NE 68510-1301 Tel. (402)474-3017 Fax (402)475-3262
E-mail: mail@lincolninterfaith.org
Web site: www.lincolninterfaith.org
Media Contact, Doug Boyd
Exec. Dir., Dr. William Caldwell
Pres., The Rev. Jay A. Vetter
Vice-Pres., John Cutler
Sec., Debra Butt
Treas., Jeff Bomberger
Prog. Dir., Jean Scali
Media Specialist, Mr. Douglas Boyd
Soccer Coach, Mr. Izzaldin Badi
Faces of the Middle East Coord., Mr. Nodri Al-Awady
Families First & Foremost Iraqi Care Coord., Mrs. Zainab Al-Batat
Faces of the Middle East Taekwon Do Instructor, Mr. Ali Zabaidi
African Multicultural Community Ctr. Coord., Mr. David Taw
African Behavioral Healthcare Specialist, Mrs. Nyalam Gatrek
Building & Grounds, Mrs. Doc Le
Major Activities: Emergency Food Pantries System; MLK, Jr. Observance; Healing Community Project; Interfaith Passover Seder; Week of Prayer Christian Unity; Festival of Faith & Culture; Holocaust Memorial Observance; Citizens Against Racism & Discrimination; HIV-AIDS; Community organization; Anti-Drug & Anti-Alcohol Abuse Projects; Youth Gang & Violence Prevention; Domestic Abuse Prevention; Migrant Child Education; Connecting Neighborhood Partnerships; American Citizenship Classes; Survival English for Pre-literate AmerAsians and Elderly Refugees; Ecumenical Deaf Ministry; Multi-Faith & Multi-Cultural Training; Faces of the Middle East Project; Crop Walk for Hunger; UNICEF Drive; New Clergy Orientation; Directory of Clergy, Congregations & Religious Resources; Multi-Faith Planning Calendar Publication; "Faith Report"; "Lincoln Faith & Culture" on Cable TV-13 and Kzum-FM Radio; African Multicultural Community Center; Faces of the Middle East Center

NEW HAMPSHIRE

New Hampshire Council of Churches*

140 Sheep Davis Road, Ste. 1, Pembroke, NH 03275 Tel. (603)224-1352 Fax (603)224-9161
E-mail: churches@nhchurches.org
Web site: www.nhchurches.org
Media Contact, Exec. Dir., David Lamarre-Vincent, P.O. Box 1087, Concord, NH 03302-1087 Tel. (603)224-1352 Fax (603)224-9161, E-mail david@nhchurches.org
Pres., Rev. David Yasenka, Triumphant Cross ELCA, 171 Zion's Hill Rd, Salem, NH 03079
Treas., Mr. Alvah Chisholm
Major Activities: Statewide Ecumenical Work For Christian Unity, Interfaith Understanding, and Social Justice

NEW JERSEY

Bergen County Council of Churches

58 James Street, Bergenfield, NJ 07621 Tel. (201)384-7505 Fax (201)384-2585
E-mail: bergenccc@hotmail.com
Web site: www.bergenccc.org
Media Contact, Pres., Rev. Dr. Stephen T. Giordano, Clinton Avenue Reformed Church, Clinton Ave. & James St., Bergenfield, NJ 07621 Tel. (201)384-2454 Fax (201)384-2585
Exec. Sec., Anne Annunziato
Major Activities: Ecumenical and Religious Institute; Brotherhood-Sisterhood Breakfast; Center for Food Action; Homeless Aid; Operation Santa Claus; Aging Services; Boy

& Girl Scouts; Easter Dawn Services; Music; Youth; Ecumenical Representation; Support of Chaplains in Jails & Hospitals; Faith & Values Online project www.njfaithandvalues.org; Welfare into Workplace

Ecclesia

700 West State St., Trenton, NJ 08618 Tel. (609) 394-9229
Media Contact, Sec., Mrs. Tina Swan
Pres., Rev. Joseph P. Ravenell
Campus Chaplains, Rev. Nancy Schulter; Rev. Robert Wittin, Rev. Richard Kocses
Major Activities: Racial Justice; Children & Youth Ministries; Advocacy; CROP Walk; Ecumenical Worship; Hospital Chaplaincy; Church Women United; Campus Chaplaincy; Congregational Empowerment; Prison Chaplaincy; Substance Abuse Ministry Training

Metropolitan Ecumenical Ministry

525 Orange St., Newark, NJ 07107 Tel. (973) 485-8100 Fax (973)485-1165
Media Contact, Consultant, Rev. M. L. Emory
Exec. Dir., C. Stephen Jones
Major Activities: Community Advocacy (education, housing, environment); Church Mission Assistance; Community and Clergy Leadership Development; Economic Development; Affordable Housing

Metropolitan Ecumenical Ministry Community Development Corp.

525 Orange St., Newark, NJ 07107 Tel. (973)481-3100 Fax (201)481-7883
E-mail: memcdc@juno.com
Exec. Dir., Jacqueline Jones
Major Activities: Housing Development; Neighborhood Revitalization; Commercial-Small Business Development; Economic Development; Community Development; Credit Union; Home Ownership Counseling; Credit Repair; Mortgage Approval; Technical Assitance To Congregations

New Jersey Council of Churches*

176 W. State St., Trenton, NJ 08608 Tel. (609) 396-9546 Fax (609)396-7646
Media Contact, Public Policy Dir., Joan Diefenbach, Esq.
Pres., Rev. Jack Johnson
Sec., Beverly McNally
Treas., Marge Christie
Major Activities: Racial Justice; Children's Issues; Theological Unity; Ethics Public Forums; Advocacy; Economic Justice

NEW MEXICO

Faith Community Assistance Center

P.O. Box 15517, Santa Fe, NM 87592 Tel. (505)438-4782 Fax (505)473-5637
Media Contact, Barbara A. Robinson
Major Activities: Faith Community Assistance Center; providing emergency assistance to the poor; Interfaith Dialogues-Celebrations-Visitations; Peace Projects; Understanding Hispanic Heritage; Newsletter

New Mexico Conference of Churches*

720 Vassar Dr NE, Albuquerque, NM 87106-2724 Tel. (505)255-1509 Fax (505)256-0071
E-mail: nmcc@nmchurches.org
Web site: www.nmchurches.org
Media Contact, Exec. Dir., Rev. Barbara E Dua
Pres., Rev. Harold T. Nilsson
Treas., Ruth E. Tribou
Exec. Dir., Rev. Dr. Barbara E. Dua
Major Activities: Affordable Housing; Social Justice Coalitions; Spiritual Life & Ministries

NEW YORK

Brooklyn Council of Churches

125 Ft. Greene Place, Brooklyn, NY 11217 Tel. (718)625-5851 Fax (718)522-1231
Media Contact, Dir., Charles Henze
Prog. Dir., Charles Henze (Deacon)
Pres., Rev. James H. Eggleston
Treas., Rev. Charles H. Straut , Jr.
Major Activities: Education Workshops; Food Pantries; Hospital and Nursing Home Chaplaincy; Church Women United; Legislative Concerns; Directory of Churches; Ecumenical Dialogue

Broome County Council of Churches, Inc.

William H. Stanton Center, 3 Otseningo St., Binghamton, NY 13903 Tel. (607)724-9130 Fax (607)724-9148
E-mail: mfrick@broomecouncil.ort
Web site: www.broomecouncil.net
Media Contact, Rev. Dr. Murray Frick
Exec. Dir., Rev. Dr. Murray Frick
Exec. Asst., Brigitte Stella
Hospital Chaplains, Betty Pomeroy; Rev. David Rockwell
Jail Chaplain, Rev. Cris Mogenson
Aging Ministry Coord., Linda McColgin
CHOW Prog. Coord., Wendy Primavera
Pres., Dr. Thomas Kelly
Treas., Rey Hull
Caregiver Prog. Coord., Joanne Kays
Community and Donor Relations, Dir., Dr. Murray Frick
Major Activities: Hospital and Jail Chaplains; Youth and Aging Ministries; Broome Bounty (Food Rescue Program); Emergency Hunger & Advocacy Program; Faith & Family Values; Ecumenical Worship and Fellowship; Media; Community Affairs; Peace with Justice; Day by Day Marriage Prep Program; Interfaith Coalition; Interfaith Volunteer Caregiver Program

Capital Area Council of Churches, Inc.

646 State St., Albany, NY 12203-3815 Tel. (518)462-5450 Fax (518)462-5450
E-mail: capareacc@aol.com
Media Contact, Admin. Asst., Kitt Jackson
Exec. Dir., Rev. John U. Miller
Admn. Dir., Kitt Jackson
Pres., Rev. Vernon Victorson
Treas., David Wood
Major Activities: Hospital Chaplaincy; Food Pantries; CROP Walk; Jail and Nursing Home Ministries; Martin Luther King Memorial Service and Scholarship Fund; Emergency Shelter for the Homeless; Campus Ministry; Ecumenical Dialogue; Forums on Social Concerns; Peace and Justice Education; Inter-Faith Programs; Legislative Concerns; Comm. Thanksgiving Day and Good Friday Services; Annual Ecumenical Musical Celebration

Capital Region Ecumenical Organization (CREO)

812 N. Church St., Schenectady, NY 12305 Tel. (518)382-7505 Fax (518)382-7505
E-mail: mishamarvel@juno.com
Media Contact, Coord., Misha Marvel
Pres., Rev. Donna Elia (PCUSA)
Vice-Pres., Rev. John U. Miller (UCC)
Treas., Rev. Dr. Charles Lindhdm (ELCA)
Sec., Ms. Kitt Jackson (RCA)
Coord., Misha Marvel
Major Activities: Promote Cooperation-Coordination Among Member Judicatories and Ecumenical Organizations in the Capital Region in Urban Ministries, Social Action

Chautaugua County Rural Ministry

127 Central Ave., P.O. Box 362, Dunkirk, NY 14048 Tel. (716)366-1787 Fax (716)366-1787
E-mail: ccrm@netsync.net
Web site: www.ccrm.netsync.net
Exec. Dir., Kathleen Peterson
Major Activities: Chautaugua County Food Bank; Collection-Distribution of Furniture, Clothing, & Appliances; Homeless Services; Advocacy for the Poor; Soup Kitchen; Emergency Food Pantry; Thrift Store

Concerned Ecumenical Ministry to the Upper West Side

286 LaFayette Ave., Buffalo, NY 14213 Tel. (716)882-2442 Fax (716)882-2477
E-mail: crieleygod@cembuffalo.org
Media Contact, Exec. Dir., The Rev. Catherine Rieley-Goddard
Pres., Ms. Priscilla Marsh
Major Activities: Community Center Serving Youth, Refugee Families, Seniors and the Hungry

Cortland County Council of Churches, Inc.

7 Calvert St., Cortland, NY 13045 Tel. (607)753-1002
Media Contact, Office Mgr., Joy Niswender
Exec. Dir., Rev. Donald M. Wilcox
Major Activities: College Campus Ministry; Hospital Chaplaincy; Nursing Home Ministry; Newspaper Column; Interfaith Relationships; Hunger Relief; CWS; Crop Walk; Leadership Education; Community Issues; Mental Health Chaplaincy; Grief Support; Jail Ministry

Council of Churches of Chemung County, Inc.

330 W. Church St., Elmira, NY 14901 Tel. (607) 734-2294
E-mail: ecumenic2000@yahoo.com
Media Contact, Exec. Dir., Joan Geldmacher, Tel. (607)734-7622
Exec. Dir., Joan Geldmacher
Pres., Father Bill Lutz, Trinity Episcopal Church, 304 N. Main St., Elmira, NY 14901
Major Activities: CWS Collection; CROP Walk; UNICEF; Institutional Chaplaincies; Radio, Easter Dawn Service; Communications Network; Produce & Distribute Complete Church Directories; Representation on Community Boards and Agencies; Ecumenical Services; Interfaith Coalition; Taskforce on Children & Families; Compeer; Interfaith Hospitality Center

Council of Churches of the City of New York

475 Riverside Dr., Rm. 727, New York, NY 10115 Tel. (212)870-1020 Fax (212)870-1025
E-mail: jehiemstra@aol.com
Media Contact, Exec. Dir., Dr. John E. Hiemstra
Exec. Dir., Dr. John E. Hiemstra
Pres., Rev. Calvin O. Butts
First Vice-Pres., Friend Carol Holmes
Second Vice-Pres., Rev. Carolyn Holloway
Third Vice-Pres., Ven. Michael Kendall
Fourth Vice-Pres., Morris Gurley
Sec., Rev.N.J. L'Heureux
Treas., Rev. Jon Norton
Major Activities: Radio & TV; Pastoral Care; Christ for the World Chapel, Kennedy International Airport; Coordination and Strategic Planning; Interfaith Coordinator, Religious Conferences; Referral & Advocacy; Youth Development; Directory of Churches and Database Available

Dutchess Interfaith Council, Inc.

9 Vassar St., Poughkeepsie, NY 12601 Tel. (914) 471-7333 Fax (914)471-7333
E-mail: dic@bestweb.net
Media Contact, Exec. Dir., Rev. Gail A. Burger
Exec. Dir., Rabbi Johnathan Case
Pres., Rev. Gilbert E, McKenzie

Treas., Edward Koziol

Major Activities: CROP Hunger Walk; Interfaith Music Festival; Public Worship Events; Interfaith Dialogue; Christian Unity; Interfaith Youth Evening; Oil Purchase Group; Tour Of Houses Of Worship; Weekly Radio Program; Racial Unity Work; Poverty Forums

Genesee County Churches United, Inc.

P.O. Box 547, Batavia, NY 14021 Tel. (716)343-6763

Media Contact, Pres., Captain Leonard Boynton, Salvation Army, 529 East Main St., Batavia, NY 14020 Tel. (716)343-6284

Pres., James Woodruff

Exec. Sec., Cheryl Talone

Chaplain, Rev. Peter Miller

Major Activities: Jail Ministry; Food Pantries; Serve Needy Families; Radio Ministry; Pulpit Exchange; Community Thanksgiving; Ecumenical Services at County Fair

Genesee-Orleans Ministry of Concern

Arnold Gregory Memorial Complex, Suite 271

243 South Main St., Albion, NY 14411 Tel. (585)589-9210 Fax (585)589-9617

E-mail: gomoc@rochester.rr.com

Media Contact, Exec. Dir., Marian M. Adrian, GNSH

Exec. Dir., Suzanne R. Noonan

Advocates, JoAnn McCowan; Cheryl Johnson

Pres., John W. Cebula, Esq.

Chaplain, Albion Correctional Facility, Sr. Dolores O'Dowd, GNSH

Major Activities: Advocacy Services for the Disadvantaged, Homeless, Ill, Incarcerated and Victims of Family Violence; Emergency Food, Shelter, Utilities, Medicines, just Friends (a mentoring program for children), Parenting Program, Furniture Program.

Greater Rochester Community of Churches

2 Riverside St., Rochester, NY 14613-1222 Tel. (585)254-2570 Fax (585)254-6551

E-mail: grcc@juno.com

Web site: www.grcc.org

Media Contact, Admin., Elder Marie E. Gibson

Pres., Rev. Richard N. Myers

Vice-Pres., Prog. and Discipleship, Gloria Ulterino

Vice-Pres., Organization, Elder Jack Wheeler

Vice-Pres., Social Justice Ministry, Deacon Marvin Mich

Sec., Sister Patricia Switzer

Treas., Gary Hoyle

Major Activities: Ecumenical Worship; Christian Unity; Interfaith Health Care Coalition; Interfaith Dialogue; Annual Faith in Action Celebration; Rochester's Religious Community Directory; Religious Information-Resources; Justice Issues; Children's Emergency Fund Commission on Christian-Jewish Relations; Commissions on Christian-Muslim Relations; Commissions on Jewish-Muslim Relations

Inter-religious Council of Central New York

3049 E. Genesee St., Syracuse, NY 13224 Tel. (315)449-3552 Fax (315)449-3103

E-mail: mbowles@irccny.org

Web site: www.irccny.org

Media Contact, Dir. of Dev., Renée Roeder McCaffrey

Exec. Dir., Dr. James B. Wiggins

Pres., The Rev. William C. Redfield

Bus. Mgr., Laura J. Haley

Director for Resource Development, Renée Roeder McCaffrey

Pastoral Care Prog., Dir., The Rev. Martha Metzler

Refugee Resettlement Prog., Dir. Hope Wallis

Senior Companion Prog., Dir., Karen O'Hara

Long Term Ombudsman Prog., Dir., Linda Kashdin

Covenant Housing Prog., Dir., Kimberlee Dupcak

Southeast Asia Center, Dir., Mai Lan Gustafsson

Community Wide Dialogue on Racism, Race Relations and Racial Healing, Beth Broadway

Inter-religious Council News, Ed., Renée Roeder McCaffrey

Major Activities: Pastoral Ministries; Community Ministries; Inter-religious and Ecumenical Relations; Diversity Education; Worship; Community Advocacy and Planning

The Long Island Council of Churches

1644 Denton Green, Hempstead, NY 11550 Tel. (516)565-0290 Fax (516)565-0291

E-mail: licchemp@aol.com

Web site: www.ncccusa.org/ecmin/licc

Media Contact, Exec. Dir., Thomas W. Goodhue

Exec. Dir., Rev. Thomas W. Goodhue

Pastoral Care, Dir., Rev. Richard Lehman

Community Resources Dir., Alric Kennedy, Tel. (516)565-0390 ext. 204

Nassau County Ofc., Social Services Sec., Yolanda Murray

Suffolk County Ofc., Food Program & Family Support, Carolyn Gumbs, Tel: (631) 727-2210

Major Activities: Pastoral Care in Jails; Emergency Food; Family Support & Advocacy; Advocacy for Peace & Justice; Church World Service; Multifaith Education; Clergy-Laity Training; Newsletter; Church Directory; AIDS Interfaith of Long Island

Network of Religious Communities

1272 Delaware Ave., Buffalo, NY 14209-2496 Tel. (716)882-4793 Fax (716)882-3797

E-mail: nrc@religiousnet.org
Web site: ReligiousNet.org
Media Contact, Co-Exec. Dir., Rev. Dr. G. Stanford Bratton
Co-Exec. Dir. & COO, Rev. Dr. G. Stanford Bratton
Co-Exec. Dir., Rev. Francis X. Mazur
Pres., Imam Fajri Ansari
Vice-Pres. for Prog., The Rev. John Powell (Mennonite Board of Missions of WNY)
Vice-Pres. for Admin., Ms. Marlene Glickman (Dir., American Jewish Committee)
Sec., The Rev. Pierre Albricht-Carrie (Lockport Clergy Association)
Treas., Mr. Daniel Kantor (Exec. Dir., Jewish Federation of Greater Buffalo)
Chairs, Inter-religious Concerns, Rabbi Charles Shalman (Buffalo Board of Rabbis) and Dr. Othman Shibly (Islamic Society of the Niagara Frontier)
Chair, Personnel, The Rev. James Croglio (Diocese of Buffalo-Roman Catholic)
Chair, Membership, The Rev. Robert Grimm (United Church of Christ)
Chair, Riefler Enablement Fund, The Rev. Charles Bang (Holy Trinity Lutheran Church)
Chair, Public Issues, Rev. Merle Showers (United Methodist Church)
Chair, Religious Leaders Forum, Rev. Paul Litwin (Diocese of Buffalo-Roman Catholic)
Chair, Church Women United, Ms. Norma Roscover (Presbytery WNY)
Financial/Office Admin., Ms. Bonnie Jehle
Church Women United Coord., Ms. Sally Giordano
Food For All, Nutrition Outreach Coord., Ms. Kelly Kowalski
Food For All, Public Policy Coord., Mr. Bruce Davidson
Major Activities: Regionwide Inter-religious Conversation, Hunger Advocacy, Food Distribution, Roll Call Against Racism, Buffalo Coalition for Common Ground, Ecumenical and Inter-religious Relations and Celebrations, Radio-TV Broadcast and Production, Church Women United, Lay-Religious Leaders Education, Community Development, Chaplaincy, Yom Hashoah Commemoration Service, Aids Memorial Service, Police-Community Relations, CROP Walks

New York State Community of Churches, Inc.*

362 State St, Albany, NY 12210-1202 Tel. (518)436-9319 Fax (518)427-6705
E-mail: nyscoc@aol.com
Web site: www.nyscommunityofchurches.org
Media Contact, Ms. Mary Lu Bowen
Exec. Dir., Ms. Mary Lu Bowen
Pres., The Rev. Geoffrey A. Black
Vice-Pres., The Rev. Clint McCoy
Corp. Sec., The Rev. Dr. Jon Norton
Treas., Bishop Marie C. Jerge
Convener, Bishop Susan M. Morrison
Coord. of Chaplaincy Services, Ms. Damaris McGuire
Public Policy Consultant, The Rev. Daniel Hahn
Comm. Consultant, The Rev. Daniel Hahn
Admin. Asst., Sylvenia F. Cochran
Major Activities: Faith & Order; Interfaith Dialogue; State Chaplaincy and Public Policy Advocacy in the following areas, Anti-Racism; Campaign Reform; Criminal Justice System Reform; Disability; Ecomomic-Social Justice; Environmental; Health care; Homelessness-Shelter; Hunger-Food Programs; Immigrant Issues; Public Education; Rural Issues; Substance Abuse; Violence; Women's Issues

The Niagara Council of Churches Inc.

St. Paul UMC, 723 Seventh St., Niagara Falls, NY 14301 Tel. (716)285-7505
Media Contact, Pres., Nessie S. Bloomquist, 7120 Laur Rd., Niagara Falls, NY 14304 Tel. (716)297-0698 Fax (716)298-1193
Exec. Dir., Ruby Babb
Pres., Nessie S. Bloomquist
Treas., Shirley Bathurst
Trustees Chair, Rev. Vincent Mattoni, 834 19th St., Niagara Falls, NY 14304
Major Activities: Ecumenical Worship; Bible Study; Christian Ed. & Social Concerns; Church Women United; Evangelism & Mission; Institutional Min. Youth Activities; Hymn Festival; Week of Prayer for Christian Unity; CWS Projects; Audio-Visual Library; UNICEF; Food Pantries and Kitchens; Community Missions, Inc.; Political Refugees; Eco-Justice Task Force; Migrant-Rural Ministries; Interfaith Coalition on Energy

Queens Federation of Churches

86-17 105th St., Richmond Hill, NY 11418-1597 Tel. (718)847-6764 Fax (718)847-7392
E-mail: qfc@queenschurches.org
Web site: www.queenschurches.org
Media Contact, Rev. N. J. L'Heureux, Jr.
Exec. Dir., Rev. N. J. L'Heureux, Jr.
York College Chaplain, Rev. Dr. Hortense Merritt
Pres., Rev. J. Karel Boersma
Treas., Annie Lee Phillips
Major Activities: Emergency Food Service; York College Campus Ministry; Blood Bank; Scouting; Christian Education Workshops; Planning and Strategy; Church Women United; Community Consultations; Seminars for Church Leaders; Online Directory of Churches and Synagogues; Christian Relations (Prot-RC); Chaplaincies; Public Policy Issues; N.Y.S. Interfaith Commission on Landmarking of Religious Property;

Queens Interfaith Hunger Network; "The Nexus of Queens" (online, weekly newspaper)

Rural Migrant Ministry

P.O. Box 4757, Poughkeepsie, NY 12602 Tel. (845)485-8627 Fax (845)485-1963
E-mail: rmmhope3@aol.com
Web site: ruralmigrantministry.org
Media Contact, Exec. Dir., Rev. Richard Witt
Exec. Dir., Rev. Richard Witt
Pres., Melinda Trotti
Major Activities: Serving the Rural Poor and Migrants Through a Ministry of Advocacy & Empowerment; Youth Program; Latino Committee; Organization and Advocacy with and for Rural Poor and Migrant Farm Workers

Schenectady Inner City Ministry

930 Albany St., Schenectady, NY 12307-1514 Tel. (518)374-2683 Fax (518)382-1871
E-mail: sicm@knick.net
Web site: www.timesunion.com/community/sicm
Media Contact, Marianne Comfort
Urban Agent, Rev. Phillip N. Grigsby
Off. Mgr., Vjuana Anderson
Business Mgr., Barbara Bieniek
Emergency Food, Patricia Obrecht
Pres., Crystal Hamelink
Food System, Marianne Comfort
Damien Ctr., Glenn Read
Youth/Cocoa House, Rachel Graham
Jobs, Etc., David Coplon
Summer Food, Rachel Graham
Housing Task Force, Rev. Phil Grigsby
Major Activities: Food Security; Advocacy; Housing; Neighborhood and Economic Issues; Ecumenical Worship and Fellowship; Community Research; Education in Congregations on Faith Responses to Social Concerns; Legislative Advocacy; CROP Walk; HIV-AIDS Ministry; Job Training and Placement Center; Summer Lunch for Youth; Study Circles Initiative on Embracing Diversity; EPRUS-Americorps; Community Crisis Nework; Housing Services and Advocacy; Youth Initiative; After-School Program; Committee for Social Justice; Theological Center; Emmett Street Initiative

Southeast Ecumenical Ministry

25 Westminster Rd., Rochester, NY 14607 Tel. (585)271-5350 Fax (585)271-8526
E-mail: sem@frontiernet.net
Media Contact, Laurie Jenkins
Dir., Laurie Jenkins
Pres., Ronald K. Fox
Major Activities: Transportation of Elderly & Disabled; Emergency Food Cupboard for Case Managers to access for their clients; Supplemental Nutrition Program for seniors; Community Health and Pharmacy Partnership (CHAPP)

Staten Island Council of Churches

2187 Victory Blvd., Staten Island, NY 10314 Tel. (718)761-6782
E-mail: sicoc@verizon.net
Media Contact, Pres., Rev. Virginia Kaada, 2187 Victory Blvd., Staten Island, NY 10314 Tel. (718)761-6782
Pres., Rev. Virginia Kaada
Exec. Sec., Rebekah A. Ellis
Major Activities: Congregational Support & Outreach; Education & Pastoral Care; Ecumenical & Interfaith Witness; Social Witness

Troy Area United Ministries

392 Second St., Troy, NY 12180 Tel. (518)274-5920 Fax (518)271-1909
E-mail: info@taum.org
Web site: www.taum.org
Media Contact, Exec. Dir., Rev. Donna Elia
Pres., Laura M. Rogers
Chaplain, R.P.I. And Russel Sage, Rev. Beth Illingworth
Damien Ctr., Dir., Glenn Read
Furniture Prog., Dir., Michael Barrett
Major Activities: College Ministry; Nursing Home Ministry; CROP Walk; Homeless and Housing Concerns; Weekend Meals Program at Homeless Shelter; Community Worship Celebrations; Racial Relations; Furniture Program; Damien Center of Troy Hospitality for persons with HIV-AIDS; Computer Ministries; Youth Ministry

Wainwright House

260 Stuyvesant Ave., Rye, NY 10580 Tel. (914) 967-6080 Fax (914)967-6114
E-mail: frandavies@wainwright.org
Web site: www.wainwright.org
Media Contact, Exec. Dir., Fran Davies
Exec. Dir., Fran Davies
Pres., Robert Laughlin
Vice-Pres., Michael Standen
Major Activities: Educational Programs, Retreat and Conference Center; Intellectual, Psychological, Physical and Spiritual Growth; Healing and Health

NORTH CAROLINA

Asheville-Buncombe Community Christian Ministry (ABCCM)

30 Cumberland Ave., Asheville, NC 28801 Tel. (828)259-5300 Fax (828)259-5923
Media Contact, Exec. Dir., Rev. Scott Rogers, Fax (828)259-5323
Exec. Dir., Rev. Scott Rogers
Pres., Stephen Williamson
Major Activities: Crisis Ministry; Jail-Prison Ministry; Shelter Ministry; Medical Ministry

Greensboro Urban Ministry

305 West Lee St., Greensboro, NC 27406 Tel.

(910)271-5959 Fax (910)271-5920
E-mail: guministry@aol.com
Web site: www.greensboro.com/gum
Media Contact, Exec. Dir., Rev. Mike Aiken
Exec. Dir., Rev. Mike Aiken
Major Activities: Emergency Financial Assistance; Emergency Housing; Hunger Relief; Interfaith and Interracial Under-standing; Justice Ministry; Chaplaincy with the Poor

North Carolina Council of Churches*

Methodist Bldg., 1307 Glenwood Ave., Suite 156, Raleigh, NC 27605-3258 Tel. (919)828-6501 Fax (919)828-9697
E-mail: nccofc@nccouncilofchurches.org
Web site: www.nccouncilofchurches.org
Media Contact, Comm. Assoc., Aleta Payne
Exec. Dir., Rev. J. George Reed
Prog. Assoc., Steve Smith
Prog. Assoc., Denise Long
Prog. Assoc., Barbara Zelter
Comm. Assoc., Aleta Payne
Pres., Mrs. Barbara Volk, 1609 Pineview Drive, Raleigh, NC 27606
Treas., Dr. James W. Ferree, 168 Brook Landing Drive, Winston-Salem, NC 27106
Major Activities: Children and Families; Health Care Justice; Christian Unity; Women's Issues; Legislative Program; Criminal Justice; Farmworker Ministry; Rural Crisis; Racial Justice; Death Penalty; Poverty and Response to Welfare Changes; Climate Change; Public Education

NORTH DAKOTA

North Dakota Conference of Churches*

9195 70th Avenue, SE, Ashley, ND 58413-9600 Tel. (701)647-2063
E-mail: ndconchu@drtel.net
Web site: ndconference.org
Media Contact, Exec. Sec., Renee Gopal
Pres., Bishop Paul Zipfel
Vice-Pres. I, Dr. Wade Schemmel
Vice-Pres. II, Rev. Terri Akkerman
Treas., Rev. Charles Cherry
Sec., Bishop Duane Danielson
Major Activities: Rural Life Ministry; Faith and Order; North Dakota 101; Victims & Offenders Ministry; Rural Life Convocation

OHIO

Akron Area Association of Churches

350 S. Portage Path, Akron, OH 44320 Tel. (330)535-3112 Fax (330)374-5041
E-mail: aaac1@juno.com
Web site: www.triple-ac.org
Media Contact, Exec. Dir., Chloe Ann Kriska
Bd. of Trustees, Pres., Rev. Dr. J. Wayman Butts
Vice-Pres., Rev. Mark Frey
Sec., Dale Kline
Treas., Ms. Sherrie Petrochuk
Major Activities: *Messiah* Sing; Interfaith Council; Newsletters; Resource Center; Community Worship; Training of Local Church Leadership; Radio Programs; Clergy and Lay Fellowship Luncheons; Neighborhood Development; Community Outreach; Church Interracial Partnerships; Pastor Peer Group Program

Alliance of Churches

470 E. Broadway, Alliance, OH 44601 Tel. (330) 821-6648
Media Contact, Dir., Lisa A. Oyster
Dir., Lisa A. Oyster
Pres., Rev. Bud Hoffman
Treas., Betty Rush
Major Activities: Christian Education; Community Relations & Service; Ecumenical Worship; Community Ministry; Peacemaking; Medical Transportation for Anyone Needing It; Emergency Financial Assistance

Churchpeople for Change and Reconciliation

Box 488, Lima, OH 45802-0488 Tel. (419)224-2086 Fax (419)224-2086
Media Contact, Exec. Dir., The Rev. Darwin Ralston
Exec. Dir., The Rev. Darwin Ralston
Major Activities: Developing Agencies for Minorities, Poor, Alienated and Despairing; Our Daily Bread Soup Kitchen

Council of Christian Communions of Greater Cincinnati

42 Calhoun St., Cincinnati, OH 45219-1525 Tel. (513)559-3151
Media Contact, Exec. Dir., Joellen W. Grady
Exec. Dir., Joellen W. Grady
Justice Chaplaincy, Assoc. Dir., Rev. Jack Marsh
Educ., Assoc., Lillie D. Bibb
Pres., Rev. Damon Lynch III
Major Activities: Christian Unity & Interfaith Cooperation; Justice Chaplaincies; Police-Clergy Team; Adult and Juvenile Jail Chaplains; Religious Education

Greater Dayton Christian Connections

601 W. Riverview Ave., Dayton, OH 45406 Tel. (937)227-9485 Fax (937)227-9407
E-mail: gdcc@donet.com
Web site: www.christianconnections.org
Media Contact, Exec. Dir., Rev. Darryl Fairchild
Exec. Dir., Darryl Fairchild
Pres., Rev. Burton Wolf
Major Activities: Information, Ecumenical and Interfaith Dialogue; Peace Making; Environmental Justice; Racial Reconciliation; Pastor

Resources; Ministry Recruitment and Placement

Mahoning Valley Association of Churches
30 W. Front St., Youngstown, OH 44503 Tel. (330)744-8946 Fax (330)774-0018
E-mail: mvac@onecom.com
Media Contact, Exec. Dir., Elsie L. Dursi
Exec. Dir., Elsie L. Dursi
Pres., Rev. Joyce Lawson
Treas., Carol Williams
Major Activities: Communications; Christian Education; Ecumenism; Social Action; Advocacy

Metropolitan Area Church Council
760 E. Broad St., Columbus, OH 43205 Tel. (614)461-7103 Fax (614) 280-0352
E-mail: church_council@yahoo.com
Media Contact, Exec. Dir., Alvin Hadley
Pres., The Rev. Melvin Richardson
Vice-Pres., The Rev. Frank Ball
Sec., Ms. Ariene Reynolds
Treas., Ms. Marilyn Shreffler
Exec. Dir., Alvin Hadley
Major Activities: Newspaper; Published nine times annually; Annual Living Faiths Awards; Quarterly Racial Unity Services; Clergy Hospital Indentification Badges; Community Computer Center; Social Concerns relating to human needs in our community; Older Adult ministries; Collaborations to facilitate unity among religious denominations.

Metropolitan Area Religious Coalition of Cincinnati
617 Vine St., Suite 1035, Cincinnati, OH 45202-2423 Tel. (513)721-4843 Fax (513)721-4891
E-mail: marcc@fuse.net
Media Contact, Dir., Rev. Duane Holm
Pres., Mr. William K. Woods
Dir., Rev. Duane Holm
Major Activities: Affordable Housing & Community-Police Relations

Ohio Council of Churches*
6877 N. High St., Ste. 206, Columbus, OH 43085-2516 Tel. (614)885-9590 Fax (614) 885-6097
E-mail: mail@ohcouncilchs.org
Web site: www.ohcouncilchs.org
Exec. Dir., Rev. Rebecca J. Tollefson
Public Policy, Dir., Tom Smith
Pres., Rev. Joseph W. Witmer
Vice Pres., Ms. Rhea Ballas
Secretary: Rev. Deacon Leo Bistak
Treas., Rev. Dr. LaTaunya M. Bynum
Major Activities: Economic & Social Justice; Ecumenical Relations; Health Care Reform; Theological Dialogue; Racial Relations; Education-Funding; Childcare-Children Issues; Poverty-Welfare; Environment, Casino Gambling, Global Warming

Pike County Outreach Council
122 E. North St., Waverly, OH 45690-1146 Tel. (740)947-7151
Dir., Judy Dixon
Major Activities: Emergency Service Program; Self Help Groups; Homeless Shelter

Toledo Ecumenical Area Ministries
444 Floyd St., Toledo, OH 43620 Tel. (419)242-7401 Fax (419)242-7404
Media Contact, Admin., Nancy Lee Atkins
Metro-Toledo Churches United, Admn., Nancy Lee Atkins
Toledo Metropolitan Mission, Exec. Dir., Nancy Lee Atkins
Major Activities: Ecumenical Relations; Interfaith Relations; Food Program; Housing Program; Social Action-Public Education; Health Care; Urban Ministry; Employment; Welfare Rights; Housing; Mental Retardation; Voter Registration-Education; Substance Abuse Treatment; Youth Leadership; Children at Risk; Elimination of Discrimination

Tuscarawas County Council for Church and Community
1458 5th St. NW, New Philadelphia, OH 44663 Tel. (330)343-6012 Fax (330)343-9845
E-mail: mooredj3@adelphia.net
Media Contact, Donna J. Moore
Exec. Dir., Donna J. Moore
Pres., Dian Nemitz, 449 Seneca Dr. SW, New Philadelphia, OH 44663
Treas., James Barnhouse, 120 N. Broadway, New Philadelphia, OH 44663
Major Activities: Human Services; Health; Family Life; Child Abuse; Housing; Educational Programs; Emergency Assistance; Legislative Concerns; Juvenile Prevention Program; Character Formation; Prevention Program for High Risk Children; Bimonthly Newsletter *The Pilot*; Home Improvement Program

West Side Ecumenical Ministry
5209 Detroit Ave, Cleveland, OH 44102 Tel. (216)651-2037 Fax (216)651-4145
E-mail: eotero@wsem.org
Web site: www.wsem.org
Media Contact, Dir. of Marketing and Public Relations, Kami L. Marquardt
Pres. & CEO, Judith Peters
Chief Operation Officer, Adam Roth
Major Activities: WSEM is dedicated to serving urban low-income families by providing programs that encourage self-sufficiency. Three food pantries and outreach centers, a job-training program, early childhood, preschool, and schoool-age child care, crisis intervention,

counseling, youth services, a theatre education program and a senior nutrition program are among the services available. WSEM serves more than 56,000 children, families, and individuals annually with a staffing of more than 300 employees and 3,200 volunteers.

OKLAHOMA

Oklahoma Conference of Churches*

301 Northwest 36th St., Oklahoma City, OK 73118 Tel. (405)525-2928 Fax (405)525-2636
E-mail: okchurches@okchurches.org
Web site: www.okchurches.org
Media Contact, Deborah Canary-Marshall
Exec. Dir., The Rev. Dr. Rita K. Newton
Pres., Rev. Mark Gibbens-Rickman
Major Activities: Christian Unity Issues; Community Building Among Members; Rural Community Care; Children's Advocacy; Day at the Legislature; Impact; Criminal Justice; Hunger & Poverty; Legislative Advocacy; Aging; Women's Issues; Interfaith Coalition and Activities

Tulsa Metropolitan Ministry

221 S. Nogales, Tulsa, OK 74127 Tel. (918)582-3147 Fax (918)582-3159
E-mail: tummtulsa@aol.com
Web site: www.tumm.org
Media Contact, Exec. Dir., Stephen Cranford
Exec. Dir., The Rev. Dr. Stephen V. Cranford
Pres., Rev. Sara Jo Waggoner
Vice-Pres., Martin Belsky
Treas., Robert Dormont
Major Activities: Religious Understanding; Legislative Issues; Christian Unity Issues; Justice Issues; Against Racism; Disability Awareness; Directory of Metro; Religious Community; Airport Interfaith Chapel; Caring Companions; Native American Issues.

OREGON

Ecumenical Ministries of Oregon*

0245 S.W. Bancroft St., Ste. B, Portland, OR 97239 Tel. (503)221-1054 Fax (503)223-7007
E-mail: emo@emoregon.org
Web site: www.emoregon.org
Media Contact, Bob Baker, Dir. of Development & Communications
Exec. Dir., David A. Leslie
Finance & Admin. Services, Dir., Gary B. Logsdon
Development & Comm., Bob Baker
Sponsors Organized to Assist Refugees, Vesna Vila
Russian Oregon Social Services, Yelena Sergeva
Portland International Community School, Skip Adams
Public Policy Dir., Phillip Kennedy-Wong
Interfaith Network for Earth Concerns, Jenny Holmes
Parent Mentor Program, Patti Clothier
HIV Day Ctr., Lowen Berman
Shared Housing, Barbara Stone
Oregon Recovery Homes, Mike Morgester
Northeast Emergency Food Program, John Elizade
Pres., The Rev. Mark Knutson
Major Activities: Ecumenical Ministries of Oregon is a statewide association of seventeen Christian denominations including Protestant, Roman Catholic and Orthodox bodies working together to improve the lives of Oregonians through theological education and dialogue, public policy advocacy, environmental ministry and community ministry programs.

PENNSYLVANIA

Allegheny Valley Association of Churches

1913 Freeport Rd., Natrona Heights, PA 15065 Tel. (724)226-0606 Fax (724)226-3197
E-mail: avac@avaoc.org
Web site: www.avaoc.org
Media Contact, Exec. Dir., Karen Snair
Exec. Dir., Karen Snair
Pres., Rev. Dr. W. James Legge, 232 Tarentum-Culmerville Rd., Tarentum, PA 15084
Treas., Libby Grimm, 312 Butternut Ln., Tarentum, PA 15084
Major Activities: Ecumenical Services; Dial-a-Devotion; Walk for Hunger; Food Bank; Emergency Aid; Cross-on-the-Hill; AVAC Hospitality Network for Homeless Families; AVAC Volunteer Caregivers; Senior Citizen Housing-Pine Ridge Heights Senior Complex; AVAC Chaplaincy Program; Summer Camp for Children, Case Management

Christian Associates of Southwest Pennsylvania

204 37th St., Suite 201, Pittsburgh, PA 15201 Tel. (412)688-9070 Fax (412)688-9091
E-mail: casp1817@aol.com
Web site: www.casp.org
Media Contact, Dir. of Comm., Bruce J. Randolph
Exec., Dir., Rev. Dr. Donald B. Green
Chair of Council, Rev. Dr. Wayne Yost
Pres., Board of Delegates, Fr. Roger Statnick
Dir. of Comm., Bruce J. Randolph
Exec. Admin. Asst., Tracy Ritchie
Dir. of Jail Chaplaincy Services, Rev. Ulli Klemm
Television Studio Dir., Earl C. Hartman, Jr.
Protestant Chaplain-Shuman Youth Detention Center, Rev. Floyd Palmer
Protestant Chaplain, Rev. Dallas Brown
Jail Admin. Asst., Karen Mack
Major Activities: Jail Chaplaincy; Youth-Incarceration Chaplaincies; Theological Dialogue-Religious Education; Racism-Interracial Understanding; Religious Leadership

Forum; Christian Associates Television (CATV); *The Call...*Newsletter; Media Ministries Internet ministry; Indigent Burial program

Christian Churches United of the Tri-County Area

413 South 19th St., Harrisburg, PA 17106-0750 Tel. (717)230-9550 Fax (717)230-9554
E-mail: ccuhbg@aol.com
Web site: christianchurchesunited.com
Media Contact, Exec. Dir., Jaqueline P. Rucker
Exec. Dir., Jaqueline P. Rucker
Pres., John Dame
Treas., Henry Greenawald
Vice-Pres., Jeanne Heath
Sec., Patricia Greenawald
HELP & LaCasa Ministries, John Scarpato, Program Director, P.O. Box 60750, Harrisburg, PA 17106-0750 Tel. (717)238-2851 Fax (717)238-1916
Major Activities: Volunteer Ministries to Prisons; HELP (Housing, Rent, Food, Medication, Transportation, Home Heating, Clothing); La Casa de Amistad (The House of Friendship) Social Services; AIDS Outreach; Prison Chaplaincy; Lend-A-Hand (Disaster Rebuilding)

Christians United in Beaver County

1098 Third St., Beaver, PA 15009 Tel. (724)774-1446 Fax (724)774-1446
Media Contact, Exec. Sec., Lois L. Smith
Exec. Sec., Lois L. Smith
Chaplains, Rev. Dennis Ugoletti; Rev. Anthony Massey; Rev. Phyllis Anston; John Pusateri, Rev. Art Peters
Pres., Mrs. Delores Tisdale, 1021-5th Street, New Brighton, PA 15066
Treas., Mr. Richard Puryear, 2 McCabe Street, Sewickley, PA 15143
Major Activities: Christian Education; Evangelism; Social Action; Church Women United; United Church Men; Ecumenism; Hospital, Detention Home and Jail Ministry, Behavioral Health Clinic.

East End Cooperative Ministry

250 N. Highland Ave., Pittsburgh, PA 15206 Tel. (412)361-5549 Fax (412)361-0151
E-mail: eecm@eecm.org
Web site: www.eecm.org
Media Contact, Exec. Dir., Myrna Zelenitz
Exec. Dir., Myrna Zelenitz
Asst. Dir., Rev. Darnell Leonard
Major Activities: Food Pantry; Soup Kitchen; Men's Emergency Shelter; Drop-In Shelter for Homeless; Meals on Wheels; Information and Referral; Programs for Children and Youth; Bridge Housing Program for Men and PennFree Housing for Women in Recovery

Ecumenical Conference of Greater Altoona

P.O. Box 771, Altoona, PA 16693 Tel. (814)942-0512 Fax (814)942-0512
E-mail: ecumenaltoona@charter.net
Media Contact, Exec. Dir., Susanna M. Tomlinson
Exec. Dir., Susanna M. Tomlinson
Major Activities: Religious Education; Workshops; Ecumenical Activities; Religious Christmas Parade; Campus Ministry; Community Concerns; Peace Forum; Religious Education for Mentally Challenged, and Interfaith Committee

Greater Bethlehem Area Council of Churches

1021 Center St., P.O. Box 1245, Bethlehem, PA 18016-1245 Tel. (610)867-8671 Fax (610) 866-9223
E-mail: gbacc@enter.net
Exec. Dir., The Rev. Patricia Dwyer MacMillan
Pres., William L. Cauller
Treas., Mr. David G. Boltz, 1831 Levering Place, Bethlehem, PA 18017
Major Activities: World-local Hunger Projects; Ecumenical Worship-Cooperation; Prison Ministry Programs; Support for Homeless and Welfare to Work Programs; Emergency Food Pantry; Support for Hospice and Share Care Programs; Regional Grave Bank; Support Summer Youth Camps and Church Sports League

Hanover Area Council of Churches

136 Carlisle St., Hanover, PA 17331-2406 Tel. (717)633-6353 Fax (717)633-1992
E-mail: opsmanhacc@netrax.net
Web site: www.hanoverareacouncilofchurches.org
Operations Mgr., Carol Hinkle
Major Activities: Meals on Wheels, Provide-a-Lunch Program, Fresh Air Program, Clothing Bank, Hospital Chaplaincy Services; Congregational & Interfaith Relations, Public Ecumenical Programs and Services, State Park Chaplaincy Services & Children's Program; Compeer; Faith at Work; CROP Walk; Stolte Scholarship Fund; Community Needs; Cold Weather Shelter; AA

Inter-Church Ministries of Erie County

2216 Peach St., Erie, PA 16502 Tel. (814)454-2411
Pres., Mary C. Stewart
Treas., Ms. Margaret Lorei
Major Activities: Local Ecumenism; Social Ministry; Continuing Education; North West Pennsylvania Conference of Bishops and Judicatory Execs.; Theological Dialogue; Coats for Kids; Voucher Program for Emergency Assistance; Worship; Advocacy

Lancaster County Council of Churches

134 E. King St., Lancaster, PA 17602 Tel. (717)291-2261 Fax (717)291-6403
E-mail: office@lccouncilofchurches.org
Media Contact, Interim Exec. Dir., Kenneth Trauger
Pres., Steve Mentzer
Prescott House, Dir., John Stoudt
Service Ministry, Dir., Jaclyn Messersmith
Major Activities: Social Ministry; Residential Ministry to Youthful Offenders; Advocacy

Lebanon County Christian Ministries

250 S. 7th St., P.O. Box 654, Lebanon, PA 17042 Tel. (717)274-2601
E-mail: lccm@lmf
Media Contact, Exec. Dir., Lillian Morales
Exec. Dir., Lillian Morales
Noon Meals Coord., Wenda Dinatale
Major Activities: H.O.P.E. (Helping Our People in Emergencies); Food & Clothing Bank; Free Meal Program; Commodity Distribution Program; Ecumenical Events

Lehigh County Conference of Churches

534 Chew St., Allentown, PA 18102 Tel. (610) 433-6421 Fax (610)439-8039
E-mail: lccc@lcconfchurch.org
Web site: www.lcconfchurch.org
Media Contact, Dir. of Dev., Ira Faro
Exec. Dir., The Rev. Dr. Christine L. Nelson
Pres., Rev. William Metzger
First Vice-Pres., Ms. Gwyn Parker
Sec., The Rev. Dr. David Charles Smith
Treas., Mr. Nelson Rabenold
Major Activities: Prison Chaplaincy Program; Social Concerns and Action; Clergy Dialogues; Daybreak Drop-In Center for Mental Health Adults; Soup Kitchen; Housing Advocacy Program; Pathways (Referral to Social Services); Street Contact via Linkage; Community Exchange; Homelessness Prevention; Pharmaceutical Assistance; Campbell Ecumenism-Unity lecture; Clothing Distribution; Aspires Mentoring Program; Ecumenical & Interfaith Services; Homeless Supportive Services

Lewisburg Council of Churches

5. S. Asper Place, Lewisburg, PA 17837 Tel. (570)524-2834
Media Contact, Guy Temple, 139 Iron Cave Lane, Lewisburg, PA 17837 Tel. (570)-524-4877
Pres., Mrs. Janet Betzer, 1103 Market St., Lewisburg, PA 17837 Tel. (570) 524-2834
Treas., Mrs. Jan Temple, 139 Iron Cave Lane, Lewisburg, PA 17837 Tel. (570)-524-4877
Major Activities: Supplementary and Emergency Food Pantries; Clothing Bank; CROP Walk; Week of Prayer for Christian Unity; Soup & Scripture Lenten Series; 3-hour Good Friday Service; Human Services Directory; Transient-Homeless Aid

Metropolitan Christian Council of Philadelphia

1501 Cherry St., Philadelphia, PA 19102-1429 Tel. (215)563-7854 Fax (215)563-6849
E-mail: geiger@mccp.org
Web site: www.mccp.org
Media Contact, Assoc. Communications, Nancy L. Nolde
Exec. Dir., Rev. C. Edward Geiger
Assoc. Communications, Nancy L. Nolde
Office Mgr., Joan G. Shipman
Pres., Rev. Steven B. Laurence
First Vice-Pres., Rev. G. Daniel Jones
Treas., A. Louis Denton, Esq.
Major Activities: Congregational Clusters; Public Policy Advocacy; Communication; Theological Dialogue (Christian & Interfaith); Women's Issues

North Hills Youth Ministry Counseling Center

802 McKnight Park Dr., Pittsburgh, PA 15237 Tel. (412)366-1300
E-mail: nhym@sgi.net
Media Contact, Exec. Dir., Rev. Ronald B. Barnes
Exec. Dir., Ronald B. Barnes
Major Activities: Elementary, Junior and Senior High School Individual and Family Counseling; Elementary Age Youth Early Intervention Counseling; Educational Programming for Churches and Schools; Youth Advocacy; Parent Education; Marital Counseling

Northside Common Ministries

P.O. Box 99861, Pittsburgh, PA 15233 Tel. (412)323-1163 Fax (412)323-1749
E-mail: ncm@city-net.com
Media Contact, Exec. Dir., Janet E. Holtz
Exec. Dir., Janet E. Holtz
Major Activities: Pleasant Valley Shelter for Homeless Men; Advocacy around Hunger, Housing, Poverty, and Racial Issues; Community Food Pantry and Service Center; Supportive Housing

Northwest Interfaith Movement

6757 Greene St., Philadelphia, PA 19119 Tel. (215)843-5600 Fax (215)843-2755
E-mail: jejohnson@nim-phila.org
Web site: www.nim-phila.org
Media Contact, Exec. Dir., Rabbi George M. Stern
Exec. Dir., Rabbi George M. Stern
Chair, Judy Weinstein

Long Term Care Program, Dir., Donald Carlin

Neighborhood Child Care Resource Prog., Dir., Leslie S. Eslinger

Major Activities: Resources amd Technical Assistance for Child Care Programs; Conflict Mediation and Support for Nursing and Boarding Home Residents

Pennsylvania Conference on Interchurch Cooperation*

P.O. Box 2835, 223 North St., Harrisburg, PA 17105 Tel. (717)238-9613 Fax (717)238-1473

E-mail: staff@pacatholic.org

Web site: www.pacatholic.org/ecumenism

Media Contact, Carolyn Astfalk

Co-Staff, Dr. Robert J. O'Hara, Jr., Rev. Gary Harke

Co-Chpsns., Bishop Joseph Martino; Bishop Donald Main.

Major Activities: Theological Consultation; Social Concerns; Public Policy; Conferences and Seminars

The Pennsylvania Council of Churches*

900 S. Arlington Ave., Ste. 100, Harrisburg, PA 17109-5089 Tel. (717)545-4761 Fax (717) 545-4765

E-mail: pcc@pachurches.org

Web site: www.pachurches.org

Media Contact, Exec. Dir., Rev. Gary L. Harke

Exec. Dir., Rev. Gary L. Harke

Dir. of Public Advocacy, The Rev. Sandra L. Strauss

Dir. of Finance & Facilities, Janet A. Gulick

Coord. for Contract Chaplaincy, Rev. Douglas Hodges

Coord. for Leisure Ministries, Dr. Paul L. Herring

Coord. for Direct Ministries, Rev. Douglas Hodges

Pres., Rev. Bishop A. Donald Main

Vice-Pres., Ms. Barbara Adams-Smelter

Sec., Rev. Dr. Warren M. Eshbach

Treas., Ms. Zedna M. Haverstock

Major Activities: Inter-church dialogue; trade association activities; faith and order; seasonal farmworker ministry; trucker-traveler ministry; institutional chaplaincy; public policy advocacy and education; leisure ministry; conferences and continuing education events; disaster response; church education; global warming project; public education initiative.

Project of Easton, Inc.

330 Ferry St., Easton, PA 18042 Tel. (215)258-4361

Pres., Dr. John H. Updegrove

Vice-Pres. Public Relations, Rev. Charles E. Staples

Vice-Pres. Operations, Don Follett

Sec., Rosemary Reese

Treas., Steve Barsony

Exec. Dir., Maryellen Shuman

Major Activities: Food Bank; Adult Literacy Program; English as a Second Language; Children's Programs; Parents as Student Support; CROP Walk; Interfaith Council; Family Literacy; Emergency Assistance; Even Start Family Literacy

Reading Berks Conference of Churches

519 Elm St., P.O.Box 957, Reading, PA 19603 Tel. (610)375-6108 Fax (610)375-6205

E-mail: rdgbrkscc@comcast.net

Web site: www.readingberksconference-ofchurches.com

Media Contact, Exec. Dir., Rev. Calvin Kurtz

Admin. Asst., Donna Boyajcan

Exec. Dir., Rev. Calvin Kurtz

Pres., John Roland

Treas., William Maslo

Major Activities: Institutional Ministry; Social Action; CROP Walk for Hunger; Emergency Assistance; Prison Chaplaincy; Hospital Chaplaincy; Interchurch-Intercultural Services; Children & Youth Ministry; Healthy Family & Marriage Initiatives; Lazarus Project

South Hills Interfaith Ministries

1900 Sleepy Hollow Rd., South Park, PA 15129 Tel. (412)854-9120 Fax (412)854-9123

Web site: www.shimcenters.org

Media Contact, Exec. Dir., Jerry Ellis

Prog. Dir., Director of Youth Programs, Sarah Henkel

Psychological Services, Don Zandier

Family Assistance Coordinator, Harry Dietz

Business Mgr., Amy Puglisi

Volunteer Coord., Barbara Houston

Major Activities: Basic Human Needs; Community Organization and Development; Interfaith Cooperation; Personal Growth; At-Risk Youth Development; Women in Transition; Elderly Support; After School Homework Club; Early Childhood Program (Pre-School); Interfaith Educational Programs & Observances

United Churches of Lycoming County

202 E. Third St., Williamsport, PA 17701 Tel. (570)322-1110 Fax (570)326-4572

E-mail: uclc@sunlink.net

Web site: www.uclc.org

Media Contact, Exec. Dir., Rev. Gwen Nelson Bernstine

Exec. Dir., Rev. Gwen Nelson Bernstine

Ofc. Sec., Linda Winter

Pres., Rev. Louis Gatti, 3200 Lycoming Creek Road, Williamsport PA 17701

Pres., Mrs. Mikey Kamienski, 515 Vallamont Dr., Williamsport, PA 17701

Treas., Mr. A. Blair Phillips, 1511 Fairview Drive, Montoursville, PA 17754
Shepherd of the Streets, Rev. J. Morris Smith, 669 Center Street., Williamsport, PA 17701
Ecumenism, Dir., Rev. Leo McKernan, 800 Mulberry Street, Montoursville PA 17754
Educ. Ministries, Dir., Mrs. Deb Best, 522 N Grier St., Williamsport, PA. 17701
Institutional Ministry, Dir., Rev. Darlene Little, 266 Wagner Rd., Williamsport, PA 17701
Radio-TV, Dir., Nan Porter, 953 South Market St., South Williamsport, PA 17702
Prison Ministry, Dir., Mrs. Evadna Cline, 3336 West Fourth St., Williamsport, PA 17701
Christian Social Concerns, Dir., Rev. Joyce Gensib, 1315 Cherry St., Williamsport, PA 17701
Major Activities: Ecumenism; Educational Ministries; Church Women United; Church World Service and CROP; Prison Ministry; Radio-TV; Nursing Homes; Fuel Bank; Food Pantry; Family Life; Shepherd of the Streets Urban Ministry; Peace Concerns; Housing Initiative; Interfaith Dialogue, Youth Ministry

Wilkinsburg Community Ministry

710 Mulberry St., Pittsburgh, PA 15221 Tel. (412)241-8072 Fax (412)241-8315
E-mail: wcm15221@juno.com
Web site: trfn.clpgh.org/wcm
Media Contact, Dir., Rev. Vivian Lovingood
Acting Dir., Elizabeth Mulvaney, MSW, LSW
Pres. of Bd., Glenna Wilson, MSW, LSW
Major Activities: Hunger Ministry;Summer Reading Camp; Teen-Moms Infant Care; Meals on Wheels; Church Camp Scholarships; Utility Assistance; Clothing-Furniture Assistance; Case Management for Elderly Homebound Persons and Families, Soup Kitchen

Wyoming Valley Council of Churches

70 Lockhart St., Wilkes-Barre, PA 18702 Tel. (570)825-8543
Media Contact, Exec. Dir., Beth Titus
Exec. Dir., Beth Titus
Ofc. Sec., Sandra Karrott
Pres., Very Rev. Joseph Martin
Treas., Rev. Dr. Robert Zanicky
Major Activities: Nursing Home Chaplaincy; Hospital Referral Service; CROP Hunger Walk; Pastoral Care Ministries; Clergy Retreats and Seminars; Meals on Wheels Fuel Service; Citizen's Voice articles

York County Council of Churches

P.O. Box 1865, York, PA 17405-1865 Tel. (717)854-9504 Fax (717)843-5295
E-mail: ycccoffice@ycchurches.org
Web site: www.ycchurches.org
Media Contact, Exec. Dir., Rev. David D. Danneberger
Pres., Mrs. Christina J. Iosue
Vice-Pres., Rev. Donald Zobler
Exec. Dir., Rev. David D. Danneberger
Major Activities: Educational Development; Spiritual Growth and Renewal; Worship and Witness; Congregational Resourcing; Outreach and Mission

RHODE ISLAND

The Rhode Island State Council of Churches*

225 Chapman Street, Ste. 303, Providence, RI 02905 Tel. (401)461-5558 Fax (401)461-5233
E-mail: ricouncil@aol.com
Web site: www.ricouncilof churches
Media Contact, Exec. Minister, The Rev. John E. Holt
Exec. Min., The Rev. John E. Holt
Admn. Asst., Peggy Macnie
Pres., Mr. Frank Cook
Treas., George Weavill
Major Activities: Urban Ministries; Institutional Chaplaincy; Advocacy-Justice & Service, Legislative Liaison; Faith & Order; Leadership Development; Campus Ministries

SOUTH CAROLINA

South Carolina Christian Action Council, Inc.*

P.O. Drawer 3248, Columbia, SC 29230 Tel. (803)786-7116 Fax (803)786-7116
E-mail: sccouncil@sccouncil.net
Web site: www.sccouncil.net
Media Contact, Exec. Minister, Rev. Brenda Kneece
Exec. Minister, Rev. Brenda Kneece
Pres., The Rt. Rev. William "Bill" Skitton
Major Activities: Advocacy and Ecumenism; Continuing Education; Interfaith Dialogue; Citizenship and Public Affairs; Publications; Race Relations; Child Advocacy; Faith and Health; Environmental Stewardship

United Ministries

606 Pendleton St., Greenville, SC 29601 Tel. (864)232-6463 Fax (864)370-3518
E-mail: info@united-ministries.org
Web site: www.united-ministries.org
Media Contact, Exec. Dir., Rev. Beth Templeton
Exec. Dir., Rev. Beth Templeton
Pres., Becky Bouton
Vice-Pres., Bo Russell
Sec., Debbee Gordon
Treas., Bill Hummers
Major Activities: Assistance with rent, utilities, prescriptions, food, heat; Place of Hope (a day shelter for people who are homeless); Assistance with getting and keeping jobs; a Middle School and GED program for adults; case management as part of all activities

SOUTH DAKOTA

Association of Christian Churches of South Dakota*

100 S. Spring Ave., Suite 106, Sioux Falls, SD 57104-3626 Tel. (605)334-1980
E-mail: office@accsd.org
Web site: www.accsd.org
Media Contact, Gary Nesdahl
Pres., Board of Dir., Dr. Gene Miller
Major Activities: Ecumenical Forums; Continuing Education for Clergy; Legislative Information; Resourcing Local Ecumenism; Native American Issues; Ecumenical Fields Ministries; Rural Economic Development; Children at Risk

TENNESSEE

Metropolitan Inter Faith Association (MIFA)

P.O. Box 3130, Memphis, TN 38173-0130 Tel. (901)527-0208 Fax (901)527-3202
Media Contact, Dir., Media Relations, Caroline Vonicessler
Exec. Dir., Margaret Craddock
Major Activities: Emergency Services (Rent, Utility, Food, Clothing Assistance); Home-Delivered Meals and Senior Support Services; Youth Services; Homeless Programs

Tennessee Association of Churches*

103 Oak St., Ashland City, TN 37015 Tel. (615)792-4631
Pres., Rev. Steve Mosley
Treas., Paul Milliken
Major Activities: Faith and Order; Christian Unity; Social Concern Ministries; Governmental Concerns; Governor's Prayer Breakfast

Volunteer Ministry Center

103 South Gay St., Knoxville, TN 37902 Tel. (423)524-3926 Fax (423)524-7065
Media Contact, Exec. Dir., Angelia Moon
Exec. Dir., Angelia Moon
Pres., David Leech
Vice-Pres., John Moxham
Treas., Doug Thompson
Major Activities: Homeless Program; Food Line; Crisis Referral Program; Subsidized Apartment Program; Counselling Program; Parenting Education for Single Parents

TEXAS

Austin Area Inter-religious Ministries

701 Tillery St., Ste. 8, Austin, TX 78705 Tel. (512)386-9145 Fax (512)385-1430
E-mail: aaim@ammaustin.org
Web site: www.ammaustin.org
Media Contact, Exec. Dir., Susan Wills, LPC
Exec. Dir., Susan Wills
Pres., Rev. Mel Waxler
Treas., Anita Maxwell
Major Activities: Youth at Risk Mentoring; Housing Rehabilitation; Broadcast Ministry; Interfaith Dialogues; Family Issues; Homeless Issues; Hunger Issues; Racial Reconciliation, ESL

Border Association for Refugees from Central America (BARCA), Inc.

P.O. Box 1725, Edinburg, TX 78540 Tel. (956) 631-7447 Fax (956)687-9266
E-mail: barcainc@aol.com
Media Contact, Exec. Dir., Ninfa Ochoa-Krueger
Exec. Dir, Ninfa Ochoa-Krueger
Outreach Services, Dir., Juanita Ledesma
Major Activities: Food, Shelter, Clothing to Newly Arrived Indigent Immigrants & Refugees; Medical and Other Emergency Aid; Special Services to Children; Speakers on Refugee and Immigrant Concerns for Church Groups; Orientation, Advocacy and Legal Services for Immigrants and Refugees

Corpus Christi Metro Ministries

1919 Leopard St., P.O. Box 4899, Corpus Christi, TX 78469-4899 Tel. (361)887-0151 Fax (361)887-7900
E-mail: edseeger@ccmetrominstries.com
Web site: www.ccmetroministries.com
Media Contact, Exec. Dir., The Reverend Robert G. Trache
Exec. Dir., The Reverend Robert G. Trache, btrache@ccmetroministries.com
Admin. Dir., Ginger Flewelling-Leeds
Volunteer Dir., Ann Cox
Fin. Coord., Sue McCown
Loaves & Fishes Dir., Ray Gomez
Emergency Services Mgr., Ann Cox
Employment Dir., Larry Curtis
Health and Human Services, Dir., Ann Cox
Major Activities: Clothing Distribution, Employment Assistance, Healthcare, Homelessness/Shelter, and Hunger/Food Programs.

East Dallas Cooperative Parish

P.O. Box 720305, Dallas, TX 75372-0305 Tel. (214)823-9149 Fax (214)823-2015
E-mail: edcp@swbell.net
Media Contact, Exec. Dir., Nancy Jellinek
Pres., Debbie Thorpe
Major Activities: Emergency Food, Clothing, Job Bank; Medical Clinic; Legal Clinic, Tutorial Education; Home Companion Service; Pre-School Education; Hispanic Ministry; Activity Center for Low Income Older Adults; Pastoral Counseling; English Language Ministry, Pre-GED program

Greater Dallas Community of Churches

624 N. Good-Latimer #100, Dallas, TX 75204-5818 Tel. (214)824-8680 Fax (214)824-8726

E-mail: gdcc@churchcommunity.org
Media Contact, Exec. Dir., Rev. Elzie Odom
Exec. Dir., Rev. Elzie Odom
AmeriCorps-Building Blocks Dir., Venita Allen-Kent
Development Vice-Pres., Charlotte Coyle
Pres., Richard Selby
Treas., John Rutzler
Major Activities: Interdenominational, Interfaith and Interracial Understanding and Joint Work; AmeriCorps-Building Blocks (Direct Service to Develop Inner City Children, Youth & Families); Summer Food & Reading; Hunger; Peacemaking; Public Policy; Social Justice; Faith & Life; Children's Health Outreach; Child Advocacy; Dismantling Racism

Interfaith Ministries for Greater Houston

3217 Montrose Blvd., Houston, TX 77006 Tel. (713)522-3955 Fax (713)520-4663
Media Contact, Exec. Dir., Betty P. Taylor
Exec. Dir., Betty P. Taylor
Pres., Charles R. Erickson
Development, Dir., Sharon Ervine
Assoc. Exec. Dir., Larry Norton
Treas., Fort D. Flowers, Jr.
Sec., Darlene Alexander
Major Activities: Community Concerns, Hunger; Older Adults; Families; Youth; Child Abuse; Refugee Services; Congregational Relations and Development; Social Service Programs, Refugee Services; Hunger Coalition; Youth Victim Witness; Family Connection; Meals on Wheels; Senior Health; RSVP; Foster Grandparents

North Dallas Shared Ministries

2530 Glenda Ln., #500, Dallas, TX 75229 Tel. (214)620-8696 Fax (214)620-0433
Media Contact, Exec. Dir., J. Dwayne Martin
Exec. Dir., J. Dwayne Martin
Major Activities: Emergency Assistance; Job Counseling; ESL

Northside Inter-Church Agency (NICA)

1600 Circle Park Blvd., Fort Worth, TX 76106-8943 Tel. (817)626-1102 Fax (817)626-9043
E-mail: nicaagency@sbcglobal.net
Web site: www.nicaagency.org
Media Contact, Exec. Dir., Connie Nahoolewa
Exec. Dir., Connie Nahoolewa
Major Activities: Food; Clothing; Counseling; Information and Referral; Furniture and Household Items; Nutrition Education; Employment Services; Thanksgiving Basket Program; "Last Resort" Christmas Program; Community Networking; Ecumenical Worship Services; Volunteer Training; Newsletter; Senior Home Repairs; School Clothing Program; Advocacy; GED Preparation; Literacy; Computer Training; English as a Second Language

San Antonio Community of Churches

1101 W. Woodlawn, San Antonio, TX 78201 Tel. (210)733-9159 Fax (210)733-5780
E-mail: sacc@juno.com
Media Contact, Exec. Dir., Dr. Kenneth Thompson
Exec. Dir., Dr. Kenneth Thompson
Pres., Rev. Thomas Robinson
Major Activities: Christian Education; Missions; Infant Formula and Medical Prescriptions for Children of Indigent Families; Continuing Education For Clergy and Laity; Media Resource Center; Social Issues; Aging Concerns; Youth Concerns; Family Concerns; Sponsor annual CROP Walk for Hunger; Peace and Anti-Violence Initiatives

San Antonio Urban Ministries

535 Bandera Rd., San Antonio, TX 78228
Media Contact, Sue Kelly
Exec. Dir., Sue Kelly
Pres., Rev. Leslie Ellison
Major Activities: Homes for Discharged Mental Patients; After School Care for Latch Key Children; Christian Based Community Ministry

Southeast Area Churches (SEARCH)

P.O. Box 51256, Fort Worth, TX 76105 Tel. (817)531-2211
Exec. Dir., Dorothy Anderson-Develrow
Major Activities: Emergency Assistance; Advocacy; Information and Referral; Community Worship; School Supplies; Direct Aid to Low Income and Elderly

Tarrant Area Community of Churches

P.O. Box 11471, Fort Worth, TX 76110-0471 Tel. (817)534-1790 Fax (817)534-1995
E-mail: revkm@flash.net
Pres., Regina Taylor
Treas., Don Hoak
Exec. Dir., Dr. Kenneth W. McIntosh
Major Activities: Eldercare Program; Children's Sabbath Sponsorship; Week of Prayer for Christian Unity; CROP Walk for Hunger Relief; Community Issues Forums; Family Pathfinders

Texas Conference of Churches*

1033 La Posada, Ste. 125, Austin, TX 78752 Tel. (512)451-0991 Fax (512)451-5348
E-mail: tcc@txconfchurches.org
Web site: www.txconfchurches.org
Media Contact, Comm. and Web Services, Caryn Wontor

Exec. Dir., Rev. Dr. George P. Bithos
Dir. of Business Admin., Caryn Wontor
Pres., Rev. Dr. T. Randall Smith
Major Activities: Faith & Order; Related Ecumenism; Christian-Jewish Relations; Church and Society Issues

United Board of Missions

1701 Bluebonnet Ave., P.O. Box 3856, Port Arthur, TX 77643-3856 Tel. (409)982-9412 Fax (409)985-3668
Media Contact, Admin. Asst., Carolyn Schwarr
Exec. Dir., Clark Moore
Pres., Glenda McCoy
Major Activities: Emergency Assistance (Food and Clothing, Rent and Utility, Medical, Dental, Transportation); Share a Toy at Christmas; Counseling; Back to School Clothing Assistance; Information and Referral; Hearing Aid Bank; Meals on Wheels; Super Pantry; Energy Conservation Programs; Job Bank Assistance to Local Residents Only

VERMONT

Vermont Ecumenical Council and Bible Society*

P.O. Box 728, Richmond, VT 05477 Tel. (802)434-7307
E-mail: info@vecbs.org
Web site: www.vecbs.org
Media Contact, Admin. Asst., Betsy Wackernagel
Exec. Officer, Rev. Dr. Leonard Rowell
Pres., Rev. Frederick Neu
Vice-Pres., Bishop Thomas Ely
Treas., Mr. Joseph Cioffi
Major Activities: Christian Unity; Bible Distribution; Social Justice; Committee on Faith and Order; Committee on Peace, Justice and the Integrity of Creation; Committee on Prayer and Worship

VIRGINIA

Virginia Council of Churches, Inc.*

1214 W. Graham Rd., Richmond, VA 23220-1409 Tel. (804)321-3300 Fax (804)329-5066
E-mail: barton@vcc-net.org
Web site: www.vcc-net.org
Media Contact, Gen. Min., Rev. Jonathan Barton
Gen. Min., Rev. Jonathan Barton
Migrant Head Start, Dir., Richard D. Cagan
Refugee Resettlement, Dir., Rev. Richard D. Cline
Weekday Rel. Educ., Coord., 2699 Lanier Lane, McGaheysville, VA 22840
Campus Ministry Forum, Coord., Rev. Steve Darr, c/o Community College Ministries, 305 Washington St., N.W., Blacksburg, VA 24060-4745
Major Activities: Faith and Order; Network Building & Coordination; Ecumenical Communications; Justice and Legislative Concerns; Educational Development; Rural Concerns; Refugee Resettlement; Migrant Ministries and Migrant Head Start; Disaster Coordination; Infant Mortality Prevention

WASHINGTON

Associated Ministries of Tacoma-Pierce County

1224 South I St., Tacoma, WA 98405-5021 Tel. (253)383-3056 Fax (253)383-2672
E-mail: info@associatedministries.org
Web site: www. associatedministries.org
Media Contact, Exec. Dir., Rev. David T. Alger
Dir. of Comm., Judy Jones
Pres., Rev. John Williams
Vice-Pres., Rev. David Wold
Sec., Karen Davey
Treas., Jeff Cunningham
Exec. Dir., Rev. David T. Alger
Deputy Dir., Maureen Fife
Dir. of Mental Health Chaplaincy, Julie Bradley
Dir. of Project Interdependence, Valorie Crout
Dir. of Paint Tacoma-Pierce Beautiful, Sallie Shawl
Dir. Of Development, S. Marion Sharp
Dir. of Hilltop Action Coalition, Jeanie Peterson
Director of Comm. and Education, Judy Jones
Director of Community Connections for Military Families, Sherrill Hendrick
Major Activities: County-wide Hunger Walk; Hunger Awareness; Economic Justice; Religious Education; Social Service Program Advocacy; Communication and Networking of Churches; Housing; Paint Tacoma-Pierce Beautiful; Mental Health Chaplaincy; Theological Dialogue; Welfare to Work Mentoring; Hilltop Action Coalition; Compeer; Homelessness; Youth Ministry; Ecumenical Formation; Community Connection for Military Families; Interfaith Roundtable

Church Council of Greater Seattle

4759 15th Ave. NE, Seattle, WA 98105-4404 Tel. (206)525-1213 Fax (206)525-1218
E-mail: info@thechurchcouncil.org
Web site: www.thechurchcouncil.org
Media Contact, Exec. Dir., The Rev. Dr. Sanford Brown
Exec. Dir., The Rev. Dr. Sanford Brown
Emergency Feeding Prog., Dir., Arthur Lee
Friend to Friend, Dir., Marilyn Soderquist
Youth Chaplaincy Program, Dir. Chaplain, Rev. Benny Wright
The Sharehouse, Dir., Michal Nortness
The Homelessness Project, Dir., Nancy Dorman
Mission for Music & Healing, Dir., Susan Gallaher & Esther "Little Dove" John
Sound Youth-AmeriCorps, Dir., Cat Koehn
Academy of Religious Broadcasting, Dir., Rev. J. Graley Taylor
Board Chair, Verlene Jones

Board Treas., The Rev. Jeb Parr
Board Sec., Susan Segall
Editor, The Source, Tricia Schug
Seattle Youth Garden Works, Dir., Conner Sharpe
SW King County Mental Health Ministry, Dir., The Rev. Stephen Jones
JOY Initiative, Prog. Dir., Rick Jump
St. Petersburg-Seattle Sister Churches Program Chair, Nigel Taber-Hamilton
Asia Pacific Task Force, Contact Person, Akio Yanagihara
Self-Managed Housing Programs, Dir., Misti Uptain
Cuba Friendshipment Committee, Chair, Monica Zapeda
Palestinian Concerns Task Force, Chair, Constance Trowbridge
Interfaith Network of Concern for the People of Iraq, Chair, The Rev. Rich Gamble & Andrew Fung
Major Activities: Children; Youth & Families; Hunger Relief; Global Peace and Justice; Housing and Homelessness; Pastoral Care; Services for the Aging; Public Witness; Interfaith and Ecumenical Relations; Publisher of the *The Source*, a monthly ecumenical newspaper

FaithTrust Institute

2400 N. 45th St, Suite 10, Seattle, WA 98103 Tel. (206)634-1903 Fax (206)634-0115
E-mail: info@faithtrustinstitute.org
Web site: www.faithtrustinstitute.org
Media Contact, Rev. Dr. Marie M. Fortune
Exec. Dir., Rev. Kathryn J. Johnson, kjohnson@faithtrustinstitute.org
Founder & Sr. Analyst, Rev. Dr. Marie M. Fortune, mfortune@faithtrustinstitute.org
Dir. of Training & Education, Rev. Thelma Burgonio-Watson, burgonio@faithtrustinstitute.org
Dir. of the Jewish Prog., Rabbi Cindy Enger, cenger@faithtrustinstitute.org
Clearinghouse Coord., Dinah Hall, dhall@faithtrustinstitute.org
Finance Dir., Marion J. Ward
Major Activities: Prevention and Response Education; Clergy and Lay Training; Video and Print Resources; Bi-national Educational Ministry

The Interfaith Association of Snohomish County

2301 Hoyt, P.O. Box 12824, Everett, WA 98206 Tel. (206)252-6672
E-mail: admin@tiasc.com
Web site: www.tiasc.com
Media Contact, Exec. Dir., Janet Pope
Exec. Dir., Janet Pope
Pres., William Comfort
Major Activities: Housing and Shelter; Economic Justice; Hunger; Interfaith Worship and Collaboration

Interfaith Council

1620 N. Monroe, Spokane, WA 99205 Tel. (509)329-1410 Fax (509)329-1409
E-mail: info@interfaithnw.org
Web site: www.interfaithnw.org
Media Contact, Dir., Kateri Caron
Director: Kateri Caron
Board Pres.: Stephen Rorie
Vice-Pres.: Elliot Fabric
Sec., Rev. Dr. Richard Erhardt
Major Activities: Camp PEACE; Multi-Cultural Human Relations; High School Youth Camp; Eastern Washington Legislative Conference; CROP Walk; Interfaith Thanksgiving Worship; Easter Sunrise Service; Dir. Of Churches & Community Agencies; Circle of Caring (for Women in Domestic Violence); Guatemala Dialogues

Interfaith Works

P.O. Box 1221, Olympia, WA 98507 Tel. (360)357-7224
E-mail: amtcoly@aol.com
Web site: www.interfaith-works.org
Media Contact, Exec. Dir., Kathy Erlandson
Exec. Dir., Cheri Gonyaw
Pres., Jim Fultonl
Treas., Mike Coday
Major Activities: Interfaith Relations; Social and Health Concerns; Community Action; Social Justice

Northwest Harvest-E. M. M.

P.O. Box 12272, Seattle, WA 98102 Tel. (206) 625-0755 Fax (206)625-7518
E-mail: nharvest@blarg.net
Web site: www. northwestharvest.org
Media Contact, Comm. Affairs Dir., Ellen Hansen
Exec. Dir., Ruth M. Velozo
Chair, Patricia Barcott
Major Activities: Northwest Harvest (Statewide Hunger Response); Cherry Street Food Bank (Community Hunger Response); Northwest Infants Corner (Special Nutritional Products for Infants and Babies)

Washington Association of Churches*

419 Occidental Ave. S., Ste. 201, Seattle, WA 98104-2886 Tel. (206)625-9790 Fax (206) 625-9791
E-mail: wac@thewac.org
Web site: www.thewac.org
Media Contact, John C. Boonstra, boonstra@thewac.org
Exec. Min., Rev. John C. Boonstra, boonstra@thewac.org
Dir. for Operations, Bette Schneider, schneider@thewac.org

Major Activities: Faith and Order; Ecumencial Dialogue; Justice Advocacy; Confronting Poverty; Hunger Action; Legislation; Denominational Ecumenical Coordination; Theological Formation; Leadership Development; Immigrant Rights Advocacy; Racial Justice Advocacy; International Solidarity; Environmental Justice Advocacy

WEST VIRGINIA

Greater Fairmont Council of Churches

P.O. Box 108, Fairmont, WV 26554 Tel. (304) 367-0962

Media Contact, Pres., Rev. Jeremiah Jasper

Pres., Rev. Jeremiah Jasper

Major Activities: Community Ecumenical Services; Youth and Adult Sports Leagues; CROP Walk Sponsor; Weekly Radio Broadcasts

The Greater Wheeling Council of Churches

1060 Chapline St., 110 Methodist Building, Wheeling, WV 26003 Tel. (304)232-5315

Media Contact, Exec. Dir., Kathy J. Burley

Exec. Dir., Kathy J. Burley

Hospital Notification Sec., Anna Lou Lenz

Pres., Martha J. Morris

Finance Chair, Rev. Robert P. Johnson; Doug Clatterbuck

Major Activities: Christian Education; Evangelism; Christian Heritage Week Celebration; Institutional Ministry; Regional Jail Chaplaincy; Church Women United; Volunteer Chaplaincy Care at OVMC Hospital; School of Religion; Hospital Notification; Hymn Sing in the Park; Anti-Gambling Crusade; Pentecost Celebration; Clergy Council; Easter Sunrise Service; Community Seder; Church Secretaries Fellowship; National Day of Prayer Service; Videotape Library-Audiotape Library; Flood Relief Network of the Upper Ohio Valley

West Virginia Council of Churches*

2207 Washington St. E., Charleston, WV 25311-2218 Tel. (304)344-3141 Fax (304)342-1506

E-mail: wvcc@wvcc.org

Web site: www.wvcc.org

Media Contact, Exec. Dir., The Rev. Dennis D. Sparks, dsparks@wvcc.org

Office Manager, Bob Rosier, bob@wvcc.org

Pres., Most Rev. Bernard W. Schmitt, D.D. (RC)

1st Vice-Pres., Rev. Dr. Randall F. Flanagan (UMC)

2nd Vice-Pres., Ms. Patricia Harris, CC (DOC)

Sec., Rev. Dr. William B. Allen (DOC)

Treas., Very Rev. Frederick P. Annie, (RC)

Major Activities: Disaster Response; Faith and Order; Family Concerns; Inter-Faith Relations; Peace and Justice; Government Concerns; Support Services Network

WISCONSIN

Christian Youth Council

1715-52nd St., Kenosha, WI 53140 Tel. (262) 654-6200 x120 Fax (414)652-4461

Media Contact, Exec. Dir., Steven L. Nelson

Exec. Dir., Steven L. Nelson

Sports Dir., Jerry Tappen

Outreach Dir., Linda Osborne

Accountant, Debbie Cutts

Class Dir., Jill Cox

Pres. & Chair of Board, Lon Knoedler

Gang Prevention Dir., Sam Sauceda

Major Activities: Leisure Time Ministry; Institutional Ministries; Ecumenical Committee; Social Concerns; Outreach Sports (with a Christian Philosophy)

Interfaith Conference of Greater Milwaukee

1442 N. Farwell Ave., Ste. 200, Milwaukee, WI 53202 Tel. (414)276-9050 Fax (414)276-8442

E-mail: ifcgm@aol.com

Media Contact, Exec. Dir., Marcus White

Chair, Rev. Velma Smith

First Vice-Chair, Archbishop Rembert G. Weakland

Second Vice-Chair, Rev. Charles Graves

Sec., Paula Simon

Treas., Rev. Mary Ann Neevel

Exec. Dir., Marcus White

Consultant in Communications, Rev. Robert P. Seater

Major Activities: Economic Issues; Racism; CROP Walk; Public Policy; Suburban and Urban Partnerships; TV Programming; Peace and International Issues Committee; Annual Membership Luncheon; Religion Diversity; Restorative Justice

Madison-area Urban Ministry

2300 S. Park St., Madison, WI 53713 Tel. (608) 256-0906 Fax (608)256-4387

E-mail: mum@emum.org

Web site: www.emun.org

Media Contact, Office Mgr., Jackie Austin

Exec. Dir., Mary K. Baum

Major Activities: Community Projects; Dialogue-Forums

Wisconsin Council of Churches*

750 Windsor St. Ste. 301, Sun Prairie, WI 53590-2149 Tel. (608)837-3108 Fax (608)837-3038

E-mail: sanderson@wichurches.org

Web site: www.wichurches.org

Media Contact, Comm. Coord., Jeanette Johnson

Exec. Dir., Exec. Dir., Scott D. Anderson

Office Manager, Jeanette Johnson

Coord. for Local Ecumenism, Rev. Kenneth Pennings

Pres., Rev. Hal Murray

Treas., Dr. Robert Bock

Accountant, Rick Fluechtling

Coord. for Prog. Support Services, Mr. Christopher Marceil

Major Activities: Social Witness; Migrant Ministry; Peace and Justice; Faith and Order; Anti-Hunger Campaign; American Indian Ministries Council; Park Ministry; Wisconsin Housing Partnership; Nonviolence, Affordable Housing; Economic Justice; Corporate Responsibility

WYOMING

Wyoming Association of Churches*

P.O. Box 20812, Cheyenne, WY 82003-7017 Tel. (307)635-4251 Fax (307)637-4737

E-mail: wychurches@wyoming.com

Web site: www.wyomingassociationofchurch-es.org

Media Contact, Mary Richey, Wyoming Church Coalition, P.O. Box 20812, Cheyenne, WY 82003

Dir., Rev. Warren Murphy

Chaplain, Rev. Kenneth Martin

Bookkeeper, Mary Richey

Office Manager, Peg Edwards

Major Activities: Alternatives to Violence; Prison Ministry; Beyond Tolerance; Malicious Harrassment; Domestic Violence; Empowering the Poor and Oppressed; Peace and Justice; Public Health Issues; Welfare Reform; Death Penalty

Index of Select Programs for U.S. Regional and Local Ecumenical Bodies

For many years the *Yearbook of American & Canadian Churches* has published the previous chapter, The Directory of U.S. Regional and Local Ecumenical Bodies. Each entry of that directory contains a brief description of the diverse programs offered by each agency. However, researchers, pastors, service organizations and theological seminaries often inquire about specific programs and which agencies carry out such programs. In response we have created this chapter, which indexes the various regional and local ecumenical agencies by twenty-five different program areas. These program areas are the twenty-five that have been the most frequent subjects of inquiry in our office. We have collected this program information directly from these organizations by means of a simple response form. There is an enormous diversity of ministries and missions conducted by these diverse organizations. Most organizations pursue several kinds of programs at once. However, some of these may focus their efforts most especially on only one of their programs; their other programs may be less well developed than their specialty. Consequently, the extent to which any of these ministries is a priority for any particular organization cannot be inferred from this list. For detailed information about the nature and extent of any particular ministry, the reader is urged to contact the organization directly using the directory of "U.S. Regional and Local Ecumenical Bodies," which is found in the pages just prior to this index.

AIDS/HIV Programs

Arizona Ecumenical Council—Phoenix, AZ
Associated Ministries of Tacoma-Pierce County—Tacoma, WA
Center City Churches—Hartford, CT
The Council of Churches of Santa Clara County—San Jose, CA
East Dallas Cooperative Parish—Dallas, TX
Ecumenical Ministries of Oregon—Portland, OR
Grand Rapids Area Center for Ecumenism (GRACE)—Grand Rapids, MI
Greater Baton Rouge Federation of Churches and Synagogues—Baton Rouge, LA
Greater Chicago Broadcast Ministries—Chicago, IL
Interfaith Community Services—St. Joseph, MO
Lehigh County Conference of Churches—Allentown, PA
Lincoln Interfaith Council—Lincoln, NE
The Long Island Council of Churches—Hempstead, NY
Metropolitan Ecumenical Ministry—Newark, NJ
New Britain Area Conference of Churches (NEWBRACC)—New Britain, CT
New Mexico Conference of Churches—Albuquerque, NM
Schenectady Inner City Ministry—Schenectady, NY
South Carolina Christian Action Council, Inc.—Columbia, SC
Southeast Ecumenical Ministry—Rochester, NY
Staten Island Council of Churches—Staten Island, NY
Troy Area United Ministries—Troy, NY
Wyoming Valley Council of Churches—Wilkes-Barre, PA
York County Council of Churches—York, PA

Anti-Gambling Programs

The Associated Churches of Fort Wayne & Allen County, Inc.—Fort Wayne, IN
Ecumenical Ministries of Iowa (EMI)—Des Moines, IA
Kentucky Council of Churches—Lexington, KY
Mahoning Valley Association of Churches—Youngstown, OH
Mississippi Religious Leadership Conference—Jackson, MS
Muskegon County Cooperating Churches—Muskegon, MI
Network of Religious Communities—Buffalo, NY
Texas Conference of Churches—Austin, TX

Anti-Racism Programs

Akron Area Association of Churches—Akron, OH
Arizona Ecumenical Council—Phoenix, AZ
Arkansas Interfaith Conference—Scott, AR
The Associated Churches of Fort Wayne & Allen County, Inc.—Fort Wayne, IN
Associated Ministries of Tacoma-Pierce County—Tacoma, WA
Association of Religious Communities—Danbury, CT
Austin Area Inter-religious Ministries—Austin, TX
Broome County Council of Churches, Inc.—Binghamton, NY
Capital Region Ecumenical Organization (CREO)—Schenectady, NY

The Capitol Region Conference of Churches—Hartford, CT
Christian Associates of Southwest Pennsylvania—Pittsburgh, PA
Christian Ministries of Delaware County—Muncie, IN
The Church Federation of Greater Indianapolis, Inc.—Indianapolis, IN
Churches United of the Quad City Area—Rock Island, IL
Colorado Council of Churches—Denver, CO
Community Emergency Assistance Program (CEAP)—Brooklyn Park, MN
Community Renewal Society—Chicago, IL
Cooperative Metropolitan Ministries—Newton, MA
Council of Churches of the City of New York—New York, NY
Council of Churches of Greater Bridgeport, Inc.—Bridgeport, CT
The Council of Churches of Santa Clara County—San Jose, CA
Council of Churches and Synagogues of Southwestern Connecticut—Stamford, CT
Dutchess Interfaith Council, Inc.—Poughkeepsie, NY
East Dallas Cooperative Parish—Dallas, TX
Ecclesia—Trenton, NJ
Ecumenical Conference of Greater Altoona—Altoona, PA
Ecumenical Ministries of Oregon—Portland, OR
Evanston Ecumenical Action Council—Evanston, IL
Faith Community Assistance Center—Santa Fe, NM
Florida Council of Churches—Altamonte Springs, FL
Fresno Metro Ministry—Fresno, CA
Georgia Christian Council—Macon, GA
Grand Rapids Area Center for Ecumenism (GRACE)—Grand Rapids, MI
Greater Baton Rouge Federation of Churches and Synagogues—Baton Rouge, LA
Greater Birmingham Ministries—Birmingham, AL
Greater Chicago Broadcast Ministries—Chicago, IL
Greater Dallas Community of Churches—Dallas, TX
Greater Dayton Christian Connections—Dayton, OH
Greater Minneapolis Council of Churches—Minneapolis, MN
Greater Rochester Community of Churches—Rochester, NY
The Greater Wheeling Council of Churches—Wheeling, WV
Greensboro Urban Ministry—Greensboro, NC
Illinois Conference of Churches—Springfield, IL
In One Accord—Battle Creek, MI
Indiana Partners for Christian Unity and Mission—Indianapolis, IN
Inter-Church Council of Greater New Bedford—New Bedford, MA
Inter-Church Ministries of Erie County—Erie, PA
Interchurch Ministries of Nebraska—Lincoln, NE
Interfaith Conference of Greater Milwaukee—Milwaukee, WI
InterFaith Conference of Metropolitan Washington—Washington, DC
Interfaith Council—Spokane, WA
Interfaith Council of Contra Costa County—Walnut Creek, CA
Inter-Faith Ministries-Wichita—Wichita, KS
Interfaith Mission Service—Huntsville, AL
Interfaith Service Bureau—Sacramento, CA
InterReligious Council of Central New York—Syracuse, NY
Kansas Ecumenical Ministries—Topeka, KS
Kentuckiana Interfaith Community—Louisville, KY
Kentucky Council of Churches—Lexington, KY
Lincoln Interfaith Council—Lincoln, NE
The Long Island Council of Churches—Hempstead, NY
Louisiana Interchurch Conference—Baton Rouge, LA
Mahoning Valley Association of Churches—Youngstown, OH
Massachusetts Council of Churches—Boston, MA
The Metropolitan Christian Council: Detroit-Windsor—Detroit, MI
Metropolitan Christian Council of Philadelphia—Philadelphia, PA
Metropolitan Ecumenical Ministry—Newark, NJ
Metropolitan Interfaith Council on Affordable Housing (MICAH)—Minneapolis, MN
Michigan Ecumenical Forum—Lansing, MI
Minnesota Council of Churches—Minneapolis, MN
Mississippi Religious Leadership Conference—Jackson, MS
Montana Association of Churches—Billings, MT
Muskegon County Cooperating Churches—Muskegon, MI
Network of Religious Communities—Buffalo, NY
New Britain Area Conference of Churches (NEWBRACC)—New Britain, CT
New Hampshire Council of Churches—Pembroke, NH
New Mexico Conference of Churches—Albuquerque, NM
North Carolina Council of Churches—Raleigh, NC
Northern California Interreligious Conference—Oakland, CA
Northside Common Ministries—Pittsburgh, PA

The Rhode Island State Council of Churches—Providence, RI
St. Paul Area Council of Churches—St. Paul, MN
San Fernando Valley Interfaith Council—Chatsworth, CA
Schenectady Inner City Ministry—Schenectady, NY
South Carolina Christian Action Council, Inc.—Columbia, SC
South Coast Interfaith Council—Long Beach, CA
South Hills Interfaith Ministries—South Park, PA
Staten Island Council of Churches—Staten Island, NY
Tarrant Area Community of Churches—Fort Worth, TX
Texas Conference of Churches—Austin, TX
Tri-Council Coordinating Commission—Minneapolis, MN
Troy Area United Ministries—Troy, NY
Tulsa Metropolitan Ministry—Tulsa, OK
United Churches of Lycoming County—Williamsport, PA
Vermont Ecumenical Council and Bible Society—Richmond, VT
Virginia Council of Churches, Inc.—Richmond, VA
Wainwright House—Rye, NY
Washington Association of Churches—Seattle, WA
West Virginia Council of Churches—Charleston, WV
Wyoming Association of Churches—Cheyenne, WY
York County Council of Churches—York, PA

Christian Education Programs

Akron Area Association of Churches—Akron, OH
Allegheny Valley Association of Churches—Natrona Heights, PA
Arizona Ecumenical Council—Phoenix, AZ
Arkansas Interfaith Conference—Scott, AR
The Associated Churches of Fort Wayne & Allen County, Inc.—Fort Wayne, IN
Associated Ministries of Tacoma-Pierce County—Tacoma, WA
Attleboro Area Council of Churches, Inc.—Attleboro, MA
Brooklyn Council of Churches—Brooklyn, NY
Christian Ministries of Delaware County—Muncie, IN
Christians United in Beaver County—Beaver, PA
Churches United of the Quad City Area—Rock Island, IL
Council of Christian Communions of Greater Cincinnati—Cincinnati, OH
The Council of Churches of Santa Clara County—San Jose, CA
Council of Churches and Synagogues of Southwestern Connecticut—Stamford, CT
East Dallas Cooperative Parish—Dallas, TX
Ecclesia—Trenton, NJ
Ecumenical Conference of Greater Altoona—Altoona, PA
Ecumenical Ministries of Oregon—Portland, OR
Evansville Area Community of Churches, Inc.—Evansville, IN
FaithTrust Institute—Seattle, WA
Georgia Christian Council—Macon, GA
Greater Bethlehem Area Council of Churches—Bethlehem, PA
Greater Chicago Broadcast Ministries—Chicago, IL
Greater Dayton Christian Connections—Dayton, OH
Greater Fairmont Council of Churches—Fairmont, WV
Greater Flint Council of Churches—Flint, MI
Greater New Orleans Federation of Churches—New Orleans, LA
Greater Rochester Community of Churches—Rochester, NY
The Greater Wheeling Council of Churches—Wheeling, WV
Greensboro Urban Ministry—Greensboro, NC
Highlands Community Ministries—Louisville, KY
Inter-Church Council of Greater New Bedford—New Bedford, MA
Interchurch Ministries of Nebraska—Lincoln, NE
InterReligious Council of Central New York—Syracuse, NY
Iowa Religious Media Services—Des Moines, IA
Kentuckiana Interfaith Community—Louisville, KY
Lincoln Interfaith Council—Lincoln, NE
The Metropolitan Christian Council: Detroit-Windsor—Detroit, MI
Metropolitan Christian Council of Philadelphia—Philadelphia, PA
Metropolitan Ecumenical Ministry—Newark, NJ
Network of Religious Communities—Buffalo, NY
New Hampshire Council of Churches—Pembroke, NH
Northern Kentucky Interfaith Commission, Inc.—Newport, KY
Oklahoma Conference of Churches—Oklahoma City, OK
Peoria Friendship House of Christian Service—Peoria, IL
Reading Berks Conference of Churches—Reading, PA
San Antonio Community of Churches—San Antonio, TX
South Coast Interfaith Council—Long Beach, CA

Staten Island Council of Churches—Staten Island, NY
Tarrant Area Community of Churches—Fort Worth, TX
Texas Conference of Churches—Austin, TX
Troy Area United Ministries—Troy, NY
Tuscarawas County Council for Church and Community—New Philadelphia, OH
United Churches of Lycoming County—Williamsport, PA
Wainwright House—Rye, NY
West Virginia Council of Churches—Charleston, WV
Wisconsin Council of Churches—Sun Prairie, WI
Wyoming Association of Churches—Cheyenne, WY
Wyoming Valley Council of Churches—Wilkes-Barre, PA

Clothing Distribution Programs

Allegheny Valley Association of Churches—Natrona Heights, PA
Arkansas Interfaith Conference—Scott, AR
Asheville-Buncombe Community Christian Ministry (ABCCM)—Asheville, NC
Associated Ministries of Tacoma-Pierce County—Tacoma, WA
Attleboro Area Council of Churches, Inc.—Attleboro, MA
Border Association for Refugees from Central America (BARCA), Inc.—Edinburg, TX
Chautaugua County Rural Ministry—Dunkirk, NY
Christian Ministries of Delaware County—Muncie, IN
Christian Service Center for Central Florida, Inc.—Orlando, FL
Community Emergency Assistance Program (CEAP)—Brooklyn Park, MN
Community Ministry of Montgomery County—Rockville, MD
Contact Ministries of Springfield—Springfield, IL
Cooperative Metropolitan Ministries—Newton, MA
Corpus Christi Metro Ministries—Corpus Christi, TX
Council of Churches of the Ozarks—Springfield, MO
East Dallas Cooperative Parish—Dallas, TX
Eastern Area Community Ministries—Louisville, KY
The Ecumenical Council of Pasadena Area Churches—Pasadena, CA
Evanston Ecumenical Action Council—Evanston, IL
Fern Creek-Highview United Ministries—Louisvlle, KY
Greater Birmingham Ministries—Birmingham, AL
Greater Fairmont Council of Churches—Fairmont, WV
Greensboro Urban Ministry—Greensboro, NC
Hanover Area Council of Churches—Hanover, PA
Interfaith Community Council, Inc.—New Albany, IN
Interfaith Community Services—St. Joseph, MO
Lancaster County Council of Churches—Lancaster, PA
Lebanon County Christian Ministries—Lebanon, PA
Lehigh County Conference of Churches—Allentown, PA
Lewisburg Council of Churches—Lewisburg, PA
The Long Island Council of Churches—Hempstead, NY
Metropolitan Ecumenical Ministry—Newark, NJ
Northside Inter-Church Agency (NICA)—Fort Worth, TX
Peoria Friendship House of Christian Service—Peoria, IL
Reading Berks Conference of Churches—Reading, PA
St. Paul Area Council of Churches—St. Paul, MN
South East Associated Ministries (SEAM)—Louisville, KY
South Hills Interfaith Ministries—South Park, PA
Staten Island Council of Churches—Staten Island, NY
Tuscarawas County Council for Church and Community—New Philadelphia, OH
West Side Ecumenical Ministry—Cleveland, OH
Wilkinsburg Community Ministry—Pittsburgh, PA

CROP Walks

Akron Area Association of Churches—Akron, OH
Asheville-Buncombe Community Christian Ministry (ABCCM)—Asheville, NC
The Associated Churches of Fort Wayne & Allen County, Inc.—Fort Wayne, IN
Attleboro Area Council of Churches, Inc.—Attleboro, MA
Austin Area Interreligious Ministries—Austin, TX
Berrien County Association of Churches—Benton Harbor, MI
Broome County Council of Churches, Inc.—Binghamton, NY
Capital Area Council of Churches, Inc.—Albany, NY
Chautaugua County Rural Ministry—Dunkirk, NY
Christian Associates of Southwest Pennsylvania—Pittsburgh, PA
Christian Ministries of Delaware County—Muncie, IN

Christian Service Center for Central Florida, Inc.—Orlando, FL
Church Community Services—Elkhart, IN
The Church Federation of Greater Indianapolis, Inc.—Indianapolis, IN
Churches United, Inc.—Cedar Rapids, IA
Churches United of the Quad City Area—Rock Island, IL
Community Emergency Assistance Program (CEAP)—Brooklyn Park, MN
Council of Churches of Chemung County, Inc.—Elmira, NY
Council of Churches of Greater Bridgeport, Inc.—Bridgeport, CT
Council of Churches of Greater Springfield—Springfield, MA
The Council of Churches of Santa Clara County—San Jose, CA
Dutchess Interfaith Council, Inc.—Poughkeepsie, NY
East Dallas Cooperative Parish—Dallas, TX
East End Cooperative Ministry—Pittsburgh, PA
Ecclesia—Trenton, NJ
The Ecumenical Council of Pasadena Area Churches—Pasadena, CA
Ecumenical Ministries—Fulton, MO
Evanston Ecumenical Action Council—Evanston, IL
Evansville Area Community of Churches, Inc.—Evansville, IN
Florida Council of Churches—Altamonte Springs, FL
Fresno Metro Ministry—Fresno, CA
Greater Bethlehem Area Council of Churches—Bethlehem, PA
Greater Dayton Christian Connections—Dayton, OH
Greater Fairmont Council of Churches—Fairmont, WV
Greater Flint Council of Churches—Flint, MI
Greater Waterbury Interfaith Ministries, Inc.—Waterbury, CT
Greensboro Urban Ministry—Greensboro, NC
Hanover Area Council of Churches—Hanover, PA
In One Accord—Battle Creek, MI
Inter-Church Ministries of Erie County—Erie, PA
Interfaith Conference of Greater Milwaukee—Milwaukee, WI
Interfaith Council—Spokane, WA
Inter-Faith Ministries-Wichita—Wichita, KS
Interfaith Works—Olympia, WA
Lancaster County Council of Churches—Lancaster, PA
Lebanon County Christian Ministries—Lebanon, PA
Lehigh County Conference of Churches—Allentown, PA
Lewisburg Council of Churches—Lewisburg, PA
Lincoln Interfaith Council—Lincoln, NE
The Long Island Council of Churches—Hempstead, NY
Mahoning Valley Association of Churches—Youngstown, OH
The Metropolitan Christian Council: Detroit-Windsor—Detroit, MI
Metropolitan Ecumenical Ministry—Newark, NJ
Muskegon County Cooperating Churches—Muskegon, MI
Network of Religious Communities—Buffalo, NY
New Britain Area Conference of Churches (NEWBRACC)—New Britain, CT
Northside Inter-Church Agency (NICA)—Fort Worth, TX
Oak Park-River Forest Community of Congregations—Oak Park, IL
Peoria Friendship House of Christian Service—Peoria, IL
Pike County Outreach Council—Waverly, OH
Reading Berks Conference of Churches—Reading, PA
St. Paul Area Council of Churches—St. Paul, MN
San Antonio Community of Churches—San Antonio, TX
San Fernando Valley Interfaith Council—Chatsworth, CA
Schenectady Inner City Ministry—Schenectady, NY
South Coast Interfaith Council—Long Beach, CA
Staten Island Council of Churches—Staten Island, NY
Tarrant Area Community of Churches—Fort Worth, TX
Troy Area United Ministries—Troy, NY
Tuscarawas County Council for Church and Community—New Philadelphia, OH
United Churches of Lycoming County—Williamsport, PA
Wilkinsburg Community Ministry—Pittsburgh, PA
Worcester County Ecumenical Council—Worcester, MA
Wyoming Valley Council of Churches—Wilkes-Barre, PA
York County Council of Churches—York, PA

Domestic Violence Programs

Arizona Ecumenical Council—Phoenix, AZ
Asheville-Buncombe Community Christian Ministry (ABCCM)—Asheville, NC
Associated Ministries of Tacoma-Pierce County—Tacoma, WA
Association of Religious Communities—Danbury, CT
Chautaugua County Rural Ministry—Dunkirk, NY
Christian Associates of Southwest Pennsylvania—Pittsburgh, PA
Colorado Council of Churches—Denver, CO

Contact Ministries of Springfield—Springfield, IL
Council of Churches of Greater Bridgeport, Inc.—Bridgeport, CT
Dutchess Interfaith Council, Inc.—Poughkeepsie, NY
The Ecumenical Council of Pasadena Area Churches—Pasadena, CA
Ecumenical Council of San Diego County—San Diego, CA
Ecumenical Ministries of Oregon—Portland, OR
FaithTrust Institute—Seattle, WA
Fresno Metro Ministry—Fresno, CA
Greater Chicago Broadcast Ministries—Chicago, IL
Greater Minneapolis Council of Churches—Minneapolis, MN
Indiana Partners for Christian Unity and Mission—Indianapolis, IN
Inter-Church Council of Greater New Bedford—New Bedford, MA
Interchurch Ministries of Nebraska—Lincoln, NE
Interfaith Council—Spokane, WA
Interfaith Service Bureau—Sacramento, CA
Interfaith Works—Olympia, WA
Lincoln Interfaith Council—Lincoln, NE
The Long Island Council of Churches—Hempstead, NY
The Metropolitan Christian Council: Detroit-Windsor—Detroit, MI
Metropolitan Ecumenical Ministry—Newark, NJ
Mississippi Religious Leadership Conference—Jackson, MS
New Hampshire Council of Churches—Pembroke, NH
New Mexico Conference of Churches—Albuquerque, NM
Peoria Friendship House of Christian Service—Peoria, IL
The Rhode Island State Council of Churches—Providence, RI
St. Paul Area Council of Churches—St. Paul, MN
San Antonio Community of Churches—San Antonio, TX
Southeast Ecumenical Ministry—Rochester, NY
Troy Area United Ministries—Troy, NY
Tulsa Metropolitan Ministry—Tulsa, OK
Vermont Ecumenical Council and Bible Society—Richmond, VT
West Side Ecumenical Ministry—Cleveland, OH
West Virginia Council of Churches—Charleston, WV
Wyoming Association of Churches—Cheyenne, WY

Economic/Social Justice Programs

Akron Area Association of Churches—Akron, OH
Arizona Ecumenical Council—Phoenix, AZ
Arkansas Interfaith Conference—Scott, AR
Asheville-Buncombe Community Christian Ministry (ABCCM)—Asheville, NC
The Associated Churches of Fort Wayne & Allen County, Inc.—Fort Wayne, IN
Associated Ministries of Tacoma-Pierce County—Tacoma, WA
Association of Christian Churches of South Dakota—Sioux Falls, SD
Austin Area Interreligious Ministries—Austin, TX
Brooklyn Council of Churches—Brooklyn, NY
Broome County Council of Churches, Inc.—Binghamton, NY
California Council of Churches-California Church Impact—Sacramento, CA
Capital Area Council of Churches, Inc.—Albany, NY
Capital Region Ecumenical Organization (CREO)—Schenectady, NY
The Capitol Region Conference of Churches—Hartford, CT
Chautaugua County Rural Ministry—Dunkirk, NY
Christian Associates of Southwest Pennsylvania—Pittsburgh, PA
Christian Community Action—New Haven, CT
Christian Ministries of Delaware County—Muncie, IN
Christian Service Center for Central Florida, Inc.—Orlando, FL
Church Council of Greater Seattle—Seattle, WA
The Church Federation of Greater Indianapolis, Inc.—Indianapolis, IN
Churches United of the Quad City Area—Rock Island, IL
Colorado Council of Churches—Denver, CO
Community Emergency Assistance Program (CEAP)—Brooklyn Park, MN
Community Ministry of Montgomery County—Rockville, MD
Community Renewal Society—Chicago, IL
Contact Ministries of Springfield—Springfield, IL
Cooperative Metropolitan Ministries—Newton, MA
Council of Churches of Chemung County, Inc.—Elmira, NY
Council of Churches of the City of New York—New York, NY
Council of Churches of Greater Bridgeport, Inc.—Bridgeport, CT
Council of Churches of Greater Springfield—Springfield, MA
The Council of Churches of Santa Clara County—San Jose, CA
Dutchess Interfaith Council, Inc.—Poughkeepsie, NY
Eastern Area Community Ministries—Louisville, KY

Ecclesia—Trenton, NJ
Ecumenical Conference of Greater Altoona—Altoona, PA
The Ecumenical Council of Pasadena Area Churches—Pasadena, CA
Ecumenical Ministries of Oregon—Portland, OR
Evanston Ecumenical Action Council—Evanston, IL
Faith Community Assistance Center—Santa Fe, NM
Florida Council of Churches—Altamonte Springs, FL
Fresno Metro Ministry—Fresno, CA
Georgia Christian Council—Macon, GA
Grand Rapids Area Center for Ecumenism (GRACE)—Grand Rapids, MI
Greater Birmingham Ministries—Birmingham, AL
Greater Chicago Broadcast Ministries—Chicago, IL
Greater Dallas Community of Churches—Dallas, TX
Greater Dayton Christian Connections—Dayton, OH
Greater Minneapolis Council of Churches—Minneapolis, MN
Greater Rochester Community of Churches—Rochester, NY
Illinois Conference of Churches—Springfield, IL
In One Accord—Battle Creek, MI
Inter-Church Council of Greater New Bedford—New Bedford, MA
Interchurch Ministries of Nebraska—Lincoln, NE
Interfaith Community Council, Inc.—New Albany, IN
Interfaith Conference of Greater Milwaukee—Milwaukee, WI
InterFaith Conference of Metropolitan Washington—Washington, DC
Interfaith Council—Spokane, WA
Interfaith Council of Contra Costa County—Walnut Creek, CA
Inter-Faith Ministries-Wichita—Wichita, KS
Interfaith Mission Service—Huntsville, AL
Interfaith Service Bureau—Sacramento, CA
Interfaith Works—Olympia, WA
InterReligious Council of Central New York—Syracuse, NY
The Joint Religious Legislative Coalition—Minneapolis, MN
Kansas Ecumenical Ministries—Topeka, KS
Kentuckiana Interfaith Community—Louisville, KY
Kentucky Council of Churches—Lexington, KY
Lehigh County Conference of Churches—Allentown, PA
Lincoln Interfaith Council—Lincoln, NE
The Long Island Council of Churches—Hempstead, NY
Madison-area Urban Ministry—Madison, WI
Mahoning Valley Association of Churches—Youngstown, OH
Maine Council of Churches—Portland, ME
Marin Interfaith Council—San Rafael, CA
Massachusetts Council of Churches—Boston, MA
Metropolitan Area Religious Coalition of Cincinnati—Cincinnati, OH
The Metropolitan Christian Council: Detroit-Windsor—Detroit, MI
Metropolitan Christian Council of Philadelphia—Philadelphia, PA
Metropolitan Ecumenical Ministry—Newark, NJ
Metropolitan Inter Faith Association (MIFA)—Memphis, TN
Metropolitan Interfaith Council on Affordable Housing (MICAH)—Minneapolis, MN
Michigan Ecumenical Forum—Lansing, MI
Minnesota Council of Churches—Minneapolis, MN
Mississippi Religious Leadership Conference—Jackson, MS
Montana Association of Churches—Billings, MT
Muskegon County Cooperating Churches—Muskegon, MI
Network of Religious Communities—Buffalo, NY
New Britain Area Conference of Churches (NEWBRACC)—New Britain, CT
New Hampshire Council of Churches—Pembroke, NH
New Mexico Conference of Churches—Albuquerque, NM
New York State Community of Churches, Inc.—Albany, NY
North Carolina Council of Churches—Raleigh, NC
North Dakota Conference of Churches—Ashley, ND
Northern California Interreligious Conference—Oakland, CA
Northern Kentucky Interfaith Commission, Inc.—Newport, KY
Northside Inter-Church Agency (NICA)—Fort Worth, TX
Northwest Interfaith Movement—Philadelphia, PA
Oak Park-River Forest Community of Congregations—Oak Park, IL
Ohio Council of Churches—Columbus, OH
Oklahoma Conference of Churches—Oklahoma City, OK
Pennsylvania Conference on Interchurch Cooperation—Harrisburg, PA
The Pennsylvania Council of Churches—Harrisburg, PA
Peoria Friendship House of Christian Service—Peoria, IL
Queens Federation of Churches—Richmond Hill, NY

The Rhode Island State Council of Churches —Providence, RI
Rural Migrant Ministry—Poughkeepsie, NY
St. Paul Area Council of Churches—St. Paul, MN
San Antonio Community of Churches—San Antonio, TX
San Fernando Valley Interfaith Council—Chatsworth, CA
Schenectady Inner City Ministry—Schenectady, NY
South Carolina Christian Action Council, Inc.—Columbia, SC
South Coast Interfaith Council—Long Beach, CA
South East Associated Ministries (SEAM)—Louisville, KY
South Louisville Community Ministries—Louisville, KY
Southern California Ecumenical Council—Pasadena, CA
Tarrant Area Community of Churches—Fort Worth, TX
Texas Conference of Churches—Austin, TX
Troy Area United Ministries—Troy, NY
Tulsa Metropolitan Ministry—Tulsa, OK
United Churches of Lycoming County—Williamsport, PA
Vermont Ecumenical Council and Bible Society—Richmond, VT
Virginia Council of Churches, Inc.—Richmond, VA
Wainwright House—Rye, NY
Washington Association of Churches—Seattle, WA
West Virginia Council of Churches—Charleston, WV
Wilkinsburg Community Ministry—Pittsburgh, PA
Wisconsin Council of Churches—Sun Prairie, WI
Worcester County Ecumenical Council—Worcester, MA
Wyoming Association of Churches—Cheyenne, WY

Employment Assistance Programs

Asheville-Buncombe Community Christian Ministry (ABCCM)—Asheville, NC
Chautaugua County Rural Ministry—Dunkirk, NY
Community Emergency Assistance Program (CEAP)—Brooklyn Park, MN
Contact Ministries of Springfield—Springfield, IL
Corpus Christi Metro Ministries—Corpus Christi, TX
Council of Churches of Greater Bridgeport, Inc.—Bridgeport, CT
East Dallas Cooperative Parish—Dallas, TX
East End Cooperative Ministry—Pittsburgh, PA
Eastern Area Community Ministries—Louisville, KY
Evanston Ecumenical Action Council—Evanston, IL
Fern Creek-Highview United Ministries—Louisvlle, KY
Genesee-Orleans Ministry of Concern—Albion, NY
Greater Dallas Community of Churches—Dallas, TX
Greater Minneapolis Council of Churches—Minneapolis, MN
Greensboro Urban Ministry—Greensboro, NC
Interfaith Community Council, Inc.—New Albany, IN
Lehigh County Conference of Churches—Allentown, PA
Lincoln Interfaith Council—Lincoln, NE
The Long Island Council of Churches—Hempstead, NY
Metropolitan Ecumenical Ministry—Newark, NJ
Northside Inter-Church Agency (NICA)—Fort Worth, TX
Peoria Friendship House of Christian Service—Peoria, IL
Schenectady Inner City Ministry—Schenectady, NY
South East Associated Ministries (SEAM)—Louisville, KY
Southeast Ecumenical Ministry—Rochester, NY
United Ministries—Greenville, SC
Virginia Council of Churches, Inc.—Richmond, VA
West Side Ecumenical Ministry—Cleveland, OH

Environmental Programs

Arizona Ecumenical Council—Phoenix, AZ
Associated Ministries of Tacoma-Pierce County—Tacoma, WA
California Council of Churches-California Church Impact—Sacramento, CA
The Capitol Region Conference of Churches —Hartford, CT
The Church Federation of Greater Indianapolis, Inc.—Indianapolis, IN
Colorado Council of Churches—Denver, CO
The Council of Churches of Santa Clara County—San Jose, CA
Ecumenical Ministries of Iowa (EMI)—Des Moines, IA
Ecumenical Ministries of Oregon—Portland, OR
Florida Council of Churches—Altamonte Springs, FL
Fresno Metro Ministry—Fresno, CA
Georgia Christian Council—Macon, GA
Grand Rapids Area Center for Ecumenism (GRACE)—Grand Rapids, MI
Greater Chicago Broadcast Ministries—Chicago, IL

Greater Dayton Christian Connections—Dayton, OH
The Greater Wheeling Council of Churches—Wheeling, WV
Inter-Church Council of Greater New Bedford—New Bedford, MA
Interchurch Ministries of Nebraska—Lincoln, NE
Interfaith Conference of Greater Milwaukee—Milwaukee, WI
InterFaith Conference of Metropolitan Washington—Washington, DC
Interfaith Mission Service—Huntsville, AL
Kentucky Council of Churches—Lexington, KY
Louisiana Interchurch Conference—Baton Rouge, LA
Maine Council of Churches—Portland, ME
Marin Interfaith Council—San Rafael, CA
Massachusetts Council of Churches—Boston, MA
The Metropolitan Christian Council: Detroit-Windsor—Detroit, MI
Metropolitan Christian Council of Philadelphia—Philadelphia, PA
Metropolitan Ecumenical Ministry—Newark, NJ
Michigan Ecumenical Forum—Lansing, MI
Mississippi Religious Leadership Conference—Jackson, MS
Montana Association of Churches—Billings, MT
Muskegon County Cooperating Churches—Muskegon, MI
Network of Religious Communities—Buffalo, NY
New Hampshire Council of Churches—Pembroke, NH
New Mexico Conference of Churches—Albuquerque, NM
North Carolina Council of Churches—Raleigh, NC
North Dakota Conference of Churches—Ashley, ND
Northern California Interreligious Conference—Oakland, CA
Ohio Council of Churches—Columbus, OH
Oklahoma Conference of Churches—Oklahoma City, OK
The Pennsylvania Council of Churches—Harrisburg, PA
The Rhode Island State Council of Churches—Providence, RI
South Carolina Christian Action Council, Inc.—Columbia, SC
South Coast Interfaith Council—Long Beach, CA
Southern California Ecumenical Council—Pasadena, CA
Staten Island Council of Churches—Staten Island, NY
United Churches of Lycoming County—Williamsport, PA
Vermont Ecumenical Council and Bible Society—Richmond, VT
Washington Association of Churches—Seattle, WA
West Virginia Council of Churches—Charleston, WV

Faith and Order Programs

Akron Area Association of Churches—Akron, OH
Allegheny Valley Association of Churches—Natrona Heights, PA
Arizona Ecumenical Council—Phoenix, AZ
Associated Ministries of Tacoma-Pierce County—Tacoma, WA
Association of Christian Churches of South Dakota—Sioux Falls, SD
Capital Area Council of Churches, Inc.—Albany, NY
Capital Region Ecumenical Organization (CREO)—Schenectady, NY
Christian Associates of Southwest Pennsylvania—Pittsburgh, PA
Church Council of Greater Seattle—Seattle, WA
The Church Federation of Greater Indianapolis, Inc.—Indianapolis, IN
Churches United of the Quad City Area—Rock Island, IL
Colorado Council of Churches—Denver, CO
Council of Churches of the City of New York—New York, NY
Council of Churches of Greater Springfield—Springfield, MA
The Council of Churches of Santa Clara County—San Jose, CA
Council of Churches and Synagogues of Southwestern Connecticut—Stamford, CT
East Dallas Cooperative Parish—Dallas, TX
Ecclesia—Trenton, NJ
Ecumenical Council of San Diego County—San Diego, CA
Ecumenical Ministries of Iowa (EMI)—Des Moines, IA
Ecumenical Ministries of Oregon—Portland, OR
Florida Council of Churches—Altamonte Springs, FL
Georgia Christian Council—Macon, GA
Grand Rapids Area Center for Ecumenism (GRACE)—Grand Rapids, MI
Greater Chicago Broadcast Ministries—Chicago, IL
Greater Dallas Community of Churches—Dallas, TX
Greater Dayton Christian Connections—Dayton, OH
Greater New Orleans Federation of Churches—New Orleans, LA
Greater Waterbury Interfaith Ministries, Inc.—Waterbury, CT
The Greater Wheeling Council of Churches—Wheeling, WV

Highlands Community Ministries—Louisville, KY
Illinois Conference of Churches—Springfield, IL
In One Accord—Battle Creek, MI
Indiana Partners for Christian Unity and Mission—Indianapolis, IN
Inter-Church Council of Greater New Bedford —New Bedford, MA
Interchurch Ministries of Nebraska—Lincoln, NE
Interfaith Community Council, Inc.—New Albany, IN
InterFaith Conference of Metropolitan Washington—Washington, DC
Interfaith Council of Contra Costa County—Walnut Creek, CA
Interfaith Works—Olympia, WA
InterReligious Council of Central New York—Syracuse, NY
Kansas Ecumenical Ministries—Topeka, KS
Kentuckiana Interfaith Community—Louisville, KY
Kentucky Council of Churches—Lexington, KY
Lehigh County Conference of Churches—Allentown, PA
Lincoln Interfaith Council—Lincoln, NE
The Long Island Council of Churches—Hempstead, NY
Louisiana Interchurch Conference—Baton Rouge, LA
Mahoning Valley Association of Churches—Youngstown, OH
Massachusetts Council of Churches—Boston, MA
The Metropolitan Christian Council: Detroit-Windsor—Detroit, MI
Metropolitan Christian Council of Philadelphia—Philadelphia, PA
Metropolitan Ecumenical Ministry—Newark, NJ
Michigan Ecumenical Forum—Lansing, MI
Minnesota Council of Churches—Minneapolis, MN
Montana Association of Churches—Billings, MT
Network of Religious Communities—Buffalo, NY
New Hampshire Council of Churches—Pembroke, NH
New Mexico Conference of Churches—Albuquerque, NM
North Carolina Council of Churches—Raleigh, NC
North Dakota Conference of Churches—Ashley, ND
Northern California Interreligious Conference —Oakland, CA
Northern Kentucky Interfaith Commission, Inc.—Newport, KY
Ohio Council of Churches—Columbus, OH
Oklahoma Conference of Churches—Oklahoma City, OK
The Pennsylvania Council of Churches—Harrisburg, PA
Queens Federation of Churches—Richmond Hill, NY
The Rhode Island State Council of Churches —Providence, RI
Schenectady Inner City Ministry—Schenectady, NY
South Carolina Christian Action Council, Inc.—Columbia, SC
Southern California Ecumenical Council—Pasadena, CA
Texas Conference of Churches—Austin, TX
Troy Area United Ministries—Troy, NY
Tulsa Metropolitan Ministry—Tulsa, OK
United Churches of Lycoming County—Williamsport, PA
Vermont Ecumenical Council and Bible Society—Richmond, VT
Virginia Council of Churches, Inc.—Richmond, VA
Wainwright House—Rye, NY
Washington Association of Churches—Seattle, WA
West Virginia Council of Churches—Charleston, WV
Wisconsin Council of Churches—Sun Prairie, WI
Worcester County Ecumenical Council—Worcester, MA
Wyoming Valley Council of Churches—Wilkes-Barre, PA

Healthcare Issues

Asheville-Buncombe Community Christian Ministry (ABCCM)—Asheville, NC
The Associated Churches of Fort Wayne & Allen County, Inc.—Fort Wayne, IN
Berrien County Association of Churches—Benton Harbor, MI
California Council of Churches-California Church Impact—Sacramento, CA
Christian Associates of Southwest Pennsylvania —Pittsburgh, PA
Churchpeople for Change and Reconciliation —Lima, OH
Community Ministries of Rockville—Rockville, MD
Community Renewal Society—Chicago, IL
Corpus Christi Metro Ministries—Corpus Christi, TX
Council of Churches of the City of New York—New York, NY
The Council of Churches of Santa Clara County—San Jose, CA
East Dallas Cooperative Parish—Dallas, TX
Eastern Area Community Ministries—Louisville, KY
Ecumenical Ministries of Iowa (EMI)—Des Moines, IA
Fresno Metro Ministry—Fresno, CA
Greater Baton Rouge Federation of Churches and Synagogues—Baton Rouge, LA

Greater Chicago Broadcast Ministries—Chicago, IL
Greater Minneapolis Council of Churches—Minneapolis, MN
Greater Rochester Community of Churches—Rochester, NY
Greensboro Urban Ministry—Greensboro, NC
Illinois Conference of Churches—Springfield, IL
Inter-Church Council of Greater New Bedford—New Bedford, MA
Inter-Church Ministries of Erie County—Erie, PA
Interchurch Ministries of Nebraska—Lincoln, NE
Interfaith Conference of Greater Milwaukee—Milwaukee, WI
Lehigh County Conference of Churches—Allentown, PA
The Long Island Council of Churches—Hempstead, NY
Louisiana Interchurch Conference—Baton Rouge, LA
Marin Interfaith Council—San Rafael, CA
Massachusetts Council of Churches—Boston, MA
The Metropolitan Christian Council: Detroit-Windsor—Detroit, MI
Metropolitan Ecumenical Ministry—Newark, NJ
Metropolitan Ecumenical Ministry Community Development Corp.—Newark, NJ
Michigan Ecumenical Forum—Lansing, MI
Mississippi Religious Leadership Conference—Jackson, MS
Montana Association of Churches—Billings, MT
Muskegon County Cooperating Churches—Muskegon, MI
Network of Religious Communities—Buffalo, NY
New Hampshire Council of Churches—Pembroke, NH
New Mexico Conference of Churches—Albuquerque, NM
Ohio Council of Churches—Columbus, OH
Oklahoma Conference of Churches—Oklahoma City, OK
Peoria Friendship House of Christian Service—Peoria, IL
Pike County Outreach Council—Waverly, OH
The Rhode Island State Council of Churches—Providence, RI
Schenectady Inner City Ministry—Schenectady, NY
South Carolina Christian Action Council, Inc.—Columbia, SC
Southeast Ecumenical Ministry—Rochester, NY
Tarrant Area Community of Churches—Fort Worth, TX
Tuscarawas County Council for Church and Community—New Philadelphia, OH
Vermont Ecumenical Council and Bible Society—Richmond, VT
Washington Association of Churches—Seattle, WA
West Virginia Council of Churches—Charleston, WV
Worcester County Ecumenical Council—Worcester, MA

Homelessness/Shelter Programs

Allegheny Valley Association of Churches—Natrona Heights, PA
Arkansas Interfaith Conference—Scott, AR
Asheville-Buncombe Community Christian Ministry (ABCCM)—Asheville, NC
The Associated Churches of Fort Wayne & Allen County, Inc.—Fort Wayne, IN
Associated Ministries of Tacoma-Pierce County—Tacoma, WA
Attleboro Area Council of Churches, Inc.—Attleboro, MA
Austin Area Interreligious Ministries—Austin, TX
Capital Area Council of Churches, Inc.—Albany, NY
The Capitol Region Conference of Churches—Hartford, CT
Center City Churches—Hartford, CT
Chautaugua County Rural Ministry—Dunkirk, NY
Christian Associates of Southwest Pennsylvania—Pittsburgh, PA
Christian Churches United of the Tri-County Area—Harrisburg, PA
Christian Community Action—New Haven, CT
Christian Ministries of Delaware County—Muncie, IN
Christian Service Center for Central Florida, Inc.—Orlando, FL
Church Council of Greater Seattle—Seattle, WA
Churches United of the Quad City Area—Rock Island, IL
Colorado Council of Churches—Denver, CO
Community Emergency Assistance Program (CEAP)—Brooklyn Park, MN
Community Ministries of Rockville—Rockville, MD
Community Ministry of Montgomery County—Rockville, MD
Community Renewal Society—Chicago, IL
Contact Ministries of Springfield—Springfield, IL
Cooperative Metropolitan Ministries—Newton, MA
Corpus Christi Metro Ministries—Corpus Christi, TX
Council of Churches of the City of New York—New York, NY
Council of Churches of Greater Bridgeport, Inc.—Bridgeport, CT

Council of Churches of Greater Springfield—Springfield, MA
East End Cooperative Ministry—Pittsburgh, PA
The Ecumenical Council of Pasadena Area Churches—Pasadena, CA
Ecumenical Council of San Diego County—San Diego, CA
Ecumenical Ministries—Fulton, MO
Ecumenical Ministries of Oregon—Portland, OR
Evanston Ecumenical Action Council—Evanston, IL
Faith Community Assistance Center—Santa Fe, NM
Genesee-Orleans Ministry of Concern—Albion, NY
Grand Rapids Area Center for Ecumenism (GRACE)—Grand Rapids, MI
Greater Bethlehem Area Council of Churches—Bethlehem, PA
Greater Chicago Broadcast Ministries—Chicago, IL
Greater Minneapolis Council of Churches—Minneapolis, MN
Greensboro Urban Ministry—Greensboro, NC
Hanover Area Council of Churches—Hanover, PA
Inter-Church Ministries of Erie County—Erie, PA
Interchurch Ministries of Nebraska—Lincoln, NE
Interfaith Community Council, Inc.—New Albany, IN
Interfaith Community Services—St. Joseph, MO
Interfaith Conference of Greater Milwaukee—Milwaukee, WI
InterFaith Conference of Metropolitan Washington—Washington, DC
Inter-Faith Ministries-Wichita—Wichita, KS
Interfaith Mission Service—Huntsville, AL
Interfaith Works—Olympia, WA
InterReligious Council of Central New York—Syracuse, NY
Lehigh County Conference of Churches—Allentown, PA
Lewisburg Council of Churches—Lewisburg, PA
The Long Island Council of Churches—Hempstead, NY
Maine Council of Churches—Portland, ME
Marin Interfaith Council—San Rafael, CA
Metropolitan Area Religious Coalition of Cincinnati—Cincinnati, OH
Metropolitan Ecumenical Ministry—Newark, NJ
Metropolitan Inter Faith Association (MIFA)—Memphis, TN
Metropolitan Interfaith Council on Affordable Housing (MICAH)—Minneapolis, MN
Michigan Ecumenical Forum—Lansing, MI
Mississippi Religious Leadership Conference—Jackson, MS
Muskegon County Cooperating Churches—Muskegon, MI
New Britain Area Conference of Churches (NEWBRACC)—New Britain, CT
New Hampshire Council of Churches—Pembroke, NH
New Mexico Conference of Churches—Albuquerque, NM
Northside Common Ministries—Pittsburgh, PA
Northside Inter-Church Agency (NICA)—Fort Worth, TX
Paducah Cooperative Ministry—Paducah, KY
Peoria Friendship House of Christian Service—Peoria, IL
Pike County Outreach Council—Waverly, OH
Reading Berks Conference of Churches—Reading, PA
The Rhode Island State Council of Churches—Providence, RI
St. Paul Area Council of Churches—St. Paul, MN
San Antonio Community of Churches—San Antonio, TX
South Louisville Community Ministries—Louisville, KY
Tarrant Area Community of Churches—Fort Worth, TX
Troy Area United Ministries—Troy, NY
Tulsa Metropolitan Ministry—Tulsa, OK
Tuscarawas County Council for Church and Community—New Philadelphia, OH
United Ministries—Greenville, SC
Wyoming Valley Council of Churches—Wilkes-Barre, PA

Hunger/Food Programs

Allegheny Valley Association of Churches—Natrona Heights, PA
Arkansas Interfaith Conference—Scott, AR
Asheville-Buncombe Community Christian Ministry (ABCCM)—Asheville, NC
The Associated Churches of Fort Wayne & Allen County, Inc.—Fort Wayne, IN
Associated Ministries of Tacoma-Pierce County—Tacoma, WA
Attleboro Area Council of Churches, Inc.—Attleboro, MA
Austin Area Interreligious Ministries—Austin, TX
Border Association for Refugees from Central America (BARCA), Inc.—Edinburg, TX
Brooklyn Council of Churches—Brooklyn, NY
Broome County Council of Churches, Inc.—Binghamton, NY
California Council of Churches-California Church Impact—Sacramento, CA
Capital Area Council of Churches, Inc.—Albany, NY
Center City Churches—Hartford, CT
Chautaugua County Rural Ministry—Dunkirk, NY

Christian Community Action—New Haven, CT
Christian Ministries of Delaware County—Muncie, IN
Christian Service Center for Central Florida, Inc.—Orlando, FL
Church Community Services—Elkhart, IN
Church Council of Greater Seattle—Seattle, WA
The Church Federation of Greater Indianapolis, Inc.—Indianapolis, IN
Churches United of the Quad City Area—Rock Island, IL
Community Emergency Assistance Program (CEAP)—Brooklyn Park, MN
Community Ministry of Montgomery County—Rockville, MD
Concerned Ecumenical Ministry to the Upper West Side—Buffalo, NY
Contact Ministries of Springfield—Springfield, IL
Corpus Christi Metro Ministries—Corpus Christi, TX
Council of Churches of the City of New York—New York, NY
Council of Churches of Greater Bridgeport, Inc.—Bridgeport, CT
Council of Churches of the Ozarks—Springfield, MO
The Council of Churches of Santa Clara County—San Jose, CA
Council of Churches and Synagogues of Southwestern Connecticut—Stamford, CT
Cross-Lines Cooperative Council—Kansas City, KS
Des Moines Area Religious Council—Des Moines, IA
Dutchess Interfaith Council, Inc.—Poughkeepsie, NY
East Dallas Cooperative Parish—Dallas, TX
East End Cooperative Ministry—Pittsburgh, PA
Eastern Area Community Ministries—Louisville, KY
Ecclesia—Trenton, NJ
The Ecumenical Council of Pasadena Area Churches—Pasadena, CA
Ecumenical Ministries of Oregon—Portland, OR
Evanston Ecumenical Action Council—Evanston, IL
Evansville Area Community of Churches, Inc.—Evansville, IN
Faith Community Assistance Center—Santa Fe, NM
Fern Creek-Highview United Ministries—Louisvlle, KY
Fresno Metro Ministry—Fresno, CA
Genesee County Churches United, Inc.—Batavia, NY
Genesee-Orleans Ministry of Concern—Albion, NY
Grand Rapids Area Center for Ecumenism (GRACE)—Grand Rapids, MI
Greater Baton Rouge Federation of Churches and Synagogues—Baton Rouge, LA
Greater Bethlehem Area Council of Churches—Bethlehem, PA
Greater Birmingham Ministries—Birmingham, AL
Greater Chicago Broadcast Ministries—Chicago, IL
Greater Dallas Community of Churches—Dallas, TX
Greater Minneapolis Council of Churches—Minneapolis, MN
Greater New Orleans Federation of Churches—New Orleans, LA
Greater Waterbury Interfaith Ministries, Inc.—Waterbury, CT
Greensboro Urban Ministry—Greensboro, NC
Hanover Area Council of Churches—Hanover, PA
Highlands Community Ministries—Louisville, KY
In One Accord—Battle Creek, MI
Inter-Church Ministries of Erie County—Erie, PA
Interchurch Ministries of Nebraska—Lincoln, NE
Interfaith Community Council, Inc.—New Albany, IN
Interfaith Community Services—St. Joseph, MO
InterFaith Conference of Metropolitan Washington—Washington, DC
Inter-Faith Ministries-Wichita—Wichita, KS
Interfaith Mission Service—Huntsville, AL
InterReligious Council of Central New York—Syracuse, NY
Kentuckiana Interfaith Community—Louisville, KY
Lancaster County Council of Churches—Lancaster, PA
Lebanon County Christian Ministries—Lebanon, PA
Lehigh County Conference of Churches—Allentown, PA
Lewisburg Council of Churches—Lewisburg, PA
Lincoln Interfaith Council—Lincoln, NE
The Long Island Council of Churches—Hempstead, NY
The Metropolitan Christian Council: Detroit-Windsor—Detroit, MI
Metropolitan Ecumenical Ministry—Newark, NJ
Minnesota Council of Churches—Minneapolis, MN
Mississippi Religious Leadership Conference—Jackson, MS
Network of Religious Communities—Buffalo, NY
New Britain Area Conference of Churches (NEWBRACC)—New Britain, CT
New Hampshire Council of Churches—Pembroke, NH

Northside Common Ministries—Pittsburgh, PA
Northside Inter-Church Agency (NICA)—Fort Worth, TX
Northwest Harvest-E. M. M.—Seattle, WA
Oak Park-River Forest Community of Congregations—Oak Park, IL
Paducah Cooperative Ministry—Paducah, KY
Peoria Friendship House of Christian Service—Peoria, IL
Pike County Outreach Council—Waverly, OH
Queens Federation of Churches—Richmond Hill, NY
Reading Berks Conference of Churches—Reading, PA
The Rhode Island State Council of Churches —Providence, RI
St. Paul Area Council of Churches—St. Paul, MN
San Antonio Community of Churches—San Antonio, TX
San Fernando Valley Interfaith Council—Chatsworth, CA
Schenectady Inner City Ministry—Schenectady, NY
South Coast Interfaith Council—Long Beach, CA
South East Associated Ministries (SEAM)—Louisville, KY
South Hills Interfaith Ministries—South Park, PA
South Louisville Community Ministries—Louisville, KY
Southeast Ecumenical Ministry—Rochester, NY
Staten Island Council of Churches—Staten Island, NY
Tulsa Metropolitan Ministry—Tulsa, OK
Tuscarawas County Council for Church and Community—New Philadelphia, OH
United Churches of Lycoming County—Williamsport, PA
United Ministries—Greenville, SC
West Central Neighborhood Ministry, Inc.—Fort Wayne, IN
West Side Ecumenical Ministry—Cleveland, OH
Wilkinsburg Community Ministry—Pittsburgh, PA
Wyoming Valley Council of Churches—Wilkes-Barre, PA
York County Council of Churches—York, PA

Immigration Issues

Association of Religious Communities—Danbury, CT
Austin Area Interreligious Ministries—Austin, TX
Border Association for Refugees from Central America (BARCA), Inc.—Edinburg, TX
Chautaugua County Rural Ministry—Dunkirk, NY
Community Emergency Assistance Program (CEAP)—Brooklyn Park, MN
Community Ministries of Rockville—Rockville, MD
Concerned Ecumenical Ministry to the Upper West Side—Buffalo, NY
Council of Churches of the City of New York—New York, NY
East Dallas Cooperative Parish—Dallas, TX
Eastern Area Community Ministries—Louisville, KY
The Ecumenical Council of Pasadena Area Churches—Pasadena, CA
Ecumenical Ministries of Oregon—Portland, OR
Fresno Metro Ministry—Fresno, CA
Greater Chicago Broadcast Ministries—Chicago, IL
Greater Minneapolis Council of Churches—Minneapolis, MN
Interchurch Ministries of Nebraska—Lincoln, NE
Interfaith Community Services—St. Joseph, MO
InterReligious Council of Central New York—Syracuse, NY
Lincoln Interfaith Council—Lincoln, NE
Marin Interfaith Council—San Rafael, CA
Minnesota Council of Churches—Minneapolis, MN
Mississippi Religious Leadership Conference —Jackson, MS
Northside Inter-Church Agency (NICA)—Fort Worth, TX
Peoria Friendship House of Christian Service—Peoria, IL
Reading Berks Conference of Churches—Reading, PA
San Antonio Community of Churches—San Antonio, TX
San Fernando Valley Interfaith Council—Chatsworth, CA
South Coast Interfaith Council—Long Beach, CA
Tulsa Metropolitan Ministry—Tulsa, OK
Virginia Council of Churches, Inc.—Richmond, VA

Interfaith Dialogue/Relationships

Akron Area Association of Churches—Akron, OH
Arizona Ecumenical Council—Phoenix, AZ
Arkansas Interfaith Conference—Scott, AR
The Associated Churches of Fort Wayne & Allen County, Inc.—Fort Wayne, IN
Associated Ministries of Tacoma-Pierce County—Tacoma, WA
Association of Religious Communities—Danbury, CT
Attleboro Area Council of Churches, Inc.—Attleboro, MA
Austin Area Interreligious Ministries—Austin, TX

Berrien County Association of Churches—Benton Harbor, MI
Brooklyn Council of Churches—Brooklyn, NY
Broome County Council of Churches, Inc.—Binghamton, NY
California Council of Churches-California Church Impact—Sacramento, CA
Capital Area Council of Churches, Inc.—Albany, NY
The Capitol Region Conference of Churches—Hartford, CT
Christian Associates of Southwest Pennsylvania—Pittsburgh, PA
Christian Ministries of Delaware County—Muncie, IN
The Church Federation of Greater Indianapolis, Inc.—Indianapolis, IN
Churches United of the Quad City Area—Rock Island, IL
Colorado Council of Churches—Denver, CO
Community Emergency Assistance Program (CEAP)—Brooklyn Park, MN
Community Ministries of Rockville—Rockville, MD
Community Ministry of Montgomery County—Rockville, MD
Community Renewal Society—Chicago, IL
Cooperative Metropolitan Ministries—Newton, MA
Council of Churches of Chemung County, Inc.—Elmira, NY
Council of Churches of the City of New York—New York, NY
Council of Churches of Greater Bridgeport, Inc.—Bridgeport, CT
Council of Churches of Greater Springfield—Springfield, MA
The Council of Churches of Santa Clara County—San Jose, CA
Council of Churches and Synagogues of Southwestern Connecticut—Stamford, CT
Des Moines Area Religious Council—Des Moines, IA
Dutchess Interfaith Council, Inc.—Poughkeepsie, NY
East Dallas Cooperative Parish—Dallas, TX
Eastern Area Community Ministries—Louisville, KY
Ecclesia—Trenton, NJ
Ecumenical Conference of Greater Altoona—Altoona, PA
The Ecumenical Council of Pasadena Area Churches—Pasadena, CA
Ecumenical Council of San Diego County—San Diego, CA
Ecumenical Ministries of Iowa (EMI)—Des Moines, IA
Ecumenical Ministries of Oregon—Portland, OR
Evanston Ecumenical Action Council—Evanston, IL
Faith Community Assistance Center—Santa Fe, NM
FaithTrust Institute—Seattle, WA
Fresno Metro Ministry—Fresno, CA
Georgia Christian Council—Macon, GA
Grand Rapids Area Center for Ecumenism (GRACE)—Grand Rapids, MI
Greater Baton Rouge Federation of Churches and Synagogues—Baton Rouge, LA
Greater Bethlehem Area Council of Churches—Bethlehem, PA
Greater Birmingham Ministries—Birmingham, AL
Greater Chicago Broadcast Ministries—Chicago, IL
Greater Dallas Community of Churches—Dallas, TX
Greater Dayton Christian Connections—Dayton, OH
Greater Flint Council of Churches—Flint, MI
Greater New Orleans Federation of Churches—New Orleans, LA
Greater Rochester Community of Churches—Rochester, NY
Greater Waterbury Interfaith Ministries, Inc.—Waterbury, CT
Greensboro Urban Ministry—Greensboro, NC
Highlands Community Ministries—Louisville, KY
Indiana Partners for Christian Unity and Mission—Indianapolis, IN
Inter-Church Council of Greater New Bedford—New Bedford, MA
Inter-Church Ministries of Erie County—Erie, PA
Interchurch Ministries of Nebraska—Lincoln, NE
Interfaith Community Council, Inc.—New Albany, IN
Interfaith Community Services—St. Joseph, MO
Interfaith Conference of Greater Milwaukee—Milwaukee, WI
InterFaith Conference of Metropolitan Washington—Washington, DC
Interfaith Council—Spokane, WA
Interfaith Council of Contra Costa County—Walnut Creek, CA
Inter-Faith Ministries-Wichita—Wichita, KS
Interfaith Mission Service—Huntsville, AL
Interfaith Service Bureau—Sacramento, CA
Interfaith Works—Olympia, WA
InterReligious Council of Central New York—Syracuse, NY
Kentuckiana Interfaith Community—Louisville, KY
Lehigh County Conference of Churches—Allentown, PA
Lewisburg Council of Churches—Lewisburg, PA
Lincoln Interfaith Council—Lincoln, NE
The Long Island Council of Churches—Hempstead, NY
Mahoning Valley Association of Churches—Youngstown, OH

Maine Council of Churches—Portland, ME
Marin Interfaith Council—San Rafael, CA
Massachusetts Council of Churches—Boston, MA
The Metropolitan Christian Council: Detroit-Windsor—Detroit, MI
Metropolitan Christian Council of Philadelphia—Philadelphia, PA
Metropolitan Ecumenical Ministry—Newark, NJ
Metropolitan Interfaith Council on Affordable Housing (MICAH)—Minneapolis, MN
Michigan Ecumenical Forum—Lansing, MI
Minnesota Council of Churches—Minneapolis, MN
Mississippi Religious Leadership Conference—Jackson, MS
Montana Association of Churches—Billings, MT
Muskegon County Cooperating Churches—Muskegon, MI
Network of Religious Communities—Buffalo, NY
New Britain Area Conference of Churches (NEWBRACC)—New Britain, CT
New Hampshire Council of Churches—Pembroke, NH
New Mexico Conference of Churches—Albuquerque, NM
North Dakota Conference of Churches—Ashley, ND
Northern California Interreligious Conference—Oakland, CA
Northern Kentucky Interfaith Commission, Inc.—Newport, KY
Northwest Interfaith Movement—Philadelphia, PA
Oklahoma Conference of Churches—Oklahoma City, OK
Paducah Cooperative Ministry—Paducah, KY
Pennsylvania Conference on Interchurch Cooperation—Harrisburg, PA
Peoria Friendship House of Christian Service—Peoria, IL
Reading Berks Conference of Churches—Reading, PA
The Rhode Island State Council of Churches—Providence, RI
St. Paul Area Council of Churches—St. Paul, MN
San Antonio Community of Churches—San Antonio, TX
San Fernando Valley Interfaith Council—Chatsworth, CA
South Carolina Christian Action Council, Inc.—Columbia, SC
South Coast Interfaith Council—Long Beach, CA
South Hills Interfaith Ministries—South Park, PA
Staten Island Council of Churches—Staten Island, NY
Texas Conference of Churches—Austin, TX
Troy Area United Ministries—Troy, NY
Tulsa Metropolitan Ministry—Tulsa, OK
Tuscarawas County Council for Church and Community—New Philadelphia, OH
United Churches of Lycoming County—Williamsport, PA
Vermont Ecumenical Council and Bible Society—Richmond, VT
Virginia Council of Churches, Inc.—Richmond, VA
Wainwright House—Rye, NY
Washington Association of Churches—Seattle, WA
West Side Ecumenical Ministry—Cleveland, OH
West Virginia Council of Churches—Charleston, WV
Wisconsin Council of Churches—Sun Prairie, WI
Worcester County Ecumenical Council—Worcester, MA
Wyoming Association of Churches—Cheyenne, WY
Wyoming Valley Council of Churches—Wilkes-Barre, PA
York County Council of Churches—York, PA

Peace Advocacy

Akron Area Association of Churches—Akron, OH
Arkansas Interfaith Conference—Scott, AR
The Associated Churches of Fort Wayne & Allen County, Inc.—Fort Wayne, IN
Church Council of Greater Seattle—Seattle, WA
Colorado Council of Churches—Denver, CO
Council of Churches of the City of New York—New York, NY
The Council of Churches of Santa Clara County—San Jose, CA
Ecumenical Conference of Greater Altoona—Altoona, PA
Ecumenical Ministries of Iowa (EMI)—Des Moines, IA
Ecumenical Ministries of Oregon—Portland, OR
Greater Chicago Broadcast Ministries—Chicago, IL
Greater Dallas Community of Churches—Dallas, TX
Indiana Partners for Christian Unity and Mission—Indianapolis, IN
Lincoln Interfaith Council—Lincoln, NE
Muskegon County Cooperating Churches—Muskegon, MI
Network of Religious Communities—Buffalo, NY
Oklahoma Conference of Churches—Oklahoma City, OK
St. Paul Area Council of Churches—St. Paul, MN

Southern California Ecumenical Council—Pasadena, CA
Staten Island Council of Churches—Staten Island, NY
Texas Conference of Churches—Austin, TX
Vermont Ecumenical Council and Bible Society—Richmond, VT

Prison Chaplaincy

Asheville-Buncombe Community Christian Ministry (ABCCM)—Asheville, NC
Association of Christian Churches of South Dakota—Sioux Falls, SD
Broome County Council of Churches, Inc.—Binghamton, NY
Capital Area Council of Churches, Inc.—Albany, NY
Christian Associates of Southwest Pennsylvania—Pittsburgh, PA
Christians United in Beaver County—Beaver, PA
Church Council of Greater Seattle—Seattle, WA
The Church Federation of Greater Indianapolis, Inc.—Indianapolis, IN
Churches United of the Quad City Area—Rock Island, IL
Churchpeople for Change and Reconciliation—Lima, OH
Council of Christian Communions of Greater Cincinnati—Cincinnati, OH
Council of Churches of the City of New York—New York, NY
Council of Churches of Greater Bridgeport, Inc.—Bridgeport, CT
Council of Churches of Greater Springfield—Springfield, MA
The Council of Churches of Santa Clara County—San Jose, CA
Ecclesia—Trenton, NJ
Ecumenical Ministries—Fulton, MO
Evansville Area Community of Churches, Inc.—Evansville, IN
Genesee County Churches United, Inc.—Batavia, NY
Greater Bethlehem Area Council of Churches—Bethlehem, PA
Greater Chicago Broadcast Ministries—Chicago, IL
Greater Minneapolis Council of Churches—Minneapolis, MN
The Greater Wheeling Council of Churches—Wheeling, WV
Interfaith Council of Contra Costa County—Walnut Creek, CA
InterReligious Council of Central New York—Syracuse, NY
Lehigh County Conference of Churches—Allentown, PA
The Long Island Council of Churches—Hempstead, NY
Louisiana Interchurch Conference—Baton Rouge, LA
Maine Council of Churches—Portland, ME
Network of Religious Communities—Buffalo, NY
New Hampshire Council of Churches—Pembroke, NH
New York State Community of Churches, Inc.—Albany, NY
Reading Berks Conference of Churches—Reading, PA
The Rhode Island State Council of Churches—Providence, RI
San Antonio Community of Churches—San Antonio, TX
United Churches of Lycoming County—Williamsport, PA
West Virginia Council of Churches—Charleston, WV
Wyoming Association of Churches—Cheyenne, WY
York County Council of Churches—York, PA

Programs with/for Persons with Disabilities

Asheville-Buncombe Community Christian Ministry (ABCCM)—Asheville, NC
Christian Ministries of Delaware County—Muncie, IN
Ecumenical Ministries of Oregon—Portland, OR
Greater Chicago Broadcast Ministries—Chicago, IL
Greater Minneapolis Council of Churches—Minneapolis, MN
Inter-Church Council of Greater New Bedford—New Bedford, MA
Inter-Faith Ministries-Wichita—Wichita, KS
InterReligious Council of Central New York—Syracuse, NY
Massachusetts Council of Churches—Boston, MA
Metropolitan Ecumenical Ministry—Newark, NJ
New Hampshire Council of Churches—Pembroke, NH
New Mexico Conference of Churches—Albuquerque, NM
Reading Berks Conference of Churches—Reading, PA
The Rhode Island State Council of Churches—Providence, RI
Southeast Ecumenical Ministry—Rochester, NY
Tulsa Metropolitan Ministry—Tulsa, OK

Public Education Advocacy

Arizona Ecumenical Council—Phoenix, AZ
Associated Ministries of Tacoma-Pierce County—Tacoma, WA
Austin Area Interreligious Ministries—Austin, TX

California Council of Churches-California Church Impact—Sacramento, CA
Christian Ministries of Delaware County—Muncie, IN
The Church Federation of Greater Indianapolis, Inc.—Indianapolis, IN
Community Emergency Assistance Program (CEAP)—Brooklyn Park, MN
Community Ministries of Rockville—Rockville, MD
Community Ministry of Montgomery County—Rockville, MD
Community Renewal Society—Chicago, IL
Contact Ministries of Springfield—Springfield, IL
Council of Churches of the City of New York—New York, NY
Council of Churches of Greater Springfield—Springfield, MA
Evanston Ecumenical Action Council—Evanston, IL
Fresno Metro Ministry—Fresno, CA
Grand Rapids Area Center for Ecumenism (GRACE)—Grand Rapids, MI
Greater Baton Rouge Federation of Churches and Synagogues—Baton Rouge, LA
Greater Bethlehem Area Council of Churches—Bethlehem, PA
Greater Birmingham Ministries—Birmingham, AL
Greater Chicago Broadcast Ministries—Chicago, IL
Greater Fairmont Council of Churches—Fairmont, WV
Greater Minneapolis Council of Churches—Minneapolis, MN
Greater Rochester Community of Churches—Rochester, NY
Greater Waterbury Interfaith Ministries, Inc.—Waterbury, CT
The Greater Wheeling Council of Churches—Wheeling, WV
In One Accord—Battle Creek, MI
Inter-Church Council of Greater New Bedford—New Bedford, MA
Interchurch Ministries of Nebraska—Lincoln, NE
Interfaith Conference of Greater Milwaukee—Milwaukee, WI
InterFaith Conference of Metropolitan Washington—Washington, DC
Interfaith Council—Spokane, WA
Lincoln Interfaith Council—Lincoln, NE
Maine Council of Churches—Portland, ME
Metropolitan Christian Council of Philadelphia—Philadelphia, PA
Metropolitan Ecumenical Ministry—Newark, NJ
Metropolitan Inter Faith Association (MIFA)—Memphis, TN
Metropolitan Interfaith Council on Affordable Housing (MICAH)—Minneapolis, MN
Mississippi Religious Leadership Conference—Jackson, MS
Network of Religious Communities—Buffalo, NY
New Hampshire Council of Churches—Pembroke, NH
New York State Community of Churches, Inc.—Albany, NY
North Carolina Council of Churches—Raleigh, NC
Oklahoma Conference of Churches—Oklahoma City, OK
The Pennsylvania Council of Churches—Harrisburg, PA
Peoria Friendship House of Christian Service—Peoria, IL
The Rhode Island State Council of Churches—Providence, RI
San Antonio Community of Churches—San Antonio, TX
South Carolina Christian Action Council, Inc.—Columbia, SC
Staten Island Council of Churches—Staten Island, NY
Tarrant Area Community of Churches—Fort Worth, TX
Tulsa Metropolitan Ministry—Tulsa, OK
Tuscarawas County Council for Church and Community—New Philadelphia, OH
West Virginia Council of Churches—Charleston, WV
Wisconsin Council of Churches—Sun Prairie, WI

Refugee Assistance Programs

Association of Religious Communities—Danbury, CT
Austin Area Interreligious Ministries—Austin, TX
Border Association for Refugees from Central America (BARCA), Inc.—Edinburg, TX
The Capitol Region Conference of Churches—Hartford, CT
Community Emergency Assistance Program (CEAP)—Brooklyn Park, MN
Council of Churches of Greater Bridgeport, Inc.—Bridgeport, CT
Ecumenical Ministries of Oregon—Portland, OR
Greater Chicago Broadcast Ministries—Chicago, IL
Greater Minneapolis Council of Churches—Minneapolis, MN
Interchurch Ministries of Nebraska—Lincoln, NE
Interfaith Service Bureau—Sacramento, CA
InterReligious Council of Central New York—Syracuse, NY
Lincoln Interfaith Council—Lincoln, NE
Metropolitan Ecumenical Ministry—Newark, NJ
Minnesota Council of Churches—Minneapolis, MN

Network of Religious Communities—Buffalo, NY
Virginia Council of Churches, Inc.—Richmond, VA

Rural Issues

Alaska Christian Conference—Fairbanks, AK
Asheville-Buncombe Community Christian Ministry (ABCCM)—Asheville, NC
Association of Christian Churches of South Dakota—Sioux Falls, SD
Berrien County Association of Churches—Benton Harbor, MI
Border Association for Refugees from Central America (BARCA), Inc.—Edinburg, TX
Chautaugua County Rural Ministry—Dunkirk, NY
Ecumenical Ministries of Iowa (EMI)—Des Moines, IA
Ecumenical Ministries of Oregon—Portland, OR
Fresno Metro Ministry—Fresno, CA
Georgia Christian Council—Macon, GA
Interchurch Ministries of Nebraska—Lincoln, NE
Interfaith Conference of Greater Milwaukee—Milwaukee, WI
Kansas Ecumenical Ministries—Topeka, KS
Kentucky Council of Churches—Lexington, KY
Louisiana Interchurch Conference—Baton Rouge, LA
Minnesota Council of Churches—Minneapolis, MN
Mississippi Religious Leadership Conference—Jackson, MS
Montana Association of Churches—Billings, MT
North Carolina Council of Churches—Raleigh, NC
North Dakota Conference of Churches—Ashley, ND
Oklahoma Conference of Churches—Oklahoma City, OK
Pike County Outreach Council—Waverly, OH
Reading Berks Conference of Churches—Reading, PA
The Rhode Island State Council of Churches—Providence, RI
Virginia Council of Churches, Inc.—Richmond, VA
West Virginia Council of Churches—Charleston, WV

Senior Citizen Programs

Arkansas Interfaith Conference—Scott, AR
Asheville-Buncombe Community Christian Ministry (ABCCM)—Asheville, NC
Associated Ministries of Tacoma-Pierce County—Tacoma, WA
Attleboro Area Council of Churches, Inc.—Attleboro, MA
Capital Area Council of Churches, Inc.—Albany, NY
The Capitol Region Conference of Churches—Hartford, CT
Christian Ministries of Delaware County—Muncie, IN
Church Council of Greater Seattle—Seattle, WA
Community Emergency Assistance Program (CEAP)—Brooklyn Park, MN
Community Ministries of Rockville—Rockville, MD
Community Renewal Society—Chicago, IL
Concerned Ecumenical Ministry to the Upper West Side—Buffalo, NY
Council of Churches of Greater Springfield—Springfield, MA
Council of Churches of the Ozarks—Springfield, MO
Council of Churches and Synagogues of Southwestern Connecticut—Stamford, CT
East Dallas Cooperative Parish—Dallas, TX
East End Cooperative Ministry—Pittsburgh, PA
Eastern Area Community Ministries—Louisville, KY
Ecumenical Ministries—Fulton, MO
Ecumenical Ministries of Oregon—Portland, OR
Fern Creek-Highview United Ministries—Louisvlle, KY
Fresno Metro Ministry—Fresno, CA
Georgia Christian Council—Macon, GA
Greater Baton Rouge Federation of Churches and Synagogues—Baton Rouge, LA
Greater Minneapolis Council of Churches—Minneapolis, MN
Highlands Community Ministries—Louisville, KY
Inter-Church Council of Greater New Bedford—New Bedford, MA
Interfaith Community Council, Inc.—New Albany, IN
Interfaith Community Services—St. Joseph, MO
Interfaith Council of Contra Costa County—Walnut Creek, CA
Inter-Faith Ministries-Wichita—Wichita, KS
InterReligious Council of Central New York—Syracuse, NY
Lincoln Interfaith Council—Lincoln, NE
The Long Island Council of Churches—Hempstead, NY
Louisiana Interchurch Conference—Baton Rouge, LA
Metropolitan Ecumenical Ministry—Newark, NJ
Metropolitan Inter Faith Association (MIFA)—Memphis, TN
Mississippi Religious Leadership Conference—Jackson, MS
New Hampshire Council of Churches—Pembroke, NH

Northside Inter-Church Agency (NICA)—Fort Worth, TX
Northwest Interfaith Movement—Philadelphia, PA
Ohio Council of Churches—Columbus, OH
Oklahoma Conference of Churches—Oklahoma City, OK
Paducah Cooperative Ministry—Paducah, KY
Peoria Friendship House of Christian Service—Peoria, IL
The Rhode Island State Council of Churches—Providence, RI
San Antonio Community of Churches—San Antonio, TX
San Fernando Valley Interfaith Council—Chatsworth, CA
South Hills Interfaith Ministries—South Park, PA
South Louisville Community Ministries—Louisville, KY
Southeast Ecumenical Ministry—Rochester, NY
Staten Island Council of Churches—Staten Island, NY
Tarrant Area Community of Churches—Fort Worth, TX
Troy Area United Ministries—Troy, NY
Tulsa Metropolitan Ministry—Tulsa, OK
Tuscarawas County Council for Church and Community—New Philadelphia, OH
United Churches of Lycoming County—Williamsport, PA
Wainwright House—Rye, NY
West Central Neighborhood Ministry, Inc.—Fort Wayne, IN
West Side Ecumenical Ministry—Cleveland, OH
Wilkinsburg Community Ministry—Pittsburgh, PA

Substance Abuse Programs

Community Ministries of Rockville—Rockville, MD
Corpus Christi Metro Ministries—Corpus Christi, TX
Council of Churches of Greater Bridgeport, Inc.—Bridgeport, CT
Council of Churches of the Ozarks—Springfield, MO
East End Cooperative Ministry—Pittsburgh, PA
Ecumenical Ministries of Iowa (EMI)—Des Moines, IA
Ecumenical Ministries of Oregon—Portland, OR
Evanston Ecumenical Action Council—Evanston, IL
Greater Chicago Broadcast Ministries—Chicago, IL
Greensboro Urban Ministry—Greensboro, NC
Hanover Area Council of Churches—Hanover, PA
Interchurch Ministries of Nebraska—Lincoln, NE
Lehigh County Conference of Churches—Allentown, PA
Lincoln Interfaith Council—Lincoln, NE
The Metropolitan Christian Council: Detroit-Windsor—Detroit, MI
Metropolitan Ecumenical Ministry—Newark, NJ
Metropolitan Ecumenical Ministry Community Development Corp.—Newark, NJ
Mississippi Religious Leadership Conference—Jackson, MS
New Hampshire Council of Churches—Pembroke, NH
Pike County Outreach Council—Waverly, OH
San Antonio Community of Churches—San Antonio, TX
Southeast Ecumenical Ministry—Rochester, NY
Staten Island Council of Churches—Staten Island, NY
Tulsa Metropolitan Ministry—Tulsa, OK
West Side Ecumenical Ministry—Cleveland, OH

Theology and Worship Programs

Arizona Ecumenical Council—Phoenix, AZ
Associated Ministries of Tacoma-Pierce County—Tacoma, WA
Association of Christian Churches of South Dakota—Sioux Falls, SD
Attleboro Area Council of Churches, Inc.—Attleboro, MA
Brooklyn Council of Churches—Brooklyn, NY
Broome County Council of Churches, Inc.—Binghamton, NY
Capital Area Council of Churches, Inc.—Albany, NY
Christian Associates of Southwest Pennsylvania—Pittsburgh, PA
Church Council of Greater Seattle—Seattle, WA
The Church Federation of Greater Indianapolis, Inc.—Indianapolis, IN
Churches United of the Quad City Area—Rock Island, IL
Colorado Council of Churches—Denver, CO
Council of Churches of the City of New York—New York, NY
Council of Churches of Greater Springfield—Springfield, MA
The Council of Churches of Santa Clara County—San Jose, CA
Council of Churches and Synagogues of Southwestern Connecticut—Stamford, CT
Dutchess Interfaith Council, Inc.—Poughkeepsie, NY
East Dallas Cooperative Parish—Dallas, TX

The Ecumenical Council of Pasadena Area Churches—Pasadena, CA
Ecumenical Ministries—Fulton, MO
Ecumenical Ministries of Iowa (EMI)—Des Moines, IA
Ecumenical Ministries of Oregon—Portland, OR
Fresno Metro Ministry—Fresno, CA
Georgia Christian Council—Macon, GA
Grand Rapids Area Center for Ecumenism (GRACE)—Grand Rapids, MI
Greater Bethlehem Area Council of Churches—Bethlehem, PA
Greater Chicago Broadcast Ministries—Chicago, IL
Greater Dallas Community of Churches—Dallas, TX
Greater Dayton Christian Connections—Dayton, OH
Greater Fairmont Council of Churches—Fairmont, WV
Greater New Orleans Federation of Churches—New Orleans, LA
Greater Rochester Community of Churches—Rochester, NY
The Greater Wheeling Council of Churches—Wheeling, WV
Greensboro Urban Ministry—Greensboro, NC
Illinois Conference of Churches—Springfield, IL
In One Accord—Battle Creek, MI
Inter-Church Council of Greater New Bedford—New Bedford, MA
Inter-Church Ministries of Erie County—Erie, PA
Interchurch Ministries of Nebraska—Lincoln, NE
Interfaith Council—Spokane, WA
Interfaith Mission Service—Huntsville, AL
InterReligious Council of Central New York—Syracuse, NY
Kentuckiana Interfaith Community—Louisville, KY
Lehigh County Conference of Churches—Allentown, PA
Lincoln Interfaith Council—Lincoln, NE
Louisiana Interchurch Conference—Baton Rouge, LA
Mahoning Valley Association of Churches—Youngstown, OH
Marin Interfaith Council—San Rafael, CA
Massachusetts Council of Churches—Boston, MA
The Metropolitan Christian Council: Detroit-Windsor—Detroit, MI
Metropolitan Christian Council of Philadelphia—Philadelphia, PA
Metropolitan Ecumenical Ministry—Newark, NJ
Michigan Ecumenical Forum—Lansing, MI
Montana Association of Churches—Billings, MT
Muskegon County Cooperating Churches—Muskegon, MI
New Britain Area Conference of Churches (NEWBRACC)—New Britain, CT
New Hampshire Council of Churches—Pembroke, NH
New Mexico Conference of Churches—Albuquerque, NM
Northern Kentucky Interfaith Commission, Inc.—Newport, KY
Oak Park-River Forest Community of Congregations—Oak Park, IL
Ohio Council of Churches—Columbus, OH
Oklahoma Conference of Churches—Oklahoma City, OK
Reading Berks Conference of Churches—Reading, PA
The Rhode Island State Council of Churches—Providence, RI
San Antonio Community of Churches—San Antonio, TX
Schenectady Inner City Ministry—Schenectady, NY
South Coast Interfaith Council—Long Beach, CA
South East Associated Ministries (SEAM)—Louisville, KY
Staten Island Council of Churches—Staten Island, NY
Tarrant Area Community of Churches—Fort Worth, TX
Texas Conference of Churches—Austin, TX
Troy Area United Ministries—Troy, NY
Tulsa Metropolitan Ministry—Tulsa, OK
United Churches of Lycoming County—Williamsport, PA
Vermont Ecumenical Council and Bible Society—Richmond, VT
Virginia Council of Churches, Inc.—Richmond, VA
Wainwright House—Rye, NY
West Virginia Council of Churches—Charleston, WV
Wisconsin Council of Churches—Sun Prairie, WI
Worcester County Ecumenical Council—Worcester, MA
Wyoming Association of Churches—Cheyenne, WY
York County Council of Churches—York, PA

Women's Issues

Associated Ministries of Tacoma-Pierce County—Tacoma, WA
Border Association for Refugees from Central America (BARCA), Inc.—Edinburg, TX
California Council of Churches-California Church Impact—Sacramento, CA
Chautaugua County Rural Ministry—Dunkirk, NY
Christian Ministries of Delaware County—Muncie, IN

Church Community Services—Elkhart, IN
Community Ministries of Rockville—Rockville, MD
Council of Churches of the City of New York—New York, NY
Council of Churches of Greater Springfield—Springfield, MA
The Council of Churches of Santa Clara County—San Jose, CA
East Dallas Cooperative Parish—Dallas, TX
Ecumenical Ministries of Oregon—Portland, OR
FaithTrust Institute—Seattle, WA
Florida Council of Churches—Altamonte Springs, FL
Fresno Metro Ministry—Fresno, CA
Genesee-Orleans Ministry of Concern—Albion, NY
Georgia Christian Council—Macon, GA
Greater Birmingham Ministries—Birmingham, AL
Greater Chicago Broadcast Ministries—Chicago, IL
Greater Dallas Community of Churches—Dallas, TX
Inter-Church Council of Greater New Bedford—New Bedford, MA
Interchurch Ministries of Nebraska—Lincoln, NE
Interfaith Community Services—St. Joseph, MO
Interfaith Council—Spokane, WA
Lincoln Interfaith Council—Lincoln, NE
The Metropolitan Christian Council: Detroit-Windsor—Detroit, MI
Metropolitan Christian Council of Philadelphia—Philadelphia, PA
Metropolitan Ecumenical Ministry—Newark, NJ
Mississippi Religious Leadership Conference—Jackson, MS
Network of Religious Communities—Buffalo, NY
New Mexico Conference of Churches—Albuquerque, NM
North Carolina Council of Churches—Raleigh, NC
Oklahoma Conference of Churches—Oklahoma City, OK
Peoria Friendship House of Christian Service—Peoria, IL
San Antonio Community of Churches—San Antonio, TX
South Hills Interfaith Ministries—South Park, PA
Tulsa Metropolitan Ministry—Tulsa, OK
United Churches of Lycoming County—Williamsport, PA
Wainwright House—Rye, NY
West Central Neighborhood Ministry, Inc.—Fort Wayne, IN
West Side Ecumenical Ministry—Cleveland, OH

Youth Activities

Arizona Ecumenical Council—Phoenix, AZ
Arkansas Interfaith Conference—Scott, AR
Associated Ministries of Tacoma-Pierce County—Tacoma, WA
Austin Area Interreligious Ministries—Austin, TX
Center City Churches—Hartford, CT
Christian Ministries of Delaware County—Muncie, IN
The Church Federation of Greater Indianapolis, Inc.—Indianapolis, IN
Colorado Council of Churches—Denver, CO
Community Renewal Society—Chicago, IL
Concerned Ecumenical Ministry to the Upper West Side—Buffalo, NY
Cooperative Metropolitan Ministries—Newton, MA
Council of Churches of the City of New York—New York, NY
Council of Churches of Greater Bridgeport, Inc.—Bridgeport, CT
The Council of Churches of Santa Clara County—San Jose, CA
Dutchess Interfaith Council, Inc.—Poughkeepsie, NY
East Dallas Cooperative Parish—Dallas, TX
East End Cooperative Ministry—Pittsburgh, PA
Eastern Area Community Ministries—Louisville, KY
Ecclesia—Trenton, NJ
Ecumenical Ministries—Fulton, MO
Evanston Ecumenical Action Council—Evanston, IL
FaithTrust Institute—Seattle, WA
Fresno Metro Ministry—Fresno, CA
Genesee-Orleans Ministry of Concern—Albion, NY
Grand Rapids Area Center for Ecumenism (GRACE)—Grand Rapids, MI
Greater Bethlehem Area Council of Churches—Bethlehem, PA
Greater Chicago Broadcast Ministries—Chicago, IL
Greater Dallas Community of Churches—Dallas, TX
Greater Fairmont Council of Churches—Fairmont, WV
Greater Minneapolis Council of Churches—Minneapolis, MN
Highlands Community Ministries—Louisville, KY
Indiana Partners for Christian Unity and Mission—Indianapolis, IN
Inter-Church Council of Greater New Bedford—New Bedford, MA
Interfaith Community Council, Inc.—New Albany, IN
Interfaith Community Services—St. Joseph, MO

Interfaith Conference of Greater Milwaukee—Milwaukee, WI
InterFaith Conference of Metropolitan Washington—Washington, DC
Interfaith Council—Spokane, WA
Inter-Faith Ministries-Wichita—Wichita, KS
Lehigh County Conference of Churches—Allentown, PA
Lincoln Interfaith Council—Lincoln, NE
Marin Interfaith Council—San Rafael, CA
The Metropolitan Christian Council: Detroit-Windsor—Detroit, MI
Metropolitan Ecumenical Ministry—Newark, NJ
Metropolitan Ecumenical Ministry Community Development Corp.—Newark, NJ
Metropolitan Inter Faith Association (MIFA)—Memphis, TN
Muskegon County Cooperating Churches—Muskegon, MI
New Britain Area Conference of Churches (NEWBRACC)—New Britain, CT
New Mexico Conference of Churches—Albuquerque, NM
North Dakota Conference of Churches—Ashley, ND
Northern California Interreligious Conference—Oakland, CA
Peoria Friendship House of Christian Service—Peoria, IL
Queens Federation of Churches—Richmond Hill, NY
Reading Berks Conference of Churches—Reading, PA
Rural Migrant Ministry—Poughkeepsie, NY
St. Paul Area Council of Churches—St. Paul, MN
San Antonio Community of Churches—San Antonio, TX
Schenectady Inner City Ministry—Schenectady, NY
South East Associated Ministries (SEAM)—Louisville, KY
South Hills Interfaith Ministries—South Park, PA
South Louisville Community Ministries—Louisville, KY
Southeast Ecumenical Ministry—Rochester, NY
Troy Area United Ministries—Troy, NY
Tulsa Metropolitan Ministry—Tulsa, OK
Tuscarawas County Council for Church and Community—New Philadelphia, OH
United Churches of Lycoming County—Williamsport, PA
Wainwright House—Rye, NY
West Central Neighborhood Ministry, Inc.—Fort Wayne, IN
West Side Ecumenical Ministry—Cleveland, OH
Worcester County Ecumenical Council—Worcester, MA

7. Canadian Regional and Local Ecumenical Bodies

Most of the organizations listed below are councils of churches in which churches participate officially, whether at the parish or judicatory level. They operate at the city, metropolitan area, or county level. Parish clusters within urban areas are not included.

Canadian local ecumenical bodies operate without paid staff, with the exception of a few which have part-time staff. In most cases, the name and address of the president or chairperson is listed. As these offices change from year to year, some of this information may be out of date by the time the *Yearbook of American & Canadian Churches* is published.

ALBERTA

Calgary Council of Churches

c/o Anna Tremblay, Ecumenical & Inter-religious Affairs, 120 17th Ave., Calgary, AB T2S 2T2 Tel. (403)218-5521

Calgary Inter-Faith Community Association

P.O. Box 93, Stn. M, Calgary, AB T2P 2G9 Tel. (403)262-5111

BRITISH COLUMBIA

Greater Victoria Council of Churches

c/o Rev. Edwin Taylor, St. Alban's Church, 1468 Ryan St. at Balmont, Victoria, BC V8R 2X1

Multifaith Action Society of British Columbia

305 41st Ave. W, Vancouver, BC V5Y 2S5

Vancouver Council of Churches

Murray Moerman, 700 Kingsway, Vancouver, BC V5V 3C1 Tel. (604)420-0761

MANITOBA

Association of Christian Churches in Manitoba

150 de la Cathedrale Ave., Winnipeg, MB R2H 0H6 Tel. (204)237-9851

NEW BRUNSWICK

Atlantic Ecumenical Council of Churches

Rev. Rufus Onyewuchi, 170 Daniel Ave., Saint John, NB E2K 4S7 Tel. (506)538-2491

First Miramichi Inter-Church Council

Pres., Ellen Robinson, Doaktown, NB E0C 1G0

Moncton Area Council of Churches

Rev. Donald Routledge, 135 Mount Royal Blvd., Moncton, NB E1E 2V5 Tel. (506)382-7725

NEWFOUNDLAND

St. John's Area Council of Churches

Rev. Canon Ralph Billard, 31 Hazelwood Cres., St. John's, NF, A1E 6B3 Tel. (709)579-0536

NOVA SCOTIA

Atlantic Ecumenical Council of Churches

Pres., Rev. John E. Boyd, Box 637, 90 Victoria St., Amherst, NS B4H 4B4

Bridgewater Inter-Church Council

Pres., Wilson Jones, 30 Parkdale Ave., Bridgewater, NS B4V 1L8

Cornwallis District Inter-Church Council

Pres., Mr. Tom Regan, Centreville, RR 2, Kings County, NS BOT 1JO

Halifax-Dartmouth Council of Churches

Mrs. Betty Short, 3 Virginia Ave., Dartmouth, NS B2W 2Z4

Industrial Cape Breton Council of Churches

Rev. Karen Ralph, 24 Huron Ave., Sydney Mines, NS B1S 1V2

Kentville Council of Churches

Rev. Canon S.J.P. Davies, 325-325 Main St., Kentville, NS B4N 1C5

Lunenburg Queens BA Association

Mrs. Nilda Chute, 56 Hillside Dr., RR 4, Bridgewater, NS B4V 2W3

Mahone Bay Interchurch Council
Patricia Joudrey, R.R. 1, Blockhouse, NS B0J 1E0

Pictou Council of Churches
Rev. D. J. Murphy, Sec., P.O. Box 70, Pictou, NS B0K 1H0

Queens County Association of Churches
Mr. Donald Burns, Box 537, Liverpool, NS B0T 1K6

ONTARIO

Burlington Inter-Church Council
Mr. Fred Townsend, 425 Breckenwood, Burlington, ON L7L 2J6

Christian Leadership Council of Downtown Toronto
Ken Bhagan, Chair, 40 Homewood Ave., #509, Toronto, ON M4Y 2K2

Ecumenical Committee
Rev. William B. Kidd, 76 Eastern Ave., Sault Ste. Marie, ON P6A 4R2

Glengarry-Prescott-Russell Christian Council
Pres., Rev. G. Labrosse, St. Eugene's, Prescott, ON K0B 1P0

The Greater Toronto Council of Christian Churches
Secretary, Father Damian MacPherson, 1155 Yonge St., Toronto M4T 1W2 Tel. (416)934-3400 ext.344

Hamilton & District Christian Churches Association
The Rev. Dr. John Johnston, 183 Chedoke Avenue, Hamilton, ON L8P 4P2 Tel. (905)529-6896 or (905)528-2730 Fax (905)521-2539

Ignace Council of Churches
Box 5, 205 Pine St., St. Ignace, ON P0T 1H0

Inter Church Council of Burlington
P.O. Box 62120 Burlington Mall R.P.O., Burlington, ON L7R 4K2 Tel. (905)333-0515 Fax (509)526-9056
Website: www.iccb.ca

Kitchener-Waterloo Council of Churches
Rev. Clarence Hauser, CR, 53 Allen St. E, Waterloo, ON N2J 1J3

London Inter-City Faith Team
David Carouthers, Chair, c/o United Church, 711 Colbourne St., London, ON N6A 3Z4

Massey Inter-Church Council
The Rev. Brian Sonnenburg, Box 238, Massey, ON P0P 1P0 Tel. (705)865-2202

Ottawa Christian Council of the Capital Area
1247 Kilborn Ave., Ottawa, ON K1H 6K9

St. Catharines & Dist. Clergy Fellowship
Rev. Victor Munro, 663 Vince St., St. Catharines, ON L2M 3V8

Spadina-Bloor Interchurch Council
Rev. Frances Combes, Chair, c/o Bathurst St. United Church, 427 Bloor St. W, Toronto, ON M5S 1X7

Stratford & District Council of Churches
Rev. Ted Heinze, Chair, 202 Erie St., Stratford, ON N5A 2M8

Thorold Inter-Faith Council
1 Dunn St., St. Catharines, ON L2T 1P3

Thunder Bay Council of Churches
Rev. Richard Darling, 1800 Moodie St. E, Thunder Bay, ON P7E 4Z2

PRINCE EDWARD ISLAND

Atlantic Ecumenical Council
The Rev. Arthur J. Pendergast, Secretary, Immaculate Conception Church, St. Louis, PEI C0B 1Z0 Tel. (902)963-2202 or (902)882-2610

Summerside Christian Council
Ms. A. Kathleen Miller, P.O. Box 1551, Summerside, PEI C1N 4K4

QUEBEC

AGAPÉ Deux-Montagnes
c/o Donald Tremblay, prêtre, cure de Saint-Agapit et president de AGAPÉ deux-Montagnes, 1002 chemin d'Oka, Deux-Montagnes, QC J7® 1L7 Tel. (450)473-9877

ACAT
Action des chrétiens pour l'abolition de la torture, 4839 rue de Bordeaux, Montréal, QC H2H 2A2 Tel. (514)890-6169.

Canadian Centre for Ecumenism/ Centre d'oecuménisme
Fr. Emmanuel Lapierre, 2065 Sherbrooke Street W, Montreal, QC H3H 1G6 Tel. (514)937-9176 Fax (514)937-2684

Centre Emmaüs
Centre de spiritualité des Églises d'Orient, 3774 chemin Queen-Mary, 3e étage, Montréal, QC, H3V 1A6 Tel. (514)276-2144
Website: www.centre-emmaus.qc.ca

Direction Chrétienne

The Rev. Glen Smith, 1450 rue City Councillors, bureau 720, Montréal, QC H3A 2E6 Tél. (514) 878-3035 Fax (514)878-8048
Email: info@direction.ca
Website: www.direction.ca

Conseil des Églises de Côte-des Neiges <<Sept Égliese—un seul Esprit>>

Notre-Dame-des-Neiges (Roman Catholic), Tel. (514)738-1987; Dominion Douglas (United Church of Canada), Tel. (514)486-1165; St. Kevin's (Roman Catholic), Tel. (514)733-5600; St. Paul's Anglican, Tel. (514)733-2908; Mount Royal United (United Church of Canada), Tel. (514)739-7741; St. Peter's Anglican, Tel. (514)739-4776; St. Pascal-Baylon (Roman Catholic), Tel. (514)738-1214.

Conseil interreligieux de Montréal

2065 rue Sherbrooke ouest, Montréal, QC, H3H 1G6 Tel. (514)937-9176 Fax (514)937-4986
Website: www.total.net/~ccocce.

The Ecumenical Group

c/o Mrs. C. Haten, 1185 Ste. Foy, St. Bruno, QC J3V 3C3

Hemmingford Ecumenical Committee

c/o Catherine Priest, Box 300, Hemmingford, QC J0L 1H0

Jewish-Christian Dialogue of Montreal

The Rabbi Leigh Lerner, Temple Emmanu-El-Beth Sholom, 4100 Sherbrooke St. West, Westmount, QC H3Z 1A5 Tel. (O)(514)937-3575 ext.207, (H)(514)937-3708

Montréal Council of Churches

The Rev. Ralph Watson, 4995 Coronation Avenue, Montréal, QC H4V 2E1 Tel. (514)482-3210

Montreal Association for the Blind Foundation

The Rev. Dr. John A. Simms, 7000 Sherbrooke St. W., Montreal, QC H4B 1R3 Tel. (514)489-8201

Muslim Christian Dialogue

Dr. Sheila McDonnough, Department of Religion, Concordia University, 1455 de Maisonneuve Blvd., Montreal, QC, H3G 1M8 Tel. (514)488-6308
Email: donou@vax2.concordia.ca

Radio Ville-Marie

Radio religieuse, 505 avenue de Mont-Cassin, Montréal, QC, H3L 1W7 Tel (514)382-3913 or (877)668-6601 Fax (514)858-0965
Email: cira@radiovm.com
Website: www.radiovm.com

ROQ

Réseau oecuménique du Québec (Quebec Ecumenical Network), le Centre canadien d'oecuménisme en assure le secretariat, 2065 rue Sherbrooke ouest, Montréal, QC. Tel. (514) 937-9176 Fax (514)937-4986
Email: ccocce@total.net

Réseau oecuménique justice et paix

C.P. 114, Succ. D. Montréal, QC H3K 3B9 Tel/Fax (514)937-2683
Email: info@justiceoaix.org

Unitas

Centre oecuménique de meditation chrétienne et de spiritualité, 3289 St-Jacques, Montréal, QC, H4C 1G8 Tel. (514)485-0009

SASKATCHEWAN

Humboldt Clergy Council

Fr. Leo Hinz, OSB, Box 1989, Humboldt, SK S0K 2A0

Melville Association of Churches

Attn., Catherine Gaw, Box 878, Melville, SK S0A 2P0

Regina Council of Churches

The Rev. Bud Harper, 5 Robinson Crescent, Regina, SK S4R 3R1 Tel. (306)545-3375

Prairie Centre for Ecumenism

Sister Anne Keffer, 250-B Second Ave. So, Saskatoon, SK S7K 1K9 Tel. (306)653-1633 Fax (306)653-1821
Email: pce@ecumenism.net

Saskatoon Council of Churches

Dr. Colin Clay, 250-B Second Ave. S, Saskatoon, SK S7K 1K9

8. Theological Seminaries and Bible Colleges in the United States

The following list includes theological seminaries, Bible colleges and departments in colleges and universities in which ministerial training is given. Many denominations have additional programs.

Inclusion in or exclusion from this list implies no judgment about the quality or accreditation of any institution. Those schools that are members of the Association of Theological Schools are marked with an asterisk (*). Those schools that are accredited by the Transnational Association of Christian Colleges and Schools are marked with (†). Additional information about enrollment in ATS member schools can be found in the "Trends in Seminary Enrollment" section of chapter III. Information about TRACS and ATS can be found in the United States Cooperative Organizations section of chapter II.

Each of the listings include, when available: the institution name, denominational sponsor, location, the president or dean of the institution, telephone and fax numbers and E-mail and Website addresses.

Abilene Christian University Graduate School of Theology* (Churches of Christ), Jack R. Reese, Dean, College of Biblical Studies, ACU Box 29422, 1850 N. Judge Ely Boulevard, CBS Room 297, Abilene, TX 79699-9422 Tel. (915)674-3700 Fax (915)674-6180
E-mail: thompson@bible.acu.edu
Web site: www.bible.acu.edu/GST

Alaska Bible College (Nondenominational), Steven J. Hostetter, President, P.O. Box 289, Glennallen, AK 99588 Tel. (907)822-3201 Fax (907)822-5027
E-mail: info@akbible.edu
Web site: www.akbible.edu

Alliance Theological Seminary* (The Christian and Missionary Alliance), David E. Schroeder, President, 350 N. Highland Ave., Nyack, NY 10960-1416 Tel. (845)353-2020 Fax (845) 727-3002
Web site: www.alliance.edu

American Baptist College (National Baptist Convention U.S.A., Inc.), Dr. Forrest E. Harris, President, 1800 Baptist World Center Dr., Nashville, TN 37207 Tel. (615)228-7877 Fax (615)226-7855
E-mail: harrisfe@abcnash.edu

American Baptist Seminary of the West* (American Baptist Churches in the U.S.A.), Keith A. Russell, President, 2606 Dwight Way, Berkeley, CA 94704-3029 Tel. (510)841-1905 Fax (510)841-2446
E-mail: krussell@absw.edu
Web site: www.absw.edu

American Christian College and Seminary (Nondenominational), Dr. Fred Hambrick, President, 4300 Highline Boulevard, Suite #202, Oklahoma, OK 73108 Tel. (405)945-0100 Fax (405)945-0311
E-mail: info@accs.edu
Web site: www.accs.edu

Anderson University School of Theology* (Church of God (Anderson, Ind.)), James L. Edwards, President, 1100 East Fifth Street, Anderson, IN 46012-3495 Tel. (765)641-4032 Fax (765)641-3851
Web site: www.anderson.edu/academics/sot

Andover Newton Theological School* (American Baptist Churches in the U.S.A.; United Church of Christ), Nick Carter, President, 210 Herrick Rd., Newton Centre, MA 02459 Tel. (617)964-1100 Fax (617)558-9785
E-mail: admissions@ants.edu
Web site: www.ants.edu

Appalachian Bible College (Nondenominational), Daniel L. Anderson, President, P.O. Box ABC, Bradley, WV 25818 Tel. (304)877-6428 Fax (304)877-5082
E-mail: abc@abc.edu
Web site: www.abc.edu

Aquinas Institute of Theology* (The Roman Catholic Church), Charles E. Bouchard, President, 3642 Lindell Blvd., St. Louis, MO 63108-3396 Tel. (314)977-3882 Fax (314) 977-7225
E-mail: aquinas@slu.edu
Web site: www.ai.edu

Arizona College of the Bible (Interdenominational), Douglas K. Winn, President, 2045 W. Northern Ave., Phoenix, AZ 85021-5197 Tel. (602)995-2670 Fax (602) 864-8183

Arlington Baptist College (Baptist), David Bryant, President, 3001 W. Division, Arlington, TX 76012-3425 Tel. (817)461-8741 Fax (817)274-1138

Asbury Theological Seminary* (Inter/Multidenominational), Jeffrey E Greenway, President, 204 N. Lexington Ave., Wilmore, KY 40390-1199 Tel. (859)858-3581
Web site: www.asburyseminary.edu

Ashland Theological Seminary* (Brethren Church (Ashland, Ohio)), Frederick J. Finks, President, 910 Center St., Ashland, OH 44805 Tel. (419)289-5161 Fax (419)289-5969
E-mail: ffinks@ashland.edu
Web site: www.ashland.edu/seminary

Assemblies of God Theological Seminary* (Assemblies of God), Byron D. Klaus, President, 1435 North Glenstone Avenue, Springfield, MO 65802-2131 Tel. (417)268-1000 Fax (417)268-1001
E-mail: agts@agseminary.edu
Web site: www.agts.edu

Associated Mennonite Biblical Seminary* (Mennonite Church; General Conference Mennonite Church), J. Nelson Kraybill, President, 3003 Benham Ave., Elkhart, IN 46517-1999 Tel. (574)295-3726 Fax (574) 295-0092
E-mail: nkraybill@ambs.edu
Web site: www.ambs.edu

Athenaeum of Ohio* (The Roman Catholic Church), Gerald R. Haemmerle, President and Rector, 6616 Beechmont Ave., Cincinnati, OH 45230-2091 Tel. (513)231-2223 Fax (513) 231-3254
E-mail: atheathenaeum.edu
Web site: www.athenaeum.edu

Atlanta Christian College (Christian Churches and Churches of Christ), R. Edwin Groover, President, 2605 Ben Hill Rd., East Point, GA 30344 Tel. (404)761-8861 Fax (404)669-2024
E-mail: admissions@acc.edu
Web site: www.acc.edu

Austin Presbyterian Theological Seminary* (Presbyterian Church (U.S.A.)), Theodore J. Wardlaw, President, 100 E. 27th St., Austin, TX 78705-5797 Tel. (512)472-6736 Fax (512) 479-0738
Web site: www.austinseminary.edu

Bangor Theological Seminary* (United Church of Christ), William C. Imes, President, 300 Union St., Bangor, ME 04401 Tel. (207)942-6781 Fax (207)942-4914
E-mail: mhuddy@bts.edu
Web site: www.bts.edu

Baptist Bible College (Baptist Bible Fellowship International), Leland Kennedy, President, 628 E. Kearney, Springfield, MO 65803 Tel. (417)268-6060 Fax (417)268-6694

Baptist Bible College and Seminary (Baptist), Jim Jeffery, President, 538 Venard Rd., Clarks Summit, PA 18411 Tel. (570)586-2400 Fax (570)586-1753
E-mail: bbc@bbc.edu
Web site: www.bbc.edu

Baptist Missionary Association Theological Seminary* (Baptist Missionary Association of America), Charley Holmes, President, 1530 E. Pine St., Jacksonville, TX 75766 Tel. (903)586-2501 Fax (903)586-0378
E-mail: bmatsem@bmats.edu
Web site: www.bmats.edu

Baptist Theological Seminary at Richmond* (Cooperative Baptist Fellowship), Thomas H. Graves, President, 3400 Brook Rd., Richmond, VA 23227 Tel. (804)355-8135 Fax (804)355-8182
E-mail: btsr@btsr.edu
Web site: www.btsr.edu

Barclay College (Interdenominational), Maurice G. Chandler, President, 607 N Kingman, Haviland, KS 67059 Tel. (620)862-5252 Fax (620)862-5403
E-mail: barclaycollege@havilandtalco.com

Barry University Department of Theology and Philosophy*, Mark E. Wedig, Chair of the Department of Theology and Philosophy, 11300 Northeast Second Avenue, Miami Shores, FL 33161-6695 Tel. (305)899-3469 Fax (305)899-3385
E-mail: theology@mail.barry.edu
Web site: www.barry.edu/TheologyPhilosophy/default.htm

Bay Ridge Christian College (Church of God (Anderson, Ind.)), Dr. Verda Beach, President, P.O. Box 726, Kendleton, TX 77451 Tel. (979)532-3982 Fax (979)532-4352
E-mail: brcccampus@wcnet.net
Web site: brcconline.org

Beacon College & Graduate School† (Nondenominational), Dr. John Durden, Dean, 6003 Veterans Parkway, Columbus, GA 31909 Tel. (706)323-5364 Fax (706)323-3236
E-mail: beacon@beacon.edu
Web site: www.beacon.edu

Beeson Divinity School of Samford University* (Inter/Multidenominational), Timothy George, Dean, 800 Lakeshore Dr., Birmingham, AL 35229-2252 Tel. (205)726-2991 Fax (205)726-2260
E-mail: bdsadmis@samford.edu
Web site: www.beesondivinity.com

Berkeley Divinity School* (Episcopal Church), Joseph H. Britton, Dean, 409 Prospect Street,

New Haven, CT 06511 Tel. (203)432-9285 Fax (203)432-9353
Web site: www.yale.edu/divinity/bds

Bethany Lutheran Theological Seminary (Evangelical Lutheran Synod), G. R. Schmeling, President, 6 Browns Court, Mankato, MN 56001 Tel. (507)344-7354 Fax (507)344-7426
E-mail: gschmeli@blc.edu
Web site: www.blts.edu

Bethany Theological Seminary* (Church of the Brethren), Eugene F. Roop, President, 615 National Rd. W., Richmond, IN 47374 Tel. (765)983-1800 Fax (765)983-1840
E-mail: roopge@bethanyseminary.edu
Web site: www.bethanyseminary.edu

Bethel Seminary of the East* (Conservative Baptist Association of America— Baptist General Conference), Douglas W. Fombelle, Dean and Executive Officer, 1605 N. Limekiln Pike, Dresher, PA 19025 Tel. (215)641-4801 Fax (215)641-4804
Web site: www.bethel.edu

Bethel Seminary San Diego* (General Bapist Conference), John Lillis, Dean, 6116 Arosa Street, San Diego, CA 92115-3902 Tel. (619)582-8188 Fax (619)583-9114
Web site: www.bethel.edu

Bethel Theological Seminary* (Baptist General Conference), George K. Brushaber, President, 3949 Bethel Dr., St. Paul, MN 55112 Tel. (651)638-6180 Fax (651)638-6002
E-mail: webmaster@bethel.edu
Web site: www.bethel.edu

Beulah Heights Bible College† (The International Pentecostal Church of Christ), Samuel R. Chand, President, 892 Berne St. SE, Atlanta, GA 30316 Tel. (404)627-2681 Fax (404)627-0702
E-mail: bhbc@beulah.org
Web site: www.beulah.org

Bexley Hall Seminary* (Episcopal Church), John R. Kevern, President and Dean, 583 Sheridan Avenue, Columbus, OH 43209-2325 Tel. (614)231-3095 Fax (614)231-3236
E-mail: bexleyhall@bexley.edu
Web site: www.bexley.edu

Bible Church of Christ Theological Institute (Nondenominational), Roy Bryant; Sr., President, 1358 Morris Ave., Bronx, NY 10456-1402 Tel. (718)588-2284 Fax (718) 992-5597
Web site: www.thebiblechurchofchrist.org

Biblical Theological Seminary* (Inter/ Multidenominational), David G. Dunbar, President, 200 N. Main St., Hatfield, PA 19440 Tel. (215)368-5000 Fax (215)368-7002
E-mail: president@biblical.edu
Web site: www.biblical.edu

Blessed John XXIII National Seminary* (Roman Catholic), Francis D. Kelly, Rector, 558 South Avenue, Weston, MA 02493-2699 Tel. (781)899-5500 Fax (781)899-9057
Web site: www.blessedjohnxxiii.edu

Boise Bible College (Christian Churches and Churches of Christ), Dr. Charles A. Crane, President, 8695 Marigold St., Boise, ID 83714 Tel. (208)376-7731 Fax (208)376-7743
E-mail: boisebible@boisebible.edu
Web site: www.boisebible.edu

Boston Baptist College† (Baptist), Dr. Harry Boyle, President, 950 Metropolitan Avenue, Boston, MA 02136 Tel. (617)364-3510 Fax (617)364-0723
E-mail: admin@boston.edu
Web site: www.boston.edu

Boston College Institute of Religious Education and Pastoral Ministry and Department of Theology* (Roman Catholic), Thomas H. Groome, Director, 31 Lawrence Ave., Chestnut Hill, MA 02467-3931 Tel. (617)552-8440 Fax (617)552-0811
Web site: www.bc.edu/irepm

Boston University School of Theology* (The United Methodist Church), Ray L. Hart, Dean, 745 Commonwealth Ave., Boston, MA 02215 Tel. (617)353-3050 Fax (617)353-3061
Web site: www.bu.edu/STH/

Brite Divinity School, Texas Christian University* (Christian Church (Disciples of Christ)), Newell Williams, President, TCU Box 298130, Ft. Worth, TX 76129-0002 Tel. (817)257-7575 Fax (817)257-7305
E-mail: t.palmer@tcu.edu
Web site: www.brite.tcu.edu/brite

Byzantine Catholic Seminary of SS. Cyril and Methodius* (Byzantine Catholic Archeparchy of Pittsburgh), John G. Petro, Rector, 3605 Perrysville Ave., Pittsburgh, PA 15214 Tel. (412)321-8383 Fax (412)321-9936

California Christian College† (Free Will Baptist), Wendell Walley, President, 4881 E. University Avenue, Fresno, CA 93703 Tel. (559)251-4215 Fax (559)251-4231
E-mail: cccfresno@aol.com
Web site: www.calchristiancollege.org

Calvary Bible College and Theological Seminary (Independent Fundamental Churches of America), James L. Anderson, President,

15800 Calvary Rd., Kansas City, MO 64147-1341 Tel. (800)326-3960 Fax (816)331-4474

Calvin Theological Seminary* (Christian Reformed Church in North America), Cornelius Plantinga, Jr., President, 3233 Burton St. S.E., Grand Rapids, MI 49546-4387 Tel. (616)957-6036 Fax (616)957-8621
E-mail: sempres@calvin.edu
Web site: www.calvinseminary.edu

Campbell University Divinity School* (Baptist State Convention of North Carolina), Michael G. Cogdill, Dean, 116 T. T. Lanier Street, PO Drawer 4050, Buies Creek, NC 27506 Tel. (910)893-1830 Fax (910)893-1835
Web site: www.campbell.edu/divinity

Candler School of Theology of Emory University* (The United Methodist Church), Russell E. Richey, Dean, 500 Kilgo Circle N.E., Emory Univ., Atlanta, GA 30322 Tel. (404)727-6324 Fax (404)727-3182
E-mail: candler@emory.edu
Web site: www.emory.edu/candler

Capital Bible Seminary* (Nondenominational), Homer Heater Jr., President, 6511 Princess Garden Parkway, Lanham, MD 20706 Tel. (301)552-1400 Fax (301)614-1024
E-mail: bfox@bible.edu
Web site: www.bible.edu

Carolina Evangelical Divinity School* (Religious Society of Friends), Frank P. Scurry, President, P.O. Box 5831, High Point, NC 27265 Tel. (336)889-2262 Fax (336)882-3370
E-mail: deansoffice@hgstnc.org

Catholic Theological Union at Chicago* (Catholic Church), Donald Senior, C.P., President, 5401 S. Cornell Ave., Chicago, IL 60615-5664 Tel. (773)324-8000 Fax (773) 324-8490
Web site: www.ctu.edu

Catholic University of America* (The Roman Catholic Church), Rev. Dr. Francis J. Maloney, Dean, 620 Michigan Avenue NE, Washington, DC 20064 Tel. (202)319-5683 Fax (202)319-4967
E-mail: cua-deansrs@cua.edu
Web site: www.religiousstudies.cua.edu

Central Baptist College (Baptist Missionary Association of Arkansas), Charles Attebery, President, 1501 College Ave., Conway, AR 72032 Tel. (501)329-6872 Fax (501)329-2941
E-mail: Cattebery@cbc.edu
Web site: www.cbc.edu

Central Baptist Theological Seminary* (Baptist), James W. McCrossen, Interim President, 741 N. 31st St., Kansas City, KS 66102-3964 Tel. (913)371-5313 Fax (913) 371-8110
E-mail: central@cbts.edu
Web site: www.cbts.edu

Central Baptist Theological Seminary in Indiana (National Baptist Convention U.S.A., Inc.), 1535 Dr. A. J. Brown Ave. N., Indianapolis, IN 46202 Tel. (317)636-6622
E-mail: henriettabrown@webtv.net

Central Bible College (Assemblies of God), M. Wayne Benson, President, 3000 N. Grant Ave., Springfield, MO 65803 Tel. (417)833-2551 Fax (417)833-5141
E-mail: info@cbcag.edu
Web site: www.cbcag.edu

Central Christian College of the Bible (Christian Churches and Churches of Christ), Russell N. James III, President, 911 E. Urbandale Dr., Moberly, MO 65270-1997 Tel. (660)263-3900 Fax (660)263-3936
E-mail: develop@cccb.edu
Web site: www.cccb.edu

Central Indian Bible College (Assemblies of God), Robert Koscak, President, P.O. Box 550, Mobridge, SD 57601 Tel. (605)845-7801 Fax (605)845-7744

Chapman School of Religious Studies of Oakland City University* (General Association of General Baptists), James W. Murray, Chancellor and President, 143 Lucretia Street, Oakland City, IN 47660 Tel. (812)749-4781 Fax (812)749-1233
E-mail: ocuexe@oak.edu
Web site: www.oak.edu

Chicago Theological Seminary* (United Church of Christ), Susan Brooks Thistlethwaite, President, 5757 South University Ave., Chicago, IL 60637-1507 Tel. (773)752-5757 Fax (773)752-5925
E-mail: sthistle@chgosem.edu
Web site: www.ctschicago.edu

Christ the King Seminary* (Catholic Church), Rev. Richard W. Siepka, President and Rector, 711 Knox Rd., P.O. Box 607, East Aurora, NY 14052-0607 Tel. (716)652-8900 Fax (716) 652-8903
E-mail: rsiepka@cks.edu
Web site: www.cks.edu

Christ the Savior Seminary (The American Carpatho-Russian Orthodox Greek Catholic Church), Nicholas Smisko, President, 225 Chandler Ave., Johnstown, PA 15906 Tel. (814)539-0116 Fax (814)536-4699
E-mail: mrosco2@excite.com

Christian Heritage College (Southern Baptist), Dr. David Jeremiah, President, 2100 Greenfield Drive, El Cajon, CA 92019 Tel. (619)441-2200 Fax (619)440-0209
E-mail: chcadm@christianheritage.edu
Web site: www.christianheritage.edu

Christian Life College† (Nondenominational), Harry Schmidt, President, 400 E. Gregory Street, Mount Prospect, IL 60056 Tel. (847)259-1840 Fax (847)259-3888
E-mail: admissions@christianlifecollege.edu
Web site: www.christianlifecollege.edu

Christian Theological Seminary* (Christian Church (Disciples of Christ)), Dr. Edward L. Wheeler, President, 1000 W. 42nd St., Indianapolis, IN 46208-3301 Tel. (317)924-1331 Fax (317)923-1961
E-mail: wheeler@cts.edu
Web site: www.cts.edu

Christian Witness Theological Seminary* (Nondenominational), Lawrence Chan, President, 1040 Oak Grove Rd., Concord, CA 94518 Tel. (925)676-5002 Fax (925)676-5220
E-mail: admin@cwts.edu

Church Divinity School of the Pacific* (Episcopal Church), Donn F. Morgan, President, 2451 Ridge Rd., Berkeley, CA 94709-1217 Tel. (510)204-0700 Fax (510) 644-0712
E-mail: mollyanne@cdsp.edu
Web site: www.cdsp.edu

Church of God Theological Seminary* (Church of God (Cleveland, Tenn.)), Steven J. Land, President, P.O. Box 3330, Cleveland, TN 37320-3330 Tel. (423)478-1131 Fax (423)478-7711
E-mail: cogseminary@wingnet.com
Web site: www.cogts.edu

Cincinnati Bible Seminary* (Christian Churches and Churches of Christ), David M. Faust, President, 2700 Glenway Ave., Cincinnati, OH 45204-3200 Tel. (513)244-8120 Fax (513)244-8434
E-mail: info@cincybible.edu
Web site: www.cincybible.edu

Circleville Bible College (Churches of Christ in Christian Union), John Conley, President, P.O. Box 458, Circleville, OH 43113 Tel. (614)474-8896 Fax (614)477-7755
E-mail: cbc@biblecollege.edu
Web site: www.biblecollege.edu

Claremont School of Theology* (The United Methodist Church), Philip A. Amerson, President, 1325 N. College Ave., Claremont, CA 91711-3199 Tel. (909)447-2500 Fax (909)626-7062
E-mail: admission@cst.edu
Web site: www.cst.edu

Clear Creek Baptist Bible College (Southern Baptist Convention), President Bill Whittaker, President, 300 Clear Creek Rd., Pineville, KY 40977 Tel. (606)337-3196 Fax (606)337-2372
E-mail: ccbbc@ccbbc.edu
Web site: www.ccbbc.edu

Clinton Junior College† (African Methodist Episcopal Zion Church), Dr. Elaine Johnson Copeland, President, 1029 Crawford Road, Rock Hill, SC 29730 Tel. (803)327-7402 Fax (803)327-3261
E-mail: ecopeland@clintonjrcollege.org
Web site: www.clintonjrcollege.org

Colegio Biblico Pentecostal de Puerto Rico (Church of God (Cleveland, Tenn.)), Dr. Lidefonso Caraballo, President, P.O. Box 901, Saint Just, PR 00978 Tel. (787)761-0640 Fax (787)748-9228

Colgate Rochester Crozer Divinity School* (American Baptist Churches in the USA), G. Thomas Halbrooks, President, 1100 S. Goodman St., Rochester, NY 14620 Tel. (585)271-1320 Fax (585)271-8013
Web site: www.crcds.edu

Colorado Christian University (Nondenominational), Larry R. Donnithorne, President, 180 S. Garrison St., Lakewood, CO 80226 Tel. (303)202-0100 Fax (303)274-7560
Web site: www.ccu.edu

Columbia Biblical Seminary and School of Missions of Columbia International University* (Inter/Multidenominational), George W. Murray, President, P.O. Box 3122, Columbia, SC 29230-3122 Tel. (803)754-4100 Fax (803)786-4209
Web site: www.ciu.edu

Columbia Theological Seminary* (Presbyterian Church (U.S.A.)), Laura S. Mendenhall, President, 701 Columbia Dr., P.O. Box 520, Decatur, GA 30031 Tel. (404)378-8821 Fax (404)377-9696
Web site: www.CTSnet.edu

Concordia Seminary* (The Lutheran Church-Missouri Synod), John Franklin Johnson, President, 801 DeMun Ave., St. Louis, MO 63105 Tel. (314)505-7010 Fax (314)505-7002
E-mail: hollisterr@csl.edu
Web site: www.csl.edu

Concordia Theological Seminary* (The Lutheran Church-Missouri Synod), Dean O.

Wenthe, President, 6600 N. Clinton St., Ft. Wayne, IN 46825-4996 Tel. (260)452-2100 Fax (260)452-2121
E-mail: wenthedo@mail.ctsfw.edu
Web site: www.ctsfw.edu

Covenant Theological Seminary* (Presbyterian Church in America), Dr. Bryan Chapell, President, 12330 Conway Rd., St. Louis, MO 63141-8697 Tel. (314)434-4044 Fax (314)434-4819
E-mail: admissions@covenantseminary.edu
Web site: www.covenantseminary.edu

Cranmer Seminary (The Episcopal Orthodox Church; The Anglican Rite Synod in the Americas; The Orthodox Anglican Communion), The Most Rev. Scott E. McLaughlin, D.D., Ph.D., President, 901 English Rd., High Point, NC 27262 Tel. (336)885-6032 Fax (336)885-6021
E-mail: seminaryinfo@orthodoxanglican.net
Web site: orthodoxanglican.net, divinity school.org

Criswell Center for Biblical Studies (Southern Baptist Convention), 4010 Gaston Ave., Dallas, TX 75246 Tel. (214)821-5433 Fax (214)818-1320

Crossroads College (Christian Churches and Churches of Christ - Nondenominational), Dr. Bill J. Luce Jr., President, 920 Mayowood Rd. S.W., Rochester, MN 55902 Tel. (507)288-4563 Fax (507)288-9046
E-mail: academic@crossroadscollege.edu
Web site: www.crossroadscollege.edu

Crown College (The Christian and Missionary Alliance), Gary M. Benedict, President, 8700 College View Dr., St. Bonifacius, MN 55375-9001 Tel. (952)446-4100 Fax (952)446-4149
E-mail: crown@crown.edu
Web site: www.crown.edu

Cummins Theological Seminary (Reformed Episcopal Church), James C. West, President, 705 S. Main St., Summerville, SC 29483 Tel. (843)873-3451 Fax (843)875-6200
E-mail: jcw121@aol.com

Dallas Christian College (Christian Churches and Churches of Christ), Dr. John Derry, President, 2700 Christian Pkwy, Dallas, TX 75234 Tel. (972)241-3371 Fax (972)241-8021
E-mail: dcc@dallas.edu
Web site: www.dallas.edu

Dallas Theological Seminary* (Inter/Multidenominational), Dr. Mark L. Bailey, President, 3909 Swiss Ave., Dallas, TX 75204 Tel. (214)824-3094 Fax (214)841-3625
Web site: www.dts.edu

Denver Seminary* (Nondenominational), Craig Williford, President, Box 100000, Denver, CO 80250-0100 Tel. (303)761-2482 Fax (303) 761-8060
E-mail: info@denverseminary.edu
Web site: www.denverseminary.edu

Samuel DeWitt Proctor School of Theology of Virginia Union University* (American Baptist Churches in the USA, National Baptist Convention, Progressive National Baptist Convention), John W. Kinney, Dean, 1500 North Lombardy Street, Richmond, VA 23330 Tel. (804)257-5715 Fax (804)342-3911
Web site: www.vuu.edu

The Disciples Divinity House of the University of Chicago* (Christian Church (Disciples of Christ)), Dr. Kristine A. Culp, Dean, 1156 E. 57th St., Chicago, IL 60637-1536 Tel. (773)643-4411 Fax (773)643-4413
E-mail: ddh.uchicago.admin@attglobal.net
Web site: ddh.uchicago.edu

Dominican House of Studies* (The Roman Catholic Church), Dwight Reginald Whitt, O.P., President, 487 Michigan Ave. N.E., Washington, DC 20017-1585 Tel. (202)529-5300 Fax (202)636-1700
E-mail: assistant@dhs.edu
Web site: www.dhs.edu

Dominican School of Philosophy and Theology* (The Roman Catholic Church), Michael Sweeney, President, 2401 Ridge Rd., Berkeley, CA 94709 Tel. (510)849-2030 Fax (510)849-1372
Web site: www.dspt.edu

Dominican Study Center of the Caribbean* (Catholic Church), Rev. Fr. Dr. Félix Struik, O.P., Regent of the Center, Apartado Postal 1968, Bayamon, PR 00960-1968 Tel. (787) 787-1826 Fax (787)798-2712
E-mail: fstruik@cedocpr.org
Web site: www.cedocpr.org

Drew University Theological School* (The United Methodist Church), Maxine C. Beach, Vice President and Dean, 36 Madison Ave., Madison, NJ 07940-4010 Tel. (973)408-3258 Fax (973)408-3534
E-mail: elopezjr@drew.edu
Web site: www.drew.edu/theo

Duke University Divinity School* (The United Methodist Church), L. Gregory Jones, Dean, Box 90968, Durham, NC 27708-0968 Tel. (888)462-3853 Fax (919)660-3535
E-mail: admissions@div.duke.edu
Web site: www.divinity.duke.edu

Earlham School of Religion* (Interdenominational-Friends), Jay Wade Marshall, Dean, 228

College Ave., Richmond, IN 47374 Tel. (800) 432-1377 Fax (765)983-1688
E-mail: woodna@earlham.edu
Web site: www.esr.earlham.edu

Eastern Baptist Theological Seminary* (American Baptist Churches in the U.S.A.), Wallace C. Smith, President, 6 Lancaster Ave., Wynnewood, PA 19096 Tel. (610)896-5000 Fax (610)649-3834
Web site: www.ebts.edu

Eastern Mennonite Seminary of Eastern Mennonite University* (Mennonite Church), Loren Swartzendruber, President, 1200 Park Road, Harrisonburg, VA 22802 Tel. (540)432-4260 Fax (540)432-4598
E-mail: info@emu.edu
Web site: www.emu.edu/seminary

Ecumenical Theological Seminary* (Inter/Multidenominational), V. Bruce Rigdon, President, 2930 Woodward Ave., Detroit, MI 48201 Tel. (313)831-5200 Fax (313)831-1353
Web site: www.etseminary.org

Eden Theological Seminary* (United Church of Christ), David M. Greenhaw, President, 475 E. Lockwood Ave., St. Louis, MO 63119-3192 Tel. (314)961-3627 Fax (314)918-2626
Web site: www.eden.edu

Rabbi Isaac Elchanan Theological Seminary (Jewish), Dr. Norman Lamm, President, 2540 Amsterdam Ave., New York, NY 10033 Tel. (212)960-5344 Fax (212)960-0061
Web site: www.yu.edu/riets

Emmanuel School of Religion* (Christian Churches and Churches of Christ), C. Robert Wetzel, President, One Walker Dr., Johnson City, TN 37601-9438 Tel. (423)926-1186 Fax (423)926-6198
E-mail: wetzelc@esr.edu
Web site: www.esr.edu

Emmaus Bible College (Christian Brethren, also known as Plymouth Brethren), Kenneth Alan Daughters, President, 2570 Asbury Rd., Dubuque, IA 52001 Tel. (563)588-8000 Fax (563)588-1216
E-mail: info@emmaus.edu
Web site: www.emmaus.edu

Episcopal Divinity School* (Episcopal Church), The Rt. Rev. Steven Charleston, President and Dean, 99 Brattle St., Cambridge, MA 02138-3494 Tel. (617)868-3450 Fax (617)864-5385
E-mail: fphillips@episdivschool.org
Web site: www.episdivschool.edu

Episcopal Theological Seminary of the Southwest* (Episcopal Church), Titus L. Presler, Dean and President, P.O. Box 2247, Austin, TX 78768-2247 Tel. (512)472-4133 Fax (512)472-3098
E-mail: salexander@etss.edu
Web site: www.etss.edu

Erskine Theological Seminary* (Associate Reformed Presbyterian Church (General Synod)), R.J. Gore, Jr., Dean, P.O. Box 668, Due West, SC 29639 Tel. (864)379-8885 Fax (864)379-2171
E-mail: gore@erskine.edu
Web site: www.erskine.edu/seminary/gore/gore.htm

Eugene Bible College (Open Bible Standard Churches, Inc.), Robert L. Whitlow, President, 2155 Bailey Hill Rd., Eugene, OR 97405 Tel. (503)485-1780 Fax (503)343-5801

Evangelical School of Theology* (The Evangelical Congregational Church), Dennis P. Hollinger, President, 121 S. College St., Myerstown, PA 17067 Tel. (717)866-5775 Fax (717)866-4667
Web site: www.evangelical.edu

Evangelical Seminary of Puerto Rico* (Inter/Multidenominational), Sergio Ojeda-Carcamo, President, Ponce de Leon Avenue 776, San Juan, PR 00925 Tel. (787)763-6700 Fax (787)751-0847
Web site: www.seminarioevangelicopr.org

Faith Baptist Bible College and Theological Seminary (General Association of Regular Baptist Churches), Richard W. Houg, President, 1900 N.W. 4th St., Ankeny, IA 50021-2152 Tel. (515)964-0601 Fax (515) 964-1638
Web site: www.faith.edu

Faith Evangelical Lutheran Seminary (Conservative Lutheran Association), R. H. Redal, President, 3504 N. Pearl St., Tacoma, WA 98407 Tel. (253)752-2020 (888)777-7675 Fax (206)759-1790
E-mail: fsinfo@faithseminary.edu
Web site: www.faithseminary.edu

Florida Center for Theological Studies* (Inter/Multidenominational), Patrick H. O'Neill, President, 111 NE First St., Eighth Floor, Miami, FL 33132 Tel. (305)379-3777 Fax (305)379-1006
Web site: www.fcfts.org

Florida Christian College (Christian Churches and Churches of Christ), A. Wayne Lowen, President, 1011 Bill Beck Blvd., Kissimmee, FL 34744 Tel. (407)847-8966 Fax (407)847-3925
E-mail: fcc@fcc.edu
Web site: www.fcc.edu

George Fox Evangelical Seminary* (Inter/Multidenominational), Jules Glanzer, Dean, 12753 SW 68th Ave., Portland, OR 97223 Tel. (503)554-6150 Fax (503)554-6111
E-mail: seminary@georgefox.edu
Web site: www.seminary.georgefox.edu

Franciscan School of Theology* (Catholic Church), William M. Cieslak, President, 1712 Euclid Ave., Berkeley, CA 94709 Tel. (510) 848-5232 Fax (510)549-9466
E-mail: wcieslak@fst.edu
Web site: www.fst.edu

Free Will Baptist Bible College (National Association of Free Will Baptists), J. Matthew Pinson, President, 3606 West End Ave., Nashville, TN 37205 Tel. (615)383-1340 Fax (615)269-6028
E-mail: president@fwbbc.edu
Web site: www.fwbcc.edu

Fuller Theological Seminary* (Multidenominational), Richard J. Mouw, President, 135 N. Oakland Ave., Pasadena, CA 91182 Tel. (626)584-5200 Fax (626)795-8767
E-mail: lguernse@fuller.edu
Web site: www.fuller.edu

Garrett-Evangelical Theological Seminary* (The United Methodist Church), Ted A. Campbell, President, 2121 Sheridan Rd., Evanston, IL 60201-3298 Tel. (847)866-3900 Fax (847)866-3957
E-mail: seminary@garrett.edu
Web site: www.garrett.edu

The General Theological Seminary* (Episcopal Church), Ward B. Ewing, President, 175 Ninth Ave., New York, NY 10011-4977 Tel. (212) 243-5150 Fax (212) 647-0294
E-mail: ewing@gts.edu
Web site: www.gts.edu

God's Bible School and College (Nondenominational), Dr. Michael Avery, President, 1810 Young St., Cincinnati, OH 45202 Tel. (513) 721-7944 Fax (513)721-3971
E-mail: president@gbs.edu
Web site: www.gbs.edu

Golden Gate Baptist Theological Seminary* (Southern Baptist Convention), Jeff Iorg, President, 201 Seminary Dr., Mill Valley, CA 94941-3197 Tel. (415)380-1300 Fax (415) 380-1302
E-mail: seminary@ggbts.edu
Web site: www.ggbts.edu

Gonzaga University Department of Religious Studies* (The Roman Catholic Church), Fr. Robert Spitzer, S.J., President, 502 East Boone, Spokane, WA 99258 Tel. (509)328-6782 Fax (509)323-5718
Web site: www.gonzaga.edu

Gordon-Conwell Theological Seminary* (Inter/Multidenominational), Walter C. Kaiser, Jr., President, 130 Essex St., South Hamilton, MA 01982 Tel. (978)468-7111 Fax (978)468-6691
E-mail: info@gcts.edu
Web site: www.gordonconwell.edu

Grace Bible College (Grace Gospel Fellowship), Kenneth B. Kemper, President, P.O. Box 910, Grand Rapids, MI 49509 Tel. (616)538-2330 Fax (616)538-0599
E-mail: gbc@gbcol.edu
Web site: www.gbcol.edu

Grace Theological Seminary* (Fellowship of Grace Brethren Churches), Ronald E. Manahan, President, 200 Seminary Dr., Winona Lake, IN 46590-1294 Tel. (574)372-5100 Fax (574)372-5139
Web site: www.grace.edu

Grace University (Independent), Dr. James Eckman, President, 1311 South 9th St., Omaha, NE 68108 Tel. (402)449-2809 Fax (402)341-9587
E-mail: jofast@graceu.edu

Graduate Theological Union* (Interdenominational), James A. Donahue, President, 2400 Ridge Rd., Berkeley, CA 94709-1212 Tel. (510)649-2400 Fax (510)649-1417
E-mail: libref@gtu.edu
Web site: www.gtu.edu

Grand Rapids Theological Seminary of Cornerstone University* (Baptist Other), Douglas L. Fagerstrom, 1001 East Beltline NE, Grand Rapids, MI 49525-5897 Tel. (616) 222-1422 Fax (616)222-1502
Web site: www.cornerstone.edu

Great Lakes Christian College (Christian Churches and Churches of Christ), Larry Carter, President, 6211 W. Willow Hwy, Lansing, MI 48917 Tel. (517)321-0242 Fax (517)321-5902

Greenville College (Free Methodist Church of North America), President Robert E. Smith, President, 315 E. College Ave., P.O. Box 159, Greenville, IL 62246 Tel. (618)664-2800 Fax (618)664-1748
E-mail: rsmith@Greenville.edu
Web site: www.greenville.edu

Haggard School of Theology at Azusa Pacific University* (Interdenominational), Jon R. Wallace, President, 901 E. Alosta, P.O. Box 7000, Azusa, CA 91702-7000 Tel. (845)969-3434 Fax (845)969-7180
Web site: www.apu.edu/theology

Harding University Graduate School of Religion* (Churches of Christ), Evertt W. Huffard, Executive Director, 1000 Cherry Rd., Memphis, TN 38117-5499 Tel. (901)761-1352 Fax (901)761-1358
E-mail: dean@hugsr.edu
Web site: www.hugsr.edu

Hartford Seminary* (Interdenominational), Heidi Hadsell, President, 77 Sherman St., Hartford, CT 06105-2260 Tel. (860)509-9500 Fax (860)509-9509
E-mail: info@hartsem.edu
Web site: www.hartsem.edu

Harvard University Divinity School* (Inter/Multidenominational), Professor William A. Graham, Dean, 45 Francis Ave., Cambridge, MA 02138 Tel. (617)495-5761 Fax (617)495-8026
Web site: www.hds.harvard.edu

Hebrew Union College-Jewish Institute of Religion (Jewish), Rabbi David Ellenson, President, 3077 University Ave., Los Angeles, CA 90007 Tel. (213)749-3424 Fax (213)747-6128
Web site: www.huc.edu

Hebrew Union College-Jewish Institute of Religion, NY (Jewish), Sheldon Zimmerman, President, 1 W. 4th St., New York, NY 10012 Tel. (212)674-5300 Fax (212)533-0129

Heritage Bible College† (Pentecostal Free Will Baptist), Dr. Dwarka Ramphal, President, 1747 Bud Hawkins Road, P.O. Box 1628, Dunn, NC 28335 Tel. (910)892-3178 Fax (910) 892-1809
E-mail: generalinfo@heritagebiblecollege.org
Web site: www.heritagebiblecollege.org

Hillsdale Free Will Baptist College† (Free Will Baptist), Carl Cheshier, President, P.O. Box 7208, Moore, OK 73153-1208 Tel. (405)912-9000 Fax (405)912-9050
E-mail: hillsdale@hc.edu
Web site: www.hc.edu

Hobe Sound Bible College (Nondenominational), P. Daniel Stetler, President, P.O. Box 1065, Hobe Sound, FL 33475 Tel. (407)546-5534 Fax (407)545-1421

Holy Cross Greek Orthodox School of Theology* (Greek Orthodox Archdiocese of America), Rev. Nicholas C. Triantafilou, President, 50 Goddard Ave., Brookline, MA 02445-7495 Tel. (617)731-3500 Fax (617) 850-1460
E-mail: admissions@hchc.edu
Web site: www.hchc.edu

Holy Trinity Orthodox Seminary (Russian Orthodox Church Outside of Russia), Archbishop Laurus Skurla, President, P.O. Box 36, Jordanville, NY 13361 Tel. (315)858-0945 Fax (315)858-0945
E-mail: seminary@telenet.net

Hood Theological Seminary* (African Methodist Episcopal Zion Church), Albert J.D. Aymer, President, 800 W. Thomas St., Salisbury, NC 28144 Tel. (704)636-7611 Fax (704)636-7699
E-mail: pwells@hoodseminary.edu
Web site: www.hoodseminary.edu

Hope International University (Christian Churches and Churches of Christ), John Derry, President, 2500 E. Nutwood Ave., Fullerton, CA 92831-3104 Tel. (714)879-3901 Fax (714) 681-7451
E-mail: slcarter@hiu.edu
Web site: www.hiu.edu

Houston Graduate School of Theology* (Friends), Keith A. Jenkins, President, 1311 Holman, Ste. 200, Houston, TX 77004-3833 Tel. (713)942-9505 Fax (713)942-9506
E-mail: hgst@hgst.edu
Web site: www.hgst.edu

Howard University School of Divinity* (Nondenominational), Bertram Melbourne, Interim Dean, 1400 Shepherd St. N.E., Washington, DC 20017 Tel. (202)806-0500 Fax (202)806-0711
Web site: www.howard.edu/schooldivinity

Huntington College, Graduate School of Christian Ministries (Church of the United Brethren in Christ), G. Blair Dowden, President, 2303 College Ave., Huntington, IN 46750 Tel. (260)359-4039 Fax (260)359-4126
E-mail: gscm@huntington.edu
Web site: www.huntington.edu/gscm

Iliff School of Theology* (United Methodist Church), J. Philip Wogaman, President, 2201 S. University Blvd., Denver, CO 80210-4798 Tel. (303)744-1287 Fax (303)777-3387
Web site: www.iliff.edu

Immaculate Conception Seminary Seton Hall University* (Catholic Church), Rev. Msgr. Robert F. Coleman, J. C. D., Rector and Dean, 400 S. Orange Ave., South Orange, NJ 07079 Tel. (973)761-9575 Fax (973)761-9577
E-mail: theology@shu.edu
Web site: www.theology.shu.edu

Indiana Wesleyan University (The Wesleyan Church), James Barnes, President, 4201 S. Washington, Marion, IN 46953-4974 Tel. (765)674-6901 Fax (765)677-2465
E-mail: james.barnes@indwes.edu
Web site: www.indwes.edu

Institute for Creation Research Graduate School† (Nondenominational), Dr. John Morris, President, 10946 Woodside Avenue North, Santee, CA 92071 Tel. (619)448-0900 Fax (619)448-3469
E-mail: kcumming@icr.edu
Web site: www.icr.org

Inter-American Adventist Theological Seminary* (Seventh-day Adventist), Jaime Castrejon, President and Dean, P.O. Box 830518, Miami, FL 33283 Tel. (305)403-4700 Fax (305)403-4600
Web site: www.interamerica.org

Interdenominational Theological Center* (Interdenominational), Dr. Michael A. Battle, President, 700 Martin Luther King, Jr. Dr. S.W., Atlanta, GA 30314-4143 Tel. (404)527-7702 Fax (404)527-7770
E-mail: info@itc.edu
Web site: www.itc.edu

International Baptist College† (Baptist), Dr. Jerry Tetreau, President, 2150 East Southern Avenue, Tempe, AZ 85282-7504 Tel. (480)838-7070 Fax (480)505-3299
E-mail: ibc4u@juno.com
Web site: www.tri-citybaptist.org

International College & Graduate School† (Nondenominational), Dr. Rick Stinton, President, 20 Dowsett Avenue, Honolulu, HI 96817 Tel. (808)595-4247 Fax (808)595-4779
E-mail: icgs@hawaii.rr.com
Web site: www.icgshawaii.org

International Theological Seminary* (Nondenominational), Joseph Tong, President, 3215-3225 N. Tyler Ave., El Monte, CA 91731 Tel. (626)448-0023 Fax (626)350-6343
Web site: www.itsla.edu

William Jessup University (Christian Churches and Churches of Christ), Bryce L. Jessup, D.D., President, 333 Sunset Blvd., Rocklin, CA 95765 Tel. (916)577-2210
E-mail: bjessup@jessup.edu
Web site: www.jessup.edu

Jesuit School of Theology at Berkeley* (Catholic Church), Joseph P. Daoust, President, 1735 LeRoy Ave., Berkeley, CA 94709-1193 Tel. (510)549-5000 Fax (510)841-8536
Web site: www.jstb.edu

Jewish Theological Seminary of America (Jewish), Ismar Schorsch, President, 3080 Broadway, New York, NY 10027-4649 Tel. (212)678-8000 Fax (212)678-8947
E-mail: webmaster@jtsa.edu
Web site: www.jtsa.edu

Johnson Bible College (Christian Churches and Churches of Christ), David L. Eubanks, President, 7900 Johnson Dr., Knoxville, TN 37998 Tel. (865)573-4517 Fax (865)251-2336
E-mail: jbc@jbc.edu
Web site: www.jbc.edu

Kansas City College and Bible School (Church of God (Holiness)), Gayle Woods, President, 7401 Metcalf Ave., Overland Park, KS 66204 Tel. (913)722-0272 Fax (913)722-2135

Kenrick-Glennon Seminary* (Catholic Church), Ted L. Wojcicki, President-Rector, 5200 Glennon Dr., St. Louis, MO 63119-4399 Tel. (314)792-6100 Fax (314)792-6500
Web site: www.kenrick.edu

Kentucky Christian College (Christian Churches and Churches of Christ), Keith P. Keeran, President, 100 Academic Parkway, Grayson, KY 41143 Tel. (606)474-3000 Fax (606)474-3155
E-mail: knights@E-mail.kcc.edu
Web site: www.kcc.edu

Kentucky Mountain Bible College (Interdenominational), Philip Speas, President, Box 10, Vancleve, KY 41385 Tel. (606) 666-5000 Fax (606)666-7744

King's College and Seminary† (Nondenominational), Paul G. Chappell, Ph.D., Dean, 14800 Sherman Way, Van Nuys, CA 91405 Tel. (818)779-8040 Fax (818)779-8241
E-mail: admissions@kingsseminary.edu
Web site: www.kingsseminary.edu, www.kingscollege.edu

Knox Theological Seminary* (Presbyterian Church in America), R. Fowler White, Administrator and Dean of the Faculty, 5554 North Federal Highway, Fort Lauderdale, FL 33308 Tel. (954)771-0376 Fax (954)351-3343
E-mail: knox@crpc.org
Web site: www.knoxseminary.org

La Sierra University School of Religion* (Seventh-day Adventist Church), Lawrence T. Geraty, President, 4500 Riverwalk Parkway, Riverside, CA 92515-8247 Tel. (951)785-2000 Fax (951)785-2901
E-mail: pr@lasierra.edu
Web site: www.lasierra.edu

Lancaster Bible College (Nondenominational), Peter W. Teague, President, P.O. Box 83403, Lancaster, PA 17601 Tel. (717)560-8278 Fax (717)560-8260
E-mail: president@lbc.edu
Web site: www.lbc.edu

Lancaster Theological Seminary* (United Church of Christ), Rev. Dr. Riess W.

Potterveld, President, 555 W. James St., Lancaster, PA 17603-2897 Tel. (717)393-0654 Fax (717)393-4254
E-mail: seminary@lancasterseminary.edu
Web site: www.lancasterseminary.edu

The John Leland Center for Theological Studies* (Baptist), K. Randel Everett, President, 1301 N. Hartford St., Arlington, VA 22201 Tel. (703)812-4757 Fax (703)812-4764
Web site: www.johnlelandcenter.edu

Lexington Theological Seminary* (Christian Church (Disciples of Christ)), R. Robert Cueni, President, 631 S. Limestone St., Lexington, KY 40508 Tel. (859)252-0361 Fax (859)281-6042
Web site: www.lextheo.edu

Liberty Baptist Theological Seminary (Independent Baptist), A. Pierre Guillermin, President, 1971 University Blvd., Lynchburg, VA 24502-2269 Tel. (804)582-2000 Fax (804)582-2304

Liberty University† (Baptist), Dr. John Borek, President, 1971 University Boulevard, Lynchburg, VA 24502 Tel. (434)582-2000 Fax (434)582-2304
E-mail: admissions@liberty.edu
Web site: www.liberty.edu

Life Pacific College (International Church of the Foursquare Gospel), Dan R. Stewart, President, 1100 Covina Blvd., San Dimas, CA 91773 Tel. (909)599-5433 Fax (909)599-6690
E-mail: info@lifepacific.edu
Web site: www.lifepacific.edu

Lincoln Christian Seminary* (Christian Churches and Churches of Christ), Keith H. Ray, President, 100 Campus View Dr., Lincoln, IL 62656 Tel. (217)732-3168 ext.2354 Fax (217)732-1821
E-mail: ttanner@lccs.edu
Web site: www.lccs.edu

Lipscomb University College of Bible and Ministry* (Churches of Christ), Terry Briley, Dean, 3901 Granny White Pike, Nashville, TN 37204-3951 Tel. (615)279-6051 Fax (615)279-6052
Web site: www.lipscomb.edu

Logos Evangelical Seminary* (Evangelical Formosan Church), Felix Liu, President, 9358 Telstar Ave., El Monte, CA 91731 Tel. (626)571-5110 Fax (626)571-5119
E-mail: logos@les.edu
Web site: www.logos-seminary.edu

Logsdon School of Theology of Hardin-Simmons University* (Baptist General Convention of Texas), Thomas Brisco, Dean, P.O. Box 16235, Abilene, TX 79698-6235 Tel. (325)670-1287 Fax (325)670-1406
Web site: www.hsutx.edu/academics/logsdon

Louisville Presbyterian Theological Seminary* (Presbyterian Church (U.S.A.)), Dean K. Thompson, President, 1044 Alta Vista Rd., Louisville, KY 40205 Tel. (502)895-3411 Fax (502)895-1096
Web site: www.lpts.edu

Loyola Marymount University Department of Theological Studies* (Roman Catholic), Jeffrey S. Siker, Chair, One LMU Drive, Los Angeles, CA 90045-2659 Tel. (310)338-7670 Fax (310)338-1947
Web site: bellarmine.imu.edu/theology

Loyola University Chicago Institute of Pastoral Studies* (Catholic Church), Robert A. Ludwig, Director, 820 N. Michigan Ave., Chicago, IL 60611 Tel. (312)915-7400 Fax (312)915-7410
Web site: www.luc.edu/depts/ips

Luther Rice Bible College & Seminary (Baptist), Dr. James Flanagan, President, 3038 Evans Mill Road, Lithonia, GA 30038 Tel. (770)484-1204 Fax (770)484-1155
E-mail: lrs@lrs.edu
Web site: www.lrs.edu

Luther Seminary* (Evangelical Lutheran Church in America), David L. Tiede, President, 2481 Como Ave., St. Paul, MN 55108 Tel. (651)641-3456 Fax (651)641-3425
E-mail: admissions@luthersem.edu
Web site: www.luthersem.edu

Lutheran Bible Institute in California (Intersynodical Lutheran), Samuel Giesy, Acting President, 5321 University Dr., Ste. G, Irvine, CA 92612-2942 Tel. (949)262-9222, (800)261-5242 Fax (949)262-0283, (877)-381-4245
E-mail: LBICalifornia@earthlink.net
Web site: www.lbic.org

Lutheran Brethren Seminary (Church of the Lutheran Brethren of America), Joel T. Nordtvedt, Ph.D., President, 815 W. Vernon, Fergus Falls, MN 56537 Tel. (218)739-3375 Fax (218)739-1259
E-mail: lbs@clba.org
Web site: www.lbs.edu

Lutheran School of Theology at Chicago* (Evangelical Lutheran Church in America), James Kenneth Echols, President, 1100 E. 55th St., Chicago, IL 60615-5199 Tel. (773)256-0700 Fax (773)256-0782
E-mail: jechols@lstc.edu
Web site: www.lstc.edu

Lutheran Theological Seminary at Gettysburg* (Evangelical Lutheran Church in America), The Rev. Michael L. Cooper-White, President, 61 Seminary Ridge, Gettysburg, PA 17325-1795 Tel. (717)334-6286 Fax (717) 334-3469
E-mail: info@ltsg.edu
Web site: www.ltsg.edu

Lutheran Theological Seminary at Philadelphia* (Evangelical Lutheran Church in America), Philip D.W. Krey, President, 7301 Germantown Ave., Philadelphia, PA 19119 Tel. (215)248-4616 Fax (215)248-4577
E-mail: mtairy@ltsp.edu
Web site: www.ltsp.edu

Lutheran Theological Southern Seminary* (Evangelical Lutheran Church in America), H. Frederick Reisz, President, 4201 North Main St., Columbia, SC 29203 Tel. (803)786-5150 Fax (803)786-6499
E-mail: Freisz@ltss.edu
Web site: www.ltss.edu

Magnolia Bible College (Churches of Christ), Dr. Leslie Ferguson, Sr., President, P.O. Box 1109, Kosciusko, MS 39090 Tel. (662)289-2896 Fax (662)289-1850
E-mail: president@magnolia.edu
Web site: www.magnolia.edu

Manhattan Christian College (Christian Churches and Churches of Christ), Kenneth Cable, President, 1415 Anderson Ave., Manhattan, KS 66502 Tel. (785)539-3571 Fax (785)539-0832
Web site: www.mccks.edu

Maple Springs Baptist Bible College and Seminary† (Nondenominational), Dr. Larry W. Jordan, President, 4130 Belt Road, Capital Heights, MD 20743 Tel. (301)736-3631 Fax (301)735-6507
E-mail: larry.jordan@msbbcs.edu
Web site: www.msbbcs.edu

Mars Hill Graduate School† (Nondenominational), Dr. Dan Allander, President, 2525 - 220th Street, Bothell, WA 98021 Tel. (425) 415-0505 Fax (425)806-5599
E-mail: info@mhgs.edu
Web site: www.mhgs.net

James and Carolyn McAfee School of Theology of Mercer University* (Cooperative Baptist Fellowship), R. Alan Culpepper, Dean of the School of Theology, 3001 Mercer University Drive, Atlanta, GA 30341-4115 Tel. (678)547-6470 Fax (678) 547-6478
Web site: www.theology.mercer.edu

McCormick Theological Seminary* (Presbyterian Church (U.S.A.)), Cynthia M. Campbell, President, 5460 S. University Ave., Chicago, IL 60615-5108 Tel. (773)947-6300 Fax (773)288-2612
E-mail: ccampbell@mccormick.edu
Web site: www.mccormick.edu

Meadville Lombard Theological School* (Unitarian Universalist), Lee Barker, President, 5701 S. Woodlawn Ave., Chicago, IL 60637 Tel. (773)256-3000 Fax (773)753-1323
E-mail: LBarker@meadville.edu
Web site: www.meadville.edu

Memphis Theological Seminary* (Cumberland Presbyterian Church), Timothy P. Weber, Interim President, 168 E. Parkway S. at Union, Memphis, TN 38104-4395 Tel. (901)458-8232 Fax (901)452-4051
E-mail: lblakeburn@mtscampus.edu
Web site: www.mtscampus.edu

Mennonite Brethren Biblical Seminary* (General Conference of Mennonite Brethren Churches), Jim Holm, President, 4824 E. Butler Ave. at Chestnut Ave., Fresno, CA 93727-5097 Tel. (559)251-8628 Fax (559) 251-7212
E-mail: fresno@mbseminary.edu
Web site: www.mbseminary.edu

George Mercer Jr. Memorial School of Theology (Episcopal Church), President, 65 Fourth St., Garden City, NY 11530 Tel. (516)248-4800 Fax (516)248-4883

Messenger College† (Pentecostal Church of God), 300 E. 50th Street, Joplin, MO 64804 Tel. (417)624-7070 Fax (417)624-1689
E-mail: info@messengercollege.edu
Web site: www.messengercollege.edu

Methodist Theological School in Ohio* (United Methodist Church), President Norman E. Dewire, President, 3081 Columbus Pike, P.O. Box 8004, Delaware, OH 43015-8004 Tel. (740)363-1146 Fax (740)362-3135
E-mail: ndewire@mtso.edu
Web site: www.mtso.edu

Michigan Theological Seminary*† (Nondenominational), Bruce W. Fong, President, 41550 E. Ann Arbor Trail, Plymouth, MI 48170-4308 Tel. (734)207-9581 Fax (734) 207-9582
E-mail: admissions@mts.edu
Web site: www.mts.edu

Mid-America Christian University (Church of God - Anderson, Ind.), Dr. John D. Fozard, President, 3500 S.W. 119th St., Oklahoma City, OK 73170 Tel. (405)691-3800 Fax (405)692-3165
E-mail: info@macu.edu
Web site: www.macu.edu

Mid-America Reformed Seminary* (Inter/Multidenominational), Cornelius P. Venema,

President, 229 Seminary Drive, Dyer, IN 46311 Tel. (219)864-2400 Fax (219)864-2410
E-mail: mars@jorsm.com
Web site: www.midamerica.edu

Midwestern Baptist Theological Seminary* (Southern Baptist Convention), Dr. R. Philip Roberts, President, 5001 N. Oak Trafficway, Kansas City, MO 64118 Tel. (816)414-3700 Fax (816)414-3799
Web site: www.mbts.edu

Moody Bible Institute (Interdenominational), Joseph M. Stowell, President, 820 N. La Salle Blvd., Chicago, IL 60610 Tel. (312)329-4000 Fax (312)329-4109
Web site: www.moody.edu

Moravian Theological Seminary* (Moravian Church in America (Unitas Fratrum)), Ervin J. Rokke, President, 1200 Main St., Bethlehem, PA 18018 Tel. (610)861-1516 Fax (610)861-1569
E-mail: seminary@moravian.edu
Web site: www.moravianseminary.edu

Moreau Seminary (Congregation of Holy Cross) (The Roman Catholic Church), Rev. Wilson Miscamble, C.S.C., President, Moreau Seminary, Notre Dame, IN 46556 Tel. (574)631-7735 Fax (574)631-9233

Morehouse School of Religion (Interdenominational Baptist), William T. Perkins, President, 645 Beckwith St. S.W., Atlanta, GA 30314 Tel. (404)527-7777 Fax (404)681-1005

Mount Angel Seminary* (Catholic Church), Richard Paperini, President Rector, One Abbey Drive, St. Benedict, OR 97373 Tel. (503)845-3951 Fax (503)845-3126
Web site: www.mtangel.edu

Mt. St. Mary's Seminary* (Catholic Church), Very Rev. Kevin C. Rhoades, Rector, 16300 Old Emmitsburg Rd., Emmitsburg, MD 21727-7797 Tel. (301)447-5295 Fax (301) 447-5636
E-mail: rhoades@msmary.edu
Web site: www.msmary.edu

Mt. St. Mary's Seminary of the West (Catholic Church), Gerald R. Haemmerle, President, 6616 Beechmont Ave., Cincinnati, OH 45230 Tel. (513)231-2223 Fax (513)231-3254
E-mail: jhaemmer@mtsm.org
Web site: mtsm.org

Multnomah Biblical Seminary* (Multnomah Biblical Seminary), Dr. Daniel R. Lockwood, President, 8435 N.E. Glisan St., Portland, OR 97220 Tel. (503)255-0332 Fax (503)251-6701
Web site: www.multnomah.edu

Mundelein Seminary of the Univ. of St. Mary-of-the-Lake (The Roman Catholic Church), John Canary, Rector-President, 1000 E. Maple, Mundelein, IL 60060-1174 Tel. (847) 566-6401 Fax (847)566-7330
E-mail: syopusml@usml.edu
Web site: www.vocations.org

Nashotah House (Theological Seminary)* (Episcopal Church), Robert S. Munday, President and Dean, 2777 Mission Rd., Nashotah, WI 53058-9793 Tel. (262)646-6500 Fax (262)646-6504
E-mail: nashotah@nashotah.edu
Web site: www.nashotah.edu

Nazarene Bible College (Church of the Nazarene), Hiram Sanders, President, 1111 Academy Park Loop, Colorado Springs, CO 80910-3704 Tel. (719)884-5000 Fax (719) 884-5199
E-mail: info@nbc.edu
Web site: www.nbc.edu

Nazarene Theological Seminary* (Church of the Nazarene), Ron Benefiel, President, 1700 E. Meyer Blvd., Kansas City, MO 64131-1246 Tel. (816)333-6254 Fax (816)333-6271
E-mail: rbenefiel@nts.edu
Web site: www.nts.edu

Nebraska Christian College (Christian Churches and Churches of Christ), Richard D. Milliken, President, 1800 Syracuse Ave., Norfolk, NE 68701-2458 Tel. (402)379-5000 Fax (402)391-5100
E-mail: info@nechristian.edu
Web site: www.nechristian.edu

New Brunswick Theological Seminary* (Reformed Church in America), Norman J. Kansfield, President, 17 Seminary Pl., New Brunswick, NJ 08901-1196 Tel. (732)247-5241 Fax (732)249-5412
E-mail: njk@nbts.edu
Web site: www.nbts.edu

New Orleans Baptist Theological Seminary* (Southern Baptist Convention), Charles S. Kelley, President, 3939 Gentilly Blvd., New Orleans, LA 70126 Tel. (504)282-4455 Fax (504)816-8023
E-mail: nobts@nobts.edu
Web site: www.nobts.edu

New York Theological Seminary* (Inter/Multidenominational), Hillary Gaston Sr., President, 475 Riverside Drive, Ste. 500, New York, NY 10115 Tel. (212)870-1250 Fax (212) 870-1236
Web site: www.nyts.edu

North American Baptist Seminary* (North American Baptist Conference), G. Michael

Hagan, President, 1525 S. Grange Ave., Sioux Falls, SD 57105-1526 Tel. (605)336-6588 Fax (605)335-9090
E-mail: admissions@nabs.edu
Web site: www.nabs.edu

North Central Bible College (Assemblies of God), Gordon L. Anderson, President, 910 Elliot Ave. S., Minneapolis, MN 55404 Tel. (612)332-3491 Fax (612)343-4778

North Park Theological Seminary* (The Evangelical Covenant Church), John E. Phelan, President and Dean, 3225 W. Foster Ave., Chicago, IL 60625 Tel. (773)244-6214 Fax (773)244-6244
E-mail: jphelan@northpark.edu
Web site: www.northpark.edu

Northeastern Seminary at Roberts Wesleyan College* (Nondenominational), John A. Martin, President, 2265 Westside Dr., Rochester, NY 14624-1977 Tel. (585)594-6800 Fax (585) 594-6801
Web site: www.nes.edu

Northern Baptist Theological Seminary* (American Baptist Churches in the U.S.A.), Charles W. Moore, President, 660 E. Butterfield Rd., Lombard, IL 60148-5698 Tel. (630)620-2100 Fax (630)620-2194
E-mail: cwmoore@northern.seminary.edu
Web site: www.seminary.edu

Northwest Baptist Seminary† (Baptist), Dr. Mark Wagner, President, 4301 N. Stevens, Tacoma,, WA 98407 Tel. (253)759-6104 Fax (253)759-3299
E-mail: nbs@nbs.edu
Web site: www.nbs.edu

Northwest College (Assemblies of God), Don H. Argue, Ed.D., President, 5520 108th Ave. N.E., P.O. Box 579, Kirkland, WA 98083-0579 Tel. (425)822-8266 Fax (425)827-0148
E-mail: mail@ncag.edu
Web site: www.nwcollege.edu

Northwest Graduate School of the Ministry† (Nondenominational), Brad Smith, Interim President, 1013 Eighth Ave, Seattle, WA 98104 Tel. (206) 264-9100 Fax (206)624-8828
E-mail: nwgs@nwgs.edu
Web site: www.nwgs.edu

Notre Dame Seminary* (Catholic Church), Patrick J. Williams, President and Rector, 2901 S. Carrollton Ave., New Orleans, LA 70118-4391 Tel. (504)866-7426 Fax (504) 866-3119
Web site: www.nds.edu

Oak Hills Christian College (Interdenominational), Dr. Daniel Clausen, President, 1600 Oak Hills Rd. S.W., Bemidji, MN 56601 Tel. (218)751-8670 Fax (218)751-8825
E-mail: dclausen@aokhills.edu
Web site: www.aokhills.edu

Oblate School of Theology* (Catholic Church), Warren Brown, President, 285 Oblate Dr., San Antonio, TX 78216-6693 Tel. (210)341-1366 Fax (210)341-4519
E-mail: oblate@connecti.com
Web site: www.ost.edu

Ozark Christian College (Christian Churches and Churches of Christ), President Dr. Kenneth D. Idleman, President, 1111 N. Main St., Joplin, MO 64801 Tel. (417)624-2518 Fax (417)624-0090
E-mail: pres@occ.edu
Web site: www.occ.edu

Pacific Lutheran Theological Seminary* (Evangelical Lutheran Church in America), Ted Peters, President, 2770 Marin Ave., Berkeley, CA 94708-1597 Tel. (510)524-5264 Fax (510)524-2408
E-mail: president@plts.edu
Web site: www.plts.edu

Pacific School of Religion* (Inter/Multidenominational), William McKinney, President, 1798 Scenic Ave., Berkeley, CA 94709 Tel. (510)848-0528 Fax (510)845-8948
E-mail: comm@psr.edu
Web site: www.psr.edu

Payne Theological Seminary* (African Methodist Episcopal Church), Leah Gaskin, Ed.D., President, P.O. Box 474, 1230 Wilberforce-Clifton Rd., Wilberforce, OH 45384-0474 Tel. (937)376-2946 Fax (937) 376-3330
E-mail: LFitchue@payne.edu
Web site: www.payne.edu

Pepperdine University (Churches of Christ), Dr. Randall Chesnutt, Chair of Religion Division, 24255 Pacific Coast Highway, Malibu, CA 90263 Tel. (310)506-4352 Fax (310)317-7271
E-mail: randall.chesnutt@pepperdine.edu
Web site: seaver.pepperdine.edu/religion

Perkins School of Theology (Southern Methodist University)* (The United Methodist Church), William B. Lawrence, Dean, P.O. Box 750133, Dallas, TX 75275-0133 Tel. (214)768-2293 Fax (214)768-4245
E-mail: theology@smu.edu
Web site: www.smu.edu/theology

Philadelphia Biblical University (Nondenominational), W. Sherrill Babb, President, 200 Manor Ave., Langhorne, PA 19047-2990 Tel. (215)752-5800 Fax (215)702-4341
E-mail: president@pbu.edu
Web site: www.pbu.edu

Phillips Theological Seminary* (Christian Church (Disciples of Christ)), William

Tabbernee, President, 901 North Mingo Road, Tulsa, OK 74116 Tel. (918)610-8303 Fax (918) 610-8404
Web site: www.ptstulsa.edu

Phoenix Seminary* (Nondenominational), Darryl DelHousaye, President, 13402 N. Scottsdale Road, Ste. B-185, Scottsdale, AZ 85254 Tel. (480)443-1020 Fax (480)443-1120
Web site: www.phoenixseminary.edu

Piedmont Baptist College† (Independent Baptist), Charles W. Petitt, President, 716 Franklin St., Winston-Salem, NC 27101 Tel. (336)725-8344 Fax (336)725-5522
E-mail: admissions@pbc.edu
Web site: www.pbc.edu

Pittsburgh Theological Seminary* (Presbyterian Church (U.S.A.)), Carnegie Samuel Calian, President, 616 N. Highland Ave., Pittsburgh, PA 15206 Tel. (412)362-5610 Fax (412)363-3260
E-mail: calian@pts.edu
Web site: www.pts.edu

Pontifical College Josephinum* (Catholic Church), Msgr. Paul J. Langsfeld, Rector and President, 7625 N. High St., Columbus, OH 43235 Tel. (614)885-5585 Fax (614)885-2307
Web site: www.pcj.edu

Pope John XXIII National Seminary (Catholic Church), Francis D. Kelly, President, 558 South Ave., Weston, MA 02193 Tel. (617)899-5500 Fax (617)899-9057

Practical Bible College (Independent Baptist), Dale E. Linebaugh, President, Box 601, Bible School Park, NY 13737 Tel. (607)729-1581 Fax (607)729-2962
E-mail: pbc@lakenet.org
Web site: www.lakenet.org/~pbc

Princeton Theological Seminary* (Presbyterian Church (U.S.A.)), Iain R. Torrance, President, P.O. Box 821, Princeton, NJ 08542-0803 Tel. (609)921-8300 Fax (609)924-2973
E-mail: comm-pub@ptsem.edu
Web site: www.ptsem.edu

Protestant Episcopal Theological Seminary in Virginia* (Episcopal Church), Martha J. Horne, Dean and President, 3737 Seminary Rd., Alexandria, VA 22304 Tel. (703)370-6600 Fax (703)370-6234
E-mail: mhorne@vts.edu
Web site: www.vts.edu

Puget Sound Christian College (Christian Churches and Churches of Christ), Randy J. Bridges, Ph.D., President, P.O. Box 13108, Everett, WA 98206-3108 Tel. (425)257-3090 Fax (425)258-1488
E-mail: president@pscc.edu
Web site: www.pscc.edu

Reconstructionist Rabbinical College (Jewish), Dan Ehrenkrantz, President, Church Rd. and Greenwood Ave., Wyncote, PA 19095 Tel. (215)576-0800 Fax (215)576-6143
E-mail: rrcinfo@rrc.edu

Reformed Bible College (Interdenominational), Nicholas V. Kroeze, President, 3333 East Beltline N.E., Grand Rapids, MI 49525-9749 Tel. (616)222-3000 Fax (616)988-3608
E-mail: administration@reformed.edu
Web site: www.reformed.edu

Reformed Episcopal Seminary* (Reformed Episcopal Church), Wayne A. Headman, President, 826 Second Ave., Blue Bell, PA 19422-1257 Tel. (610)292-9852 Fax (610) 292-9853
E-mail: reseminary.edu
Web site: www.reseminary.edu

Reformed Presbyterian Theological Seminary* (Reformed Presbyterian Church of North America), Jerry F. O'Neill, President, 7418 Penn Ave., Pittsburgh, PA 15208-2594 Tel. (412)731-8690 Fax (412)731-4834
E-mail: rpseminary@aol.com
Web site: www.rpts.edu

Reformed Theological Seminary* (Inter/Multidenominational), Dr. Robert C. Cannada, Jr., President, 5422 Clinton Blvd., Jackson, MS 39209-3099 Tel. (601)923-1600 Fax (601) 923-1654
E-mail: rts.orlando@rts.edu
Web site: www.rts.edu

Regent University School of Divinity* (Nondenominational/Evangelical), Vinson Synan, Dean, 1000 Regent University Dr, Virginia Beach, VA 23464-9870 Tel. Fax (757)226-4597
E-mail: vinssyn@regent.edu
Web site: www.regent.edu/acad/schdiv

Roanoke Bible College (Christian Churches and Churches of Christ), William A. Griffin, President, 715 N. Poindexter St, Elizabeth City, NC 27909-4054 Tel. (252)334-2070 Fax (252)334-2071
E-mail: wag@roanokebible.edu
Web site: www.roanokebible.edu

Oral Roberts University School of Theology* (Inter/Multidenominational), Dr. Thomson K. Mathew, Dean, 7777 S. Lewis Ave., Tulsa, OK 74171 Tel. (918)495-7016 Fax (918)495-6259
E-mail: jcope@oru.edu
Web site: www.oru.edu

Sacred Heart Major Seminary* (The Roman Catholic Church), Steven C. Boguslawski, President, 2701 Chicago Blvd., Detroit, MI 48206 Tel. (313)883-8501 Fax (313)868-6440
Web site: www.shmsonline.org

Sacred Heart School of Theology* (Catholic Church), Thomas P. Cassidy, S.C.J., President-Rector, P.O. Box 429, Hales Corners, WI 53130-0429 Tel. (414)425-8300 Fax (414) 529-6999
E-mail: rector@shst.edu
Web site: www.shst.edu

St. Bernard's School of Theology and Ministry* (Catholic Church), Patricia A. Schoelles, President, 120 French Road, Rochester, NY 14618 Tel. (585)271-3657 Fax (585)271-2045
E-mail: pschoelles@sbi.edu
Web site: www.stbernards.edu

St. Charles Borromeo Seminary* (Catholic Church), Rev. Joseph G. Prior, M.Div., M.A., S.S.L., S.T.D., President and Rector, 100 East Wynnewood Rd., Wynnewood, PA 19096-3001 Tel. (610)667-3394 Fax (610)667-0452
Web site: www.scs.edu

St. Francis Seminary* (Catholic Church), Very Rev. Michael G. Witczak, Rector, 3257 S. Lake Dr., St. Francis, WI 53235 Tel. (414)747-6400 Fax (414)747-6442
E-mail: mwitczak@sfs.edu
Web site: www.sfs.edu

St. John Vianney Theological Seminary* (Roman Catholic Church), Michael Glenn, Rector, 1300 S. Steele St., Denver, CO 80210-2599 Tel. (303)282-3427 Fax (303)282-3453

St. John's Seminary* (Catholic Church), John Farren, Rector and President, 127 Lake St., Brighton, MA 02135 Tel. (617)254-2610 Fax (617)787-2336
Web site: www.sjs.edu

St. John's Seminary* (Catholic Church), Helmut Hefner, Rector and President, 5012 Seminary Rd., Camarillo, CA 93012-2598 Tel. (805)482-2755 Fax (805)482-0637
Web site: www.stjohnsem.edu

St. John's University, School of Theology-Seminary* (Catholic Church), William J. Cahoy, Dean, Box 7288, Collegeville, MN 56321-7288 Tel. (320)363-2622 Fax (320) 363-3145
Web site: www.csbsju.edu/sot

St. Joseph's Seminary* (Catholic Church), Peter G. Finn, President, 201 Seminary Ave., Yonkers, NY 10704 Tel. (914)968-6200 Fax (914)968-7912
Web site: www.ny-archdiocese.org/pastoral/seminary.cfm

St. Louis Christian College (Christian Churches and Churches of Christ), Kenneth L. Beck, President, 1360 Grandview Dr., Florissant, MO 63033 Tel. (314)837-6777 Fax (314)837-8291
E-mail: questions@slcc4ministry.edu
Web site: www.slcc4ministry.edu

St. Mary Seminary and Graduate School of Theology* (Catholic Church), Thomas W. Tifft, President, 28700 Euclid Ave., Wickliffe, OH 44092-2585 Tel. (440)943-7600 Fax (440)943-7577
Web site: www.stmarysem.edu

St. Mary's Seminary (The Roman Catholic Church), Very Rev. Brendan Cahill, Rector, 9845 Memorial Dr., Houston, TX 77024-3498 Tel. (713)686-4345 Fax (713)681-7550

St. Mary's Seminary and University* (The Roman Catholic Church), Robert F. Leavitt, President and Rector, 5400 Roland Ave., Baltimore, MD 21210 Tel. (410)864-4000 Fax (410)864-4278
Web site: www.stmarys.edu

Saint Meinrad School of Theology* (Catholic Church), Mark O'Keefe, President, 200 Hill Drive, St. Meinrad, IN 47577 Tel. (812)357-6611 Fax (812)357-6964
E-mail: theology@saintmeinrad.edu
Web site: www.saintmeinrad.edu

St. Patrick's Seminary and University* (Catholic Church), Gerald L. Brown, President and Rector, 320 Middlefield Rd., Menlo Park, CA 94025 Tel. (650)325-5621 Fax (650)322-0997
Web site: www.stpatricksseminary.org

Saint Paul School of Theology* (The United Methodist Church), Myron F. McCoy, President, 5123 Truman Rd., Kansas City, MO 64127-2499 Tel. (816)483-9600 Fax (816) 483-9605
E-mail: spst@spst.edu
Web site: www.spst.edu

St. Paul Seminary School of Divinity of the University of St. Thomas* (Catholic Church), Frederick F. Campbell, Vice-President and Rector, 2260 Summit Ave., St. Paul, MN 55105 Tel. (651)962-5050 Fax (651)962-5790
Web site: www.stthomas.edu/spssod

St. Petersburg Theological Seminary† (Inter/Multidenominational), Dr. Myron P. Miller, President, 10830 Navajo Dr., St. Petersburg, FL 33708 Tel. (727)399-0276 Fax (727)399-1324
E-mail: sptsoffice@aol.com
Web site: www.sptseminary.edu

St. Tikhon's Orthodox Theological Seminary* (The Orthodox Church in America), Metropolitan Herman (Swaiko), President, Very Rev. Michael G. Dahulich, Ph.D., Dean, President, Box 130, St. Tikhon's Rd., South Canaan, PA 18459-0121 Tel. (570)937-4411 Fax (570)937-3100
E-mail: info@stots.edu (General Information), fr.michael@stots.edu (Dean's Office), admissions@stots.edu (Admissions), acadean@stots. edu (Academic Dean)
Web site: www.stots.edu

St. Vincent de Paul Regional Seminary* (Roman Catholic), Stephen C. Bosso, Rector and President, 10701 South Military Trail, Boynton Beach, FL 33436-4899 Tel. (561)732-4424 Fax (561)737-2205
E-mail: cduque@svdp.edu
Web site: www.svdp.edu

St. Vincent Seminary* (Catholic Church), Very Rev. Kurt Belsole, O.S.B., Rector, 300 Fraser Purchase Rd., Latrobe, PA 15650-2690 Tel. (724)537-4592 Fax (724)532-5052
E-mail: kurt.belsole@E-mail.stvincent.edu
Web site: benedictine.stvincent.edu/seminary

St. Vladimir's Orthodox Theological Seminary* (The Orthodox Church in America), John H. Erickson, Dean, 575 Scarsdale Rd., Crestwood, NY 10707-1699 Tel. (914)961-8313 Fax (914)961-4507
E-mail: info@svots.edu
Web site: www.svots.edu

SS. Cyril and Methodius Seminary* (Catholic Church), Very Rev. Jaroslaw Zaniewski, Rector, 3535 Indian Trail, Orchard Lake, MI 48324-1623 Tel. (248)683-0310 Fax (248)738-6735
E-mail: sscms.dean@comcast.net
Web site: www.orchardlakeseminary.org

San Francisco Theological Seminary* (Presbyterian Church (U.S.A.)), Rev. Dr. Philip W. Butin, President, 105 Seminary Rd., San Anselmo, CA 94960 Tel. (415)451-2800 Fax (415)451-2811
E-mail: sftsinfo@sfts.edu
Web site: www.sfts.edu

Savonarola Theological Seminary (Polish National Catholic Church of America), Prime Bishop Robert M. Nemkovich, Rector, 1031 Cedar Ave., Scranton, PA 18505 Tel. (570)343-0100
E-mail: pncccenter@adelphia.net

Seabury-Western Theological Seminary* (Episcopal Church), James B. Lemler, Dean and President, 2122 Sheridan Rd., Evanston, IL 60201-2976 Tel. (847)328-9300 Fax (847)328-9624
E-mail: seabury@seabury.edu
Web site: www.seabury.edu

Seattle University School of Theology and Ministry* (Catholic Church and 10 Mainline Protestant Denominations and Associations), Rev. Patrick Howell, S.J., Dean, 901 12th Avenue, P.O. Box 222000, Seattle, WA 98122-1090 Tel. (206)296-5330 Fax (206)296-5329
E-mail: millerdi@seattleu.edu
Web site: www.seattleu.edu/theomin

Seminario Evangelico de Puerto Rico (Interdenominational), Samuel Pagán, President, 776 Ponce de León Ave., San Juan, PR 00925 Tel. (787)763-6700 Fax (787)751-0847
E-mail: drspagan@icepr.com or jvaldes@tld.net
Web site: netministries.org/see/charmin/CM01399

Seminary of the Immaculate Conception* (Catholic Church), Msgr. Francis J. Schneider, J.C.D., President, 440 West Neck Rd., Huntington, NY 11743 Tel. (631)423-0483 Fax (631)423-2346
Web site: www.icseminary.edu

Seventh-day Adventist Theological Seminary of Andrews University* (Seventh-Day Adventist Church), John K. McVay, Dean, Andrews University, Berrien Springs, MI 49104-1500 Tel. (269)471-3537 Fax (269)471-6202
E-mail: seminary@andrews.edu
Web site: www.andrews.edu/sem

Seventh Day Baptist School of Ministry (Seventh Day Baptist General Conference), Gordon P. Lawton, Dean of School of Ministry, 3120 Kennedy Rd., P.O. Box 1678, Janesville, WI 53547 Tel. (608)752-5055 Fax (608)752-7711
E-mail: dean@sdbministry.org
Web site: sdbministry.org

Sewanee: The University of the South School of Theology* (Episcopal Church), The Rev. Dr. Willian S. Stafford, Dean, 335 Tennessee Ave., Sewanee, TN 37383-0001 Tel. (800)722-1974 Fax (931)598-1412
E-mail: theology@sewanee.edu
Web site: www.sewanee.edu

Shasta Bible College and Graduate School† (Baptist), Dr. David Nicholas, President, 2951

Goodwater Avenue, Redding, CA 96002 Tel. (530)221-4275 Fax (530)221-6929
E-mail: sbcadm@shasta.edu
Web site: www.shasta.edu

Shaw University Divinity School* (General Baptist State Convention, N.C.), James T. Roberson, Jr., President, P.O. Box 2090, Raleigh, NC 27602 Tel. (919)546-8569 Fax (919)546-8571
Web site: www.shawuniversity.edu

Simpson College (The Christian and Missionary Alliance), James M. Grant, President, 2211 College View Dr., Redding, CA 96003 Tel. (916)224-5600 Fax (916)224-5608

Southeastern Baptist College (Baptist Missionary Association of America), Jentry W. Bond, President, 4229 Highway 15N, Laurel, MS 39440 Tel. (601)426-6346 Fax (601)426-6346

Southeastern Baptist Theological Seminary* (Southern Baptist Convention), Daniel L. Akin, President, P.O. Box 1889, Wake Forest, NC 27588-1889 Tel. (919)556-3101 Fax (919) 556-8550
Web site: www.sebts.edu

Southeastern Bible College (Interdenominational), Dr. Don Hawkins, President, 2545 Valleyvale Rd., Birmingham, AL 35244 Tel. (205)408-7073 or (205)970-9200 Fax (205) 970-9207
E-mail: 102064.406@compuserve.com
Web site: www.sebc.edu

Southeastern College of the Assemblies of God (Assemblies of God), Mark Rutland, President, 1000 Longfellow Blvd., Lakeland, FL 33801 Tel. (863)667-5000 Fax (863)667-5200
E-mail: info@secollege.edu
Web site: www.secollege.edu

Southern Baptist Theological Seminary* (Southern Baptist Convention), R. Albert Mohler, Jr., President, 2825 Lexington Rd., Louisville, KY 40280- Tel. (502)897-4011 Fax (502)899-1770
E-mail: communications@sbts.edu
Web site: www.sbts.edu

Southern California Bible College & Seminary† (Southern Baptist Convention), Dr. Gary F. Coombs, President, 2075 East Madison Avenue, El Cajon, CA 92019 Tel. (619)442-9841 Fax (619)442-4510
E-mail: info@scbcs.edu
Web site: www.scbcs.edu

Southern Evangelical Seminary† (Interdenominational), Dr. Norman Geisler, President, 3000 Tilley Morris Road, Matthews, NC 28104 Tel. (704)847-5600 Fax (704)845-1747
E-mail: ses@ses.edu
Web site: www.ses.edu

Southern Methodist College† (Independent Denomination), Dr. John P. Hucks, Acting President, 541 Broughton Street, P.O. Box 1027, Orangeburg, SC 29116-1027 Tel. (803)534-7826 Fax (803)534-7827
E-mail: smced@smcollege.edu
Web site: www.southernmethodistcollege.org

Southern Wesleyan University (The Wesleyan Church), President David J. Spittal, President, 907 Wesleyan Dr., P.O. Box 1020, Central, SC 29630-1020 Tel. (864)644-5000 Fax (864) 644-5900
E-mail: dspittal@swu.edu
Web site: www.swu.edu

Southwestern Assemblies of God University (Assemblies of God), Delmer R. Guynes, President, 1200 Sycamore St., Waxahachie, TX 75165 Tel. (972)937-4010 Fax (972)923-0488

Southwestern Baptist Theological Seminary* (Southern Baptist Convention), Paige Patterson, President, 2001 W. Seminary Dr., Fort Worth, TX 76115 Tel. (817)923-1921 Fax (817)923-0610
Web site: www.swbts.edu

Southwestern College (Conservative Baptist Association of America), Brent D. Garrison, President, 2625 E. Cactus Rd., Phoenix, AZ 85032 Tel. (602)992-6101 Fax (602)404-2159

Starr King School for the Ministry* (Unitarian Universalist Association), Rebecca Parker, President, 2441 LeConte Ave., Berkeley, CA 94709 Tel. (510)845-6232 Fax (510)845-6273
Web site: www.sksm.edu

Swedenborgian House of Studies at the Pacific School of Religion (The Swedenborgian Church), Dr. James F. Lawrence, Dean, 1798 Scenic Ave., Berkeley, CA 94709 Tel. (510)849-8228 Fax (510)849-8296
E-mail: jlawrence@shs.psr.edu

Talbot School of Theology of Biola University* (Inter/Multidenominational), Clyde Cook, President, 13800 Biola Ave., La Mirada, CA 90639-0001 Tel. (562)903-4816 Fax (562) 903-4759
E-mail: talbot.receptionist@biola.edu
Web site: www.talbot.edu

Temple Baptist Seminary† (Interdenominational), Dr. Barkev Trachian, President, 1815

Union Ave., Chattanooga, TN 37404 Tel. (423)493-4221 Fax (423)493-4471
E-mail: tbsinfo@templebaptistseminary.edu
Web site: www.templebaptistseminary.edu

Tennessee Temple University†, 1815 Union Avenue, Chattanooga, TN 37404 Tel. (423) 493-4202 Fax (423)493-4114
E-mail: ttuinfo@tntemple.edu
Web site: www.tntemple.edu

Theological School of the Protestant Reformed Churches (Protestant Reformed Churches in America), Robert D. Decker, President, 4949 Ivanrest Ave., Grandville, MI 49418 Tel. (616)531-1490 Fax (616)531-3033
E-mail: doezema@prca.org
Web site: www.prca.org/seminary.html

Toccoa Falls College (The Christian and Missionary Alliance), Dr. W. Wayne Gardner, President, P.O. Box 800777, Toccoa Falls, GA 30598 Tel. (706)886-6831 Fax (706)282-6005
E-mail: president@tfc.edu
Web site: www.tfc.edu

Trevecca Nazarene University (Church of the Nazarene), Millard Reed, President, 333 Murfreesboro Rd., Nashville, TN 37210-2877 Tel. (615)248-1200 Fax (615)248-7728
Web site: www.trevecca.edu

Trinity Baptist College† (Baptist), Tom Messer, Pastor, 800 Hammond Boulevard, Jacksonville, FL 32221 Tel. (904)596-2400 Fax (904)596-2531
E-mail: trinity@tbc.edu
Web site: www.tbc.edu

Trinity Bible College (Assemblies of God), Dennis D. Niles, President, 50 S. 6th Ave., Ellendale, ND 58436 Tel. (701)349-3621 Fax (701)349-5443

Trinity College of Florida (Nondenominational), Bill W. Lanpher, President, 2430 Welbilt Blvd., New Port Richey, FL 34655-4401 Tel. (727)376-6911 Fax (727)376-0781
E-mail: admissions@trinitycollege.edu
Web site: www.trinitycollege.edu

Trinity Episcopal School for Ministry* (Episcopal Church), The Very Rev. Dr. Paul F.M. Zahl, Dean and President, 311 Eleventh St., Ambridge, PA 15003 Tel. (724)266-3838 Fax (724)266-4617
E-mail: tesm@tesm.edu
Web site: www.tesm.edu

Trinity Evangelical Divinity School of Trinity International University* (Evangelical Free Church of America), Gregory L. Waybright, President, 2065 Half Day Rd., Deerfield, IL 60015 Tel. (847) 945-8800 Fax (847)317-8141
Web site: www.tiu.edu/divinity

Trinity Lutheran College (Interdenominational-Lutheran), John M. Stamm, President, 4221-228th Ave., S.E., Issaquah, WA 98029-9299 Tel. (425)392-0400 Fax (425)392-0404
E-mail: info@tlc.edu
Web site: www.tlc.edu

Trinity Lutheran Seminary* (Evangelical Lutheran Church in America), Mark R. Ramseth, President, 2199 East Main Street, Columbus, OH 43209-2334 Tel. (614)235-4136 Fax (614)238-0263
Web site: www.TrinityLutheranSeminary.edu

George W. Truett Theological Seminary of Baylor University* (Baptist General Convention of Texas), Paul W. Powell, Dean, P.O. Box 97126, Waco, TX 76798-7126 Tel. (254)710-3755 Fax (254)710-3753
Web site: www.baylor.edu/seminary

Turner School Of Theology of Southern Christian University* (Churches of Christ), President Dr. Rex A. Turner, Jr., President, 1200 Taylor Rd., Montgomery, AL 36117-3553 Tel. (334)387-3877 Fax (334)387-3878
E-mail: southernchristian@southernchristian.edu
Web site: www.southernchristian.edu

William Tyndale College (Interdenominational), Robert E. Hagerty, President, 35700 W. Twelve Mile Rd., Farmington Hills, MI 48331 Tel. (248)553-7200 Fax (248)553-5963
Web site: www.williamtyndale.edu

Union Theological Seminary* (Inter/Multidenominational), Joseph C. Hough Jr., President, 3041 Broadway at 121st Street, New York, NY 10027-0003 Tel. (212)662-7100 Fax (212)280-1440
Web site: www.uts.columbia.edu

Union Theological Seminary and Presbyterian School of Christian Education* (Presbyterian Church (U.S.A.)), Louis B. Weeks, President, 3401 Brook Rd., Richmond, VA 23227 Tel. (800)229-2990 Fax (804)355-3919
E-mail: gbirch@union-psce.edu
Web site: www.union-psce.edu

United Theological Seminary* (The United Methodist Church), Rev. Dr. G. Edwin Zeiders, President and Chief Exec. Officer, 1810 Harvard Blvd., Dayton, OH 45406-4599 Tel. (937)278-5817 Fax (937)278-1218
E-mail: utscom@united.edu
Web site: www.united.edu

United Theological Seminary of the Twin Cities* (United Church of Christ), Wilson

Yates, President, 3000 Fifth St. N.W., New Brighton, MN 55112 Tel. (651)633-4311 Fax (651)633-4315
E-mail: general@unitedseminary-mn.org
Web site: www.unitedseminary-mn.org

University of Chicago Divinity School* (Interdenominational), Richard Rosengarten, Dean, 1025 E. 58th St., Chicago, IL 60637 Tel. (773)702-8221 Fax (773)702-6048
Web site: www.uchicago.edu/divinity

University of Dubuque Theological Seminary* (Presbyterian Church (U.S.A.)), Jeffrey Bullock, President, 2000 University Ave., Dubuque, IA 52001-5099 Tel. (563)589-3122 Fax (563)589-3110
E-mail: udtsadms@dbq.edu
Web site: www.UDTSeminary.net

University of Notre Dame Department of Theology* (The Roman Catholic Church), John C. Cavadini, Department Chair, 130 Malloy Hall, Notre Dame, IN 46556-5639 Tel. (574)631-6662 Fax (574)631-4291
Web site: www.nd.edu/~theo

University of St. Mary of the Lake Mundelein Seminary* (Roman Catholic), John F. Canary, Rector and President, 1000 E. Maple Avenue, Mundelein, IL 60060 Tel. (847)566-6401 Fax (847)566-7330
Web site: www.usml.edu

University of St. Thomas School of Theology* (The Roman Catholic Church), Sandra Magie, President, 9845 Memorial Dr., Houston, TX 77024 Tel. (713)686-4345 Fax (713)683-8673
Web site: www.stthom.edu

Urshan Graduate School of Theology* (United Pentecostal Church International), David Bernard, President, P.O. Box 40, Hazelwood, MO 63042 Tel. (512)832-5433 Fax (512)832-9108
E-mail: ugst@upci.org
Web site: www.ugst.org

Valley Forge Christian College (Assemblies of God), Don Meyer, President, 1401 Charlestown Rd., Phoenixville, PA 19460 Tel. (610)935-0450 Fax (610)935-9353
E-mail: admissions@vfcc.edu
Web site: www.vfcc.edu

Vanderbilt University Divinity School* (Inter/Multidenominational), James Hudnut-Beumler, Dean, 411 21st Av. So., Nashville, TN 37240 Tel. (615)322-2776 Fax (615)343-9957
E-mail: james.hudnut-beumler@vanderbilt.edu
Web site: divinity.lib.vanderbilt.edu/vds/vds-home.htm

Vennard College (Interdenominational), Dr. Bruce Moyer, President, Box 29, University Park, IA 52595 Tel. (641)673-8391 Fax (641) 673-8365
E-mail: bruce.moyer@vennard.edu
Web site: www.vennard.edu

Virginia Union University (School of Theology) (American Baptist Churches in the USA, National Baptist Convention, USA, Inc., Progressive National Baptist Convention, Inc., Lott Carey), John W. Kinney, Dean, President, 1500 N. Lombardy St., Richmond, VA 23220 Tel. (804)257-5715 Fax (804)342-3911

Wake Forest University Divinity School* (Inter/Multidenominational), Bill J. Leonard, Dean, P.O. Box 7719, Winston-Salem, NC 27109-7719 Tel. (336)758-5121 Fax (336) 758-4316
Web site: www.wfu.edu

Walla Walla College (School of Theology) (Seventh-day Adventist Church), Ernest Bursey, Dean, President, 204 S. College Ave., College Place, WA 99324-1198 Tel. (509)527-2194 Fax (509)527-2253
E-mail: burser@wwc.edu
Web site: www.wwc.edu

Wartburg Theological Seminary* (Evangelical Lutheran Church in America), Duane H. Larson, President, 333 Wartburg Pl., P.O. Box 5004, Dubuque, IA 52004-5004 Tel. (563)589-0200 Fax (563)589-0333
E-mail: mailbox@wartburgseminary.edu
Web site: www.wartburgseminary.edu

Washington Baptist College and Seminary* (Baptist), Johng O. Lee, President, 4300 Evergreen Lane, Annandale, VA 22003 Tel. (703)333-5904 Fax (703)333-5906
Web site: www.wbcs.edu

Washington Theological Consortium (Non-denominational), Daniel McLellan, O.F.M, President, 487 Michigan Ave. N.E., Washington, DC 20017 Tel. (202)832-2675 Fax (202)526-0818
E-mail: wtc@washtheocon.org
Web site: www.washtheocon.org

Washington Theological Union* (Roman Catholic Church), Daniel McLellan, O.F.M., President, 6896 Laurel St. N.W., Washington, DC 20012-2016 Tel. (202)726-8800 Fax (202) 726-1716
E-mail: mclellan@wtu.edu
Web site: www.wtu.edu

Wesley Biblical Seminary* (Interdenominational), Ronald E. Smith, President, P.O. Box 9938, Jackson, MS 39286-0938 Tel. (601)366-8880 Fax (601)366-8832
Web site: www.wbs.edu

John Wesley College (Interdenominational), Brian C. Donley, President, 2314 N. Centennial St., High Point, NC 27265 Tel. (336) 889-2262 Fax (336)889-2261
E-mail: admissions@johnwesley.edu
Web site: www.johnwesley.edu

Wesley Theological Seminary* (The United Methodist Church), David F. McAllister-Wilson, President, 4500 Massachusetts Ave. N.W., Washington, DC 20016-5690 Tel. (800)885-8600 or (800)882-4987 Fax (202) 885-8605
E-mail: caldridge@wesleysem.edu
Web site: www.Wesleysem.edu

Western Seminary* (Conservative Baptist Association of America), Bert E. Downs, President, 5511 S.E. Hawthorne Blvd., Portland, OR 97215 Tel. (503)517-1800 Fax (503)517-1801
Web site: westernseminary.edu

Western Theological Seminary* (Reformed Church in America), Dennis N. Voskuil, President, 101 E. 13th St., Holland, MI 49423 Tel. (616)392-8555 Fax (616)392-7717
Web site: www.westernsem.edu

Westminster Theological Seminary* (Presbyterian Church in America), Samuel T. Logan, President, Chestnut Hill, P.O. Box 27009, Philadelphia, PA 19118 Tel. (215)887-5511 Fax (215)887-5404
E-mail: slogan@wts.edu
Web site: www.wts.edu

Westminster Theological Seminary in California* (Nondenominational), W. Robert Godfrey, President, 1725 Bear Valley Pkwy, Escondido, CA 92027-4128 Tel. (760)480-8474 Fax (760)480-0252
E-mail: info@wscal.edu
Web site: www.wscal.edu

Weston Jesuit School of Theology* (Roman Catholic Church), Robert Manning, President, 3 Phillips Place, Cambridge, MA 02138-3495 Tel. (617)492-1960 Fax (617)492-5833
E-mail: Admissionsinfo@wjst.edu
Web site: www.wjst.edu

M. Christopher White School of Divinity of Gardner-Webb University* (Baptist State Convention of North Carolina), Robert W. Canoy, Dean, 110 N. Main Street, Noel Hall, Boiling Springs, NC 28017 Tel. (704)406-4400 Fax (704)406-3935
Web site: www.divinity.gardner-webb.edu

Williamson Christian College† (Nondenominational), Dr. Ken Oosting, President, 200 Seaboard Lane, Franklin, TN 37067 Tel. (615)771-7821 Fax (615)771-7810
E-mail: info@williamsoncc.edu
Web site: www.williamsoncc.edu

Winebrenner Theological Seminary* (Churches of God, General Conference), David E. Draper, President, 950 N. Main Street, Findlay, OH 45840 Tel. (419)434 4200 Fax (419)434 4267
E-mail: wts@winebrenner.edu
Web site: www.winebrenner.edu

Wisconsin Lutheran Seminary (Wisconsin Evangelical Lutheran Synod), Paul O. Wendland, President, 11831 N. Seminary Dr., 65W, Mequon, WI 53092-1597 Tel. (262)242-8100 Fax (262)242-8110
E-mail: president@wls.wels.net
Web site: www.wls.wels.net

Word of Life Bible Institute† (Nondenominational), Dr. Joe Jordan, Chancellor, P.O. Box 129, 4200 Glendale Road, Pottersville, NY 12860 Tel. (518)494-4723 Fax (518)494-7474
E-mail: admissions@wol.org
Web site: www.wol.org

Yale University Divinity School* (Inter/Multidenominational), Harold W. Attridge, Dean, 409 Prospect Sreet, New Haven, CT 06511-2167 Tel. (203)432-5303 Fax (203) 432-5356
E-mail: divinity.admissions@yale.edu
Web site: www.yale.edu/divinity

9. Theological Seminaries and Bible Colleges in Canada

The following list includes theological seminaries and departments in colleges and universities in which ministerial training is provided. Many denominations have additional programs. The list has been developed from direct correspondence with the institutions. Inclusion in or exclusion from this list implies no judgment about the quality or accreditation of any institution. Those schools that are members of the Association of Theological Schools are marked with an asterisk (*). Each of the listings includes: the institution name, denominational sponsor, when appropriate, location, the president or dean, telephone and fax numbers when known, and E-mail and Web site addresses when available.

Acadia Divinity College* (Convention of the Atlantic Baptist Church), Lee M. McDonald, 31 Horton Street, Wolfville, NS B4P 2R6 Tel. (902)585-2210 Fax (902)585-2233
E-mail: adcinfo@acadiau.ca
Web site: adc.acadiau.ca

Alberta Bible College (Christian Churches and Churches of Christ in Canada), Ronald A. Fraser, 635 Northmount Dr. N.W., Calgary, AB T2K 3J6 Tel. (403)282-2994 Fax (403) 282-3084
E-mail: generalinquiries@abc-ca.org
Web site: www.abc-ca.org

Arthur Turner Training School (The Anglican Church of Canada), Roy Bowkett, Box 378, Pangnirtung, NU X0A 0R0 Tel. (867)473-8375 Fax (867)473-8375

Associated Canadian Theological Schools of Trinity Western University* (Baptist General Conference of Canada, Evangelical Free Church of Canada, The Fellowship of Evangelical Baptist Churches in Canada, Christian and Missionary Alliance, Canadian Conference of Mennonite Brethren Churches), Dr. Phil Zylla, 7600 Glover Rd., Langley, BC V2Y 1Y1 Tel. (604)513-2044 Fax (604)513-2045
E-mail: acts@twu.ca
Web site: www.acts.twu.ca

Atlantic School of Theology* (Interdenominational), The Rev. Canon Eric Beresford, 660 Francklyn St., Halifax, NS B3H 3B5 Tel. (902)423-6801 Fax (902)492-4048
Web site: www.astheology.ns.ca

Baptist Leadership Training School (Canadian Baptist Ministries), Hugh Fraser, 4330 16th St. SW, Calgary, AB T2T 4H9 Tel. (403)243-3770 Fax (403)287-1930
E-mail: blts@imag.net
Web site: www.yet.ca

Bethany Bible College-Canada (The Wesleyan Church), Dr. David S. Medders, 26 Western St., Sussex, NB E4E 1E6 Tel. (506)432-4400 Fax (506)432-4425
E-mail: meddersd@bethany-ca.edu
Web site: www.bethany-ca.edu

Bethany College Bible Institute (Mennonite), Rick Schellenberg, Box 160, Hepburn, SK S0K 1Z0 Tel. (306)947-2175 Fax (306)947-4229
E-mail: info@bethany.sk.ca
Web site: www.bethany.sk.ca

Briercrest Seminary* (Interdenominational), Dwayne Uglem, 510 College Dr., Caronport, SK S0H 0S0 Tel. (800)667-5199 Fax (306) 756-5500
E-mail: seminary@briercrest.ca
Web site: www.briercrest.ca

Canadian Bible College & Canadian Theological Seminary of Alliance University College* (Christian and Missionary Alliance in Canada), Dr. George Durance, 630, 833-4th Avenue SW, Calgary, AB T2P 3T5 Tel. (403)410-2000 Fax (403) 571-2556
E-mail: gdurance@auc-nuc.ca
Web site: www.auc-nuc.ca

Canadian Lutheran Bible Institute (Lutheran), Pastor Harold Rust, 4837 52A St., Camrose, AB T4V 1W5 Tel. (780)672-4454 Fax (780) 672-4455
E-mail: clbi@clbi.edu
Web site: www.clbi.edu

Canadian Mennonite University (Mennonite Brethren Churches Mennonite Church Canada), Gerald Gerbrandt, 500 Shaftesbury Blvd, Winnipeg, MB R3P 2N2 Tel. (204)487-3300 Fax (204)487-3858
E-mail: reception@cmu.ca
Web site: www.cmu.ca

Canadian Nazarene University College (Church of the Nazarene Canada), Riley Coulter, 610-833 4th Ave. SW, Calgary, AB T2P 3T5 Tel. (403)571-2550 Fax (403)571-2556
E-mail: reception@auc-nuc.ca
Web site: www.auc-nuc.ca

Canadian Southern Baptist Seminary* (Canadian Convention of Southern Baptists), G. Richard Blackby, 200 Seminary View, Cochrane, AB T4C 2G1 Tel. (403)932-6622 Fax (403)932-7049
E-mail: csbs@compuserve.com
Web site: www.csbs.edu

Carey Theological College* (Baptist Union of Western Canada), Brian F. Stelck, 5920 Iona Drive, Vancouver, BC V6T 1J6 Tel. (604)224-4308 Fax (604)224-5014
Web site: www.careytheologicalcollege.ca

Central Pentecostal College, University of Saskatchewan (The Pentecostal Assemblies of Canada), D. Munk, 1303 Jackson Ave., Saskatoon, SK S7H 2M9 Tel. (306)374-6655 Fax (306)373-6968
E-mail: admissions@cpc-paoc.edu
Web site: www.cpc-paoc.edu

Centre for Christian Studies (The Anglican Church of Canada, The United Church of Canada), Caryn Douglas, 60 Maryland, Winnipeg, MB R3G 1K7 Tel. (204)783-4490 Fax (204)786-3012
E-mail: info@ccsonline.ca
Web site: www.ccsonline.ca

College Biblique Québec (The Pentecostal Assemblies of Canada), William Raccah, 740 Lebourgneuf, Ste. 100, Ancienne Lorette, QC G2J 1E2 Tel. (418)622-7552 Fax (418)622-1470

Collège Dominicain de Philosophie et de Théologie (The Roman Catholic Church in Canada), Gabor Csepregi, 96 Avenue Empress, Ottawa, ON K1R 7G3 Tel. (613) 233-5696 Fax (613)233-6064
E-mail: service.accueil@collegedominicain.ca
Web site: www.collegedominicain.ca

College of Emmanuel and St. Chad (The Anglican Church of Canada), Dr. Walter Deller, 1337 College Dr., Saskatoon, SK S7N 0W6 Tel. (306)975-3753 Fax (306)934-2683
E-mail: emmanuel.stchad@usask.ca
Web site: www.usask.ca/stu/emmanuel

Columbia Bible College (Mennonite), Dr. Paul Wartman, 2940 Clearbrook Rd., Abbotsford, BC V2T 2Z8 Tel. (604)853-3358 Fax (604) 853-3063
E-mail: info@columbiabc.edu
Web site: www.columbiabc.edu

Concordia Lutheran Seminary* (Lutheran Church-Canada), Arthur D. Bacon, 7040 Ada Blvd., Edmonton, AB T5B 4E3 Tel. (780)474-1468 Fax (780)479-3067
E-mail: info@concordiasem.ab.ca
Web site: www.concordiasem.ab.ca

Concordia Lutheran Theological Seminary* (Lutheran Church-Canada), Roger Humann, 470 Glenridge Ave., St. Catharines, ON L2T 4C3 Tel. (905)688-2362 Fax (905)688-9744
E-mail: concordia@brocku.ca
Web site: www.brocku.ca/concordiaseminary

Covenant Bible College (The Evangelical Covenant Church of Canada), 630 Westchester Road, Strathmore, AB T1P 1H8 Tel. (403)934-6200 Fax (403)934-6220
E-mail: office@covenantbiblecollege.ab.ca
Web site: www.covenantbiblecollege.ab.ca

Ecole de Theologie Evangelique de Montreal (Canadian Conference of Mennonite Brethren Churches), Eric Wingender, 1775, boul Édouard-Laurin, Ville Saint-Laurent, QC H4L 2B9 Tel. (514)331-0878 Fax (514)331-0879
E-mail: iblinstitute@proxyma.net

Emmanuel Bible College (The Evangelical Missionary Church of Canada), Thomas E. Dow, 100 Fergus Ave., Kitchener, ON N2A 2H2 Tel. (519)894-8900 Fax (519)894-5331
E-mail: dmin@ebcollege.on.ca
Web site: www.ebcollege.on.ca

Emmanuel College of Victoria University* (The United Church of Canada), The Rev. Dr. Peter Wyatt, 75 Queens Park Crescent East, Toronto, ON M5S 1K7 Tel. (416)585-4539 Fax (416)585-4516
E-mail: ec.office@utoronto.ca
Web site: vicu.utoronto.ca

Faculté de Théologie Évangélique (Interdenominational), Amar Djaballah, 2285 Avenue Papineau, Montréal, QC H2K 4J5 Tel. (514)526-2003 Fax (514)526-6887
E-mail: reg@fteacadia.ca
Web site: www.fteacadia.ca

Faith Alive Bible College (Nondenominational), David Pierce, 637 University Dr., Saskatoon, SK S7N 0H8 Tel. (306)652-2230 Fax (306) 665-1125
E-mail: faithalive@dlcwest.com

Full Gospel Bible Institute (Apostolic Church of Pentecost of Canada Inc.), Rev. Lauren E. Miller, Box 579, Eston, SK S0L 1A0 Tel. (306)962-3621 Fax (306)962-3810
E-mail: fgbi@fgbi.sk.ca
Web site: fgbi.sk.ca

Gardner College, A Centre for Christian Studies (Church of God (Anderson, Ind.)), John Alan Howard, 4707 56th St., Camrose, AB T4V 2C4 Tel. (780)672-0171 Fax (780) 672-2465
E-mail: gardnercollege@gardnercollege.org
Web site: www.gardnercollege.org

Grand Seminaire de Montréal* (The Roman Catholic Church in Canada), Marcel Demers, p.s.s., 2065 Sherbrooke Ouest, Montréal, QC H3H 1G6 Tel. (514)935-1169 Fax (514)935-5497
E-mail: Information Generale, info@gsdm.qc.ca or Bibliotheque, biblio@gsdm.qc.ca
Web site: www.gsdm.qc.ca

Great Lakes Bible College (Churches of Christ in Canada), Mr. J. Arthur Ford, 470 Glenelm Crescent, Waterloo, ON N2L 5C8 Tel. (519) 884-4310 Fax (519)884-4412
E-mail: learn@glbc.on.ca
Web site: www.glbc.on.ca

Heritage Theological Seminary*, Marvin R. Brubacher, 175 Holiday Inn Dr., Cambridge, ON N3C 3T2 Tel. (519)651-2869 or 800-465-1961 Fax (519)651-2870
E-mail: recruitment@heritage-theo.edu
Web site: www.heritageseminary.net or www.heritagecollege.net

Huron University College Faculty of Theology* (The Anglican Church of Canada), Dr. Ramona Lumpkin, 1349 Western Rd., London, ON N6G 1H3 Tel. (519)438-7224 Fax (519)438-9981
E-mail: huron@uwo.ca
Web site: www.huronuc.on.ca

Institut Biblique Beree (The Pentecostal Assemblies of Canada), André L. Gagnon, 1711 Est Boul. Henri-Bourassa, Montréal, QC H2C 1J5 Tel. (514)385-4238 Fax (514)385-4238

Institute for Christian Studies (Nondenominational), Harry Fernhout, 229 College St., Suite 200, Toronto, ON M5T 1R4 Tel. (416)979-2331 or 1 (888)326-5347 Fax (416) 979-2332
E-mail: E-mail@icscanada.edu
Web site: www.icscanada.edu

International Bible College (Church of God (Cleveland, Tenn.)), Cheryl Busse, 401 Trinity La., Moose Jaw, SK S6H 0E3 Tel. (306)692-4041 Fax (306)692-7968
E-mail: ibc@cofg.net
Web site: www.ibc.cofg.net

Key-Way-Tin Bible Institute (Nondenominational), Dir. Dave Petkau, Box 540, Lac La Biche, AB T0A 2C0 Tel. (780) 623-4565 Fax (780)623-1788
E-mail: kbi@telusplanet.net

Knox College* (The Presbyterian Church in Canada), J. Dorcas Gordon, 59 St. George St., Toronto, ON M5S 2E6 Tel. (416)978-4500 Fax (416)971-2133
E-mail: knox.college@utoronto.ca
Web site: www.utoronto.ca/knox

Living Faith Bible College (Fellowship of Christian Assemblies (Canada)), Dan Pope, Box 100, Caroline, AB T0M 0M0 Tel. (403) 722-2225, (800)838-2975 Fax (403)722-2459
E-mail: office@lfbc.net
Web site: www.lfbc.net

Lutheran Theological Seminary* (Evangelical Lutheran Church in Canada), Erwin Buck, 114 Seminary Crescent, Saskatoon, SK S7N 0X3 Tel. (306)966-7850 Fax (306)966-7852
E-mail: lutheran.seminary@usask.ca
Web site: www.usask.ca/stu/luther

Maritime Christian College (Christian Churches and Churches of Christ), Fred C. Osborne, 503 University Ave., Charlottetown, PE C1A 7Z4 Tel. (902)628-8887 Fax (902) 892-3959
E-mail: registrar@maritimechristiancollege.pe.ca
Web site: www.maritimechristiancollege.pe.ca

Master's College and Seminary (The Pentecostal Assemblies of Canada), Dr. Evon G. Horton, 3080 Yonge St., Box 70, Suite 3040, Toronto, ON M4N 3N1 Tel. (416)482-2224 Fax (416)482-7004
E-mail: info@mcs.edu
Web site: www.mcs.edu

McGill University Faculty of Religious Studies* (Interdenominational), B. Barry Levy, 3520 University St., Montréal, QC H3A 2A7 Tel. (514)398-4125 Fax (514)398-6665
Web site: www.mcgill.ca/religiousstudies

McMaster Divinity College* (Baptist Convention of Ontario and Quebec (BCOQ)), Stanley E. Porter, 1280 Main St. West, Hamilton, ON L8S 4K1 Tel. (905)525-9140x24401 Fax (905)577-4782
E-mail: divinity@mcmaster.ca
Web site: www.macdiv.ca

Millar College of the Bible (Interdenominational), A. Brian Atmore, Box 25, Pambrun, SK S0N 1W0 Tel. (306)582-2033 Fax (306)582-2027

Montreal Diocesan Theological College (The Anglican Church of Canada), Bishop of Montreal, 3473 University St., Montreal, QC H3A 2A8 Tel. (514)849-3004 Fax (514)849-4113
E-mail: diocoll@netrover.com
Web site: www.montreal.anglican.org/mdtc

Montreal School of Theology* (Inter/Multidenominational), Dr. John Vissers, 3473 University St., Montréal, QC H3A 2A8 Tel. (514)849-8511 Fax (514)849-4113
E-mail: jvissers@presbyteriancollege.ca
Web site: www.mcgill.ca/religion/jbtc.htm

Mount Carmel Bible School (Transdenominational), Gordon King, 4725 106 Ave., Edmonton, AB T6A 1E7 Tel. (780)465-3015 Toll-free 1(800) 561-6443 Fax (780)466-2485
E-mail: mail@mountcarmel.net
Web site: www.mountcarmel.net

National Native Bible College (Elim Fellowship of Evangelical Churches and Ministers), Michael Hart, Box 478, Deseronto, ON K0K 1X0 Tel. (613)396-2311

Newman Theological College* (The Catholic Church in Canada), Rev. John (Jack) Gallagher, 15611 St. Albert Trail, Edmonton, AB T6V 1H3 Tel. (780)447-2993 Fax (780) 447-2685
E-mail: patricia.hauck@newman.edu
Web site: www.newman.edu

Nipawin Bible Institute (Interdenominational), Mr. Wes Fehr, Box 1986, Nipawin, SK S0E 1E0 Tel. (306)862-5095 Fax (306)862-3651
E-mail: info@nipawin.org
Web site: www.nipawin.org

Northwest Baptist Theological College and Seminary (The Fellowship of Evangelical Baptist Churches of Canada), Dr. Larry Perkins, 7600 Glover Rd., Langley, BC V2Y 1Y1 Tel. (604)888-7592 Fax (604)513-8511
E-mail: nbs@twu.ca
Web site: www.nbseminary.com

Ontario Christian Seminary (Christian Churches and Churches of Christ in Canada), James R. Cormode, 260 High Park Ave., Toronto, ON M6P 3J9 Tel. (416)769-7115 Fax (416)769-7047

Pacific Life Bible College (Foursquare), Rob Buzza, 15100 66 A Ave., Surrey, BC V3S 2A6 Tel. (604)597-9082 Fax (604)597-9090
E-mail: paclife@pacificlife.edu
Web site: www.pacificlife.edu

Parole de Vie Bethel/Word of Life Bethel (Nondenominational), Mark Strout, 1175, ch. Woodward, Lennoxville, QC J1M 2A2 Tel. (819)823-8435 Fax (819)823-2468
E-mail: quebec@pdvb.org
Web site: www.pdvb.org

Peace River Bible Institute (Interdenominational), Rod Masterson, Box 99, Sexsmith, AB T0H 3C0 Tel. (780)568-3962 Fax (780)568-4431
E-mail: prbi@prbi.edu
Web site: www.prbi.edu

Prairie Graduate School (Interdenominational), Dr. Charlotte Kinvig Bates, 330 6th Ave., Three Hills, AB T0M 2N0 Tel. (403)443-5511 Fax (403)443-5540
E-mail: prairie@prairie.edu
Web site: www.pbi.ab.ca

The Presbyterian College, Montreal* (Presbyterian Church in Canada), John Vissers, 3495 University St., Montreal, QC H3A 2A8 Tel. (514)288-5256 Fax (514)288-8072
E-mail: info@presbyteriancollege.ca
Web site: www.presbyteriancollege.ca

Providence College and Theological Seminary* (Inter/Multidenominational), August H. Konkel, General Delivery, Otterburne, MB R0A 1G0 Tel. (204)433-7488 Fax (204)433-7158
E-mail: info@prov.ca
Web site: www.prov.ca

Queens College Faculty of Theology* (The Anglican Church of Canada), John Mellis, 210 Prince Phillip Dr.. Suite 3000, St. Johns, NF A1B 3R6 Tel. (709)753-0116 Fax (709)753-1214
E-mail: queens@mun.ca
Web site: www.mun.ca/queens

Queen's Theological College* (The United Church of Canada), M. Jean Stairs, Room 212 Theological Hall, Kingston, ON K7L 3N6 Tel. (613)533-2110 Fax (613)533-6879
E-mail: theology@post.queensu.ca
Web site: www.queensu.ca/theology

Reformed Episcopal Theological College (Reformed Episcopal Church of Canada), Rt. Rev. Michael Fedechko, 320 Armstrong St., Box 2532, New Liskeard, ON P0J 1P0 Tel. (705)647-4565 Fax (705)647-4565
E-mail: fed@nt.net
Web site: www.retcc.com

Regent College* (Interdenominational), Rod Wilson, PhD, 5800 University Blvd., Vancouver, BC V6T 2E4 Tel. (800)663-8664 or (604)224-3245 Fax (604)224-3097
E-mail: administration@regent-college.edu
Web site: www.regent-college.edu

Regis College* (The Roman Catholic Church in Canada), Joseph G. Schner, S.J, 15 St. Mary St., Toronto, ON M4Y 2R5 Tel. (416)922-5474 Fax (416)922-2898
E-mail: regis.registrar@utoronto.ca
Web site: www.regiscollege.ca

Rocky Mountain College, Centre for Biblical Studies (The Evangelical Missionary Church of Canada), Gordon Dirks, 4039 Brentwood Rd. NW, Calgary, AB T2L 1L1 Tel. (403)284-5100 Fax (403)220-9567
E-mail: admissions@rockymountaincollege.ca
Web site: www.rockymountaincollege.ca

St. Andrew's College* (The United Church of Canada), Dr. Tom Faulkner, 1121 College Dr., Saskatoon, SK S7N 0W3 Tel. (306)966-8970; (877)644-8970 Fax (306)966-8981
Web site: www.standrews.ca

St. Augustine's Seminary of Toronto* (The Roman Catholic Church in Canada), Rev. Msgr. A. Robert Nusca, 2661 Kingston Rd., Toronto, ON M1M 1M3 Tel. (416)261-7207 Fax (416)261-2529
E-mail: info@staugustines.on.ca
Web site: www.staugustines.on.ca

St. John's College, Univ. of Manitoba, Faculty of Theology (The Anglican Church of Canada), Dr. Janet A. Hoskins, 92 Dysart Rd., Winnipeg, MB R3T 2M5 Tel. (204)474-8531 Fax (204)474-7610
E-mail: stjohns_college@umanitoba.ca
Web site: www.umanitoba.ca/colleges/st_johns

Saint Paul University, Faculty of Theology (The Roman Catholic Church in Canada), Normand Bonneau, Ph.D., 223 Main St., Ottawa, ON K1S 1C4 Tel. (613)236-1393 x. 2246 Fax (613)751-4016
E-mail: fquesnel@ustpaul.uottawa.ca
Web site: www.ustpaul.ca

St. Peter's Seminary* (The Roman Catholic Church in Canada), William T. McGrattan, 1040 Waterloo St. North, London, ON N6A 3Y1 Tel. (519)432-1824 Fax (519)432-0964
Web site: www.stpetersseminary.ca

St. Stephen's College (The United Church of Canada), Dr. Tom Faulkner, 8810 112th St., Edmonton, AB T6G 2J6 Tel. (800)661-4956 Fax (780)433-8875
E-mail: westema@ualberta.ca
Web site: www.ststephenscollege.ca

Salvation Army College for Officer Training (The Salvation Army in Canada), Wayne N. Pritchett, 2130 Bayview Ave., North York, ON M4N 3K6 Tel. (416)481-6131 Fax (416)481-6810 Library (416)481-2895

The Salvation Army William and Catherine Booth College (The Salvation Army in Canada), Dr. Jonathan S. Raymond, 447 Webb Pl., Winnipeg, MB R3B 2P2 Tel. (204)947-6701 Fax (204)942-3856
E-mail: wcbc@boothcollege.ca
Web site: www.boothcollege.ca

Steinbach Bible College (Mennonite), Abe Bergen, 50 PTH 12 N, Steinbach, MB R5G 1T4 Tel. (204)326-6451 Fax (204)326-6908
E-mail: info@sbcollege.mb.ca
Web site: www.sbcollege.mb.ca

Summit Pacific College (The Pentecostal Assemblies of Canada), James G. Richards, Box 1700, Abbotsford, BC V2S 7E7 Tel. (604)853-7491 Fax (604)853-8951
E-mail: pr@summitpacific.ca
Web site: www.summitpacific.ca

Taylor College of Mission and Evangelism (Church Army Canada), Rev. Capt. David Edwards, 105 Mountain View Drive, Saint John, NB E2J 5B5 Tel. (866)693-8975 Fax (506)657-8217
E-mail: edwa@nbnet.nb.ca
Web site: www.taylorcollege.com or www.churcharmy.com/taylor

Taylor Seminary* (North American Baptist Conference), Dr. Marvin L. Dewey, 11525-23 Ave., Edmonton, AB T6J 4T3 Tel. (780)431-5200 Fax (780)436-9416
E-mail: marvin.dewey@taylor-edu.ca
Web site: www.taylor-edu.ca

Theological College of the Canadian Reformed Churches (Canadian and American Reformed Churches), C. Van Dam, 110 West 27th St., Hamilton, ON L9C 5A1 Tel. (905)575-3688 Fax (905)575-0799
Web site: www.canrc.org/college

Toronto Baptist Seminary and Bible College (Baptist), Dr. Glendon G. Thompson, 130 Gerrard St., E., Toronto, ON M5A 3T4 Tel. (416)925-3263 Fax (416)925-8305
E-mail: tbs@tbs.edu
Web site: www.tbs.edu

Toronto School of Theology* (Inter/Multi-denominational), Christopher J.L. Lind, 47 Queens Park Crescent E., Toronto, ON M5S 2C3 Tel. (416)978-4039 Fax (416)978-7821
E-mail: registrar.tst@utoronto.ca
Web site: www.tst.edu

Trinity College Faculty of Divinity* (The Anglican Church of Canada), David Neelands, 6 Hoskin Ave., Toronto, ON M5S 1H8 Tel. (416)978-2146 Fax (416)978-4949
E-mail: divinity@trinity.utoronto.ca
Web site: www.trinity.utoronto.ca/divinity

Tyndale University College & Seminary* (Transdenominational), Dr. Brian C. Stiller, 25 Ballyconnor Ct., Toronto, ON M2M 4B3 Tel. (416)226-6380 Fax (416)226-9464
E-mail: info@tyndale.ca
Web site: www.tyndale.ca

United Theological College/Le Séminaire Uni (The United Church of Canada), Rev. Philip Joudrey, 3521 rue Université, Montréal, QC H3A 2A9 Tel. (514)849-2042 Fax (514)849-8634
E-mail: admin@utc.ca
Web site: www.utc.ca

Université Laval, Faculté de Théologie et de Sciences Religieuses (The Roman Catholic Church in Canada), Jacques Racine, Cité Universitaire, Quebec, QC G1K 7P4 Tel. (418)656-3576 Fax (418)656-3273
E-mail: ftsr@ftsr.ulaval.ca
Web site: www.ftsr.ulaval.ca

Université de Montréal, Faculté de théologie (The Roman Catholic Church in Canada), Jean-Marc Charron, C. P. 6128 Succ. Centre Ville, Montréal, QC H3C 3J7 Tel. (514)343-7160 Fax (514)343-5738
E-mail: theologie@ere.umontreal.ca
Web site: www.theo.umontreal.ca

Université de Sherbrooke, Faculté de theologié, d'éthique et de philosophie (The Roman Catholic Church in Canada), Jean-François Malherbe, 1111, rue Saint-Charles Ouest, Tourquest—Bureau 310, Longueuil, QC J4K 5G4 Tel. (450)670-7157 Fax (450) 670-1959
E-mail: jf.malherbe@sympatico.ca
Web site: www.usherb.ca/longueuil

University of St. Michael's College Faculty of Theology* (Roman Catholic Church), Dr. Anne T. Anderson, CSJ, 81 St. Mary St., Toronto, ON M5S 1J4 Tel. (416)926-7265 Fax (416)926-7294
Web site: www.utoronto.ca/stmikes

The University of Winnipeg Faculty of Theology* (Multidenominational and the United Church of Canada), Gordon E. MacDermid, 515 Portage Ave., Winnipeg, MB R3B 2E9 Tel. (204)786-9390 Fax (204)772-2584
E-mail: theology@uwinnipeg.ca
Web site: www.uwinnipeg.ca/academic/theology

Vancouver School of Theology* (Inter/Multi-denominational), Dr. Kenneth G. MacQueen, 6000 Iona Dr., Vancouver, BC V6T 1L4 Tel. (866)822-9031 Fax (604)822-9212
E-mail: vstinfo@vst.edu
Web site: www.vst.edu

Vanguard College (The Pentecostal Assemblies of Canada), Stephen Hertzog, 12140 103 St., Edmonton, AB T5G 2J9 Tel. (780)452-0808 Fax (780)452-5803
E-mail: info@vanguardcollege.com
Web site: www.vanguardcollege.com

Waterloo Lutheran Seminary* (Evangelical Lutheran Church in Canada), Richard C. Crossman, 75 University Ave. W., Waterloo, ON N2L 3C5 Tel. (519)884-1970 Fax (519)725-2434
E-mail: seminary@wlu.ca
Web site: www.wlu.ca/~wwwsem

Western Christian College (Churches of Christ in Canada), John McMillan, 100-4400 4th Ave., Regina, SK S4T 0H8 Tel. (306)545-1515 Fax (306)352-2198
E-mail: president@westernchristian.ca
Web site: www.westernchristian.ca

Wycliffe College* (The Anglican Church of Canada), Rev. Dr. George R. Sumner, Jr., 5 Hoskin Ave., Toronto, ON M5S 1H7 Tel. (416)946-3535 Fax (416)946-3545
E-mail: wycliffe.college@utoronto.ca
Web site: www.utoronto.ca/wycliffe

10. Religious Periodicals in the United States

This directory lists publications primarily of the organizations listed in Directory 3, "Religious Bodies in the United States." Some independent publications are also listed. The list does not include all publications prepared by religious bodies, and not all the publications listed here are necessarily the official publication of a particular church. Regional publications and newsletters are not included. A more extensive list of religious periodicals published in the United States can be found in *Gale Directory of Publications and Broadcast Media*, (Gale Research, Inc., P.O. Box 33477, Detroit MI 48232-5477).

Each entry in this directory contains: the title of the periodical, frequency of publication, religious affiliation, editor's name, address, telephone and fax number and E-mail and Web site addresses when available. The frequency of publication, which appears in parenthesis after the name of the publication, is represented by a "W." for weekly; "M." for monthly; "Q." for quarterly; "I." for Internet.

21st Century Christian, (M.) Churches of Christ, M. Norvel Young and Prentice A. Meador, Jr., Box 40304, Nashville, TN 37204 Tel. (800)331-5991 Fax (615)385-5915

Action, (10-Y.) Churches of Christ, Dr. R. H. Tex Williams, P.O. Box 2169, Cedar Park, TX 78630-2169 Tel. (512)345-8191 Fax (512) 401-8265
E-mail: wbsinfo@wbschool.org
Web site: www.wbschool.org

Adra Today, (Q.) Seventh-day Adventist Church, Beth Schaefer, 12501 Old Columbia Pike, Silver Spring, MD 20904-6600 Tel. (301)680-6355 Fax (301)680-6370
E-mail: 74617.2105@compuserve.com
Web site: www.adra.org

The Adult Quarterly, (Q.) Associate Reformed Presbyterian Church (General Synod), Mr. William B. Evans, PhD, P.O. Box 275, Due West, SC 29639 Tel. (864)379-8896
E-mail: wbevans@erskine.edu

Advent Christian News, (M.) Advent Christian Church, Rev. Keith D. Wheaton, P.O. Box 23152, Charlotte, NC 28227 Tel. (704)545-6161 Fax (704)573-0712
E-mail: Acpub@Adventchristian.org

The Adventist Chaplain, (Q.) Seventh-day Adventist Church, Martin W. Feldbush, Adventist Chaplaincy Ministries, 12501 Old Columbia Pike, Silver Spring, MD 20904-6600 Tel. (301)680-6780 Fax (301)680-6783
E-mail: acm@gc.adventist.org
Web site: www.adventistchaplains.org

Adventist Review, (W.) Seventh-day Adventist Church, W. G. Johnsson, 12501 Old Columbia Pike, Silver Spring, MD 20904-6600 Tel. (301)680-6560 Fax (301)680-6638
E-mail: letters@adventistreview.org
Web site: www.adventistreview.org

Again Magazine, (Q.) The Antiochian Orthodox Christian Archdiocese of North America, R. Thomas Zell, P.O. Box 76, Ben Lomond, CA 95005-0076 Tel. (831)336-5118 Fax (831) 336-8882
E-mail: marketing@conciliarpress.com
Web site: www.conciliarpress.com

Agape Magazine, (bi-M.) Coptic Orthodox Church, Bishop Serapion, P.O.Box 4960, Diamond Bar, CA 91765 Tel. (909)865-8378 Fax (909)865-8348
E-mail: agape@lacopts.org
Web site: lacopts.org

AIM Magazine, (Q.) Free Will Baptists, National Association of, Ida Lewis, Home Missions Office, P.O. Box 5002, Antioch, TN 37011-5002 Tel. (615)731-6812 Fax (615) 731-7655
E-mail: ida@nafwb.org
Web site: www.homemissions.net

Alive Now, (bi-M.) The United Methodist Church, Melissa Tidwell, P.O. Box 340004, Nashville, TN 37203-0004 Tel. (615)340-7218
E-mail: alivenow@upperroom.org
Web site: www.alivenow.org

The Allegheny Wesleyan Methodist, (M.) The Allegheny Wesleyan Methodist Connection (Original Allegheny Conference), William Cope, P.O. Box 357, Salem, OH 44460 Tel. (330)337-9376 Fax (330)337-9700
E-mail: awmc@juno.com

Alliance Life, (M.) The Christian and Missionary Alliance, Mark Failing, P.O. Box 35000, Colorado Springs, CO 80935 Tel. (719)599-5999 Fax (719)599-8234
E-mail: alife@cmalliance.org
Web site: www.alliancelife.org

The A.M.E. Christian Recorder, (bi-W.) African Methodist Episcopal Church, Ricky

Spain, 1134 11th St NW, Suite 202, Washington, D.C. 20001 Tel. (202)216-4294 Fax (202)216-4293
E-mail: rspain5737@aol.com
Web site: www.amecnet.org

American Baptist Quarterly, (Q.) American Baptist Churches in the USA, Dr. Robert E. Johnson, P.O. Box 851, Valley Forge, PA 19482-0851 Tel. (610)768-2269 Fax (610)768-2266
E-mail: dbvanbro@abc-usa.org
Web site: www.cbts.edu/rejohnsonweb/AB Quarterly

American Baptists In Mission, (Q.) American Baptist Churches in the USA, Richard W. Schramm, P.O. Box 851, Valley Forge, PA 19482-0851 Tel. (610)768-2077 Fax (610) 768-2320
E-mail: richard.schramm@abc-usa.org
Web site: www.abc-usa.org

American Bible Society Record, (Q.) Nondenominational, Francine Lange, 1865 Broadway, New York, NY 10023-7505 Tel. (212)408-1399 Fax (212)408-1456
E-mail: absrecord@americanbible.org
Web site: www.americanbible.org

The Anchor of Faith, (M.) The Anglican Orthodox Church, The Most Rev. Jerry L. Ogles, Anglican Orthodox Church, P.O. Box 128, Statesville, NC 28687-0128 Tel. (704) 873-8365 Fax (704)873-5359
E-mail: aocusa@energyunited.net
Web site: www.anglicanorthodoxchurch.org

Annual Catholic Directory, The, (Y.) The Catholic Church, Michelle Laque Johnson, 222 N. 17th St., Philadelphia, PA 19103 Tel. (215)587-3660 Fax (215)587-3979

El Aposento Alto, (bi-M.) The United Methodist Church, Carmen Gaud, P.O. Box 340004, Nashville, TN 37203-0004 Tel. (615)340-7253 Fax (615)340-7267
E-mail: ElAposentoAlto@upperroom.org
Web site: www.upperroom.org

The Armenian Church, (2-Y.) Diocese of the Armenian Church of America, Arpie McQueen, 630 Second Avenue, New York, NY 10016 Tel. (212)686-0710 Fax (212)779-3558
E-mail: tac@armeniandiocese.org
Web site: www.armenianchurch.org

The Associate Reformed Presbyterian, (M.) Associate Reformed Presbyterian Church (General Synod), Mrs. Sabrina M. Cooper, One Cleveland St., Greenville, SC 29601 Tel. (864)232-8297 Fax (864)271-3729
E-mail: arpmaged@arpsynod.org
Web site: www.arpmagazine.org

Attack, A Magazine for Christian Men, (Q.) National Association for Free Will Baptists, James E. Vallance, P.O. Box 5002, Antioch, TN 37011-5002 Tel. (615)731-4950 Fax (615) 731-0771

Awake!, (bi-W.) Jehovah's Witnesses, Watch Tower Society, 25 Columbia Heights, Brooklyn, NY 11201-2483 Tel. (718)560-5000
Web site: watchtower.org

The Banner, (M.) Christian Reformed Church in North America, Robert DeMoor, 2850 Kalamazoo Ave., S.E., Grand Rapids, MI 49560 Tel. (616)224-0732 Fax (616)224-0834
E-mail: editorial@thebanner.org
Web site: www.thebanner.org

The Banner of Truth, (M.) Netherlands Reformed Congregations, J. den Hoed, 1113 Bridgeview Dr., Lynden, WA 98264 Tel. (360)354-4203 Fax (360)354-7565

The Baptist Bible Tribune, (M.) Baptist Bible Fellowship International, Mike Randall, P.O. Box 309, Springfield, MO 65801-0309 Tel. (417)831-3996 Fax (417)831-1470
E-mail: editors@tribune.org
Web site: www.tribune.org

Baptist Bulletin, (M.) General Association of Regular Baptist Churches, David M. Gower, 1300 N. Meacham Rd., Schaumburg, IL 60173-4806 Tel. (847)843-1600 Fax (847) 843-3757
E-mail: baptistbulletin@garbc.org
Web site: www.garbc.org

Baptist History Heritage, (3-Y.) Baptist History and Heritage Society, Pamela R. Durso, P.O. Box 728, Brentwood, TN 37021-0728 Tel. (615)371-7937 Fax (615)371-7939
E-mail: pdurso@tubaptist.org
Web site: www.baptisthistory.org

Baptist Peacemaker, (Q.) Baptist, Katie Cook, 4800 Wedgewood Dr., Charlotte, NC 28210 Tel. (704)521-6051 Fax (704)521-6053
E-mail: bpfna@bpfna.org
Web site: www.bpfna.org

Baptist Peacemaker, (Q.) Baptist, Katie Cook, 4800 Wedgewood Drive, Charlotte, NC 28210 Tel. (704)521-6051 Fax (704)521-6053
E-mail: bpfna@bpfna.org
Web site: www.bpfna.org

The Baptist Preacher, (bi-M.) Baptist Bible Fellowship International, Mike Randall, P.O. Box 309 HSJ, Springfield, MO 65801 Tel. (417)831-3996 Fax (417)831-1470
E-mail: editors@tribune.org
Web site: www.tribune.org

The Baptist Preacher's Journal, (Q.) Baptist Bible Fellowship International, Keith Bassham, P.O.Box 309, Springfield, MO 65801 Tel. (417)831-3996 Fax (417)831-1470
E-mail: editor@tribune.org
Web site: tribune.org

Missions Ministry, (Q.) Progressive National Baptist Convention, Inc., Justus Y. Reeves, 601 50th St. NE, Washington, DC 20019 Tel. (202)396-0558 Fax (202)398-4998
E-mail: justusreeves@aol.com
Web site: www.PNBC.org

Baptist Witness, (M.) Primitive Baptists, Lasserre Bradley, Jr., Box 17037, Cincinnati, OH 45217 Tel. (513)821-7289 Fax (513)821-7303
E-mail: bbh45217@aol.com
Web site: www.BaptistBibleHour.org

BGC World, (8-Y.) Baptist General Conference, Bob Putman, 2002 S. Arlington Heights Rd., Arlington Heights, IL 60005 Tel. (847)228-0200 Fax (847)228-5376
E-mail: bgcworld@bgcworld.org
Web site: www.bgcworld.org

The Bible Advocate, (10-Y.) The Church of God (Seventh Day), Denver, CO, Calvin Burrell, P.O. Box 33677, Denver, CO 80233 Tel. (303)452-7973 Fax (303)452-0657
E-mail: bibleadvocate@cog7.org
Web site: www.cog7.org/BA

The Brethren Evangelist, (4-6-Y.) 524 College Ave., Ashland, OH 44805 Tel. (419)289-1708 Fax (419)281-0450
E-mail: brethren@brethrenchurch.org
Web site: www.brethrenchurch.org

Brethren Journal, (10-Y.) Unity of Brethren, Rev. Milton Maly, 6703 FM 2502, Brenham, TX 77833-9803 Tel. (409)830-8762
Web site: www.unityofthebrethren.org

Brethren Life and Thought, (Q.) Church of the Brethren, Carol Gardner, Bethany Seminary, 615 National Road West, Richmond, IN 47374-4019 Fax (765)983-1840
E-mail: gardnca@bethanyseminary.edu

The Bridegroom's Messenger, (bi-M.) The International Pentecostal Church of Christ, Janice Boyce, 121 W. Hunters Trail, Elizabeth City, NC 27909 Tel. (919)338-3003 Fax (919) 338-3003

The Burning Bush, (Q.) The Metropolitan Church Association, Inc. (Wesleyan), Rev. Gary Bowell, The Metropolitan Church Assoc., 2425 West Ramsey Ave, Milwaukee, WI 53221-4907 Tel. (414)282-8539
E-mail: metrochurch assn@wi.rr.com

Call to Unity: Resourcing the Church for Ecumenical Ministry, (bi-M.) Christian Church (Disciples of Christ), Robert K. Welsh, P.O. Box 1986, Indianapolis, IN 46206-1986 Tel. (317)713-2586 Fax (317)713-2588
E-mail: rwelsh@ccu.disciples.org
Web site: www.disciples.org/ccu

Calvary Messenger, (M.) Beachy Amish Mennonite Churches, Paul L. Miller, 7809 Soul Herren Road, Partridge, KS 67566 Tel. (620)567-2286 Fax (620)567-2286
E-mail: paullmiller@mindspring.com

Campus Life, (9-Y.) Nondenominational, Christopher Lutes, 465 Gunderson Dr., Carol Stream, IL 60188 Tel. (630)260-6200 Fax (630)260-0114
E-mail: clmag@campuslife.net
Web site: www.campuslife.net

Caring, (Q.) Assemblies of God, Owen Wilkie, Gospel Publishing House, 1445 N. Boonville Ave., Springfield, MO 65802 Tel. (417)862-2781 Fax (417)862-0503
E-mail: benevolences@ag.org
Web site: www.benevolences.ag.org

Cathedral Age, (Q.) Interdenominational, Craig W. Stapert, Washington National Cathedral, 3101 Wisconsin Ave., NW, Washington, DC 20016-5098 Tel. (202)537-5681 Fax (202) 364-6600
E-mail: cathedral_age@cathedral.org
Web site: www.cathedralage.org

Catholic Chronicle, (bi-W.) The Catholic Church, Christine Alexander, P.O. Box 1866, Toledo, OH 43603-1866 Tel. (419)244-6711 ext. 232 Fax (419)244-0468
E-mail: ccnews@toledodiocese.org
Web site: www.catholicchronicle.org

Catholic Digest, (M.) The Catholic Church, Joop Koopman, 185 Willow St., Mystic, CT 06355 Tel. (800)321-0411 Fax (860)536-5600
E-mail: jkoopman@bayard-inc.com
Web site: www.CatholicDigest.org

Catholic Herald, (W.) The Catholic Church, Fr. Thomas Brundage, 3501 S. Lake Dr., St. Francis, WI 53235-0913 Tel. (414)769-3500 Fax (414)769-3468
E-mail: chnonline@archmil.org
Web site: www.chnonline.org

Catholic Light, (bi-W.) The Catholic Church, William R. Genello, 300 Wyoming Ave., Scranton, PA 18503 Tel. (570)207-2229 Fax (570)207-2271
E-mail: william-genello@dioceseofscranton.org
Web site: www.dioceseofscranton.org

The Catholic Peace Voice, (bi-M.) The Catholic Church, Dave Robinson, 532 W. 8th Street, Erie, PA 16502 Tel. (814)453-4955 Fax (814)452-4784
E-mail: info@paxchristiusa.org
Web site: www.paxchristiusa.org

The Catholic Review, (W.) The Catholic Church, Daniel L. Medinger, Associate Publisher, P.O. Box 777, Baltimore, MD 21203 Tel. (443)524-3150 Fax (443)524-3155
E-mail: mail@catholicreview.org
Web site: www.catholicreview.org

Catholic Standard and Times, (W.) The Catholic Church, Michelle Laque Johnson, 222 N. 17th St., Philadelphia, PA 19103 Tel. (215)587-3660 Fax (215)587-3979
E-mail: standard@adphila.org
Web site: www.cst-phl.com

Catholic Trends, (bi-W.) The Catholic Church, David E. Gibson, 3211 Fourth St. NE, Washington, DC 20017-1100 Tel. (202)541-3250 Fax (202)541-3255
E-mail: cns@catholicnews.com
Web site: www.catholicnews.com

The Catholic Worker, (7-Y.) The Roman Catholic Church, Joanne Kennedy & Padraic O'Neal, Managing Editors, 36 E. First St., New York, NY 10003 Tel. (212)777-9617

Cela Biedrs, (bi-M.) The Latvian Evangelical Lutheran Church in America, Vieturs Bamban, 14170 S.W. 22nd St., Beaverton, OR 97008 Tel. (503)781-6724
E-mail: celabiedrs@yahoo.com

Celebration: An Ecumenical Worship Resource, (M.) Interdenominational, Patrick Marrin, P.O. Box 419493, Kansas City, MO 64141-6493 Tel. (816)531-0538 Fax (816) 968-2291
E-mail: patmarrin@aol.com
Web site: www.ncrpub.com

The Challenge, (Q.) The Bible Church of Christ, Inc., A.M. Jones, 1358 Morris Ave., Bronx, NY 10456 Tel. (718)588-2284 Fax (718)992-5597
Web site: www.thebiblechurchofchrist.org

Charisma, (M.) Nondenominational, J. Lee Grady, 600 Rinehart Rd., Lake Mary, FL 32746 Tel. (407)333-0600 Fax (407)333-7133
E-mail: grady@strang.com
Web site: www.charismamag.com

The Children's Friend, (Braille), (Q.) Seventh-Day Adventist Church, Gaylena Gibson, P.O. Box 6097, Lincoln, NE 68506 Tel. (402)488-0981 Fax (402)488-7582
E-mail: editorial@christianrecord.org
Web site: www.ChristianRecord.org

Christadelphian Advocate, (M.) Christadelphians, James I. Millay, 27 Delphian Road, Springfield, VT 05156-9335 Tel. (802) 885.2316 Fax (802)885.2319
E-mail: jimillay@vermontel.net
Web site: www.christadelphian-advocate.org

Christadelphian Tidings, (M.) Christadelphians, Donald H. Styles, 42076 Hartford Dr., Canton, MI 48187 Tel. (313)844-2426 Fax (313)844-8304

The Christian Baptist, (Q.) Primitive Baptists, Elder S. T. Tolley, P.O. Box 68, Atwood, TN 38220 Tel. (901)662-7417
E-mail: cbl@aeneas.net

Christian Bible Teacher, (M.) Churches of Christ, Bob Connel, P.O. Box 7385, Ft. Worth, TX 76111 Tel. (817)838-2644 Fax (817)838-2644

The Christian Century, (bi-M.) Nondenominational, John Buchanan, 104 South Michigan Ave. Suite 700, Chicago, IL 60603 Tel. (312)263-7510 Fax (312)263-7540
E-mail: main@christiancentury.org
Web site: www.christiancentury.org

The Christian Chronicle, (M.) Churches of Christ, Bailey McBride, Box 11000, Oklahoma City, OK 73136-1100 Tel. (405) 425-5070 Fax (405)425-5076
Web site: www.christianchronicle.org

The Christian Community, (8-Y.) International Council of Community Churches, Rev. Michael E. Livingston, 21116 Washington Pkwy., Frankfort, IL 60423 Tel. (815)464-5690 Fax (815)464-5692
E-mail: ICCC60423@sbcglobal.net
Web site: icccusa.com

The Christian Contender, (M.) Mennonite Church, James Boll, Box 3, Highway 172, Crockett, KY 41413 Tel. (606)522-4348 Fax (606)522-4896

The Christian Index, (M.) Christian Methodist Episcopal Church, Dr. Kenneth E. Jones, P.O. Box 431, Fairfield, AL 35064 Tel. (205)929-1410 Fax (205)744-0010
E-mail: goodoc@aol.com
Web site: www.c-m-e.org

Christian Journal, (M.) Churches Of Christ, J.E. Snelson, P.O. Box 7385, Ft. Worth, TX 76111 Tel. (817)838-2644

Christian Leader, (M.) U.S. Conference of Mennonite Brethren Churches, Connie Faber, Box 220, Hillsboro, KS 67063 Tel. (316)947-5543 Fax (316)947-3266
E-mail: chleader@southwind.net

Christian Monthly, (M.) Apostolic Lutheran Church of America, Linda Mattson, P.O. Box 2126, Battle Ground, WA 98604 Tel. (360) 687-6493 Fax (360)687-6493
E-mail: christianm@apostolic-lutheran.org
Web site: www.Apostolic-Lutheran.org

Christian Record (Braille), (Q.) Seventh-day Adventist Church, Gaylena Gibson, P.O. Box 6097, Lincoln, NE 68506 Tel. (402)488-0981 Fax (402)488-7582
E-mail: editorial@christianrecord.org
Web site: www.ChristianRecord.org

The Christian Science Journal, (M. & Q.) Church of Christ, Scientist, Mary M. Trammell, Editor in Chief; William G. Dawley, Editor, One Norway St., Boston, MA 02115-3195 Tel. (617)450-2000 Fax (617) 450-2930
E-mail: trammellm@csps.com or dawleyw@csps.com
Web site: www.csjournal.com

The Christian Science Monitor, (D. & W.) Church of Christ, Scientist, David T. Cook, One Norway St., Boston, MA 02115 Tel. (617)450-2000 Fax (617)450-7575
Web site: www.csmonitor.com

Christian Science Quarterly Weekly Bible Lessons, (M. & Q.) Church of Christ, Scientist, Carol Humphry, Circulation Marketing Manager, One Norway St., C-40, Boston, MA 02115 Tel. (617)450-2000 Fax (617)450-2930
E-mail: service@csps.com
Web site: www.BibleLesson.com

Christian Science Sentinel, (W.) Church of Christ, Scientist, Mary M. Trammell, One Norway St., Boston, MA 02115-3195 Tel. (617)450-2000 Fax (617)450-2930
E-mail: sentinel@csps.com or trammellm@csps.com
Web site: www.cssentinel.com

Christian Social Action, (bi-M.) The United Methodist Church, 100 Maryland Ave. NE, Washington, D.C. 20002 Tel. (202)488-5621 Fax (202)488-1617
Web site: www.umc-gbcs.org

Christian Standard, (W.) Christian Churches and Churches of Christ, Mark A. Taylor, 8121 Hamilton Ave., Cincinnati, OH 45231 Tel. (513)931-4050 Fax (513)931-0950
E-mail: christianstd@standardpub.com
Web site: www.christianstandard.com

The Christian Union Witness, (10-Y.) Christian Union, Joseph Cunningham, P.O. Box 361, Greenfield, OH 45123 Tel. (937)981-2760 Fax (937)981-2760
E-mail: ohiocu@bright.net
Web site: christianunionbright.net

Christian Woman, (bi-M.) Churches of Christ, Sandra Humphrey, Box 150, Nashville, TN 37202 Tel. (615)254-8781 Fax (615)254-7411

The Church Advocate, (Q.) Churches of God, General Conference, Rachel L. Foreman, P.O. Box 926, 700 E. Melrose Ave., Findlay, OH 45839 Tel. (419)424-1961 Fax (419)424-3433
E-mail: communications@cggc.org
Web site: www.cggc.org

Church of God Evangel, (M.) Church of God (Cleveland, Tenn.), Bill George, P.O. Box 2250, Cleveland, TN 37320 Tel. (423)478-7592 Fax (423)478-7616
E-mail: bill_george@pathwaypress.org
Web site: www.pathwaypress.org

Church of God Progress Journal, (bi-M.) Church of God General Conference (Oregon, IL & Morrow, GA), Tom Colburn, Box 100,000, Morrow, GA 30260 Tel. (404)362-0052 Fax (404)362-9307
E-mail: info@abc-coggc.org
Web site: www.abc-coggc.org

The Church Herald, (11-Y.) Reformed Church in America, Christina Van Eyl, 4500 60th St. SE, Grand Rapids, MI 49512 Tel. (616)698-7071
E-mail: herald@rca.org
Web site: herald.rca.org

The Church Herald, (11-Y.) Reformed Church in America, Christina Van Eyl, 4500 60th St., SE, Grand Rapids, MI 49512 Tel. (616)698-7071 Fax (616)698-6606
E-mail: herald@rca.org
Web site: www.rca.org/herald

Church History: Studies in Christianity and Culture, (Q.) Scholarly, John Corrigan, Amanda Porterfield, Religion Department, M05 Dodd Hall - Florida State University, Tallahassee, FL 32306-1520 Tel. (850)644-1020 Fax (850)644-7225
E-mail: john.corrigan@fsu.edu
Web site: www.churchhistory.org

The Church Messenger, (bi-W.) The American Carpatho-Russian Orthodox Greek Catholic Church, V. Rev. Michael Rosco, 145 Broad St., Perth Amboy, NJ 08861 Tel. (732)826-4442
E-mail: mrosco2@excite.com
Web site: www.acrod.org/news/messenger1.html

Church School Herald, (Q.) African Methodist Episcopal Zion Church, Ms. Mary A. Love,

P.O. Box 26769, Charlotte, NC 28221-6769 Tel. (704)599-4630 ext. 324 Fax (704)688-2548
E-mail: MaLove@amezhqtr.org

Church & Society Magazine, (bi-M.) Presbyterian Church (U.S.A.), Rev. Dr. Bobbi Wells Hargleroad, 100 Witherspoon St., Louisville, KY 40202-1396 Tel. (502)569-5810 Fax (502)569-8116
E-mail: c-s@ctr.pcusa.org
Web site: www.horebpcusa.org/churchsociety

Church & Society Magazine, (bi-M.) Presbyterian Church (U.S.A.), Bobbi Wells Hargleroad, 100 Witherspoon St., Louisville, KY 40202-1396 Tel. (502)569-5810
E-mail: C-S@ctr.pcusa.org
Web site: www.pcusa.org/churchsociety

Church Talk, (Q.) General Association of General Baptists, Mike Warren, 100 Stinson Drive, Poplar Bluff, MO 63901 Tel. (573)785-7746 Fax (573)785-0564
E-mail: cmdir@generalbaptist.com
Web site: generalbaptist.com

Churchwoman, (Q.) Interdenominational, Annie Llamoso-Songco, 475 Riverside Dr., Suite 500, New York, NY 10115 Tel. (212)870-3339 Fax (212)870-2338
E-mail: allamoso@churchwomen.org
Web site: www.churchwomen.org

Circuit Rider, (bi-M.) The United Methodist Church, Jill S. Reddig, 201 Eighth Ave. S, Nashville, TN 37203 Tel. (615)749-6538 Fax (615)749-6061
E-mail: jreddig@umpublishing.org
Web site: www.circuitrider.com

Clarion Herald, (bi-W.) The Catholic Church, Peter P. Finney, Jr., P. O. Box 53247, 1000 Howard Ave. Suite 400, New Orleans, LA 70153 Tel. (504)596-3035 Fax (504)596-3020
E-mail: clarionherald@clarionherald.org
Web site: www.clarionherald.org

Clergy Comminique, (2-Y.) International Council of Community Churches, Michael Livingston, 21116 Washington Pky., Frankfort, IL 60423-3112 Tel. (815)464-5690 Fax (815)464-5692
E-mail: iccc60423@aol.com
Web site: icccusa.com

The Clergy Journal, (9-Y.) Nondenominational, Sharilyn A. Figueroa, Managing Editor & Clyde J. Steckel, Executive Editor, 6160 Carmen Avenue E, Inver Grove Heights, MN 55076-4422 Tel. (800)328-0200 Fax (651) 457-4617
E-mail: fig@logostaff.com
Web site: www.joinhands.com

Club Connection, (Q.) Assemblies of God, Debby Seler, 1445 Boonville Ave., Springfield, MO 65802-1894 Tel. (417)862-2781 Fax (417)862-0503
E-mail: clubconnection@ag.org
Web site: www.missionettes.ag.org

CoLaborer, (bi-M.) National Association of Free Will Baptists, Sarah Fletcher, Women Nationally Active for Christ, P.O. Box 5002, Antioch, TN 37011-5002 Tel. (615)731-6812 Fax (615)731-0771
E-mail: wnac@nafwb.org

College and University Dialogue, (3-Y.) Seventh-day Adventist Church, John M. Fowler, 12501 Old Columbia Pike, Silver Spring, MD 20904-6600 Fax (301)622-9627
Web site: dialogue.adventist.org

Collegiate Quarterly, (Q.) Seventh-day Adventist Church, Gary B. Swanson, 12501 Old Columbia Pike, Silver Spring, MD 20904 Tel. (301)680-6160 Fax (301)680-6155

Columbia, (M.) The Catholic Church, Tim S. Hickey, One Columbus Plaza, New Haven, CT 06510 Tel. (203)752-4398 Fax (203)752-4109
E-mail: tim.hickey@kofc-supreme.com
Web site: www.kofc.org

The Commission, (7-Y.) International Mission Board, Southern Baptist Convention, Kathy Sharp, Box 6767, Richmond, VA 23230-0767 Tel. (804)219-1253 Fax (804)219-1410
E-mail: commission@imb.org
Web site: www.tconline.org

Common Lot, (Q.) United Church of Christ, Martha J. Hunter, 700 Prospect Ave., Cleveland, OH 44115 Tel. (216)736-2150 Fax (216)736-2156

Commonweal, (bi-W.) The Catholic Church, Paul Baumann, 475 Riverside Drive, Room 405, New York, NY 10115 Tel. (212)662-4200 Fax (212)662-4183
E-mail: editors@commonwealmagazine.org
Web site: www.commonwealmagazine.org

Communion, (bi-M.) Church of God (Anderson, Indiana), Arthur Kelly, P.O. Box 2420, 1201 E. 5th Street, Anderson, IN 46018-2420 Tel. (765)642-0256 Fax (765)652-5652
E-mail: AKelly@chog.org
Web site: chog.org/news/communion.asp

The Congregationalist, (5-Y.) National Association Congregational Christian Churches, Rev. James E. Eaton, 87 Broadway, Norwich, CT 06360 Tel. (860)889-1363 Fax (860)887-5715
E-mail: jeaton@unitedcongregational.org
Web site: www.congregationalist.org

Connections, (M.) The Alliance of Baptists in the U.S.A, Rev. Dr. Stan Hastey, 1328 16th St. N.W., Washington, DC 20036 Tel. (202)745-7609 Fax (202)745-0023
Web site: allianceofbaptists.org

Conqueror, (bi-M.) United Pentecostal Church International, John F. Sills, 8855 Dunn Rd., Hazelwood, MO 63042 Tel. (314)837-7300 Fax (314)837-4503
E-mail: GYouth8855@aol.com

Context, (M.) Nondenominational, Martin Marty, 205 W. Monroe St., Chicago, IL 60606-5013 Tel. (312)236-7782 Fax (312)236-8207
E-mail: editors@uscatholic.org
Web site: www.contextonline.org

Covenant, (Q.) Presbyterian Church in America, Eileen O'Gorman, Covenant Theological Seminary, 123330 Conway Road, St. Louis, MO 63141 Tel. (314)434-4044 Fax (314)434-4819
E-mail: eileen.ogorman@covenantseminary.edu
Web site: www.convenantseminary.edu

Cornerstone Connections, (Q.) Seventh-day Adventist Church, Gary B. Swanson, 12501 Old Columbia Pike, Silver Spring, MD 20904 Tel. (301)680-6160 Fax (301)680-6155

The Covenant Companion, (M.) Evangelical Covenant Church, Jane K. Swanson-Nystrom, Managing Editor, Donald L. Meyer, 5101 N. Francisco Ave., Chicago, IL 60625 Tel. (773)906-3328 Fax (773)784-4366
E-mail: communication@covchurch.org
Web site: www.covchurch.org/cov/companion

Covenant Home Altar, (Q.) Evangelical Covenant Church, Jane K. Swanson-Nystrom, 5101 N. Francisco Ave., Chicago, IL 60625 Tel. (773)784-3000 Fax (773)784-4366
E-mail: communication@covchurch.org

Covenant Quarterly, (Q.) Evangelical Covenant Church, Paul E. Koptak, 3225 W. Foster Ave., Chicago, IL 60625-4895 Tel. (773)244-6242
E-mail: pkoptak@northpark.edu

The Covenanter Witness, (11-Y.) Reformed Presbyterian Church of North America, Drew Gordon and Lynne Gordon, 7408 Penn Ave., Pittsburgh, PA 15208 Tel. (412)241-0436 Fax (412)731-8861
E-mail: info@psalms4u.com
Web site: www.psalms4u.com

Credinta–The Faith, (Q.) The Romanian Orthodox Church in America, V. Rev. Archim. Dr. Vasile Vasilac, 45-03 48th Ave., Woodside, Queens, NY 11377 Tel. (313)893-8390

The Cumberland Presbyterian, (11-Y.) Cumberland Presbyterian Church, Patricia P. White, Cumberland Presbyterian Church, 1978 Union Ave., Memphis, TN 38104 Tel. (615)731-5556
E-mail: cpmag@comcast.net
Web site: www.cumberland.org/cpmag

Currents in Theology and Mission, (bi-M.) Evangelical Lutheran Church in America, Ralph W. Klein, 1100 E. 55th St., Chicago, IL 60615 Tel. (773)256-0751 Fax (773)256-0782
E-mail: currents@lstc.edu
Web site: www.lstc.edu/pub_peo/pub/currents.html

Cutting Edge, (Q.) Association of Vineyard Churches, Jeff Bailey, VCF of Evanston, 1800 Ridge Ave., Evanston, IL 60201 Tel. (847)328-4544 Fax (847)328-5153
E-mail: cuttingedge@vineyardusa.org
Web site: www.vineyardusa.org/publications/newsletters/cutting_edge

Decision, (11-Y.) Nondenominational, Bob Paulson, 1 Billy Graham Parkway, Charlotte, NC 28201-0001 Tel. (704)401-2432 Fax (704)401-3009
E-mail: decision@bgea.org
Web site: www.decisionmag.org

DisciplesWorld, (10-Y.) Christian Church (Disciples of Christ) in the United States and Canada, Verity A. Jones, P.O. Box 11469, Indianapolis, IN 46201-0469 Tel. (317)375-8846 Fax (317)375-8849
Web site: www.disciplesworld.com

Ecu-Link, (Several Per Year) Interdenominational, Sarah Vilankulu, 475 Riverside Drive, 8th Floor, New York, NY 10115-0050 Tel. (212)870-2227 Fax (212) 870-2030
E-mail: svilankulu@ncccusa.org
Web site: www.ncccusa.org

Ecumenical Trends, (M.) Nondenominational, James Loughran, SA, Graymoor Ecumenical & Interreligious Institute, P.O. Box 300, Garrison, NY 10524-0300 Tel. (845)424-3671 ext. 3323 Fax (845)424-2163
E-mail: jloughran@atonementfriars.org
Web site: www.geii.org

Eleventh Hour Messenger, (bi-M.) Wesleyan Holiness Association of Churches, John Brewer, 11411 N US Hwy 27, Fountain City, IN 47341-9757 Tel. (317)584-3199

Elim Herald, (2-Y.) Elim Fellowship, Bernard J. Evans, 1703 Dalton Road, P.O. Box 57A, Lima, NY 14485 Tel. (585)582-2790 Fax (585)624-1229

E-mail: executive@elimfellowship.org
Web site: www.elimfellowhip.org

Enrichment: A Journal for Pentecostal Ministry, (Q.) Assemblies of God, Gary Allen; Rick Knoth, Managing Editor, 1445 N. Boonville Ave., Springfield, MO 65802 Tel. (417)862-2781 Fax (417)862-0416
E-mail: gallen@ag.org
Web site: www.enrichmentjournal.ag.org

The Ensign, (M.) The Church of Jesus Christ of Latter-day Saints, Brian K. Kelly, Managing Editor, 50 E North Temple Street, 24th Fl, Salt Lake City, UT 84150 Tel. (801)240-2950 Fax (801)240-5732

Episcopal Life, (M.) The Episcopal Church, Jerrold Hames, 815 Second Ave., New York, NY 10017-4503 Tel. (800)334-7626 Fax (212)949-8059
E-mail: jhames@episcopalchurch.org
Web site: www.episcopal-life.org

Equip, (bi-M.) Presbyterian Church in America, Dr. Charles Dunahoo, 1700 N. Brown Road Ste. 102, Lawrenceville, GA 30043 Tel. (678)825-1100 Fax (678)825-1101
E-mail: cep@pcanet.org
Web site: pcanet.org

The Evangel, (Q.) The Evangelical Church Alliance, Dr. Henry A. (Hank) Roso, P.O. Box 9, Bradley, IL 60915 Tel. (815)937-0720 Fax (815)937-0001
E-mail: info@ecainternatinal.org
Web site: www.ecainternational.org

The Evangel, (bi-M.) American Association of Lutheran Churches, The, Rev. Charles D. Eidum, 801 W. 106th St, Suite 203, Minneapolis, MN 55420-5603 Tel. (952)884-7784 Fax (952)884-7894
E-mail: aa2taalc@aol.com
Web site: www.taalc.com

The Evangelical Advocate, (M.) Churches of Christ in Christian Union, Ralph Hux, P.O. Box 30, Circleville, OH 43113 Tel. (740)474-8856 Fax (740)477-7766
E-mail: doc@cccuhg.org
Web site: www.cccuhq.org

Evangelical Beacon, (bi-M.) The Evangelical Free Church of America, Ms. Carol Madison, 901 East 78th St., Minneapolis, MN 55420-1300 Tel. (877)293-5653 Fax (952)853-8488
E-mail: beacon@efca.org
Web site: www.efca.org

Evangelical Challenge, (Q.) The Evangelical Church, Shirley Roehl, 9421 West River Road, Minneapolis, MN 55444 Tel. (763)424-2589 Fax (763)424-9230
E-mail: ecdenom@usfamily.net
Web site: www.theevangelicalchurch.org

The Evangelist, (W.) The Roman Catholic Church, James Breig, 40 N. Main Ave., Albany, NY 12203 Tel. (518)453-6688 Fax (518)453-8448
E-mail: james.breig@rcda.org
Web site: www.evangelist.org

Explorations, (Q.) Nondenominational, Irvin J. Borowsky, 321 Chestnut Street, 4th Floor, Philadelphia, PA 19106-2779 Tel. (215)925-2800 Fax (215)925-3800
E-mail: aii@interfaith-scholars.org

Extension, (M.) The Roman Catholic Church, Bradley Collins, 150 S. Wacker Drive, 20th Floor, Chicago, IL 60606 Tel. (312)236-7240 Fax (312)236-5276
E-mail: magazine@catholic-extension.org
Web site: www.catholic-extension.org

Face to Face, (Q.) Community of Christ, Richard A. Brown, Herald Publishing House, 1001 W. Walnut Street, Independence, MO 64050-3562 Tel. (816)833-1000 ext. 2144 Fax (816)521-3043
E-mail: rbrown@cofchrist.org
Web site: www.cofchrist.org

Faith & Fellowship, (M.) Church of the Lutheran Brethren of America, Brent Juliot, P.O. Box 655, Fergus Falls, MN 56538 Tel. (218)736-7357 Fax (218)736-2200
E-mail: ffpress@clba.org
Web site: www.faithandfellowship.org

Faith-Life, (bi-M.) Lutheran, Pastor Marcus Albrecht, 2107 N. Alexander St., Appleton, WI 54911 Tel. (920)733-1839 Fax (920)733-4834
E-mail: malbrecht@milwpc.com

Fellowship, (bi-M.) Interfaith, Richard Deats, P.O. Box 271, Nyack, NY 10960-0271 Tel. (845)358-4601 Fax (845)358-4924
E-mail: fellowship@forusa.org
Web site: www.forusa.org/

Fellowship Focus, (bi-M.) Fellowship of Evangelical Bible Churches, Sharon K. Berg, 3339 N 109th Plz, Omaha, NE 68164-2908 Tel. (402)965-3860 Fax (402)965-3871
E-mail: fellowshipfocus@febcministries.org
Web site: www.febcministries.org

Fellowship News, (M.) Bible Fellowship Church, Carol Snyder, 3000 Fellowship Drive, Whitehall, PA 18052-3343 Tel. (717)337-3408 Fax (215)536-2120
E-mail: ccsnyder@supernet.com
Web site: www.bfc.org

Fellowship Tidings, (Q.) Full Gospel Fellowship of Churches and Ministers Intern, S. K. Biffle, 1000 N. Beltline Road, Irving, TX 75061 Tel. (214)492-1254 Fax (214)492-1736
E-mail: FGFCMI@aol.com
Web site: www.fgfcmi.org

FGConnections, (3-Y.) Friends General Conference, Barbara Hirshkowitz, 1216 Arch Street 2B, Philadelphia, PA 19107 Tel. (215)561-1700 Fax (215)561-0759
E-mail: connections@fgcquaker.org
Web site: www.fgcquaker.org/connect

Firm Foundation, (M.) Churches of Christ, H. A. Dobbs, P.O. Box 690192, Houston, TX 77269-0192 Tel. (713)469-3102 Fax (713) 469-7115
E-mail: HAD@onramp.net

First Things: A Monthly Journal of Religion & Public Life, (10-Y.) Interdenominational, Richard J. Neuhaus, 156 Fifth Ave., Ste. 400, New York, NY 10010 Tel. (212)627-1985 Fax (212)627-2184
E-mail: ft@firstthings.com
Web site: www.firstthings.com

The Flaming Sword, (M.) Bible Holiness Church, Susan Davolt, 10th St. & College Ave., Independence, KS 67301 Tel. (316)331-2580 Fax (316)331-2580

Foresee, (bi-M.) Conservative Congregational Christian Conference, Carol Wells, 7582 Currell Blvd., #108, St. Paul, MN 55125 Tel. (651)739-1474 Fax (651)739-0750
E-mail: dmjohnson@ccccusa.org
Web site: www.ccccusa.org

Forum Letter, (M.) Independent, Intra-Lutheran (companion publication to the quarterly, *Lutheran Forum*), Pastor Russell E. Saltzman, Ruskin Heights Lutheran Church, 10801 Ruskin Way, Kansas City, MO 64134 Tel. (816)761-6815 Fax (816)761-6523
E-mail: Saltzman@integritynetwork.net
Web site: www.alpb.org

Forward, (Q.) United Pentecostal Church International, Rev. J. L. Hall, 8855 Dunn Rd., Hazelwood, MO 63042 Tel. (314)837-7300 Fax (314)837-4503

Forward in Christ, (M.) Wisconsin Evangelical Lutheran Synod, Gary Baumler, 2929 N. Mayfair Rd., Milwaukee, WI 53222 Tel. (414)256-3210 Fax (414)256-3862
E-mail: fic@sab.wels.net
Web site: www.wels.net

Foursquare World Advance, (Q. w/ bonus issue) International Church of the Foursquare Gospel, Dr. Ron Williams, P.O. Box 26902, 1910 W. Sunset Blvd., Ste 400, Los Angeles, CA 90026-0176 Tel. (213)989-4230 Fax (213)989-4544
E-mail: comm@foursquare.org
Web site: www.advancemagazine.org

Free Will Baptist Bible College Bulletin, (bi-M.) National Association of Free Will Baptists, Bert Tippett, 3606 West End Ave., Nashville, TN 37205 Tel. (615)383-1340 Fax (615)269-6028
E-mail: bert@fwbbc.edu
Web site: www.fwbbc.edu

Free Will Baptist Gem, (M.) National Association of Free Will Baptists, Gary Fry, P.O. Box 991, Lebanon, MO 65536 Tel. (417)532-6537 Fax (417)588-7068
E-mail: gwfry@webound.com

Friend Magazine, (M.) The Church of Jesus Christ of Latter-day Saints, Vivian Paulsen, 50 E. South Temple Street, 24th Fl., Salt Lake City, UT 84150 Tel. (801)240-2210 Fax (801)240-2270

Friends Bulletin, (10-Y.) Religious Society of Friends, Anthony Manousos, 5238 Andalucia Court, Whittier, CA 90601 Tel. (562)699-5670 Fax (562)692-2472
E-mail: friendsbul@aol.com
Web site: www.quaker.org/fb and www.quaker.org/western

Friends Journal, (M.) Religious Society of Friends (Quakers), Susan Corson-Finnerty, Publisher & Exec. Editor, 1216 Arch St., 2A, Philadelphia, PA 19107-2835 Tel. (215)563-8629 Fax (215)568-1377
E-mail: info@friendsjournal.org
Web site: www.friendsjournal.org

The Friends Voice, (3-Y.) Evangelical Friends International—North America Region, Becky Towne, Sr. Editor, Kathy Boblyer, Assoc. Editor, 2748 E. Pikes Peak Ave, Colorado Springs, CO 80909 Tel. (719)632-5721 Fax (719)635-4011
E-mail: voicephotos@codenet.net
Web site: evangelical-friends.org

Front Line, (Q.) Conservative Baptist Association of America, Al Russell, P.O. Box 58, Long Prairie, MN 56347 Tel. (320)732-8072 Fax (509)356-7112
E-mail: chaplruss@earthlink.net
Web site: www.cbchaplains.net

Full Gospel Ministries Outreach Report, (Q.) Full Gospel Assemblies International, Simeon Strauser, P.O. Box 1230, Coatsville, PA 19320 Tel. (610)857-2357 Fax (610)857-3109

The Gem, (W.) Churches of God, General Conference, Rachel Foreman, P.O. Box 926, Findlay, OH 45839 Tel. (419)424-1961 Fax (419) 424-3433
E-mail: communications@cggc.org
Web site: www.cggc.org

God's Field, (bi-W.) Polish National Catholic Church of America, Rev. Anthony Mikovsky (English) and Rt. Rev. Casimir Grotnik (Polish), 1006 Pittston Ave., Scranton, PA 18505-4109 Tel. (570)346-9131 Fax (570) 346-2188
E-mail: GodsField@adelphia.net
Web site: www.pncc.org

Good News–Buna Vestire, (Q.) The Romanian Orthodox Episcopate of America, The Romanian Orthodox Deanery of Canada, Psa. Alice Nenson, 2855 Helmsing St., Regina, SK S4V 0W7 CANADA Tel. (306)761-2379 Fax (306)525-9650
E-mail: danenson@accesscomm.ca

Gospel Advocate, (M.) Churches of Christ, Neil W. Anderson, 1006 Elm Hill Pike, Nashville, TN 37202 Tel. (615)254-8781 Fax (615)254-7411
E-mail: info@gospeladvocate.com
Web site: www.gospeladvocate.com

The Gospel Herald, (M.) Church of God, Mountain Assembly, Inc., Scott Isham, P.O. Box 157, Jellico, TN 37762 Tel. (423)784-8260 Fax (423)784-3258
E-mail: cgmahdq@jellico.com
Web site: www.cgmahdq.org

The Gospel Light, (2-Y.) The Bible Church of Christ, Inc., Carole Crenshaw, 1358 Morris Ave., Bronx, NY 10456 Tel. (718)588-2284 Fax (718)992-5597
Web site: www.thebiblechurchofchrist.org

The Gospel Messenger, (M.) Congregational Holiness Church, Inc., Cullen L. Hicks, Congregational Holiness Church, 3888 Fayetteville Highway, Griffin, GA 30223 Tel. (770)228-4833 Fax (770)228-1177
E-mail: CHChurch@bellsouth.net
Web site: www.CHChurch.com

The Gospel Truth, (bi-M.) Church of the Living God, C.W.F.F., W.E. Crumes, 430 Forest Avenue, Cincinnati, OH 45229 Tel. (513)569-5660 Fax (513)569-5661
E-mail: cwff430@aol.com

Grow Magazine, (Q.) Church of the Nazarene, Jim Dorsey, 6401 The Paseo, Kansas City, MO 64131 Tel. (816)333-7000 ext. 2828 Fax (816)523-1872
E-mail: jdorsey@nazarene.org
Web site: www.growmagazine.org

Guide, (W.) Seventh-day Adventist Church, Randy Fishell, 55 W. Oak Ridge Dr., Hagerstown, MD 21740 Tel. (301)393-4037 Fax (301)393-4055
E-mail: guide@rhpa.org
Web site: www.guidemagazine.org

The Handmaiden, (Q.) The Antiochian Orthodox Christian Archdiocese of North America, Virginia Nieuwsma, P.O. Box 76, Ben Lomond, CA 95005-0076 Tel. (831)336-5118 Fax (831)336-8882
E-mail: czell@conciliarpress.com
Web site: www.conciliarpress.com

The Happy Harvester, (M.) Church of God of Prophecy, Diane Pace, P.O. Box 2910, Cleveland, TN 37320-2910 Tel. (423)559-5435 Fax (423)559-5444
E-mail: JoDiPace@wingnet.net

Heartbeat, (bi-M.) National Association of Free Will Baptists, Deborah St. Lawrence, Foreign Missions Office, P.O. Box 5002, Antioch, TN 37011-5002 Tel. (615)731-6812 Fax (615) 731-5345
E-mail: Heartbeat@NAFWB.org
Web site: www.nafwb.org/fm

Herald, (M.) Community of Christ, Linda L. Booth, 1001 W. Walnut, Independence, MO 64050 Tel. (816)833-1000 Fax (816)521-3043
E-mail: jhannah@cofochrist.org
Web site: www.heraldhouse.org or www.cofchrist.org

The Herald of Christian Science, (M. & Q.) Church of Christ, Scientist, Mary M. Trammell, The Christian Science Publishing Society, One Norway St., Boston, MA 02115-3195 Tel. (617)450-2000 Fax (617)450-2930
E-mail: trammellm@csps.com/herald@csps.com
Web site: www.csherald.com

Heritage, (Q.) Assemblies of God, Wayne E. Warner, 1445 Boonville Ave., Springfield, MO 65802 Tel. (417)862-1447 Fax (417)862-6203
E-mail: wwarner@ag.org
Web site: www.agheritage.org

High Adventure, (Q.) Assemblies of God, Jerry Parks, Gospel Publishing House, 1445 N. Boonville Ave., Springfield, MO 65802-1894 Tel. (417)862-2781 Fax (417)831-8230
E-mail: rangers@ag.org
Web site: www.royalrangers.org

Higher Way, (Q.) Apostolic Faith Mission of Portland, Oregon, Darrel D. Lee, 6615 S.E. 52nd Ave., Portland, OR 97206 Tel. (503)777-1741 Fax (503)777-1743
E-mail: kbarrett@apostolicfaith.org
Web site: www.apostolicfaith.org

Holiness Today, (bi-M.) Church of the Nazarene, David J. Felter, 6401 The Paseo, Kansas City, MO 64131 Tel. (816)333-7000 Fax (816)333-1748
E-mail: HolinessToday@nazarene.org
Web site: www.holinesstoday.com

Homiletic and Pastoral Review, (M.) The Roman Catholic Church, Kenneth Baker, 50 S Franklin Tpk, P.O. Box 297, Ramsey, NJ 07446 Tel. (201)236-9336

Horizons, (M.) Christian Churches and Churches of Christ, Reggie Hundley, Box 13111, Knoxville, TN 37920-0111 Tel. (800)655-8524 Fax (865)573-5950
E-mail: msa@missionservices.org
Web site: www.missionservices.org

Horizons, (7-Y.) Presbyterian Church (U.S.A.), Leah Ellison Bradley, Susan Jackson Dowd, Presbyterian Women, 100 Witherspoon St., Louisville, KY 40202-1396 Tel. (502)569-5368 Fax (502)569-8085
E-mail: lbradley@ctr.pcusa.org
Web site: www.pcusa.org/horizons

The Inclusive Pulpit, (Y.) International Council of Community Churches, Robert Tuckett, 21116 Washington Pky., Frankfort, IL 60423-3112 Tel. (815)464-5690 Fax (815)464-5692
E-mail: iccc60423@aol.com
Web site: icccusa.com

Insight Into, (bi-M.) Netherlands Reformed Congregations, Mr. Schipper, 4732 E. C Avenue, Kalamazoo, MI 49004 Tel. (269)349-9448

InterLit, (Q.) Nondenominational, Kim A. Pettit, 4050 Lee Vance View Drive, Colorado Springs, CO 80918 Tel. (719)536-0100 Fax (719)536-3266
E-mail: ccmintl@ccmi.org
Web site: www.ccmi.org

International Bulletin of Missionary Research, (Q.) Nondenominational, Jonathan J. Bonk, Overseas Ministries Study Center, 490 Prospect St., New Haven, CT 06511-2196 Tel. (203)624-6672 Fax (203)865-2857
E-mail: ibmr@OMSC.org
Web site: www.OMSC.org or www.DACB.org

Interpretation: A Journal of Bible and Theology, (Q.) Presbyterian Church (U.S.A.), Co-Editors, James Brashler and Sam Balentine, 3401 Brook Rd., Richmond, VA 23227 Tel. (804)278-4296 Fax (804)278-4208
E-mail: E-mail@interpretation.org
Web site: www.interpretation.org

el Intérprete, (bi-M.) The United Methodist Church, Martha E. Rovira Raber, P.O. Box 320, Nashville, TN 37202-0320 Tel. (615)742-5115 Fax (615)742-5460
E-mail: mraber@umcom.org
Web site: www.interpretermagazine.org

Interpreter, (8-Y.) The United Methodist Church, M. Garlinda Burton, P.O. Box 320, Nashville, TN 37202-0320 Tel. (615)742-5102 Fax (615)742-5460
E-mail: gburton@umcom.org
Web site: www.interpretermagazine.org

IPHC Experience, (bi-M.) International Pentecostal Holiness Church, Shirley Spencer, P.O. Box 12609, Oklahoma City, OK 73157 Tel. (405)787-7110 Fax (405)789-3957
Web site: www.iphc.org/wms

John Three Sixteen, (Q.) Bible Holiness Church, Mary Cunningham, 10th St. & College Ave., Independence, KS 67301 Tel. (316)331-2580 Fax (316)331-2580

Journal of Adventist Education, (5-Y.) Seventh-Day Adventist Church, Beverly J. Robinson-Rumble, 12501 Old Columbia Pike, Silver Spring, MD 20904-6600 Tel. (301)680-5075 / (301)680-5069 Fax (301)622-9627
E-mail: rumbleb@gc.adventist.org or goffc@gc.adventist.org
Web site: education.gc.adventist.org/jae

Journal of the American Academy of Religion, (Q.) Nondenominational, Glenn Yocum, Whittier College, P.O. Box 634, Whittier, CA 90608-0634 Tel. (562)907-4200 Fax (562) 907-4910
E-mail: gyocum@whittier.edu
Web site: www.aarweb.org

Journal of Christian Education, (Q.) African Methodist Episcopal Church, Kenneth H. Hill, 500 Eighth Ave., S., Nashville, TN 37203 Tel. (615)242-1420 Fax (615)726-1866
E-mail: ameced@edge.net
Web site: www.ameced.com

Journal of Ecumenical Studies, (Q.) Interdenominational/Interfaith, Leonard Swidler, Temple Univ. (022-38), 1114 West Berks St.-Anderson 511, Philadelphia, PA 19122-6090 Tel. (215)204-7714 Fax (215)204-4569
E-mail: nkrody@astro.temple.edu

The Journal of Pastoral Care & Counseling, (Q.) Nondenominational, Orlo Strunk Jr., 1068 Harbor Dr. SW, Calabash, NC 28467 Tel. (910)579-5084 Fax (910)579-5084
E-mail: jpcp@jpcp.org
Web site: www.jpcp.org

Journal of Presbyterian History, (Q.) Presbyterian Church (U.S.A.), James H. Moorhead, Frederick J. Heuser, Jr., Tricia Manning, Managing Editor, 425 Lombard St.,

Philadelphia, PA 19147 Tel. (215)627-1852 Fax (215)627-0509
E-mail: tmanning@history.pcusa.org
Web site: www.history.pcusa.org

Journal From the Radical Reformation, (Q.) Church of God General Conference (Morrow, GA), Kent Ross and Anthony Buzzard, Sr., Box 100,000, Morrow, GA 30260-7000 Tel. (404)362-0052 Fax (404)362-9307
E-mail: kenthross@cs.com
Web site: www.abc-coggc.org

Journal of Theology, (Q.) Church of the Lutheran Confession, Prof. Paul Schaller, Immanuel Lutheran College, 501 Grover Rd., Eau Claire, WI 54701-7199 Tel. (715)832-9936 Fax (715)836-6634
E-mail: schallers@usa.net
Web site: www.primenet.com/~clcpub/clc/clc.html

The Joyful Noiseletter, (10-Y.) Interdenominational, Cal Samra, P.O. Box 895, Portage, MI 49081-0895 Tel. (616)324-0990 Fax (616) 324-3984
E-mail: joyfulnz@aol.com
Web site: www.joyfulnoiseletter.com

Judaism, (Q.) Jewish, Murray Baumgarten, 15 E. 84th St., New York, NY 10028 Tel. (212)879-4500 Fax (212)249-3672
E-mail: judaism@cats.ucsc.edu

Keeping in Touch, (bi-W.) Universal Fellowship of Metropolitan Community Churches, James N. Birkitt, Jr., 8704 Santa Monica Blvd, 2nd Fl., West Hollywood, CA 90069-4548 Tel. (310)360-8640 Fax (310)360-8680
E-mail: info@mccchurch.org
Web site: www.mccchurch.org

Key Lay Notes, (2-Y.) International Council of Community Churches, Stephan Nash, 21116 Washington Pky., Frankfort, IL 60423-3112 Tel. (815)464-5690 Fax (815)464-5692
E-mail: iccc60423@aol.com
Web site: icccusa.com

The Lantern, (bi-M.) National Baptist Convention of America, Inc., Robert Jeffrey, 1320 Pierre Avenue, Shreveport, LA 71103 Tel. (318)221-3701 Fax (318)222-7512

Leadership: A Practical Journal for Church Leaders, (Q.) Nondenominational, Marshall Shelley, 465 Gundersen Dr., Carol Stream, IL 60188 Tel. (630)260-6200 Fax (630)260-0114
E-mail: LJeditor@leadershipjournal.net
Web site: www.leadershipjournal.net

Learning and Living, (Q.) Netherlands Reformed Congregations, David Engelsma, 1000 Ball NE, Grand Rapids, MI 49505 Tel. (616)458-4367 Fax (616)458-8532
E-mail: engelsma@plymouthchristian.put.k12.mi.us

Liahona, The Church of Jesus Christ of Latter-day Saints, Marvin K. Gardner, 50 East North Temple St., 24th Floor, Salt Lake City, UT 84150-3220 Tel. (801)240-2490 Fax (801) 240-4225
E-mail: CUR-Liahona-IMag@ldschurch.org
Web site: www.lds.org

Liberty, (bi-M.) Seventh-day Adventist Church, Clifford R. Goldstein, 12501 Old Columbia Pike, Silver Spring, MD 20904 Tel. (301)680-6691 Fax (301)680-6695

Lifeglow, (Q.) Seventh-day Adventist Church, Large Print, Gaylena Gibson, Christian Record Services, Inc., P.O. Box 6097, Lincoln, NE 68506 Tel. (402)488-0981 Fax (402)488-7582
E-mail: editorial@christianrecord.org
Web site: www.christianrecord.org

Light and Life Magazine, (bi-M.) Free Methodist Church, Douglas M. Newton, P.O. Box 535002, Indianapolis, IN 46253-5002 Tel. (317)244-3660
E-mail: llmeditor@fmcna.org
Web site: www.freemethodistchurch.org

Liguorian, (10-Y.) The Roman Catholic Church, William J. Parker, C.SS.R., 1 Liguori Dr., Liguori, MO 63057 Tel. (636)464-2500 Fax (636)464-8449
E-mail: liguorianeditor@liguori.org
Web site: www.liguorian.org

Listen, (Sep.-May) Seventh-day Adventist Church, Céleste Walker, 55 W. Oak Ridge Dr., Hagerstown, MD 21740 Tel. (301)393-4082 Fax (301)393-4055
E-mail: listen@healthconnection.org
Web site: www.listenmagazine.org

Living Orthodoxy, (bi-M.) The Russian Orthodox Church Outside of Russia, Fr. Gregory Williams, 1180 Orthodox Way, Liberty, TN 37095 Tel. (615)536-5239 Fax (615)536-5945
E-mail: info@sjkb.org
Web site: www.sjkb.org

The Long Island Catholic, (W.) The Roman Catholic Church, Elizabeth O'Connor, P. O. Box 9000, 200 W Centennial Ave Suite 201, Roosevelt, NY 11575 Tel. (516)594-1000 Fax (516)594-1092
Web site: www.licatholic.org

The Lookout, (W.) Christian Churches and Churches of Christ, Shawn McMullen, 8121

Hamilton Ave., Cincinnati, OH 45231 Tel. (513)931-4050 Fax (513)931-0950
E-mail: lookout@standardpub.com
Web site: www.lookoutmag.com

Lumicon Digital Productions, (I.) Independent, Protestant, Rev. Dr. Tom Boomershine, UMR Communications, P.O. Box 660275, Dallas, TX 75266-0275 Tel. (214)630-6495 Fax (214) 630-0079
E-mail: tboom@umr.org
Web site: www.lumicon.org

The Lutheran, (M.) Evangelical Lutheran Church in America, Rev. David L. Miller, 8765 W. Higgins Rd., Chicago, IL 60631-4183 Tel. (773)380-2540 Fax (773)380-2751
E-mail: lutheran@elca.org
Web site: www.thelutheran.org

The Lutheran Ambassador, (16-Y.) The Association of Free Lutheran Congregations, Craig Johnson, 575 34th Street, Astoria, OR 97103 Tel. (541)687-8643 Fax (541)683-8496
E-mail: cjohnson@efn.org

The Lutheran Educator, (Q.) Wisconsin Evangelical Lutheran Synod, Prof. John R. Isch, Martin Luther College, 1995 Luther Ct., New Ulm, MN 56073 Tel. (507)354-8221 Fax (507)354-8225
E-mail: lutheraneducator@mlc-wels.edu

Lutheran Forum, (Q.) Interdenominational Lutheran, Ronald B. Bagnall, 207 Hillcrest Ave., Trenton, NJ 08618 Tel. (856)696-0417

The Lutheran Layman, (bi-M.) The Lutheran Church—Missouri Synod, Gerald Perschbacher, 660 Mason Ridge Center Dr, St. Louis, MO 63141-8557 Tel. (314)317-4100 Fax (314) 317-4295

Lutheran Partners, (bi-M.) Evangelical Lutheran Church in America, William Decker, 8765 W. Higgins Rd., Chicago, IL 60631-4195 Tel. (773)380-2884 Fax (773)380-2829
E-mail: lutheran_partners@ecunet.org or lpartmag@elca.org
Web site: www.elca.org/lp

Lutheran Sentinel, (M.) Evangelical Lutheran Synod, Theodore Gullixson, 105 Indian Ave., Forest City, IA 50436 Tel. (641)585-1683 Fax (641)585-1683
E-mail: elsentinel@wctatel.net

The Lutheran Spokesman, (M.) Church of the Lutheran Confession, Rev. Paul Fleischer, 1741 E. 22nd St., Cheyenne, WY 82001 Tel. (307)638-8006
E-mail: paulgf@lakes.com
Web site: www.lutheranspokeman.org

Lutheran Synod Quarterly, (Q.) Evangelical Lutheran Synod, G.R. Schmeling, Bethany Lutheran Theological Semi, 6 Browns Ct., Mankato, MN 56001 Tel. (507)344-7855 Fax (507)344-7426
E-mail: elsynod@blc.edu
Web site: www.blts.edu

The Lutheran Witness, (M.) The Lutheran Church—Missouri Synod, Rev. David Mahsman, 1333 S. Kirkwood Road, St. Louis, MO 63122-7295 Tel. (314)965-9000 Fax (314)966-1126
E-mail: lutheran.witness@lcms.org
Web site: www.lcms.org/witness

Lutheran Woman Today, (10-Y.) Evangelical Lutheran Church in America, Nancy Goldberger, 8765 W. Higgins Rd., Chicago, IL 60631-4101 Tel. (773)380-2730 Fax (773) 380-2419
E-mail: lwt@elca.org
Web site: www.elca.org/wo/lwthome.html

Lyceum Spotlight, (10-Y.) National Spiritualist Association of Churches, Rev. Cosie Allen, 1418 Hall St., Grand Rapids, MI 49506 Tel. (616)241-2761 Fax (616)241-4703
E-mail: cosie@dnx.net
Web site: www.nsac.org/spotlight

Magyar Egyhaz—Magyar Church, (Q.) Hungarian Reformed Church in America, Stephen Szabo, 464 Forest Ave., Paramus, NJ 7652 Tel. (201)262-2338 Fax (845)359-5771

Mar Thoma Messenger, (Q.) Mar Thoma Syrian Church of India, Abraham Mattackal, 2320 S. Merrick Ave, Merrick, NY 11566 Tel. (516)377-3311 Fax (516)377-3322
E-mail: marthoma@aol.com

Maranatha, (Q.) Advent Christian Church, Dawn Rutan, P.O. Box 23152, Charlotte, NC 28227 Tel. (704)545-6161 Fax (704)573-0712
E-mail: acpub@adventchristian.org
Web site: www.adventchristian.org

Marriage Partnership, (Q.) Nondenominational, Ginger Kolbaba, Managing Editor, 465 Gundersen Dr., Carol Stream, IL 60188 Tel. (630)260-6200 Fax (630)260-0114
E-mail: mp@marriagepartnership.com
Web site: www.marriagepartnership.com

Mature Years, (Q.) The United Methodist Church, Marvin W. Cropsey, 201 Eighth Ave. S., Nashville, TN 37202 Tel. (615)749-6292 Fax (615)749-6512
E-mail: matureyears@umpublishing.org

The Mennonite, (24-Y.) Mennonite Church USA, Everett Thomas, 1700 S. Main St., Goshen, IN 46526 Tel. (219)535-6051 Fax (219)535-6050
E-mail: editor@themennonite.org
Web site: www.themennonite.org

Mennonite Historical Bulletin, (Q.) Mennonite Church USA, John E. Sharp, 1700 South Main St., Goshen, IN 46526 Tel. (574)535-7477 Fax (574)535-7756
E-mail: archives@goshen.edu
Web site: www.mcusa-archives.org

Mennonite Quarterly Review, (Q.) Mennonite Church, John D. Roth, 1700 S. Main St., Goshen, IN 46526 Tel. (574)535-7433 Fax (574)535-7438
E-mail: MQR@goshen.edu
Web site: www.goshen.edu/mgr

Message, (bi-M.) Seventh-day Adventist Church, Dr. Ron C. Smith, 55 West Oak Ridge Dr., Hagerstown, MD 21740 Tel. (301)393-4099 Fax (301)393-4100
E-mail: pharris@rhpa.org OR ronsmith@rhpa.org
Web site: MESSAGEMAGAZINE.org

Message of the Open Bible, (bi-M.) Open Bible Standard Churches, Inc., Andrea Johnson, 2020 Bell Ave., Des Moines, IA 50315-1096 Tel. (515)288-6761 Fax (515)288-2510
E-mail: message@openbible.org
Web site: www.openbible.org

The Messenger, (M.) Pentecostal Free Will Baptist Church, Inc., George Thomas, P.O. Box 1568, Dunn, NC 28335 Tel. (910)892-4161 Fax (910)892-6876

The Messenger, (M.) The Swedenborgian Church, Patte LeVan, P.O. Box 985, Julian, CA 92036 Tel. (760)765-2915
E-mail: messenger@julianweb.com
Web site: www.swedenborg.org

Messenger, (11-Y.) Church of the Brethren, Walt Wiltschek, 1451 Dundee Ave., Elgin, IL 60120 Tel. (847)742-5100 Fax (847)742-1407
E-mail: wmcfadden_gb@brethren.org

Messenger of Truth, (bi-W.) Church of God in Christ (Mennonite), Gladwin Koehn, P.O. Box 230, Moundridge, KS 67107 Tel. (620)345-2532 Fax (620)345-2582
E-mail: gospelpublishers@cogicm.org

Methodist History, (Q.) The United Methodist Church, Charles Yrigoyen Jr., P.O. Box 127, Madison, NJ 07940 Tel. (973)408-3189 Fax (973)408-3909
E-mail: cyrigoyen@gcah.org
Web site: www.gcah.org

Ministry, (M.) Seventh-day Adventist Church, Willmore D. Eva, 12501 Old Columbia Pike, Silver Spring, MD 20904 Tel. (301)680-6510 Fax (301)680-6502
E-mail: 74532.2425@compuserve.com

Mission, Adult, and Youth Children's Editions, (Q.) Seventh-day Adventist Church, Charlotte Ishkanian, 12501 Old Columbia Pike, Silver Spring, MD 20904 Tel. (301)680-6167 Fax (301)680-6155
E-mail: 74532.2435@compuserve.com

Mission Connection, (Q.) Wisconsin Evangelical Lutheran Synod, Rev. Gary Baumler, 2929 N. Mayfair Rd., Milwaukee, WI 53222 Tel. (414)256-3210 Fax (414)256-3862
E-mail: mc@sab.wels.net

Mission Herald, (bi-M.) National Baptist Convention, U.S.A., Inc., Dr. Bruce N. Alick, 701 S. 19th Street, Philadelphia, PA 19146 Tel. (215)735-9853 Fax (215)735-1721

Mission Report, (Q.) Presbyterian Church in America, Fred Marsh, 1700 North Brown Road, Mission to North America, Ste. 101, Lawerenceville, GA 30044 Tel. (678)825-1200 Fax (678)825-1201
E-mail: mna@pcanet.org
Web site: pcanet.org/mna

Missionary Church Today, (bi-M.) The Missionary Church, Rev. Thomas Murphy, P.O. Box 9127, Ft. Wayne, IN 46899 Tel. (260)747-2027 Fax (260)747-5331
E-mail: tom_murphy@mcusa.org
Web site: www.mcusa.org

The Missionary Messenger, (bi-M.) Christian Methodist Episcopal Church, Doris F. Boyd, 213 Viking Dr., W., Cordova, TN 38018 Tel. (901)757-1103 Fax (901)751-2104
E-mail: doris.boyd@williams.com

The Missionary Messenger, (bi-M.) Cumberland Presbyterian Church, Michael G. Sharpe, 1978 Union Ave., Memphis, TN 38104 Tel. (901)276-9988 Fax (901)276-4578
E-mail: messenger@cumberland.org
Web site: www.cumberland.org/bom/Communication_nd_Publication_Unit/MissionaryMessenger. htm

Missionary Seer, (bi-M.) African Methodist Episcopal Zion Church, Rev. Kermit J. DeGraffenreidt, 475 Riverside Dr., Rm. 1935, New York, NY 10115 Tel. (212)870-2952 Fax (212)870-2808
E-mail: domkd5@aol.com

The Missionary Signal, (bi-M.) Churches of God, General Conference, Rachel Foreman, P.O. Box 926, Findlay, OH 45839 Tel. (419)424-1961 Fax (419)424-3433
E-mail: communications@cggc.org
Web site: cggc.org

The Moravian, (10-Y.) Moravian Church in North America (Unitas Fratrum), Deanna L. Hollenbach, Dir. Of Communication, Interprovincial Bd. Of Communication, 1021 Center St., P.O. Box 1245, Bethlehem, PA 18016 Tel. (610)867-0593 Fax (610)866-9223
E-mail: pubs@mcnp.org
Web site: www.moravian.org

The Mother Church, (bi-M.) Western Diocese of the Armenian Church of North America, Archpriest Fr. Sipan Mekhsian, 3325 N. Glenoaks Blvd., Burbank, CA 91504 Tel. (818)558-7474 Fax (818)558-6333
E-mail: armenianchwd@earthlink.net
Web site: www.armenianchurchwd.com

NABtoday, (bi-M.) North American Baptist Conference, Marilyn Schaer, 1 S. 210 Summit Ave., Oakbrook Terrace, IL 60181 Tel. (630) 495-2000 Fax (630)495-3301
E-mail: NABtoday@nabconf.org
Web site: NABConference.org

NAE Washington Insight, (M.) Interdenominational, Rev. Richard Cizik, 718 Capitol Square Place, SW, Washington, DC 20024 Tel. (202)789-1011
E-mail: rcizik@aol.com
Web site: www.nae.net

National Catholic Reporter, (44-Y.) The Catholic Church, Tom Roberts, P.O. Box 419281, Kansas City, MO 64141 Tel. (816) 531-0538 Fax (816)968-2280
E-mail: editor@natcath.org
Web site: www.NCRonline.org

The National Spiritualist Summit, (M.) National Spiritualist Association of Churches, Rev. Sandra Pfortmiller, 3521 W. Topeka Dr., Glendale, AZ 85308-2325 Tel. (623)581-6686 Fax (623)581-5544
E-mail: G2s2pfort@aol.com
Web site: www.nsac.org

Network, (Q.) Presbyterian Church in America, Susan Fikse, 1600 North Brown Road, Lawrenceville, GA 30047 Tel. (678)823-0004 Fax (678)823-0027
Web site: pca.org

New Church Life, (M.) General Church of the New Jerusalem, Rev. Donald L. Rose, Box 277, Bryn Athyn, PA 19009 Tel. (215)947-6225 ext. 209 Fax (215)938-1871
E-mail: DonR@BACS-GC.org
Web site: www.newchurch.org

New Horizons in the Orthodox Presbyterian Church, (11-Y.) The Orthodox Presbyterian Church, Danny E. Olinger, 607 N. Easton Rd., Bldg. E, P.O. Box P, Willow Grove, PA 19090-0920 Tel. (215)830-0900 Fax (215)830-0350
E-mail: olinger.1@opc.org
Web site: www.opc.org/

New Oxford Review, (11-Y.) The Catholic Church, Dale Vree, 1069 Kains Ave., Berkeley, CA 94706 Tel. (510)526-5374 Fax (510)526-3492
Web site: www.newoxfordreview.org

New World Outlook, (bi-M.) Mission magazine of the United Methodist Church, Christie R. House, 475 Riverside Dr., Rm. 1476, New York, NY 10115 Tel. (212)870-3765 Fax (212) 870-3654
E-mail: NWO@gbgm-umc.org
Web site: gbgm-umc.org/now

Newscope, (W.) The United Methodist Church, Andrew J. Schleicher, P.O. Box 801, Nashville, TN 37202 Tel. (615)749-6320 Fax (615)749-6512
E-mail: aschleicher@umpublishing.org
Web site: www.umph.org

Newsline, (I.; Bi-W.) Church of the Brethern, Cheryl Brumbaugh-Cayford, 1451 Dundee Ave., Elgin, IL 60120-1694 Tel. (847)742-5100 Fax (847)742-6103
E-mail: cobnews@aol.com

NONE, Fellowship of Evangelical Church, 1420 Kerrway Ct., Fort Wayne, IN 46805 Tel. (260)423-3649 Fax (260)420-1905
E-mail: emchdq@aol.com
Web site: www.fecministries.org

North American Baptist Conference, (bi-M.) North American Baptist Conference, Lucinda Armas, 1 S. 210 Summit Ave., Oakbrook Terrace, IL 60184 Tel. (630)495-2000 Fax (630)495-3300
E-mail: serve@nabconference.org
Web site: www.nabconference.org

The North American Catholic, (M.) North American Old Roman Catholic Church, Theodore J. Remalt, 4154 W. Berteau Ave, Chicago, IL 60641 Tel. (312)685-0461 Fax (312) 485-0461
E-mail: chapelhall@aol.com

The North American Challenge, (M.) Home Missions Division of The United

Pentecostal Church International, Joseph Fiorino, 8855 Dunn Rd., Hazelwood, MO 63042-2299 Tel. (314)837-7300 Fax (314)837-5632

NRB Magazine, (9-Y.) Nondenominational, Christine Pryor, National Religious Broadcasters, 9510 Technology Drive, Manassas, VA 20110 Tel. (703)330-7000 Fax (703)330-6996
E-mail: cpryor@nrb.org
Web site: www.nrb.org

On Course, (bi-M.) Assemblies of God, Kristi Arnold and Amber Weigand-Buckley (Interim co-editors), 1445 N. Boonville Ave., Springfield, MO 65802-1894 Tel. (417)862-2781 Fax (417)862-1693
E-mail: oncourse@ag.org
Web site: oncourse.ag.org

On the Line, (M.) Mennonite Church, Mary C. Meyer, 616 Walnut Ave., Scottdale, PA 15683 Tel. (724)887-8500 Fax (724)887-3111
E-mail: otl@mph.org
Web site: www.mph.org/otl

On Mission, (Q.) Southern Baptist Convention, Carolyn Curtis, 4200 North Point Pkwy., Alpharetta, GA 30202-4174 Tel. (770)410-6394 Fax (770)410-6105
Web site: www.onmission.com

Orthodox America, (8-Y.) The Russian Orthodox Church Outside of Russia, Mary Mansur, P.O. Box 383, Richfield Springs, NY 13439-0383 Tel. (315)858-1518
E-mail: info@orthodoxamerica.org
Web site: www.orthodoxamerica.org

The Orthodox Church, (M.) The Orthodox Church in America, Very Rev. John Matusiak, Managing Editor, Very Rev. Leonid Kishkovsky, Editor, Editorial Office, One Wheaton Center #912, Wheaton, IL 60187 Tel. (630)668-3071 Fax (630)668-5712
E-mail: tocmed@hotmail.com
Web site: www.oca.org

Orthodox Family, (Q.) The Russian Orthodox Church Outside of Russia, George Johnson and Deborah Johnson, P.O. Box 45, Beltsville, MD 20705 Tel. Fax (301)890-3552
E-mail: 1lew@cais.com
Web site: www.roca.org/orthodox

Orthodox Life, (bi-M.) The Russian Orthodox Church Outside of Russia, Fr. Luke, Holy Trinity Monastery, P.O Box 36, Jordanville, NY 13361-0036 Tel. (315)858-0940 Fax (315)858-0505
E-mail: 72204.1465@compuserve.com

The Orthodox Observer, (M.) Greek Orthodox Archdiocese of America, Stavros H. Papagermanos, 8 E. 79th St., New York, NY 10021 Tel. (212)570-3555 Fax (212)774-0239
E-mail: observer@goarch.org
Web site: www.observer.goarch.org

Orthodox Russia (English translation of Pravoslavnaya Rus), (24-Y.) The Russian Orthodox Church Outside of Russia, Archbishop Laurus, Holy Trinity Monastery, P.O. Box 36, Jordanville, NY 13361-0036 Tel. (315)858-0940 Fax (315)858-0505
E-mail: orthrus@telenet.net

The Other Side, (bi-M.) Interdenominational, Dee Dee Risher, 300 W. Apsley St., Philadelphia, PA 19144-4221 Tel. (215)849-2178 Fax (215)849-3755
E-mail: editors@theotherside.org
Web site: www.theotherside.org

Our Daily Bread, (M.) The Swedenborgian Church, Lee Woofenden, P.O. Box 396, Bridgewater, MA 02324 Tel. (508)946-1767 Fax (508)946-1757
E-mail: odb@swedenborg.org
Web site: www.swedenborg.org/odb/index.cfm

Our Little Friend, (W.) Seventh-Day Adventist Church, Aileen Andres Sox, P.O. Box 5353, Nampa, ID 83653-5353 Tel. (208)465-2500 Fax (208)465-2531
E-mail: ailsox@pacificpress.com
Web site: www.pacificpress.com

Our Sunday Visitor, (W.) The Catholic Church, Gerald Korson, 200 Noll Plaza, Huntington, IN 46750 Tel. (219)356-8400
E-mail: oursunvis@osv.com
Web site: www.osv.com

Outreach, (bi-M.) Armenian Apostolic Church of America, Iris Papazian, 138 E. 39th St., New York, NY 10016 Tel. (212)689-7810 Fax (212)689-7168
E-mail: info@armenianprelacy.org
Web site: www.armenianprelacy.org

Pastor Talk, (Q.) General Association of General Baptists, Fred Brittian, 100 Stinson Drive, Poplar Bluff, MO 63901 Fax (573)785-0564
E-mail: pmdir@generalbaptist.com

Pastoral Life, (M.) The Catholic Church, Matthew Roehrig, 9531 Akron-Canfield Road, Canfield, OH 44406-0595 Tel. (330)533-5503
E-mail: plmagazine@hotmail.com
Web site: www.albahouse.org

The Path of Orthodoxy (Serbian), (M.) Serbian Orthodox Church in the U.S.A. and Canada, V. Rev. Nedeljko Lunich, 300 Striker Ave., Joliet, IL 60436 Tel. (815)741-1023 Fax (815) 741-1883
E-mail: nedlunich300@comcast.net

Paul, (Q.) Netherlands Reformed Congregations, J. Spans, 47 Main Street E., Norwich, ON NOJ 1PO CANADA Tel. (519)863-3306 Fax (519)863-2793

Today's Pentecostal Evangel, (W.) Assemblies of God, Hal Donaldson, Gospel Publishing House, 1445 N. Boonville Ave., Springfield, MO 65802-1894 Tel. (417)862-2781 Fax (417)862-0416
E-mail: pe@ag.org
Web site: www.pe.ag.org

Pentecostal Evangel, Missions World Edition, (M.) Assemblies of God, Hal Donaldson, Editor in Chief, Gospel Publishing House, 1445 N. Boonville Ave., Springfield, MO 65802 Tel. (417)862-2781 Fax (417)862-0416
E-mail: pe@ag.org
Web site: www.pe.ag.org

The Pentecostal Herald, (M.) United Pentecostal Church International, Rev. J. L. Hall, 8855 Dunn Rd., Hazelwood, MO 63042 Tel. (314)837-7300 Fax (314)837-4503

Pentecostal Leader, (bi-M.) The International Pentecostal Church of Christ, Clyde M. Hughes, P.O. Box 439, London, OH 43140 Tel. (740)852-4722 Fax (740)852-0348
E-mail: hqipcc@aol.com
Web site: www.IPCC.CC

The Pentecostal Messenger, (M.) Pentecostal Church of God (Joplin, MO), John Mallinak, P.O. Box 850, Joplin, MO 64802 Tel. (417)624-7050 Fax (417)624-7102
E-mail: johnm@pcg.org
Web site: www.pcg.org

Perspectives, (10-Y.) Reformed Church in America, Roy M. Anker, David E. Timmer, Leanne Van Dyk (co-editors), P.O. Box 1196, Holland, MI 49422-1196 Tel. (616)392-8555 ext. 131 Fax (616)392-7717
E-mail: perspectives@hotmail.com
Web site: www.perspectivesjournal.org

Perspectives on Science and Christian Faith, (Q.) Nondenominational, Dr. Roman J. Miller, 4956 Singers Glen Rd., Harrisonburg, VA 22802 Tel. (540)432-4412 Fax (540)432-4488
E-mail: millerrj@rica.net
Web site: www.asa3.org

The Pilot–America's Oldest Catholic Newspaper, (W.) The Roman Catholic Archdiocese of Boston, Antonio Enrique, 2121 Commonwealth Ave., Brighton, MA 02135 Tel. (617) 746-5889 Fax (617)783-2684
E-mail: editorial@bostonpilot.org
Web site: www.rcab.org

Pockets, (11-Y.) The United Methodist Church, Lynn W. Gilliam, P.O. Box 340004, Nashville, TN 37203-0004 Tel. (615)340-7333 Fax (615) 340-7267
E-mail: pockets@upperroom.org
Web site: www.pockets.org

Polka, (Q.) Polish National Catholic Church of America, Cecelia Lallo, 1127 Frieda St., Dickson City, PA 18519-1304 Tel. (570)489-4364 Fax (570)346-2188

Pravoslavnaya Rus (Russian), (24-Y.) The Russian Orthodox Church Outside of Russia, Archbishop Laurus, Holy Trinity Monastery, P.O. Box 36, Jordanville, NY 13361-0036 Tel. (315)858-0940 Fax (315)858-0505
E-mail: orthrus@telenet.net

Pravoslavnaya Zhisn (Monthly Supplement to Pravoslavnaya Rus), (M.) The Russian Orthodox Church Outside of Russia, Archbishop Laurus, Holy Trinity Monastery, P.O. Box 36, Jordanville, NY 13361-0036 Tel. (315)858-0940 Fax (315)858-0505
E-mail: Orthrus@telenet.net

Preacher's Magazine, (bi-M.) Church of the Nazarene, Randal Denney, 6401 Paseo Blvd, Kansas City, MO 64131-1213

Presbyterian News Service "The News," (bi-M.) Presbyterian Church (U.S.A.), Jerry L. VanMarter, 100 Witherspoon St., Rm. 5418, Louisville, KY 40202 Tel. (502)569-5493 Fax (502)569-8073
E-mail: JVanMart@ctr.pcusa.org
Web site: www.pcusa.org/pcnews

Presbyterian Outlook, (43-Y.) Robert H. Bullock Jr., Box 85623, Richmond, VA 23285-5623 Tel. (804)359-8442 Fax (804)353-6369
E-mail: rbullock@pres-outlook.com
Web site: www.pres-outlook.com

Presbyterians Today, (10-Y.) Presbyterian Church (U.S.A.), Eva Stimson, 100 Witherspoon St., Louisville, KY 40202-1396 Tel. (502)569-5637 Fax (502)569-8632
Web site: www.pcusa.org/today

Primary Source, (Q.) American Baptist Historical Society, Deborah Van Broekhoven, P.O. Box 851, Valley Forge, PA 19482-0851 Tel. Fax (610)768-2266
E-mail: dbvanbro@abc-usa.org
Web site: www.abc-usa.org/abhs

Primary Treasure, (W.) Seventh-day Adventist Church, Aileen Andres Sox, P.O. Box 5353, Nampa, ID 83653-5353 Tel. (208)465-2500 Fax (208)465-2531
E-mail: ailsox@pacificpress.com
Web site: www.pacificpress.com

Priority, (M.) Missionary Church, Dr. Thomas Murphy, P.O. Box 9127, Ft. Wayne, IN 46899 Tel. (260)747-2027 Fax (260)747-5331
E-mail: mcdenomusa@aol.com
Web site: mcusa.org

Pulse, (M.) The Church of God (Seventh Day), Denver, Colorado, Hope Dais, P.O. Box 33677, 330 W. 152nd Ave., Denver, CO 80233 Tel. (303)452-7973 Fax (303)452-0657
E-mail: offices@cog7.org
Web site: cog7.org

Purpose, (M.) Mennonite Church Canada and USA, James E. Horsch, 616 Walnut Ave., Scottdale, PA 15683 Tel. (724)887-8500 Fax (724)887-3111
E-mail: horsch@mph.org
Web site: www.mph.org

PYM News, (5-Y.) Philadelphia Yearly Meeting of the Religious Society of Friends, Allen R. Reeder, 1515 Cherry St., Philadelphia, PA 19102-1479 Tel. (215)241-7000 Fax (215) 567-2096
Web site: www.pym.org

Quaker Life, (10-Y.) Friends United Meeting, Patricia Edwards-Konic, 101 Quaker Hill Dr., Richmond, IN 47374-1980 Tel. (765)962-7573 Fax (765)966-1293
E-mail: QuakerLife@fum.org
Web site: www.fum.org

Quarterly Review, (Q.) The United Methodist Church, Hendrik R. Pieterse, Box 340007, Nashville, TN 37203-0007 Tel. (615)340-7334 Fax (615)340-7048
E-mail: hpieterse@gbhem.org
Web site: www.quarterlyreview.org

Quarterly Review, A.M.E. Zion, (Q.) African Methodist Episcopal Zion Church, Rev. James D. Armstrong, P.O. Box 33247, Charlotte, NC 28233 Tel. (704)599-4630 Fax (704)688-2544
E-mail: jaarmstrong@amezhqtr.org

Reflections, (bi-M.) United Pentecostal Church International, Melissa Anderson, 8855 Dunn Rd, Hazelwood, MO 63042 Tel. (918)371-2659 Fax (918)371-6320
E-mail: manderson@tums.org
Web site: www.upci.org/ladies

Reformed Worship, (Q.) Christian Reformed Church in North America, Emily R. Brink, 2850 Kalamazoo Ave. SE, Grand Rapids, MI 49560-0001 Tel. (800)777-7270 Fax (616) 224-0834
E-mail: info@reformedworship.org
Web site: www.reformedworship.org

Rejoice!, (Q.) Mennonite Church, Byron Rempel-Burkholder, 600 Shaftesbury Blvd., Winnipeg, MB R3P 0M4 CANADA Tel. (204)888-6781 Fax (204)831-5675
E-mail: byronrb@mph.org
Web site: www.mph.org/rejoice

Report From The Capital, (10-Y.) Baptist Joint Committee, Larry Chesser, 200 Maryland Ave. NE, Washington, DC 20002-5797 Tel. (202) 544-4226 Fax (202)544-2094
E-mail: lchesser@bjcpa.org
Web site: www.bjcpa.org

Reporter, (M.) The Lutheran Church—Missouri Synod, David Mahsman, 1333 S. Kirkwood Rd., St. Louis, MO 63122-7295 Tel. (314)996-9000 Fax (314)966-1126
E-mail: REPORTER@lcms.org
Web site: reporter.lcms.org

Reporter Interactive, (D.) Independent, Protestant, Cynthia B. Astle, UMR Communications, P.O. Box 660275, Dallas, TX 75266-0275 Tel. (214)630-6495 Fax (214)630-0079
E-mail: news@umr.org
Web site: www.lumicon.org

The Rescue Herald, (3-Y.) American Rescue Workers, Rev. Col. Robert N. Coles, National Field Office, 1209 Hamilton Blvd., Hagerstown, MD 21742 Tel. (301)797-0061 Fax (301)797-1480
E-mail: chiefcoles@aol.com
Web site: www.arwus.com

Response, (M.) The United Methodist Church, Dana Jones, 475 Riverside Dr., Room 1356, New York, NY 10115 Tel. (212)870-3755 Fax (212)870-3940

The Restitution Herald, (bi-M.) Church of God General Conference (Oregon, IL & Morrow, GA), Jeffery Fletcher, Box 100,000, Morrow, GA 30260-7000 Tel. (504)543-0290 Fax (404)362-9307

Restoration Herald, (M.) Christian Churches and Churches of Christ, H. Lee Mason, 7133 Central Parks Blvd., Mason, OH 45040 Tel. (513)229-8000 Fax (513)229-8003
E-mail: thecra@aol.com
Web site: www.thecra.org

Restoration Quarterly, (Q.) Churches of Christ, James W. Thompson, Box 28227, Abilene, TX 79699-8227 Tel. (915)674-3781 Fax (915) 674-3776

E-mail: rq@bible.acu.edu
Web site: www.rq.acu.edu

Review for Religious, (Q.) The Roman Catholic Church, David L. Fleming, S.J., 3601 Lindell Blvd., St. Louis, MO 63108 Tel. (314)977-7363 Fax (314)977-7362
E-mail: review@slu.edu
Web site: www.reviewforreligious.org

Review of Religious Research, (Q.) Non-denominational, Patricia Wittberg, Sociology Department, Indiana University Purdue University, Indianapolis, IN 46202 Tel. (317)274-4478 Fax (317)278-3654
E-mail: pwittber@iupui.edu
Web site: rra.hartsem.edu

Road to Emmaus, (Q.) Orthodox Christian, Nun Nectaria, 1516 N. Delaware, Indianapolis, IN 46202 Tel. (317)637-1897 Fax (317)631-1334
E-mail: csb@indy.net
Web site: www.roadtoemmaus.net

Rocky Mountain Christian, (M.) Churches of Christ, Ron L. Carter, P.O. Box 26620, Colorado Springs, CO 80936 Tel. (719)598-4197 Fax (719)528-1549
E-mail: 76102.2461@compuserve.com

Sabbath Recorder, (M.) Seventh Day Baptist General Conference, USA and Canada, Rev. Kevin J. Butler, 3120 Kennedy Rd., P.O. Box 1678, Janesville, WI 53547 Tel. (608)752-5055 Fax (608)752-7711
E-mail: sdbmedia@charter.net
Web site: www.seventhdaybaptist.org

Sabbath School Leadership, (M.) Seventh-day Adventist Church, Faith Crumbly, Review and Herald Publishing Assoc., 55 W. Oak Ridge Dr., Hagerstown, MD 21740 Tel. (301)393-4090 Fax (301)393-4055
E-mail: sabbathschoolleadership@rhpa.org
Web site: www.rhpa.org

Saint Anthony Messenger, (M.) Roman Catholic, Pat McCloskey, O.F.M., St. Anthony Messenger Editorial, Dept., 28 W. Liberty St., Cincinnati, OH 45202 Tel. (513)241-5616 Fax (513)241-0399
E-mail: StAnthony@AmericanCatholic.org
Web site: www.americancatholic.org

Saint Willibrord Journal, (Q.) Christ Catholic Church, The Rev. Monsignor Charles E. Harrison, P.O. Box 271751, Houston, TX 77277-1751 Tel. (713)515-8206 Fax (713) 622-5311
Web site: www.christcatholic.org

Saints Herald, (M.) Community of Christ, Linda Booth, The Herald Publishing House, P.O. Box 390, Independence, MO 64051-0390 Tel. (816)521-3015 Fax (816)521-3066
E-mail: comdiv@rlds.org
Web site: www.heraldhouse.org

SBC Life, (10-Y.) Southern Baptist Convention, Bill Merrell, 901 Commerce St., Nashville, TN 37203 Tel. (615)244-2355 Fax (615)782-8684
E-mail: jrevell@sbc.net
Web site: sbc.net

The Schwenkfeldian, (3-Y.) The Schwenkfelder Church, Gerald Heebner, 105 Seminary Street, Pennsburg, PA 18073 Tel. (215)679-3103 Fax (215)679-8175
E-mail: info@schwenfelder.com
Web site: www.schwenkfelder.com

Searching Together, (Q.) Sovereign Grace Believers, Jon Zens, Box 548, St. Croix Falls, WI 54024 Tel. (651)465-6516 Fax (651)465-5101
E-mail: jzens@searchingtogether.org
Web site: www.searchingtogether.org

The Secret Place, (Q.) American Baptist Churches USA, Kathleen Hayes, Senior Editor, P.O. Box 851, Valley Forge, PA 19482-0851 Tel. (610)768-2240 Fax (610)768-2441
E-mail: thesecretplace@abc-usa.org

Seeds for the Parish, (bi-M.) Evangelical Lutheran Church in America, Kate Elliott, 8765 W. Higgins Rd., Chicago, IL 60631-4101 Tel. (773)380-2949 Fax (773)380-1465
E-mail: kelliott@elca.org
Web site: www.elca.org/co/seeds/index.html

Shalom!, (Q.) Brethren in Christ Church, Harriet Bicksler, 127 Holly Drive, Mechanicsburg, PA 17055-5527 Tel. (717)795-9151
E-mail: bickhouse@aol.com
Web site: bic-church.org/shalom

Shiloh's Messenger of Wisdom, (M.) Israelite House of David, William Robertson, P.O. Box 1067, Benton Harbor, MI 49023

Signs of the Times, (M.) Seventh-day Adventist Church, Marvin Moore, P.O. Box 5353, Nampa, ID 83653-5353 Tel. (208)465-2577 Fax (208)465-2531

The Silver Lining, (M.) Apostolic Christian Churches of America, Bruce Leman, R.R. 2, Box 50, Roanoke, IL 61561-9625 Tel. (309)923-7777 Fax (309)923-7359

Social Questions Bulletin, (bi-M.) The United Methodist Church, Rev. Kathryn J. Johnson, 212 East Capitol St., NE, Washington, DC 20003 Tel. (202)546-8806 Fax (202)546-6811

E-mail: mfsa@olg.com
Web site: www.olg.com/mfsa

Sojourners, (bi-M.) Ecumenical, Jim Wallis, 2401 15th St. NW, Washington, D.C. 20009 Tel. (202)328-8842 Fax (202)328-8757
E-mail: sojourners@sojo.net
Web site: www.sojo.net

Solia Calendar, (Y.) The Romanian Orthodox Episcopate of America, The Department of Publications of the Romanian Orthodox Episcopate of America, P.O. Box 185, Grass Lake, MI 49240-0185 Tel. (517)522-4800 Fax (517)522-5907
E-mail: solia@roea.org
Web site: roea.org

Solia–The Herald, (M.) The Romanian Orthodox Episcopate of America, Rev. Archdeacon David Oancea, P.O. Box 185, Grass Lake, MI 49240-0185 Tel. (517)522-3656 Fax (517)522-5907
E-mail: solia@roea.org
Web site: www.roea.org

Sound of Grace, (Q.) Soverign Grace Believers, 5317 Wye Creek Dr, Frederick, MD 21703-6938

The Southern Methodist, (bi-M.) Southern Methodist Church, Thomas M. Owens, Sr., P.O. Box 39, Orangeburg, SC 29116-0039 Tel. (803)534-9853 Fax (803)535-3881
E-mail: foundry@bellsouth.net

Spirit, (Q.) Volunteers of America, Arthur Smith and Denis N. Baker, 1809 Carrollton Ave, New Orleans, LA 70118-2829 Tel. (504)897-1731

The Spiritual Sword, (Q.) Churches of Christ, Alan E. Highers, 1511 Getwell Rd., Memphis, TN 38111 Tel. (901)743-0464 Fax (901)743-2197
E-mail: getwellcc@aol.com
Web site: www.getwellchurchofchrist.org

Spotlight, (10-Y.) National Spiritualist Association of Churches, 1418 Hall SE, Grand Rapids, MI 49506-3960 Tel. (616)241-2761 Fax (616) 241-4703
E-mail: spotlight@nsac.org
Web site: www.nsac.org/spotlight

The Standard Bearer, (21-Y.) Protestant Reformed Churches in America, David J. Engelsma, 4949 Ivanrest Ave., Grandville, MI 49418 Tel. (616)531-1490 Fax (616)531-3033
E-mail: engelsma@prca.org
Web site: www.rfpa.org/sb.asp

Star of Zion, (bi-W.) African Methodist Episcopal Zion Church, Mr. Mike Lisby, P.O. Box 26770, Charlotte, NC 28221-6770 Tel. (704)599-4630 ext.318 Fax (704)688-2546
E-mail: editor@thestarofzion.org
Web site: www.thestarofzion.org

Stewardship USA, (Q.) Nondenominational, Raymond Barnett Knudsen, II, 4818 Quarton Rd., Bloomfield Hills, MI 48302 Tel. (248) 737-0895 Fax (248)737-0895

Story Friends, (24-Y.) Mennonite Church, Rose Mary Stutzman, 616 Walnut Ave., Scottdale, PA 15683 Tel. (574)887-8500 Fax (574)887-3111
E-mail: editor@themennonite.org
Web site: www.themennonite.org

The Student (Braille & Cassette), (M.) Seventh-day Adventist Church, Jerry Stevens, P.O. Box 6097, Lincoln, NE 68506-0097 Tel. (402)488-0981 Fax (402)488-7582
E-mail: info@christianrecord.org
Web site: www.ChristianRecord.org

Sunday, (Q.) Interdenominational, Timothy A. Norton, 2930 Flowers Rd., S., Atlanta, GA 30341-5532 Tel. (770)936-5376 Fax (770)936-5385
E-mail: tnorton@ldausa.org
Web site: www.sundayonline.org

The Tablet, (W.) The Catholic Church, Ed Wilkinson, 653 Hicks St., Brooklyn, NY 11231 Tel. (718)858-3838 Fax (718)858-2112

Theology Digest, (Q.) The Catholic Church, Bernhard Asen, Rosemary Jermann, co-editors, 3800 Lindell Blvd., St. Louis, MO 63108 Tel. (314)977-3410 Fax (314)977-3704
E-mail: thdigest@slu.edu

Theology Today, (Q.) Nondenominational, Patrick D. Miller, Ellen T. Charry, P.O. Box 821, Princeton, NJ 08542-0803 Tel. (609)497-7714 Fax (609)497-1826
E-mail: theology.today@ptsem.edu
Web site: theologytoday.ptsem.edu

These Days, (Q.) Interdenominational, Vince Patton, 100 Witherspoon St., Louisville, KY 40202-1396 Tel. (502)569-5080 Fax (502)569-5113
Web site: www.ppcpub.com

The Three-Fold Vision, (M.) Apostolic Faith Mission Church of God, Alice Walker, 156 Walker Street, Munford, AL 36268 Tel. (256) 358-9763
E-mail: alicemtwalker156.aol

Timbrel: The Publication for Mennonite Women, (bi-M.) Mennonite Church USA and Mennonite Church Canada, Cathleen Hockman-Wert, 420 SE Richland Ave., Corvallis, OR 97333 Tel. (541)752-0444
E-mail: timbrel@mennonitewomenUSA.org
Web site: www.mennonitewomenusa.org

Today's Christian, (bi-M.) Nondenominational, Managing Editor: Ed Gilbreath, 465 Gundersen Dr., Carol Stream, IL 60188 Tel. (630)260-6200 Fax (630)260-0114
E-mail: tceditor@todays-christian.com
Web site: www.todays-christian.com

Today's Christian Woman, (bi-M.) Nondenominational, Jane Johnson Struck, 465 Gundersen Dr., Carol Stream, IL 60188 Tel. (630)260-6200 Fax (630)260-0114
E-mail: TCWedit@christiantoday.com
Web site: www.todayschristianwoman.com

Tomorrow Magazine, (Q.) American Baptist Churches in the USA, Sara E. Hopkins, 475 Riverside Dr., Room 1700, New York, NY 10115-0049 Tel. (800)986-6222 Fax (800) 986-6782

The Tover of St. Cassian, (2-Y.) Apostolic Episcopal Church, Rt. Rev. Francis C. Spataro DD, Order of Corporate Reunion-US Council-Society of St. Cassian, 80-46 234th Street, Jamaica, NY 11427 Tel. (718)740-4134
E-mail: vil11427@yahoo.com
Web site: vgusa.InJesus.com

Truth, (Q.) Grace Gospel Fellowship, Phil Cereghino, 2125 Martindale SW, Grand Rapids, MI 49509 Tel. (616)247-1999 Fax (616) 241-2542
E-mail: ggfinc@aol.com
Web site: www.ggfusa.org

Truth Magazine, (bi-W.) Churches of Christ, Mike Willis, Box 9670, Bowling Green, KY 42102 Tel. (800)428-0121
Web site: truthmagazine.com

Turnings, (bi-M.) Conservative Baptist Association of America, Dr. Dennis L. Gorton, 1501 W. Mineral Ave., Suite B, Littleton, CO 80120 Tel. (720)283-3030 ext. 1830 Fax (720) 283-3333
E-mail: CBA@CBAmerica.org
Web site: www.CBAmerica.org

Ubique, (Q.) The Liberal Catholic Church—Province of the United States, Rev. Brian Satterlee, 2033 22nd Ave. #302, Greeley, CO 80631
E-mail: frbsatt@hotmail.com
Web site: www.thelcc.org

Ukrainian Orthodox Herald, Ukrainian Orthodox Church in America (Ecumenical Patriarchate), Rev. Dr. Anthony Ugolnik, P.O. Box 774, Allentown, PA 18105

UMR Communications, Inc., (D., W., Bi-W.) Independent, Protestant, Cynthia B. Astle, P.O. Box 660275, Dallas, TX 75266-0275 Tel. (214)630-6495 Fax (214)630-0079
E-mail: info@umr.org
Web site: www.umr.org, www.reporterinteractive. org (news site), www.lumicon.org

United Church News, (10-Y.) United Church of Christ, W. Evan Golder, 700 Prospect Ave., Cleveland, OH 44115 Tel. (216)736-2218 Fax (216)736-2223
E-mail: goldere@ucc.org
Web site: www.ucc.org

The United Methodist Reporter, (W.) Independent, Protestant, Cynthia B. Astle, UMR Communications, P.O. Box 660275, Dallas, TX 75266-0275 Tel. (214)630-6495 Fax (214)630-0079
E-mail: news@umr.org
Web site: www.umr.org

The Upper Room, (bi-M.) The United Methodist Church, Steven D. Bryant, P. O. Box 340004, Nashville, TN 37203-0004 Tel. (877)899-2780 Fax (615)340-7289
E-mail: sbryant@upperroom.org
Web site: www.upperroom.org

U.S. Catholic, (M.) The Catholic Church, Rev. John Molyneux, 205 W. Monroe St., Chicago, IL 60606 Tel. (312)236-7782 Fax (312)236-8207
E-mail: editors@uscatholic.org
Web site: www.uscatholic.org

UU World, (bi-M.) Unitarian Universalist Association of Congregations, Tom Stites, 25 Beacon St., Boston, MA 02108-2803 Tel. (617)948-6518 Fax (617)742-7025
E-mail: world@uua.org
Web site: www.uuworld.org

Vibrant Life, (bi-M.) Seventh-day Adventist Church, Charles Mills, 55 W. Oak Ridge Dr., Hagerstown, MD 21740 Tel. (301)393-4019 Fax (301)393-4055
E-mail: vibrantlife@rhpa.org
Web site: www.vibrantlife.com

Victory (Youth Sunday School/Bible Study Curriculum), (Q.) Church of God of Prophecy, David Bryan, P.O. Box 2910, Cleveland, TN 37320-2910 Tel. (423)559-5321 Fax (423)559-5461
E-mail: david@cogop.org
Web site: www.cogop.org

The Vindicator, (M.) Old German Baptist Brethren Church, Steven L. Bayer, 6952 N. Montgomery Co. Line Rd., Englewood, OH 45322-9748 Tel. (937)884-7531 Fax (937) 884-7531

Vira, (Q.) Ukrainian Orthodox Church of the U.S.A., Hieromonk Daniel, P.O. Box 495,

South Bound Brook, NJ 08880 Tel. (732)356-0090 Fax (732)356-9437
E-mail: virafaith@aol.com

The Visitor, (bi-M.) Brethren in Christ Church, Ron Ross, P.O.Box A, Grantham, PA 17027 Tel. (717)697-2634
E-mail: rross@messiah.edu
Web site: www.bic-church.org/visitor

Vista, (Q.) Christian Church of North America, General Council, Eric Towse, 1294 Rutledge Rd., Transfer, PA 16154 Tel. (412)962-3501 Fax (412)962-1766
E-mail: ccna@nauticom.net
Web site: www.ccna.org

The Voice, (bi-M.) IFCA International, Inc., Les Lofquist, P.O. Box 810, Grandville, MI 49468-0810 Tel. (616)531-1840 Fax (616) 531-1814
E-mail: Voice@ifca.org

The Voice, (Q.) The Bible Church of Christ, Inc., Montrose Bushrod, 1358 Morris Ave., Bronx, NY 10456 Tel. (718)588-2284 Fax (718)992-5597
Web site: www.thebiblechurchofchrist.org

Voice of Mission, (Q.) African Methodist Episcopal Church, George Flowers, 1587 Savannah Highway, Suite A, Charleston, SC 29407 Tel. (843)852-2645 Fax (843)852-2648
E-mail: gwmame@bellsouth.net
Web site: amegobalmissions.com

The War Cry, (bi-M.) The Salvation Army, Marlene Chase, Editor in Chief, Jeff McDonald, Managing Editor, 615 Slaters Lane, Alexandria, VA 22314 Tel. (703)684-5500 Fax (703)684-5539
E-mail: warcry@usn.salvationarmy.org
Web site: publications.salvationarmyusa.org

Watchtower, (bi-W.) Jehovah's Witnesses, Watch Tower Society, 25 Columbia Heights, Brooklyn, NY 11201-2483 Tel. (718)560-5000 Fax (718)560-8850
Web site: watchtower.org

Weavings: A Journal of the Christian Spiritual Life, (bi-M.) The United Methodist Church, John S. Mogabgab, 1908 Grand Avenue, Nashville, TN 37212 Tel. (615)340-7254 Fax (615)340-7267
E-mail: weavings@upperroom.org
Web site: www.upperroom.org/weavings

Wesleyan Life, (Q.) The Wesleyan Church, Norman G. Wilson, P.O. Box 50434, Indianapolis, IN 46250-0434 Tel. (317)774-7909 Fax (317)774-7913
E-mail: wilsonn@wesleyan.org
Web site: www.wesleyan.org

Wesleyan World, (Q.) The Wesleyan Church, Joy Bray, P.O. Box 50434, Indianapolis, IN 46250 Tel. (317)774-7950 Fax (317)774-7958
E-mail: ghpm@wesleyan.org
Web site: www.praygivego.com

The White Wing Messenger, (bi-W.) Church of God of Prophecy, Virginia E. Chatham, P.O. Box 3000, Cleveland, TN 37320-3000 Tel. (423)559-5413 Fax (423)559-5444
E-mail: jenny@wingnet.net
Web site: www.cogop.org

Window on the World, (3-Y.) The Evangelical Congregational Church, Patricia Strain, 100 W. Park Ave, Myerstown, PA 17067 Tel. (717)866-7584 Fax (717)866-7383
E-mail: ecglobalministries@eccenter.com
Web site: www.eccenter.com

Wineskins, (bi-M.) Churches of Christ, Mike Cope and Rubel Shelly, Box 41028, Nashville, TN 37024-1028 Tel. (615)373-5004 Fax (615)373-5006
E-mail: wineskinsmagazine@msn.com
Web site: www.wineskins.org

The Winner, (9-Y.) Nondenominational, Anita Jacobs, The Health Connection, P.O. Box 859, Hagerstown, MD 21741 Tel. (301)393-4082 Fax (301)393-4055
E-mail: winner@healthconnection.org
Web site: www.winnermagazine.org

Wisconsin Lutheran Quarterly, (Q.) Wisconsin Evangelical Lutheran Synod, John F. Brug, 11831 N. Seminary Dr., Mequon, WI 53092 Tel. (262)242-8139 Fax (262)242-8110
E-mail: brugj@wls.wels.net
Web site: www.wls.wels.net

With: The Magazine for Radical Christian Youth, (bi-M.) Mennonite Church USA, Carol Duerksen, P.O. Box 347, 722 Main Street, Newton, KS 67114 Tel. (316)283-5100 Fax (316)283-0454
E-mail: carold@mennoniteusa.org
Web site: withonline.org

The Witness, (10-Y.) Nondenominational, Julie A. Wortman, 7000 Michigan Ave., Detroit, MI 48210 Tel. (313)841-1967 Fax (313)841-1956
E-mail: office@thewitness.org
Web site: www.thewitness.org

Woman to Woman, (M.) General Association of General Baptists, Stephana Deckard, 100 Stinson Dr., Poplar Bluff, MO 63901 Tel. (573)785-7746 Fax (573)785-0564
E-mail: wmdir@generalbaptist.com

Woman's Touch, (bi-M.) Assemblies of God, Arlene Allen, 1445 N. Boonville Ave., Springfield, MO 65802-1894 Tel. (417)862-

2781 Fax (417)862-0503
E-mail: womanstouch@ag.org
Web site: www.womanstouch.ag.org

Women's Missionary Magazine, (9-Y.) African Methodist Episcopal Church, Dr. Bettye J. Allen, 17129 Bennett Dr., South Holland, IL 60473 Tel. (708)339-5997 Fax (708)339-5987
E-mail: bettye1901@aol.com

The Word, (10-Y.) The Antiochian Orthodox Christian Archdiocese of North America, V. Rev. John Abdalah, 635 Miranda Dr., Pittsburgh, PA 15241-2041 Tel. (412)681-2988 Fax (412)831-5554
E-mail: frjpa@aol.com
Web site: www.antiochian.org

Word and Work, (11-Y.) Churches of Christ, Alex V. Wilson, 2518 Portland Ave., Louisville, KY 40212 Tel. (502)897-2831

The Worker, (Q.) Progressive National Baptist Convention, Inc., Mattie A. Robinson, 601 50th St. NE, Washington, DC 20019 Tel. (202)398-5343 Fax (202)398-4998
E-mail: info@pnbc.org
Web site: www.pnbc.org

World Harvest Today, (Q.) United Pentecostal Church International, J. S. Leaman, 8855 Dunn Rd., Hazelwood, MO 63042 Tel. (314) 837-7300 Fax (314)837-2387

World Parish: International Organ of the World Methodist Council, (s-M.) Interdenominational Methodist (Christian World Communion of Methodist and WMC-Related Churches), George Freeman, P.O. Box 518, Lake Junaluska, NC 28745 Tel. (828)456-9432 Fax (828)456-9433
E-mail: georgefreeman@mindspring.com, georgefreeman@charter.net
Web site: www.worldmethodistcouncil.org

Worldorama, (M.) Pentecostal Holiness Church, International, Donald Duncan, P.O. Box 12609, Oklahoma City, OK 73157 Tel. (405)787-7110 Fax (405)787-7729
E-mail: donald@iphc.org

Worship, (bi-M.) The Catholic Church, R. Kevin Seasoltz, St. John's Abbey, Collegeville, MN 56321 Tel. (320)363-3883 Fax (320)363-3145
E-mail: kseasoltz@csbsju.edu
Web site: www.sja.org/worship

Worship Arts, (bi-M.) Nondenominational, David A. Wiltse, P.O. Box 6247, Grand Rapids, MI 49516-6247 Tel. (616)459-4503 Fax (616) 459-1051
E-mail: graphics@iserv.net

Young & Alive, (Q.) Seventh-Day Adventist Church, Braille and Large Print, Gaylena Gibson, P.O. Box 6097, Lincoln, NE 68506 Tel. (402)488-0981 Fax (402)488-7582
E-mail: editorial@christianrecord.org
Web site: www.christianrecord.org

Youth Ministry Accent, (Q.) Seventh-day Adventist Church, David S.F. Wong, 12501 Old Columbia Pike, Silver Spring, MD 20904-6600 Tel. (301)680-6180 Fax (301)680-6155
E-mail: 74532.1426@compuserve.com

YPD Newsletter, (3-M.) African Methodist Episcopal Church, Adrienne A. Morris and Andrea Smith, 327 Washington Avenue, Wyoming, OH 45215 Tel. (513)821-1481 Fax (513)821-3073
E-mail: amconndri@cs.com
Web site: ameypd.org

Zion's Advocate, (M.) Church of Christ, Gordon McCann, P.O. Box 472, Independence, MO 64051-0472 Tel. (816)796-6255

11. Religious Periodicals in Canada

The religious periodicals below constitute a basic core of important journals and periodicals circulated in Canada. The list does not include all publications prepared by religious bodies, and not all the publications listed here are necessarily the official publication of a particular church. Each entry gives: the title of the periodical, frequency of publication, religious affiliation, editor's name, address, telephone and fax number and E-mail and Web site addresses when available. The frequency of publication, which appears in parentheses after the name of the publication, is represented by a "W." for weekly; "M." for monthly; "Q." for quarterly.

Again, (Q.) The Antiochian Orthodox Christian Archdiocese of North America, R. Thomas Zell, Conciliar Press, P.O. Box 76, Ben Lomond, CA 95005-0076 Tel. (800)967-7377 Fax (831)336-8882
E-mail: tzell@conciliarpress.com
Web site: www.conciliarpress.com

The Anglican, (10-Y.) The Anglican Church of Canada, Stuart Mann, 135 Adelaide St. E., Toronto, ON M5C 1L8 Tel. (416)363-6021 Fax (416)363-7678
E-mail: smann@toronto.anglican.ca
Web site: www.toronto.anglican.ca

Anglican Journal, (10-Y.) The Anglican Church of Canada, Leanne Larmondin, 80 Hayden St., Toronto, ON M4Y 3G2 Tel. (416)924-9199 ext. 306 Fax (416)921-4452
E-mail: editor@national.anglican.ca
Web site: www.anglicanjournal.com

Armenian Evangelical Church Newsletter, (Q.) Armenian Evangelical Church, Yessayi Sarmazian, 2600 14th Avenue, Markham, ON L3R 3X1 Tel. (905)305-8144 Fax (905)305-8125
E-mail: aectoronto@yahoo.com

Aujourd'hui Credo, (10-Y.) The United Church of Canada, David Fines, 1332 Victoria, Longueuil, QC J4V 1L8 Tel. (450)446-7733 Fax (450)466-2664
E-mail: davidfines@egliseunce.org
Web site: www.united-church/credo

The Baptist Horizon, (M.) Canadian Convention of Southern Baptists, Nancy McGough, P.O. Box 300, Cochrane, AB T0L 0W0 Tel. (403)932-5688 Fax (403)932-4937
E-mail: office@ccsb.ca

B.C. Fellowship Baptist, (Q.) The Fellowship of Evangelical Baptist Churches in BC and Yukon, Bruce Christensen, #201-26620-56th Ave, Langley, BC V4W 3X5 Tel. (604)607-1192 Fax (604)607-1193
E-mail: fellowship@shaw.ca

Blackboard Bulletin, (10-Y.) Old Order Amish Church, Rt. 4, Aylmer, ON N5H 2R3

Die Botschaft, (W.) Old Order Amish Church, James Weaver, Brookshire Publishing, Inc., 200 Hazel St., Lancaster, PA 17603 Tel. (717)392-1321 Fax (717)392-2078

The Budget, (W.) Old Order Amish Church, Fannie Erb-Miller, P.O. Box 249, Sugarcreek, OH 44681 Tel. (330)852-4634 Fax (330)852-4421
E-mail: budgetnews@aol.com

Cahiers de Spiritualite Ignatienne, (Q.) The Roman Catholic Church in Canada, Rene Champagne, Gaetane Guillemette, 2370 Rue Nicolas-Pinel, Ste-Foy, QC G1V 4L6 Tel. (418)653-6353 Fax (418)653-1208
E-mail: cahiersi@centremanrese.org
Web site: www.centremanrese.org

Canada Lutheran, (8-Y.) Evangelical Lutheran Church in Canada, 302-393 Portage Avenue, Winnipeg, MB R3B 3H6 Tel. (204)984-9170 Fax (204)984-9185
E-mail: canaluth@elcic.ca
Web site: www.elcic.ca/clweb

Canada Update, (Q.) The Church of God of Prophecy in Canada, 5145 Tomkin Road, Mississaugh, ON L4W 1P1 Tel. (905)625-1278 Fax (905)843-3990

Canadian Adventist Messenger, (12-Y.) Seventh-day Adventist Church in Canada, Carolyn Willis, 1148 King St. E., Oshawa, ON L1H 1H8 Tel. (905)433-0011 Fax (905)433-0982
E-mail: cwillis@sdacc.org
Web site: www.sdacc.org

The Canadian Baptist, (10-Y.) Baptist Convention of Ontario and Quebec, Larry Matthews, 195 The West Mall, Suite 414, Etobicoke, ON M9C 5K1 Tel. (416)622-8600 Fax (416)622-0780
E-mail: thecb@baptist.ca

The Canadian Friend, (bi-M.) Canadian Yearly Meeting of the Religious Society of Friends, Anne Marie Zilliacus, 218 Third Ave., Ottawa, ON K1S 2K3 Tel. (613)567-8628 Fax (613) 567-1078
E-mail: zilli@cyberus.ca

The Canadian Lutheran, (9-Y.) Lutheran Church—Canada, Ida Backman, Interim Editor, 3074 Portage Ave., Winnipeg, MB R3K 0Y2 Tel. (204)895-3433 ext.24 Fax (204) 897-4319
E-mail: communications@lutheranchurch.ca
Web site: www.lutheranchurch.ca

Canadian Mennonite, (bi-W.) Mennonite Church Canada, Ron Rempel, Suite C5, 490 Dutton Dr., Waterloo, ON N2L 6H7 Tel. (519)884-3810 Fax (519)884-3331
E-mail: editor@canadianmennonite.org
Web site: www.canadianmennonite.org

Canadian Orthodox Messenger, (Q.) Orthodox Church in America (Canada Section), Nun Sophia (Zion), P.O. Box 179, Spencerville, ON K0E 1X0 Tel. (613)925-0645 Fax (613) 925-1521
E-mail: sophia@ripnet.com

The Catalyst, (6-Y.) Nondenominational, Murray MacAdam, Citizens for Public Justice, 229 College St. #311, Toronto, ON M5T 1R4 Tel. (416)979-2443 Fax (416)979-2458
E-mail: cpj@cpj.ca
Web site: www.cpj.ca

The Catholic Register, (W.) The Roman Catholic Church in Canada, Joseph Sinasac, 1155 Yonge St., Suite 401, Toronto, ON M4Y 1W2 Tel. (416)934-3410 Fax (416)934-3409
E-mail: editor@catholicregister.org
Web site: www.catholicregister.org

The Catholic Times (Montreal), (10-Y.) The Roman Catholic Church in Canada, Eric Durocher, 2005 St. Marc St., Montreal, QC H3H 2G8 Tel. (514)937-2301 Fax (514)937-3051

Channels, (3-Y.) Presbyterian Church in Canada, Calvin Brown, Managing Editor, Dal Schindell, Renewal Fellowship, 3819 Bloor St W, Etobicoke, ON M9B 1K7 Tel. (416)233-6581 Fax (416)233-1743
E-mail: cbbrown@rogers.com
Web site: www.presbycan.ca/rfpc

Chinese Herald, (bi-M.) Canadian Conference of Mennonite Brethren Churches, Joseph Kwan, 8143 Burnlake Drive, Burnaby, BC V5A 3R6 Tel. (604)421-4100 Fax (604)421-4100
E-mail: chineseherald@mbconf.ca

Church of God Beacon, (Q.) Church of God (Cleveland, Tenn.), Andrew Binda, P.O. Box 2036, Brampton Commercial Service Center, Brampton, ON L6T 3T0 Tel. (905)793-2213 Fax (905)793-9173
E-mail: afinda@cogontario.com

Clarion- The Canadian Reformed Magazine, (bi-W.) Canadian and American Reformed Churches, J. Visscher, One Beghin Ave., Winnipeg, MB R2J 3X5 Tel. (204)663-9000 Fax (204)663-9202
E-mail: clarion@premier.mb.ca
Web site: premier.mb.ca/clarion.html

CLBI-Cross Roads, (6-Y.) Lutheran, Dean J. Rostand, 4837-52A St., Camrose, AB T4V 1W5 Tel. (780)672-4454 Fax (780)672-4455
E-mail: communications@clbi.edu
Web site: www.clbi.edu

College News & Updates, (6-Y.) Church of God (Anderson, Ind.), John Alan Howard, 4707 56th St, Camrose, AB T4V 2C4 Tel. (780)672-0171 Fax (780)672-2465
E-mail: info@gardnercollege.org
Web site: www.gardnercollege.org

The Communicator, (3-Y.) The Roman Catholic Church in Canada, Box 2400, London, ON N6A 4G3 Tel. (519)439-7514 Fax (519)439-0207
E-mail: info@arccc.ca
Web site: arccc.ca/news.htm

Connexions, (4-Y.) Interdenominational, Ulli Diemer, 489 College St., Suite 305, Toronto, ON M6G 1A5 Tel. (416)964-1511
Web site: www.connexions.org

The Covenant Messenger, (5-Y.) The Evangelical Covenant Church of Canada, Ingrid Wildman, P.O.Box 34025 RPO Fort Richmond, Winnipeg, MB R3T 5T5 Tel. (204)269-3437 Fax (204)269-3584
E-mail: messengr@escape.ca
Web site: www.canadacovenantchurch.org

Crux, (Q.) Nondenominational, Donald Lewis, Regent College, 5800 University Blvd., Vancouver, BC V6T 2E4 Tel. (604)224-3245 Fax (604)224-3097
E-mail: crux@regent.college.edu
Web site: www.cruxonline.net

Diakonia-A Magazine of Office-Bearers, (4-Y.) Canadian and American Reformed Churches, J. Visscher, Brookside Publishing, 3911 Mt. Lehman Rd., Abbotsford, BC V4X 2M9 Tel. (604)856-4127 Fax (604)856-6724

The Diary, (M.) Old Order Amish Church, Don Carpenter, P.O. Box 98, Gordonville, PA 17529 Tel. (717)529-3938 Fax (717)529-3292

Ecumenism-Oecumenisme, (Q.) Interdenominational, 2065 Sherbrooke St. W, Montreal, QC H3H 1G6 Tel. (514)937-9176 Fax (514)937-4986
E-mail: ccocce@total.net
Web site: www.total.net/~ccocce

The Edge (Christian Youth Magazine), (10-Y.) The Salvation Army in Canada, John McAlister, 2 Overlea Blvd., Toronto, ON M4H 1P4 Tel. (416)422-6116 Fax (416)422-6120
E-mail: edge@can.salvationarmy.org
Web site: www.salvationarmy.ca

Eesti Kirik, (Q.) The Estonian Evangelical Lutheran Church Abroad, Rev. U. Petersoo, 383 Jarvis St., Toronto, ON M5B 2C7 Tel. (416)925-5465 Fax (416)925-5688

EMMC Recorder, (M.) Evangelical Mennonite Mission Conference, Lil Goertzen, Box 52059 Niakwa P.O., Winnipeg, MB R2M 5P9 Tel. (204)253-7929 Fax (204)256-7384
E-mail: info@emmc.ca
Web site: www.emmc.ca

En Avant!, (12-Y.) The Salvation Army in Canada, Marie-Michèle Roy, 2050 Rue Stanley, Bureau 400, Montreal, QB H3A 3G3 Tel. (514)288-2848 Fax (514)288-4657
E-mail: enavant@can.salvationarmy.org

Esprit, (Q.) Evangelical Lutheran Church in Canada (Evangelical Lutheran Women), Gayle Johannesson, 302-393 Portage Avenue, Winnipeg, MB R3B 3H6 Tel. (204)984-9160 Fax (204)984-9162
E-mail: esprit@elcic.ca
Web site: www.elw.ca

Evangel—The Good News of Jesus Christ, (4-Y.) Canadian and American Reformed Churches, D. Moes, 21804 52nd Ave., Langley, BC V2Y 1L3 Tel. (604)576-2124 Fax (604)576-2101
E-mail: canrc@uniserve.com or jvisscher@telus.ca

Evangel Voice-Voce Evangelica, (Q.) Canadian Assemblies of God, Rev. Daniel Costanza, 140 Woodbridge Ave., Suite 400, Woodbridge, ON L4L 4K9 Tel. (905)850-1578 Fax (905)850-1578
E-mail: bethel@idirect.com
Web site: www.the-ipcc.org

The Evangelical Baptist, (5-Y.) The Fellowship of Evangelical Baptist Churches in Canada, Terry D. Cuthbert, 679 Southgate Dr., Suite 100, Guelph, ON N1G 4S2 Tel. (519)821-4830 Fax (519)821-9829
E-mail: president@fellowship.ca
Web site: www.fellowship.ca

Faith & Friends, (M.) The Salvation Army in Canada, Geoff Moulton, 2 Overlea Blvd., Toronto, ON M4H 1P4 Tel. (416)422-6110 Fax (416)422-6120
Web site: faithandfriends.sallynet.org

Faith Today, (bi-M.) Evangelical Fellowship of Canada, Gail Reid, M.I.P. Box 3745, Markham, ON L3R 0Y4 Tel. (905)479-5885 Fax (905)479-4742
E-mail: ft@efc-canada.com
Web site: www.faithtoday.ca

Family Life, (11-Y.) Old Order Amish Church, Joseph Stoll and David Luthy, Old Order Amish Church, Rt. 4, Aylmer, ON N5H 2R3

Family Life Network Newsline, (3-Y.) Canadian Conference of Mennonite Brethren Churches, Dorothy Siebert, 225 Riverton Ave., Winnipeg, MB R2L 0N1 Tel. (204)667-9576 Fax (204)669-6079
E-mail: info@fln.ca
Web site: www.fln.ca

Fellowship Magazine, (4-Y.) The United Church of Canada, Rev. Diane Walker Bob McC, Box 237, Barrie, ON L4M 4T2 Tel. (705)737-0114 or (800)678-2607 Fax (705) 737-1086
E-mail: felmag@csolve.net
Web site: www.fellowshipmagazine.org

Foi & Vie, (12-Y.) The Salvation Army in Canada, Marie-Michele Roy, 2050 Rue Stanley, Bureau 400, Montreal, QC H3A 3G3 Tel. (514)288-2848 ext. 236 Fax (514)288-4657
E-mail: foivie@can.salvationarmy.org

Glad Tidings, (6-Y.) Presbyterian Church in Canada, Holly Wilson, Women's Missionary Society, 50 Wynford Dr., Toronto, ON M3C 1J7 Tel. (800)619-7301/(416)441-1111 Fax (416)441-2825
E-mail: hwilson@presbyterian.ca
Web site: www.presbyterian.ca/wms

Good Tidings, (10-Y.) The Pentecostal Assemblies of Newfoundland and Labrador, H. Paul Foster, 57 Thorburn Rd., P.O. Box 8895, Sta. A, St. John's, NL A1B 3T2 Tel. (709)753-6314 Fax (709)753-4945
E-mail: paon@paon.nf.ca

The Gospel Contact, (4-Y.) Church of God (Anderson, Ind.), Editorial Committee, 4717 56th St., Camrose, AB T4V 2C4 Tel. (780) 672-0772 Fax (780)672-6888
E-mail: winscho@chog.ca
Web site: www.chog.ca

Gospel Herald, (M.) Churches of Christ in Canada, Wayne Turner and Max E. Craddock, 4904 King St., Beamsville, ON L0R 1B6 Tel. (905)563-7503 Fax (905)563-7503
E-mail: editorial@gospelherald.org
Web site: www.gospelherald.org

The Gospel Standard, (M.) Nondenominational, Perry F. Rockwood, Box 1660, Halifax, NS

B3J 3A1 Tel. (902)423-5540 Fax (902)423-0820

Gospel Tidings, (M.) Independent Holiness Church, Marilyn E. Votary, 1564 John Quinn Rd., Greely, ON K4P 1J9 Tel. (613)821-2237 Fax (613)821-4663
E-mail: marilynv@hotmail.com
Web site: www.holiness.ca

The Grape Vine, (12-Y.) Reformed Episcopal Church in Canada, Richard Montgomery, 626 Blanshard Street, Victoria, BC V8W 3G6 Tel. (250)383-8915 Fax (250)383-8916
E-mail: office@churchofourlord.org
Web site: www.churchofourlord.org

Hallelujah!, (bi-M.) The Bible Holiness Movement, Wesley H. Wakefield, Box 223, Postal Stn. A, Vancouver, BC V6C 2M3 Tel. (250)492-3376

Herold der Wahrheit, (M.) Old Order Amish Church, Cephas Kauffman, 1827 110th St., Kalona, IA 52247

Horizons, (bi-M.) The Salvation Army in Canada, 2 Overlea Blvd., Toronto, ON M4H 1P4 Tel. (416)425-6118 Fax (416)422-6120

IdeaBank, (Q.) Canadian Conference of Mennonite Brethren Churches, Sharon Johnson, Christian Ed. Office, 3-169 Riverton Ave., Winnipeg, MB R2L 2E5 Tel. (204)669-6575 Fax (204)654-1865
E-mail: cem@mbconf.ca
Web site: www.mbconf.ca

Insight*Insound*In Touch, (6-Y. (Insight); 6-Y. (In Sound); 4-Y. (In Touch)) Interdenominational. *Insight* (large print newspaper); *In Sound* (audio magazine); *In Touch* (Braille newspaper), Rebekah Chevalier, Graham Down, John Milton Society for the Blind in Canada, 40 St. Clair Ave. E., Suite 202, Toronto, ON M4T 1M9 Tel. (416)960-3953 Fax (416)960-3570
E-mail: admin@jmsblind.ca
Web site: www.jmsblind.ca

Intercom, (Q.) The Fellowship of Evangelical Baptist Churches in Canada, Terry D. Cuthbert, 679 Southgate Dr., Suite 100, Guelph, ON N1G 4S2 Tel. (519)821-4830 Fax (519)821-9829
E-mail: president@fellowship.ca
Web site: www.fellowship.ca

ISKRA, (20-Y.) Union of Spiritual Communities of Christ (Orthodox Doukhobors in Canada), Dmitri E. (Jim) Popoff, Box 760, Grand Forks, BC V0H 1H0 Tel. (604)442-8252 Fax (604)442-3433
E-mail: iskra@sunshinecable.com

Istocnik, (4-Y.) Serbian Orthodox Church in the U.S.A. and Canada, Diocese of Canada, Very Rev. Vasilije Tomic, 7470 McNiven Rd., RR 3, Campbellville, ON L0P 1B0 Tel. (905)878-0043 Fax (905)878-1909
E-mail: vladika@istocnik.com
Web site: www.istocnik.com

Leader, (Q.) Mennonite Church USA, 600 Shaftesbury Blvd., Winnipeg, MB R3P 0M4 Tel. (204)888-6781 Fax (204)831-2454
E-mail: byronrb@mph.org
Web site: www.leaderonline.org

Le Lien, (11-Y.) Canadian Conference of Mennonite Brethren Churches, Annie Brosseau, 1775 Edouard-Laurin, St. Laurent, QC H4L 2B9 Tel. (514)331-0878 Fax (514) 331-0879
E-mail: lelien@total.net
Web site: www.mbconf.ca/comm/lelien

Liturgie, Foi et Culture (Bulletin Natl. de Liturgie), (4-Y.) The Roman Catholic Church in Canada, Service des Editions de la CECC, Office national de liturgie, 3530 Rue Adam, Montreal, QC H1W 1Y8 Tel. (514)522-4930 Fax (514)522-1557
E-mail: onl.cecc@ccb.ca
Web site: www.cccb.ca

Mandate, (4-Y.) The United Church of Canada, Rebekah Chevalier, 3250 Bloor St W., Suite 300, Etobicoke, ON M8X 2Y4 Tel. (416)231-5931 Fax (416)231-3103
E-mail: rchevali@united-church.ca
Web site: www.united-church.ca/mandate

The Mantle, (M.) Independent Assemblies of God International (Canada), Philip Rassmussen, P.O. Box 2130, Laguna Hills, CA 92654-9901 Tel. (514)522-4930 Fax (514) 522-1557

Mennonite Brethren Herald, (3-W.) Canadian Conference of Mennonite Brethren Churches, Susan Brandt, Acting Editor, 3-169 Riverton Ave., Winnipeg, MB R2L 2E5 Tel. (204)654-5760 Fax (204)654-1865
E-mail: mbherald@mbconf.ca
Web site: www.mbherald.com

Mennonite Historian, (Q.) Canadian Conference of Mennonite Brethren Churches, Mennonite Church Canada, Abe Dueck and Alf Redekopp, Ctr. for Menn. Brethren Studies, 169 Riverton Ave., Winnipeg, MB R2L 2E5 Tel. (204)669-6575 Fax (204)654-1865
E-mail: adueck@mbconf.ca
Web site: mbconf.ca/mbstudies

Die Mennonitische Post, (bi-M.) Mennonite Central Committee Canada, Kennert

Giesbrecht, 383 Main St., Steinbach, MB R5G 1S1 Tel. (204)326-6790 Fax (204)326-6302
E-mail: mennpost@mts.net

Mennonitische Rundschau, (M.) Canadian Conference of Mennonite Brethren Churches, Brigitte Penner; Marianne Dulder, 3-169 Riverton Ave., Winnipeg, MB R2L 2E5 Tel. (204)669-6575 Fax (204)654-1865
E-mail: MR@mbconf.ca
Web site: www.mbconf.ca

The Messenger, (bi-M.) Church of God (in Eastern Canada), Rosemary Krashel, 20625 Winston Churchill Blvd., Alton, ON LON 1AO Tel. (514)938-9994
E-mail: rosemarykrushel@sympatico.ca

The Messenger, (Q.) The Reformed Episcopal Church of Canada, Rt. Rev. Michael Fedechko, 320 Armstrong St., New Liskeard, ON P0J 1P0 Tel. (705)647-4565 Fax (705) 647-4565
E-mail: fed@nt.net
Web site: www.forministry.com/rec-canada

The Messenger, (22-Y.) The Evangelical Mennonite Conference, Terry Smith, Editor; Becky Buhler, Assistant Editor, 440 Main Street, Steinbach, MB R5G 1Z5 Tel. (204) 326-6401 Fax (204)326-1613
E-mail: emcmessenger@mts.net
Web site: www.emconf.ca/messenger

MinistryMatters, (3-Y.) The Anglican Church of Canada, Vianney (Sam) Carriere, 80 Hayden St., Toronto, ON M4Y 3G2 Tel. (905)833-6200 Fax (905)833-2116
E-mail: matters@national.anglican.ca
Web site: www.ministrymatters.ca

Missions Today, (bi-M.) Roman Catholic, Patricia McKinnon, Society for the Propagation of the Faith, 3329 Danforth Ave., Scarborough, ON M1L 4T3 Tel. (416)699-7077 or 800-897-8865 Fax (416)699-9019
E-mail: missions@eda.net
Web site: www.eda.net/~missions

Mosaic, (Q.) Canadian Baptist Ministries, Jennifer Lau, 7185 Millcreek Dr., Mississauga, ON L5N 5R4 Tel. (905)821-3533 Fax (905) 826-3441
E-mail: mosaic@cbmin.org
Web site: www.cbmin.org

National Bulletin on Liturgy, (4-Y.) The Roman Catholic Church in Canada, Zita Maier, 2500 Don Reid Drive, Ottawa, ON K1H 2J2 Tel. (613)241-9461 ext. 221 Fax (613)241-8117
E-mail: liturgy@cccb.ca
Web site: www.cccb.ca

The New Freeman, (W.) The Roman Catholic Church in Canada, Margie Traftan, One Bayard Dr., Saint John, NB E2L 3L5 Tel. (506)653-6806 Fax (506)653-6818
E-mail: tnf@nbnet.nb.ca

News of Québec, (3-Y.) Christian Brethren (also known as Plymouth Brethren), Richard E. Strout, P.O. Box 1054, Sherbrooke, QC J1H 5L3 Tel. (819)820-1693 Fax (819)821-9287

Orthodox Way, (M.) Greek Orthodox Metropolis of Toronto (Canada), Orthodox Way Committee, 86 Overlea Blvd., 4th Floor, Toronto, ON M4H 1C6 Tel. (416)429-5757 Fax (416)429-4588
E-mail: greekomt@on.aibn.com
Web site: www.gocanada.org

Passport, (3-Y.) Interdenominational, Lois Penner, Briercrest Family of Schools, 510 College Dr., Caronport, SK S0H 0S0 Tel. (306)756-3200 Fax (306)756-3366
E-mail: info@briercrest.ca
Web site: www.briercrest.ca

Pourastan, (bi-M.) Armenian Holy Apostolic Church, St. Gregory the Illuminator Armenian Cathedral of Montreal, 615 Stuart Ave., Outremont, QC H2V 3H2 Tel. (514)279-3066 Fax (514)279-8008
E-mail: sourpkrikor@qc.aibn.com
Web site: www.sourpkrikor.org

Prairie Messenger, (W.) The Roman Catholic Church in Canada, Peter Novecosky, O.S.B., Box 190, 11 College Drive, Muenster, SK S0K 2Y0 Tel. (306)682-1772 Fax (306)682-5285
E-mail: pm.editor@stpeters.sk.ca
Web site: www.stpeters.sk.ca/prairie_messenger

The Presbyterian Message, (10-Y.) Presbyterian Church in Canada, Janice Carter, Kouchibouguac, NB E0A 2A0 Tel. (506)876-4379
E-mail: mjcarter@nb.sympatico.ca

Presbyterian Record, (11-Y.) The Presbyterian Church in Canada, Rev. David Harris, 50 Wynford Dr., Toronto, ON M3C 1J7 Tel. (416)441-1111 Fax (416)441-2825
E-mail: pcrecord@presbyterian.ca
Web site: www.presbyterian.ca/record

Presence, (8-Y.) The Roman Catholic Church in Canada, Jean-Claude Breton, 2715 Chemin de la Cote Ste-Catherine, Montreal, QC H3T 1B6 Tel. (514)739-9797 Fax (514)739-1664
E-mail: presence@presencemag.qc.ca

The Pulse, (4-Y.) Evangelical Free Church of Canada, Dr. Ron Unruh, Editor-in-Chief;

Tracy Morris, Managing Editor, Box 850, LCDI, Langley, BC V3A 8S6 Tel. (604)888-8668 Fax (604)888-3108
E-mail: efcc@twu.ca
Web site: www.efcc.ca

Quaker Concern, (Q.) Canadian Yearly Meeting of the Religious Society of Friends, Jane Orion Smith, 60 Lowther Ave., Toronto, ON M5R 1C7 Tel. (416)920-5213 Fax (416)920-5214
E-mail: cfsc-office@quaker.ca
Web site: www.cfsc.quaker.ca

Reformed Perspective—A Magazine for the Christian Family, (M.) Canadian and American Reformed Churches and United Reformed Churches in North America, Jon Dykstra, 13820-106 A Avenue, Edmonton, AB T5N 1C9 Tel. (780)452-3978 Fax
E-mail: editor@reformedperspective.ca
Web site: www.reformedperspective.ca

Relations, (8-Y.) The Roman Catholic Church in Canada, Jean-Marc Biron, 25 Jarry Ouest, Montreal, QC H2P 1S6 Tel. (514)387-2541 Fax (514)387-0206
E-mail: relations@cjf.qc.ca
Web site: www.cjf.qc.ca

RESCUE, (bi-M.) Association of Gospel Rescue Missions, Philip Rydman, 1045 Swift, N. Kansas City, MO 64116 Tel. (816)471-8020 Fax (816)471-3718
E-mail: pwydman@agrm.org
Web site: www.agrm.org

Revival News, (Q.) Interdenominational, Harold Lutzer & Neill K. Foster, Canadian Revival Fellowship, Box 584, Regina, SK S4P 3A3 Tel. (306)522-3685 Fax (306)522-3686
E-mail: crfellowship@accesscomm.ca
Web site: www.revivalfellowship.com

Rupert's Land News, (10-Y.) The Anglican Church of Canada, Irvin J. Kroeker, Anglican Centre, 935 Nesbitt Bay, Winnipeg, MB R3T 1W6 Tel. (204)992-4205 Fax (204)992-4219
E-mail: rlnews@rupertsland.ca

St. Luke Magazine, (M.) Christ Catholic Church International, Donald W. Mullan, 5165 Palmer Ave., Niagara Falls, ON L2E 6S8 Tel. (905)354-2329 Fax (905)354-9934
E-mail: dmullan1@cogeco.ca

Scarboro Missions, (7-Y.) The Roman Catholic Church in Canada, G. Curry, S.F.M., 2685 Kingston Rd., Scarborough, ON M1M 1M4 Tel. (416)261-7135 or 800-260-4815 (In Canada) Fax (416)261-0820
E-mail: sfmmag@scarboromissions.ca
Web site: www.scarboromissions.ca

The Shantyman, (6-Y.) Nondenominational, Ken Godevenos, Editor in Chief; Phil Hood, Managing Editor, 1885 Clements Rd., Unite 226, Pickering, ON L1W 3V4 Tel. (905)686-2030 Fax (905)427-0334
E-mail: shanty@pathcom.com
Web site: www.shantymen.org

Sister Triangle, (Q.) Churches of Christ, Marilyn Muller, P.O. 948, Dauphin, MB R7N 3J5 Tel. (204)638-9812 Fax (204)638-6231
E-mail: dmmuller@mb.sympatico.ca

SR- Studies in Religion- Sciences religieuses, (Q.) Nondenominational, Dr. Kay Koppedrayer, Dept. of Religion & Culture, Wilfrid Laurier University, Waterloo, ON N2L 3C5 Tel. (519)884-0710 x3329 Fax (519)884-9387
E-mail: kkoppedr@wlu.ca
Web site: info.wlu.ca/~wwwpress/jrls/sr

Testimony, (M.) The Pentecostal Assemblies of Canada, Richard P. Hiebert, 2450 Milltower Ct., Mississauga, ON L5N 5Z6 Tel. (905)542-7400 Fax (905)542-7313
E-mail: testimony@PAOC.org

Topic, (10-Y.) The Anglican Church of Canada, Neale Adams, 580-401 W. Georgia St., Vancouver, BC V6B 5A1 Tel. (604)684-6306 ext. 223 Fax (604)684-7017
E-mail: nadams@vancouver.anglican.ca
Web site: www.vancouver.anglican.ca

United Church Observer, (M.) The United Church of Canada, Muriel Duncan, 478 Huron St., Toronto, ON M5R 2R3 Tel. (416)960-8500 Fax (416)960-8477
E-mail: general@ucobserver.org
Web site: www.ucobserver.org

La Vie Chretienne (French), (M.) Presbyterian Church in Canada, Jean Porret, P.O. Box 272, Suzz. Rosemont, Montreal, QC H1X 3B8 Tel. (514)737-4168

La Vie des Communautes religieuses, (5-Y.) The Roman Catholic Church in Canada, Religious Communities (Consortium), 251 St-Jean-Baptiste, Nicolet, QC J3T 1X9 Tel. (819)293-8736 Fax (819)293-2419
E-mail: viecr@sogetel.net

Vie Liturgique, (6-Y.) The Roman Catholic Church in Canada, Novalis, 4475 Rue Frontenac, Montreal, QC H2H 2S2 Tel. (800) 668-2547 Fax (514)278-3030
E-mail: info@novalis-inc.com
Web site: www.novalis.ca

VIP Communique, Foursquare Gospel Church of Canada, Timothy Peterson, 8459-160th St.,

Suite 100, Surrey, BC V3S 3T9 Tel. (604)543-8414 Fax (604)543-8417
E-mail: foursquare@foursquare.ca
Web site: www.foursquare.ca

Visnyk—The Herald, (2-M.) Ukrainian Orthodox Church of Canada, Rt. Rev. Fr. William Makarenko, 9 St. John's Ave., Winnipeg, MB R2W 1G8 Tel. (204)586-3093 Fax (204)582-5241
E-mail: visnky@uocc.ca
Web site: www.uocc.ca

The War Cry, (M.) The Salvation Army in Canada and Bermuda, Major Kenneth Smith, Associate Editor, 2 Overlea Blvd., Toronto, ON M4H 1P4 Tel. (416)425-2111 Fax (416)422-6120
E-mail: warcry@can.salvationarmy.org
Web site: salvationarmy.ca

Word Alive, (Q.) Nondenominational, Dwayne Janke & Dave Crough, Wycliffe Bible Translators of Canada Inc., 4316 10 St. NE, Calgary, AB T2E 6K3 Tel. (403)250-5411 Fax (403)250-2623
E-mail: editors_wam@wycliffe.ca
Web site: www.wycliffe.ca

Young Companion, (11-Y.) Old Order Amish Church, Joseph Stoll and Christian Stoll, Old Order Amish Church, Rt. 4, Aylmer, ON N5H 2R3

12. Church Archives and Historical Records Collections

American and Canadian history is interwoven with the social and cultural experience of religious life and thought. Most repositories of primary research materials in North America will include some documentation on religion and church communities. This directory is not intended to replace standard bibliographic guides to those resources. The intent is to give a new researcher entry to major archival holdings of religious collections and to programs of national scope. In the interest of space, no attempt has been made to list the specific contents of the archives or to include the numerous specialized research libraries of North America. The repositories listed herein are able to redirect inquirers to significant regional and local church archives, and specialized collections such as those of religious orders, educational and charitable organizations, and personal papers. This directory has been thoroughly re-edited to include updated entries and contact information.

Repositories marked with an asterisk (*) are designated by their denomination as their official archives. The reference departments at these archives will assist researchers in locating primary material of geographic or subject focus of the Episcopal Church, USA.

UNITED STATES

Adventist

Adventist Heritage Center, James White Library, Andrews University, Berrien Springs, MI 49104, Curator: Jim Ford Tel. (269)471-3274, Fax (269)471-2646, ahc@andrews.edu, Website: http://www.andrews.edu/library/ahc/index.html

Large collection of Millerite and Seventh-day Adventist materials.

Aurora University, Charles B. Phillips Library, 347 S. Gladstone, Aurora, IL 60506, Volunteer Curator: David T. Arthur Tel. (630)844-5437, Fax (630)844-3848, jhuggins@aurora.edu

Adventual archival materials on the Millerite/Early Adventist movement (1830-1860), also denominational archives relating to Advent Christian Church, Life, and Advent Union, and (to a lesser extent) Evangelical Adventists and Age-to-Come Adventists.

Department of Archives and Special Collections/Ellen G. White Estate Branch Office, Loma Linda University Library, Loma Linda, CA 92350, Chairman/Dir.: Elder Merlin D. Burt Tel. (909)558-4942, Fax (909)558-0381, whiteestate@llu.edu, Website: http://www.llu.edu/llu/library/heritage

Photographs, sound and video recordings, personal papers, and library pertaining to the Seventh-day Adventist Church.

Ellen G. White Estate, Inc., 12501 Old Columbia Pike, Silver Spring, MD 20904, Archivist: Tim Poirier Tel. (301)680-6540, Fax (301)680-6559, Website: http://www.whiteestate.org

Records include letters and manuscripts (1840s to 1915), pamphlets and publications, and the White papers.

*General Conference of Seventh-day Adventists: Archives and Statistics, 12501 Old Columbia Pike, Silver Spring, MD 20904-6600, Dir.: Bert Haloviak Tel. (301)680-5022, Fax (301)680-5038, HaloviakB@GC.Adventist.org, Website: http://www.adventistarchives.org

Repository of the records created at the world administrative center of the Seventh-day Adventist Church. Includes the period from the 1860s to the present.

Assemblies of God

*Flower Pentecostal Heritage Center, 1445 Boonville Ave., Springfield, MO 65802, Dir.: Wayne Warner Tel. (417)862-1447 ext. 4400, Fax (417)862-6203, archives@ag.org, Website: http://www.agheritage.org

Official repository for materials related to the Assemblies of God, as well as materials related to the early Pentecostal movement in general.

Baptist

*American Baptist Archives Center, P.O. Box 851, Valley Forge, PA 19482-0851, Archivist: Betty Layton Tel. (610)768-2374, Fax (610)768-2266, Website: http://www.abc-usa.org/abhs

Repository for the non-current records of the national boards and administrative organizations of American Baptist Churches in the USA. Collections include mission files, publications, correspondence, official minutes, and annual reports.

American Baptist–Samuel Colgate Historical Library, 1106 S. Goodman St., Rochester, NY 14620-2532, Dir.: Stuart W. Campbell Tel. (716)473-1740, Fax (716)473-1740 [Call first], Website: http://www.crds.edu/abhs/default.htm

Manuscript holdings include collections of Baptist ministers, missionaries, and scholars, as well as some records of Baptist churches, associations, and national and international bodies.

Andover Newton Theological School, Franklin Trask Library, 169 Herrick Rd., Newton

Centre, MA 02459, Associate Dir. for Special Collections: Diana Yount Tel. (617)964-1100 ext. 252, Fax (617)965-9756, dyount@ants.edu, Website: http://www.ants.edu

The collections document Baptist, Congregational, and United Church history, including personal papers relating to national denominational work and foreign missions, with emphasis on New England Church history.

Primitive Baptist Library of Carthage, Illinois, 416 Main St., Carthage, IL 62321, Dir. of Library: Elder Robert Webb Tel. (217)357-3723, Fax (217)357-3723, bwebb9@juno.com, Website: http://www.carthage.lib.il.us/community/churches/primbap/pbl.html

Collects the records of congregations and associations.

*Seventh-day Baptist Historical Society, 3120 Kennedy Rd., P.O. Box 1678, Janesville, WI 53547, Historian: Don A. Sanford Tel. (608)752-5055, Fax (608)752-7711, sdbhist@inwave.com, Website: http://www.seventhday-baptist.org

Serves as a depository for records of Seventh-day Baptists, Sabbath, and Sabbath-keeping Baptists since the mid-seventeenth century.

*Southern Baptists Historical Library & Archives, 901 Commerce St., Suite 400, Nashville, TN 37203-3630, Dir. and Archivist: Bill Sumners Tel. (615)244-0344, Fax (615) 782-4821, bill@sbhla.org, Website: http://www.sbhla.org

Central depository of the Southern Baptist Convention. Materials include official records of denominational agencies, personal papers of denominational leaders and missionaries, records of related Baptist organizations, and annual proceedings of national and regional bodies.

Brethren in Christ

*Brethren in Christ Historical Library and Archives, One College Ave., P.O. Box 3002, Grantham, PA 17027, Dir.: Dori I. Steckbeck Tel. (717)691-6048, Fax (717)691-6042, archives@messiah.edu, Website: http://www.messiah.edu/archives

Records of general church boards and agencies, regional conferences, congregations, organizations, and church institutions, including Messiah College; also includes historical library and special collections (manuscripts, oral history, and photographs).

Church of the Brethren

*Brethren Historical Library and Archives, 1451 Dundee Ave., Elgin IL 60120, Dir.: Kenneth M. Shaffer Jr. Tel. (847)742-5100, Fax (847) 742-6103, kshaffer_gb@brethren.org, Website: http:// www.brethren.org/genbd/bhla

Archival materials dating from 1800-present relating to the cultural, socioeconomic, theological, genealogical, and institutional history of the Church of the Brethren.

Churches of Christ

Center for Restoration Studies, Abilene Christian University, 221 Brown Library, P.O. Box 29208, Abilene, TX 79699, Librarian: Craig Churchill Tel. (325)674-2347, Fax (325)674-2202, churchill @ acu.edu, Website: http:// www.bible.acu.edu/crs

Materials in various formats including archival materials connected with the Stone-Campbell Restoration Movement. The chief focus is on the Church of Christ in the twentieth century.

Emmanuel School of Religion Library, One Walker Dr., Johnson City, TN 37601-9438, Dir.: Thomas E. Stokes Tel. (423)926-1186, Fax (423)926-6198, library@esr.edu, Website: http://www.esr.edu

Materials related to the Stone-Campbell/Restoration Movement tradition. Collection includes items from the Christian Church and Churches of Christ, the a cappella Churches of Christ, and the Christian Church (Disciples of Christ)

Churches of God, General Conference

*Winebrenner Theological Seminary, 701 E. Melrose Ave., Findlay, OH 45804, Dir. of Library Services: Margaret Hirschy Tel. (419) 422-4824, Fax (419)422-3999, wts@winebrenner.edu, Website: http://www.winebrenner. edu

Archival materials of the Churches of God, General Conference including local conference journals.

Disciples of Christ

Christian Theological Seminary Library, 1000 W. 42nd St., Indianapolis, IN 46208-3301, Serials Librarian and Archivist: Don Haymes Tel. (317)931-2368 (Monday–Thursday), Fax (317)931-2363, don.haymes@cts.edu (Monday–Thursday), Website: http://www.cts.edu

Archival documents, materials, and artifacts of Disciples of Christ, Christian Churches, Churches of Christ, and related movements; documents of Indiana religious history; documents of ecumenical endeavors in Indiana and the American Midwest; documents of local ecumenical organizations and ministries nationwide.

*Disciples of Christ Historical Society, 1101 19th Ave. South, Nashville, TN 37212, Dir. of Library and Archives: Sara Harwell Tel. (615) 327-1444, mail@dishistsoc.org, Website: http://www.dishistsoc.org

Collects documents of the Stone-Campbell Movement.

Episcopal

*Archives of the Episcopal Church, P.O. Box 2247, Austin, TX 78768-2247, Dir.: Mark J.

Duffy Tel. (512)472-6816, Fax (512)480-0437, Research@EpiscopalArchives.org, Website: http://www.EpiscopalArchives.org

Repository for the official records of the national church, its corporate bodies, and affiliated agencies; personal papers; and some diocesan archives. Contact the Archives for reference to diocesan and parochial church records.

Evangelical Congregation Church

*Archives of the Evangelical Congregational Church, Evangelical School of Theology, Rostad Library, 121 S. College St., Myerstown, PA 17067, Archivist: Terry M. Heisey Tel. (717)866-5775, Fax (717)866-4667, theisey@evangelical.edu, Website: http://www.eccenter.com

Repository of records of the administrative units of the denomination, affiliated organizations, and closed churches. Also collected are records of local congregations and materials related to the United Evangelical Church and the Evangelical Association.

Friends

Friends Historical Library of Swarthmore College, 500 College Ave., Swarthmore, PA 19081-1399, Curator: Christopher Densmore, Tel. (610)328-8496, Fax (610)690-5728, friends@swarthmore.edu, Website: http://www.swarthmore.edu/library/friends

Official depository for records of Philadelphia, Baltimore, New York and Lake Erie Yearly Meetings of the Religious Society of Friends. Also depository for several Quaker organizations, including Friends General Conference and Pendle Hill. Comprehensive collection of printed materials concerning Quakers.

Special Collections/Quaker Collection, Haverford College, 370 Lancaster Ave., Haverford, PA 19041-1392, Quaker Bibliographer: Emma Jones Lapsansky Tel. (610)896-1161, Fax (610)896-1102, elapsans@haverford.edu, Website: http://www.haverford.edu/library/special

Repository for material relating to the Society of Friends (Quakers), especially to the segment known from 1827 to the mid-20th century as "Orthodox," in the Delaware Valley.

Interdenominational

American Bible Society Library and Archives, 1865 Broadway, New York, NY 10023-9980, Dir.: Mary F. Cordat Tel. (212)408-1258, Fax (212)408-1526, mcordato@americanbible.org, Website: http://www.americanbible.org

Billy Graham Center Archives, Wheaton College, 500 College Ave., Wheaton, Il 60187-5593, Dir. of Archives: Paul Ericksen Tel. (630)752-5910, Fax (630)752-5916, bgcarc@wheaton.edu, Website: http://www. wheaton.edu/bgc/archives

Repository of 600-plus collections that document the history of evangelism and missions by North American nondenominational Protestants, especially Billy Graham. Extensive resources are available through the Archives' Website, including online exhibits. Fee-based services include some short-term borrowing and in-depth research.

David du Plessis Archives, Fuller Theological Seminary, 135 N. Oakland, Pasadena, CA 91182, Archivist: To be appointed, Tel. (626)584-5311, Fax (626)584-5644, archive@fuller.edu, Website: http://www.fuller.edu/archive

Collects material related to the Pentecostal and Charismatic movements, also includes material related to Charles Fuller and the Old *Fashioned Revival Hour* broadcast, Fuller Theological Seminary, and the Evangelical traditions.

Graduate Theological Union Archives, 2400 Ridge Rd., Berkeley, CA 94709, Archivist: Lucinda Glenn Tel. (510)649-2507, Fax (510) 649-2508, Website: http://library.gtu.edu/archives/index.html

Holy Spirit Research Center, Oral Roberts University (LRC 5E 02), 7777 S. Lewis Ave., Tulsa OK 74171, Dir.: Mark E. Roberts Tel. (918)495-6898, Fax (918)495-6662, hsrc@oru.edu, Website: http://www.oru.edu/university/library/holyspirit

Pentecostal and Charismatic records, with emphasis on divine healing.

National Council of Churches Archives, Department of History and Records Management Services, Presbyterian Church (USA), 425 Lombard St., Philadelphia, PA 19147-1516, Manager: Margery N. Sly Tel. (215)627-1852, Fax (215)627-0509, preshist@shrsys.hslc.org, Website: http://www.libertynet.org/pacscl/phs/

Schomburg Center for Research in Black Culture, 515 Malcolm X Blvd., New York, NY 10037, Curator: Diana Lachatanere Tel. (212) 491-2224, Fax (212)491-6067, scmarbref@nypl.org, Website: http://www.schomburgcenter.org

Manuscripts, archives, and rare books division.

Union Theological Seminary, Burke Library, 3041 Broadway, New York, NY 10027, Archivist and Head of Special Collections: Claire McCurdy Tel. (212)280-1502, Fax (212) 280-1456, awt@uts.columbia.edu, Website: http://www.uts.columbia.edu

University of Chicago, Regenstein Library, 1100 E. 57th St., Chicago, IL 60537-1502, Bibliographer for Humanities: Curtis Bochanyin Tel. (773)702-8442, boc7@midway.uchicago.edu, Website: http://www.lib.uchicago.edu/e/su/rel/

Yale Divinity School Library, 409 Prospect St., New Haven, CT 06511, Research Services Librarian: Martha Smalley Tel. (203)432-6374, Fax (203)432-3906, divinity.library@yale.edu, Website: http://www.library.yale.edu/div

Jewish

American Jewish Historical Society, Center for Jewish History, 15 W. 16th St., New York, NY 10011, Dir.: Michael Feldberg Tel. (212)294-6162 (NY), Fax (212)294-6161 (NY), ajhs@ajhs.org, Website: http://www.ajhs.org

Friedman Memorial Library, 2 Thornton Rd., Waltham, MA 02453, Dir.: Michael Feldberg Tel. (781)891-8110, Fax (781)899-9208, mfeldberg@ajhs.cjh.org, Website: http://www.ajhs.org

Archival repositories of the Jewish people in America, including significant religious contributions to American life.

Jacob Rader Marcus Center of the American Jewish Archives, 3101 Clifton Ave., Cincinnati, OH 45220, Associate Archivist: Christine A. Crandall Tel. (513)221-1875 ext. 319, Fax (513)221-7812, ccrandall@huc.edu, Website: http://www.americanjewisharchives.org

Materials documenting the Jewish experience in the Western Hemisphere with emphasis on the Reform movement. Included in the collection are congregational and organizational records, personal papers of rabbis and secular leaders, and genealogical materials.

Latter-day Saints

*Archives, Church of Jesus Christ of the Latter-day Saints, 50 E. North Temple, Salt Lake City, UT 84150-3800, Dir.: Steven R. Sorensen Tel. (801)240-2273, Fax (801)240-6134

Repository of official records of church departments, missions, congregations, and associated organizations. Includes personal papers of church leaders and members.

Family History Library, 35 N. West Temple, Salt Lake City, UT 84150-3400 Tel. (801)240-2331, Fax (801)240-5551, fhl@ldschurch.org, Website: http://www.familysearch.org

International collection of microfilmed records significant to family history. Includes the following subjects: biography, census, civil, court and church records, directories, emigration/immigration, and genealogy, history (local), Jewish records, land and property, maps, military history, military records, naturalization records, newspapers, obituaries, probate and public records, taxation, and vital records.

Lutheran

*Archives of the Evangelical Lutheran Church in America, 8765 West Higgins Rd., Chicago, IL 60631-4198, Chief Archivist: Elisabeth Wittman Tel. (847)690-9410, Fax (847)690-9502, archives@elca.org, Website: http://www.elca.org/os/archives

Official repository for the churchwide offices of the ELCA and its predecessors. For further information on synod and regional archives, contact the Chicago archives or check the ELCA World Wide Web site. For ELCA college and seminary archives, contact those institutions directly, or consult the ELCA Archives.

*Concordia Historical Institute, Dept. of Archives and History, The Lutheran Church–Missouri Synod, 801 De Mun Ave., St. Louis, MO 63105-3199, Dir.: Martin Noland Tel. (314)505-7900, Fax (314)505-7901, chi@chi.lcms.org, Website: http://chi. lcms.org/

Official repository of The Lutheran Church-Missouri Synod. Collects synodical and congregational records, personal papers, and records of Lutheran agencies.

Mennonite

*Center for Mennonite Brethren Studies, 1717 S. Chestnut, Fresno, CA 93702, Archivist: Kevin Enns-Rempel Tel. (559)453-2225, Fax (559) 453-2124, kennsrem@fresno.edu, Website: http://www.fresno.edu/affiliation/cmbs

Official repository for the General Conference of Mennonite Brethren churches.

*Mennonite Church USA Archives–Goshen, 1700 S. Main, Goshen, IN 46526, Dir.: John E. Sharp Tel. (574)535-7477, Fax (574)535-7756, johnes@goshen.edu, Website: http://www.mcusa-archives.org

One of two repositories of the official organizational records of Mennonite Church USA and personal papers of leaders and members.

*Mennonite Church USA Archives–North Newton, Bethel College, 300 E. 27th St., North Newton, KS 67117-0531, Archivist: John Thiesen Tel. (316)284-5304, Fax (316) 284-5843, mla@bethelks.edu, Website: http://www.bethelks.edu/services/mla

An official repository for the Mennonite Church USA, its predecessor, the General Conference Mennonite Church, and several other organizations.

Methodist

B. L. Fisher Library, Asbury Theological Seminary, 204 N. Lexington Ave., Wilmore, KY 40390, Archivist and Special Collections Librarian: Bill Kostlevy Tel. (859)858-2235, Fax (859)858-2350, bill_kostlevy@asburyseminary.edu

Documents the Holiness Movement and evangelical currents in the United Methodist Church. Holdings include records of related associations, camp meetings, personal papers, and periodicals.

Center for Evangelical United Brethren Heritage, United Theological Seminary, 1810 Harvard Blvd., Dayton, OH 45406-4599, Dir.: Sarah D.

Brooks Blair Tel. (937)278-5817, Fax (937) 275-5701, eubcenter@united.edu, Website: http:// www.united.edu/eubcenter

Documents predecessor and cognate church bodies of the United Methodist Church including the Evangelical Association, United Brethren in Christ, United Evangelical, Evangelical, Evangelical United Brethren, Evangelical Congregational, and Evangelical of North America.

*General Commission on Archives and History, The United Methodist Church, P.O. Box 127, Madison, NJ 07940, Archivist/Records Administrator: L. Dale Patterson Tel. (973) 408-3189, Fax (973)408-3909, gcah@gcah.org, Website: http://www.gcah.org

Collects administrative and episcopal records and personal papers of missionaries and leaders. Holds limited genealogical information on ordained ministers. Will direct researchers to local and regional collections of congregational records and information on United Methodism and its predecessors.

*Heritage Hall at Livingstone College, 701 W. Monroe St., Salisbury, NC 28144, Dir.: Phyllis H. Galloway Tel. (704) 638-5664

Records of the African Methodist Episcopal Zion Church.

*Office of the Historiographer of the African Methodist Episcopal Church, P.O. Box 301, Williamstown, MA 02167, Historiographer: Dennis C. Dickerson Tel. (413)597-2484, Fax (413)597-3673, dennis.c.dickerson@williams.edu

General and annual conference minutes, reports of various departments such as missions and publications, and congregational histories and other local materials. The materials are housed in the office of the historiographer and other designated locations.

Moravian

Moravian Archives, Southern Province, Drawer L, Winston-Salem, NC 27108, Archivist: C. Daniel Crews Tel. (336)722-1742, Fax (336) 725-4514, nblum@mcsp.org, Website: http:// www.moravianarchives.org

Repository of the records of the Moravian Church, Southern Province, its congregations, and its members.

The Moravian Archives, 41 W. Locust St., Bethlehem, PA 18018-2757, Archivist: Vernon H. Nelson Tel. (610)866-3255, Fax (610)866-9210, morarchbeth@enter.net, Website: http:// www.moravianchurcharchives.org

Records of the Northern Province of the Moravian Church in America, including affiliated provinces in the Eastern West Indies, Nicaragua, Honduras, Labrador, and Alaska.

Nazarene

*Nazarene Archives, Church of the Nazarene, 6401 The Paseo, Kansas City, MO 64131, Archives Manager: Stan Ingersol Tel. (816)333-7000 ext. 2437, Fax (816)361-4983, singersol@nazarene.org, Website: http://www.nazarene.org/archives/index.html

While the focus is on collections pertaining to general agencies, leaders, and study commissions, the Archives also has collections on congregations, districts, universities, seminaries, and social ministries in the U.S. and worldwide.

Pentecostal

*Hal Bernard Dixon Jr. Pentecostal Research Center, 260 11th St. NE, Cleveland, TN 37311, Dir.: David G. Roebuck Tel. (423)614-8576, Fax (423)614-8555, dixon_research@leeuniversity.edu, Website: http://www.leeuniversity.edu/library/dixon

Official repository of the Church of God (Cleveland, TN). Also collects other Pentecostal and Charismatic materials.

*International Pentecostal Holiness Church Archives and Research Center, P.O. Box 12609, Oklahoma City, OK 73157, Dir.: Harold D. Hunter Tel. (405)787-7110, Fax (405)789-3957, archives@iphc.org, Website: http://www.pctii.org/arc/archives.html

Official repository for records and publications produced by the international headquarters, conferences, and influential leaders.

United Pentecostal Church International Historical Center, 8855 Dunn Rd., Hazelwood, MO 63042, Chpsn., Historical Committee: J. L. Hall Tel. (314)837-7300, Fax (314)837-4503, main@upci.org, Website: http://www.upci.org

Collects a variety of Pentecostal archives, primarily the United Pentecostal (Oneness) Branch.

Polish National Catholic

*Polish National Catholic Church Commission on History and Archives, 1031 Cedar Ave., Scranton, PA 18505, Chpsn: Joseph Wieczerzak Tel. (570)343-0100, Fax (570) 343-0100 or (570)346-2188, josephwie@aol.com

Documents pertaining to the church's national office, parishes, Prime Bishop, leaders, and organizations.

Reformed

*Heritage Hall, Calvin College, 1855 Knollcrest Circle SE, Grand Rapids, MI 49546-4402, Curator of Archives: Richard H. Harms Tel. (616)526-6313, Fax (616)526-6470, rharms@calvin.edu, Website: http://www.calvin.edu/hh

Repository of the official records of the Christian Reformed Church in North America, including its classes, congregations, and denominational agencies and committees.

*Historical Foundation of the Cumberland Presbyterian Church and the Cumberland Presbyterian Church in America, 1978 Union

Ave., Memphis, TN 38104, Archivist: Susan Knight Gore Tel. (901)276-8602, Fax (901) 272-3913, skg@cumberland.org, Website: http://www.cumberland.org/hfcpc Official archives of the Cumberland Presbyterian Church and the Cumberland Presbyterian Church in America.

*Reformed Church Archives, 21 Seminary Pl., New Brunswick, NJ 08901-1159, Archivist: Russell Gasero Tel. (732)246-1779, Fax (732) 249-5412, rgasero@rca.org, Website: http://www.rca.org

Official repository for denominational records including congregations, classes, synods, missions, and national offices from 1628 to the present.

*Presbyterian Historical Society, Presbyterian Church (USA) (2 offices): Headquarters, 425 Lombard St., Philadelphia, PA 19147-1516, Deputy Dir.: Margery N. Sly Tel. (215)627-1852, Fax (215)627-0509, refdesk@history.pcusa.org, Website: http://www.history.pcusa.org

Southern Regional Office, P.O. Box 849, Montreat, NC 28757, Deputy Dir.–Southern Regional Office: William Bynum Tel. (828)669-7061, Fax (828)669-5369, refdesk@history.pcusa.org, Website: http://www.history.pcusa.org

Collects the official records of the Church's national offices and agencies, synods, presbyteries, and some congregations. The Society also houses records of the Church's predecessor denominations, personal papers of prominent Presbyterians, and records of ecumenical organizations. The Southern Regional Office in Montreat, N.C. documents the fourteen southern states.

*Presbyterian Church in America Historical Center, 12330 Conway Rd., St. Louis, MO 63141, Dir.: Wayne Sparkman Tel. (314)469-9077, wsparkman@pcanet.org, Website: http://www.pcanet.org/history

The Historical Center serves as the official archive of the Presbyterian Church in America, and holds records of five other Presbyterian churches: Reformed (Evangelical Synod), Evangelical, Bible, Bible (Columbus Synod), Reformed (General Synod); also includes manuscript collections of some 60 individuals.

Princeton Theological Seminary Libraries, Library Place and Mercer St., P.O. Box 111, Princeton, NJ 08542-0803, Librarian for Archives and Special Collections: William O. Harris Tel. (609)497-7950, Fax (609)497-1826, william.harris@ptsem.edu, Website: http://www.ptsem.edu/grow/library/index.htm

Documents the history of American Presbyterianism, with an extensive collection of alumni biographies, congregational histories, and missionary reports.

Roman Catholic

The Catholic University of America (CUA), The American Catholic History Research Center and University Archives (Life Cycle Institute), 101 LCI, Washington, D.C. 20064, Archivist: Timothy Meagher Tel. (202)319-5065, Fax (202)319-6554, meagher@cua.edu, Website: http://libraries.cua.edu/achrcua/archives.html

Marquette University, Department of Special Collections and Archives, P.O. Box 3141, Milwaukee, WI 93201-3141, Department Head: Charles Elston Tel. (414)288-7256, Fax (414)288-6709, charles.elston@marquette.edu, Website: http://www.marquette.edu/library/collections/archives/index.html

Collection strengths are in the areas of Catholic social action, American missions and missionaries, and other work with Native Americans and African Americans.

US Catholic Documentary Heritage Project. For holdings information on various dioceses and religious orders, see the Website. Website: www.uschs.com

University of Notre Dame Archives, 607 Hesburgh Library, Notre Dame, IN 46556, Curator of Manuscripts: William Kevin Cawley Tel. (574)631-6448, Fax (574)631-7980, archives@nd.edu, Website: http://archives.nd.edu

Papers of bishops and prominent Catholics and records of Catholic organizations. Includes parish histories, but few parish records. Covers U.S. only.

Salvation Army

*Salvation Army Archives and Research Center, 615 Slaters Ln., Alexandria, VA 22313, Archivist: Susan Mitchem Tel. (703)684-5500, Fax (703)299-5552, archives@usn.salvationarmy.org, Website: http://www.salvationarmy.org

Holds the documents of Salvation Army history, personalities, and events in the United States from 1880.

Swedenborgian

*Bryn Athyn College of the New Church, Swedenborg Library, 2875 College Dr., P.O. Box 740, Bryn Athyn, PA 19009-0740, Dir.: Carroll C. Odhner Tel. (215)938-2547, Fax (215)938-2637, ccodhner@newchurch.edu, Website: http://www.newchurch.edu/college/facilities/swedlib.html

Unitarian Universalist Association

*Andover–Harvard Theological Library, Harvard Divinity School, 45 Francis Ave., Cambridge, MA 02138, Curator: Frances O'Donnell Tel. (617)496-5153, Fax (617)496-4111, frances_odonnell@harvard.edu, Website: http://www.hds.harvard.edu/library/bms/index. html

Institutional archives of the Unitarian Universalist Association including the Unitarian Universalist Service Committee; also houses records of many congregations, personal papers of ministers and other individuals.

Unitarian and Universalist

Meadville/Lombard Theological School Library, 5701 S. Woodlawn Ave., Chicago, IL 60637, Dir.: Neil W. Gerdes Tel. (773)256-3000 ext. 225, Fax (773)256-3007, ngerdes@meadville.edu, Website: http://www.meadville.edu

Repository for materials relating to Unitarian Universalism in particular and liberal religion in general. Includes personal papers of several noted UU ministers, and church records from many UU churches in the Midwest.

United Church of Christ

Andover Newton Theological School, Franklin Trask Library, 169 Herrick Rd., Newton Centre, MA 02459, Associate Dir. for Special Collections: Diana Yount Tel. (617)964-1100 ext. 252, Fax (617)965-9756, dyount@ants.edu, Website: http://www.ants.edu

Collections document Baptist, Congregational, and UCC history. Some personal papers relating to national denominational work and foreign missionary activity; majority of collections relate to New England history.

Archives of the Evangelical Synod of North America, Eden Theological Seminary, Luhr Library, 475 E. Lockwood Ave., Webster Groves, MO 63119-3192, Assistant Archivist: Val Detjen Tel. (314)918-2515, vdetjen@eden.edu

Archival records include organization records, Evangelical Synod Congregational records, personal papers, and immigration records.

Congregational Library, 14 Beacon St., Boston, MA 02108, Archivist: Jessica Steytler Tel. (617)523-0470, Fax (617)523-0491, jsteytler@14beacon.org, Website: http://www.14beacon.org

Documentation on the Congregational, Congregational Christian, Christian, and United Church of Christ throughout the world, including local church records, associations, charitable organizations, and papers of clergy, missionaries, and others.

Elon University Library, P.O. Box 187, Elon, NC 27244, Archivist/Technical Services Librarian: Connie L. Keller Tel. (336)278-6578, Fax (336) 278-6638, keller@elon.edu

Collection of membership records and other archival material on the predecessor churches of the UCC: Christian Church and the Southern Conference of the Christian Church, also maintains records of churches that no longer exist.

*Evangelical and Reformed Historical Society, Lancaster Theological Seminary, 555 W. James St., Lancaster, PA 17603, Archivist: Richard R. Berg Tel. (717)290-8704, Fax (717)393-4254, erhs@lancasterseminary.edu, Website: http://www.erhs.info

Manuscripts and transcriptions of early German Reformed Church (U.S.) 1725-1863, Reformed Church in the United States 1863-1934, and Evangelical and Reformed Church 1934-1957; records of coetus, synods, classes, pastoral records, and personal papers.

*United Church of Christ Archives, 700 Prospect Ave., Cleveland, OH 44115, Archivist: Bridgette A. Kelly Tel. (216)736-2106, Fax (216)736-2203, kellyb@ucc.org, Website: http://www.ucc.org/aboutus/archives/index.html

Records created in the national setting of the church since its founding in 1957, including the General Synod, Executive Council, officers, instrumentalities, and bodies created by and/or related to the General Synod.

Standard Guides to Church Archives

Edmund L. Binsfield, "Church Archives in the United States and Canada: A Bibliography," in *American Archivist*, v. 21, no. 3 (July 1958) pp. 311-332, 219 entries.

Nelson R. Burr, "Sources for the Study of American Church History in the Library of Congress" (1953); 13 pp. Reprinted from *Church History*, v. XXII, no. 3 (Sept. 1953).

Canadian Archival Resources on the Internet: University of Saskatchewan Archives, Web site maintained by Cheryl Avery and Steve Billington at http://www.usask.ca/archives/menu.html

Donald L. DeWitt, "Articles Describing Archives and Manuscript Collections in the United States: An Annotated Bibliography," in *Bibliographies and Indexes in Library and Information Science*, no. 11 (1997).

Andrea Hinding, ed. *Women's History Sources: A Guide to Archives and Manuscript Collections in the U.S.* (New York, Bowker, 1979) 2 vols.

Kay Kirkham, *A Survey of American Church Records, for the Period Before the Civil War, East of the Mississippi River* (Salt Lake City, 1959-60) 2 vols. Includes the depositories and bibliographies.

Martha Lund Smalley, "Archives and Manuscript Collections in Theological Libraries," in *The American Theological Library Association*, ed. by M. Graham (1996) pp. 122-130.

Evangeline Thomas, *Women's Religious History Sources: A Guide to Repositories in the United States* (New York, Bowker, 1983).

U.S. National Historical Publications and Records Commission, Directory of Archives and Manuscript Repositories in the United States (Washington, D.C., 1988).

U.S. Library of Congress, Washington, D.C., The National Union Catalog of Manuscript Collections, serially published from 1959 to

1993. Contains many entries for collections of church archives. Researchers may consult the cumulative paper indexes or use the NUCMC home page to access the RLIN database of archives and manuscripts collections at http:/lcweb.loc.gov/coll/nucmc/nucmc.html

CANADA

Anglican

*Anglican Church of Canada/General Synod Archives, 600 Jarvis St., Toronto, ON M4Y 2J6—as of 2004 new address: 80 Hayden Street, Toronto, ON M4Y 3G2—Archivist: To be announced, Tel. (416)924-9199 ext. 278, Fax (416)968-7983, archives@national.anglican.ca, Website: http://www.anglican.ca

Collects the permanent records of the General Synod, its committees, and its employees. The Archives has a national scope, and provides referral services on local Church records.

Baptist

*Atlantic Baptist Historical Collection of the Acadia University Archives, Vaughan Memorial Library, Wolfville, NS BOP 1XO, Archivist: Patricia Townsend Tel. (902)585-1412, Fax (902)585-1748, patricia.townsend @acadiau.ca, Website: http://www.acadiau.ca/vaughan/archives

Records of associations and churches of the United Baptist Convention of the Atlantic Provinces, also personal papers of pastors and missionaries.

Canadian Baptist Archives, McMaster Divinity College, Hamilton, ON L8S 4K1, Dir.: Kenneth R. Morgan Tel. (905)525-9140 ext. 23511, Fax (905)577-4782, morgankr@ mcmaster.ca, Website: http://www.macdiv.ca

Friends

Canadian Yearly Meeting Archives, Pickering College, 16945 Bayview Ave., New Market, ON L3Y 4X2, Yearly Meeting Archivist: Jane Zavitz-Bond Tel. (905)895-1700, Fax (905) 895-9076

Holds the extant records for Quakers in Canada beginning with Adolphus in 1798 to the present, including the records of the Canadian Friends Service Committee.

Interdenominational

Canadian Council of Churches Archives, on deposit in National Archives of Canada, 395 Wellington, Ottawa, ON K1A 0N3 Tel. Research Services Division: (613)992-3884 or (866)578-7777, Genealogical Assistance: (613)996-7458, Fax (613)995-6274, reference@archives.ca, Website: http://www.archives.ca

National Archives of Canada, 395 Wellington, Ottawa, ON K1A 0N3, Dir.: Ian E. Wilson Tel. Research Services Division: (613)992-388 or (866)578-7777, Genealogical Assistance: (613)996-7458, Fax (613)995-6274, reference @archives.ca, Website: http://www. archives.ca

Records of interdenominational and ecumenical organizations, missionary societies, denominational churches, parish registers, and papers of prominent clergy.

Jewish

Canadian Jewish Congress National Archives, 1590 Ave. Docteur Penfield, Montreal, QC H3G 1C5, Dir. of Archives: Janice Rosen Tel. (514)931-7531 ext. 2, Fax (514)931-0548, archives@cjc.ca, Website: http://www.cjc.ca (see "National Archives" section)

Collects documentation on all aspects of social, political, and cultural history of the Jewish presence in Quebec and Canada.

Lutheran

*Archives of the Evangelical Lutheran Church in Canada, 302-393 Portage Ave., Winnipeg, MB R3B 3H6, Dir. of Administration: Rhonda Lorch Tel. (204)984-9165, Fax (204)984-9185, rlorch@elcic.ca, Website: http://www.elcic.ca

Official repository for the ELCIC and its predecessor bodies, the Evangelical Lutheran Church of Canada and the Evangelical Lutheran Church of America–Canada Section.

Lutheran Historical Institute, 7100 Ada Blvd., Edmonton, AB T5B 4E4, Archivist: Karen Baron, kbaron@lccabc.ca, Website: http://www.lccarchives.ca

Mennonite

*Centre for Mennonite Brethren Studies, 1-169 Riverton Ave., Winnipeg, MB R2L 2E5, Dir.: Dr. Heinrich Loewen Tel. (204)669-6575, Fax (204)654-1865, cmbs@mbconf.ca, Website: http://www.mbconf.ca/mbstudies/index.html

Institutional records of the boards and agencies of the Mennonite Brethren Church in Canada with some holdings pertaining to other parts of North America; also personal papers of leaders.

*Mennonite Heritage Centre, 600 Shaftesbury Blvd., Winnipeg, MB R3P 0M4, Dir.: Alf Redekopp Tel. (204)888-6781, Fax (204)831-5675, aredekopp@mennonitechurch.ca, Website: http://www.mennonitechurch.ca/programs/archives/

Institutional records and personal papers of leaders within the Mennonite Community; holdings include the records of the Conference and related agencies.

Pentecostal

*Pentecostal Assemblies of Canada, 2450 Milltower Ct., Mississauga, ON L5N 5Z6, Dir.

of Archives: James D. Craig Tel. (905) 542-7400, Fax (905)542-7313, archives@paoc.org, Website: http://www. paoc.org

Repository of archival records created by the Pentecostal Assemblies of Canada.

Reformed

*Presbyterian Church in Canada Archives and Records, 50 Wynford Dr., North York, ON M3C 1J7, Archivist/Records Administrator: Kim M. Arnold Tel. (416)441-1111 ext. 310, Fax (416)441-2825, karnold@presbyterian.ca, Website: http://www.presbyterian.ca

Records of the Presbyterian Church in Canada, its officials, ministers, congregations, and organizations.

Roman Catholic

Research Centre for the Religious History of Canada, St. Paul University, 223 Main St., Ottawa, ON K1S 1C4, Dir.: Pierre Hurtubise Tel. (613)236-1393 ext. 2270; Exec. Sec.: Jean-Marie LeBlanc Tel. (613)236-1393 ext. 2225; Fax (613)782-3001, crh-rc-rhc@ust-paul.ca, Website: http://www.ustpaul.ca

Holds 1300 linear feet of documents, mainly records on deposit from other institutions, and also guides to many Canadian Catholic archives.

Salvation Army

The Salvation Army, George Scott Railton Heritage Centre, 2130 Bayview Ave., Toronto, ON M4N 3K6, Dir.: Major Ira Barrow; Archivist: Major Barbara Bawks; Tel. (416) 481-4441, Fax (416)481-6096, heritage_center@can.salvationarmy.org, Website: http://www.heritage.salvationarmy.ca

Records relative to The Salvation Army include publications; also financial, personnel, social welfare, and immigration records.

United Church of Canada

*United Church of Canada Central Archives, Victoria University, 73 Queen's Park Crescent E, Toronto, ON M5S 1K7, Chief Archivist: Sharon Larade Tel. (416)585-4563, Fax (416) 585-4584, uccvu.archives@utoronto.ca, Website: http://www.united-church.ca/archives/ home.htm

Records of the United Church of Canada and its antecedent denominations (Methodist, Presbyterian, Congregational and Evangelical United Brethren Churches) and local and Conference records of the United Church in Ontario. Call or view the web page for information on the United Church Conference Archives Network.

III

STATISTICAL SECTION

Guide to Statistical Tables

Since questions regarding religious affiliation are no longer a part of the United States Census, the *Yearbook of American & Canadian Churches* is as near an "official" record of denominational statistics as is available.

Because these data represent the most complete annual compilation of church statistics, there is a temptation to expect more than is reasonable. These tables provide the answers to very simple and straightforward questions. Officials in church bodies were asked: "How many members does your organization have?" "How many clergy?" and "How much money does your organization spend?" Each respondent interprets the questions according to the policies of the organization.

Caution should, therefore, be exercised when comparing statistics across denominational lines, comparing statistics from one year to another, and adding together statistics from different denominations.

Some particular methodological issues, and therefore cautions in interpretation, include the following considerations:

1. Definitions of membership, clergy, and other important characteristics differ from religious body to religious body. In this section, **Full or Confirmed Membership** refers to those with full communicant status. **Inclusive Membership** refers to those who are full communicants or confirmed members plus other members baptized, non-confirmed or non-communicant. Each church determines the age at which a young person is considered a member. Churches also vary in their approaches to statistics. For some, very careful counts are made of members. Other groups only make estimates.

2. Each year the data are collected with the same questions. While most denominations have consistent reporting practices from one year to the next, any change in practices is not noted in the tables. Church mergers and splits can also influence the statistics when they are compared over a number of years. Churches have different reporting schedules and some do not report on a regular basis.

3. The two problems listed above make adding figures from different denominations problematic. However, an additional complication is that individuals who attend two different churches may be included more than once. For example, a person who attends the Church of God in Christ Wednesday evening and an AME service on Sunday morning will likely be included in both counts.

4. Churches were asked to report figures for the full year ending December 31, 2003. Churches actually collect statistics according to their own ecclesial calendars. Data collected consistently from year to year accurately reflect trends over time, irrespective of when customarily collected. Caution should, therefore, be exercised when comparing statistics across denominational lines, comparing statistics from one year to another, and adding together statistics from different denominations.

Table 1. Membership Statistics in Canada

Religious Body	Year Reporting	Number of Churches Reporting	Full Communicant or Confirmed Members	Inclusive Membership	Number of Pastors Serving Parishes	Total Number of Clergy	Number of Sunday or Sabbath Schools	Total Enrollment
The Anglican Church of Canada	2000	2,872	650,997	650,997	1,579	3,631	1,715	55,366
The Antiochian Orthodox Christian Archdiocese of North America	2003	16	105,000	150,000	30	31	16	1,300
Apostolic Christian Church (Nazarene)	1985	14		830	49	49		
The Apostolic Church in Canada	2002	20	1,450	1,740	22	28	17	687
Apostolic Church of Pentecost of Canada, Inc.	2003	155	25,000	25,000	341	450		
Armenian Holy Apostolic Church—Canadian Diocese	2000	15	85,000	85,000	10	47	5	424
Associated Gospel Churches	2003	139	11,056	11,056	127	257		
Association of Regular Baptist Churches (Canada)	1994	12			8	11		
Baptist Convention of Ontario and Quebec		373	43,283	57,263	333	625		
Baptist General Conference of Canada	1999	92		7,045	95	143		4,079
Baptist Union of Western Canada	2000	155	20,427	20,427	279	530		
The Bible Holiness Movement	2002	25	751	1,001	14	14	24	
Brethren in Christ Church, Canadian Conference	2003		3,287	3,287	81	81		

Table 1. Membership Statistics in Canada *(continued)*

Religious Body	Year Reporting	Number of Churches Reporting	Full Communicant or Confirmed Members	Inclusive Membership	Number of Pastors Serving Parishes	Total Number of Clergy	Number of Sunday or Sabbath Schools	Total Enrollment
Canadian and American Reformed Churches	2003	52	8,838	15,799	45	67		
Canadian Baptist Ministries	1996	1,133	129,055	129,055				
Canadian Conference of Mennonite Brethren Churches	2003	246	36,028	36,028				
Canadian Convention of Southern Baptists	2002	196	10,622	10,622	150	176	126	5,579
Canadian District of the Moravian Church in America, Northern Province	2003	9	1,139	1,563	6	9	8	353
Canadian Evangelical Christian Churches	2003	25	600	2,000	53	100	40	4,000
Canadian Yearly Meeting of the Religious Society of Friends	2002	24	1,175	1,232	0	0	24	101
Christian Brethren (also known as Plymouth Brethren)	2003	580		47,000		250	500	
Christian Church (Disciples of Christ) in Canada	2002	25	1,599	2,631	24	32	23	390
Christian Churches/Churches of Christ	2003	62	5,500	9,500	75	105	60	3,300
Christian and Missionary Alliance in Canada	2003	423	42,019	123,114	1,004	1,361	384	39,510
Christian Reformed Church in North America	2002	243	50,557	81,469	187	322		

Table 1. Membership Statistics in Canada *(continued)*

Religious Body	Year Reporting	Number of Churches Reporting	Full Communicant or Confirmed Members	Inclusive Membership	Number of Pastors Serving Parishes	Total Number of Clergy	Number of Sunday or Sabbath Schools	Total Enrollment
Church of God (Anderson, Ind.)	2002	48	3,711	3,711	41	88	37	1,794
Church of God (Cleveland, Tenn.)	2003	135	11,993	11,993	135	175	105	5,599
Church of God in Christ (Mennonite)	2003	50	4,496	4,496	163	177	50	
Church of God of Prophecy Canada East	2003	26	3,830	3,830	64	78	29	1,357
The Church of Jesus Christ of Latter-day Saints in Canada	2003	479	153,243	166,442	1,437	1,614	1,437	122,539
Church of the Lutheran Brethren	2002	9	376	622	9	10	9	476
Church of the Nazarene in Canada	2003	165	12,530	12,624	123	276	145	16,124
Churches of Christ in Canada		151	6,857	6,587	122	120		
Community of Christ	2003	75	11,536	11,536	1,100	1,100		
Congregational Christian Churches in Canada		95		7,500	174	235		
Convention of Atlantic Baptist Churches	2003	539	62,766	62,766	282	619	314	
The Coptic Orthodox Church in Canada	2002	24	45,000		33	33		
The Estonian Evangelical Lutheran Church Abroad	2003	11	4,996	4,996	78	10	2	60
The Evangelical Covenant Church of Canada	2002	21	1,384	1,384	6	25		1,763

Table 1. Membership Statistics in Canada *(continued)*

Religious Body	Year Reporting	Number of Churches Reporting	Full Communicant or Confirmed Members	Inclusive Membership	Number of Pastors Serving Parishes	Total Number of Clergy	Number of Sunday or Sabbath Schools	Total Enrollment
Evangelical Free Church of Canada	2003	139	8,356	8,356	203	203	132	
Evangelical Lutheran Church in Canada	2002	623	142,865	199,236	485	866	447	17,926
The Evangelical Mennonite Conference	2001	50	7,000	7,000		220	50	
Evangelical Mennonite Mission Conference	1997	44	4,633	4,633	75	201		
The Evangelical Missionary Church of Canada	2003	130	10,390	10,390	218	309		0
The Fellowship of Evangelical Baptist Churches in Canada	2002	493	71,073					
Foursquare Gospel Church of Canada	2003	56	3,332	3,332	126	147		1,317
Free Methodist Church in Canada	2003	149	7,603	7,603	123	223		5,955
Free Will Baptists	1998	10	347		3	4	8	
Greek Orthodox Metropolis of Toronto (Canada)	2003	76	350,000	350,000	58	69	76	
Independent Assemblies of God International (Canada)	2003	379			736	736		
Independent Holiness Church	1994	5		150	4	10	4	118
Jehovah's Witnesses	2003	1,332	111,781	111,781				

Table 1. Membership Statistics in Canada *(continued)*

Religious Body	Year Reporting	Number of Churches Reporting	Full Communicant or Confirmed Members	Inclusive Membership	Number of Pastors Serving Parishes	Total Number of Clergy	Number of Sunday or Sabbath Schools	Total Enrollment
Lutheran Church—Canada	2001	328	58,545	79,178	248	378	2,069	8,911
Mennonite Church—Canada	2003	233	34,478	34,478				
North American Baptist Conference	2002	124	16,873	16,873	133	202	124	
The Old Catholic Church of Canada	2000	4	30	100	4	5	0	0
Open Bible Faith Fellowship of Canada	2003	75	2,500	9.000	164	256	77	3,900
Orthodox Church in America (Archdiocese of Canada)	2003	61	2,000	10,000	58	62	20	450
Patriarchal Parishes of the Russian Orthodox Church in Canada	2003	24	1,200	1,200	5	6	4	128
The Pentecostal Assemblies of Canada	2001	1,108		232,000		1,850	616	30,044
The Pentecostal Assemblies of Newfoundland	2001	126	11,910	25,431	210	312	101	6,067
Presbyterian Church in America (Canadian Section)	2003	19	732	1,109				464
Presbyterian Church in Canada	2003	979	125,509	196,475		1,323	979	
Reformed Church in Canada	2003	41	3,812	5,781	33	70		
The Reformed Episcopal Church of Canada	2001	11	420	505	10	13	3	25

Table 1. Membership Statistics in Canada *(continued)*

Religious Body	Year Reporting	Number of Churches Reporting	Full Communicant or Confirmed Members	Inclusive Membership	Number of Pastors Serving Parishes	Total Number of Clergy	Number of Sunday or Sabbath Schools	Total Enrollment
Reinland Mennonite Church	1995	6	877	1,816	10	13	5	347
The Roman Catholic Church in Canada	2003	5,391	12,987,637	12,987,637		8,641		
The Romanian Orthodox Church in America (Canadian Parishes)	2003	21	3,000	6,500	23	23	20	296
The Romanian Orthodox Episcopate of America (Jackson, MI)	2003	22	900	1,400	13	16	12	
The Salvation Army in Canada		356	21,645	75,732	567	1,923		
Serbian Orthodox Church in the U.S.A. and Canada, Diocese of Canada	2003	23	8,500	230,000	26	31	14	1,979
Seventh-day Adventist Church in Canada	2003	331	52,955	52,955	184	319	400	27,942
Syrian Orthodox Church of Antioch	1995	5	2,500	2,500	3	4		
Ukranian Orthodox Church of Canada	1988	258		120,000	75	91		
Union d'Églises Baptistes Françaises au Canada	2003	34	1,805	1,805	32	41	68	
United Brethren Church in Canada	1992	9	835	835	5	12	9	447
The United Church of Canada	2002	3,640	625,000	1,518,000	2,003	4,156	2,832	61,380

Table 1. Membership Statistics in Canada *(continued)*

Religious Body	Year Reporting	Number of Churches Reporting	Full Communicant or Confirmed Members	Inclusive Membership	Number of Pastors Serving Parishes	Total Number of Clergy	Number of Sunday or Sabbath Schools	Total Enrollment
United Pentecostal Church in Canada	1997	199				340		
Universal Fellowship of Metropolitan Community Churches	1992	12	50	1,500	8	9	1	36
The Wesleyan Church of Canada	2002	89	5,977	6,481	131	201	80	5,306
TOTALS		**25,749**	**16,243,151**	**18,093,898**	**14,255**	**36,164**	**13,221**	**437,839**

Table 2. Membership Statistics in the United States

Religious Body	Year Reporting	Number of Churches Reporting	Full Communicant or Confirmed Members	Inclusive Membership	Number of Pastors Serving Parishes	Total Number of Clergy	Number of Sunday or Sabbath Schools	Total Enrollment
African Methodist Episcopal Church*	1999	4,174	1,857,186	2,500,000	7,741	14,428	6,128	303,199
African Methodist Episcopal Zion Church*	2003	3,236	1,211,387	1,432,795	3,285	3,827	2,508	72,969
Albanian Orthodox Diocese of America	2003	2	2,311	2,311	3	3	2	55
The Allegheny Wesleyan Methodist Connection (Original Allegheny Conference)	2003	109	1,619	1,765	81	170	106	5,404
The Alliance of Baptists*	2002	128	63,870	63,870	286	286		
The American Association of Lutheran Churches	1999	101	14,095	18,252	91	141	83	3,612
The American Baptist Association	2000	1,760	275,000	275,000	1,740	1,760		
American Baptist Churches in the U.S.A.*	2003	5,834	1,433,075	1,433,075	4,277	8,577		146,718
The American Carpatho-Russian Orthodox Greek Catholic Church	2003	80	13,377	13,377	71	102	76	
American Evangelical Christian Churches	2001	180	15,470	18,412	192	268	180	14,935
American Rescue Workers	2001	15	3,000	3,000	35	35	8	300
The Antiochian Orthodox Christian Archdiocese of North America*	2003	226	390,000	390,000	400	450	230	20,000
Apostolic Catholic Orthodox Church	2003	10	10,000	25,000	13	21	4	
Apostolic Christian Church (Nazarene)	1993	63	3,723	3,723	217	234	55	

Table 2. Membership Statistics in the United States *(continued)*

Religious Body	Year Reporting	Number of Churches Reporting	Full Communicant or Confirmed Members	Inclusive Membership	Number of Pastors Serving Parishes	Total Number of Clergy	Number of Sunday or Sabbath Schools	Total Enrollment
Apostolic Christian Churches of America	2003	86	12,780	12,780	311	412	84	6,280
Apostolic Episcopal Church	2002	250	18,000	18,000	300	320	50	1,150
Apostolic Faith Mission Church of God	2003	21	8,220	10,330	44	92	21	3,887
Apostolic Faith Mission of Portland, Oregon	1994	54	4,500	4,500	60	85	54	
Apostolic Orthodox Catholic Church of North America	2000	3	2,400	2,400	4	21		
Armenian Apostolic Church of America	2003	34	360,000	360,000	34	44	25	1,789
Armenian Apostolic Church, Diocese of America*	1991	72	14,000	414,000	49	70		
Assemblies of God	2003	12,222	1,584,076	2,729,562	18,937	32,556	11,388	1,401,428
Associate Reformed Presbyterian Church (General Synod)	2003	268	35,418	40,703	227	399	206	16,706
The Association of Free Lutheran Congregations	2003	257	29,200	39,409	144	223	211	11,576
Association of Vineyard Churches	2003	600	140,000	140,000	700	1,200		54,000
Baptist Bible Fellowship International	2003	4,500	1,200,000	1,200,000				
Baptist General Conference	2002	902	145,148	145,148				65,735
Baptist Missionary Association of America	1999	1,334	234,732	234,732	1,525	3,055	1,300	88,921
Beachy Amish Mennonite Churches	2003	185	10,773	10,773	535	565		

Table 2. Membership Statistics in the United States *(continued)*

Religious Body	Year Reporting	Number of Churches Reporting	Full Communicant or Confirmed Members	Inclusive Membership	Number of Pastors Serving Parishes	Total Number of Clergy	Number of Sunday or Sabbath Schools	Total Enrollment
Berean Fellowship of Churches	2003	54	10,000	10,000				
The Bible Church of Christ, Inc.	1993	6	4,150	6,850	11	52	6	
Bible Fellowship Church	2003	57	7,427	7,427	60	127	52	5,623
Brethren in Christ Church	2001	232	20,739	20,739	151	295		12,404
Brethren Church (Ashland, Ohio)	2003	115	10,240	10,240	89	202	105	
The Catholic Church	2002	19,431	67,259,768	67,259,768	29,483	44,212		
Christ Catholic Church	2003	6	1,797	2,887	7	7	1	23
Christ Community Church (Evangelical-Protestant)	2002	3	1,027	1,690	5	9	1	369
Christian Brethren (also known as Plymouth Brethren)	2003	1,150	86,000	86,000		600	1,000	
Christian Church (Disciples of Christ) in the United States and Canada*	2003	3,717	492,691	770,793	3,412	7,197	3,267	181,489
Christian Church of North America, General Council	2003	90	363	363	100	162	90	
Christian Churches and Churches of Christ	1988	5,579	1,071,616	1,071,616	5,525			
The Christian Congregation, Inc.	2003	1,482	120,972	120,972	1,566	1,567	1,333	40,293
Christian Methodist Episcopal Church*	2002	3,300	850,000	850,000	3,001	3,407	2,485	68,155
The Christian and Missionary Alliance	2003	1,961	194,074	400,909	1,598	2,226		
Christian Reformed Church in North America	2003	761	136,088	190,587	676	1,290		

Table 2. Membership Statistics in the United States *(continued)*

Religious Body	Year Reporting	Number of Churches Reporting	Full Communicant or Confirmed Members	Inclusive Membership	Number of Pastors Serving Parishes	Total Number of Clergy	Number of Sunday or Sabbath Schools	Total Enrollment
Christian Union	2003	107	5,306	6,163	135	195	101	4,708
Church of the Brethren*	2003	1,062	132,481	132,481	796	1,874	773	36,739
The Church of Christ (Holiness) U.S.A.	2002	159	10,321	10,321	191	229	145	7,168
Church of God (Anderson, Indiana)	2002	2,290	247,007	247,007	3,445	6,114	2,290	137,178
The Church of God in Christ	1991	15,300	5,499,875	5,499,875	28,988	33,593		
Church of God in Christ, Mennonite	2003	118	13,307	13,307	472	501	118	
Church of God (Cleveland, Tennessee)	2003	6,623	961,390	961,390	5,084	15,337	5,199	301,542
Church of God General Conference (Oregon, IL and Morrow, GA)	2002	90	3,860	5,018	67	81	64	2,051
Church of God, Mountain Assembly, Inc.	2003	118	8,000	8,000				
Church of God of Prophecy	2003	1,879	80,976	105,976	2,500	5,047	1,730	114,000
The Church of God (Seventh Day), Denver, Colorado	2001	200	9,000	11,000	90	130	200	
The Church of Illumination	2000	4	1,200	1,200		16	1	216
The Church of Jesus Christ (Bickertonites)	1989	63	2,707	2,707	183	262		
The Church of Jesus Christ of Latter-day Saints	2003	12,112	4,935,548	5,503,192	36,336	40,761	12,112	4,218,956
Church of the Living God (Motto, Christian Workers for Fellowship)	2002	120	20,000	20,000	105	214	65	
Church of the Lutheran Brethren of America	2002	108	8,194	13,702	145	229	101	8,843

Table 2. Membership Statistics in the United States *(continued)*

Religious Body	Year Reporting	Number of Churches Reporting	Full Communicant or Confirmed Members	Inclusive Membership	Number of Pastors Serving Parishes	Total Number of Clergy	Number of Sunday or Sabbath Schools	Total Enrollment
Church of the Lutheran Confession	2003	77	6,365	8,390	64	90	67	943
Church of the Nazarene	2003	4,922	616,069	621,048	4,705	10,271	4,738	777,441
Church of the United Brethren in Christ	2002	217	22,740	22,740	180	323		12,661
Churches of Christ	1999	15,000	1,500,000	1,500,000	14,500	16,350	12,500	1,600,000
Churches of Christ in Christian Union	2003	228	11,504	11,504	301	628		10,538
Churches of God, General Conference	2003	331	32,961	32,961	271	470	331	14,130
Community of Christ	2003	904	163,850	163,850		16,026		
Congregational Holiness Church	2001	190	9,565	9,565	190	305	190	
Conservative Baptist Association of America (CBAmerica)	2002	1,200	200,000	200,000	1,800	2,100		
Conservative Congregational Christian Conference	2002	259	40,041	40,041	267	539	229	12,717
Conservative Lutheran Association	2002	3	852	1,267	8	29	3	120
Coptic Orthodox Church*	2000	100	250,000	300,000	140	145	100	5,500
Cumberland Presbyterian Church	2003	774	83,742	83,742	635	890	650	36,559
Cumberland Presbyterian Church in America	1996	152	15,142	15,142	141	156	152	9,465
Episcopal Church*	2002	7,305	1,902,525	2,320,221	6,060	16,493	6,419	303,061
The Estonian Evangelical Lutheran Church	2001	21	3,508	3,508	10	12		

Table 2. Membership Statistics in the United States *(continued)*

Religious Body	Year Reporting	Number of Churches Reporting	Full Communicant or Confirmed Members	Inclusive Membership	Number of Pastors Serving Parishes	Total Number of Clergy	Number of Sunday or Sabbath Schools	Total Enrollment
The Evangelical Church	2000	133	12,475	12,475	164	255	125	8,000
The Evangelical Congregational Church	2003	146	20,743	20,743	169	252		
The Evangelical Covenant Church	2003	734	105,956	105,956		1,297	748	102,768
The Evangelical Free Church of America	2003	1,420	130,000	350,000	2,025	2,733		
Evangelical Friends International—North American Region	2003	288	25,423	39,913				
Evangelical Lutheran Church in America*	2003	10,657	3,724,321	4,984,925	9,225	17,666	7,904	773,367
Evangelical Lutheran Synod	2003	140	16,674	21,047	125	166	116	2,802
Evangelical Methodist Church	1997	123	8,615	8,615	105	215	120	6,547
Evangelical Presbyterian Church	2003	194	65,669	71,755	284	501	144	31,889
Fellowship of Evangelical Bible Churches	2003	16	2,020	2,020	16	47	16	1,704
Fellowship of Evangelical Churches	2003	37	13,043	13,043	103	178	37	4,898
Fellowship of Fundamental Bible Churches	1998	22	1,125	1,125	29	46	22	1,036
Fellowship of Grace Brethren Churches	1997	260	30,371	30,371		564		
Free Methodist Church of North America	2003	1,008	63,538	71,459		1,888		41,282

Table 2. Membership Statistics in the United States *(continued)*

Religious Body	Year Reporting	Number of Churches Reporting	Full Communicant or Confirmed Members	Inclusive Membership	Number of Pastors Serving Parishes	Total Number of Clergy	Number of Sunday or Sabbath Schools	Total Enrollment
Friends General Conference	2002	650	34,000	34,000			400	
Friends United Meeting*	2002	427	37,595	42,680	306	355	273	
Full Gospel Assemblies International	2002	41	3,075	3,075	224		41	
Full Gospel Fellowship of Churches and Ministers International	2003	902	345,000	346,800	2,210	2,707	899	
Fundamental Methodist Church, Inc.	1993	12	682	787	17	22	12	454
General Association of General Baptists	2002	692	67,231	85,924	1,035	1,185	1,086	21,424
General Association of Regular Baptist Churches	2002	1,415	129,407	129,407				
General Church of the New Jerusalem	2003	35	3,301	6,522	31	68		
General Conference of Mennonite Brethren Churches	1996	368	50,915	82,130	590			34,668
Grace Gospel Fellowship	1992	128	60,000	60,000	160	196	128	
Greek Orthodox Archdiocese of America*	2003	510	1,500,000	1,500,000	570	803	500	
The Holy Eastern Orthodox Catholic and Apostolic Church in North America, Inc.	2001	17	4,138	4,138	9		17	
Hungarian Reformed Church in America*	2001	27	6,000	6,000	27	30		
Hutterian Brethren	2000	444	36,800	43,000	600	600		

Table 2. Membership Statistics in the United States *(continued)*

Religious Body	Year Reporting	Number of Churches Reporting	Full Communicant or Confirmed Members	Inclusive Membership	Number of Pastors Serving Parishes	Total Number of Clergy	Number of Sunday or Sabbath Schools	Total Enrollment
IFCA International, Inc.	1998	659	61,655	61,655			659	57,768
International Church of the Foursquare Gospel	2003	1,888	251,614	326,614	5,506	7,254	1,450	61,000
International Council of Community Churches*	2003	126	108,806	108,806	283	374		
The International Pentecostal Church of Christ	2002	67	2,004	4,961	51	157	48	1,918
International Pentecostal Holiness Church	2003	1,964	222,960	276,916	2,743	2,910		133,239
Jehovah's Witnesses	2003	12,054	1,041,030	1,041,030				
Korean Presbyterian Church in America, General Assembly of the*	2003	302	38,500	55,000	465	583		17,760
The Latvian Evangelical Lutheran Church in America	2002	68	12,124	13,584	43	63		
Liberal Catholic Church (International)	2003	10	1,000	6,000	16	20	3	
The Liberal Catholic Church—Province of the United States of America	2003	21	5,800	5,800	50	53		
The Lutheran Church—Missouri Synod (LCMS)	2003	6,160	1,894,822	2,488,936	5,281	8,515	5,330	471,492
Mar Thoma Syrian Church of India*	2003	72	25,000	35,000	45	50	58	4,300

Table 2. Membership Statistics in the United States *(continued)*

Religious Body	Year Reporting	Number of Churches Reporting	Full Communicant or Confirmed Members	Inclusive Membership	Number of Pastors Serving Parishes	Total Number of Clergy	Number of Sunday or Sabbath Schools	Total Enrollment
Mennonite Church USA	2002	964	112,688	112,688	738			
The Missionary Church	2003	391	36,162	36,162	645	1,020		25,911
Moravian Church in America (Unitas Fratrum)*	2003	92	19,456	24,650	90	161	90	5,574
National Association of Congregational Christian Churches	2001	432	65,392	65,392	507	650		
National Association of Free Will Baptists	2003	2,458	198,795	198,795	2,155	4,069	2,458	124,724
National Baptist Convention of America, Inc.*	2000		3,500,000	3,500,000			9,000	
National Baptist Convention, U.S.A., Inc.*		9,000	5,000,000	5,000,000			9,000	
National Missionary Baptist Convention of America*	1992		2,500,000	2,500,000				
National Organization of the New Apostolic Church of North America	2003	348	37,605	37,605	1,740	1,740	293	3,581
National Primitive Baptist Convention, Inc.	2002	1,565	600,000	600,000				
Netherlands Reformed Congregations	2003	27	4,523	9,524	9	10		
North American Baptist Conference	2002	270	47,692	47,692	287	421	270	
North American Old Roman Catholic Church (Archdiocese of New York)	2002	8	590	615	8	9	4	18

Table 2. Membership Statistics in the United States *(continued)*

Religious Body	Year Reporting	Number of Churches Reporting	Full Communicant or Confirmed Members	Inclusive Membership	Number of Pastors Serving Parishes	Total Number of Clergy	Number of Sunday or Sabbath Schools	Total Enrollment
Old German Baptist Brethren Church	2003	55	6,285	6,285	266	266		
Old Order Amish Church	2001	898	80,820	80,820	3,592	3,617	55	
Open Bible Standard Churches	2000	314	38,000	38,000	500	1,028		
The Orthodox Church in America*	2003	731	930,000	1,000,000	798	876	509	
The Orthodox Presbyterian Church	2003	241	19,725	27,582	310	437	230	13,105
Patriarchal Parishes of the Russian Orthodox Church in the U.S.A.*		31	7,000	7,000	45	48		
Pentecostal Assemblies of the World, Inc.	1998	1,750	1,500,000	1,500,000	4,500	4,500		
Pentecostal Church of God	2003	1,190	46,000	104,000		1,706		
Pentecostal Fire-Baptized Holiness Church	1996	27	223	223		28	25	400
Philadelphia Yearly Meeting of the Religious Society of Friends*	2003	104	11,874	11,874			80	2,500
Polish National Catholic Church of America	2003			60,000	120	154		
Presbyterian Church in America	2003	1,546	255,492	315,981	3,310	3,310		114,644
Presbyterian Church (U.S.A.)*	2003	11,064	2,405,311	3,241,309	8,945	21,248	8,882	1,110,115
Primitive Advent Christian Church	1993	10	345	345	11	11	10	292
Primitive Methodist Church in the U.S.A.	2003	79	4,124	4,480	52	91	65	2,737

Table 2. Membership Statistics in the United States *(continued)*

Religious Body	Year Reporting	Number of Churches Reporting	Full Communicant or Confirmed Members	Inclusive Membership	Number of Pastors Serving Parishes	Total Number of Clergy	Number of Sunday or Sabbath Schools	Total Enrollment
Progressive National Baptist Convention, Inc.*	1995	2,000	2,500,000	2,500,000				
Protestant Reformed Churches in America	2003	28	4,068	7,080	23	41	23	
Reformed Catholic Church	1997	100	25,000	25,000	80	100		
Reformed Church in America*	2003	897	168,801	278,739	828	1,811		
Reformed Church in the United States	2002	48	3,258	4,369	42	50	48	951
Reformed Episcopal Church	2003	142	8,631	11,281	185	211		
Reformed Mennonite Church	2003	10	251	263				
Reformed Presbyterian Church of North America	2003	83	4,440	6,259	75	148		
Religious Society of Friends (Conservative)	1994	1,200	104,000	104,000				
The Romanian Orthodox Episcopate of America	2002	22	1,000	1,500	16	19	12	
The Russian Orthodox Church Outside of Russia	2003	180	480,000	480,000	190	196	25	2,120
The Salvation Army	2003	1,329	115,251	564,885	2,658	5,443	1,329	103,730
The Schwenkfelder Church	2003	6	2,633	2,633	9	12	6	654
Separate Baptists in Christ	1992	100	8,000	8,000	95	140	100	
Serbian Orthodox Church in the U.S.A. and Canada*	1986	68	67,000	67,000	60	82		

Table 2. Membership Statistics in the United States *(continued)*

Religious Body	Year Reporting	Number of Churches Reporting	Full Communicant or Confirmed Members	Inclusive Membership	Number of Pastors Serving Parishes	Total Number of Clergy	Number of Sunday or Sabbath Schools	Total Enrollment
Seventh-day Adventist Church	2003	4,683	935,428	935,428	2,544	5,060	5,019	515,306
Seventh Day Baptist General Conference, USA and Canada	2003	98	4,800	5,600	55	75		
Southern Baptist Convention	2003	42,972	16,439,603	16,439,603	96,466	112,922	39,718	8,193,284
Southern Methodist Church	2003	108	6,493	6,493	123	163	108	3,987
Sovereign Grace Believers	2002	350	4,000	4,000	450	450	350	
The Swedenborgian Church*	2003	40	1,452	1,677	26	60		
Syrian (Syriac) Orthodox Church of Antioch*	2003	31	32,500	32,500	26	29	22	1,585
The Syro-Russian Orthodox Catholic Church	2003	120	21,000	22,500	100	121	37	1,305
True Orthodox Church of Greece (Synod of Metropolitan Cyprian), American Exarchate	1999	9	1,095	1,095	18	19		
Ukrainian Orthodox Church of the U.S.A.*	2000	115	8,000	13,000	103	124	65	500
Unitarian Universalist Association of Congregations	2002	1,010	214,738	214,738	1,267	171	1,010	1,819
The United Catholic Church, Inc.	2003	21	504	624	27	32		
United Christian Church		10	334	334	8	14	9	448

Table 2. Membership Statistics in the United States *(continued)*

Religious Body	Year Reporting	Number of Churches Reporting	Full Communicant or Confirmed Members	Inclusive Membership	Number of Pastors Serving Parishes	Total Number of Clergy	Number of Sunday or Sabbath Schools	Total Enrollment
United Church of Christ*	2003	5,738	1,296,652	1,296,652	4,219	10,323	4,889	291,609
The United Methodist Church*	2002	35,102	8,251,175	8,251,175	24,269	44,987	32,245	3,573,954
The United Pentecostal Churches of Christ	2000	62	7,059	7,059	466	483	62	2,289
United Zion Church	2003	12	748	748	13	23	11	631
Unity of the Brethren	1998	27	2,548	3,218	25	39	24	1,442
Universal Fellowship of Metropolitan Community Churches	1998	300	44,000	44,000	324	372		
The Wesleyan Church	2003	1,609	113,927	124,550	2,047	3,323	1,604	400,652
Wisconsin Evangelical Lutheran Synod	2003	1,259	314,840	400,622	1,267	1,795	1,196	49,960
Totals		**324,407**	**154,943,201**	**163,128,935**	**394,034**	**586,098**	**218,356**	**26,459,699**

**National Council of Churches member communion*

Table 3. Membership Statistics for the National Council of the Churches of Christ in the U.S.A.

Religious Body	Year Reporting	Number of Churches Reporting	Inclusive Membership	Number of Pastors Serving Parishes
African Methodist Episcopal Church	1999	4,174	2,500,000	7,741
The African Methodist Episcopal Zion Church	2003	3,236	1,432,795	3,285
The Alliance of Baptists	2002	128	63,870	286
American Baptist Churches in the U.S.A.	2003	5,834	1,433,075	4,277
The Antiochian Orthodox Christian Archdiocese of North America	2003	226	390,000	400
Armenian Apostolic Church, Diocese of America	1991	72	414,000	49
Christian Church (Disciples of Christ) in the United States and Canada	2003	3,717	770,793	3,412
Christian Methodist Episcopal Church	2002	3,300	850,000	3,001
Church of the Brethren	2003	1,062	132,481	796
Coptic Orthodox Church	2000	100	300,000	140
Episcopal Church	2002	7,305	2,320,221	6,060
Evangelical Lutheran Church in America	2003	10,657	4,984,925	9,225
Friends United Meeting	2002	427	42,680	306
Greek Orthodox Archdiocese of America	2003	510	1,500,000	570
Hungarian Reformed Church in America	2001	27	6,000	27
International Council of Community Churches	2003	126	108,806	283
Korean Presbyterian Church in America, General Assembly of the	2003	302	55,000	465
Malankara Orthodox Syrian Church, Diocese of America				

Table 3. Membership Statistics for the National Council of the Churches of Christ in the U.S.A. *(continued)*

Religious Body	Year Reporting	Number of Churches Reporting	Inclusive Membership	Number of Pastors Serving Parishes
Mar Thoma Syrian Church of India	2003	72	35,000	45
Moravian Church in America (Unitas Fratrum)	2003	92	24,650	90
National Baptist Convention of America, Inc.	2000		3,500,000	
National Baptist Convention, U.S.A., Inc.		9,000	5,000,000	
National Missionary Baptist Convention of America	1992		2,500,000	
The Orthodox Church in America	2003	731	1,000,000	798
Patriarchal Parishes of the Russian Orthodox Church in the U.S.A.		31	7,000	45
Philadelphia Yearly Meeting of the Religious Society of Friends	2003	104	11,874	
Polish National Catholic Church of America	2003		60,000	120
Presbyterian Church (U.S.A.)	2003	11,064	3,241,309	8,945
Progressive National Baptist Convention, Inc.	1995	2,000	2,500,000	
Reformed Church in America	2003	897	278,739	828
Serbian Orthodox Church in the U.S.A. and Canada	1986	68	67,000	60
The Swedenborgian Church	2003	40	1,677	26
Syrian (Syriac) Orthodox Church of Antioch	2003	31	32,500	26
Ukrainian Orthodox Church of the U.S.A.	2000	115	13,000	103
United Church of Christ	2003	5,738	1,296,652	4,219
The United Methodist Church	2002	35,102	8,251,175	24,269
Totals		**106,288**	**45,125,222**	**79,897**

Table 4. Selected Statistics of Church

				TOTAL CONTRIBUTIONS		
Religious Body	**Year**	**Full or Confirmed Members**	**Inclusive Members**	**Total Contributions**	**Per Capita Full or Confirmed Members**	**Per Capita Inclusive Members**
The Apostolic Church in Canada	2002	1,450	1,740	$1,705,737.17	$1,176.37	$980.31
Armenian Holy Apostolic Church—Canadian Diocese	2000	85,000	85,000	$855,000.00	$10.06	$10.06
Baptist Union of Western Canada	1999	20,427	20,427	$5,107,654.00	$250.04	$250.04
The Bible Holiness Movement	2002	751	1,001	$280,664.50	$373.72	$280.38
Canadian District of the Moravian Church in America, Northern Province	2003	1,139	1,563	$1,468,581.00	$1,289.36	$939.59
Canadian Evangelical Christian Churches	2003	600	2,000	$56,000.00	$93.33	$28.00
Christian Church (Disciples of Christ) in Canada	2002	1,599	2,631	$1,449,009.00	$906.20	$550.74
Christian and Missionary Alliance in Canada	2003	42,019	123,114	$146,093,331.00	$3,476.84	$1,186.65
Church of God (Anderson, Ind.)	2002	3,711	3,711	$936,321.00	$252.31	$252.31
Church of the Lutheran Brethren	2002	376	622	$650,359.00	$1,729.68	$1,045.59
Church of the Nazarene in Canada	2003	12,530	12,624	$13,745,519.00	$1,097.01	$1,088.84
Convention of the Atlantic Baptist Churches	2003	62,766	62,766	$36,457,660.00	$580.85	$580.85
Evangelical Lutheran Church in Canada	2002	142,865	199,236	$61,270,705.00	$428.87	$307.53
Foursquare Gospel Church of Canada	1996	3,332	3,332	$4,376,923.00	$1,313.60	$1,313.60
Free Methodist Church in Canada	2003	7,603	7,603	$14,331,942.00	$1,885.04	$1,885.04
North American Baptist Conference	2002	16,873	16,873	$32,107,049.66	$1,902.87	$1,902.87
Presbyterian Church in America (Canadian Section)	2003	732	1,109	$1,281,232.00	$1,750.32	$1,155.30
Reformed Church in Canada	2003	3,812	$5,781	$3,784,718.00	$992.84	$654.68
The Reformed Episcopal Church of Canada	2001	420	505	$221,452.00	$527.27	$438.52
Seventh-day Adventist Church in Canada	2003	52,955	52,955	$57,690,201.00	$1,089.42	$1,089.42
Union d'Eglises Baptistes Françaises au Canada	2003	1,805	1,805	$867,852.00	$480.80	$480.80
The United Church of Canada	2002	625,000	1,518,000	$328,501,000.00	$525.60	$216.40
Totals		978,998	2,014,667	$703,821,274	$718.92	$349.35

STATISTICAL SECTION

Finances—Canadian Churches

CONGREGATIONAL FINANCES			BENEVOLENCES			
Total Congregational Contributions	Per Capita Full or Confirmed Members	Per Capita Inclusive Members	Total Benevolences	Per Capita Full or Confirmed Members	Per Capita Inclusive Members	Benevolences as a Percentage of Total Giving
$1,506,103.89	$1,038.69	$865.58	$199,633.28	$137.68	$114.73	12%
$430,000.00	$5.06	$5.06	$425,000.00	$5.00	$5.00	50%
$562,511.00	$27.54	$27.54	$4,545,143.00	$222.51	$222.51	89%
$51,474.50	$68.54	$51.42	$229,190.00	$305.18	$228.96	82%
$1,356,242.00	$1,190.73	$867.72	$112,339.00	$98.63	$71.87	8%
$40,000.00	$66.67	$20.00	$16,000.00	$26.67	$8.00	29%
$1,230,384.00	$769.47	$467.65	$218,625.00	$136.73	$83.10	15%
$127,136,716.00	$3,025.70	$1,032.67	$18,956,615.00	$451.14	$153.98	13%
			$936,321.00	$252.31	$252.31	100%
$530,911.00	$1,412.00.	$853.55	$119,448.00	$317.68	$192.04	18%
$11,287,797.00	$900.86	$894.15	$2,457,722.00	$196.15	$194.69	18%
$36,457,660.00	$580.85	$580.85	$2,962,889.00	$47.21	$47.21	8%
$52,343,354.00	$366.38	$262.72	$7,518,028.00	$52.62	$37.73	12%
$4,248,451.00	$1,275.05	$1,275.05	$128,472.00	$38.56	$38.56	3%
$12,892,061.00	$1,695.65	$1,695.65		$0.00	$0.00	0%
$26,408,218.00	$1,565.12	$1,565.12	$5,698,831.66	$337.75	$337.75	18%
$1,146,263.00	$1,565.93	$1,033.60	$134,969.00	$184.38	$121.70	11%
$3,000,806.00	$787.20	$519.08	$783,912.00	$205.64	$135.60	21%
$96,000	$228.57	$190.10	$125,452.00	$298.70	$248.42	57%
$21,321,121.00	$402.63	$402.63	$36,369,080.00	$686.79	$686.79	63%
$439,852.00	$243.69	$243.69	$428,000.00	$237.12	$237.12	49%
$284,973,000.00	$455.96	$187.73	$43,528,000.00	$69.64	$28.67	13%
$583,552,594	$596.07	$289.65	$120,382,365	$122.96	$59.75	17%

Table 5. Selected Statistics of Church

				TOTAL CONTRIBUTIONS		
Religious Body	**Year**	**Full or Confirmed Members**	**Inclusive Members**	**Total Contributions**	**Per Capita Full or Confirmed Members**	**Per Capita Inclusive Members**
Albanian Orthodox Diocese of America	2003	2,311	2,311	$133,000.00	$57.55	$57.55
The Allegheny Wesleyan Methodist Connection (Original Allegheny Conference)	2003	1,619	1,765	$5,216,941.65	$3,222.32	$2,955.77
American Baptist Churches in the U.S.A.*	2003	1,433,075	1,433,075	$424,003,347.00	$295.87	$295.87
American Evangelical Christian Churches	2003	15,470	18,412	$2,911,172.00	$188.18	$158.11
The Antiochian Orthodox Christian Archdiocese of North America*	2003	390,000	390,000	$4,387,000.00	$11.25	$11.25
Apostolic Faith Mission Church of God	2003	8,220	10,330	$1,082,000.00	$131.63	$104.74
Associate Reformed Presbyterian Church (General Synod)	2003	35,418	40,703	$44,279,992.00	$1,250.21	$1,087.88
Baptist Missionary Association of America	1998	234,732	234,732	$70,087,434.00	$298.58	$298.58
Berean Fellowship of Churches	2000	10,000	10,000	$10,309,605.00	$1,030.96	$1,030.96
Bible Fellowship Church	2003	7,427	7,427	$14,253,397.00	$1,919.13	$1,919.13
Brethren in Christ Church	2001	20,739	20,739	$36,431,223.00	$1,756.65	$1,756.65
Christ Community Church (Evangelical-Protestant)	2000	1,027	1,690	$1,107,628.00	$1,078.51	$655.40
Christian Church (Disciples of Christ) in the United States and Canada*	2003	492,691	770,793	$503,410,382.00	$1,021.76	$653.11
The Christian and Missionary Alliance	2003	194,074	400,909	$365,115,588.00	$1,881.32	$910.72
Christian Union	2002	5,306	6,163	$3,952,933.43	$744.99	$641.40
Church of the Brethren*	2003	132,481	132,481	$93,876,819.00	$708.61	$708.61
The Church of Christ (Holiness) U.S.A.	2002	10,321	10,321	$9,740,580.00	$943.76	$943.76
Church of the Lutheran Brethren of America	2001	8,194	13,702	$14,103,909.00	$1,721.25	$1,029.33
Church of the Lutheran Confession	2003	6,365	8,390	$5,855,961.00	$920.03	$697.97
Church of the Nazarene	2003	616,069	621,048	$728,931,987.00	$1,183.20	$1,173.71
Churches of Christ	1997	1,500,000	1,500,000	$1,445,000,000.00	$963.33	$963.33
Churches of God, General Conference	2003	32,961	32,961	$27,675,460.00	$839.64	$839.64
Community of Christ	2002	163,850	163,850	$42,535,613.00	$259.60	$259.60
Conservative Congregational Christian Conference	2002	40,041	40,041	44,938,493.00	$1,122.31	$1,122.31
Cumberland Presbyterian Church	2003	83,742	83,742	$49,168,885	$580.34	$580.34

Finances—United States Churches

CONGREGATIONAL FINANCES			BENEVOLENCES			
Total Congregation Contributions	**Per Capita Full or Confirmed Members**	**Per Capita Inclusive Members**	**Total Benevolences**	**Per Capita Full or Confirmed Members**	**Per Capita Inclusive Members**	**Benevolences as a Percentage**
$125,000.00	$54.09	$54.09	$8,000.00	$3.46	$3.46	6%
$4,131,410.28	$2,551.83	$2,340.74	$1,085,531.37	$670.49	$615.03	21%
364,868,764.00	$254.61	$254.61	$59,134,583.00	$41.26	$41.26	14%
$2,900,500.00	$187.49	$157.53	$10,672.00	$0.69	$0.58	<1%
$1,967,000.00	$5.04	$5.04	$2,420,000.00	$6.21	$6.21	55%
$304,000.00	$36.98	$29.43	$778,000.00	$94.65	$75.31	72%
36,664,331.00	$1,035.19	$900.78	$7,615,661.00	$215.02	$187.10	17%
57,481,427.00	$244.88	$244.88	$12,606,007.00	$53.70	$53.70	18%
$9,277,940.00	$927.79	$927.79	$1,031,665.00	$103.17	$103.17	10%
11,294,071.00	$1,520.68	$1,520.68	$2,959,326.00	$398.46	$398.46	21%
29,566,287.00	$1,425.64	$1,425.64	$6,864,936.00	$331.02	$331.02	19%
$904,628.00	$880.85	$535.28	$203,000.00	$197.66	$120.12	18%
457,918,554.00	$929.42	$594.09	$45,491,828.00	$92.33	$59.02	9%
321,068,596.00	$1,654.36	$800.85	$44,046,992.00	$226.96	$109.87	12%
$3,197,057.61	$602.54	$518.75	$755,875.82	$142.46	$122.65	19%
73,120,173.00	$551.93	$551.93	$20,756,646.00	$156.68	$156.68	22%
$9,178,816.00	$889.33	$889.33	$561,764.00	$54.43	$54.43	6%
11,905,251.00	$1,452.92	$868.87	$2,198,658.00	$268.33	$160.46	16%
$4,999,122.00	$785.41	$595.84	$856,839.00	$134.62	$102.13	15%
$595,552,079	$966.70	$958.95	$133,379,908.00	$216.50	$214.77	18%
1,414,000,000.00	$942.67	$942.67	$31,000,000.00	$20.67	$20.67	2%
$22,702,989.00	$688.78	$688.78	$4,972,471.00	$150.86	$150.86	18%
$18,217,887.00	$111.19	$111.19	$24,317,726.00	$148.41	$148.41	57%
36,747,983.00	$917.76	$917.76	$8,190,510.00	$204.55	$204.55	18%
41,950,671.00	$500.95	500.95	$7,218,214.00	$86.20	$86.20	15%

Table 5. Selected Statistics of Churc[h]

				TOTAL CONTRIBUTIONS		
Religious Body	Year	Full or Confirmed Members	Inclusive Members	Total Contributions	Per Capita Full or Confirmed Members	Per Capita Inclusive Members
Cumberland Presbyterian Church in America	1996	15,142	15,142	$40,408,524.00	$2,668.64	$2,668.64
Episcopal Church*	2002	1,902,525	2,320,221	$2,070,493,919.00	$1,088.29	$892.37
The Evangelical Church	2000	12,475	12,475	$15,632,985.00	$1,253.15	$1,253.15
The Evangelical Congregational Church	2003	20,743	20,743	$19,628,647.00	$946.28	$946.28
The Evangelical Covenant Church	2002	105,956	105,956	$256,582,437.00	$2,421.59	$2,421.59
Evangelical Lutheran Church in America*	2003	3,724,321	4,984,925	$2,518,612,907.00	$676.26	$505.25
Evangelical Lutheran Synod	2003	16,674	21,047	$13,013,890	$780.49	$618.33
Fellowship of Evangelical Bible Churches	2003	2,020	2,020	$3,260,129.00	$1,613.93	$1,613.93
Fellowship of Evangelical Churches	2003	13,043	13,043	$18,418,273.00	$1,412.12	$1,412.12
Free Methodist Church of North America	2003	63,538	71,459	$129,071,159.00	$2,031.40	$1,806.23
General Association of General Baptists	2002	67,231	85,924	$33,922,637.00	$504.57	$394.80
General Conference of Mennonite Brethren Churches	1996	50,915	82,130	$65,851,481.00	$1,293.36	$801.80
International Church of the Foursquare Gospel	2003	251,614	326,614	$533,993,579.00	$2,122.27	$1,634.94
The International Pentecostal Church of Christ	2002	2,004	4,961	$3,551,761.42	$1,772.34	$715.94
The Latvian Evangelical Lutheran Church in America	2002	12,124	13,584	$3,094,000.00	$255.20	$227.77
The Lutheran Church Missouri Synod (LCMS)	2003	1,894,822	2,488,936	$1,256,382,217.00	$663.06	$504.79
Mar Thoma Syrian Church of India*	2002	25,000	35,000	$2,875,000.00	$115.00	$82.14
The Missionary Church	2003	36,162	36,162	$83,371,445.00	$2,305.50	$2,305.50
Moravian Church in America (Unitas Fratrum)*	2003	19,456	24,650	$17,864,570.00	$918.20	$724.73
National Association of Free Will Baptists	2001	198,795	198,795	$97,416,530.00	$490.04	$490.04
North American Baptist Conference	2002	47,692	47,692	$65,765,687.49	$1,378.97	$1,378.97
The Orthodox Presbyterian Church	2003	19,725	27,582	$36,644,100.00	$1,857.75	$1,328.55
Presbyterian Church in America	2003	255,492	315,981	$529,220,570.00	$2,071.38	$1,674.85
Presbyterian Church (U.S.A.)*	2003	2,405,311	3,241,309	$2,743,637,755.00	$1,140.66	$846.46
Primitive Methodist Church in the U.S.A.	2003	4,124	4,480	$4,771,104.00	$1,156.91	$1,064.98

Finances—United States Churches *(continued)*

CONGREGATIONAL FINANCES			BENEVOLENCES			
Total Congregation Contributions	Per Capita Full or Confirmed Members	Per Capita Inclusive Members	Total Benevolences	Per Capita Full or Confirmed Members	Per Capita Inclusive Members	Benevolences as a Percentage
$34,921,064.00	$2,306.24	2,306.24	$5,487,460.00	$362.40	$362.40	14%
$1,811,142,440.00	$951.97	$780.59	$279,394,072.00	$146.85	$120.42	13%
$12,784,502.00	$1,024.81	$1,024.81	$2,848,483.00	$228.34	$228.34	18%
$17,648,320.00	$850.81	$850.81	$1,980,327.00	$95.47	$95.47	10%
$233,937,868.00	$2,207.88	$2,207.88	$22,644,569.00	$213.72	$213.72	9%
$2,287,110,767.00	$614.10	$458.81	$231,502,140.00	$62.16	$46.44	9%
$12,018,180.00	$720.77	$571.02	$995,710	$59.72	$47.51	8%
$2,448,800.00	$1,212.28	$1,212.28	$811,329.00	$401.65	$401.65	25%
$16,525,789.00	$1,267.02	$1,267.02	$1,892,484.00	$145.10	$145.10	10%
$122,723,869.00	$1,931.50	$1,717.40	$6,347,290.00	$99.90	$88.82	5%
$31,000,633.00	$461.11	$360.79	$2,922,004.00	$43.46	$34.01	9%
$50,832,814.00	$998.39	$618.93	$15,018,667.00	$294.98	$182.86	23%
$490,130,528.00	$1,947.95	$1,500.64	$43,863,051.00	$174.33	$134.30	8%
$2,648,634.00	$1,321.67	$533.89	$903,127.42	$450.66	$182.05	25%
$2,598,000.00	$214.29	$191.25	$496,000.00	$40.91	$36.51	16%
$1,313,212,373.00	$693.05	$527.62	$125,169,844.00	$66.06	$50.29	10%
$2,405,000.00	$96.20	$67.71	$475,000.00	$19.00	$13.57	17%
$69,273,225.00	$1,915.64	$1,915.64	$14,098,220.00	$389.86	$389.86	17%
$16,939,268.00	$870.64	$687.19	$925,302.00	$47.56	$37.54	5%
$74,182,690.00	$373.16	$373.16	$23,233,840.00	$116.87	$116.87	24%
$56,813,620.00	$1,191.26	$1,191.26	$8,952,067.49	$187.71	$187.71	14%
$30,972,500.00	$1,570.22	$1,122.92	$5,671,600.00	$287.53	$205.63	15%
$428,961,213.00	$1,678.96	$1,357.55	$100,259,357.00	$392.42	$317.30	19%
$2,361,944,688.00	$981.97	$728.70	$381,693,067.00	$158.69	$117.76	14%
$4,100,475.00	$994.30	$915.28	$670,629.00	$162.62	$149.69	14%

Table 5. Selected Statistics of Church

Religious Body	Year	Full or Confirmed Members	Inclusive Members	TOTAL CONTRIBUTIONS		
				Total Contributions	Per Capita Full or Confirmed Members	Per Capita Inclusive Members
Reformed Presbyterian Church of North America	2003	4,400	$6,259	$8,129,526.00	$1,830.97	$1,298.85
Reformed Church in America*	2003	168,801	278,739	$275,354,238.00	$1,631.24	$987.86
Reformed Church in the United States	2002	3,258	4,369	$6,241,428.00	$1,915.72	$1,428.57
The Schwenkfelder Church	2003	2,633	2,633	$1,758,559.00	$667.89	$667.89
Seventh-day Adventist Church	2003	935,428	935,428	$1,088,682,947.00	$1,163.83	$1,163.83
Southern Baptist Convention	2003	16,439,603	16,439,603	$9,648,530,640.00	$586.91	$586.91
Syro-Russian Orthodox Catholic Church	2003	21,000	22,500	$108,500.00	$5.17	$4.82
United Church of Christ*	2003	1,296,652	1,296,652	$878,974,911.00	$677.88	$677.88
The United Methodist Church*	2002	8,251,175	8,251,175	$5,242,691,229.00	$635.39	$635.39
Unity of the Brethren	1998	2,548	3,218	$165,184.00	$64.83	$51.33
Universal Fellowship of Metropolitan Community Churches	1998	44,000	44,000	$1,570,860.00	$35.70	$35.70
The Wesleyan Church	2003	113,927	124,550	$257,241,001.00	$2,257.95	$2,065.36
Wisconsin Evangelical Lutheran Synod	2003	314,840	400,622	$348,269,908.00	$1,106.18	$869.32

**National Council of Churches member communion*

Summary Statitistics

Nation	Number Reporting	Full or Confirmed Members	Inclusive Member-ship	TOTAL CONTRIBUTIONS		
				Total Contributions	Per Capita Full or Confirmed Members	Per Capita Inclusive Members
United States	63	44,211,342	48,266,164	$32,269,713,588	$729.90	$668.58
Canada	22	978,998	2,014,667	$703,821,274	$718.92	$349.35

Finances—United States Churches (*continued*)

CONGREGATIONAL FINANCES			BENEVOLENCES			
Total Congregation Contributions	Per Capita Full or Confirmed Members	Per Capita Inclusive Members	Total Benevolences	Per Capita Full or Confirmed Members	Per Capita Inclusive Members	Benevolences as a Percentage
$7,422,347.00	$1,671.70	$1,885.87	$707,179.00	$159.27	$112.99	9%
$235,422,160.00	$1,394.67	$844.60	$39,932,078.00	$236.56	$143.26	15%
$5,398,445.00	$1,629.66	$1,215.25	$931,983.00	$286.06	$213.32	15%
$1,517,827.00	$576.46	$576.46	$240,732.00	$91.43	$91.43	14%
$348,219,525.00	$372.26	$372.26	$740,463,422.00	$791.58	$791.58	68%
$8,546,166,798.00	$519.85	$519.85	$1,102,363,842.00	$67.06	$67.06	11%
$50,000.00	$2.38	$2.22	$58,500.00	$2.79	$2.60	54%
$802,327,537.00	$618.77	$618.77	$76,647,374.00	$59.11	$59.11	9%
$4,236,235,774.00	$513.41	$513.41	$1,006,455,455.00	$121.98	$121.98	19%
$51,465.00	$20.20	$15.99	$113,719.00	$44.63	$35.34	69%
$1,415,000.00	$32.16	$32.16	$155,860.00	$3.54	$3.54	10%
$224,791,915.00	$1,973.12	$1,804.83	$32,449,086.00	$284.82	$260.53	13%
$297,307,248.00	$944.31	$742.11	$50,962,660.00	$161.87	$127.21	15%

# of Church Finances

CONGREGATIONAL FINANCES			BENEVOLENCES			
Total Congregational Contributions	Per Capita Full or Confirmed Members	Per Capita Inclusive Members	Total Belevolences	Per Capita Full or Confirmed Members	Per Capita Inclusive Members	Benevolences as a Percentage of Total Contributions
$27,723,558,838	$627.07	$574.39	$4,748,202,343	$107.40	$98.38	15%
$583,552,594	$596.07	$289.65	$120,382,365	$122.96	$59.75	17%

STATISTICAL SECTION

Trends in Seminary Enrollment

Data Provided by The Association of Theological Schools (ATS) in the United States and Canada

Table 1: ATS total student enrollment figures include the number of individuals enrolled in degree programs as well as persons enrolled in non-degree programs of study. Growth in total enrollment is a function of both increased enrollment in the seminaries and the increased number of member schools in the Association.

Table 1 Number of Member Schools from 1988 to 2003

Year	Number of Schools	Total Enrollment	Canada		United States		By Membership	
			Head Count	FTE	Head Count	FTE	Accredited	Non-Accredited
1988	207	55,746	3,995	2,679	51,751	34,827	51,683	4,063
1989	205	56,178	4,142	2,668	52,036	35,013	52,949	3,229
1990	211	59,003	4,053	2,636	54,950	37,590	54,052	4,951
1991	211	59,897	4,648	2,631	55,249	36,456	55,028	4,869
1992	220	63,484	4,897	2,999	58,587	39,554	57,784	5,700
1993	219	63,429	5,040	3,150	58,389	39,506	57,823	5,606
1994	226	65,089	5,241	3,212	59,848	40,293	60,490	4,599
1995	224	64,480	5,203	3,267	59,277	39,834	59,813	4,667
1996	233	65,637	5,568	3,304	60,069	40,111	60,527	5,110
1997	229	65,361	5,544	3,225	59,817	40,022	61,498	3,863
1998	237	68,875	5,847	3,683	63,028	40,994	64,412	4,463
1999	237	70,432	6,010	3,224	64,422	41,528	65,674	4,758
2000	243	72,728	5,868	3,251	68,860	44,627	69,850	2,878
2001	243	73,925	6,254	3,342	67,671	45,094	70,942	2,983
2002	244	76,530	6,643	3,512	69,887	44,557	73,615	2,895
2003	243	78,709	6,925	3,653	71,784	46,553	75,660	3,017

Table 2: ATS computes enrollment both by the total number of individual students (Head Count) and the equivalent of full-time students (FTE). If all students were enrolled full-time, the head count number and the full-time equivalency number would be the same. The FTE is calculated by dividing the total number of credits required for the degree by the number of semesters prescribed for degree duration to determine the average academic load. The total of credit hours taken by all students in a given degree program in a semester is then divided by the average academic load. During the past five years, full-time equivalent enrollment as a percentage of head count enrollment has generally decreased, indicating an increasing number of part-time students. The enrollment figures this year move somewhat against the trend.

Table 2 Head Count and FTE for all Member Schools 1988 to 2003

Year	Head Count	% Change	FTE	% Change	FTE % of Head Count
1988	55,746	-0.04	37,506	-2.15	67.3%
1989	56,178	0.77	37,681	0.47	67.1%
1990	59,003	5.03	40,226	6.75	68.2%
1991	59,897	1.52	39,087	-2.83	65.3%
1992	63,484	5.99	42,553	8.87	67.0%
1993	63,429	0.09	42,656	0.24	67.2%
1994	65,089	2.62	43,505	1.99	66.8%
1995	64,480	-0.94	43,101	-0.93	66.8%
1996	65,637	1.79	43,414	0.73	66.1%
1997	65,361	-0.42	43,247	-0.38	66.2%
1998	68,875	5.38	44,678	3.31	64.9%
1999	70,432	2.17	44,845	0.68	63.7%
2000	72,728	3.26	47,876	6.76	65.8%
2001	73,925	1.65	48,435	1.17	65.5%
2002	76,550	3.50	48,130	-0.76	62.8%
2003	78,709	2.8	50,206	4.35	63.8%

Table 3: ATS member schools offer a variety of degree programs, Table 3 displays enrollment by categories of degree programs. The Master of Divinity (M.Div.) degree is the normative degree to prepare persons for ordained ministry and for pastoral and religious leadership responsibilities in congregations. Over the past five years, from fall 1999 to fall 2003, the M.Div. experienced the largest increase in the *number* of students enrolled, an increase of 11.5%. In the same five-year period, the greatest increases by *percentage* in student head count enrollment were in the Master of Arts in a variety of specialized ministry areas (24%) within the Basic Ministerial Leadership (Non-M.Div.) category. This is followed by an increase of 11% in the "Others" and General Theological Studies category.

Table 3 Head Count Enrollment by Degree Categories 1988–2003
(Categories based on accrediting standards—adopted in 1996)

Year	Basic Ministerial Leadership		General Theological Studies	Advanced Ministerial Leadership	Advanced Theological Research	Others
	(M.Div.)	(Non-M.Div.)				
1988	26,581	5,131	5,423	6,511	4,203	7,897
1989	25,954	5,080	5,485	7,004	4,186	8,469
1990	25,615	5,284	6,144	7,417	5,046	9,497
1991	25,710	5,805	6,105	7,598	5,044	9,635
1992	26,956	5,812	6,872	7,961	5,036	10,847
1993	27,264	6,536	7,131	8,302	5,157	9,039
1994	27,240	6,891	7,229	7,841	5,330	10,558
1995	27,497	6,964	7,211	8,233	5,302	9,273
1996	28,035	7,474	7,157	8,315	5,499	9,157
1997	28,283	7,463	7,048	8,195	5,391	8,981
1998	29,263	8,066	7,601	8,641	5,712	9,591
1999	29,842	8,361	7,862	8,743	5,396	10,228
2000	30,427	9,098	8,436	8,758	5,692	10,317
2001	31,128	8,652	8,503	8,790	5,756	11,096
2002	32,005	9,493	8,626	9,209	5,653	11,544
2003	33,287	10,343	8,708	9,213	5,804	11,354

Table 4: In fall 2002, women constituted 35% of the total enrollment in all ATS schools and 31% of the head count enrollment in the MDiv degree program. When ATS first began gathering enrollment data by gender in 1972, women represented 10.2% of the enrollment and 4.7% of the MDiv enrollment. Only once in the past 29 years has the number of women students decreased from one year to the next, that being in 1993, with a 0.65% decrease.

Table 4 Women Student Head Count Enrollment 1988-2003

Year	Number of Students	% Annual Increase	% of Total Enrollment
1988	16,326	0.00	29.29%
1989	16,525	1.20	29.42%
1990	17,498	5.56	29.66%
1991	18,188	3.79	30.37%
1992	19,856	8.40	31.28%
1993	19,727	-0.65	31.10%
1994	20,564	4.07	31.59%
1995	20,795	1.12	32.25%
1996	21,523	3.50	32.76%
1997	21,652	0.60	33.10%
1998	23,176	7.04	33.65%
1999	24,057	3.73	34.16%
2000	25,391	5.55	34.91%
2001	25,999	2.39	35.17%
2002	27,328	5.06	35.70%
2003	27,920	2.2	35.50%

Tables 5, 6, 7: Enrollment of North American racial/ethnic minority students in ATS schools has grown from 6% of total head count enrollment in 1977 to 21% in 2003. Over the past five years (1998 to 2003), the number of African American students increased by 19%; Hispanic students by 27%; and Pacific/Asian American students by 11%. The number of white students increased 14% over the same period. Tables 5, 6, and 7 show the number of African American, Hispanic, and Pacific/Asian American students enrolled by year.

Table 5 African American Student Head Count Enrollment 1988-2003

Year	Number of Students	% Annual Increase	% of Total Enrollment
1988	3,660	8.72	6.57%
1989	3,925	6.75	6.99%
1990	4,265	7.97	7.23%
1991	4,658	8.44	7.78%
1992	5,558	16.19	8.75%
1993	5,223	-6.41	8.23%
1994	5,526	5.48	8.49%
1995	5,698	3.11	8.84%
1996	5,550	-2.60	8.45%
1997	5,802	4.54	8.87%
1998	6,328	9.07	9.19%
1999	6,854	8.31	9.73%
2000	7,161	4.48	9.85%
2001	7,462	4.20	10.09%
2002	8,192	9.78	10.71%
2003	8,144	-0.59	10.30%

Table 6 Hispanic Student Head Count Enrollment 1988–2003

Year	Number of Students	% Annual Increase	% of Total Enrollment
1988	1,415	1.13	2.54%
1989	1,485	4.71	2.64%
1990	1,912	22.33	3.24%
1991	1,626	-17.59	2.71%
1992	1,689	3.73	2.66%
1993	1,790	5.64	2.82%
1994	1,799	0.50	2.76%
1995	1,817	1.00	2.82%
1996	1,785	-1.76	2.72%
1997	1,915	7.28	2.93%
1998	2,175	13.58	3.16%
1999	2,256	3.72	3.10%
2000	2,685	19.02	3.69%
2001	2,756	2.64	3.72%
2002	2,449	-11.64	3.20%
2003	2,863	16.90	3.60%

Table 7 Pacific/Asian American Student Head Count Enrollment 1988–2003

Year	Number of Students	% Annual Increase	% of Total Enrollment
1988	1,963	13.75	3.52%
1989	2,062	4.80	3.67%
1990	2,437	15.39	4.13%
1991	2,649	8.00	4.42%
1992	3,142	15.69	4.95%
1993	3,631	13.47	5.72%
1994	3,876	6.32	5.95%
1995	4,245	9.52	6.58%
1996	4,492	5.82	6.84%
1997	4,545	1.18	6.95%
1998	4,992	8.95	7.25%
1999	4,932	-1.20	6.78%
2000	5,003	1.44	6.88%
2001	5,021	0.36	6.79%
2002	5,005	-0.32	6.54%
2003	5,499	9.87	7.00%

IV

A CALENDAR FOR CHURCH USE

2005–2008

This Calendar presents the major days of religious observances for Christians, Jews, Baha'is, and Muslims; and, within the Christian community, major dates observed by Roman Catholic, Eastern and Oriental Orthodox, Episcopal, and Lutheran churches. Within each of these traditions many other observances such as saints' days exist, but only those regarded as the most important are listed. Dates of interest to many Protestant communions are also included.

In the Orthodox dates, immovable observances are listed in accordance with the Gregorian calendar. Movable dates (those depending on the date of Easter) will often differ from Western observance, since the date of Easter (*Pascha*) in the Orthodox communions does not always correlate with the date for Easter of the Western churches. For Orthodox churches that use the old Julian calendar, observances are held thirteen days later than listed here.

Jewish and Muslim holidays begin after sunset the day previous to the date listed in this Calendar. For Jews and Muslims, who follow differing lunar calendars, the dates of major observances are translated into Gregorian dates. Since the actual beginning of a new month in the Islamic calendar is determined by the appearance of the new moon, the corresponding dates given here on the Gregorian calendar may vary by geographic location and practice. Following the lunar calendar, Muslim dates fall roughly eleven days earlier each year on the Gregorian calendar. Practice concerning transliteration of the titles of holidays varies widely as well.

(Note: This listing reflects the first full day of holidays extending over two or more days. "RC" stands for Roman Catholic, "O" for Orthodox, "E" for Episcopal, "L" for Lutheran, "ECU" for Ecumenical, "M" for Muslim).

Event	2005	2006	2007	2008
New Year's Day (RC-Solemnity of Mary; O-Circumcision of Jesus Christ; E-Feast of Holy Name; L-Naming of Jesus) (RC, O, E, L)	Jan 01	Jan 01	Jan 01	Jan 01
Epiphany Sunday (RC)	Jan 02	Jan 01	Jan 07	Jan 06
Armenian Christmas (O)	Jan 06	Jan 06	Jan 06	Jan 06
Epiphany (RC, O, E, L)	Jan 06	Jan 06	Jan 06	Jan 06
First Sunday After Epiphany (Feast of the Baptism of Our Lord) (Christian)	Jan 09	Jan 08	Jan 14	Jan 13
Feast Day of St. John the Baptist (Armenian O)	Jan 13	Jan 13	Jan 13	Jan 13
Ecumenical Sunday (ECU)	Jan 16	Jan 15	Jan 21	Jan 20
Week of Prayer for Christian Unity, Canada (ECU)	Jan 17	Jan 16	Jan 22	Jan 21
Week of Prayer for Christian Unity (ECU)	Jan 18	Jan 18	Jan 18	Jan 18
Theophany (Oriental O)	Jan 19	Jan 19	Jan 19	Jan 19
Waqf al-Arafah (Eve of 'Id al-Adha) (M)	Jan 19	Jan 08 Dec 30	Dec 19	Dec 7
'Id al-Adha (Festival of Sacrifice at time of Pilgrimage to Mecca) (M)	Jan 21	Jan 10 Dec 31	Dec 20	Dec 08
Tu B'Shevat (J)	Jan 25	Feb 13	Feb 03	Jan 22
Presentation of Jesus in the Temple (Candlemas; Purification of the Virgin Mary; O-The Meeting of Our Lord and Savior Jesus Christ) (Christian)	Feb 02	Feb 02	Feb 02	Feb 02
Ash Wednesday (Western Churches)	Feb 09	Mar 01	Feb 21	Feb 06

Event	2005	2006	2007	2008
Muharram Begins (First Day of the Month of Muharram; Muslim New Year) (M)	Feb 10	Jan 31	Jan 20	Jan 10 Dec 29
Ashura' (Martyrdom of Imam Hussein) (M [Shi'a])	Feb 19	Feb 09	Jan 29	Jan 19
Brotherhood Week (Interfaith)	Feb 20	Feb 19	Feb 18	Feb 17
Great Lent (First Day of Lent) (O)	Feb 23	Mar 14	Mar 06	Feb 19
Baha'i Fasting Season begins (19 days) (Baha'i)	Mar 02	Mar 02	Mar 02	Mar 02
World Day of Prayer (ECU)	Mar 04	Mar 3	Mar 02	Mar 07
Great Lent (First Day of Lent) (O)	Mar 14	Mar 06	Feb 19	Feb 06
Joseph, Husband of Mary (RC, E, L)	Mar 19	Mar 19	Mar 19	Mar 19
Holy Week (Western Churches)	Mar 20	Apr 09	Apr 01	Mar 16
Feast of Naw-Ruz (Baha'i New Year) (Baha'i)	Mar 21	Mar 21	Mar 21	Mar 21
Holy Thursday (Western Churches)	Mar 24	Apr 13	Apr 05	Mar 20
The Annunciation (Christian)	Mar 25	Mar 25	Mar 25	Mar 25
Good Friday (Friday of the Passion of Our Lord) (Western Churches)	Mar 25	Apr 14	Apr 06	Mar 21
Purim (J)	Mar 25	Mar 14	Mar 04	Mar 21
Easter (Western Churches)	Mar 27	Apr 16	Apr 08	Mar 23
Feast of Ridvan (Declaration of Baha'u'llah) (12 days) (Baha'i)	Apr 21	Apr 21	Apr 21	Apr 21
Mawlid al-Nabi (Anniversary of the Prophet Muhammed's Birthday) (M)	Apr 21	Apr 11	Mar 31	Mar 20
Holy Week (O)	Apr 24	Apr 16	Apr 01	Apr 20
Palm Sunday (O)	Apr 24	Apr 16	Apr 01	Apr 20
Passover (Pesach) (8 days) (J)	Apr 24	Apr 13	Apr 03	Apr 20
Holy Thursday (O)	Apr 28	Apr 20	Apr 05	Apr 24
Holy Friday (Good Friday; Burial of Jesus) (O)	Apr 29	Apr 21	Apr 06	Apr 25
Pascha (Orthodox Easter) (O)	May 01	Apr 23	Apr 08	Apr 27
Ascension Thursday (Western Churches)	May 05	May 25	May 17	May 01
National Day of Prayer (ECU)	May 05	May 04	May 03	May 02
May Friendship Day (ECU)	May 06	May 05	May 04	May 03
Yom Hashoah (J)	May 06	Apr 25	Apr 15	May 02
Rural Life Sunday (ECU)	May 08	May 14	May 13	May 12
Yom Haatzma'ut (J)	May 12	May 03	Apr 23	May 10
Pentecost (Whitsunday) (Western Churches)	May 15	Jun 04	May 27	May 11
Holy Trinity (RC, E, L)	May 22	Jun 11	Jun 03	May 18
Declaration of the Bab (Baha'i)	May 23	May 23	May 23	May 23
Lag B'Omer (J)	May 27	May 16	May 06	May 23
Ascension of Baha'u'llah (Baha'i)	May 29	May 29	May 29	May 29
Corpus Christi (RC)	May 29	Jun 18	Jun 10	May 25
Visitation of the Blessed Virgin Mary (RC, E, L)	May 31	May 31	May 31	May 31
Ascension Day (O)	Jun 02	Jun 11	May 17	Jun 05
Sacred Heart of Jesus (RC)	Jun 03	Jun 23	Jun 15	May 30
Martyrdom of the Bab (Baha'i)	Jun 09	Jun 09	Jun 09	Jun 09
Shavuout (Pentecost) (2 days) (J)	Jun 13	Jun 02	May 23	Jun 09
Pentecost (O)	Jun 19	Jun 11	May 27	Jun 15
Nativity of St. John the Baptist (RC, E, L)	Jun 24	Jun 24	Jun 24	Jun 24
Saint Peter and Saint Paul, Apostles of Christ (O)	Jun 29	Jun 29	Jun 29	Jun 29
Feast Day of the Twelve Apostles of Christ (O)	Jun 30	Jun 30	Jun 30	Jun 30
Transfiguration of the Lord (RC, O, E)	Aug 06	Aug 06	Aug 06	Aug 06
Tish'a B'Av (J)	Aug 14	Aug 03	Jul 24	Aug 10
Assumption of the Blessed Virgin Mary (E-Feast of the Blessed Virgin Mary; O-Falling Asleep (Domition) of the Blessed Virgin) (RC, O, E)	Aug 15	Aug 15	Aug 15	Aug 15
Laylat al-Miraj (Ascension of the Prophet (M)	Sep 01	Aug 22	Aug 11	Jul 31
The Birth of the Blessed Virgin (RC, O)	Sep 08	Sep 08	Sep 08	Sep 08
Holy Cross Day (RC-Triumph of the Cross; O-Adoration of the Holy Cross) (Christian)	Sep 14	Sep 14	Sep 14	Sep 14
Laylat-ul-Bara'h (Night of Forgiveness) (M)	Sep 19	Sep 09	Aug 29	Aug 16
Michaelmas (St. Michael and All Angels) (Christian)	Sep 29	Sep 29	Sep 29	Sep 29

Event	2005	2006	2007	2008
Laylat at Bar'a (M)	Sep 30	Sep 19	Sep 09	Aug 29
World Communion Sunday (ECU)	Oct 02	Oct 01	Oct 07	Oct 05
Ramadan Begins (First day of the month of Ramadan) (M)	Oct 04	Sep 24	Sep 13	Sep 01
Rosh Hashanah (New Year) (2 days) (J)	Oct 04	Sep 23	Sep 13	Sep 30
Laity Sunday (ECU)	Oct 09	Oct 08	Oct 14	Oct 12
Thanksgiving Day (Canada) (National)	Oct 10	Oct 09	Oct 08	Oct 13
Yom Kippur (Day of Atonement) (J)	Oct 13	Oct 02	Sep 22	Oct 09
Sukkot (Tabernacles) (7 days) (J)	Oct 18	Oct 07	Sep 27	Oct 14
Birth of the Bab (Baha'i)	Oct 20	Oct 20	Oct 20	Oct 20
Shmini Atzeret (Solemn Assembly) (J)	Oct 25	Oct 15	Oct 04	Oct 21
Shimchat Torah (Rejoicing of the Law) (J)	Oct 26	Oct 15	Oct 05	Oct 22
Laylat al-Qadr (Night of Destiny, Revelation of the Holy Qur'an) (M)	Oct 30	Oct 20	Oct 09	Sep 27
Reformation Sunday (L)	Oct 30	Oct 29	Oct 28	Oct 26
Reformation Day (L)	Oct 31	Oct 31	Oct 31	Oct 31
All Saints Day (RC, E, L)	Nov 01	Nov 01	Nov 01	Nov 01
'Id al-Fitr (Festival of the End of Ramadan; First day of the month of Shawwal) (M)	Nov 03	Oct 24	Oct 13	Aug 01
World Community Day (ECU)	Nov 03	Nov 02	Nov 01	Nov 06
Birth of Baha'u'llah (Baha'i)	Nov 12	Nov 12	Nov 12	Nov 12
Bible Sunday (ECU)	Nov 20	Nov 19	Nov 18	Nov 23
Last Sunday After Pentecost (L—Feast of Christ the King) (RC, L)	Nov 20	Nov 26	Nov 25	Nov 23
National Bible Week (ECU)	Nov 20	Nov 19	Nov 18	Nov 23
Thanksgiving Sunday (U.S.) (Christian)	Nov 20	Nov 19	Nov 18	Nov 23
Presentation of the Blessed Virgin Mary in the Temple (Presentation of the Theotokos) (O)	Nov 21	Nov 21	Nov 21	Nov 21
Thanksgiving Day (U.S.) (National)	Nov 24	Nov 23	Nov 22	Nov 27
The Day of the Covenant (Baha'i)	Nov 26	Nov 26	Nov 26	Nov 26
First Sunday of Advent (Advent Sunday) (Christian)	Nov 27	Dec 03	Dec 02	Nov 30
Ascension of 'Abdu'l-Baha (Baha'i)	Nov 28	Nov 28	Nov 28	Nov 28
Feast Day of St. Andrew the Apostle (RC, O, E, L)	Nov 30	Nov 30	Nov 30	Nov 30
Immaculate Conception of the Blessed Virgin Mary (RC)	Dec 08	Dec 08	Dec 08	Dec 08
Fourth Sunday of Advent (Christmas Sunday) (Christian)	Dec 18	Dec 24	Dec 23	Dec 21
Christmas (Christian, Except Armenian)	Dec 25	Dec 25	Dec 25	Dec 25
Hanukkah (Chanukah, Festival of Lights) (8 days) (J)	Dec 26	Dec 16	Dec 05	Dec 22

V

INDEXES
Organizations

AAR (American Academy of Religion)........211
ABCCM (Asheville-Buncombe Community Christian Ministry) 250
ACAT...288
Advent Christian Church..................................61
African Methodist Episcopal Church 11, 13, 61, 365, 378
African Methodist Episcopal Zion Church, The 11, 62, 365, 378
AGAPÉ Deux-Montagnes..............................288
Akron Area Association of Churches............251
Alaska Christian Conference.........................227
Alban Institute, Inc., The................................23
Albanian Orthodox Archdiocese in America ..64
Albanian Orthodox Diocese of America 65, 365, 382
Alcohol and Drug Concerns Inc......................53
Allegheny Valley Association of Churches.......253
Allegheny Wesleyan Methodist Connection, The (Original Allegheny Conference) 65, 365, 382
Alliance of Baptists, The.................65, 365, 378
Alliance of Churches.....................................251
AMERC (Appalachian Ministries Educational Resource Center)..25
American Academy of Religion (AAR)........211
American Association of Lutheran Churches, The...66, 365
American Baptist Association, The.........66, 365
American Baptist Churches in the U.S.A. 11, 12, 14, 66, 365, 378, 382
American Bible Society 23
American Buddhist Congress........................220
American Carpatho-Russian Orthodox Greek Catholic Church, The 68, 365
American Council of Christian Churches.......24
American Evangelical Christian Churches 68, 365, 382
American Friends Service Committee............24
American Hindus Against Defamation 221
American Jewish Committee 223
American Religion Data Archive (ARDA)...212
American Rescue Workers......................69, 365
American Theological Library Association, The..24
American Tract Society..................................25
American Waldensian Society, The.................25
Amish. *See* Old Order Amish Church
Anglican Church of Canada, The..........179, 358
Anglican Orthodox Church. *See* The Episcopal Orthodox Church
Anti-Defamation League of B'nai B'rith, The 223
Antiochian Orthodox Christian Archdiocese of North America, The ....69, 180, 358, 365, ...378, 382
Apostolic Catholic Assyrian Church of the East, North American Dioceses 70
Apostolic Catholic Orthodox Church.......70, 365
Apostolic Christian Church (Nazarene) 71, 180, 358, 365
Apostolic Christian Churches of America 71, 366
Apostolic Church in Canada, The 181, 358, 380
Apostolic Church of Pentecost of Canada, Inc 181, 358
Apostolic Episcopal Church....................72, 366
Apostolic Faith Mission Church of God 72, 366, 382
Apostolic Faith Mission of Portland, Oregon 73, 366
Apostolic Lutheran Church of America..........73
Apostolic Orthodox Catholic Church of North America 73, 366
Appalachian Ministries Educational Resource Center (AMERC) 25
ARDA (American Religion Data Archive) 212
Arizona Ecumenical Council 227
Arkansas Interfaith Conference.....................228
Armenian Apostolic Church, Diocese of America 75, 366, 378
Armenian Apostolic Church of America 74, 366
Armenian Evangelical Church 181
Armenian Holy Apostolic Church—Canadian Diocese 181, 358, 380
Arrowhead Interfaith Council 242
Asheville-Buncombe Community Christian Ministry (ABCCM)..................................250
Assemblies of God..........11, 12, 13, 14, 75, 366
Assemblies of God International Fellowship (Independent/Not affiliated)........................76
Associate Reformed Presbyterian Church (General Synod)..........................77, 366, 382
Associated Church Press, The.........................26

Associated Churches of Fort Wayne & Allen County, Inc., The 234
Associated Gospel Churches 181, 358
Associated Gospel Churches, The 26
Associated Ministries of Tacoma-Pierce County 260
Association of Canadian Bible Colleges 53
Association of Catholic Diocesan Archivists 26
Association of Christian Churches in Manitoba 287
Association of Christian Churches of South Dakota 258
Association for the Development of Religious Information Services 27
Association of Free Lutheran Congregations, The 77, 366
Association of Gospel Rescue Missions 27
Association of Regular Baptist Churches (Canada) 182, 358
Association of Religious Communities 230
Association of Statisticians of American Religious Bodies 27
Association of Theological Schools 212
Association of Theological Schools in the United States and Canada, The 28
Association of Vineyard Churches 78, 366
Atlantic Ecumenical Council 289
Atlantic Ecumenical Council of Churches 287
ATS (Association of Theological Schools) 212
Attleboro Area Council of Churches, Inc. 239
Auburn Theological Seminary 213
Austin Area Inter-religious Ministries 258

Baha'i National Center of the U.S.A., The 219
Baptist Bible Fellowship International 11, 78, 366
Baptist Convention of Ontario and Quebec 182, 358
Baptist General Conference 79, 366
Baptist General Conference of Canada 182, 358
Baptist Missionary Association of America 79, 366, 382
Baptist Union of Western Canada 183, 358, 380
BARCA (Border Association for Refugees from Central America), Inc. 258
Barna Group, Ltd., The 213
Bay Area Ecumenical Forum 240
Beachy Amish Mennonite Churches 80, 366
Berean Fellowship of Churches 80, 367, 382
Bergen County Council of Churches 245
Berrien County Association of Churches 240
Bible Church of Christ, Inc., The 80, 367
Bible Fellowship Church 81, 367, 382
Bible Holiness Church 81
Bible Holiness Movement, The 183, 358, 380
Bible Way Church of Our Lord Jesus Christ World Wide, Inc. 81
Blanton-Peale Institute 28
Border Association for Refugees from Central America (BARCA), Inc. 258
Bread For The World 28
Brethren in Christ Church 82, 367, 382
Brethren in Christ Church, Canadian Conference 183, 358
Brethren Church (Ashland, Ohio) 82, 367
Bridgewater Inter-Church Council 287
British Methodist Episcopal Church of Canada 184
Brooklyn Council of Churches 246
Broome County Council of Churches, Inc. 246
Buddhist Churches of America 220
Buddhist Council of the Midwest 220
Buddhist Peace Fellowship, The 221
Buddhist Sangha Council of Southern California 220
Burlington Inter-Church Council 288

CAIR (Council for American-Islamic Relations) 222
Calgary Council of Churches 287
Calgary Inter-Faith Community Association 287
California Council of Churches-California Church Impact 228
Campus Crusade for Christ International 28
Canadian and American Reformed Churches 184, 359
Canadian Baptist Ministries 184, 359
Canadian Bible Society 53
Canadian Centre for Ecumenism 54
Canadian Centre for Ecumenism/Centre d'oe cuménisme 288
Canadian Conference of Mennonite Brethren Churches 184, 359
Canadian Convention of Southern Baptists 184, 359
Canadian Council of Churches, The 54
Canadian District of the Moravian Church in America, Northern Province 185, 359, 380
Canadian Evangelical Christian Churches 185, 359, 380
Canadian Evangelical Theological Association 54
Canadian Society of Biblical Studies-Société Canadienne des Études Bibliques 55
Canadian Tract Society 55
Canadian Yearly Meeting of the Religious Society of Friends 185, 359
Cape Cod Council of Churches, Inc., The 239
Capital Area Council of Churches, Inc. 247
Capital Region Conference of Churches, The 230
Capital Region Ecumenical Organization (CREO) 247
CARA (Center for Applied Research in the Apostolate) 28
Catholic Church, The 11, 12, 13, 14, 82, 367
CEAP (Community Emergency Assistance Program) 242
Center for Applied Research in the Apostolate (CARA) 28
Center City Churches 230
Center on Conscience & War (NISBCO) 29
Center for Parish Development 29

INDEX

Center for the Study of Religion and American Culture 214
Centre Emmaüs 288
Central Maryland Ecumenical Council.........239
Chaplaincy of Full Gospel Churches 29
Chautaugua County Rural Ministry 247
Christ Catholic Church...........................84, 367
Christ Catholic Church International 185
Christ Community Church (Evangelical-Protestant) 84, 367, 382
Christadelphians 84
Christian Associates of Southwest Pennsylvania 253
Christian Brethren (also known as Plymouth Brethren) 85, 186, 359, 367
Christian Church (Disciples of Christ) in Canada.......................................186, 359, 380
Christian Church (Disciples of Christ) in the United States and Canada....85, 367, 378, 382
Christian Church of North America, General Council 87, 367
Christian Churches/Churches of Christ 11, 88, 186, 359, 367
Christian Churches United of the Tri-County Area 254
Christian Community Action 231
Christian Conference of Connecticut 231
Christian Congregation, Inc., The 88, 367
Christian Council of Delaware and Maryland's Eastern Shore, The 232
Christian Council on Persons with Disabilities 30
Christian Endeavor International 30
Christian Leadership Council of Downtown Toronto 288
Christian Management Association.................30
Christian Methodist Episcopal Church 89, 367, 378
Christian Ministries of Delaware County 234
Christian Ministry in the National Parks, A....30
Christian and Missionary Alliance, The 89, 367, 382
Christian and Missionary Alliance in Canada 187, 359, 380
Christian Reformed Church in North America 91, 187, 359, 367
Christian Service Center for Central Florida, Inc. 232
Christian Union 91, 368, 382
Christian Youth Council 262
Christians United in Beaver County 254
Church Army in Canada, The 55
Church of the Brethren 91, 368, 378, 382
Church of Christ 92
Church of Christ (Holiness) U.S.A., The 92, 368, 382
Church of Christ, Scientist 93
Church Community Services 234
Church Council of Greater Seattle 260
Church Federation of Greater Indianapolis, Inc., The 234
Church Growth Center—Home of Church Doctor Ministries..31
Church of God (Anderson, Indiana) 93, 188, 360, 368, 380
Church of God (Cleveland, Tennessee) 11, 13, 95, 188, 360, 368
Church of God, Mountain Assembly, Inc 97, 368
Church of God, The (Seventh Day), Denver, Colorado 97, 368
Church of God in Christ, International 94
Church of God in Christ, Mennonite 95, 188, 360, 368
Church of God in Christ, The.............11, 13, 94, 368
Church of God by Faith, Inc. 96
Church of God General Conference (Oregon, IL and Morrow, GA) 96, 368
Church of God of Prophecy 97, 368
Church of God of Prophecy Canada East, The..188, 360
Church of Illumination, The...................98, 368
Church of Jesus Christ, The (Bickertonites) 98, 368
Church of Jesus Christ of Latter-day Saints, The 11, 12, 13, 14, 98, 368
Church of Jesus Christ of Latter-day Saints in Canada, The...189, 360
Church of the Living God (Motto, Christian Workers for Fellowship) 99, 368
Church of the Lutheran Brethren..........189, 360, 380
Church of the Lutheran Brethren of America 99, 368, 382
Church of the Lutheran Confession......100, 369, 382
Church of the Nazarene 100, 369, 382
Church of the Nazarene in Canada 190, 360, 380
Church of Our Lord Jesus Christ of the Apostolic Faith, Inc. 101
Church of the United Brethren in Christ 101, 369
Church Women United in the U.S.A...............31
Churches of Christ 11, 101, 369, 382
Churches of Christ in Canada 190, 360
Churches of Christ in Christian Union 102, 369
Churches' Council on Theological Education in Canada, An Ecumenical Foundation, The.........55
Churches of God, General Conference 102, 369, 382
Churches United, Inc....................................235
Churches United of the Quad City Area 233
Churches Uniting in Christ 31
Churchpeople for Change and Reconciliation 251
Colorado Council of Churches......................230
Community of Christ.......103, 190, 360, 369, 382
Community Emergency Assistance Program (CEAP) 242
Community Ministries of Rockville 239
Community Ministry of Montgomery County 239
Community Renewal Society.......................233
Concerned Ecumenical Ministry to the Upper West Side 247
Congregational Christian Churches in Canada 191, 360

INDEX

Congregational Holiness Church 103, 369
Conseil des Églises de Côte-des Neiges <<Sept Église—un seul Esprit>>............................289
Conseil interreligieux de Montréal 289
Conservative Baptist Association of America (CB America) 103, 369
Conservative Congregational Christian Conference 104, 369, 382
Conservative Lutheran Association 104, 369
Contact Ministries of Springfield.................233
Convention of Atlantic Baptist Churches 191, 360, 380
Cooperative Metropolitan Ministries 239
Coptic Orthodox Church..............104, 369, 378
Coptic Orthodox Church in Canada, The 191, 360
Cornwallis District Inter-Church Council...........287
Corpus Christi Metro Ministries 258
Cortland County Council of Churches, Inc.........247
Council for American-Islamic Relations (CAIR) 222
Council of Christian Communions of Greater Cincinnati 251
Council of Churches of Chemung County, Inc 247
Council of Churches of the City of New York 247
Council of Churches of Greater Bridgeport, Inc. 231
Council of Churches of Greater Springfield 239
Council of Churches of Greater Washington, The..232
Council of Churches of the Ozarks..............244
Council of Churches and Synagogues of Southwestern Connecticut.......................231
Council of Churches of Santa Clara County, The..228
Council of Hindu Temples of North America 221
CREO (Capital Region Ecumenical Organization) 247
Cross-Lines Cooperative Council 236
Cumberland Presbyterian Church 105, 369, 382
Cumberland Presbyterian Church in America 105, 369, 384

Day 1/Episcopal Media Center 32
Des Moines Area Religious Council............236
Direction Chrétienne 289
Disciples of Christ. *See* Christian Church (Disciples of Christ) in the United States and Canada
Dutchess Interfaith Council, Inc. 247

East Dallas Cooperative Parish 258
East End Cooperative Ministry 254
Eastern Area Community Ministries............236
Ecclesia...246
Ecumenical Committee 288
Ecumenical Conference of Greater Altoona 254
Ecumenical Council of Pasadena Area Churches, The..228
Ecumenical Council of San Diego County.......228
Ecumenical Group, The...............................289
Ecumenical Ministries.................................244
Ecumenical Ministries of Iowa (EMI) 236
Ecumenical Ministries of Oregon 253
Elim Fellowship 106
Elim Fellowship of Evangelical Churches and Ministers 192
EMI (Ecumenical Ministries of Iowa) 236
empty tomb, inc...214
Episcopal Church......11, 14, 106, 369, 378, 384
Episcopal Orthodox Church, The.................109
Estonian Evangelical Lutheran Church, The 110, 369
Estonian Evangelical Lutheran Church Abroad, The...192, 360
Evangelical Church, The..............110, 370, 384
Evangelical Church Alliance, The................110
Evangelical Churches. *See* Fellowship of Evangelical Churches
Evangelical Congregational Church, The 111, 370, 384
Evangelical Council for Financial Accountability 32
Evangelical Covenant Church, The 111, 370, 384
Evangelical Covenant Church of Canada, The 192, 360
Evangelical Fellowship of Canada..................56
Evangelical Free Church of America, The 112, 370
Evangelical Free Church of Canada 192, 361
Evangelical Friends International—North American Region..............................112, 370
Evangelical Lutheran Church in America 11, 12, 14, 113, 370, 378, 384
Evangelical Lutheran Church in Canada 193, 361, 380
Evangelical Lutheran Synod 116, 370, 384
Evangelical Mennonite Church. *See* Fellowship of Evangelical Churches
Evangelical Mennonite Conference, The 193, 361
Evangelical Mennonite Mission Conference 194, 361
Evangelical Methodist Church.............116, 370
Evangelical Missionary Church of Canada, The 194, 361
Evangelical Presbyterian Church 116, 370
Evangelical Press Association.........................33
Evanston Ecumenical Action Council...........233
Evansville Area Community of Churches, Inc 235

Faith Community Assistance Center............246
Faith & Values Media....................................33
FaithTrust Institute 261
Federation of Christian Ministries 33
Federation of Jain Associations in North America 223

Fellowship of Evangelical Baptist Churches in Canada, The....................................194, 361
Fellowship of Evangelical Bible Churches 117, 370, 384
Fellowship of Evangelical Churches 118, 370, 384
Fellowship of Fundamental Bible Churches 118, 370
Fellowship of Grace Brethren Churches 119, 370
Fern Creek-Highview United Ministries.......237
First Miramichi Inter-Church Council 287
Florida Council of Churches 232
Foundation for a Conference on Faith and Order in North America..34
Foursquare Gospel Church of Canada 194, 361, 380
Free Christian Zion Church of Christ 119
Free Methodist Church in Canada 195, 361, 380
Free Methodist Church of North America 119, 370, 384
Free Will Baptists.................................195, 361
Fresno Metro Ministry 228
Friends General Conference.................120, 371
Friends International. *See* Evangelical Friends International—North American Region
Friends United Meeting 121, 371, 378
Friends World Committee for Consultation (Section of the Americas)...........................34
Full Gospel Assemblies International 122, 371
Full Gospel Fellowship of Churches and Ministers International 123, 371
Fund for Theological Education, Inc., The.........34
Fundamental Methodist Church, Inc........123, 371

GEII (Graymoor Ecumenical & Interreligious Institute)...34
General Association of General Baptists 123, 371, 384
General Association of Regular Baptist Churches...124, 371
General Church of the New Jerusalem 124, 195, 371
General Conference of Mennonite Brethren Churches..................................124, 371, 384
Genesee County Churches United, Inc. 248
Genesee-Orleans Ministry of Concern..........248
Georgia Christian Council............................232
Glengarry-Prescott-Russell Christian Council 288
Glenmary Research Center 34
Grace Gospel Fellowship......................125, 371
GRACE (Grand Rapids Area Center for Ecumenism)...241
Grand Rapids Area Center for Ecumenism (GRACE)..241
Graymoor Ecumenical & Interreligious Institute (GEII) 34
Greater Baton Rouge Federation of Churches and Synagogues.......................................238
Greater Bethlehem Area Council of Churches 254
Greater Birmingham Ministries 227
Greater Chicago Broadcast Ministries 233
Greater Dallas Community of Churches.......258
Greater Dayton Christian Connections 251
Greater Fairmont Council of Churches.........262
Greater Flint Council of Churches................241
Greater Lawrence Council of Churches........240
Greater Minneapolis Council of Churches....242
Greater New Orleans Federation of Churches 238
Greater Rochester Community of Churches 248
Greater Toronto Council of Churches, The 288
Greater Victoria Council of Churches...........287
Greater Waterbury Interfaith Ministries, Inc. 231
Greater Wheeling Council of Churches, The 262
Greek Orthodox Archdiocese of America 11, 13, 125, 371, 378
Greek Orthodox Metropolis of Toronto (Canada) 195, 361
Greensboro Urban Ministry 250

Halifax-Dartmouth Council of Churches......287
Hamilton & District Christian Churches Association 288
Hanover Area Council of Churches 254
Hartford Institute for Religion Research of Hartford Seminary, The............................215
Hazard-Perry County Community Ministries, Inc..237
Hemmingford Ecumenical Committee 289
Highlands Community Ministries 237
Holy Eastern Orthodox Catholic and Apostolic Church in North America, Inc., The 127, 371, 384
Holy Ukrainian Autocephalic Orthodox Church in Exile 127
House of God, Which is the Church of the Living God, the Pillar and Ground of the Truth, Inc. 127
Humboldt Clergy Council 289
Hungarian Reformed Church in America 127, 371, 378
Hutterian Brethren................................128, 371
Hyde Park & Kenwood Interfaith Council, The 233

ICNA (The Islamic Circle of North America) 222
IFCA International, Inc. 128, 372
IFCO (Interreligious Foundation for Community Organization)..37
Ignace Council of Churches..........................288
Illinois Conference of Churches 233
In One Accord 241
Independent Assemblies of God International (Canada) 196, 361
Independent Holiness Church 196, 361
Indiana Partners for Christian Unity and Mission 235
Industrial Cape Breton Council of Churches 287

Institute for Ecumenical and Cultural Research 215
Institute for the Study of American Evangelicals (ISAE) 216
Institute for the Study of American Religion....216
Inter Church Council of Burlington....288
Interchurch Communications....56
Inter-Church Council of Greater New Bedford 240
Inter-Church Ministries of Erie County....254
Interchurch Ministries of Nebraska....245
Interfaith Association of Snohomish County, The....261
Interfaith Community Council, Inc.....235
Interfaith Community Services....244
Interfaith Conference of Greater Milwaukee 262
InterFaith Conference of Metropolitan Washington 232
Interfaith Council....261
Interfaith Council of Boulder....230
Interfaith Council of Contra Costa County....229
Interfaith Impact for Justice and Peace....35
Interfaith Ministries for Greater Houston....259
Interfaith Ministries-Wichita....236
Interfaith Mission Service....227
Interfaith Partnership of Metropolitan St. Louis 244
Interfaith Service Bureau....229
Interfaith Worker Justice....36
Interfaith Works....261
International Church of the Foursquare Gospel 128, 372, 384
International Council of Community Churches 129, 372, 378
International Pentecostal Church of Christ, The 129, 372, 384
International Pentecostal Holiness Church 130, 372
International Society for Krishna Consciousness, The....221
Inter-religious Council of Central New York 248
Interreligious Foundation for Community Organization (IFCO)....37
Inter-Varsity Christian Fellowship of Canada 56
Inter-Varsity Christian Fellowship of the U.S.A. 35
Iowa Religious Media Services....236
ISAE (Institute for the Study of American Evangelicals)....216
ISNA (The Islamic Society of North America) .. 222
Islamic Circle of North America, The (ICNA) 222
Islamic Society of North America, The (ISNA) 222
Italian Pentecostal Church of Canada, The....196

Jackson County Interfaith Council, The....241
Jehovah's Witnesses 11, 13, 14, 130, 196, 361, 372
Jewish-Christian Dialogue of Montreal....289
Jewish Council for Public Affairs....224
Jewish Reconstructionist Federation....224
J.M. Dawson Institute of Church-State Studies at Baylor University....217
Joint Religious Legislative Coalition, The....243
John Howard Society of Ontario....57
John Milton Society for the Blind in Canada 57

Kairos Institute, Inc., The....37
Kansas Ecumenical Ministries....236
Kentuckiana Interfaith Community....237
Kentucky Council of Churches....237
Kentville Council of Churches....287
Kitchener-Waterloo Council of Churches....288
Korean Presbyterian Church in America, General Assembly of the....131, 372, 378

Lafayette Urban Ministry....235
Lancaster County Council of Churches....255
Latter-day Saints. *See* Church of Jesus Christ of Latter-day Saints, The
Latvian Evangelical Lutheran Church in America, The....131, 372, 384
LCMS (Lutheran Church—Missouri Synod, The)....11, 12
Lebanon County Christian Ministries....255
Lehigh County Conference of Churches....255
Lewisburg Council of Churches....255
Liberal Catholic Church (International) 131, 372
Liberal Catholic Church, The—Province of the United States of America....132, 372
Lincoln Interfaith Council....245
Liturgical Conference, The....37
Lombard Mennonite Peace Center....38
London Inter-City Faith Team....288
Long Island Council of Churches, The....248
Lord's Day Alliance of the United States, The 38
Louisiana Interchurch Conference....238
Louisville Institute, The....217
Lunenburg Queens BA Association....287
Lutheran Association, Conservative. *See* Conservative Lutheran Association
Lutheran Church. *See* American Association of Lutheran Churches
Lutheran Church in America. *See* Evangelical Lutheran Church in America
Lutheran Church of America. *See* Apostolic Lutheran Church of America
Lutheran Church-Canada....196, 362
Lutheran Church, The—Missouri Synod (LCMS) 11, 12, 132, 372, 384
Lutheran Council in Canada....57
Lutheran Synod. *See* Evangelical Lutheran Synod
Lutheran World Relief....38

Madison-area Urban Ministry....262
Mahone Bay Interchurch Council....288
Mahoning Valley Association of Churches....252
Maine Council of Churches....238

INDEX

Malankara Orthodox Syrian Church, Diocese of America 133, 378
Manchester Area Conference of Churches 231
Mar Thoma Syrian Church of India 136, 372, 379, 384
Marin Interfaith Council 229
Massachusetts Commission on Christian Unity 240
Massachusetts Council of Churches 240
Massey Inter-Church Council 288
MCCC (Mennonite Central Committee Canada) 57
Melville Association of Churches 289
Mennonite Brethren Churches. *See* General Conference of Mennonite Brethren Churches
Mennonite Central Committee Canada (MCCC) 57
Mennonite Central Committee, The................38
Mennonite Church Canada....................197, 362
Mennonite Church of God in Christ. *See* Church of God in Christ, Mennonite
Mennonite Church USA........................136, 373
Methodist Church. *See* United Methodist Church, The
Methodist Church, Evangelical. *See* Evangelical United Methodist Church
Methodist Church, Fundamental. *See* Fundamental Methodist Church, Inc.
Metropolitan Area Church Council 252
Metropolitan Area Religious Coalition of Cincinnati 252
Metropolitan Christian Council: Detroit-Windsor, The 241
Metropolitan Christian Council of Philadelphia 255
Metropolitan Ecumenical Ministry 246
Metropolitan Ecumenical Ministry Community Development Corp. 246
Metropolitan Inter Faith Association (MIFA)..... 258
Metropolitan Interfaith Council on Affordable Housing (MICAH) 243
MICAH (Metropolitan Interfaith Council on Affordable Housing)...............................243
Michigan Ecumenical Forum 241
MIFA (Metropolitan Inter Faith Association) 258
Ministries United South Central Louisville (M.U.S.C.L., Inc.) 237
Minnesota Council of Churches....................243
Missionary Church, The................137, 373, 384
Mississippi Religious Leadership Conference 244
Moncton Area Council of Churches 287
Montana Association of Churches 244
Montreal Association for the Blind Foundation 289
Montréal Council of Churches......................289
Moravian Church in America (Unitas Fratrum) 138, 373, 379, 384
Mormons. *See* Church of Jesus Christ of Latter-day Saints, The
MPAC (Muslim Public Affairs Council).......222
Multifaith Action Society of British Columbia 287
M.U.S.C.L., Inc. (Ministries United South Central Louisville)....................................237
Muskegon County Cooperating Churches 241
Muslim American Society, The.....................222
Muslim Christian Dialogue 289
Muslim Public Affairs Council (MPAC).......222

NARF (Native American Rights Fund) 225
National Association of Congregational Christian Churches..138, 373
National Association of Ecumenical and Interreligious Staff......................................39
National Association of Evangelicals, The 39
National Association of Free Will Baptists 138, 373, 384
National Baptist Convention of America, Inc. 11, 13, 139, 373, 379
National Baptist Convention, U.S.A., Inc.......... ....11, 13, 139, 373, 379
National Bible Association.............................40
National Conference for Community and Justice, The 40
National Conference on Ministry to the Armed Forces 40
National Congress of American Indians (NCAI) 225
National Council of the Churches of Christ in the U.S.A. 41
National Institute of Business and Industrial Chaplains 43
National Interfaith Cable Coalition, Inc. (NICC) 43
National Interfaith Coalition on Aging 43
National Missionary Baptist Convention of America........................11, 13, 140, 373, 379
National Organization of the New Apostolic Church of North America.................140, 373
National Primitive Baptist Convention, Inc. 140, 373
National Religious Broadcasters 43
National Spiritual Assembly of the Baha'is of the United States, The 219
National Spiritualist Association of Churches 141
National Woman's Christian Temperance Union 44
Native American Rights Fund (NARF) 225
NCAI (National Congress of American Indians) 225
Netherlands Reformed Congregation.......141, 373
Network of Religious Communities 248
New Britain Area Conference of Churches (NEWBRACC)..231
New Church. *See* General Church of the New Jerusalem
New Hampshire Council of Churches 245
New Jersey Council of Churches..................246
New Mexico Conference of Churches..........246
New York State Community of Churches, Inc 249
Niagara Council of Churches Inc., The 249

INDEX

NICA (Northside Inter-Church Agency).......259
NICC (National Interfaith Cable Coalition, Inc.) 43
NISBCO (Center on Conscience & War) 29
North American Baptist Conference 141, 197, 362, 373, 380, 386
North American Baptist Fellowship................44
North American Old Roman Catholic Church (Archdiocese of New York) 142, 373
North Carolina Council of Churches 251
North Dakota Conference of Churches.........251
North Dallas Shared Ministries....................259
North Hills Youth Ministry Counseling Center 255
Northern California Inter-religious Conference 229
Northern Kentucky Interfaith Commission, Inc. 238
Northside Common Ministries.....................255
Northside Inter-Church Agency (NICA).......259
Northwest Harvest-E.M.M...........................261
Northwest Interfaith Movement...................255

Oak Park-River Forest Community of Congregations 234
Ohio Council of Churches............................252
Oikocredit-Ecumenical Development Cooperative Society...44
Oklahoma Conference of Churches 253
Old Catholic Church of Canada, The.......198, 362
Old German Baptist Brethren Church......142, 374
Old Order Amish Church.............142, 198, 374
Old Order (Wisler) Mennonite Church.........142
Open Bible Faith Fellowship of Canada............ ....198, 362
Open Bible Standard Churches............142, 374
(Original) Church of God, Inc., The 143
Orthodox Church in America, The 11, 13, 143, 374, 379
Orthodox Church in America (Archdiocese of Canada)...198, 362
Orthodox Presbyterian Church, The 144, 374, 386
Ottawa Christian Council of the Capital Area 288

Pacific and Asian American Center for Theology and Strategies (PACTS)..............................229
PACTS (Pacific and Asian American Center for Theology and Strategies...........................229
Paducah Cooperative Ministry......................238
Parish Resource Center, Inc. 45
Patriarchal Parishes of the Russian Orthodox Church in Canada.............................199, 362
Patriarchal Parishes of the Russian Orthodox Church in the U.S.A.................144, 374, 379
Pennsylvania Conference on Interchurch Cooperation 256
Pennsylvania Council of Churches, The.......256
Pentecostal Assemblies of Canada, The 199, 362
Pentecostal Assemblies of Newfoundland, The 199, 362
Pentecostal Assemblies of the World, Inc. 11, 13, 144, 374
Pentecostal-Charismatic Churches of North America 45
Pentecostal Church of God 144, 374
Pentecostal Fire-Baptized Holiness Church 145, 374
Pentecostal Free Will Baptist Church, Inc., The 145
Peoria Friendship House of Christian Service 234
Philadelphia Yearly Meeting of the Religious Society of Friends 145, 374, 379
Pictou Council of Churches 288
Pike Country Outreach Council 252
Pillar of Fire 145
Pluralism Project, The..................................218
Plymouth Brethren. *See* Christian Brethren
Polish National Catholic Church of America 146, 374, 379
Pomona Inland Valley Council of Churches 229
Prairie Centre for Ecumenism.......................289
Presbyterian Church. *See* Evangelical Presbyterian Church
Presbyterian Church (U.S.A.) 11, 12, 14, 147, 374, 379, 386
Presbyterian Church in America......146, 374, 386
Presbyterian Church in America (Canadian Section) 200, 362, 380
Presbyterian Church in Canada.............200, 362
Primitive Advent Christian Church.......148, 374
Primitive Baptists 149
Primitive Methodist Church in the U.S.A. 149, 374, 386
Progressive National Baptist Convention, Inc. 11, 13, 149, 375, 379
Project of Easton, Inc. 256
Project Equality, Inc. 46
Project Ploughshares 58
Protestant Reformed Churches in America 150, 375

Quakers. *See* Friends General Conference
Quakers, Conservative. *See* Religious Society of Friends (Conservative)
Quakers, Philadelphia. *See* Philadelphia Yearly Meeting of the Religious Society of Friends
Quakers, International. *See* Evangelical Friends International—North American Region
Quakers, Unaffiliated Meetings. *See* Religious Society of Friends (Unaffiliated Meetings)
Queens County Association of Churches 288
Queens Federation of Churches 249

Radio Ville-Marie...289
Reading Berks Conference of Churches 256
Reformed Catholic Church 150, 375
Reformed Church in America 150, 375, 379, 386
Reformed Church in Canada.........200, 362, 380
Reformed Church in the United States 151, 375, 386

INDEX

Reformed Episcopal Church 151, 375
Reformed Episcopal Church of Canada, The 201, 362, 380
Reformed Mennonite Church................152, 375
Reformed Methodist Union Episcopal Church 152
Reformed Presbyterian Church of North America 153, 386
Reformed Zion Union Apostolic Church......153
Regina Council of Churches 289
Regional Council for Christian Ministry, Inc., The................233
Regional Council of Churches of Atlanta, The 232
Reinland Mennonite Church 201, 363
Religion Communicators Council, Inc., The 46
Religion In American Life, Inc. 46
Religion News Service................47
Religion Newswriters Association 47
Religions for Peace-USA, Inc. 47
Religious Action Center of Reform Judaism 224
Religious Conference Management Association, Inc. 47
Religious Society of Friends (Conservative) 153, 375
Religious Society of Friends (Unaffiliated Meetings) 153
Religious Television Associates 58
Reorganized Church of Jesus Christ of Latter-day Saints. *See* Community of Christ
Réseau oecuménique justice et paix..............289
Rhode Island State Council of Churches, The 257
Roman Catholic Church in Canada, The 201, 363
Romanian Orthodox Church in America, The 154
Romanian Orthodox Church in America (Canadian Parishes)................203, 363
Romanian Orthodox Episcopate of America, The................154, 375
Romanian Orthodox Episcopate of America, The (Jackson, MI) 203, 363
ROQ................289
Rural Migrant Ministry 250
Russian Orthodox Church. *See* Patriarchal Parishes of the Russian Orthodox Church in the USA
Russian Orthodox Church Outside of Russia, The................154, 375

Salvation Army, The................154, 375
Salvation Army in Canada, The 204, 363
San Antonio Community of Churches 259
San Antonio Urban Ministries................259
San Fernando Valley Interfaith Council........229
Saskatoon Council of Churches 289
Schenectady Inner City Ministry 250
Schwenkfelder Church, The..........155, 375, 386
Scripture Union 58
SCUPE (Seminary Consortium for Urban Pastoral Education, The) 48
SEAM (South East Associated Ministries).......238
SEARCH (Southeast Area Churches) 259
Seminary Consortium for Urban Pastoral Education, The (SCUPE) 48
Separate Baptists in Christ................155, 375
Serbian Orthodox Church in the U.S.A. and Canada................156, 375, 379
Serbian Orthodox Church in the U.S.A. and Canada, Diocese of Canada 204, 363
Seventh-day Adventist Church 156, 376, 386
Seventh-day Adventist Church in Canada 204, 363, 380
Seventh Day Baptist General Conference, USA and Canada................157, 376
Siddhacalam/International Mahavira Jain Mission 223
Sikh Center of Orange County, The..............226
South Carolina Christian Action Council, Inc. 257
South Coast Interfaith Council................230
South East Associated Ministries (SEAM).......238
South Hills Interfaith Ministries 256
South Louisville Community Ministries.......238
Southeast Area Churches (SEARCH) 259
Southeast Ecumenical Ministry................250
Southern Baptist Convention 11, 12, 158, 376, 386
Southern California Ecumenical Council 230
Southern Methodist Church 159, 376
Sovereign Grace Believers................159, 376
Spadina-Bloor Interchurch Council 288
St. Catharines & Dist. Clergy Fellowship.....288
St. John's Area Council of Churches 287
St. Matthews Area Ministries................238
St. Paul Area Council of Churches 243
Staten Island Council of Churches................250
Stratford & District Council of Churches.....288
Student Christian Movement of Canada 59
Summerside Christian Council 288
Swedenborgian Church, The.........160, 376, 379
Syriac Orthodox Church of Antioch 204, 363
Syrian (Syriac) Orthodox Church of Antioch 160, 376, 379
Syro-Russian Orthodox Catholic Church 161, 376, 386

Tarrant Area Community of Churches..........259
Tennessee Association of Churches 258
Texas Buddhist Council 221
Texas Conference of Churches................259
Thorold Inter-Faith Council 288
Thunder Bay Council of Churches 288
Toledo Ecumenical Area Ministries..............252
Transnational Association of Christian Colleges and Schools 48
Tri-Council Coordinating Commission.........244
Triumph the Church and Kingdom of God in Christ Inc. (International)................162
Troy Area United Ministries 250
True Orthodox Church of Greece (Synod of Metropolitan Cyprian), American Exarchate 162, 376
Tulsa Metropolitan Ministry 253

INDEX

Tuscarawas County Council for Church and Community 252

Ukrainian Orthodox Church of Canada 205, 363
Ukrainian Orthodox Church of the U.S.A. 163, 376, 379
Union d'Eglises Baptistes Françaises au Canada 205, 363, 380
Union of Orthodox Jewish Congregations of America, The 224
Union of Reform Judaism 224
Union of Spiritual Communities of Christ (Orthodox Doukhobors in Canada) 205
Unitarian Universalist Association of Congregations 164, 376
Unitas 289
United Board of Missions 260
United Brethren Church in Canada 206, 363
United Catholic Church, Inc., The 164, 376
United Christian Church 165, 376
United Church of Canada, The 206, 363, 380
United Church of Christ 11, 14, 165, 377, 379, 386
United Churches of Lycoming County 256
United Holy Church of America, Inc. 167
United House of Prayer for All People 168
United Methodist Church, The 11, 12, 14, 168, 377, 379, 386
United Ministries 257
United Ministries in Higher Education 48
United Pentecostal Church in Canada 207, 364
United Pentecostal Church International 171
United Pentecostal Churches of Christ, The 171, 377
United Religions Initiative 49
United Religious Community of St. Joseph County 235
United Synagogue of Conservative Judaism, The 225
United Zion Church 172, 377
Unity of the Brethren 172, 377, 386
Universal Fellowship of Metropolitan Community Churches 172, 208, 364, 377, 386

Vancouver Council of Churches 287
Vellore Christian Medical College Board (USA), Inc. 50
Vermont Ecumenical Council and Bible Society 260
Virginia Council of Churches, Inc. 260
Volunteer Ministry Center 258
Volunteers of America 173

Wainwright House 250
Washington Association of Churches 261
Wesleyan Church, The 173, 377, 386
Wesleyan Church of Canada, The 208, 364
Wesleyan Holiness Association of Churches 174
West Central Neighborhood Ministry, Inc. 235
West Side Ecumenical Ministry 252
West Virginia Council of Churches 262
Westside Interfaith Council 230
Wilkinsburg Community Ministry 257
Wisconsin Council of Churches 262
Wisconsin Evangelical Lutheran Synod 174, 377, 386
Women's Inter-Church Council of Canada 59
Worcester County Ecumenical Council 240
World Council of Churches, United States Office 50
World Day of Prayer 50
World Methodist Council-North American Section 50
World Vision 51
World Vision Canada 59
Wyoming Association of Churches 263
Wyoming Valley Council of Churches 257

YMCA of the USA 51
York County Council of Churches 257
Young Men's Christian Association in Canada 59
Young Women's Christian Association of-du Canada 60
Youth for Christ-Canada 60
Youth for Christ–USA 52
YWCA of the U.S.A. 52

Individuals

Abbott, Grant 243
Abbott, Z. Allen 67
Abboud, Jon W. 152
Abdalah, John 339
Aboodi, Timotheos Aphrem 205
Abraham, Raphael 163
Ackerman, Keith L. 109
Adams, Don 131
Adams, Dorothy 65
Adams, Gladstone B., III .107
Adams, James Marshall .109
Adams, Margaret 237
Adams, Michael J. 104
Adams, Neale 345
Adams, Skip 253
Adams-Smelter, Barbara 256
Addington, R. James 242, 243, 244
Addington, Timothy 112
Addland, Thomas V. 66
Adego, Epainitus 121
Adira, Titus 121
Adkinson, Oleda 96
Adnams, Ian 197
Adolf, Don 194
Adrian, Marian M. 248
Aenz, Agnes 239
Ahonen, E. 199
Aiken, David A., Sr. 64
Aiken, Mike 251
Aja, Antonio (Tony) 237
Aja, Loyd 148
Ajer, Margaret Schmitt ..114
Akers, Kenneth 139
Akin, Daniel L. 307
Akkerman, Terri 251
Alagiah, Sabapath 49
Al-Awady, Nodri 245
Al-Batat, Zainab 245
Albert, Leonard 96
Albrecht, Betty 184
Albrecht, James 100
Albrecht, Marcus 324
Albricht-Carrie, Pierre ...249
Albright, Jacob 111, 169
Alchin, Errol 192
Alcosser, Lois 231
Aldred, Ray 56
Aleksy II 144
Aleshire, Daniel O. ..28, 212
Alexander, Christine 319
Alexander, Darlene 259
Alexander, Jean M. 167
Alexander, John Neil 107
Alexios (Metropolitan) ..126
Alford, Anthony M., Sr. .233
Alford, Delton 96
Alger, David T. 260
Algera, Fred 201
Alguire, Frances M. 51
Alick, Bruce N. 330
Allander, Dan 301
Allen, Arlene 339
Allen, Bettye J. 339
Allen, Cosie 329
Allen, David W. 207
Allen, David, Jr. 149
Allen, Gary 324
Allen, John 28
Allen, Richard 61
Allen, Sherman 97, 189
Allen, Virginia 80
Allen, William B. ...87, 262
Allen-Kent, Venita 259
Allmen, Robert J. 150
Al-Marayati, Salam 222
Almen, Lowell G. 113
Almquist, Roy G. 115
Alpine, W.H. 139
Alsdurf, Edna 51
Alston, Roosevelt 168
Alston, Wallace M., Jr. ...34
Alterbarmakian, Varouj ...75
Alverez, Gracela 51
Alvis, Rick 27
Ambrose, Richard 227
Ambrus, Zoltan 127
Amerson, Philip A. 294
Amjad-Ali, Charles 36
Ammann, Jacob 118, 198
Ammerman, E.H. Jim 30
Amorim, Nilton D. 204
Amos, Barbara 46
Andenya, Wilson 121
Anders, Andrea 96
Anders, Linda 155
Anderson, Anne T. 316
Anderson, Billy 103
Anderson, Daniel L. 290
Anderson, David A. 233
Anderson, David 47
Anderson, Dennis 242
Anderson, E. Byron 38
Anderson, Gordon L. ...303
Anderson, James L. 292
Anderson, Jeffrey ..112, 192
Anderson, Jim 154
Anderson, John A. 66
Anderson, John 243
Anderson, Jon V. 114
Anderson, Kristi 243
Anderson, Melissa 334
Anderson, Nancy L. 243
Anderson, Neil W. ..102, 326
Anderson, Paul 106
Anderson, Scott D. 262
Anderson, Vinton 34
Anderson, Vjuana 250
Anderson, William J. 179
Anderson-Develrow, Dorothy 259
Andonios (Bishop) 126
Andreas (Archbishop) ...162
Andres, Oseas 69
Andrews, Roger 118
Andrews, Ruth 56
Andriy (Archimandrite) ..163
Angeline, Peter 57
Angie, Frank 130
Ankeny, Mark 113
Anker, Roy M. 333
Annie, Frederick P. 262
Annis, Sharon 121
Annunziato, Anne 245
Ansari, Imam Fajri 249
Ansell, Fred A. 67
Anston, Phyllis 254
Anthony (Metropolitan) .126
Anthony, Lewis 232
Antony (Archbishop) 163, 164
Apostola, Nicholas .154, 203
Appel, Robert 157
Aquila, Dominic 200
Archer, Barbara 245
Ard, Robert 228
Argue, David 76
Argue, Don H. 303
Armas, Lucinda 331
Armiger, Thomas E. 174
Armstrong, Calvin 168
Armstrong, George 49
Armstrong, James D. .63, 334
Armstrong, Ken 79
Arnold, Don 123
Arnold, Kim M. 355
Arnold, Kristi 332
Arsenios (Metropolitan-Bishop) 72
Arslanian, Hagop 181
Arthur (Bishop) 127
Arthur, David T. 347
Artis, Lois 86
Asbury, Francis 61, 169
Asen, Bernhard 336
Ashdown, David N. 180
Ashford, Anne 229

INDEX

Ashlay, Pamla 141
Asir, John 162
Astfalk, Carolyn 256
Astin, Claude S., Jr. 69
Astin, Dawn R. 69
Astin, Sam (Claude S., III) 69
Astle, Cynthia B. . . .334, 337
Astley, Nolan D. 197
Atagotaalnuk, Andrew P. .179
Atkins, Nancy Lee 252
Atmore, A. Brian 313
Attai, Monday S. 183
Attebery, Charles 293
Attridge, Harold W. 310
Aubrey, Michael 102
Augsburger, Bryce 124
Augsburger, Lynette 118
Augsburger, Rick 42
Augson, Albert 168
Austin, George 144
Austin, Jackie 262
Authier, Ken 129
Auxentios (Bishop) 163
Avakian, Karl 181
Avera, Alan 77
Avery, Cheryl 353
Avery, Michael 297
Avey, Thomas 119
Aykazian, Vicken 41
Ayloush, Hussam 36
Aymer, Albert J.D. 298
Aymond, Gregory M. 83
Azmy, Isaac Boulos 105

Baak, David P. 241
Babb, Ruby 249
Babb, W. Sherrill 303
Babcock, Calvin 157
Backman, Ida 341
Bacon, Arthur D. 312
Badi, Izzaldin 245
Bagley, Louis 167
Bagnall, Ronald B. 329
Bailey, Jeff 323
Bailey, Joey 148
Bailey, Leslee 103
Bailey, Mark L. 295
Bailey, Orrin 104
Baillargeon, Gaëtan 202
Baillie, Kenneth 155
Bainbridge, Harry B., III
. 108
Baird, Bob 78
Baird, John 117
Baker, Bob 253
Baker, Charles 125
Baker, Denis N. 336
Baker, Kenneth 327
Baker, Marsha 25
Baker, Michael L. . . .95, 188
Baldwin, David N. 158
Baldwin, M. Winston, Jr.
. 166
Baldwin, Nancy 138
Baldwin, Raymond C. . . .149
Balentine, Sam 327
Baletka, Jim 172
Balfour, Edward 133
Ball, David 199
Ball, Frank 252
Ballantyne, V.A. 110
Ballard, M. Russell 99
Ballas, Rhea 252
Balogh, Balint 127
Bamban, Vieturs 320
Banaszak, Karen 240
Bancroft, Timothy 43
Bane, David C., Jr. 109
Banek, Walter 152
Bang, Charles 249
Bankhead, Robert 129
Bankord, Mark A. 30
Banks, Rosa T. 157
Bannister, Kathryn 50
Baranowski, Bernice 54
Barber, Jay A., Jr. 94
Barbour, Johnny, Jr. 62
Barcott, Patricia 261
Barfoot, Gillian 59
Bariteau, Benoît 202
Barkat, Samuel 35
Barker, Lee 301
Barker, Randy 145
Barkman, Len 194
Barna, George 213
Barnabas, Mathews Mar
. 136
Barnes, James 298
Barnes, Kurt 107
Barnes, Ronald B. 255
Barnes, Thane 159
Barnett-Cowan, Alyson . .179
Barnhouse, James 252
Barnwell, Ray E., Sr. 174
Baron, Karen 354
Barrentine, Jimmy L. . . .158
Barrett, Michael 250
Barrows, Ken 190
Barry, Jane 228
Barsamian, Khajag . . .46, 75
Barsony, Steve 256
Bartlett, Carol 120
Bartlett, Eileen 238
Bartlett, Patrick 41
Bartlett, William G. 207
Bartol, Rachel 236
Barton, Jonathan 260
Bass, Steve 158
Bassett, W. Todd 155
Bassham, Keith 319
Bates, Charlotte Kinvig . .314
Bates, Dale 124
Batey, Gary 129
Bathurst, Shirley 249
Batstone, A. Earl 200
Battle, Michael A. 299
Battler, Jack 57
Battram, Janet 235
Batts, Carl 140
Bauer, Martha 160
Baugham, Billy 26
Baugham, Eva 26
Baum, Mary K. 262
Baumann, Paul 322
Baumgarten, Murray 328
Baumgartner, Will 232
Baumler, Gary 325, 330
Bawai, Mar 70
Bawks, Barbara 355
Bayer, Steven L. . . .142, 338
Bayiha, Suzie, II 50
Beach, Maxine C. 295
Beach, Verda 291
Beacham, A.D., Jr. 130
Beachy, LeRoy 142
Beals, Charlotte 137
Beane, Marian 120
Beard, C. Ronald 77
Beaupe, Richard 57
Beaver, R. Pierce 20
Beck, Kenneth L. 305
Beck, Sarai Schnucker . .236
Becker, Bruce 175
Becker, Susan 31
Beckett, Malcolm 191
Beckman, Mike 36, 37
Beckmann, David 28
Beckwith, Peter H. 109
Becton, C.M. 207
Bedgood, Douglas, Sr. . . .88
Bediako, Matthew A. . . .156
Behrakis, George 126
Beinikis, Vilmars 131
Beizer, Lance 71
Bekken, Dean 132
Bekker, Gary 91
Bell, Brian 183
Bell, Nancy 54, 182
Bellamy, James C. 168
Bellavin, Tikhon 72
Bellefleur, Beverley 200
Bellinger, Carolyn 195
Bellinger, James 195
Bellous, Ken 182
Belrose, Danny A. 103
Belrose, Darrell 190
Belsky, Martin 253
Belsole, Kurt 306
Belton, Victor T. 133
Bender, Robert 229
Bendyna, Mary E. 29
Benedict, Gary M. 295
Benefiel, Ron 302
Benjamin (Bishop) 161
Benjamin I (Patriarch) 68
Benjamin, Waveney 50
Bennett, Gordon D. 83
Bennett, Robertson H. 46
Bennett, Vicki 202

Bennison, Charles E., Jr. 108
Benoway, Edward R. 116
Benson, M. Wayne 293
Benson, Willie, Jr. 119
Beresford, Eric 311
Berg, Peter 141
Berg, Richard R. 353
Berg, Robert D. 115
Berg, Ron 142
Berg, Sharon K. 324
Berge, Arthur 190
Bergen, Abe 315
Bergen, Abe 53
Berger, David G. 244
Berghes, DeLandes 70
Bergin, Karen 231
Berlamino, Cheryl 24
Berman, Lowen 253
Bernard, David 309
Bernstine, Gwen Nelson 256
Bernthal, Mark 100
Bertalan, Imre 127
Berube, Albert J. 142
Beshara, Sophronios 74
Best, Deb 257
Betancourt, Esdras 96
Betzer, Dan 76
Betzer, Janet 255
Bevens, Stephen B. 29
Beverley, James 216
Beyer, Carl 167
Beyer, Teresa A. 143
Bhagan, Ken 288
Bibb, Lillie D. 251
Bickerton, William 98
Bicksler, Harriet 335
Bieniek, Barbara 250
Biffle, Nita 123
Biffle, S.K. 123, 325
Biffle, Steven K. 123
Billard, Ralph 287
Billington, Steve 353
Bilyew, Janet 101
Binda, Andrew 95, 341
Bingham, Maurice D. 92, 93
Binsfield, Edmund L. . . .353
Birchard, Bruce 120
Birkitt, James N., Jr. 173, 328
Birney, Walter 88
Biron, Jean-Marc 345
Birse, Douglas 184
Bishop, Cecil 51, 63
Bishop, Paul M. 86
Bistak, Leo 252
Bithos, George P. 260
Bitner, Terry 232
Bjork, Bruce 242
Bjork, Kryssis 242
Bjornberg, Allan C. 114
Black, Geoffrey A. . . .167, 249
Black, J.B., Jr. 234
Black, Ron 123, 124
Blackburn, Martha 174
Blackburn, Richard G. . . .38
Blackby, G. Richard 312
Blackwell, George L. 64
Blackwell, Phil 233
Blades, Wayne 123
Blair, Sarah D. Brooks . .351
Blaire, Stephen E. 83
Blake, Bruce P. 170
Blake, Canute 188
Blake, Harry 139
Blakeman, Jeannine 237
Blanchett, David I. 227
Bland, James C. 147
Blanding, Ann 153
Blanton, Smiley 28
Bliss, Dale 96
Blom, Paul J. 115
Bloom, Peter 55
Bloomquist, Nessie S. . . .249
Blouin, Francis 239
Blount, Bill A. 44
Blount, Robert 168
Blowers, David 65
Blumhofer, Edith 216
Blythe, David 68
Boblyer, Kathy 325
Bobo, Kim 37
Bochanyin, Curtis 349
Bock, Robert 263
Bodner, Keith 55
Boe, Eugene 100
Boehlke, Craig A. 114
Boehm, John Philip 151
Boehm, Martin 101, 206
Boeker, Paul 117, 118
Boerger, Wm Chris 114
Boersma, J. Karel 249
Bogard, Ben M. 66
Boguslawski, Steven C. . .305
Bohl, Robert 148
Bojey, Fred 206
Boland, J. Kevin 83
Boler, James E. 167
Boles, J.A. 140
Bolick, Leonard H. 116
Bolinder, Garth T. 112
Boling, Daniel F. 96
Boll, James 320
Bolt, John 91, 187
Boltz, David G. 254
Bomberger, Jeff 245
Bombick, Betsy 138
Bomgardner, LeRoy 165
Bond, Jane Zavitz 185
Bond, Jentry W. 307
Bond, Jim L. 101
Bond, Judy 232
Bond, Linda 155
Bonk, Jonathan J. 327
Bonneau, Normand 315
Bonner, Harrison 32
Bonner, Margie J. 64
Bonner, William L. 101
Bonney, Timothy D. 235
Bonnot, Bernard (Bob) . . .229
Boomershine, Tom 329
Boone, Martha Moody . . .31
Boonstra, John C. . . .36, 261
Booth, Ballington 173
Booth, Linda 326, 335
Booth, Maud 173
Booth, Robby 129
Booth, Robert H. 152
Booth, William 69, 154
Borden, M. Daniel 168
Borden, Paul D. 67
Borek, John 300
Borgdorff, Peter 91, 187
Borowsky, Irvin J. 324
Boschman, Ed 124
Bosh, Larry 155
Bossio, Patrick, Sr. 88
Bosso, Stephen C. 306
Boto, Augie 158
Bouchard, Charles E. . . .290
Bouffides-Walsh, Catherine 126
Boulva, Michèle 203
Bouman, Stephen P. 115
Bouras, Nicholas 126
Bourdette, Wesley R. 87
Bourne, Hugh 149
Bouton, Becky 257
Bowell, Gary 319
Bowen, Mary Lu 249
Bowen-Bailey, Doug 242
Bowie, E.L. 99
Bowkett, Roy 311
Bowman, Christopher D. . .92
Bowman, Robert M. 164
Boyajcan, Donna 256
Boyce, H. Gene 130
Boyce, Janice 130, 319
Boyd, Doris F. 330
Boyd, Douglas 245
Boyd, John E. 287
Boyd, T.B., III 140
Boyer, Wayne W. 102
Boyle, Harry 292
Boyles, James B. 179
Boyles, Lemuel 41
Boynton, Leonard 248
Bracelin, Frank 84
Bradford, Bose 168
Bradford, Karole 236
Bradley, Curtis 186
Bradley, James G. 231
Bradley, Julie 260
Bradley, Lasserre, Jr. 149, 319
Bradsell, Kenneth 151, 201
Brady, A. Glenn 144
Brame, Nicholas 129

INDEX

Brandebura, Michael 199
Brandt, Susan 343
Branham, Craig 80
Brashler, James 327
Bratton, G. Stanford 249
Braun, Alan 185
Braver, Barbara L. 107
Bravo-Guzman, Pedro 72
Brawner, John 113
Braxton, Edward K. 83
Bray, Donald L. 174
Bray, Imam Mahdi 36
Bray, Joy 338
Brazier, Arthus 144
Bregar, Janet A. 230
Breig, James 324
Bremer, Calvin L. 91
Brennan, Mary Pat 45
Brennan, Peter B. 72
Brennemann, Howard . . .137
Brenton, B. Dean 200
Bresee, Phineas 100
Breton, Jean-Claude 344
Brewer, John 174
Brewer, John 324
Brice, James T. 77
Brickhouse, Smith N. 92
Bridges, Dorothy 242
Bridges, James E. 76
Bridges, Randy J. 304
Briggs, Robert L. 23
Bright, John 96
Briley, Terry 300
Brill, Debra 157
Brink, Emily R. 334
Brink, Shari 151
Brinks, Robert 148
Brinser, Gerald 165
Brinser, Matthias 172
Brisco, Thomas 300
Briscoe, John 41
Britt, Kevin M. 83
Brittain, Fred 124
Brittian, Fred 333
Britton, Joseph H. 291
Broad, Dwayne 195
Broadfield, Edward 145
Broadway, Beth 248
Brodeur, Adele 54
Brom, Robert H. 83
Brookhart, C. Franklin . .108
Brooks, George 144
Brooks, James W. 167
Brooks, John 113
Brooks, Thomas 73
Brookshire, Mary Sue 65
Broomfield, Oree, Sr. 89
Brosseau, Annie 343
Brothers, William Francis .70
Brower, E. Alex 64
Brown, A.J. 293
Brown, Arthur 120
Brown, Barry R. 57
Brown, Carroll E. 231
Brown, Charles 172
Brown, Cynthia Vasil 65
Brown, Dallas 253
Brown, Daniel 129
Brown, Don J. 79
Brown, Donice 73
Brown, E. Lynn 89
Brown, E. 196
Brown, Elizabeth 82
Brown, Gary 111
Brown, Gerald L. 305
Brown, Gus H. 90
Brown, Harry 235
Brown, J. Richard 196
Brown, J.R. 131
Brown, James R. 68
Brown, Jeffrey P. 90
Brown, John W. 185, 186
Brown, Mark A. 25
Brown, Patricia L. 245
Brown, Philip 148
Brown, Ray 80
Brown, Richard A. 324
Brown, Sanford 260
Brown, Tod D. 83
Brown, Vivian W. 64
Brown, W. Wayne 67
Brown, Warner H., Jr. 171
Brown, Warren M. 62, 63
Brown, Warren 303
Brownlee, Richard D. 148
Brubacher, Marvin R. 313
Brubaker, John 82
Bruce, George L.R. 180
Bruehl, J. Roger 28
Brug, John F. 338
Brumbaugh-Cayford, Cheryl 92, 331
Brundage, Thomas 319
Bruno, C. José 90
Bruno, J. Jon 108
Brushaber, George K. 79, 292
Brust, Donald M. 90
Bryan, David 338
Bryan, Jamie Brooke 172
Bryan, Ron 121
Bryant, Darue 81
Bryant, David 290
Bryant, John R. 51, 62
Bryant, Juanita 89
Bryant, Roy, Sr. 80, 81, 292
Bryant, S.N. 97
Bryant, Sissieretta 80
Bryant, Steven D. 337
Buchanan, John 320
Buchanan, Kimberleigh . .233
Buck, Charles 166
Buck, Erwin 313
Buckle, Clarence 200
Buckle, Terry 180
Buechlein, Daniel M [[or Buechelin?]]. 84
Buegler, David D. 133
Bueno, John 76
Buick, William W. 124
Bula, Omega C. 207
Bull, Norman 195
Bulloch, Wendy 207
Bullock, Jeffrey 309
Bullock, M. Wyvetta 113
Bullock, Robert H., Jr. 333
Bullock, Warren 76
Burbridge, Michael F. 84
Burden, Keith 138
Burden, Roy A. 200
Burdick, Brent 204
Bures, Sally 45
Burg, Randall S. 90
Burger, Delores 27
Burger, Elizabeth 68
Burger, Gail A. 247
Burger, Stephen E. 27
Burgess, Morgan 119
Burgio, Ron 106
Burgo, Peter 90
Burgonio-Watson, Thelma 261
Burkat, Howard 33, 43
Burke, Anne 83
Burke, C. Don 145
Burke, Michael 207
Burkhardt, Patricia 31
Burleigh, Elizabeth F. 71
Burley, Kathy J. 262
Burnett, Joe G. 108
Burney, Artie 80, 81
Burnham, Gary 96
Burns, Donald 288
Burns, Patricia 55
Burns, Robert J. 55
Burr, Nelson R. 353
Burrell, Calvin 319
Burrell, Willie 144
Burris, Glenn C., Jr. 129
Bursey, Ernest 309
Burt, Lindsey 198
Burt, Merlin D. 347
Burton, Anthony 180
Burton, M. Garlinda 327
Busby, Dan 32
Bush, Richard E. 90
Bushkofsky, Linda Post . .114
Bushrod, Montrose 338
Bush-Simmons, La Quetta 229
Buslon, Jim 198
Buss, P.M. 195
Busse, Cheryl 95, 188, 313
Bustle, Louie 101
Bustram, James 119
Buswell, J. Oliver 128
Butimore, David, Sr. 66
Butin, Philip W. 306

INDEX

Butler, Kevin J. 157, 335
Butler, Lisa 141
Butler, Ramsey 144
Butler, Thomas 141
Butt, Debra 245
Butts, Calvin O. 247
Butts, J. Wayman 251
Buxton, Zane 148
Buzza, John 243
Buzza, Rob 314
Buzzard, Anthony, Sr. 328
Buzzell, Sandra 239
Byler, J. Ron 137
Bynum, LaTaunya M. . . .252
Bynum, William 352
Byrd, Ron 124

Cabana, Denise 231
Cabigting, Ruben 132
Cable, Kenneth 301
Cabrera, Brigido 151
Cadieux, Vincent 202
Cady, Donald D. 174
Cagan, Richard D. 260
Cahill, Brendan 305
Cahoy, William J. 305
Caldwell, Bruce 109
Caldwell, William 245
Calhoun, Mary 121
Calian, Carnegie Samuel
. 304
Caliandro, Arthur 28
Callaway, Susan L. 103
Calvin, John 155
Camenga, Andrew 157
Cameron, Lawrence M. . .165
Camp, Peggy 174
Camp, Richard P., Jr. 31
Camp, Steve 167
Campbell, Alexander
. . . . .85, 186
Campbell, Cynthia M.
. . . . .28, 301
Campbell, Donald G. . . .148
Campbell, Ella 151
Campbell, Frederick F. . .305
Campbell, G. Robert 207
Campbell, Greg 129
Campbell, John D. 188
Campbell, Joseph 93
Campbell, Phillip 133
Campbell, Stuart W. 347
Campbell, Ted A. 297
Campbell, Thomas 85, 186
Campbell, Virginia 237
Campos, Jose Luis 157
Canary, John F. 302, 309
Canary-Marshall, Deborah
. 253
Canfield, Paul V. 143
Cannada, Robert C., Jr. . . .304
Cannaday, Antoinette 81
Cannon, Edward 81
Canon, Rose 127
Canoy, Robert W. 310
Caouette, Karen 238
Capets, James 122
Caraballo, Ildefonso
. . . . .95, 188, 294
Carder, Kenneth L. 170
Carey, William 16
Carfora, Carmel Henry . . .70
Carlin, Donald 256
Carlsen, William A. 67
Carlson, David 242
Carlson, Dennis N. 157
Carlson, George G. 115
Carlson, Kenneth P. 112
Carlson, Robert W. 43
Carmi, Laila 50
Carmical, Leon J. 79
Carmichael, Cassandra 41
Caron, Kateri 261
Carouthers, David 288
Carpenter, Don 341
Carpenter, Paul 118
Carpenter, Ronald, Sr. 130
Carr, Clarence 62, 63
Carriere, Vianney (Sam)
. . . . .179, 344
Carroll, Jeff 119
Carroll, Leon 25
Carroo, Winston 42
Carson, John L. 77
Carson, Kathy 49
Carter, Ethel Ware 233
Carter, Janice 344
Carter, Larry 297
Carter, Nick 290
Carter, Pamela 145
Carter, Ron L. 335
Cartes, Ann 140
Cartier, Jacques 202
Carver, Hugh 96
Cary, Lovell R. 96
Cary, Timothy 26
Case, Johnathan 247
Casebolt, James 243
Casey-Lee, Diane 239
Cashwell, G.B. 130
Cassian (Bishop) 127
Cassidy, Thomas P. 305
Casteel, Richard 129
Castle, Gretchen 121, 145
Castrejon, Jaime 299
Cauller, William L. 254
Cavadini, John C. 309
Cavalero, Robert 40
Cavanaugh, Donald 23
Cave, Evelyn 235
Cawley, William Kevin . . .352
Cayce, W. Hartsel 149
Cazabon, Gilles 203
Cebula, John W. 248
Cell, Howard 145
Cepure, Uldis 131
Cereghino, Phil 337
Chabolla, Tom 36
Chadden, Shane 58
Chadick, Bonnie 236
Chadwick, Joanne 113
Chafe, Joanne 202
Chamberlain, Larry 119
Chamberlain, Ray W., Jr.
. . . . .123, 170
Chambers, James R. 172
Chambers, Steven 207
Chambers-Young, Thelma
. 41
Chamness, Ben R. 170
Champion, Willie C. 89
Chan, Lawrence 294
Chand, Samuel R.
. . . . .48, 130, 292
Chandler, Maurice G. 291
Chane, John Bryson 109
Chang, Richard S.O. 108
Channan, James 49
Chapell, Bryan 147, 295
Chapman, Clare J. 41
Chapman, John 88
Chapman, Morris H. 158
Chappell, Paul G. 299
Chappelle, Richard Allen, Sr.
. . . . .62, 64
Charles, Mark 88
Charleston, Steven 296
Charron, Jean-Marc 316
Charry, Ellen T. 336
Chase, Deana 120, 122
Chase, Marlene 338
Chase, Noel 236
Chatham, Virginia E. 338
Chauncey, H. Doyle 159
Chavez, Linda 36
Chavez, Silvia 26
Cheatham, Shirlie 119
Chemberlin, Peg 243, 244
Cheney, Charles Edward
. 152
Cherry, Charles 251
Cheshier, Carl 298
Chesnutt, Randall 303
Chesser, Larry 334
Chetti, Samuel S. 67
Chevalier, Rebekah 343
Chidsey, Linda 120, 122
Childers, John D. 96
Chiles, Lois 68
Chisholm, Alva 245
Chivers, Charlie 30
Chmura, Joyce 232
Choe, Richard C. 207
Choi, Seung Koo 131
Choloyan, Oshagan 75
Chondo, Javan 122
Chow, Rita K. 43
Christensen, Bruce 340
Christensen, Clifford R. . . .104

Christianson, Lawrence . . .138
Christie, Joyce 59
Christie, Marge 246
Christie, Paul C. 231
Christopher (Bishop) 127
Christopher (Metropolitan) 156
Christopher, Sharon Brown 169
Chrysostomos (Archbishop) 162, 163
Chu, Thomas 107
Church, Ted 153
Churchill, Craig 348
Chute, Nilda 287
Ciceva-Aleksic, Marija 50
Cieslak, William M. 297
Cilpam, Ha Giao 91
Cimer, Mary Lee 122
Cinson, Victor 38
Cioffi, Joseph 260
Citronnelli, Eddie 81
Cizik, Rich 39
Cizik, Richard 331
Clanton, John 124
Clark, Charles 68
Clark, Cicel 159
Clark, Frank B. 228
Clark, James I., Jr. 101
Clark, Jeffery A. 159
Clark, Katharine 120
Clark, Neal 66
Clark, Robert 37
Clark, Tim 159
Clarke, John R. 179
Clarke, Levi 97, 189
Clatterbuck, Doug 262
Clausen, Daniel 303
Clay, Colin 289
Cleave, Dwayne 197
Clement, Marilyn 36, 37
Clements, Kerry 148
Clements, Larry 66
Clements, Philip J. 40
Clements, Sam 97, 189
Clemenz, Lorin 235
Clifford, Mary Montgomery 141
Cline, Douglas M. 96
Cline, Evadna 257
Cline, George 129
Cline, Richard D. 260
Clippard, David 159
Clothier, Patti 253
Cloud, Randy 66
Cloud, Sanford, Jr. 40
Clowes, William 149
Coates, Gerald 120
Coates, Ken 229
Coats, John W. 68
Cobarn, Trevor 88
Coble, Edgar O. 87
Cochran, Sylvenia F. 249
Coday, Mike 261
Coffey, David 129
Coffin, Percy D. 180
Coffin, Peter R. 180
Cogdill, Michael G. 293
Cohen, Albert G. 230
Colas, Ralph 24
Colburn, Tom 321
Cole, Brian 112
Cole, Jack 124
Cole, John K. 144
Coleman, Caesar D. 89
Coleman, Catherine 229
Coleman, K. Virginia . . .207
Coleman, Robert F. 298
Coles, Robert N. 69, 334
Collazo, Manny 86
Colligan, John 24
Collins, Arnie 52
Collins, Bradley 324
Collins, David 182
Collins, F. Donald 79
Collins, Jacqueline 184
Collins, Leland C. 232
Collins, Les D. 142
Collins, Michael R. 158
Collins, Sam 94
Collins, W. Darwin 87
Collis, John 126
Collymore, Carlisle 168
Colon, John 107
Columbus, Christopher 82
Combes, Frances 288
Comfort, Marianne 250
Comfort, William 261
Compton, Gordon 31
Conant, Lawrence 160
Condrea, Nicolae 154, 203
Cone, Claude W. 159
Conley, Jean 33
Conley, John 294
Conley, Michael 33
Conn, C. Paul 95, 188
Connel, Bob 320
Conner, Len 27
Connors, G.C. 199
Constantine (Metropolitan) 163
Contogeorge, Christopher 74
Converse, Susan . . .151, 201
Cook, Charles J. 29
Cook, Clyde 307
Cook, David T. 321
Cook, Frank 257
Cook, Gary 45
Cook, Katie 318
Cooksey, David 82
Coomas, Doug 184
Coombs, Gary F. 307
Cooney, Eugène 202
Coons-Torn, Marja 167
Coop, Linda 113
Cooper, Brian 181
Cooper, Irving S. 132
Cooper, Sabrina M. . . .77, 318
Cooper-White, Michael L. 301
Coorilos, Euyakim Mar . . .136
Coote, Robert T. 21, 22
Cope, Kenneth 146
Cope, Mike 338
Cope, William 65, 317
Copeland, Chris 65
Copeland, Elaine Johnson 294
Copeland, Shelley 230
Cope-Robinson, Lyn 121, 122
Copley, Steve 228
Coplon, David 250
Corbett, Ardelia M. 167
Corbett, Daniel 97, 189
Corbin, Randall B. 90
Cordat, Mary F. 349
Corkum, Celest 204
Corkum, Ken 204
Cormode, James R. 314
Cornelius, Brian 207
Cornelius, Fred R. 97
Corrigan, John 321
Corson-Finnerty, Susan . . .325
Costanza, Daniel 342
Côté, P. Richard 202
Cotton, Edmund G. 119
Cottrell, Ralph 79
Coulston, James A. 116
Coulter, Riley 311
Councell, George E. 108
Courter, Gini 164
Cousin, Philip Robert, Sr. 61, 62
Cowan, Mattew 156
Cowin, Suzanne 93
Cox, Ann 258
Cox, Brian 56
Cox, Jill 262
Cox, John R. 140
Coyle, Charlotte 259
Coyner, Michael J. 169
Crabtree, Charles T. 76
Crabtree, David Foy 167
Craddock, Margaret 258
Craddock, Max E. 342
Craddock, Max 190
Craft, Betty Jo 38
Craft, Roger L. 28
Craft, Roy 233
Craig, James D. 355
Cramm, Stassi D. 103
Crandall, Christine A. . . .350
Crane, Charles A. 292
Cranford, Stephen V. 253
Crank, Charles 76
Cranmer, Gilbert 98
Crapson, Winnie 236

INDEX

Craven, Paul J. 38
Crawford, Bud 192
Crawford, Florence L. 73
Crawford, Peggy 39
Crawford, S. Rea 146
Crawley, David P. 179, 180
Creighton, Michael 107
Creighton, Philip 58
Crenshaw, Carole 326
Cress, James A. 157
Crews, C. Daniel 351
Crews, Warren 244
Crick, Robert D. 95, 188
Crim, Blanche 31
Crist, Jessica 244
Crist, Larry 87
Crocker, Richard 80
Crockett, Joseph 24
Croft, Donna 55
Croglio, James 249
Croneberger, Jack P. 108
Crook, Eleanor Butt 28
Cropsey, Marvin W. 330
Cross, Marie T. 148
Cross, Roger 52
Crossman, Richard C.
. . . . .56, 316
Crouch, Peter D. 42
Crough, Dave 346
Crout, Valorie 260
Crowder, Sandra B. 64
Cruger, Douglas 239
Crum, John 73
Crumbly, Faith 335
Crumes, W.E. 99, 326
Crumpler, A.B. 130
Crutchfield, Carmichael 89
Cruver, Rob W. 146
Cruz, John 23
Csepregi, Gabor 312
Cueni, R. Robert 300
Culbertson, William 112
Cullen, Edward P. 83
Cullen, James 179
Culp, Kristine A. 295
Culpepper, R. Alan
. . . . .233, 301
Cummins, D. Duane 86
Cummins, George D.
. . . . .151, 152
Cunningham, Jack . . .171, 207
Cunningham, Jeff 260
Cunningham, Johnny 73
Cunningham, Joseph
. . . . .91, 321
Cunningham, Mary 327
Cunningham, Paul G. . . .101
Cunningham, Ronald M. . . .89
Cunningham, Ronald 32
Cureton, Charles 137
Curry, G. 345
Curry, Marvin 171
Curry, Michael B. 108
Curtis, Carolyn 332
Curtis, Larry 258
Cushman-Wood, Darren . . .36
Custer, James 119
Cuthbert, Richard 68
Cuthbert, Terry D.
. . . . .194, 342, 343
Cutler, John 245
Cutler, Lelia 141
Cutts, Debbie 262
Cyprian (Metropolitan)
. . . . .162, 163
Dabrowski, Rajmund . . .156
Dadds, David 234
Dadourian, Haig 75
Dahl, Judy 173
Dahulich, Michael G. . . .306
Dais, Hope 334
Dale, Diana C. 43, 71
Dale, William 143
Dalenberg, Jack 151
Dallenbach, Robert B. . . .146
Dame, John 254
Danhof, Henry 150
Daniel, Clifton, III 108
Daniel, Hieromonk 338
Daniel, W.N. 140
Daniels, David Rwhynica, Jr.
. 62
Daniels, Henrietta 64
Daniels, Mary Martha . . .106
Danielson, Duane C.
. . . . .114, 251
Danneberger, David D. . . .257
Daoust, Joseph P. 299
Darby, John Nelson 85
Darden, Samuel 73
Darling, Richard 288
Darr, Steve 260
Dart, Christopher 243
Dart, Helen 154
Dasa, Anuttama 47
Daugherty, Billy Joe 45
Daughters, Kenneth Alan
. 296
Daum, Roger 80
Davey, Karen 260
David, Rebecca 33
Davidson, Brian 78
Davidson, Bruce 249
Davies, Fran 250
Davies, Pat 198
Davies, S.J.P. 287
Davies, Susan E. 34
Davies-Flindall, Dorothy
. 179
Davis, Ashley 236
Davis, Bessie 73
Davis, Charles 144
Davis, Derek 217
Davis, Dollie 145
Davis, Earl 41
Davis, Edward 117
Davis, F. Benjamin 140
Davis, G. Lindsey 170
Davis, George 198
Davis, Harper 237
Davis, James Levert 62
Davis, Jim 228
Davis, Kathleen 230
Davis, Melvin 238
Davis, Richard 171
Davis, Robert 238
Davis, Sarah Frances 62
Davis, Stephanie 168
Davis, Stephen P. 158
Davis, Tyrone T. 89
Davolt, Philip 81
Davolt, Susan 325
Dawidziuk, Jan 146
Dawkins, David 144
Dawley, William G. 321
Day, Jeff 238
De Marco, Eugene 88
Dearing, Carla 241
Deats, Richard 324
Deckard, Stephana 339
Deckenback, John R. 167
Decker, Robert D. 308
Decker, William 329
DeConcini, Barbara 211
Dee, Choe Chong 183
deFreese, David L. 114
DeGraffenreidt, Kermit J.
. . . . .63, 331
DeGroot-Nesdahl, Andrea F.
. 114
DeHaan, M.R. 128
deJong, H. Wayne 91
Del Valle, Harry Fred . . .148
Delac, Katria 216
DelHousaye, Darryl 304
DellaForesta, John 196
Deller, Walter 312
Delmonte, Elisabeth 50
Delsaut, Phil 194
Demers, Marcel 313
Demeter, Andor 127
Demetrios (Archbishop)
. . . . .34, 125
DeMoor, Robert 318
Demos, Emanuel G. 126
Denis, Mary Frances 206
Denney, Randal 333
Dennie, Steve 101
Dennis, Donald R. 145
Dennison, Don 103
Denny, Jesse W. 94
Densmore, Christopher . . .349
Denton, A. Louis 255
Depner, Horst 188
Derderian, Hovnan 75, 181
Derry, John 295, 298
DeSelm, Joel 137
Desgagne, Jean 53
DeTilla, Paul 138

Detjen, Val 353
Detterick, John J. 148
DeVeaux, William Phillips 36, 62
Devia, Julian 41
DeVoe, Jerry M., Jr. 153
DeVries, Janet 148
Dew, William W., Jr. 171
DeWall, Clem 33
DeWarf, Martha 31
Dewey, Marvin L. 315
DeWinter, Deborah 50
Dewire, Norman E. 301
DeWitt, Donald L. 353
DeWitt, Jesse 36
Dewling, Gregory R. 200
Dewling, Robert H. 200
Diakiw, William . . .163, 164
Diaz, Louis 112
Diaz-Montanez, Cristino 67
Dickerson, Dennis C. 23, 62, 351
Dicks, Ronald M. 200
Diefenbach, Joan 246
Diehl, James H. 101
Diehl, Paul J., Jr. 87
Diekelman, William R. . . .133
Diemer, Ulli 341
Dietterich, Paul M. 29
Dietz, Harry 256
Diggs, Harold S. 150
Dillaman, Rockwell L. . . .90
Dilley, Gary 101
DiLorenzo, Francis X. 83
Dimitrios (Bishop) 126
Dimitriou, Jerry 126
Dinatale, Wenda 255
Dinkha, Mar, IV 70
Dinunzio, Ron 117
Dion, Peter 126
Dirks, Gordon 315
Dirmann, Kimberly 129
DiStaulo, David 196
Dividson, Janet 201
Dixon, Brad 102
Dixon, Judy 252
Dixon, Michael A. 101
Djaballah, Amar 312
Dmitri (Archbishop) 143
Dobbin, Karen 236
Dobbs, H.A. 325
Dodds, Ed 27
Doezema, Don 150
Dolan, Timothy M. 83
Donahue, James A. 297
Donald (Bishop) 127
Donaldson, Hal 333
Donges, David A. 116
Donley, Brian C. 310
Donnithorne, Larry R. . . .294
Donohoe, Linda 54
Donoyan, Avo 75
Doran, Thomas G. 83
Dorland, Arthur G. 185
Dorman, Nancy 260
Dormont, Robert 253
Dorn, Michael P. 197
Dorrington, Charles W. 152, 201
Dorsey, Daniel 34
Dorsey, Jim 326
Dortch, Mimi 228
Doster, Dean 158
Doty, Sherri L. 76
Dougans, James V. 235
Dougherty, Cindy 86
Douglas, Caryn 312
Douglas, Dominion 289
Douglas, Scott 227
Douglas, William 97
Douglass, Steve 28
Dow, Lorenzo 149
Dow, Thomas E. 312
Dowd, Susan Jackson . . .327
Dowden, G. Blair 101, 298
Dowell, W.E. 78
Dowie, John Alexander 84
Down, Graham 343
Downey, Ray 187
Downey, William S.H. 132
Downs, Bert E. 104, 310
Downs, Michael A. 166
Downs, Timothy C. 167
Doyle, Barrie 187
Doyle, Seamus 244
Draper, David E. 310
Draper, James T., Jr. 158
Dreisbach, Frances 145
Dresselhaus, Richard 76
Drew, Walter Ed 30
Driedger, Connie 187
Driggers, B. Carlisle 159
Driscoll, Virginia 121
Drummond, C.W. 162
Drur, Stephen 171
Dua, Barbara E. 246
Duda, Betty 133
Dueck, Abe 343
Duerksen, Carol 338
Duff, Donald J. 144
Duff, Susan 237
Duffy, Mark J. 107, 349
Dufresne, Edward R. 240
Dugas, Jacqueline 56
Duggins, Dominic 34
Duke, Dennis 95
Duke, Thomas 244
Dulan, C. Garland 156
Dulder, Marianne 344
Dunahoo, Charles 147, 324
Dunbar, David G. 292
Dunbar, R.G. 123
Duncan, Donald 339
Duncan, Larry 97, 189
Duncan, M. Donald 130
Duncan, Muriel 345
Duncan, Philip M., II . . .107
Duncan, Robert W., Jr. . .109
Duncan, Ronald V. 94
Dunham, Rosetta J. 64
Dunkerson, Ruddy 166
Dunkin, Ralph W. 116
Dunn, Craig A. 174
Dunn, Sharon R. 95
Dunnam, Maxie D. 51
Dunston, Ann 80
Dupcak, Kimberlee 248
Durakis, Thomas 24
Durance, George 311
Durden, John 291
Durocher, Eric 341
Dursi, Elsie L. 252
Durso, Pamela R. 318
Duvall, Charles 32
Dvorak, Robert C. . . .112, 231
Dwight, David A. 112
Dyck, Dan 197
Dyck, Darrell 194
Dyck, Ed 183
Dykstra, Jon 345

Eads, Ora W. 88
Early, Margaret 233
Eastman, Donald 173
Eatherton, Robert L. 103
Eaton, James E. 323
Eberhardt, Jack 124
Eberly, Leon 172
Echohawk, John 225
Echols, James Kenneth . . .300
Eck, Diana L. 218
Eckes, Lois 242
Eckhardt, Ellen E. 140
Eckler, Sharon 236, 237
Eckman, James 297
Eddy, Mary Baker 93
Edgar, Robert W. 41
Edgren, John Alexis 79
Edlund, Mark 158
Edney, Lowell 168
Edwards, David 240, 315
Edwards, Gregory 43
Edwards, Harold 99
Edwards, Herbert 101
Edwards, James L. 94, 290
Edwards, Jonathan 153
Edwards, Marion M. 170
Edwards, Peg 263
Edwards, William H. 87
Edwards-Konic, Patricia 121, 334
Egge, Joel 100
Eggleston, James H. 246
Egly, Henry 118
Egnew, Bruce E. 83
Ehrenkrantz, Dan 304
Ehresman, David 238
Ehrmantraut, Janet M. 87

Eibl, Shawnda 28
Eidson, E. Larry 38
Eidum, Charles D. . . .66, 324
Ekamrak, Carl 138
Ekemam, Samuel Chuka, Sr. 62, 63
Ekeroth, George E. 77
Ekeroth, M.J. 77
Elam, Betty 33, 43
Elford, Keith 51, 195
Elgin, Bette 122
Elia, Donna 247, 250
Eliason, Leland V. 28
Elizade, John 253
Ellenson, David 298
Elliott, G. Keith 194
Elliott, Kate 335
Ellis, David 123
Ellis, Davis L. 144
Ellis, Howard 192
Ellis, Jerry 256
Ellis, Jesse Delano, II 171, 172
Ellis, Rebekah A. 250
Ellis, Sandra 199
Ellis, Wayne 72
Ellison, Leslie 259
Ellyatt, David 196
Elmore, Don 79
Elrod, Rachael 237
Elston, Charles 352
Ely, Thomas C. 109, 260
El-Yateem, Grace G. 113
Embree, Dorothy 239
Emerson, Daniel E. 52
Emory, M.L. 246
Endecott, Clayton 97, 189
Endel, Leo 158
Engbrecht, Dave 137
Engebretson, Donn 111
Engel, A. Gayle 166
Engel, Bradley C. 114
Engelhard, David H. 91, 187
Engelsma, David J. 328, 336
Enger, Cindy 261
Engstrom, Jon R. 123
Enns-Rempel, Kevin 350
Enrique, Antonio 333
Enslin, Christian 195
Epp, Gerald 118
Epp, Ruth 118
Epstein, Jerome M. 225
Epting, C. Christopher 107
Erb-Miller, Fanny 340
Erdman, Greg 155, 156
Erhardt, Richard 261
Ericksen, Paul 349
Erickson, C.E. 235
Erickson, Charles R. 259
Erickson, Duane 110
Erickson, Gary 171
Erickson, James 160
Erickson, John H. 306
Ericson, Charles 231
Erlandson, Kathy 261
Ervine, Sharon 259
Eschenbrenner, Jim 91
Eshbach, Warren M. 256
Eslinger, Leslie S. 256
Essey, Basil 69, 70
Esterle, Stan 237
Estey, Denise 242
Estill, Dennis 129
Estocin, Frank 163, 164
Estwani, Sheikh Bassam .232
Eubanks, David L. 299
Eva, Willmore D. 330
Evangelos (Metropolitan) 126
Evans, Alton 143
Evans, Bernard J. 106, 192, 324
Evans, Gene 123
Evans, Irvin 168
Evans, Marie 234
Evans, William B. 138, 139, 317
Evenson, Carl R. 115
Everett, K. Randel 300
Evison, Ian 23
Ewell, Thomas C. 239
Ewing, Finis 105
Ewing, Ward B. 297
Eyring, Henry B. 99

Faber, Connie 321
Fabric, Elliot 261
Fadelle, Norman 85
Fagerstrom, Douglas L. . . .297
Failing, Mark 317
Fairchild, Darryl 251
Falco, Chris 42
Fandrey, James E. 133
Fannin, Robert E. 170
Farabee-Lewis, Iris 239
Faris, Robert 56
Farley, Lawrence 198
Farlow, Gary 122
Farmer, Jeffrey E. . . .45, 143
Farmer, Paul 235
Faro, Ira 255
Farren, John 305
Fast, Ken 27
Fast, Rick 58
Faulkner, Tom 315
Faust, David M. 294
Faust, James E. 99
Favicha, Raymond 122
Favreau, Claude 192
Fawcett, Bruce 191
Fay, William P. 83
Feamster-Roll, Gerry 237
Fecher, Roger J. 33
Fedak, Wasyly 205
Fedchenkov, Benjamin . . .74
Fedechko, Michael 152, 201, 314, 344
Fehr, Wes 314
Feldberg, Michael 350
Feldbush, Martin W. 156, 317
Feldman, James 29
Feliciano, Gloria 50
Felipa, Luis F. 90
Feller, Henriette 205
Felter, David J. 327
Fendt, John W., Jr. 140
Ferber, Otto 185
Ferguson, Leslie, Sr. 301
Ferkenstad, Craig 116
Ferlino, Jack 25
Fernhout, Harry 313
Ferree, James W. 251
Ferrell, Ernest 140
Ferrer, Abednego 91
Ferris, Ronald 179
Fetherlin, Robert L. 90
Field, Ron 43
Fife, Maureen 260
Figueroa, Sharilyn A. . . .322
Fikse, Susan 331
Finch, Morris, Jr. 87
Finck, Murray D. 114
Fincke, George B. 152
Fines, David 340
Finke, Roger 212
Finks, Frederick J. 291
Finlay, Terence E. 179, 180
Finn, Charles W. 131
Finn, Peter G. 305
Finney, Peter P., Jr. 322
Finzel, Hans 104
Fiorino, Joseph 332
Fischer, Harvey 98
Fishell, Randy 326
Fisher, Fred S., Sr. 97, 189
Fisher, Gerald 183
Fisher, Violet L. 169
Fisk, J. Victor 122
Fites, Donald V. 51
Fitzgerald, Russell G. 48
Fix, Senia 164
Flaaten, Jan Olav 228
Flach, Dennis 117
Flanagan, James 300
Flanagan, Randall F. 262
Fleischer, Daniel 100
Fleischer, Paul 329
Fleischmann, Konrad . . .141
Fleming, David L. 335
Flesher, Chuck 26
Fletcher, Alfred 67
Fletcher, James 24
Fletcher, Jeffery 335
Fletcher, Judy R. 148
Fletcher, Ruth A. 87
Fletcher, Sarah 322

Flewelling-Leeds, Ginger 258
Flores, Robert 129
Flowers, Fort D., Jr. 259
Flowers, George F. 62, 338
Flowers, Marles 94
Flowers, Ronald M. 156
Fluechtling, Rick 263
Fluegel, Elizabeth 133
Fluit, Charlie 59
Fluker, Sharon Watson 34
Flynn, Harry J. 84
Folds, Gloria 46
Follett, Don 256
Folts, James E. 109
Fombelle, Douglas W. ...292
Fong, Bruce W. 301
Ford, Brian 204
Ford, C. Barney 35
Ford, J. Arthur 313
Ford, Jim 347
Ford, Lowell 68
Ford, Marie LaMarre 231
Foreman, Rachel L. 102, 103, 321, 326, 331
Forlines, James 139
Forlines, Leroy 139
Forro, Alexander 127
Forsberg, Robert 229
Forsee, Tom 227
Fortune, Marie M. 261
Foss, Richard J. 114
Foster, H. Paul 342
Foster, Julie 234
Foster, Neill K. 345
Fouke-Mpoyo, Carol ..41, 42
Fountain, Peter 186
Fowler, John M. 322
Fox, Ronald K. 250
Foxman, Abraham H. 224
Fozard, John D. 94, 301
Frade, Leopold 109
Francis, Maureen 40
Franklin, John 55
Franklin, Mark 24, 119
Franklin, Robert M. 34
Franks, Lonnie 140
Franzmeier, Briana 242
Frase, Donald M. 174
Fraser, Hugh 311
Fraser, Ian S. 207
Fraser, Ronald A. 311
Frazier, Susan 129
Freed, Kathy 236
Freedholm, Herbert M. ...112
Freeman, David 187
Freeman, Edward A. 139
Freeman, George 339
Freeman, Hillary 242
Freeman, Linda Danby 49
Freiheit, Warren D. 115
Freitag, Herbert 129
Freitag, Merle 133
French, Juletha N. 64
Frenchak, David 48
Frericks, Sandra 233
Fretheim, James A. 112
Freund, Richard C. 140
Frew, Don 49
Frey, Mark 251
Frick, Murray 246
Friedrich, James 228
Friend, Kendra 103
Friesen, Jeff 118
Friesen, William H. 201
Frisch, Deborah 153
Fritsche, James 197
Frobisher, Martin 179
Froehlich, Samuel H. 71, 181
Frowe, Caroline 233
Fry, Gary 325
Fryling, Robert A. 35
Fuchs, Lorelei F. 35
Fugh, Clement W. 62
Fuller, Roy 237
Fullwood, James 68
Fulton, Jim 261
Fulwider, Bryan 232
Fung, Andrew 261
Funk, Abe 56, 182
Futral, James R. 159

Gabriel (Bishop) 154
Gaddie, Ron 237
Gaddy, Todd 171
Gaewski, David R. 167
Gage, J. Marshall 40
Gagnon, André L. 313
Galegor, Steve 119
Gallagher, John (Jack) ...314
Gallaher, Susan 260
Galloway, Phyllis H. 63, 351
Galvan, Elias G. 171
Gamble, Rich 261
Gammill, Nancy 236
Gandolfo, Lucian 88
Ganote, Lora 234
Garbidakis, Nicholas 24
Gardiner, Kelvin J. 90
Gardner, Brittany 129
Gardner, Carol 319
Gardner, Harry G. 44, 191
Gardner, Joan 41
Gardner, Marvin K. 328
Gardner, W. Wayne 308
Garis, Mark 82
Garment, Robert 117
Garner, Darlene 173
Garner, Don 121
Garrett, Phillip 237
Garrison, Brent D. 307
Garrison, J. Michael 109
Garrison, L. Alton 76
Garrison, Mary Lou 92
Garriss, Stephen 145
Garton, Jean 133
Gasero, Russell 352
Gaskin, Leah 303
Gast, Mary Susan 166
Gaston, Hillary, Sr. 302
Gaston, Sandra L. 64
Gatrek, Nyalam 245
Gatti, Louis 256
Gaud, Carmen 318
Gaudette, Pierre 203
Gaumond, André 202
Gautier, Haggeo 232
Gautier, Mary 27
Gaw, Catherine H. ...207, 289
Geernaert, Donna 34
Geiger, C. Edward 255
Geisler, Norman 307
Geldmacher, Joan 247
Genello, William R. 320
Gensib, Joyce 257
Gentle, Stanley 82
Gentles, Jestina 168
George (Bishop) 161
George Edward Battle, Jr. 62, 63
George, Barbara 46
George, Bill 321
George, Francis Cardinal ..83
George, J. Don 76
George, Richard 88
George, Timothy 291
George, William 89
Georgije (Bishop) 156, 204
Gepert, Robert Ronald 109
Gerasimos (Bishop) 126
Geraty, Lawrence T. 299
Gerbrandt, Gerald 311
Gerdau, Carlson 107
Gerdes, Neil W. 353
Gethers, Leroy 153
Getz, Greg 137
Geulsgeugian, Bernard 181
Geyser, P. 151
Geyser, Thomas 88
Ghabrial, Theresa 231
Ghougassian, Vazken 75
Giacoletto, Kenneth P. 68
Gibbens-Rickman, Mark 253
Gibbs, Charles P. 49
Gibbs, Wendell N., Jr. ...108
Gibson, David E. 320
Gibson, Frank G., Jr. 25
Gibson, Gaylena 320, 321, 328, 339
Gibson, Marie E. 248
Giesbrecht, Kennert 344
Giesy, Samuel 300
Gilbert, Jack 34
Gilbert, Wanda 217
Gilbert-Cougar, John 186
Gilbertson, Leon C. 57

INDEX

Gilbreath, Ed 337
Giles, Ann 148
Gill, Deborah 76
Gillette, Charisse 86
Gilley, James W. 157
Gilliam, Lynn W. 333
Gillians, Larry 53
Gilliard, Catherine 111
Gillies, Susan E. 67, 245
Gillming, Keith 78
Gillum, Perry 97, 189
Gilmore, Marshall, Sr. 89
Gilmore, Ronald M. 83
Gingerich, Elmer 80
Gingerich, Melvin 80
Ginter, William 118
Giordano, Sally 249
Giordano, Stephen T. 245
Girton-Mitchell, Brenda
. . . . .41, 42
Gist, Richard 45
Gladfelter, Irl A. 72
Gladish, Michael D. 195
Glagau, Ralph R. 95
Glanzer, Jules 297
Glass, Arless 171
Glenn, Lucinda 349
Glenn, Michael 44, 305
Glickman, Marlene 249
Glodo, Michael 117
Gnat, Thomas J. 146
Godevenos, Ken 345
Godfrey, W. Robert 310
Goebel, Samuel 110
Goertzen, Lil 194
Goertzen, Lil 342
Goff, Jim 156
Goff, Phillip 214
Goforth, C.W. 145
Gohdes, Stephen . . .138, 185
Goldberger, Nancy 329
Goldberger, Pierre 207
Golder, Morris 144
Golder, W. Evan 337
Goldstein, Clifford R. . . .328
Gomez, Jose H. 84
Gomez, Ray 258
Gonyaw, Cheri 261
Gonzalez, Geraldo 49
Gonzalez, Tony 228
Goodhue, Thomas W. . . .248
Goodin, David L. 90
Goodpaster, Larry M. . . .170
Goods, Gayle 299
Goodwin, Douglas 207
Goodyear, Paul 204
Gootjes, N.H. 184
Gopal, Renee 251
Gorazd (Most Reverend) . . .74
Gordon, Debbee 257
Gordon, Dorcas 56
Gordon, Drew 323
Gordon, J. Dorcas 313
Gordon, Lynne 323
Gore, Ralph J., Jr. 77, 296
Gore, Susan K. 105, 352
Gorton, Dennis L. . . .104, 337
Gorzoch, Michael 231
Goslee, Cindi 121
Gosner, Robert 153
Gould, Charles W. 173
Goulet, Mary Jean 202
Gover, Mary Pyke 52
Gower, David M. 124, 318
Grace, C.M. 168
Grace, Doug 41
Grady, J. Lee 320
Grady, Joellen W. 251
Graham, Ellen 234
Graham, J.B. 159
Graham, Jannice 50
Graham, Michael 240
Graham, Rachel 250
Graham, Vernon R. 234
Graham, William A. 298
Grainger, David 233
Gramm, Pat 155
Granberg-Michaelson, Wesley
. . . . .151, 201
Granitsas, Nicholas 104
Grant, F.W. 85
Grant, James M. 307
Grant, Sumner M. 68
Graves, Charles 262
Graves, David 101
Graves, James R. 66
Graves, Thomas H. 291
Graves, William H., Sr. 89
Gray, Arthur J., II 129
Gray, Davis 105
Gray, Duncan Montgomery, III
. 108
Gray, Duncan, II 244
Gray, Jane 31
Gray, Melva 67
Gray, Stephen C. 166
Graz, John 157
Greagrey, R. Alan 145
Grecco, Richard . . .202, 203
Greco, John 24
Green, Daniel 153
Green, Donald B. 253
Green, Dwight 94
Green, E. David 103
Green, Peter 138
Green, S. 168
Green, Samuel Lawrence, Sr.
. 62
Green, Stanley 137
Greenawald, Henry 254
Greenawald, Patricia 254
Greenhaw, David M. 296
Greening, John 124
Greenleaf, Helen 164
Greenway, Jeffrey E. 291
Greenwood, Greg 238
Gregersen, Bruce 207
Gregg, William O. 108
Grégoire, Léo 202
Gregory (Reverend) 143
Gregory, Chester, Sr. 168
Gregory, Wilton D. 83
Greiman, Clayton 151
Grein, Richard F. 34
Grier, David 198
Grieves, Brian 107
Griffin, Arlee, Jr. 67
Griffin, Ashley 238
Griffin, Robert 173
Griffin, William A. 304
Griffith, Craig 24
Grigsby, Phillip N. 250
Grimard, Roland 205
Grime, Paul 133
Grimes, Barry Q. 200
Grimm, Libby 253
Grimm, Robert 249
Griswold, Frank Tracy 107
Groome, Thomas H. 292
Groover, Clarence 101
Groover, Gentle L. 101
Groover, R. Edwin 291
Groseclose, Michael 172
Gross, Glenn M. 152
Gross, Joseph 146
Gross, Philip J. 128
Gross, Trevón 23
Grossman, Randall A. 81
Grossman, Robert 151
Grossman, W. 151
Grote, Royal U., Jr. 152
Grotegut, Stan 230
Grotnik, Casimir . . .146, 326
Groves, Anthony Norris 85
Grubbs, Bonita 231
Grubbs, J. Perry 94
Grubbs, Lari R. 86
Grudzen, Gerald 33
Guentert, Richard L. 87
Guernsey, Lucy 230
Guffey, Edith A. 166
Guibord, Gwynne 230
Guido, Sam 72
Guidry, Carolyn Tyler 62
Guillebeau, Julie 244
Guillemette, Gaetane 340
Guillermin, A. Pierre 300
Guinness, Howard 56
Guirguis, Ammonius 192
Guiterrez, Rosalia 49
Gulick, Edwin F., Jr. 108
Gulick, Janet A. 256
Gullette, Reginald 81
Gullixson, Theodore 329
Gumbs, Carolyn 248
Gunn, Joe 202
Guretzki, David 55
Gurgel, Karl R. 175
Gurley, Morris 247

INDEX

Guskjolen, J.I. 199
Gustafsson, Mai Lan 248
Guthrie, Donald 245
Gutierrez, Aina 37
Guynes, Delmer R. 307
Gwinn, James A. 44

Haas, Steve 51
Habecker, Eugene B. 23
Habegger, Ronald J. 118
Hackett, Charles 76
Hackner, James 181
Hadjinicolaou, John 198
Hadley, Alvin 252
Hadsell, Heidi 298
Haemmerle, Gerald R. 291, 302
Hagan, G. Michael 303
Hagan, Orville 95, 188
Hagedorn, Harold J. 175
Hagerty, Robert E. 308
Haggray, Jeffrey 67, 158
Hague, Barth 137
Hahn, Daniel 249
Hai, Iftekhar 49
Haight, David B. 99
Halbrooks, G. Thomas 294
Haldane, James 186
Haldane, Robert 186
Hale, Joe 51
Hales, Robert D. 99
Haley, Laura J. 248
Hall, A.Z., Jr. 94
Hall, Beverly 98
Hall, David A., Sr. 94
Hall, Dinah 261
Hall, Gregory V. 94
Hall, J.L. . . .171, 325, 333, 351
Hall, LisaRose 30
Hall, Marvin 122
Hall, Will 158
Hallberg, Donald M. 114
Hallstrand, Sarah 67
Haloviak, Bert 156
Haloviak, Bert 347
Hamb, Elnora P. 89
Hambrick, Fred 290
Hamel, William J. 112
Hamelink, Crystal 250
Hames, Jerald 107
Hames, Jerrold 324
Hamilton, Jeff 129
Hamilton, Karen 54
Hamilton, Thomas 24
Hamilton, W.W. 94
Hamlett, James P. 86
Hammer, Bill 237
Hammock, Cheryl 48
Hammond, F. Melvin 99
Hammons, Roger 149
Hampton, Charles 132
Hampton, John E. 144
Hancock, Carol L. 51, 207
Handysides, Allan R. 157
Haney, Kenneth F. 171
Hankins, David E. 158
Hanley, Richard 236
Hanse, Brian W. 38
Hansen, David 166
Hansen, Duane 113
Hansen, Ellen 261
Hansen, Gary L. 115
Hansen, Traynor ("Frosty"), Jr. 125
Hanson, Lloyd 229
Hanson, Mark S. 113
Hanus, Jerome G. 83
Hanzlik, Darcy 242
Hapke, Lark 166
Hardenbrook, Jim 92
Hardesty, Jane 78
Hardy, Ralph, Jr. 33, 43
Hargleroad, Bobbi Wells 322
Hargrave, Ervin 129
Harke, Gary L. 256
Harkins, Derrick 44
Harmelink, Herman, III . . .129
Harms, Forrest 236
Harms, Harold 118
Harms, Richard H. 351
Harms, Steve 229
Harp, Roger C. 148
Harper, Bud 289
Harper, Terry L. 159
Harriger, James 27
Harrington, Bernard J. 83, 84
Harris, Alvin 92
Harris, David A. 223
Harris, David 344
Harris, Elsie 167
Harris, Forrest E. 290
Harris, Grove 218
Harris, Jerome V. 62
Harris, Nanci 53
Harris, Patricia 262
Harris, Phil 91
Harris, Roger 182
Harris, Virginia S. 93
Harris, William O. 352
Harrison, Charles E. 335
Harrison, Dan 102
Harrison, Matthew 133
Harry, Emily 37
Hart, Donald G. 166
Hart, Jack 54
Hart, Ken 129
Hart, Maurice 123
Hart, Michael 314
Hart, Ray L. 292
Hart, Stephanie 215
Hartford, Barbara H. 49
Hartke, Gary 101
Hartman, Earl C., Jr. 253
Hartman, Patricia 111
Hartung, Bruce 133
Hartwig, Raymond L. 133
Harvey, Carole (Kate) H. 68
Harvey, Donald F. 180
Harvey, Jane Hull 35, 36
Harwell, Sara 348
Hasan, Imam John 228
Haskins, Roger W., Jr. . . .120
Hassinger, Susan W. 169
Hastey, Stan 65, 323
Hatcher, Warren 153
Haten, C. 289
Hatfield, Archibald 195
Hatlie, Susan Allers 242
Hauser, Clarence 288
Haverstock, Zedna M. . . .256
Hawaweeny, Raphael 69
Hawk, David 133
Hawkin, David J. 55
Hawkins, Don 307
Hawkins, O.S. 158
Haworth, Sharon 120
Hayes, Kathleen 335
Hayes, Lindsey 130
Hayes, Mona 31
Hayford, Jim 129
Haymes, Don 348
Hayner, Stephen A. 35
Hazuda, Ronald A. 68
Hazzard, David E. 199
Headman, Wayne A. 304
Heagy, David 165
Hearn, Greg 130
Heaslip, Clifford 207
Heater, Homer, Jr. 293
Heath, Jeanne 254
Heath, Preston 145
Heath, Tiffany 37
Heckenmueller, Teri 34
Heckles, Jane E. 166
Heckman, Bud 47
Heebner, Gerald 335
Hefner, Helmut 305
Heidebrecht, Paul 117
Heidkamp, Mary 36
Hein, Marvin 124, 125
Heine, Joy 37
Heinze, Ted 288
Heisey, Terry M. 349
Heleine, Berton G. 68
Heller, Ena 24
Helton, Charles L. 89
Helton, James 123
Helton, Mary Beth 238
Heminway, L. Marshall . . .132
Henderson, Dorsey F., Jr. 109
Henderson, James 148
Henderson, Katharine R. 213
Henderson, Susan 167
Henderson, Veryl F. 158

INDEX

Hendrick, Sherrill 260
Hendricks, Harry 99
Hendrickson, Mary Lynn .26
Hendrix, Carol S. 115
Hendrix, Kitsie 117
Hendrixson, Joe M. 236
Henkel, Sarah 256
Hennessy, Janet 238
Henning, Cornal Garnett, Sr. 62
Henry, Frederick B. 202,203
Henry, Patrick 215
Henze, Charles 246
Heppner, Jack 194
Herbrandson, DeWayne 30
Heretz, Michael 164
Herlong, Bertram N. 109
Herman (Metropolitan) 65, 143
Herman, Alvin 190
Herman, Harry 144
Hernandez, Lucia 37
Hernando, Mirasal 183
Hernando, Vincente 183
Herpe, Tina 37
Herr, John 152
Herring, Paul L. 256
Herrling, Karen 36
Herron, Brian 242
Hershkowitz, Thomas . . .107
Hertzog, Glenn 138
Hertzog, Stephen 316
Herzog, Daniel W. 107
Hess, Henry 187
Hess, Larry G. 96
Hessel, Karen McLean 36, 42
Hesselbein, Frances 173
Hester, Yvonne 240
Heuser, Frederick J., Jr. 148, 328
Heyward, Isaiah 95
Hickcox, Michael A. 47
Hickey, Tim S. 322
Hicks, Cullen L. 326
Hicks, Dan 129
Hicks, Maurice M. 184
Hicks, Roy 194
Hicks, Wayne 103
Hicks, William 98
Hiebert, Marilyn 184
Hiebert, Richard P. 345
Hiemstra, John E. 247
Higgens, Stan 30
Higham, Susan 152
Highers, Alan E. 336
Hill, Barbarie 121
Hill, Darcel 243
Hill, Kenneth H. 327
Hill, Nick 97
Hill, R. Eugene 69
Hill, Ronald K. 150
Hill, Ruth Y. 111
Hilliard, William Alexander 63
Hilsden, R.T. 199
Hiltz, Frederick J. 180
Hincke, Karen 59
Hinckley, Gordon B. 99
Hinding, Andrea 353
Hinkle, Carol 254
Hinton, Arthur 106
Hinz, Leo 289
Hinz, Mary Ann 240
Hirschy, Charles A. 103
Hirschy, Margaret 348
Hirschy, Paul 101
Hirshkowitz, Barbara . . .325
Ho, Esther 229
Hoak, Don 259
Hobbs (Reverend) 145
Hobgood, William Chris . . .86
Hockensmith, David W., Jr. 244
Hockman-Wert, Cathleen .337
Hodder, Gary 204
Hodges, Douglas 256
Hodges, James 71, 181
Hodgins, Donald E. 208
Hodgson, Bob 23, 191
Hodur, F. 146
Hoed, J. den 318
Hoefflin, Walter R. 129
Hoeksema, Herman 150
Hoffman, Bud 251
Hoffman, George 165
Hoffman, Jane Fisler 166
Hoffman, Karl H. 140
Hoffman, Michael 96
Hoffman, Warren L. . . .82, 183
Hoffmeister, Desmond . . .67
Hofstad, Robert D. 114
Hogan, Ed 77
Hogston, Delphine . . .241, 242
Hoke, Terry 82
Holbrook, Mark G. 30
Holdefer, Helen 227
Holdeman, John 95, 188
Holden, Ron 191
Holden, Stephen 43
Holdren, David W. 174
Holland, Grace 82
Holland, Jeffrey R. 99
Holland, Melford E., Jr. . . .107
Hollenbach, Deanna L. 138, 185,331
Holley, Darrell 139
Hollinger, Dennis P. 111, 296
Hollingsworth, Mark, Jr. 108
Holloway, Callon W., Jr. 115
Holloway, Carolyn 247
Holly, Mary Lynn 169
Holm, Duane 252
Holm, Jim 301
Holmberg, Joseph 243
Holmes, Carol 247
Holmes, Charley 79, 291
Holmes, Mary Swalla 236
Holmes, N.J. 130
Holmes, Roy A. 62, 63
Holmgren, A.A. 76
Holmstrom, Virginia 68
Holowell, Barry C.B. . . .179
Holsinger, James W., Jr. 51
Holt, Jeanette 65
Holt, John E. 257
Holtz, Janet E. 255
Homes, Jenny 253
Homoki, Lee 125
Honold, John 129
Hood, George 155
Hood, Phil 345
Hoogendoorn, Case 48
Hoople, William Howard 100
Hoover, Amos B. 142
Hope, Monica 81
Hopkins, John L. 169
Hopkins, Sara E. 337
Hopyan, Takvor 75
Horjus, Kenneth 91
Horne, Martha J. 304
Horner, David G. 112
Horner, R.C. 183
Hornshuh, Fred L. 142
Horsch, James E. 334
Horton, Evon G. 313
Horton, Jotham 173
Horvath, Carolyn 33
Hoskins, Janet A. 315
Hossler, William 137
Hostetter, Steven J. 290
Hotchkiss, Gregory K. 152
Houg, Richard W. 296
Hougen, Phillip L. 115
Hough, Joseph C., Jr. 308
Houle, Jacques 95, 188
House, Alvin 68
House, Christie R. 331
Houseal, Rich 27
Houser, Charles 24
Houser, Jim 236
Houston, Barbara 256
Hovis, Carol 229
Hovsepian, Vatche 75
Howard, John Alan 312, 341
Howard, Randy 97, 189
Howard, Roscoe J., III 157
Howard, S. Johnson 108
Howe, Barry R. 109
Howe, Bruce H.W. 180
Howe, John H. 107
Howell, Bruce 171

Howell, James R. 153
Howell, Patrick 306
Howerton, Ronnie 123
Howland, William H. 187
Hoy, G. Philip 235
Hoyle, Gary 248
Hoyt, Thomas L., Jr.
. . . . .41, 51, 89
Huang, C.P. 233
Hubbard, Bede 202
Hubbart, Mike 120
Hucks, John P. 307
Hucks, John T., Jr. 159
Hudnut-Beumler, James
. 309
Hudson, Henry 179
Hudson, James L. 148
Hudson, Steven 112
Huffard, Evertt W. 298
Hugh, Ivor T. 230
Hughes, Alfred C. 84
Hughes, Clyde M. . . .129, 333
Hughes, Dustin 130
Hughes, Gethin B. 109
Hughes, Sarah 237
Hughes, Sherly M. 168
Huh, Young Chin 131
Huie, Janice Riggle 170
Hull, Rey 246
Hulteen, William 167
Hultquist, Timothy A. 46
Humann, Roger 312
Humme, Larryl 151
Hummers, Bill 257
Humphrey, John 106
Humphrey, Sandra 321
Humphry, Carol 321
Hundley, Michael 237
Hundley, Reggie 327
Hunerdosse, Marion 91
Hungler, Tim 238
Hunn, Ken 82
Hunt, Art 117
Hunt, Frank, II 77
Hunt, Gerald 57
Hunt, Janet E. 28
Hunt, Patricia 145
Hunt, Raymon 63
Hunter, A. Scott 200
Hunter, David 239
Hunter, Harold D. 351
Hunter, Kent R. 31
Hunter, Louis, Sr. 62, 63
Hunter, Martha J. 322
Hunter, Nancy L. 200
Hunter, Robert 138
Hunter, Ron 139
Hunter, Stewart 56
Huntley, Harvey 116
Huntly, Juliet 207
Hurley, John 164
Huron, Rod 88
Hurt, Donna 138
Hurtubise, Pierre 355
Hus, Jan 138
Huszagh, Elenie K. 41
Hutcheon, Cyprian 198
Hutchings, L.W. 183
Hutchins, H.J. 159
Hutchinson, Brett 30
Hutchinson, Connie 30
Hutchinson, Moira 58
Hutchinson, William W.
. 170
Hutchison, Andrew S.
. . . . .179, 180
Hutter, Jacob 128
Hux, Ralph 102, 324
Hyvonen, Randall 166

Iakovos (Metropolitan) . . .126
Ickes, Wayne 113
Idleman, Kenneth D. 303
Ignatieff, Andrew 179
Ihloff, Robert W. 108
Ihreborg, Christer 198
Iker, Jack L. 108
Ilia (Bishop) 65
Illingworth, Beth 250
Imbens, Annie 49
Imes, William C. 291
Ingersol, Stan 351
Ingham, Michael C. 180
Ingle, Jim 118
Inglis, Charles 179
Ingram, Daryl B. 62
Ingram, Gregory 32, 62
Inskeep, Kenneth W. 114
Inyangu, Frederick 122
Ionita, Ioan 154, 203
Iorg, Jeff 159, 297
Iosue, Christina J. 257
Ippolito, Luigi 196
Irinev (Reverend) 143
Irish, Carolyn T. 109
Irish, Esther 68
Irons, Neil L. 51, 169
Irvio, Wanda 237
Irwin, B.H. 130
Irwin, H.E. 182
Irwin, John W. 58
Isaiah (Metropolitan) 126
Isch, John R. 329
Isenhower, Joe 133
Isham, Scott 326
Ishkanian, Charlotte 330
Isiye, Tom 121
Isner, Vince 41, 42
Isom, Beverly 234
Isom, Dotcy I. 89
Itty, Johnny 108
Ives, Ivan G. 113
Ives, S. Clifton 170

Jaaguste, Evi 192
Jackson, Bernice Powell . . .166
Jackson, Daniel R. 204
Jackson, Elmira 64
Jackson, Kitt 247
Jackson, Mary 80
Jackson, Norman W. 166
Jackson, Phil 138
Jackson, Scott 51
Jackson, Susan 244
Jackson-Skelton, Christina L.
. 113
Jacob, Marjorie 157
Jacobs, Anita 338
Jacobs, Sam G. 83
Jacobsen, Michael W. . . .145
Jacobus, Russell E. 108
Jacques, Camille 202
Jaggard, Art 236
Jaharis, Michael 126
Jahr, Armin 100
Jakubik, Arranna 172
James (Archbishop) 127
James, Dorothy 233
James, Joseph F. 120
James, Russell N., III 293
James, Timothy M. 86
Janes, Burton K. 200
Janke, Dwayne 346
Janssen, Angela 48
Jarmus, Andrew 205
Jarrell, Michael 238
Jarrett, Nathaniel, Jr. . . .62, 63
Jasper, Jeremiah 262
Jeavons, Thomas 121, 145
Jefferson, Jonathan K.
. 101
Jeffery, Jim 291
Jeffrey, Robert 328
Jehle, Bonnie 249
Jelinek, James L. . . .108, 243
Jellinek, Nancy 258
Jemerson, Robert 41
Jenkins, Charles E., III 108
Jenkins, Keith A. 298
Jenkins, Laurie 250
Jenkins, Marty 129
Jenness, Jeffery A. 94
Jennings, Charles 69
Jenson, Robert W. 34
Jeremiah, David 294
Jerge, Marie C. 115, 249
Jermann, Rosemary 336
Jernigan, C.B. 100
Jesske, T.J. 110
Jessup, Bryce L. 299
Jewel, Bill 238
Jewell, Thomas R. 87
Jillions, John 198
Job (Reverend) 143
Jobson, Harriet Tumlin 32
Johannesson, Gayle 342
John (Bishop) 161
John (Chorbishop) 161
John Paul II 82

INDEX

John, Esther "Little Dove" 260
Johns, Cheryl Bridges 34
Johns-Boehme, Steven 237
Johnson, A. Wayne 140
Johnson, Alfred 169
Johnson, Andrea 330
Johnson, Arthur F. 77
Johnson, B.M. 76
Johnson, Ben 73
Johnson, Bill 66
Johnson, Cheryl 248
Johnson, Craig 114, 329
Johnson, David W. 112
Johnson, Deborah 332
Johnson, Del L. 157
Johnson, Diane 104
Johnson, Don E. 109
Johnson, Eleanor 179
Johnson, Evelyn M.R. 112
Johnson, George 332
Johnson, H.J. 140
Johnson, Harold C. 66
Johnson, Henry L. 144
Johnson, Holly 28
Johnson, Jack 246
Johnson, Jacqueline 225
Johnson, Jeanette 262
Johnson, Jeffrey 120
Johnson, Jeron 144
Johnson, John Franklin . .294
Johnson, Joseph 63
Johnson, Kathryn J. 261, 356
Johnson, Ken 129
Johnson, M. 136
Johnson, Margaret 67
Johnson, Mel 173
Johnson, Michelle Laque 318, 320
Johnson, Nelson 36
Johnson, Paul 79
Johnson, Robert E. 318
Johnson, Robert H. 109
Johnson, Robert P. 262
Johnson, Rod 192
Johnson, Rodney McNeil 172
Johnson, Rosie 168
Johnson, Sally A. 111
Johnson, Sharon 343
Johnson, Thomas R. 28
Johnson, Thomas S. 46
Johnson, Todd 38
Johnson, W. Robert, III 62, 63
Johnson, W. Talmadge . . .101
Johnson, William E. 153
Johnson, William R. 166
Johnsson, W.G. 317
Johnston, John 288
Joiner, Jamie J. 145
Jones, A.M. 80, 81, 320
Jones, Barbara E. 87
Jones, Brooker T. 144
Jones, C. Stephen 246
Jones, Carol 193
Jones, Cassandra 167
Jones, Charles H. 68
Jones, Clifton 144
Jones, Dana 334
Jones, E. Edward 139
Jones, Elbert 99
Jones, G. Daniel 255
Jones, Gary A. 93
Jones, Greg 191
Jones, Jacqueline 246
Jones, Jerry 171
Jones, Jesse 168
Jones, Joyce 204
Jones, Judy 260
Jones, Kenneth E. 89, 320
Jones, L. Gregory 295
Jones, Larry 192
Jones, Lindsay E. 93
Jones, Mike 139
Jones, Paul Griffin, II 244
Jones, Paul 62
Jones, Ralph E. 115
Jones, Stephen M. 103
Jones, Stephen 261
Jones, Terrence J. 64
Jones, Tim 96
Jones, Verity A. 323
Jones, Verlene 260
Jones, Walter D. 93
Jones, Wilbur L. 101
Jones, Wilson 287
Jordan, Anthony L. 159
Jordan, Charese L. 37
Jordan, Joe 310
Jordan, L.G. 139
Jordan, Larry W. 301
Joseph (Chorbishop) 161
Joseph (Hierodeacon) . . .144
Joseph, Emmanuel 70
Joseph, John 136
Joseph, Ralph E. 153
Joshua, Kazi 48
Joudrey, Patricia 288
Joudrey, Philip 316
Jourdain, Cheryl 207
Jovan (Bishop) 156
Joy, Norman C. 200
Judd, Peter A. 103
Judge, Beverly 33, 43
Julien, Tom 119
Juliot, Brent 100, 190, 324
Jump, Rick 261
Jupin, J. Michael 238
Juras, Julia Sibley 39
Just, Donald R. 115
Justman, James A. 115
Juuti, Richard C. 73

Kaada, Virginia 250
Kaguni, Samuel 121
Kaiser, John 234
Kaiser, Walter C. 297
Kalcik, Sharon K. 245
Kalmanek, Edward 33
Kalmanek, Judy 33
Kamienski, Mikey 256
Kammerer, Charlene P. . . .170
Kane, Mary 243
Kanouse, Kevin S. 115
Kansfield, Norman J. . . .302
Kantor, Daniel 249
Kapanke, John G. 114
Kapeluck, Michael 164
Kaplan, Clemis Eugene . .161
Karaman, Dennis G. 88
Karim, Cyril Aphrem . . .161
Karli, Robert J. 113
Karrott, Sandra 257
Karssen, Paul 151
Karsten, Albert 91
Kaseman, Mansfield M. 239
Kashdin, Linda 248
Kashmar, Mary 229
Kashuck, Claire 239
Kasimer, Sol 60
Kauffman, Cephas 343
Kautz, William 111
Kays, Joanne 246
Kazanjian, Shant 75
Kearns, Curtis A., Jr. 148
Keating, A.C. 198
Keaton, Jonathan D. 169
Keeler, William Cardinal 34, 46, 83
Keener, Lamar 33
Keeney, Delmas L. 92
Keeney, Mervin B. 92
Keeran, Keith P. 299
Keffer, Anne 289
Keiller, James B. 130
Keith, Judith B. 105
Keith, Raymond J., Jr. 101
Keleher, James P. 83, 84
Keller, Connie L. 353
Keller, Helen 57
Keller, Ron L. 241
Kelley, Jack 130
Kelly, Arthur 322
Kelly, Brian K. 324
Kelly, Bridgette A. 353
Kelly, Charles S. 302
Kelly, Doug 148
Kelly, Francis D. 292, 304
Kelly, John 74
Kelly, Ronald D. 174
Kelly, Sue 259
Kelly, Thomas 246
Kelly, William 85
Kelsey, James A. 108
Kelshaw, Terence 109
Kemper, Ken 125

INDEX

Kemper, Kenneth B. 297
Kemper, Nancy Jo 237
Kendall, Michael 247
Kendall, Stephen 200
Kennaugh, R.S. 198
Kennebrew, Vernon 93
Kennedy, Alric 248
Kennedy, Cindy 243
Kennedy, Joanne 320
Kennedy, Johnny 73
Kennedy, Leland 291
Kennedy-Wong, Phillip 253
Kent, Allen 68
Kent, Edgar 130
Kepa, Peter Mar 127
Kersey, Tay 104
Kersten, David 112
Kersten, G.H. 141
Kesohole, Erastus 121
Kessler, Diane C. 240
Ketcham, Donald 172
Ketli, Vahe 75
Keurian, Alice 126
Kevern, John R. 292
Keyes, Randy 171
Keyser, Judy E. 92
Khamis, Aprim 70
Khasufa, Sylvester 122
Khatchadourian, Ashag . . .230
Khory, George 49
Khouri, Antoun 69, 70
Khoury, Demetri 69
Khrimian, Mgrditch 75
Kibble, Alvin M. 157
Kicanas, Gerald F. 83, 84
Kidd, John S. 231
Kidd, William B. 288
Kidwell, Gary W. 86
Kienitz, Richard 110
Kiernan, Jim 236
Kieschnick, Gerald B. . . .133
Kiesner, Mary Ellen 114
Kiley, Clete 36
Kilgore, Gary 120
Kilgore, James 97
Killam, Gillis 56
Killoren, Eileen 229
Killpack, Jennifer 103
Kim, Hae-Jong 169
Kim, Nam Soo 76
Kimer, Stan 173
Kind, Kerry D. 174
King, Arthur 106
King, Donald G. 157
King, Eileen 50
King, Eric 94
King, Fred G. 90
King, Gordon 314
King, James R., Jr. 170
King, Johnny 207
King, Robert L. 133
King, Samuel 105
King, Stephen 24
Kinkaid, Julie 242
Kinnaman, David 213
Kinney, John W. 295, 309
Kirchhoff, Bernard 42
Kireopoulos, Antonios 42
Kirk, Jennifer 49
Kirkham, Kay 353
Kirkland, Theodore Larry 62
Kirkpatrick, Clifton 148
Kirkpatrick, Susan 121
Kishkovsky, Leonid 47, 50, 332
Kisia, Joseph 121
Kisner, Elaine 241
Kitui, John 121
Kivuya, Thomas 122
Kjera, Timothy 162
Klaus, Byron D. 291
Klein, Ralph W. 323
Klein, Stephen 242
Kleinfelter, Kenneth 172
Klemm, Ulli 253
Kline, Dale 251
Kline, Thomas L. 124
Klinsing, P. David 90
Klusmeyer, W. Michie 109
Klutz, C.H. 70
Knapp, Martin Wells 173
Kneece, Brenda 257
Knight, Keith 57, 200
Knoche, H. Gerard 116
Knoedler, Lon 262
Knoth, Rick 324
Knowles, Louis L. 50
Knudsen, Chilton R. 108
Knudsen, Herbert L. 87
Knudsen, Raymond Barnett, II 336
Knutson, Mark 253
Kobel, Jon 92
Kober, Theodore A. 133
Kochis, Michael 163
Kocian, Dorothy 172
Kocses, Richard 246
Koehn, Cat 260
Koehn, Dale 95, 188
Koehn, Gladwin 330
Koelpin, Daniel 175
Koepke, Donald R. 43
Koh, Linda 156
Kohlbruegge, H. 151
Kokesch, William 57, 202
Koko, Patricia C. 234
Kolb, Leonard R. 140
Kolbaba, Ginger 329
Kolsti, Carol 31
Kondratick, Robert S. . . .143
Kong, Joseph S. 90, 91
Konkel, August H. 314
Konsolo, Ephraim 121
Kooistra, Paul D. 147
Koopman, Joop 319
Kopp, Herb 124
Koppedrayer, Kay 345
Koptak, Paul E. 323
Korgen, Jeffry 36
Korson, Gerald 332
Koscak, Robert 293
Kostlevy, Bill 350
Kostura, Carol 230
Kovalski, Gerald 157
Kowalski, Kelly 249
Koziol, Edward 248
Krahn, Robert 183
Krashel, Rosemary 344
Kraus, Gene 166
Krause, Henry 197
Krauss, Reinhard 230
Kraybill, J. Nelson 291
Krell, Barbara 233
Krestrick, Robert C. 197
Krey, Philip D.W. 301
Krieger, W.J. 151
Kring, S. 182
Kriska, Chloe Ann 251
Krober, Leslie L. 120
Kroeker, Irvin J. 345
Kroeze, Nicholas V. 304
Krueger, Delton 29
Kruschel, Peter 175
Kruse, Steven T. 113
Krutz, C. Dana 32, 238
Krywolap, George 164
Kucharek, Wilma S. 115
Kuchta, Thomas 133
Kugars, Girts 131
Kuhlman, Dexter 117
Kuhn, Robert T. 133
Kuik, Antoinette van 53
Kun, Zolton 127
Kunda, Theresa E. 138
Kunder, William 207
Kunselman, James 65
Kupelian, Gilda 75
Kurima, Andrew H.S. . . .122
Kurtz, Calvin 256
Kuruvila, Alexander 50
Kutosi, Peter 121
Kutter, Joseph 68
Kuykendall, Russell E. 187
Kuyper, Abraham 22
Kvam, Roger A. 38
Kwan, Joseph 341
Kwok, Jack P. 159
Kyrill (Reverend) 143

L'Heureux, N.J., Jr. 247, 249
La Plante, Gerard 186
Laar, Erwin van 54
Labrosse, G. 288
Lacey, Paul 24
Lachatanere, Diana 349

INDEX

LaCoste, Catherine Louise
. 26
Lacy, Homer, Jr. 237
LaFosse, Mona Tokarek 55
Lahey, Raymond 202
Laitner, Christine 160
Lakey, Othal H. 89
Lallo, Cecelia 333
Lamarre-Vincent, David
. 245
Lamb, Jerry A. 108
Lambert, Jerry 101
Lamm, Norman 296
Lance, Paul 230
Lance, Rick 158
Land, Brian 117
Land, Richard D. 158
Land, Stephen J. 188
Land, Steven J. 95, 294
Landahl, Paul R. 115
Landers, Bedford F. 159
Landmesser, Leora 41
Landon, Dennis L. 86
Lane, Dan G. 238
Lane, Gwendolyn 167
Lane, Hardist 233
Lanes, T.A. 77
Lang, Kristy 98
Lang, Kurt 98
Lang, Wendell 158
Lange, Francine 318
Langfitt, John N. 148
Langille, Fran 129, 240
Langley, Ken 84
Langsfeld, Paul J. 304
Lanpher, Bill W. 308
Lansing, Steven H. 114
Lapacka, J. Thomas 133
Lapierre, Emmanuel 288
Lapierre, François 202
Lapsansky, Emma Jones
. 349
Larade, Sharon 207, 355
Larkin, Michael 129
Larmondin, Leanne 340
Larson, April Ulring 115
Larson, Duane H. 309
Larson, Rebecca S. 113
Larson, Ronald 79
Last, Michael A. 115
Lau, David 100
Lau, Jennifer 344
Laughlin, Robert 250
Laurence, Steven B. 255
Laurus (Archbishop)
. . . . .332, 333
Laurus (Metropolitan) 154
Lav, Iris 232
Lavigne, David P. 185
Law, Sylvia H. 94
Law, William F., Jr. 32
Lawrence, Caleb J. 180
Lawrence, James F. 307
Lawrence, William B. . . .303
Lawson, Jim 37
Lawson, Joyce 252
Lawson, Phil 229
Lawson, R.C. 101
Lawton, Gordon P.
. . . . .157, 306
Layne, Samuel A. 144
Layton, Betty 347
Laza, Kent 172
Le, Mrs. Doc 245
Leag, Riley 244
Leaman, J.S. 339
Leavitt, Robert F. 305
Leddy, Jennifer 202, 203
Ledeboer (Reverend) 141
Ledesma, Juanita 258
Lee, Arthur 260
Lee, C.R. 144
Lee, Darrel D. 73, 327
Lee, David H. 158
Lee, Harold L. 157
Lee, Jinwol 49
Lee, Johng O. 309
Lee, Linda 169
Lee, Luther 173
Lee, Nathan 100
Lee, Peter J. 109
Lee, Randall R. 41, 114
Lee, Robert L. 78
Leech, David 258
Leech, Robert E. 148
Legge, W. James 253
Leggett, Harvey E. 140
Leggett, James D. 45, 130
Lehman, Edwin 197
Lehman, Richard 248
Leibrecht, John J. 29
Leidel, Edwin M., Jr. 108
Leiper, Henry Smith 50
Lekic, Mike 204
Leman, Bruce 336
Lemke, Steven 175
Lemler, James B. 107, 306
Lemming, Patrick 162
Lemon, Robert E. 156
LeMone, Archie, Jr. 150
Leng, Janet 39
Lennick, Robert B. 46
Lenz, Anna Lou 262
Leon, Linda M. de 48
Leonard, Bill J. 26, 309
Leonard, Darnell 254
Leonhardt, Tom 33
Leopold, Phyllis J. 230
Lerner, Leigh 289
Lesher, Thomas 165
Leslie, David A. 253
Leung, Donna 182
Levada, William J. 83
LeVan, Patte 330
Levy, B. Barry 313
Lew, Khristina 52
Lewis, Beth A. 114
Lewis, C.A. 99
Lewis, Donald 341
Lewis, Ed 119
Lewis, Greg E. 133
Lewis, Harry 207
Lewis, Hosea 162
Lewis, Ida 317
Lewis, James W. 217
Lewis, Richard Allen 62
Lewis, Robert L., Jr. 43, 71
Lewis, Vicki L. 64
Lewis, William L. 103
Liebling, Mordechai
. . . . .36, 224
Liechty, Eric 137
Liegl, Sara 243
Light, Gordon 180
Light, Rod 129
Lightbody, C. Stuart 187
Liimatta, Michael 27
Likis, Betty 227
Lilande, Joshuah 122
Lillis, John 292
Lima, David 240
Lincoln, P. John 136
Lind, Christopher J.L. . . .315
Lindgren, A. Bruce 103
Lindhal, Kay 49
Lindhdm, Charles 247
Lindner, Eileen W. 41
Lindsay, Emery 93
Lindsay, Joseph 233
Lindsay, R. Rex 158
Lindsey, W.D. "Doc" 159
Linebaugh, Dale E. 304
Ling, Mary 98
Lingle, Mark 230
Linsey, Nathaniel L. 89
Liolin, Arthur E. 65
Lipscomb, John B. 109
Lisby, Micahel 63
Lisby, Mike 336
Little, Darlene 257
Little, Edward S., III 108
Little, Jeannine 236
Little, Michael D. 44
Little, Vanuel C. 144
Litwin, Paul 249
Liu, Felix 300
Livingston, John 150, 201
Livingston, Michael E.
. . . . . . .41, 129, 320, 322
Llamoso-Songco, Annie . . .322
Llewellyn, Karen MacKay
. 54
Lloyd, Roy 23
Lobenstine, Clark 232
Locklear, Helen 148
Lockwood, Daniel R. 302
Loewen, Heinrich 354
Loewen, Paul 184
Lofquist, Les 128, 338

Lofton-Brook, Oliver 204
Logan, Samuel T. 310
Logsdon, Gary B. 253
Lohrmann, Marcus C. . . .115
Lollike, Inge Lise 50
Lomax, Mark A. 233
Long, Denise 251
Long, Sotello V. 87
Looney, Bill 80
Looper, Kirk 157
Lopez, Hector 166
Lopoukhine, Nikita 198
Lopushinsky, Roman 199
Lorch, Rhonda 354
Lord, Frank 231
Lorei, Margaret 254
Lorimer, Paul D. 187
Lotz, Linda 36
Loughran, James 35, 323
Louttit, Henry, Jr. 108
Love, Mary A. 63, 322
Love, Ralph E., Sr. 168
Love-Jones, Vivian 31
Lovett, Sidney 45
Lovingood, Vivian 257
Lowe, Asa 129
Lowe, Samuel L. 94
Lowen, A. Wayne 296
Lowery, Joseph Echols 37
Lowery, T.L. 95, 188
Loy, David 236
Lucas, C.B. 149
Lucas, J.P. 95
Lucco, Richard 112
Luce, Bill J., Jr. 295
Luckett, Catherine 129
Ludwig, John P., Jr. 165
Ludwig, Koloman K. . . .167
Ludwig, Robert A. 300
Luebbert, Karen 244
Luedtke, Joel 243
Luginbill, Betty 31
Luginbuhl, David 56, 204
Luke (Father) 332
Luke, L.M. 139
Lumpkin, Ramona 313
Lumsden, Jorge 117
Lundgren, Dean A. 111
Lundin, Jack 49
Lundy, Sarah E. 96
Lunich, Nedeljko 156, 333
Lutes, Christopher 319
Luther, Martin 155
Luthy, David 198, 342
Lutterell, Gwen 204
Luttrell, Bill 204
Lutz, Bill 247
Lutz, James E. 67
Lutzer, Harold 345
Luz, David W. 155
Lyght, Ernest Shaw 169
Lykins, Terry 130
Lyle, Charles 182
Lynch, Damon, III 251
Lyons, Arthur 48
Lyons, Deborah 145
Lysyj, Anatol 164

MacAdam, Murray 341
MacArthur, John 128
MacDermid, Gordon E. 316
MacDonald, Margaret E. 244
MacDonald, Mark . . .107, 227
Machen, J. Gresham 144
Mack, Alexander 82, 91
Mack, Karen 253
Mack, Paget 72
MacKenzie, Daryl 191
MacKenzie, Margaret 60
Mackey, Bill F. 158
Mackin, Eileen 33
Mackintosh, C.H. 85
Macklin, Jerry 94
MacLagan, Lynn 239
MacMillan, Patricia Dwyer 254
Macnie, Peggy 257
MacPherson, D. Bruce 109
MacPherson, Damian 288
MacQueen, Kenneth G. . . .316
Maddo, Robert 232
Madison, Carol 324
Madison, S.C. 168
Magarrell, Gary 207
Maggs, Robert W., Jr. . . .148
Magie, Sandra 309
Magnus, Brian 206
Magnus, Paul 56
Magnus, Richard A., Jr. . . .113
Magrill, Richard 105
Mahe, Sally 49
Maher, Philip 59
Maheras, John 240
Mahlman, Margaret 173
Mahnke, Jon 175
Mahon, Chris 145
Mahsman, David 133, 329, 334
Maida, Adam Cardinal 83
Maier, Paul L. 133
Maier, Zita 344
Main, A. Donald 116, 256
Mains, Bill 183
Makarenko, William 205
Maki, Lynn I. 207
Malayang, José A. 166
Malcolm, Barbara 230
Maldonado, Luis Fernando Hoyos 186
Malenge, Zablon Isaac 122
Maleske, A. 197
Malherbe, Jean-François 316
Malinovic, Mirko 204
Malliet, Jim 35
Mallinak, John 333
Malloy, David 83
Maloney, Francis J. 293
Maly, Jean 172
Maly, Milton 172, 319
Mammedaty, Kim 166
Manahan, Ron 119
Manahan, Ronald E. 119
Manahan, Ronald E. 297
Manes, John 98
Mangassarian, Silva 181
Manhard, Mike 242
Manis, H. Lee 24
Mann, David 137
Mann, Eric 82
Mann, Gayle 235
Mann, Stuart 340
Manning, Deborah 243
Manning, Robert 310
Manning, Tricia 328
Manning, Vicki 41
Mannoia, Kevin W. 34
Manon, John C. 117
Manousos, Anthony 325
Manseau, William 33
Mansholt, Gerald L. 114
Mansur, Mary 332
Mantha, Ray 60
Manthei, Jim 31
Manz, John R. 83
Mapson, Charlrean B. 64
Marani, Samson 122
Marceil, Christopher 263
Marcum, John P. 27
Mardirossian, Moushegh . . .75
Marenko, William 346
Mariner, John E. 77
Marini, Christine 88
Mark (Archbishop) 199
Mark (Reverend) 143
Marks, Kirk 111
Markus, Carol O. 52
Marquardt, Kami L. 252
Marrin, Patrick 320
Marsh, Fred 330
Marsh, Jack 251
Marsh, Priscilla 247
Marshall, Carolyn M. . . .169
Marshall, Jay Wade 295
Marshall, Paul 56, 107
Martens, Ed 194
Martin, Beth Ann 69
Martin, Clyde 172
Martin, Gord 186
Martin, J. Bruce 153
Martin, J. Dwayne 259
Martin, John A. 303
Martin, John T. 190
Martin, Joseph 257
Martin, Kenneth 263
Martin, Paul E. 69
Martinez, Joel N. 170

INDEX

Martinez, Julie 133
Martinez, Margarita 116
Martino, Joseph 256
Martin-Schramm, James B. 113
Martinson, Bradley 100
Martinson, Ronald D. . . .114
Marty, Martin 323
Marvel, Misha 247
Marx, Robert 36
Maslo, William 256
Mason, Charles Harrison . . .94
Mason, Debra 47
Mason, Donald E. 233
Mason, H. Lee 335
Mason, Larry D. 67
Mason, Linda J. 94
Massey, Anthony 254
Massey, Frank 120, 121
Massey, Stephen K. 69
Mast, Gregg 151, 201
Masterson, Rod 314
Matagi-Vilitama, Joanna S. 50
Mathew, Thomson K. . . .304
Mathews, Michael 122
Mathies, Ronald J.R. 39
Matiz, Jose Ruben Garcia 186
Matlack, Lucius C. 173
Matson, Louise 242
Matsuura, Junko 50
Mattackal, Abraham 329
Matthew, Lamar 120, 121
Matthews, Cecil 117
Matthews, Daniel Paul 33, 43
Matthews, F. Clayton . . .107
Matthews, Larry 340
Matthews, Mary J. 64
Matthews, Victoria 34, 180
Mattoni, Vincent 249
Mattson, Linda 321
Matusiak, John 143, 332
Mauney, James F. 116
Mauney, Patrick 107
Mawhinney, John A. 25
Maximos (Metropolitan) 126
Maxson, Benjamin C. . . .157
Maxwell, Anita 258
Maxwell, Arthur 53
Maxwell, Laurie 229
Maxwell, Neal A. 99
May, David G. 241
May, Felton Edwin 170
May, Lisa 26
May, Nareth 90
May, Thomas R. 40
Mayan, Ralph 57, 197
Mayberry, Larry 96
Mayer, Kevin 236
Mayernick, Carol L. 235
Mays, Barbara 121
Mays, Rod 147
Maze, Larry E. 107
Mazur, Francis X. 249
Mbachi, Charles 121
Mbato, Hannington 122
McAdam, Kerry 120
McAdams, Zena S. 86
McAdow, Samuel 105
McAlister, John 342
McAlister, Lorne D. 199
McAllister-Wilson, David F. 310
McAnally, Ben 148
McAuliffe, Jane Dammen 211
McBride, Bailey 320
McBride, Larry 238
McCaffrey, Renée Roeder 248
McCain, Jacquelyn B. 167, 168
McCain, Paul 133
McCallister, Cline 130
McCann, Gordon 339
McCann, Jeff 48
McCardle, Jody 243
McCarrell, Billy 128
McCarrick, Theodore Cardinal 84
McClain, Agnes S. 113
McClain, Gene 68
McClesky, J. Lawrence . . .170
McCloskey, Pat 335
McCloud, E. Earle 62
McClure, George 121
McClure, Marian 148
McCoid, Donald J. 34, 115
McColgin, Linda 246
McCollum, Odell 167
McCombs, Jerry L. 64
McConnell, Alvester 168
McConnell, Bill 167
McCool, Marilyn 101
McCormack, Alan 202
McCown, Sue 258
McCoy, Clint 249
McCoy, Glenda 260
McCoy, James E. 62, 63
McCoy, Myron F. 305
McCreary, Leroy 129
McCrossen, James W. . . .293
McCullough, John L. 42
McCurdy, Claire 349
McCutchen, Retha 121
McCutcheon, Rick 185
McCutheon, Rick 120
McDaniel, Paula 241
McDermott, Pat 238
McDonald, Jeff 338
McDonald, Lee M. 311
McDonnell, Carol 235
McDonnough, Sheila 289
McDonough, Linda 124
McDowell, Leon A. 145
McEntee, Peggy 238
McFadden, Wendy 92
McFarland, James K. . . .153
McFerran, L.M. (Mac) . . .186
McGee, J. Vernon 128
McGibbon, Carol Ann 48
McGinnis, Robert S., Jr. .132
McGlynn, Sheilagh 59
McGough, Nancy 340
McGovern, Mike 129
McGrattan, William T. 315
McGraw, Tom 236
McGray, Asa 195
McGuire, Damaris 249
McHugh, Matthew 28
McIntire, Carl 144
McIntosh, Kenneth W. 259
McJunkin, James E., Jr. . . .67
McKain, George E., II 64
McKay, Ginger 172
McKee, Joan 234
McKelvey, Jack M. 109
McKenzie, Gilbert E. . . .247
McKenzie, Vashti Murphy 32, 62
McKernan, Leo 257
McKinney, Brent 121, 122
McKinney, George D. 45
McKinney, William 303
McKinnon, Patricia 344
McKnight, James E., Jr. 96
McKnight, John 24
McLarty, Alan 167
McLaughlin, Gretchen 120
McLaughlin, John L. 55
McLaughlin, Scott E. 109, 295
McLean, Sallie 37
McLellan, Daniel 309
McMahill, David 166
McMillan, John 316
McMillan, Susan 204
McMillen, Bill 124
McMorrow, Kevin 35
McMullen, Shawn 329
McMurray, Robert 144
McMurray, W. Grant 103, 190
McNair, David C. 38
McNally, Beverly 246
McNamara, Dexter 229
McNamara, Mary 28
McNeil, J.E. 29
McNish, Mary Ellen 24
McPherson, Aimee Semple 128
McQueen, Arpie 318
McSwain, Laurin M. 32
McVay, John K. 306
McWain, Bonnie 231
Meade, Kenneth 88

Meador, Prentice A., Jr. . . .317
Meagher, Timothy 352
Mean, John D. 207
Mecham, Marilyn P. 245
Medders, David S. 311
Medinger, Daniel L. 320
Medley, A. Roy 67
Meek, Gary 27
Meier, Gordon F. 90
Mekhsian, Sipan 331
Melanchthon, Phillip 155
Melbourne, Bertram 298
Melchizedek (Mar) 186
Melczek, Dale J. 83
Mellis, John 314
Melton, J. Gordon 216
Mendenhall, Laura S. . . .294
Mendez, John N. 39
Mendoza, Salvador 46
Menes, Nadia 50
Mengel, Gail 31
Menitoff, Paul J. 33, 43
Menlove, Coleen K. 99
Menning, Bruce 151
Meno, John 161
Mentzer, Steve 255
Mercer, Amy 238
Mercer, David R. 52
Mercurius (Bishop) 144
Merillat, Pam 137
Merrell, A. William 158
Merrell, Bill 335
Merrill, John 68
Merrill, Nancy 28, 212
Merritt, Hortense 249
Meschisen, Eugene 163
Mesiti, Martha 46
Mesner, Neil 121
Messer, Tom 308
Messersmith, Jaclyn 255
Messiah, Wilfred Jacobus 62
Messias, Pedro 130
Messina, Carol 138
Methodios (Metropolitan) 126
Metzger, William 255
Metzler, Martha 248
Meyer, Don 309
Meyer, Mary C. 332
Meyer, Ron 117
Meyer, William 133
Meyerhoffer, Anne Marie 232
Mgonja, Assah E. 50
Micahelius, Domine Jonas 201
Micevych, Paul 163
Mich, Marvin 248
Michalius, Domine Jonas 150
Micon, Joseph 235
Middeke, Paul W. 133
Middendorf, Jesse C. 101
Middleton, Edward Russell 153
Miericke, Kurt A. 112
Mikovsky, Anthony 146, 326
Miley, James E. 116
Millay, James I. 320
Millen, George 110
Miller, A. Kathleen 288
Miller, Alan C. 167
Miller, Carol 232
Miller, Charles S. 113
Miller, Claude E.W. 180
Miller, David 63, 64, 329
Miller, Gene 166, 258
Miller, Geraldine 94
Miller, John Henry, Sr. . . .63
Miller, John U. 247
Miller, Keith 111
Miller, Lauren E. 312
Miller, Lawrence Michael 165
Miller, Len 204
Miller, Marcus J. 115
Miller, Mark H. 167
Miller, Mary C. 111, 112
Miller, Mary 29
Miller, Myron P. 306
Miller, Patrick D. 336
Miller, Paul L. 80, 319
Miller, Peter 248
Miller, Rick 104
Miller, Robert J. 123
Miller, Roman J. 333
Miller, Steven A. 108
Miller, Ted 233
Miller, Vernon 80
Milliken, Paul 258
Milliken, Richard D. 302
Mills, Charles 337
Mills, Wes 181
Miloro, Frank P. 68
Minden, Pamela 121
Ming, Donald 51
Minnix, Janet 119
Minor, Ronald R. 145
Minura, Kyle 229
Miranda, Jesse 76
Mirchuk, Nadia 164
Mirek, Art 69
Miscamble, Wilson 302
Missick, Glen 151
Mitchell, Bennie 36
Mitchell, Christine 55
Mitchell, James K. 93
Mitchell, Lisa H. 241
Mitchell, Lois P. 191
Mitchem, Susan 352
Mitrophan (Bishop) 156
Mittman, F. Russell 167
Mobley, John P. 86
Mock, George 240
Moerman, Murray 287
Moes, D. 342
Moffett, Marilyn 235
Mogabgab, John S. 338
Mogenson, Cris 246
Mohammed, Imam W. Deen 222
Mohler, R. Albert, Jr. 307
Mojica, Miguel 97, 189
Moldstad, John A. 116
Molyneux, John 337
Moncher, Gary 95
Moncure, Rhymes H., Jr. 170
Monroe, Bill 78
Monroe, Kenneth 63
Monson, Thomas S. 99
Montalvo, Gabriel 82
Montanez, Jose D. 95, 188
Monteith, Fred 207
Montgomery, Carl Halloway, II 172
Montgomery, Kathleen C. 164
Montgomery, Richard 229, 343
Montgomery, Robert 227
Montmorency-Laval, François de 202
Mood, Jacques 141
Moody, Carlis L. 94
Moody, Dwight L. 16
Moody, Robert M. 108
Moon, Angelia 258
Moon, Hyung J. 90
Mooney, Bernice 27
Moore, Charles W. 303
Moore, Clark 260
Moore, Donna J. 252
Moore, Douglas 199
Moore, Hugh 234
Moore, Kenneth W. . . .87, 245
Moore, Larry J. 174
Moore, Marvin 336
Moore, P.J. 104
Moore, Robert A. 96
Moore, Thomas E. 69
Moore, Willis 232
Moorhead, James H. 328
Moorjani-Vaswani, Shakuntala 49
Morales, Lillian 255
Morand, Blaise 202
Mordecai, Patricia C. . . .107
Moreau, Dorylas 202
Moretz, Lawrence 155
Morgan, Brent R. 129
Morgan, Dennis 24
Morgan, Donn F. 294
Morgan, Gerald 241
Morgan, Kenneth R. 354
Morgan, Ronald 79
Morgester, Mike 253

INDEX

Morissette, Pierre 202
Morlino, Robert C. 83
Morris, Adrienne A. 339
Morris, Calvin S. 233
Morris, Fred 232
Morris, John 299
Morris, Martha J. 262
Morris, Tracy 345
Morris, William W. 170
Morrison, Susan M. 169
Morrison, Susan M. 249
Morrison, William C., Jr. . . .86
Morrissey, James 145
Morrow, William D. 199
Morrow, William 55
Morse, Daniel R. 152
Mortelliti, David 196
Morton, Cindy 236
Morton, Raymond E. 153
Morushca, Polycarp 203
Mosaad, Mohamed 49
Moses, Tom 97
Mosier, Charles R. 145
Mosley, Steve 258
Mostert, Thomas J., Jr. 157
Mott, John R. 16, 20
Moulton, Geoff 342
Moulton, Lorinda R. 200
Moury, Fred 111
Mouw, Richard J. . . .34, 297
Mowatt, Ann 60
Moxham, John 258
Moyer, Bruce 110, 309
Moyer, David 167
Mstyslav (Metropolitan) 163
Mueller, Craig 38
Mueller, George 85
Mueller, Wayne D. 175
Muganda, Baraka G. 157
Muhlenberg, Henry Melchior 113
Mukulu, Andrew 121
Mukwanja, H.M. 121
Mulama, David A. 122
Mulama, Joseph Anyonge 122
Mulder, Gary 91
Mullan, Donald W. 186, 345
Mullen, David G. 114
Muller, Marilyn 345
Mulongo, Andrew Namasaka 122
Mulvaney, Elizabeth 257
Mummert, S. Christine 113
Munday, Robert S. 302
Munk, D. 312
Munro, Victor 288
Muravski, A. 199
Murdoch, John 41
Murdy, Peter 104
Murphy, D.J. 288
Murphy, Sue 233
Murphy, Thomas 330, 334
Murphy, Tom 137
Murphy, Warren 263
Murray, Billy D., Sr. 97, 189
Murray, Edward J. 33, 43
Murray, George W. 294
Murray, Hal 263
Murray, Harold 58
Murray, James W. 293
Murray, James 124
Murray, Michele 55
Murray, Yolanda 248
Murry, George V. 84
Musindi, Meschack 122
Musungu, Philip 121
Mutti, Albert Frederick 170
Muyskens, Samuel 39, 236
Muzingo, Cathy 145
Mwanzi, Solomon 122
Myers, Gary 119
Myers, James 114
Myers, Jerry 69
Myers, Richard N. 248
Myers-Wirt, Cathy 87
Mylonas, Efstathios 230
Mysorekar, Uma 221

N'goma, Joyce 49
Nadasdy, Dean L. 133
Nadauld, Margaret 99
Nafzger, Samuel 133
Nahoolewa, Connie 259
Naik, Deepak 49
Nakasone, Ronald 229
Nakonachny, John . . .163, 164
Namwembe, Despina 49
Nance, Cynthia 36
Nanfelt, Peter N. 90
Nash, Stephan 328
Naten, Loyd L. 145
Nathaniel (Reverend) . . .143
Navarre, Joy Sorensen . . .243
Naylor, Susan 190
Neal, Annie Wynn 166
Neal, Joseph C., Jr. 89
Neal, Ricardo 239
Neale, Archie 122
Nectaria, Nun 335
Nederveen, G. 184
Needham, Philip 155
Neel, Paul Gregory 148
Neelands, David 315
Neely, Constance D. 241
Neely, Cynthia 93
Nees, Tom 101
Neevel, Mary Ann 262
Neff, David 33
Neils, Michael 114, 228
Nelson, Arnold C., Jr. 86
Nelson, Beter T. 73
Nelson, Christine L. 255
Nelson, Dean W. 114
Nelson, Elden K. 78
Nelson, Gart 184
Nelson, J. Herbert 36
Nelson, Jodi 243
Nelson, Judy 192
Nelson, Paul D. 32
Nelson, Russell M. 99
Nelson, Steven L. 262
Nelson, Vernon H. 351
Nemitz, Dian 252
Nemkovich, Robert M. 146, 306
Nenson, Alice 326
Nenson, David 203
Nesbitt, Phyllis M. 53
Nesdahl, Gary 258
Nesmith, Virginia 42
Netterfield, Cal 182
Nettleton, Minot B. 231
Neu, Frederick 260
Neufeld, Dietmar 55
Neufeld, John 55
Neufeld, Waldy 53
Neuhaus, Richard J. 325
Newhall, Jeffrey 129
Newhouse, Herbert 149
Newport, Leroy 81
Newton, Alan 67
Newton, Douglas M. 328
Newton, Rita K. 253
Ngoya, John 121
Nguyen, Tai Anh 90
Nicholas (Metropolitan) 126
Nicholas, David 306
Nichols, John D. 95, 188
Nichols, Terrence L. 90
Nicholson, Betty 123
Nickerson, Anne 240
Nicodemus, Eugene J. 38
Nielsen, Nancy 49
Nielson, E. Kenneth 35
Nielson, Niel 147
Nienstedt, John C. 83
Nieto, Amelia 230
Nieuwsma, Virginia 326
Nighswander, Dan 197
Nikolai (Reverend) 143
Nikon (Reverend) 143
Niles, Dennis D. 308
Nilsson, Harold T. 246
Nippak, Ivar 192
Niswender, Joy 247
Njegovan, James D. 179
Njoroge, James 242
Noffsinger, Stanley J. 92
Nolan, Charles 26
Noland, Martin 133, 350
Nolde, Nancy L. 255
Noli, Fan Stylian 65
Noli, Theophan 74

Nolla, Ormara 50
Noonan, Suzanne R. 248
Nordhem, Paula 242
Nordtvedt, Joel T. 300
Norlin, Dennis A. 25
Norman (Bishop) 161
Norman, Clarence 106
Norris, Alfred L. 170
Norris, Dennis E. 67
Norris, Jeffrey A. 90
Norris, Judy 238
Norris, Larry R. 103
Norris, Richard Franklin . . .62
Northam, Gerald M. 204
Nortness, Michal 260
Norton, Jon 247, 249
Norton, Larry 259
Norton, Timothy A. . . .38, 336
Norwood, Mathew A. . . .101
Novak, Mark A. 112
Novecosky, Peter . . .203, 344
Nunn, Harry, Sr. 77
Nusca, A. Robert 315
Nyenzo, Evans 121

O'Brien, Brendan M. . . .202
O'Brien, Edwin F. 83
O'Connor, Elizabeth 329
O'Donnell, Frances 352
O'Dowd, Dolores 248
O'Farrell, Mark T. 90
O'Flaherty, Edward 240
O'Gorman, Eileen 323
O'Hair, J.C. 125
O'Hara, Karen 248
O'Hara, Robert J., Jr. . . .256
O'Keefe, Mark 305
O'Neal, Grace 129
O'Neal, Padraic 320
O'Neill, Jerry F. 304
O'Neill, Patrick H. 296
O'Neill, Robert J. 107
Oakes, Gwyn 171
Oaks, Dallin H. 99
Oancea, David
. . . . .154, 203, 336
Oates, Lonnie F. 87
Oates, Stephen E. 145
Obengerger, Glenn 116
Obrecht, Patricia 250
Ochoa-Krueger, Ninfa . . .258
Oden, William B. 170
Odhner, Carroll C. 352
Odom, Elzie 259
Odoms, John 239
Ofiesh, Aftimios 74, 127
Ogle, Jonathan 29
Ogles, Jerry L. 318
Ogui, Koshin 220
Oguma, Joseph Lavuna . .122
Ohl, C. Wallis, Jr. 108
Ojeda-Carcamo, Sergio . . .296
Olekshy, Ovest 198
Olfert, Lester 194
Olinger, Danny E. 331
Oliva, José L. 37
Oliver, Willie B. 153
Olsen, Donald P. 138
Olsen, Ron 207
Olson, Stanley N. 113
Olubalang, Alan A. 69
Omland, Richard R. 114
Onyewuchi, Rufus 287
Oosting, Ken 310
Ophoff, George 150
Orewiler, Teri 129
Orser, George 195
Ortiz, Jose 39
Osborn, Kenneth W. 157
Osborne, Brenda 68
Osborne, Fred C. 313
Osborne, Linda 262
Osodo, Lam Kisanya 121
Oswald, Duane 137
Ottenhoff, Don B. 215
Otterbein, Philip William
. . . . .101, 169, 206
Otterson, Michael 98
Otzelberger, E. Ann 141
Oubre, Sinclair 36
Ough, Bruce R. 169
Owen, Dean 51
Owen, John 66
Owen, Moses 138
Owen, Timothy P. 90
Owens, Chandler D. 94
Owens, Thomas M., Sr. . . .336
Oyando, Gilbert Akenga
. 121
Oyster, Lisa A. 251

Pace, Diane 326
Packard, George 107
Packer, Boyd K. 99
Padilla, Rafael Malpica . . .113
Paez, Leticia 52
Pagán, Samuel 306
Pagano, Nicholas 24
Page, Allen 239
Page, Bill D. 241
Palmberg, Glenn R. 111
Palmer, Floyd 253
Palmer, Gregory V. 169
Palmer, Paul 138
Palmer, Robert M. 71
Palmieri, Paul 98
Palmquist, Gustaf 79
Palumbo, Billie L. 145
Panasuk, Katherine 242
Pantupong, Woranut 50
Papagermanos, Stavros H.
. 332
Papazian, Iris 332
Paperini, Richard 302
Pappajohn, John 126
Paquette, Mario 202
Parchia, Earl 144
Parish, Donny 80
Park, Michael 157
Parker, George Lee 87
Parker, Gerald 234
Parker, Gwyn 255
Parker, Jane 237
Parker, Rebecca 307
Parker, Ronald L. 86
Parker, Tom 238
Parker, William 153, 328
Parkin, Bonnie D. 99
Parkins, Richard 107
Parks, J.H. 97
Parks, Jerry 326
Parr, Jeb 261
Parrish, Carol 129
Parrish, Walter L., II 67
Parrott, Rod 230
Parry, Walter P. 228
Parsley, Henry N., Jr. . . .107
Parsons, Gradye 148
Parsons, Reginald 148
Pastukhiv, Serhij K. 127
Patten, Bebe 188
Patterson, L. Dale 351
Patterson, Paige 307
Pattillo, Wesley M. "Pat"
. 42
Patton, Marcia 67
Patton, Vince 336
Patzer, Jere D. 157
Paulsen, Jan 156
Paulsen, Vivian 325
Paulson, Bob 323
Paup, Edward W. 171
Payiavlas, John 126
Payne, Aleta 251
Payne, James T. 152
Payne, Margaret G. 115
Peacock, Jean Marie 148
Peale, Norman Vincent 28
Pearce, Paul 183
Pearson, Jean 243
Pearson, John 30
Peddle, Alvin F. 200
Peifer, Elvin H. 82
Pelavin, Mark 37
Pell, Archie 55
Pellechia, James N.
. . . . .131, 196
Pelles, Rosalyn 37
Pelotte, Donald E. 83
Pember, Arlyn 76
Pena, Carlos F. 113
Pence, Jerry 174
Pendergast, Arthur J. 288
Pendleton, J.M. 66
Penfield, Jack 231
Pennel, Joe E., Jr. 170
Penner, A.F. (Bud) 182
Penner, Brigitte 344
Penner, David 194

INDEX

Penner, Lois 344
Penner, Rick 56
Penner, Ron 53
Pennings, Kenneth 262
Pennywell, Clarence C. . . .139
Peper, Mike 78
Peplowski, Thaddeus S. 146
Pepper, Donald R. 38
Perkins, Davis 148
Perkins, Larry 314
Perkins, William T. 302
Perkins-Hughes, Vera . . .167
Perrin, Clive 231
Perry, L. Tom 99
Perry, Roger 231
Perry, Troy 172, 173, 208
Perschbacher, Gerald 329
Persell, William D. 107
Persson, Bertil 72
Perucca, Kirk P. 46
Perzynska, Kinga 26
Peter (Reverend) 143
Peter, Ignatius, III 161
Peterkin, Valerie 231
Peters, Art 254
Peters, Donald 39, 58
Peters, Isaac 117
Peters, Judith 252
Peters, Marshall 67
Peters, Ted 303
Peterson, Brian 33
Peterson, David 41
Peterson, Jay 244
Peterson, Jeanie 260
Peterson, Kathleen 247
Peterson, Roland 112
Peterson, Timothy . . .195, 345
Peterson, Wendy 56
Petersoo, Udo 192, 342
Petitt, Charles W. 304
Petkau, Dave 313
Petrie, Lou 79
Petro, John G. 292
Petrochuk, Sherrie 251
Petroff, Valerie 53
Pettit, Kim A. 327
Pfortmiller, Sandra 331
Phelan, John E. 303
Phelan, John E., Jr. 112
Phillips, A. Blair 257
Phillips, Annie Lee 249
Phillips, Aubrey 192
Phillips, Carole 184
Phillips, David J. 90
Phillips, Donald D. 180
Phillips, Stephen 103
Phillips, Sue Watlov 243
Philpott, P.W. 182
Phipps, Ron 137
Pickle, Claudette 105
Pierce, David 312
Pierce, Garland 42
Pierce, R.W. 199
Piescik, Joseph 231
Pieterse, Hendrik R. 334
Pile, Gregory R. 115
Pinach, Dennis 198
Pinkston, Ron 129
Pinson, J. Matthew 297
Pinson, Mathew 138
Piper, O.E. 140
Pishko, Daria 164
Pitner, Kim 129
Pitt, Benjamin A. 144
Pittman, Wallace B., Jr. . . .145
Pitts, Clifford R. 167
Pitts, Tyrone S. 149
Plantinga, Cornelius, Jr. 293
Platt, Allyson D. 240
Plett, Harvey 194
Pleus, Adrian C.H. 233
Plummer, Glenn R. 44
Plummer, Steven T. 108
Poage, Bennett D. 25
Poandl, Robert 34
Poe, James 26
Poesnecker, Gerald E. 98
Pohl, Faye 44
Poirier, Jim 190
Poirier, Tim 347
Poist, William 65
Poitier, Annette 50
Polasek, Joseph 172
Polding, M. Fred 90
Polite, William 153
Pollema, Vernon 151
Pollington, Cody 68
Polston, Jimmy 156
Pomeroy, Betty 246
Pomykal, Janet 172
Ponnaiya, Joyce 50
Poole, Frank 148
Pooler, David 237
Poon, Abraham H. 90
Pope, Dan 313
Pope, Janet 261
Pope, Kenneth 69
Popoff, Dmitri E. (Jim) . . .343
Popovich, Edward 122
Popp, Nathaniel 154, 203
Porch, James M. 159
Porret, Jean 345
Porter, Jerry D. 101
Porter, John 122
Porter, Nan 257
Porter, Stanley E. 313
Porter, Waring 117
Porterfield, Amanda 321
Posey, Michael 129
Posterski, Don 59
Potter, Jim 191
Potterveld, Riess W. 300
Powell, Barbara A. 166
Powell, Christopher . . .80, 81
Powell, F. Neff 109
Powell, George H. 191
Powell, Jerry 145
Powell, Joel 145
Powell, John 249
Powell, Joseph 153
Powell, Larry 139
Powell, Paul W. 308
Powell, Raymond, Sr. 99
Powers, Diane 40
Powers, Reggie O. 145
Prachar, T. 197
Premawardhana, Shanta 42
Prendergast, Terrence . . .202
Presher, David F. 90
Presler, Titus L. 296
Prestol, Juan R. 157
Preus, Christan A. 133
Price, Donald R. 66
Price, Kenneth 109
Price, P. 106
Price, R. 168
Priest, Catherine 289
Primavera, Wendy 246
Prince, T.J. 140
Priniski, Mary 37
Prior, Joseph G. 305
Pritchett, Wayne 204, 315
Probus, Lawrence 51
Prosser, Robert 105
Provance, Terry 45
Prudente, Karen 50
Pruter, Karl 84
Pryor, Christine 332
Puckett, John L. 88
Pue, Carson 56
Puglisi, Amy 256
Pugsley, John W. 40
Pulins, Juris 131
Puryear, Richard 254
Pusateri, John 254
Putnam, Bob 319
Pyles, Franklin 187
Pyles, Maurine 120

Quackenbush, David 196
Quay, Ronald 233
Quessy, Herve L. 142
Quevedo, Jose Moises Moncada 186
Quiett, Harry V. 173
Quinlan, Bill 186
Quinn, Michaelita 33
Quinn, Thomas 33
Quirog, Bonifacio 49

Rabenold, Nelson 255
Raber, Martha E. Rovira . . .327
Rabs, Carol 240
Raccah, William 312
Racine, Jacques 316
Rader, Sharon Zimmerman 169

INDEX

Radius, Lesley M. 233
Ragsdale, John 111
Raines, James Ray 79
Rajan, Frederick E.N. . . .113
Ralph, Karen 287
Ralston, Darwin 251
Ramirez, Laura 230
Ramphal, Dwarka 145
Ramphal, Dwarka 298
Ramsden, Pamela 107
Ramseth, Mark R. 308
Randal, Ed 117
Randall, Benjamin 195
Randall, Mike 318
Randels, J. Richard 238
Randolph, Bruce J. 253
Rankin, Jerry A. 158
Rankin, Nancy 228
Ransom, Robert 137
Rasell, Edith 36
Rasmussen, Donald R. 67
Rassmussen, Philip 343
Rathbun, Peter 23
Ravenell, Joseph P. 246
Ray, Keith H. 300
Raymond, Jonathan S. . . .315
Read, Glenn 250
Read, James 56
Read, O.J. 88
Realpe, Marcelo 90
Reaney, Dwayne 196
Rebeck, Victoria A. 26
Reccord, Robert E. 158
Redal, R.H. 104, 296
Redd, Eugene 144
Reddick, Lawrence L., III 89
Reddig, Jill S. 322
Reddin, George 79
Redding, Phil L. 145
Redding, Sharon K. 145
Redekopp, Alf 343, 354
Redfield, William C. 248
Redhead, Bob 204
Reece, Scott 129
Reed, J. George 251
Reed, Jeremiah 144
Reed, Michael B. 72
Reed, Millard 308
Reed, Rodger Hall, Sr. 232
Reeder, Allen R. 334
Rees, Seth C. 173
Reese, Jack R. 290
Reese, Ron 102
Reese, Rosemary 256
Reeves, Justus Y. 319
Reeves, Steve 66
Regan, Tom 287
Regehr, Ernie 58
Regier, Rob 56
Register, Wayne 31
Regnier, Julie 51
Rehling, Tom 166
Reichter, Arlo R. 67
Reid, Gail 342
Reid-MacNevin, Susan 57
Reierson, Gary B. 242, 244
Reilly, Thomas J. 203
Reimer, Gerald 194
Reimer, Klaas 193
Reimer, Milton 104
Reimer, Willie 184
Reinert, Peter 232
Reinheimer, Larry 198
Reiser, Linda 133
Reisz, H. Frederick 301
Reiter, Steven J. 111
Reithmaier, Jan 33
Reithmaier, Paul 33
Remalt, Theodore J. 332
Rempel, Rob 341
Rempel, Ron 137
Rempel, Valerie 125
Rempel-Burkholder, Byron 334
Rendall, Joanne 42
Retzman, Alan 195
Retzr, Gordon L. 157
Revis, Charles 67
Reyes, José, Sr. 189
Reynolds, Ariene 252
Reynolds, H.F. 100, 190
Reynolds, Kristine 243
Reynolds, Paul V. 207
Rhéaume, Serge 54
Rhoades, Kevin C. 302
Rhoads, Armen O. 174
Rhoden, H. Robert 76
Rhodes, Arthur 95, 188
Rhodes, Schuyler 37
Ricard, John H. 84
Ricardo (Bishop-elect) 161
Ricci, Angelo 74
Rice, Clayton 200
Rice, Gene D. 95, 188
Richard, André 202
Richard, Thomas M. 138
Richards, James G. 315
Richards, James W. 159
Richardson, Adam Jefferson, Jr. 62
Richardson, John M. 87
Richardson, Kathleen . . .242
Richardson, Melvin 252
Richardson, Ralph 56, 191
Richardson, Wendell 78
Richert, Jean 231
Riches, Leonard W. 152
Richey, John R. 142
Richey, Mary 263
Richey, Russell E. 293
Richmond, Ben 121
Richmond, Raymond, Jr. . . .64
Ridings, Dean 33
Rieley-Goddard, Catherine 247
Riemenschneider, Dan 137
Ries, Thomas 133
Rigdon, Sidney 98
Rigdon, V. Bruce 296
Riggs, Ann K. 41, 42
Riggs, Don R. 242
Riley, Adele M. 64
Riley, E. Roy 114, 115
Riley, Meg 37
Rimbo, Robert A. 115
Rinden, David 100
Rinehart, Neil 137
Rinnel, Rod 232
Ripp, Peggy 33
Ripp, Phil 33
Risher, Dee Dee 332
Risser, Paul C. 129
Risso, Francisco 37
Ritchie, Tracy 253
Ritts, Kerry R. 149
Rivera, Regina W. 64
Rivers, Francis 25
Rivers, Willie Mae 94
Robben, Jerome 186
Robbins, Earldean V.S. . . .148
Roberson, James T., Jr. 307
Roberson, Joseph 42
Roberts, Edward 144
Roberts, James P., Jr. 131
Roberts, Mark E. 349
Roberts, R. Philip 302
Roberts, Robert H. 67
Roberts, Sharon 24
Roberts, Tom 331
Roberts, Tommy 124
Robertson, Cory 49
Robertson, Creighton L. 109
Robertson, William 335
Robinson, Anita 81
Robinson, Barbara A. 246
Robinson, Dave 320
Robinson, David 123
Robinson, Densimore 140
Robinson, Ellen 287
Robinson, John 96
Robinson, Joyce 238
Robinson, Judith 179
Robinson, Julian B. 95, 188
Robinson, Kenneth N. 103
Robinson, Kenneth O., Sr. 167, 168
Robinson, Mattie A. 339
Robinson, Paul 243
Robinson, Thomas E. . . .148
Robinson, Thomas 259
Robinson, Tommy 81
Robinson, V. Gene 108
Robinson-Rumble, Beverly J. 327
Rochester, Enoch Benjamin 63

INDEX

Rochon, Igumen Irenee . . .198
Rockwell, David 246
Rockwood, Perry F. 342
Roe, R. Richard 228
Roebuck, David G. . . .96, 351
Roegner, Robert 133
Roehl, Ronald 100
Roehl, Shirley 324
Roehrig, Matthew 333
Rogelstad, David 184
Rogers, Huie 82
Rogers, Joy 241
Rogers, Laura M. 250
Rogers, Scott 250
Rogers-Witte, Ann C. . . .166
Rogness, Matthew 100
Rogness, Peter 114
Rokke, Ervin J. 302
Roland, David 111
Roland, John 256
Rolf, Kathy 234
Rollins, Richard A. 139
Rollins, Robert L. 167
Roloff, Marvin L. 42
Romero, Carlos 137
Romero, Daniel F. 166
Ronsvalle, John L. 214
Ronsvalle, Sylvia 214
Roop, Eugene F. 292
Roozen, David A. 215
Rorie, Stephen 261
Rosario, Luis 167
Rosco, Michael 322
Roscover, Norma 249
Rose, Donald L. 124, 331
Rose, J. Hugh 171
Rose, Jonathan 49
Rose, Lou 236
Rose, Whaid 98
Rosen, Janice 354
Rosengarten, Richard 309
Rosenthal, Hannah 224
Rosier, Bob 262
Rosner, Patrice 42
Roso, Henry A. (Hank) . . .324
Ross, David E. 61
Ross, Eugene 166
Ross, Kent 328
Ross, Mary Jane 215
Ross, Nan 32
Ross, Patricia 227
Ross, Ron 338
Rossi, Loren 234
Rost, Nori 173
Rostan, June 25
Rostand, Dean J. 341
Roth, Adam 252
Roth, Jared D. 129
Roth, John D. 330
Roth, Ronald 175
Rothamel, John, Jr. 141
Rothmeyer, Sue E. 113
Rottino, Kathleen 141
Rourk, David C. 96
Rourke, Marguerite 234
Rouse, Michael 37
Roussy, Louis 205
Routledge, Donald 287
Rowell, Leonard 260
Rowley, Robert D., Jr. . . .108
Roy, Marie-Michèle 342
Roy, Stephen 53
Royston, James H. 159
Rozeboom, John A. 91
Rubin, Fred, Sr. 101
Rucker, Jaqueline P. 254
Rucks, Karen L. 239
Rudy, Frederick J. 30
Ruffin, Jeff 99
Ruge, Mark 196
Rundbraaten, Edwin 190
Rupert, Allan 149
Rupp, Alan 118
Rusch, William G. 34
Rusche, Brian A. 243
Rush, Betty 251
Rush, Henry 229
Rush, Robert D. 105
Russell, Al 325
Russell, Barbara 244
Russell, Bo 257
Russell, Charles Taze . . .130
Russell, Dorothy 44
Russell, Gary E. 90
Russell, Joseph 153
Russell, Keith A. 290
Rust, Harold 190, 311
Rutan, Dawn 329
Ruth, Gary 24
Rutherford, F. Thomas
. . . . .86, 186
Rutland, Mark 307
Rutzler, John 259
Ryan, Barb 133
Ryan, Bridget 242
Ryan, James R. 230
Ryan, Skip 147
Ryan, Sylvester D. 84
Rydman, Philip 27, 345
Ryrie, Charles 128
Ryskamp, Andrew 91
Rystephanuk, David 199

Saenz, Agnes 239
Safari, Nelly 54
Sage, R.P.I. 250
Sage, Russel 250
Sailors, Ronnette L. 245
Salge, Carol 235
Saliba, Philip 69, 70, 180
Salico, Dale V. 67
Sallows, Martha 235
Salmon, Edward L., Jr. . .109
Salmon, John 187
Saltzman, Russell E. 325
Salvas, M. Sylvain 202
Salzman, Ron 142
Samra, Cal 328
Samuel (Bishop) 161
Samuel, Athanasius Y. . . .160
Samuel, Lloyd U. 72
Samuel, S.A. 183
Samuels, Thomas W. 140
Samuelson, Cecil O., Jr. . .99
Sanchagrin, Kenneth M. . .34
Sande, Jonathan M. 121
Sanders, Bill 237
Sanders, Chris 37
Sanders, Hiram 302
Sanders, Kay 237
Sanders, Robert L. 101
Sandford, Christopher . . .242
Sandleback, Nancy 26
Sandler, Abraham 91
Sanford, Don A. . . .157, 348
Sanford, Kristi 37
Sanner, Dick 25
Santiago, Carlos 129
Santiago, Felix 97, 189
Saperstein, David 224
Sapp, W. David 38
Sarajian, Richard 75
Sarly, Robert 240
Sarmazian, Yessayi
. . . . .181, 340
Sartain, J. Peter 83
Sarwa, Andrzej J. 186
Satterfield, Ray 65
Satterlee, Brian 337
Sauceda, Sam 262
Sauls, Stacy F. 108
Saunders, Dwight 129
Saunders, Willard 144
Savas (Bishop) 126
Sawatzky, Leonard 194
Sawyer, Randy 139
Sawyer, Robert E. 138
Sayre, Larry D. 67
Scali, Jean 245
Scar, William 230
Scarfe, Alan 108
Schaal, Wendell J. 38
Schaefer, Beth 317
Schaer, Marilyn
. . . . .142, 198, 331
Schaller, Paul 328
Schaper, Michael 81
Schell, Steve 129
Schellenberg, Rick 311
Schemmel, Wade 166, 251
Schiemann, D. 197
Schiemant, Donald 122
Schierenbeck, John 100
Schilling, Ira 159
Schindell, Dal 341
Schipper, Mr. 327
Schlabach, Darrel 137
Schlatter, Michael 151
Schlatter, William R. 72

INDEX

Schleicher, Andrew J. . . .331
Schlemmer, Douglas 68
Schlenker, Janet 230
Schlonecker, William G. . . .81
Schlosser, Rick 228
Schmeling, G.R. . . .292, 329
Schmidt, Bill 233
Schmidt, Harry 123, 294
Schmitt, Bernard W. 262
Schneider, Bette 261
Schneider, Don C. 157
Schneider, Francis J. 306
Schneider, Theodore F. . .116
Schner, Joseph G. 314
Schnurr, Dennis M. 83
Schoder-Ehri, Bill 120
Schoelles, Patricia A. . . .305
Schoenhals, Floyd M. . . .114
Schofield, John-David . . .109
Schofield, Rod 113
Schofield-Bodt, Brian . . .231
Schoonmaker, Wendy . . .233
Schoonover, Wayne 125
Schori, Katharine Jefferts 108
Schorsch, Ismar 299
Schoubye, Harald 66
Schrader, David 191
Schrag, James M. 137
Schramm, Richard W. 67, 318
Schrock, Simon 80
Schrock, Wayne 80
Schrodt, Paul 25
Schroeder, David E. 290
Schueddig, Louis C. 32
Schug, Tricia 261
Schulter, Nancy 246
Schultz, Harvey 118
Schultz, Raymond 57, 193
Schultz, Stephen R. 79
Schutt, David 151, 201
Schwarr, Carolyn 260
Schwenkfeld von Ossig, Caspar 155
Schwich, Kathie Bender .114
Scott, Alphonso 144
Scott, Basil M. 83
Scott, John 24
Scott, Orange 173
Scott, Philip L. 144
Scott, Richard G. 99
Scott, W. Peter 207
Scovil, Larry 104
Scruggs, Endia 106
Scruggs, Terri 187
Scruton, Gordon P. 109
Scudder, Ida S. 50
Scurry, Frank P. 293
Seabury, Samuel 106
Seasoltz, R. Kevin 339
Seater, Robert P. 262
Segall, Susan 261
Seide, Emmanuel 90, 91
Seifert, Stan 118
Selby, Richard 259
Seler, Debby 322
Sellers, Asbury R. 96
Semel, Rita 49
Senior, Donald 28, 293
Senth, Colin 121
Seppala, Ivan M. 73
Seraphim (Bishop) .161, 198
Seraphim (Reverend) 143
Serapion (Bishop) . . .105, 317
Sergeva, Yelena 253
Serratelli, Arthur J. 84
Sessions, Jim 37
Sewell, Wayne 66
Seymour, W.J. 72
Shada, Doug 80
Shafer, Eric C. 114
Shaffer, Kenneth M., Jr. 348
Shaffer, Steve 118
Shah, Ajay 221
Shahan, Robert 107
Shaheen, Michael 69
Shahidi, Munirah 49
Shalman, Charles 249
Shamana, Beverly J. 171
Shand, James J. 108
Shannon, S.E. 99
Sharkey, Carole 35
Sharp, Arthur 138
Sharp, Bill 117
Sharp, Donald 48
Sharp, John E. 330, 350
Sharp, Kathy 322
Sharp, S. Marion 260
Sharp, Tammy 27
Sharpe, Conner 261
Sharpe, Michael . . .105, 330
Shaver, Ruth 239
Shaw, Barbara L. 64
Shaw, Carla 46
Shaw, Curt 122
Shaw, M. Thomas 108
Shaw, Milton 132
Shaw, Richard 239
Shaw, William J. 139
Shawl, Sallie 260
Shea, William B. 38
Sheard, J. Drew 94
Sheehan, Lourdes 83
Sheehan, Michael J. 83
Sheeks, Bill F. 95, 188
Sheffield, Dan 195
Sheie, Myrna J. 113
Sheldon, William A. 92
Shellabarger, Thomas 37
Shelley, Marshall 328
Shelly, Rubel 338
Shelton, Don W. 87
Shelton, Tom 138
Shenouda III (Pope) 104, 192
Shepherd, D.A. 199
Shepherd, Oscar 129
Shepherd, Thomas 239
Shequel, Sleiman 70
Sherer, Ann Brookshire . . .170
Sherry, Brian 24
Sherry, Jon 41
Sherry, Paul 36, 42
Sherwin, Wally 53
Sheveland, Gerald 79
Shibly, Othman 249
Shields, Janis 24
Shinachi, Enoch 122
Shipley, Joseph 88
Shipman, Joan G. 255
Shisanya, Jonathan 122
Shivachi, Nilson 122
Shlensky, Evely Laser 37
Shockley, Howard 117
Shockley, Nathan 174
Short, Betty 287
Short, Peter B. 206
Showers, Merle 249
Shreffler, Marilyn 252
Shrenes, Thomas A. 115
Shuman, Maryellen 256
Shurr, Dan 194
Shute, Michael 191
Sibley, Wallace J. 96
Sickbert, Bryan W. 166
Sides, Richard 138
Sidner, Art 243
Sidorak, Stephen J., Jr. 231
Siebert, Dorothy 342
Siepka, Richard W. 293
Sigismund, John 164
Sigman, Michael W. 111
Signer, Ray 49
Siker, Jeffrey S. 300
Sills, John F. 323
Silvey, James L. 79
Simcox, Lynne 166
Simiyu, Benson 122
Simiyu, Maurice 121
Simms, John A. 289
Simon, Leon 162
Simon, Mark 129
Simon, Menno 152
Simon, Paula 262
Simons, Menno 118
Simpson, A.B. 89, 187
Simpson, John 241
Simpson, Susan V. 124
Sims, E.G. 105
Sims, John 95, 188
Sinasac, Joseph 341
Sinclair, Aftimios L. 74
Sinclair, James H. 206
Singh, Mohinder 49
Singleton, Richard 241
Singley, Martin, III 129
Sinkford, William 164

Sisk, Mark 108
Sitaras, Constantine L. . .126
Skeadas, Georgia 126
Skeene, Andrea 239
Skelton, William 44
Skidmore, W. Chris Benham 237
Skiles, Neal 91
Skinner, Douglas 86
Skinner, Mrs. Bill 80
Skitton, William "Bill" 257
Skocypec, Emil 163, 164
Skurla, Laurus 298
Skylstad, William S. 83
Slater, Sherri 242
Slattery, Edward J. 83
Slie, Samuel N. 231
Sly, Margery N. 148, 349, 352
Small, Frank 181
Small, Hazel 184
Smalley, Martha Lund . . .353
Smalley, Martha 350
Smedberg, Barry 229
Smeeton, Don 96
Smiley, Wayne 73
Smisko, Nicholas . . .68, 293
Smith, Alexei 230
Smith, Alycia 234
Smith, Andrea 339
Smith, Andrew D. . . .107, 231
Smith, Arthur 336
Smith, Autholene 80
Smith, Bennett W., Sr. . . .149
Smith, Brad 303
Smith, Bruce 189
Smith, Cherie 65
Smith, Craig S. 90
Smith, David Charles . . .255
Smith, Diana E. 27
Smith, Donald 230
Smith, Elias Dempsey . . .162
Smith, Eric C. 166
Smith, Eric 137
Smith, Francis L. 144
Smith, G. Wayne 108
Smith, Glen 289
Smith, Glenn 56
Smith, Gordon 55
Smith, Guy H., III 77
Smith, Isaac V. 88
Smith, J. Morris 257
Smith, Jane Orion 345
Smith, Joseph 92, 98, 189
Smith, Joseph, III 190
Smith, Joseph, Jr. 190
Smith, Kenneth 346
Smith, Ker 186
Smith, Lawrence 132
Smith, Leroy, Jr. 99
Smith, Lois L. 254
Smith, Marilyn McCann 115
Smith, Marvin 80
Smith, Michael Gene . . .108
Smith, R. Bruce 55
Smith, Rebecca 235
Smith, Richard 203
Smith, Robert E. 297
Smith, Robert 186
Smith, Ron C. 330
Smith, Ron 231
Smith, Ronald E. 309
Smith, Ronald 103
Smith, S.S. 153
Smith, Steve 251
Smith, Susan J. 227
Smith, T. Randall 260
Smith, Terry M. 194
Smith, Terry 344
Smith, Tom 252
Smith, Velma 262
Smith, Victor P. 93
Smith, Wallace C. 296
Smith, William L. 144
Smith, Zollie 76
Smock, Robert W. 81
Snair, Karen 253
Snellgrove, P. David 148
Snelson, J.E. 321
Snow, Sharon 129
Snowman, Sharon L. 141
Snyder, Carol 325
Snyder, Joni 237
Snyder, Richard D. 51, 120
Sobel, Ronald B. 46
Soderquist, Marilyn 260
Solimon, Ronald J. 113
Solomon, Frank S. 101
Sommer, Donald 125
Sommer, Sally Weaver 120
Sommers, Gordon 46
Sonnenburg, Brian 288
Soper, John F. 90
Sophronios (Bishop) 127
Sorensen, Gordon 182
Sorensen, Steven R. 350
Sotirios (Metropolitan) 196
Sovin, Shenork 54
Sowers, Betsy 240
Sox, Aileen Andres .332, 334
Spain, Ricky 318
Spans, J. 333
Sparkman, Alan 145
Sparkman, Wayne 352
Sparks, Dennis D. 262
Sparks, William 57
Spataro, Francis C. 72, 337
Speas, Philip 299
Speer, James 80
Spence, Ralph 180
Spencer, Shirley 327
Sperzel, Ceil 235
Spindt, Judith A. 115
Spittal, David J. 307
Spitzer, Lee 67
Spitzer, Robert 297
Spleth, Richard L. 87
Sprague, C. Joseph 169
Sprague, Roy 128
Spriggs, J. Wayne 90
Sprinkle, Randy 159
Spurgeon, Don 102
St. Lawrence, Deborah 326
St. Pierre, Bill 185
St.-Gelais, Raymond 203
Stafford, E.E. 139
Stafford, Willian S. 306
Stahr, James A. 85, 186
Stair, Randel 147
Stairs, M. Jean 314
Staller, Thomas 119
Stallings, James O. 67
Stamm, John M. 308
Stamn, John 165
Standen, Michael 250
Stanford, Alan 44
Stanley, Heidi 53
Stanton, James M. 107
Stapert, Craig W. 319
Staples, Charles E. 256
Stark, J. 151
Starnes, Darryl B. 64
Starr, Barbara 141
Statnick, Roger 253
Stauch, Karimah 49
Stauffer, Rick 117
Stavert, Bruce 180
Stearns, Richard 51
Steckbeck, Dori I. 348
Stefanis, Anthony 126
Steinmetz, Larry 27
Steinwand, Randy L. 60
Stelck, Brian F. 312
Stelck, Brian 183
Stella, Brigitte 246
Stemmle, Carol 237
Stenbakken, Ardis D. 157
Stenberg, Luther 190
Stendahl, John 114, 240
Stenson, Jane 43
Stephanopoulos, Nikki . .125
Stephanopoulos, Robert G. 126
Stephen (Archbishop) . . .161
Stephens, Mary 237
Stephens, P.F. 153
Stephens, Robert 239
Stephenson, Carl H. 207
Stephenson, Robert E. . . .103
Stern, George M. 255
Stetler, P. Daniel 298
Stevens, Bruce G. 148
Stevens, Jerry 336
Stevens, Ruth J. 64
Stewart, A.G., Sr. 89
Stewart, Betty 122
Stewart, Dan R. 300
Stewart, Danny 87

Stewart, Glen J. 87
Stewart, Jewelle 130
Stewart, Jonathan 30
Stewart, Kimberly 172
Stewart, Lois R. 146
Stewart, Mary C. 254
Stewart, Richard 23
Stewart, Robert E. 87
Stewart, William E. 190
Stewart-Rhude, Eileen 56
Steytler, Jessica 353
Stief, Ron 37
Stiller, Brian C. 315
Stiller, Brian 56
Stimson, Eva 334
Stinnett, Daniel 183
Stinnett, J. Dwight 67
Stinnett, Mrs. Daniel 183
Stinson, Benoni 123
Stinton, Rick 299
Stites, Tom 337
Stith, Betty V. 64
Stith, Rhandi M. 64
Stockman, Carol 240
Stokes, Thomas E. 348
Stoll, Christian 346
Stoll, Joseph 342, 346
Stolov, Yehuda 49
Stoltzfus, Margaret 121
Stommel, Elizabeth 239
Stone, Barbara 253
Stone, Barton W. 85
Stone, Jack
. . . . .48, 51, 101, 190
Stopperich, J.R. 235
Stortz, Dennis 133
Stoudt, John 255
Stowell, Joseph M. 302
Strain, Patricia 338
Strand, David 133
Strand, Jim 26
Straughan, Gary 138
Strauser, AnnaMae 122
Strauser, Carol 122
Strauser, Charles Elwood
. 122
Strauser, Simeon 122, 326
Strauss, Sandra L. 256
Straut, Charles H., Jr. 246
Strawser, Craig L. 90
Strickland, Marshall H., I
. 63
Strobel, David R. 115
Strohmaier, Sharon E.
. 236
Strommen, E. Peter 114
Strope, David 124
Stroup, John 129
Strout, Mark 314
Strout, Richard E. 344
Struchen, Shirley W. 42
Struchen, Shirley Whipple
. 47
Struck, Jane Johnson 337
Struik, Félix 295
Strunk, Orlo, Jr. 328
Strutz, Robert 110
Stuart, Robert F. 232
Stuck, James R. 115
Studivant, G.W. 153
Stuehrenberg, Paul F. 25
Stumme-Diers, Paul W. . . .115
Sturtevant, Elwood 237
Stutzman, Rose Mary . . .336
Styles, Donald H. 320
Subotic, Zivorad 204
Subramanian, Siva 232
Suhrheinrich, Heidi 238
Sullivan, Anita 123
Sullivan, Bernard 64
Sullivan, Jack, Jr. 87
Sullivan, John 158
Sullivan, Linda 240
Sullivan, Monroe 37
Sullivan, Rosemari 107
Sullivan, Veronica 35
Sumner, George R., Jr. 316
Sumners, Bill 348
Sumter, Tyrone 80
Sunderland, LaRoy 173
Sure, Heng 49
Sutto, Zoltan S. 241
Sutton, Edgar N. 66
Sutton, Ray R. 152
Svennungsen, Ann 34
Swaiko, Herman 306
Swain, Lawrence O. 67
Swan, Richard 239
Swan, Sandra 107
Swan, Tina 246
Swank, Sandy 236
Swanson, Douglas 243
Swanson, Gary B. . . .322, 323
Swanson, Paul R. 114
Swanson-Nystrom, Jane K.
. 323
Swartling, David D. 114
Swartwood, Theresa 236
Swartz, Fred W. 92
Swartzendruber, Loren . .296
Swatkowski, Ray 79
Swedenborg, Emanuel
. . . . .124, 160, 195
Sweeden, Patsie 87
Sweeney, Michael 295
Swenson, Kristin 49
Swenson, Lester 242
Swenson, Mary Ann 171
Swidler, Leonard 327
Swinburne, R. Douglas 90
Swindle, Zephaniah 162
Swing, William 49, 107
Switzer, Patricia 248
Sydnot, Calvin H. 62
Sydow, James 100
Syeed, Sayyid M. 222
Synan, Vinson 304
Szabo, Stephen 127, 329
Szymczak, Thomas 234

Tabbernee, William 304
Taber-Hamilton, Nigel
. 261
Taillon, Gerald 159, 185
Talbert, Melvin G. 32
Talbot, Lydia 233
Talbot, Nathan 93
Talcott, Sarah 49
Talone, Cheryl 248
Talton, Chester 108
Tamayo, James A. 83
Tammen, Mark 148
Tan, Hong Kia 173
Tandon, Atul 51
Tanis, Justin 173
Tanis, Phil 151, 201
Tappen, Jerry 262
Tarr, Candace 88
Tarr, Rita 233
Tate, Mary L. 127
Tatum, Craig 241
Taturn, Ed 145
Taw, David 245
Taylor, Al 96
Taylor, Betty P. 259
Taylor, Edwin 287
Taylor, Hudson 16
Taylor, J. Graley 260
Taylor, Joyce 95
Taylor, L. Roy 147
Taylor, Mark 102, 321
Taylor, Nancy 167
Taylor, Regina 259
Taylor, Steve 119
Taylor, Victor 89
Taylor, Wayne 130
Teague, Peter W. 299
Tebbutt, Peter 207
Tedesco, John 88
Temple, Guy 255
Temple, Jan 255
Templeton, Beth 257
Templeton, John M., Jr. 40
Teodorovych, Ioan (John)
. 163
Terry, Bob 26
Tesch, Walter F. 133
Tetreau, Jerry 299
Thell, Barbara 242
Theodosius (Metropolitan)
. 143
Theriault, Donald J. 203
Thibodeau, Francois 202
Thiesen, John 350
Thiessen, David 194
Thiessen, Henry 194
This, Craig 27
Thistlethwaite, Susan Brooks
. 293

Thomann, David A. 81
Thomas, Andrea S. 235
Thomas, Arnold I. 167
Thomas, D. Karl 181
Thomas, Dominic 98
Thomas, Evangeline 353
Thomas, Everett 330
Thomas, Freeman M. . . .144
Thomas, George 330
Thomas, James P. 103
Thomas, John 85, 166
Thomas, Ralph 35
Thomas, Reginald H. . . .149
Thomas, T.V. 187
Thomas-Breitfeld, Leota .113
Thomason, Jeanette 33
Thompson, Brice 97, 189
Thompson, Daniel M. . . .232
Thompson, Dean K. 300
Thompson, Doug 258
Thompson, Else 114
Thompson, Glendon G. . . .315
Thompson, Herbert, Jr. 109
Thompson, Houston 235
Thompson, James W. . . .335
Thompson, Ken 119, 259
Thompson, Leonard, Sr. . .67
Thompson, Richard Keith 63
Thomson, H. Rogers 71
Thon, Carol 235
Thopil, Markose 144
Thornton, Bobby C. 79
Thorpe, Debbie 258
Thune, Robert L. 90
Thurton, Winston 56
Tidwell, Melissa 317
Tiede, David L. 300
Tiemann, Ray 115
Tifft, Thomas W. 305
Tikhon (Reverend) 143
Tilley, Barbara 42
Timmer, David E. 333
Timmerman, Larry J. 95
Tindal, Douglas 57
Tinsley, Charles 229
Tippett, Bert 325
Tipton, Daniel 102
Tisch, Joseph L. 132
Tisdale, Delores 254
Tisdale, Janet 141
Titus, Beth 257
Titus, Devi 129
Titus, Richard C. 227
Tizzard, Brian 59
Tkachuk, Rod 199
Tobin, Thomas J. 83
Tolbert, Mark C. 144
Tolbert, Rosa 73
Tolbert, T.C., Jr. 73
Tolbert, T.C., Sr. 73
Tolborh, Moses 80
Tollefson, Rebecca J. 252
Tolley, S.T. 149, 320
Tom, Phil 37
Tombaugh, Richard F. . . .107
Tomic, Vasilije 343
Tomlinson, A.J. 97, 188
Tomlinson, M.A. 97
Tomlinson, Susanna M. . .254
Toner, Margaret 203
Tong, Joseph 299
Toompuu, Marie 182
Toot, Gloria 160
Tooze, George 68
Toppins, Helen Garay 120, 122
Torok, Stefan M. 127
Torrance, Iain R. 304
Torrance, John 182
Torrens, Gary 148
Tortoriello, John 122
Torvik, John R. 112
Towne, Becky 325
Towns, L. Ferrell 90
Townsend, Fred 288
Townsend, Patricia 354
Towse, Eric 338
Toycen, Dave 59
Trache, Robert G. 258
Trachian, Barkev 307
Tracz, Nick 37
Traftan, Margie 344
Trammell, Mary M. 93, 321, 326
Trapp, Edwin A., Jr. 133
Trask, Thomas 46, 76
Trauger, Kenneth 255
Trautman, Donald W. 83
Treanor, John J. 26
Trees, Richard 129
Treit, Elroy 197
Trejo, José 243
Tremblay, Ann 287
Tremblay, Donald 288
Trevino, Max A. 157
Trevino, Yoland 49
Triantafilou, Nicholas 126, 298
Tribou, Ruth E. 246
Trine, Melinda 24
Tripp, Linda 59
Trosen, Robert 110
Trotter, LaTonya 49
Trotti, Melinda 250
Trowbridge, Constance . . .261
Trowbridge, Kathleen . . .239
Truss, James 73
Trusty, Bill 238
Tsapwe, Simon 121
Tschetter, Charles 118
Tse, James N. 32
Tsimbaki, Matthew 121
Tucker, Neville 64
Tucker, Tommy 238
Tuckett, Robert 327
Tune, Leslie C. 41, 42
Tunnicliffe, Geoff 56
Turner, B.G. 129
Turner, Carl A. 144
Turner, Emil 158
Turner, Rex A., Jr. 308
Turner, Wayne 342
Twedt-Ball, Karla 236
Tweet, Margaret 31
Tyler, Robert D. 99
Tyndall, Margaret 52
Tyrrell, Wilfred L. 35
Tyson, James E. 144

Udall, William B. 239
Ufford-Chase, Rich 148
Uglem, Dwayne 311
Ugoletti, Dennis 254
Ugolnik, Anthony 337
Ulery, Kent J. 166
Ullestad, Steven L. 115
Ulterino, Gloria 248
Umble, Jeni Hiett 234
Unruh, Ron 193
Unruh, Ron 344
Up De Graff, Morse 147
Updegrove, John H. 256
Uptain, Misti 261
Upton, John V., Jr. 159
Ursham, N.A. 171
Usgaard, Harold L. 114
Utterback, J. Michael 96

Valentine, Pamela 64
Valenzuela, Carmen 242, 243, 244
Vallance, James E. 318
Vallée, André 54, 202
Van Broekhoven, Deborah334
Van Dam, C. 315
Van Dyk, Leanne 333
Van Eyl, Christina 321
Van Leer, Thomas 242
Van Marter, Jerry 26
VanBeusekom, Hein 132
VanBroekhoven, Deborah B. 68
Vandee, Daniel 183
Vandee, Mrs. Daniel 183
Vander Molen, Steven 151, 201
Vanderslice, Kenneth W. . . .79
Vandervelde, George 34
Vang, Timothy T. 90
Vanhaverbeke, Sylvia Lisk 50
VanMarter, Jerry L. 333
Vansen, Beatrice 29
VanWyngaarden, Bill 48
Vanyi, Laszlo B. 127
Vargas, David A. 86
Varick, James 62
Varley, Peter 53

Varsbergs, Anita 131
Vasilac, Vasile 323
Vasko, Rebecca 214
Vasquez, Manuel 157
Vassiouchkine, Alexei ...199
Vaughn, Dan 121
Veazey, Stephen M. 103
Veenstra, William 91
Veeraswamy, B. 81
Veillette, Martin 202
Veliko, Lydia 32
Velozo, Ruth M. 261
Venema, Cornelius P. ...301
Verhoef, A.H. 141
Verigin, John J., Sr. 206
Verigin, Peter V. ...205, 206
Verlautz, James 243
Vermillion, William 110
Vest, R. Lamar
.........23, 45, 95, 188
Vetter, Jay A. 245
Vettrus, Richard 100
Vickery, David 77
Victor (Metropolitan) ...127
Victorson, Vernon 247
Vidolo, Japheth 122
Vila, Vesna 253
Vilankulu, Sarah 42, 323
Vilathi, Timotheos 161
Villafane, Eldin 34
Villalba, Eddie 98
Vinton, Samuel 125
Viola, Virginia 35
Visscher, J. 341
Vissers, John 313, 314
Vlad, Mike 98
Vladimir (Prince) 74
Vlazny, John G. 83, 84
Vogel-Borne, Jonathan 122
Volk, Barbara 251
Von Gunten, David 137
Von Wade, Melvin, Sr. 140
Vonicessler, Caroline 258
vonRosenberg, Charles ...108
Voskuil, Betty 41
Voskuil, Dennis N. 310
Votary, Marilyn E. 343
Votary, R.E. 196
Vree, Dale 331
Vreeland, Richard L. 50
Vsevolod (Archbishop) ...163
Vu, Hung 244

Wachal, Anne E. 233
Wackernagel, Betsy 260
Wade, Charles R. 159
Wade, Cheryl H. 67
Wade, James 62
Wagener, Ginny 230
Waggoner, Berten A. 78
Waggoner, James E., Jr. ...109
Waggoner, Sara Jo 253
Waghray, Rajyashri 42
Wagner, Jane 173
Wagner, Mark 303
Wagner, Norman L. 144
Wagner, Rebecca 239
Waites, Bob 159
Wakefield, M.J. 183
Wakefield, Wesley H.
.............183, 343
Wakefield, William James Elijah 183
Walden, Jay 97
Walden, Mark 48
Waldner, Jacob 128
Walgraeve, Walter M.C. 72
Walker, Alice 337
Walker, Céleste 328
Walker, Diane 342
Walker, Frank 151
Walker, Gail 37
Walker, George W.C., Sr.
...............62, 63
Walker, Jewett L. 64
Walker, Orris G., Jr. 108
Walker, Paul H. 188
Walker, Paul L. 95, 188
Walker, Reba 166
Walker, Riley H. 67
Walker-Smith, Angelique
.................234
Walking Elk, Leslie 242
Wall, Aaron 117
Wall, Jim 145
Wall, Raymond W. 95, 188
Wallace, Carl P. 166
Wallace, D. 196
Wallace, Duncan D. 180
Wallace, Jon R. 297
Wallace, Peter M. 32
Wallace, Robert 67
Walles, Caroline 245
Walles, Charles A. 112
Walley, Wendell 292
Wallis, Hope 248
Wallis, Jim 336
Walsh, Gary 56
Walsh, Robert 53
Walter, Bob 49
Walter, Ewa 50
Walter, Martin 128
Walters, Norman 144
Walther, Bob 142
Waltz, David C. 159
Walvoord, John 128
Walz, Bob 243
Wamala, Francis 122
Wan, Enoch 22
Wang, Karen 41
Wangberg, Rolf P. 114
Wangensteen, Peg 243
Wantz, Joh 234
Ward, Marion J. 261
Ward, Michael, Sr. 68
Ward, Sarah F. 44
Wardlaw, Theodore J. ...291
Warkie, Peter 144
Warner, Daniel S. 93
Warner, Vincent W. 108
Warner, Wayne 326, 347
Warren, Cindy 31
Warren, David 124
Warren, Leodis 144
Warren, Mike 124, 322
Warren, Patty 227
Warren, Ronald B. 116
Wartman, Paul 312
Washington, Don A. 239
Wasielewski, Charles, Sr.
..................68
Wasserman, Joseph 230
Watkins, David J. 81
Watkins, David T. 79
Watkins, Dennis W. 96
Watson, B. Michael
.............170, 232
Watson, Ralph 289
Watson, Robert 98
Watt, Laura 235
Watt, Neil 204
Wattson, Paul 35
Wauls, Robert 144
Wawire, Blastus 122
Waxler, Mel 258
Waybright, Gregory L. 308
Waynick, Catherine M. ...108
Weakland, Rembert G. 262
Weaver, David 42
Weaver, James 340
Weaver, Peter D. 169
Weavill, George 257
Webb, Robert 348
Webb, Suzanne 32
Webber, Robert D. 45
Weber, Francis J. 26
Weber, Timothy P. 301
Webster, Joe L. 168
Webster, Robert Vaughn 62
Wedgwood, James I. 132
Wedig, Mark E. 291
Weeks, Dewayne 145
Weeks, Louis B. 308
Weeks, Thomas J. 144
Weeks, Thomas W., Sr.
..................144
Weigand-Buckley, Amber
.................332
Weikel, Calvin 130
Weiler, Jean-Jacques 52
Weinacht, Alan 121
Weinreb, Tzvi Hersh 224
Weinstein, Judy 256
Weir, Moses 105
Weisgerber, V. James
...............202, 203
Welch, J.M. 199
Welch, Mike 198
Welch, Shirley 63

Wells, Carol 104, 325
Wells, D.R. 199
Wells, Martin D. 114
Welscott, Richard 151, 201
Welsh, Bobby 158
Welsh, Robert K. 86, 319
Welty, Marcel A. 41
Wendland, Paul O. 310
Wendorf, Mark 37
Wenger, Lee 165
Wenski, Thomas G. 83
Wenthe, Dean O. 295
Werner, George L. 107
Werner, Paul 40
Werner, Tom 117
Wert, Rita 44
Wesley, John 169
West, Barbara J. 152
West, James C. 295
West, James C., Sr. 152
West, Jonathan 25
Westberg, M. Victor 93
Westbrook, Don 123
Westcott, Barbara Spaulding
. 241
Wetzel, C. Robert 296
Wetzel, Daniel R. 90
Wexler, Marcie 208
Weyeneth, Benedict 71
Whalon, Pierre 107, 109
Whatley, Wesley 30
Wheaton, Keith D. 317
Wheeland, Duane A. 90
Wheeler, Barbara G. 213
Wheeler, Edward L. 294
Wheeler, Jack 248
Wheeler, Roger 129
Whitaker, Timothy Wayne
. 170
White, Alma Bridwell
. . . . .145, 146
White, Barbara 39
White, David O. 230
White, Douglas 111
White, Ellen G. 98
White, Frank O. 94
White, J. Robert 158
White, J.C. 95
White, Jerry E. 30
White, Jim 244
White, K. Gordon 240
White, Kent 146
White, Marcus 262
White, Patricia P. 323
White, Patricia 105
White, R. Fowler 299
White, Raymond W. 127
White, Reid R., Jr. 64
White, Richard 94
White, Robert 151
White, Terry 33
White, Woodie W. 169
WhiteEagle, Sheila 243
Whitehead, Evan 182
Whitfield, D. Max 170
Whiting, D. Douglas 45
Whitlow, Robert L. 296
Whitmore, Keith B. 108
Whitney, Dale 230
Whitt, Dwight Reginald
. 295
Whittaker, Bill 294
Whittaker, Fermin A. 158
Whittley, LuVoinia 94
Wickmann, David L. 138
Wideman, James 159
Wiebe, Dave 184
Wiebe, Henry 201
Wiebe, Jim 188
Wiebe, Virgil 80
Wieczerzak, Joseph 351
Wiens, Hart 54
Wieser, Walter W. 183
Wiesner, Gerald 202
Wigger, Barbara 124
Wiggins, Donald A. 90
Wiggins, James B. 248
Wiggins, Lonnie 66
Wiginton, Melissa 34
Wilbert, Ora 88
Wilcox, Donald M. 247
Wilcox, William 239
Wildman, Ingrid 341
Wiley, Galen 119
Wilke, LeRoy 133
Wilkerson, Jack 158
Wilkie, Owen 319
Wilkinson, Bruce 51
Wilkinson, Ed 336
Willemsma, Tena 26
Williams, Annie M. 64
Williams, Arsenia 141
Williams, Bertha 44, 167
Williams, Carl E., Sr. 95
Williams, Carol 252
Williams, Connie B. 64
Williams, Dennis L. 86
Williams, Dorothy R. 50
Williams, Edward 82
Williams, Elijah 167, 168
Williams, Elvonia 95
Williams, F.W. 72
Williams, George 51
Williams, Gregory 328
Williams, Horace K. 95
Williams, Jesse F. 171
Williams, John L. 148
Williams, John P., Jr. 113
Williams, John 260
Williams, Michael A. 67
Williams, Milton Alexander
. 63
Williams, Newell 292
Williams, Oswill 45
Williams, Patrick J. 303
Williams, Preston Warren, II
. 62
Williams, R.H. Tex 317
Williams, Robert 107
Williams, Roger 67
Williams, Ron 128, 325
Williams, Ronald 45
Williams, Roy 137
Williams, Sam 113
Williams, W. Michelle James
. 172
Williamson, Edward W. . . .116
Williamson, Elaine 234
Williamson, Henry M. 89
Williamson, Jack 40
Williamson, Portia Turner
. 34
Williamson, Stephen 250
Williford, Craig 295
Willingham, Jerome 64
Willis, Carolyn 340
Willis, Mike 337
Wills, Susan 258
Wills, Wanda Bryant 86
Wilson, Alex V. 339
Wilson, Dori 230
Wilson, Earle L. 51, 174
Wilson, Glenna 257
Wilson, H. C. 208
Wilson, Helen Tibbs 227
Wilson, Holly 342
Wilson, Ian E. 354
Wilson, Jeffrey K. 157
Wilson, Johanna 236
Wilson, John 235
Wilson, Larry E. 144
Wilson, Nancy L. 173
Wilson, Norman G.
. . . . .174, 338
Wilson, Robert W. 174
Wilson, Rod 314
Wilson, Ronald 33, 103
Wilson-Reiner, Warren 121
Wilt, Marge 33
Wilt, Tom 33
Wiltschek, Walt 330
Wiltse, David A. 339
Wimber, John 78
Wimberly, Don A. 109
Winbush, R.L.H. 94
Winbush, Robina 148
Wind, James P. 23
Wine (Sister) 153
Winebrenner, John 102
Wines, Roger 149
Wingender, Eric 312
Winger, Brian 206
Winger, Darrell S. 82
Wingle, James 202
Wingren, Gunnar 77
Winn, Douglas K. 290
Winn, Robert 93
Winnowski, Michael 54
Winsor, Eva M. 200

INDEX

Winsor, Gary D. 200
Winter, Linda 256
Winter, Roy 92
Winters, Carolyn M. 227
Wipf, Jacob 128
Wipf, John 128
Wirt, Douglas 87
Wirthlin, Joseph B. 99
Wise, Phillip D. 44
Wisler, Jacob 142
Witczak, Michael G. 305
Witmer, Joseph W. 252
Witt, Richard 250
Wittberg, Patricia 335
Wittin, Robert 246
Wittman, Elisabeth 350
Woelbern, James 28
Wogaman, J. Philip 298
Woida, Duane 229
Wojcicki, Ted L. 299
Wojtyla, Karol 82
Wold, David 260
Wolf, Burton 251
Wolf, Geralyn 109
Wolf, Patricia 42
Wolfe, Bennet 93
Wolfe, Dean E. 108
Wolfe, Robert 208
Wolford, Kathryn F. 38
Wolfram, Donald J. 146
Wollersheim, Gary M. . . .115
Woloschak, Gayle 163
Womack, Anne 25
Wong, David S.F. 339
Wontor, Caryn 259, 260
Wood, Bertice Y. 32
Wood, David 247
Wood, Edward R. 130
Wood, George O. 76
Wood, Robert Stanley . . .106
Woodbury, Clayton R. 67
Woodrich, Noya 242
Woodring, DeWayne S. . . .48
Woodruff, James 248
Woods, C. Stacey 35
Woods, William K. 252
Woodson, Darryl D. 172
Woodward, George 198
Woodward, Jim 238
Woodworth, Rodger 117
Woofenden, Lee 332
Woolfolk, Thomas E. . . .101
Workman, Marjorie 139
Workowski, Joan 152
Worley, Lloyd 132
Wormley, Mildred 150
Worthington, Melvin 48
Wortman, Julie A. 339
Wright, Abraham 32
Wright, Benny 260
Wright, Harold 229
Wright, Hilman 153
Wright, Walter L. 157
Wright, Wayne P. 107, 232
Wright-Riggins, Aidsand F. 68
Wuerch, Harry 196
Wukwanja, Geoffrey M. .121
Wyatt, Addie 37
Wyatt, Peter 312
Wylie, Ken 233
Wylie-Kellermann, Bill . . .48
Wynick, Karmen 24
Wyse, Mark 118

Yaldezian, John 75
Yanagihara, Akio 261
Yasenka, David 245
Yates, Jonathan 140
Yates, Wilson 309
Yeats, John 158
Yeglikian, Albert 181
Yi, Maria Renya 121
Yntema, Philip 198
Yocum, Glenn 327
Yoffie, Eric H. 224
York, Tim 138
Yost, Wayne 253
Young, Brigham 189
Young, Donald A. 180
Young, Lyle 93
Young, M. Norvel 317
Young, Martha 239
Young, McKinley 50, 62
Young, Ronald L. 144
Yount, Diana 348, 353
Youth, Edwina S. 50
Yrigoyen, Charles, Jr. . . .330
Yuille, William 186

Zabaidi, Ali 245
Zabel, Nancy 44
Zacharias, Carl 194
Zackrison, James W. 157
Zaffuto, Ferdinand 196
Zahl, Paul F.M. 308
Zain, Thomas 70, 180
Zakian, Chris 75
Zander, Vera 31
Zandier, Don 256
Zanicky, Robert 257
Zaniewski, Jaroslaw 306
Zapeda, Monica 261
Zastrow, Dale 66
Zavala, Gabina 37
Zavitz-Bond, Jane 354
Zawierucha, Bazyl 163, 164
Zehlaoui, Joseph 69, 70
Zehr, Marvin 236
Zeiders, G. Edwin 308
Zelenitz, Myrna 254
Zell, R. Thomas 317, 340
Zeller, Stephanie 106
Zellmek, Paul 159
Zelter, Barbara 251
Zens, Jon 160
Zens, Jon 335
Zilliacus, Anne Marie 340
Zilmer, Norman D. 85
Zimmerman, Sheldon 298
Zintak, Nancy 32
Zion, Sophia 199, 341
Zipfel, Paul 251
Zobel, Tom 27
Zobler, Donald 257
Zottoli, Carmine 88
Zuk (Bishop) 127
Zurek, M. 205
Zwingli, Ulrich 155
Zylla, Phil 311